THE VITAMINS

Chemistry, Physiology, Pathology

VOLUME II

THE
VITAMINS

Chemistry, Physiology, Pathology

VOLUME II

EDITED
BY

W. H. Sebrell, Jr.

Director, National Institutes of Health
Bethesda, Maryland

Robert S. Harris

Professor of Biochemistry of Nutrition
Massachusetts Institute of Technology
Cambridge, Massachusetts

ACADEMIC PRESS INC., PUBLISHERS

New York · 1954

CONTRIBUTORS TO VOLUME II

H. J. Almquist (389–399, 400–419, 444–447)*
Vice President and Research Director
The Grange Company
Modesto, California

Charles H. Best (104–128, 129–130)
University of Toronto
Toronto, Canada

Charles E. Bills (132–223)
6403 Murray Hill Road
Baltimore, Maryland

George M. Briggs (628–630, 633–669, 682–687)
National Institute of Arthritis and Metabolic Diseases
National Institutes of Health
Bethesda, Maryland

Erwin Chargaff (329–338)
College of Physicians and Surgeons
630 West 168th Street
New York, N. Y.

T. J. Cunha (367–371, 381–382)
Agricultural Experiment Station
University of Florida
Gainesville, Florida

Floyd S. Daft (628–630, 633–669, 682–687)
National Institute of Arthritis and Metabolic Diseases
National Institutes of Health
Bethesda, Maryland

George A. Emerson (311–317)
Department of Pediatrics
University of Texas Medical Branch
Galveston, Texas

Wendell H. Griffith (2–103, 128–129)
Department of Physiological Chemistry
School of Medicine
University of California Medical Center
Los Angeles, California

Arild E. Hansen (300–317)
Department of Pediatrics
University of Texas Medical Branch
Galveston, Texas

Robert S. Harris (2, 132, 268, 322, 388, 399–400, 452, 591)
Department of Food Technology
Massachusetts Institute of Technology
Cambridge, Massachusetts

W. Stanley Hartroft (104–128, 129–130)
University of Toronto
Toronto, Canada

Ralph T. Holman (268–300, 318–319)
The Hormel Institute
University of Minnesota
Austin, Minnesota

J. M. Hundley (452–538, 540–550, 551–587)
National Institute of Arthritis and Metabolic Diseases
National Institutes of Health
Bethesda, Maryland

James H. Jones (223–232, 253–256)
School of Veterinary Medicine
University of Pennsylvania
Philadelphia, Pennsylvania

Abram Kanof (232–253, 257–266)
Department of Pediatrics
The Jewish Hospital of Brooklyn
Brooklyn, New York

Benjamin Kramer (232–253, 257–266)
Department of Pediatrics
The Jewish Hospital of Brooklyn
Brooklyn, New York

Henry A. Lardy (323–329, 342–351)
Institute for Vitamin Research
University of Wisconsin
Madison, Wisconsin

Samuel Lepkovsky (591–598, 626–627, 680–681)
Agricultural Experimental Station
University of California
Berkeley, California

* Numbers in parentheses indicate the pages on which each author's contribution or contributions may be found.

v

FRITZ LIPMANN (598–625)
Biochemical Research Laboratory
Massachusetts General Hospital
Harvard Medical School
Boston, Massachusetts

ARTHUR H. LIVERMORE (351–361, 363–366)
Department of Chemistry
Reed College
Portland, Oregon

COLIN C. LUCAS (104–128, 129–130)
University of Toronto
Toronto, Canada

A. T. MILHORAT (371–381, 382–386)
Payne Whitney Psychiatric Clinic
The New York Hospital
New York, N. Y.

JOSEPH F. NYC (2–103, 128–129)
Department of Physiological Chemistry
School of Medicine
University of California Medical Center
Los Angeles, California

CHARLES A. OWEN, JR. (419–444, 447–448)
Mayo Clinic
Rochester, Minnesota

ELAINE P. RALLI (669–678, 687–694)
Department of Medicine
New York University
477 First Avenue
New York, N. Y.

E. E. SNELL (361–362, 366–367, 538–540, 550–551, 630–633, 678–680)
Department of Chemistry
University of Texas
Austin, Texas

E. R. WEIDLEIN, JR. (339–342)
Mellon Institute of Industrial Research
University of Pittsburgh
Pittsburgh, Pennsylvania

HILDA F. WIESE (300–311)
Department of Pediatrics
University of Texas Medical Branch
Galveston, Texas

CONTENTS OF VOLUME II

CONTENTS OF VOLUME I AND III

CHOLINE

I. Nomenclature and Formula

ROBERT S. HARRIS

Accepted name: Choline
Obsolete name: Bilineurine
Empirical formula: $C_5H_{15}O_2N$
Chemical name: β-Hydroxyethyltrimethylammonium hydroxide
Structure:

$$(CH_3)_3N\!-\!CH_2\!-\!CH_2OH$$
$$|$$
$$OH$$

II. Chemistry

WENDELL H. GRIFFITH and JOSEPH F. NYC

A. ISOLATION

Choline is widely distributed in biological materials as free choline, as acetylcholine, and as more complex phospholipids and their metabolic intermediates. It is an integral part of the lecithins, which accounts for its occurrence, in combination at least, in all plant and animal cells. It is also one of the bases of the sphingomyelins of animal tissues. Phosphorylcholine, glycerylphosphorylcholine, and the ester of phosphorylcholine with sphingosine have been reported to occur, but it is uncertain to what extent these components of phospholipids normally exist free in tissues. Choline is characterized by a trimethyl quaternary nitrogen. Substances related to choline in this respect, include glycine betaine, carnitine, and ergothionine. From the viewpoint of lability of methyl groups, related compounds are methionine, dimethyl-β-propiothetin, and dimethylthetin. The latter is of considerable importance in laboratory studies but is not known to occur naturally.

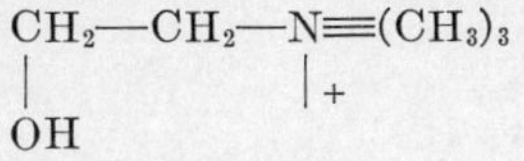

$$CH_2—CH_2—N≡(CH_3)_3$$
$$|\qquad\qquad |+$$
$$OH$$

Choline

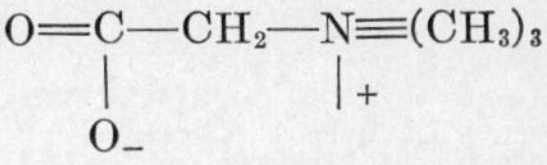

$$O=C—CH_2—N≡(CH_3)_3$$
$$|\qquad\qquad\quad |+$$
$$O_-$$

Betaine

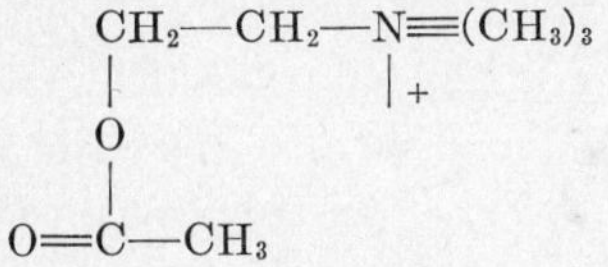

$$CH_2—CH_2—N≡(CH_3)_3$$
$$|\qquad\qquad |+$$
$$O$$
$$|$$
$$O=C—CH_3$$

Acetylcholine

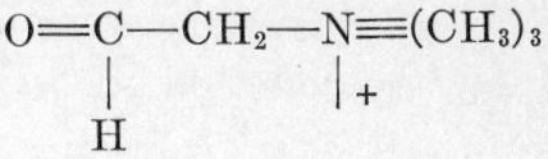

$$O=C—CH_2—N≡(CH_3)_3$$
$$|\qquad\qquad\quad |+$$
$$H$$

Betaine aldehyde

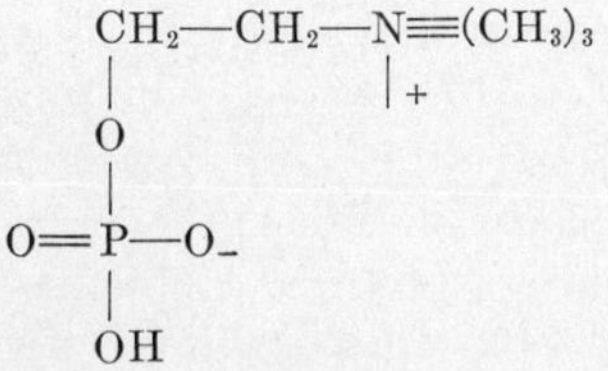

$$CH_2—CH_2—N≡(CH_3)_3$$
$$|\qquad\qquad |+$$
$$O$$
$$|$$
$$O=P—O_-$$
$$|$$
$$OH$$

Phosphorylcholine

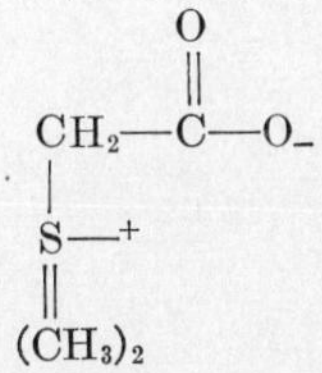

$$O$$
$$\|$$
$$CH_2—C—O_-$$
$$|$$
$$S—^+$$
$$\|$$
$$(CH_3)_2$$

Dimethylthetin

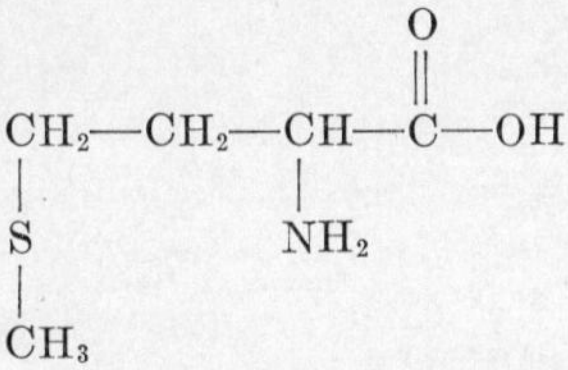

$$O$$
$$\|$$
$$CH_2—CH_2—CH—C—OH$$
$$|\qquad\qquad\quad |$$
$$S\qquad\qquad NH_2$$
$$|$$
$$CH_3$$

Methionine

$$O$$
$$\|$$
$$CH_2—CH_2—C—O_-$$
$$|$$
$$S—^+$$
$$\|$$
$$(CH_3)_2$$

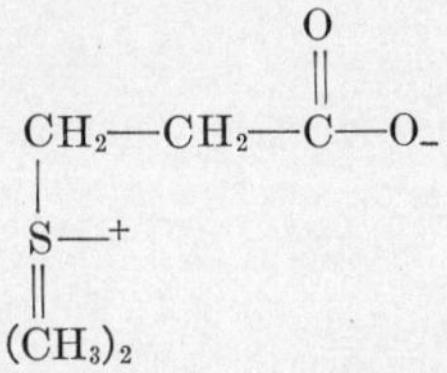

Dimethyl-β-propiothetin

Surprisingly, the first isolations of choline were not from materials rich in the complex lipids but from hog bile by Strecker[1] in 1849 and from an alkaloid of white mustard seed (*Sinapis alba*) by Babo and Hirschbrunn[2] in 1852. The latter workers named their product sinkaline, whereas Strecker[3] in 1862 applied the name choline to the substance obtained from bile. Subsequently, Liebreich[4] separated a fraction from hydrolyzed crude brain lecithin (protagon), which he named neurine. Dybkowsky[5] soon found that Liebrich's base was choline and not the vinyl compound known as neurine at the present time, and Claus and Keesé[6] demonstrated the identity of sinkaline and choline.

Choline has been obtained from a great variety of tissues and fluids

[1] A. Strecker, *Ann.* **70**, 149 (1849).
[2] L. von Babo and M. Hirschbrunn, *Ann.* **84**, 10 (1852).
[3] A. Strecker, *Ann.* **123**, 353 (1862).
[4] O. Liebreich, *Ann.* **134**, 29 (1865).
[5] W. Dybkowsky, *J. prakt. Chem.* **100**, 153 (1867).
[6] A. Claus and C. Keesé, *J. prakt. Chem.* **102**, 24 (1867).

since these original isolations. Wrede and Bruch[7] extracted various tissues with hot acidulated water, and the choline in these extracts was isolated and weighed as the chloroaurate. Bischoff et al.,[8] using a reineckate precipitation, reported finding up to 45 mg. of free choline (calculated as the chloride) per kilogram of muscle. Heesch[9] prepared extracts of blood serum which had been treated with trichloroacetic acid and found in these extracts 2.5 to 10 mg. of choline per liter of blood. Strack et al.[10] have presented data which suggest that much of the evidence for the presence of free choline in biological materials is unreliable, owing to delay in the preparation of extracts, with resulting release of choline by autolysis. They found that dog's liver contained 0 to 43 mg. of choline if extracted immediately after death of the animal and 136 to 164 mg. of choline per kilogram of liver if extracts were made 5 hours after death. A similar slow release of free choline occurred in experiments in which the fresh tissue was suspended in alcohol. Strack et al.[11] did not find free choline in rabbit, dog, or beef muscle. On careful investigation the substance in muscle which was precipitated as the reineckate and reported as choline by Bischoff et al.[8] was found to be carnitine.

Many solvents have been tested with respect to the thoroughness with which total choline, combined and free, is extracted from natural products. Among these are benzene, petroleum ether, ethyl ether, ethanol, methanol, acetone, chloroform, and mixtures thereof. None has proved to have any special advantage over methanol itself.[12, 13] Engel[12] employed multiple extractions of samples with methanol in a Bailey-Walker extractor. The more convenient method of extraction with the Soxhlet apparatus is generally preferred. Glick[14] has recommended the mixing of powdered samples with No. 2 pulverized pumice, after weighing, to prevent caking of the sample and the resultant channeling of the extracting solvent.

The residue of the methanol extracts of samples must be hydrolyzed if the total choline content is to be determined. Barium hydroxide has been favored as the alkali for the digestion process because there is no loss of choline when pure choline solutions are used.[15-18] Gulewitsch[15] studied the

[7] F. Wrede and E. Bruch, Hoppe-Seyler's Z. physiol. Chem. 195, 255 (1931).

[8] G. Bischoff, W. Grab, and J. Kapfhammer, Hoppe-Seyler's Z. physiol. Chem. 207, 57 (1932).

[9] O. Heesch, Arch. ges. Physiol. 209, 779 (1925).

[10] E. Strack, E. Neubaur, and H. Geissendörfer, Hoppe-Seyler's Z. physiol. Chem. 220, 217 (1933).

[11] E. Strack, P. Wördehoff, E. Neubaur, and H. Geissendörfer, Hoppe-Seyler's Z. physiol. Chem. 233, 189 (1935).

[12] R. W. Engel, J. Biol. Chem. 144, 701 (1942).

[13] M. Rhian, R. J. Evans, and J. L. St. John, J. Nutrition 25, 1 (1943).

[14] D. Glick, J. Biol. Chem. 156, 643 (1944).

[15] W. Gulewitsch, Hoppe-Seyler's Z. physiol. Chem. 24, 513 (1898).

effect of heating choline in aqueous baryta as well as in alcoholic solutions of sodium ethylate and found only a negligible breakdown of choline after boiling in baryta solution for 6 hours or after heating in a 5% sodium alcoholate solution for 24 hours.

Beattie[19] studied the acid hydrolysis of a lecithin emulsion prepared from a commercial egg lecithin preparation and hydrolyzed in 7.8% hydrochloric acid at 110°. The maximum value of free choline was obtained after hydrolysis for 21 hours. Acid hydrolysis has been used also in the liberation of choline from bound forms in tissues.[20-22] Ducet and Kahane[22] refluxed animal and vegetable tissues with 30% nitric acid until a clear solution was obtained. After neutralization of the solution with powdered calcium carbonate and dilution with several volumes of water, 10 ml. of 50% ferric sulfate and 5 g. of calcium carbonate were added for each gram of dry tissue originally taken. The mixture was heated to boiling and filtered. The filtrate and washings containing the choline were concentrated to a small volume, and the choline was precipitated by one of the reagents generally employed for this purpose. These workers found that no choline was destroyed during this procedure.

The earliest methods which were employed for isolating choline from biological extracts were dependent on the use of various sensitive though non-specific precipitants. Choline may be precipitated from alcoholic solutions as the double salt of platinum, gold, or mercury chlorides.[15, 23, 24] Precipitation as the reineckate or the periodide has been employed most extensively for the removal of choline from aqueous solution.

Beattie[19] observed that a quantitative precipitation of free choline as the reineckate can be obtained in solutions containing as little as 0.03 mg. of choline chloride per milliliter and that the choline in about 7 to 10 ml. of a solution of this concentration can be quantitatively determined. The slight extent to which other substances interfere with the reineckate precipitation and estimation of choline in animal tissues and fluids was demonstrated by Beattie by analysis of tissue extracts, a tryptic digest, and urine before and after the addition of known amounts of choline chloride (Table I).

[16] B. N. Erickson, I. Avrin, D. M. Teague, and H. H. Williams, *J. Biol. Chem.* **135,** 671 (1940).

[17] H. P. Jacobi, C. A. Baumann, and W. J. Meek, *J. Biol. Chem.* **138,** 571 (1941).

[18] J. Kapfhammer and C. Bischoff, *Hoppe-Seyler's Z. physiol. Chem.* **191,** 179 (1930).

[19] F. J. R. Beattie, *Biochem. J.* **30,** 1554 (1936).

[20] J. D. Fletcher, C. H. Best, and O. M. Solandt, *Biochem. J.* **29,** 2278 (1935).

[21] R. W. Luecke and P. B. Pearson, *J. Biol. Chem.* **153,** 259 (1944); **155,** 507 (1944).

[22] G. Ducet and E. Kahane, *Bull. soc. chim. biol.* **28,** 794 (1946).

[23] A. Lohmann, *Arch. ges. Physiol.* **122,** 203 (1908).

[24] C. T. Mörner, *Hoppe-Seyler's Z. physiol. Chem.* **22,** 514 (1896).

On the basis of a careful study of the reineckate method, as originally modified by Jacobi et al.[17] and Engel,[12] Glick[14] has proposed the following procedure for the isolation of choline from natural materials:

A weighed sample, containing the equivalent of 2 to 5 mg. of choline chloride, is placed in an alundum thimble of medium porosity (80 mm. long and 22 mm. in diameter) for extraction in a Soxhlet apparatus fitted with a 125-ml. boiling flask. About 100 ml. of methanol is used as the solvent, and the extraction is allowed to proceed for 24 hours. With some finely divided materials such as flour, the tendency to form a hard cake makes it desirable to mix the sample intimately with No. 2 pulverized pumice to facilitate the extraction. The boiling flask containing the methanol extract is placed on a steam bath and, when only a few milliliters of solvent remains, 30 ml. of a saturated solution of barium hydroxide is added and the heating is continued for 90 minutes. After the mixture is cooled, a drop of 1 % alcoholic thymolphthalein is added to the hydrolyzate and glacial acetic is

TABLE I

RECOVERY OF ADDED CHOLINE BY THE REINECKATE PROCEDURE[19]

	Choline chloride, mg./ml.			
	Originally present	Amount added	Total amount	Amount recovered
Kidney extract	0.13	0.69	0.85	0.72
Liver extract	0.18	0.77	0.94	0.76
Tryptic digest	None	1.50	1.56	1.56
Urine	None	1.50	1.56	1.56

introduced until the blue color is just discharged by one drop. The liquid is then filtered by suction through a sintered glass filter tube of medium porosity (15 to 30 ml. capacity) into a 125-ml. suction flask. The boiling flask is rinsed with small portions of distilled water, and the rinsings are used to wash the filter, a total of about 15 ml. of water being used. To the combined filtrate and washings is added 6 ml. of a 2 % solution of reineckate salt in methanol, and the flask is placed in a refrigerator at about 5° for 2 hours. The choline reineckate precipitate is filtered with suction into a 30-ml. sintered glass filter tube of medium porosity. The dried precipitate is washed three times with 2.5-ml. portions of n-propanol and again dried by means of the suction.

The above procedure avoids the precipitation of betaine reineckate which is insoluble in acid solutions but soluble in slightly alkaline solutions. However, it has been noted[25] that dimethylaminoethanol appears to be carried down in part in the choline reineckate precipitate when a solution containing the two bases is treated with reineckate at a slightly alkaline pH.

[25] T. H. Jukes, A. C. Dornbush, and J. J. Oleson, Federation Proc. 4, 157 (1945).

According to Coujard[26] treatment of tissue sections with reineckate precipitates choline reineckate as birefringent crystals which are readily seen with a polarizing microscope. Keenan[27] has described microscopic procedures for the quantitative detection of traces of choline as the reineckate and as the chloroplatinate.

The periodide separation is generally considered to be one of the most sensitive methods of precipitating choline. Griess and Harrow[28] had utilized the insolubility of the periodide to isolate choline as early as 1885. In 1896 Florence[29] described a medico-legal test for semen stains based upon the typical crystals formed when this material was treated with iodine in potassium iodide solution. Bocarius[30] isolated the typical Florence crystals and proved by chemical identification that choline was the substance which gave the insoluble periodide. Booth[31] estimated that in aqueous solutions potassium triiodide gives a precipitate with choline at a dilution of about 1:50,000. Staněk[32] studied the chemical composition of the choline periodide precipitate and the conditions under which it is formed. A detailed study of the periodide procedure for the isolation and subsequent estimation of choline was made by Kiesel.[33]

Choline may also be precipitated from water with phosphotungstic, silicotungstic, and phosphomolybdic acids.[15, 34] Ackerman[35] used dipicrylamine as a precipitant, the choline salt being only slightly soluble in water (0.02 g. in 100 ml. of water at 20°). The low solubility of the salt permitted the separation of choline from betaine and aminoethanol. Schoorl[36] published descriptions and enlarged micrographs of the double salts of choline hydrochloride with the following reagents: platinum chloride, sodium gold chloride, mercuric chloride, mercuric iodide, potassium bismuth iodide, picric acid, and picrolonic acid.

Several combined water-soluble forms of choline have been isolated from biological materials. In 1929 Dale and Dudley[37] succeeded in isolating acetylcholine from an extract of horse spleen in sufficient quantities for chemical identification. Since that time the acetylcholine in tissues has

[26] R. Coujard, *Compt. rend. soc. biol.* **142**, 15 (1948).
[27] G. L. Keenan, *J. Assoc. Offic. Agr. Chemists* **26**, 96 (1943).
[28] P. Griess and G. Harrow, *Ber.* **18**, 717 (1885).
[29] A. Florence, *Arch. Anthropol.* **II**, 11 (1896).
[30] N. Bocarius, *Hoppe-Seyler's Z. physiol. Chem.* **34**, 339 (1901).
[31] F. J. Booth, *Biochem. J.* **29**, 2064 (1935).
[32] V. Staněk, *Hoppe-Seyler's Z. physiol. Chem.* **46**, 280 (1905); **47**, 83 (1906); **48**, 334 (1906).
[33] A. Kiesel, *Hoppe-Seyler's Z. physiol. Chem.* **53**, 215 (1907).
[34] L. Lematte, G. Bionot, E. Kahane, and M. Kahane, *Compt. rend.* **191**, 1130 (1930).
[35] D. Ackermann, *Hoppe-Seyler's Z. physiol. Chem.* **281**, 197 (1944).
[36] N. Schoorl, *Pharm. Weekblad.* **55**, 363 (1918).
[37] H. H. Dale and H. W. Dudley, *J. Physiol. (London)* **68**, 97 (1929).

been widely studied. A summary of the early work on acetylcholine has been published by Gaddum.[38]

Hunt[39] described a biological test for choline based on its conversion to acetylcholine and the demonstration of the effect of the ester in lowering blood pressure in cats or rabbits or in decreasing the amplitude of the beat of the frog's heart. Ackermann and Mauer[40] prepared the acetylcholine salt of dipicrylamine, insoluble red crystals yielding a red solution with acetone suitable for colorimetric estimation. Rossi et al.[41] compared various derivatives and found that the formation of the crystalline silicotungstate was a useful method of distinguishing choline and acetylcholine.

Inukai and Nakahara[42] isolated phosphorylcholine from beef liver. A yield of 0.3 g. of the crystalline picrate was obtained from 200 kg. of fresh beef liver. The crystals, which were an addition compound of 1 mole of picric acid and 2 moles of the ester, softened at 225° and melted at 228°. Both the synthesis and hydrolysis of phosphorylcholine by intestinal phosphatase have been reported.[43, 44] The enzymatic cleavage of phosphorylcholine has been studied extensively by Baccari.[45, 46]

Isolation from animal tissues of a water-soluble substance believed to be the phosphorylcholine ester of sphingosine has been reported by a number of investigators.[10, 47-51] King and Aloisi[52] isolated glycerylphosphoric acid from an acid extract of beef pancreas and assumed that it resulted from hydrolysis of glycerylphosphorylcholine (GPC). Schmidt et al.[53] isolated the latter compound from incubated pancreas and, on the basis of difficulties in the isolation of homogeneous products of this type, questioned the identity of the product previously isolated by King and Small[51] and believed by them to be sphingosylphosphorylcholine. Kahane and Lévy[54-55]

[38] J. H. Gaddum, Ann. Rev. Biochem. 4, 311 (1935).
[39] R. Hunt, J. Pharmacol. Exptl. Therap. 7, 301 (1915).
[40] D. Ackermann and H. Mauer, Hoppe-Seyler's Z. physiol. Chem. 279, 114 (1943).
[41] L. Rossi, A. D. Marenzi, and R. Lobo, Anales. farm. y bioquim. (Buenos Aires) 13, 31 (1942).
[42] F. Inukai and W. Nakahara, Proc. Imp. Acad. (Tokyo) 11, 260 (1935).
[43] S. Bouchilloux and A. Tissieres, Bull. soc. chim. biol. 29, 955 (1947).
[44] J. Roche and S. Bouchilloux, Arch. sci. physiol. 2, 283 (1948).
[45] V. Baccari, Boll. soc. ital. biol. sper. 21, 48 (1946).
[46] V. Baccari and G. Auricchio, Boll. soc. ital. biol. sper. 22, 559 (1946).
[47] E. Strack, E. Neubaur and H. Geissendörfer, Hoppe-Seyler's Z. physiol. Chem. 229, 25 (1934).
[48] F. J. Booth, Biochem. J. 29, 2071 (1935).
[49] F. J. Booth and T. H. Milroy, J. Physiol. (London) 84, 32P (1935).
[50] D. H. Smyth, Biochem. J. 29, 2067 (1935).
[51] E. J. King and C. W. Small, Biochem. J. 33, 1135 (1939).
[52] E. J. King and M. Aloisi, Biochem. J. 39, 470 (1945).
[53] G. Schmidt, B. Hershman, and S. J. Thannhauser, J. Biol. Chem. 161, 523 (1945).
[54] E. Kahane and J. Lévy, Compt. rend. 219, 431 (1944).

presented evidence for the hydrolysis of lecithin to GPC by rat intestine, and Shapiro[56] has demonstrated the formation of GPC from lecithin, by a cell-free extract of pancreas.

Cyclic choline sulfate was isolated from *Aspergillus sydowi* by Woolley and Peterson,[57] who obtained it both from an autolyzate and from an acetone extract of defatted mycelium. The yield was 0.26 % based on the weight of the dry mycelium. The isolated cyclic sulfate was believed to be identical with a synthetic product of the formula $C_5H_{13}O_4NS$ which had been previously synthesized from choline chloride and sulfuric acid by Schmidt and Wagner.[58] Its use as a source of sulfur by *Aspergillus oryzae* has been reported.[59]

As yet no methods exist for the accurate isolation and determination of the different forms of choline in biological materials, particularly free choline and combined water-soluble choline. Kahane and Lévy[60] defined water-soluble choline as the total found in aqueous extracts of tissues after suitable precipitation and filtration. Ferric hydroxide formed within the mixture by addition of ferric sulfate and calcium carbonate was recommended as the best precipitating agent. The choline of lecithin would not be included in the total water-soluble choline.

Several attempts have been made to devise procedures for the separation of free choline from combined water-soluble choline as well as from other water-soluble substances which may interfere with its isolation and quantitative determination. Gebauer-Fuelnegg and Kendall[61] applied electrodialysis to the separation of histidine from histamine or choline, and also to the separation of an artificial mixture of protein or gelatin from histamine or choline. This is reported to be a suitable method for the separation of relatively strong, crystalloidal bases from mixtures with amphoteric or more weakly basic substances.

Horowitz and Beadle[62] used Permutit columns to separate choline from non-basic interfering substances. They found that a Permutit column measuring 110 × 0.6 mm., containing approximately 1 g. of Permutit, completely removes the choline from 5 ml. of a solution containing up to 0.5 mg. of choline per milliliter. Repeated tests showed that the absorbed choline is quantitatively eluted with 10 ml. of 5 % sodium chloride.

[55] E. Kahane and J. Lévy, *Helv. Chim. Acta* **29,** 1322 (1946).
[56] B. Shapiro, *Nature* **169,** 29 (1952).
[57] D. W. Woolley and W. H. Peterson, *J. Biol. Chem.* **122,** 213 (1937).
[58] E. Schmidt and W. Wagner, *Ann.* **337,** 51 (1904).
[59] F. Egami and M. Itabashi, *Igaku to Seibutsugaku* **19,** 292 (1951).
[60] E. Kahane and J. Lévy, *Bull. soc. chim. biol.* **21,** 223 (1939).
[61] E. Gebauer-Fuelnegg and A. I. Kendall, *Ber.* **64B,** 1067 (1931).
[62] N. H. Horowitz and G. W. Beadle, *J. Biol. Chem.* **150,** 325 (1943).

Ducet[63] observed that free choline can be quantitatively adsorbed on silica gel whereas the combined water-soluble choline remains in the solvent.

The isolation of choline by paper chromatography was investigated by Munier and Macheboeuf.[64] These workers report that non-alkaloidal substances such as choline and betaine are readily separated from alkaloids because their partition coefficients in various solvent systems are different. Choline is detected on the paper strips by the blue color formed when the chromatograms are treated with solutions containing phosphomolybdic acid, acetic acid and stannous chloride. R_f values are given by these workers for choline when it is chromatogrammed with various solvent mixtures containing n-butanol, acetic acid, and water.

B. PHYSICAL AND CHEMICAL PROPERTIES

Choline, hydroxyethyltrimethylammonium hydroxide, can be obtained with difficulty as a colorless crystalline mass by drying under high vacuum over P_2O_5.[28, 65] It is a strong base, decomposes ammonium salts, and has a marked tendency to absorb water and carbon dioxide from the air. Choline has no well-defined melting or boiling point but breaks down when heated into trimethylamine and glycol. Dimethylaminoethanol and dimethylvinylamine are also formed in lesser amounts by thermal decomposition of the base.[65] Dilute water solutions of the base are stable to heat, but concentrated solutions give off trimethylamine when boiled.[66]

Choline is soluble in water, in formaldehyde, and in absolute methyl and ethyl alcohols. It is sparingly soluble in amyl alcohol, chloroform, dry acetone, and wet ether. Choline is insoluble in dry ether, carbon tetrachloride, carbon sulfide, toluene, benzene, and petroleum ether.[67, 68]

Edsall[69] reported the Raman spectrum for choline chloride, and the ultraviolet absorption spectrum of the base is described by Castille and Ruppal[70] and by Graubner.[71]

C. CONSTITUTION AND SYNTHESIS

The correct structure of choline was determined by Baeyer[72] and by Wurtz,[73] who carried out the first syntheses, using the reaction of tri-

[63] G. Ducet, *Compt. rend.* **226**, 1045 (1948).
[64] R. Munier and M. Macheboeuf, *Bull. soc. chim. biol.* **31**, 1144 (1949).
[65] K. H. Meyer and H. Hopff, *Ber.* **54**, 2274 (1921).
[66] A. Wurtz, *Compt. rend.* **66**, 772 (1868).
[67] W. Roman, *Biochem. Z.* **219**, 218 (1930).
[68] G. Klien and H. Linser, *Biochem. Z.* **250**, 220 (1932).
[69] J. T. Edsall, *J. Am. Chem. Soc.* **65**, 1767 (1943).
[70] A. Castille and M. Ruppal, *Bull acad. roy. méd. Belg.* **56**, 263 (1926).
[71] W. Graubner, *Z. ges. exptl. Med.* **63**, 527 (1928).
[72] A. Baeyer, *Ann.* **140**, 306 (1866); **142**, 322 (1867).
[73] A. Wurtz, *Compt. rend.* **65**, 1015 (1867).

methylamine either on ethylene chlorohydrin or on ethylene oxide with the formation of the chloride or the free base, respectively.

Several of the early synthetic methods for choline were based on (2-bromoethyl)trimethylammonium bromide as the starting compound. This substance is easily prepared by reacting trimethylamine with ethylene bromide according to the following equation:

$$(CH_3)_3N + BrCH_2CH_2Br \rightarrow Br(CH_3)_3NCH_2CH_2Br$$

Bode[74] converted the brominated product into choline by heating it in a solution of silver nitrate. Krüger and Bergell[75] effected the same conversion by heating its aqueous solution for 4 hours at 160° in a sealed tube. Lucius[76] heated the compound for 1 hour in an alcoholic solution of potassium hydroxide at 120° and obtained a mixture of choline and neurine (vinyltrimethylammonium hydroxide).

Choline has been synthesized also by the exhaustive methylation of aminoethanol with methyl iodide in a methanolic solution of potassium hydroxide,[77] by modifications of the original methods of Wurtz[73] using trimethylamine,[78-79a] by preparation of dimethylaminoethanol and its conversion to choline through the methiodide,[80] and by hydrolysis of 2-(ethoxymethoxy)ethyl-trimethylammonium formate formed from the corresponding dimethylamine derivative and methyl formate.[81]

The general problem involving the synthesis of hydroxy bases and of homologs of choline was studied by von Braun.[80] This worker has shown that, by means of the compounds $Br(CH_2)_xOBz$ and $NHMe_2$, bases of the type $Me_2H(CH_2)_xOBz$ can be prepared. These are quantitatively converted to the hydroxy bases, $Me_2N(CH_2)_xOH$, by alkaline hydrolysis. The methiodide of the product can then be treated with silver chloride to give $Me_3NCl(CH_2)_xOH$.

The synthesis of choline with the hydrogens of the methyl groups replaced by deuterium was first undertaken by du Vigneaud[82] and his coworkers. Deuteriomethyl alcohol was converted with phosphorus and iodine to deuteriomethyliodide. The iodide with aminoethanol yielded choline with an overall yield of 64% based on deuteriomethyl alcohol.

[74] J. Bode, Ann. 267, 268 (1891).
[75] M. Krüger and P. Bergell, Ber. 36, 290 (1903).
[76] R. Lucius, Arch. Pharm. 245, 248 (1907).
[77] G. Trier, Hoppe-Seyler's Z. physiol. Chem. 80, 409 (1912).
[78] R. R. Renshaw, J. Am. Chem. Soc. 32, 128 (1910).
[79] F. Körner, French Pat. 736,107 (April 29, 1932).
[79a] H. Hopff and K. Vierling, German Pat. 801,210 (December 28, 1950).
[80] J. von Braun, Ber. 49, 966 (1916).
[81] W. F. Gresham, U. S. Pat. 2,457,226 (December 28, 1948).
[82] V. du Vigneaud, J. P. Chandler, M. Cohn, and G. B. Brown, J. Biol. Chem. 134, 787 (1940).

Walz et al.[83] synthesized choline and acetylcholine labeled in the ethylene chain with isotopic carbon-14. Acetylene-C[14], obtained from active carbonate in the usual manner,[84] was reduced to ethylene by reaction with chromous chloride according to the method of Arrol and Glascock.[85] The labeled ethylene was converted to ethylene bromohydrin-1,2-C[14] with N-bromoacetamide. The bromohydrin with excess trimethylamine in ether yielded choline bromide with an 83% yield based on the bromohydrin. Dauben and Gee[86] have published an alternative procedure starting with carboxyl-labeled sodium acetate. This was converted to chloroacetic acid which was esterified with diazoethane. The resulting chloroacetate was allowed to react with dimethylamine, and the product was reduced to N,N-dimethylaminoethanol with lithium aluminum hydride. The substituted ethanol was further methylated with methyl iodide, and the choline iodide converted into choline chloride with C[14] in the alcoholic carbon.

An improved synthesis of phosphorylcholine has been described by Baer.[87, 88] The compound was prepared by the catalytic hydrogenation of diphenylphosphorylcholine produced by the reaction of diphenylphosphoryl chloride and choline chloride in pyridine.

Glycerylphosphoric acid esters of choline have been prepared by Ravazzoni and Fenaroli[89] and by Aloisi and Buffa[90] from bromocholine picrate and the silver α- and β-glycerylphosphates. These authors suggest that previous workers may have confused the choline salts of the glycerylphosphates with the choline esters. The choline salts form readily and block esterification. Baer and Kates[91, 92] prepared and studied the hydrolysis of L-α-glycerylphosphorylcholine and noted a reversible shifting of the phosphoric acid between the α- and β-carbons.

Salts of choline and of the common acids, including acetic, carbonic, hydrochloric, nitric, oxalic, picric, picrolonic, and sulfuric acids, are soluble in water and in ethanol, whereas the acid tartrate, chloroplatinate, monophosphate, and ruffinate are insoluble in ethanol. Double salts with cadmium chloride and with zinc chloride are also soluble in water and insoluble in ethanol. Double salts with gold chloride and with mercuric chloride are insoluble in water. Other water-insoluble salts include the hexaiodide,

[83] D. E. Walz, M. Fields, and J. A. Gibbs, *J. Am. Chem. Soc.* **73**, 2968 (1951).
[84] W. J. Arrol and R. Glascock, *Nature* **159**, 810 (1947).
[85] W. J. Arrol and R. Glascock, *J. Chem. Soc.* **1950** *Suppl.*, Issue 2, S 335.
[86] W. G. Dauben and M. Gee, *J. Am. Chem. Soc.* **74**, 1078 (1952).
[87] E. Baer and C. S. McArthur, *J. Biol. Chem.* **154**, 451 (1944).
[88] E. Baer, *J. Am. Chem. Soc.* **69**, 1253 (1947).
[89] C. Ravazzoni and A. Fenaroli, *Ann. chim. applicata* **30**, 318 (1940).
[90] M. Aloisi and P. Buffa, *Biochem. J.* **43**, 157 (1948).
[91] E. Baer and M. Kates, *J. Am. Chem. Soc.* **70**, 1394 (1948).
[92] E. Baer and M. Kates, *J. Biol. Chem.* **175**, 79 (1948).

periodate, enneaiodide, phosphotungstate, phosphomolybdate, reineckate, and salts with Mayer's reagent (potassium mercuric iodide) and with Kraut's reagent (potassium bismuth iodide). The chloroplatinate is moderately soluble in water but very insoluble in ethanol. The flavianate is sparingly soluble in ethanol and is insoluble in N-butanol.

The properties of some of the more important salts are listed below:

Chloride ($C_5H_{14}ONCl$): Soluble in water, methanol, ethanol, and formaldehyde; less soluble in carbon tetrachloride, chloroform, and acetone; insoluble in carbon disulfide, benzene, toluene, ether, and petroleum ether; deliquescent; stable up to 180°, decomposing on heating to give dimethylaminoethanol and methyl chloride.

Reineckate ($C_{15}H_{14}ON \cdot C_4H_7N_6S_4Cr$): Melts above 250°;[93] soluble in water at 18° up to 0.02 %, in 10 % hydrochloric acid up to 0.03 %; in the presence of excess ammonium reineckate the solubility in water is greatly depressed;[94] insoluble in dilute ammonia, 0.1 N sodium hydroxide, ethanol, benzene, and ether, but has an appreciable solubility in acetone.[95, 96]

Periodides: Periodides of choline are precipitated by iodine in potassium iodide solution, either as an insoluble oil or as a crystalline material, depending upon the conditions.[28, 32]

Hexaiodide ($C_5H_{14}ON \cdot I \cdot I_5$): Black greenish iridescent oil obtained when potassium triiodide solution is added to an excess of choline chloride; very insoluble in water and soluble in ethanol; converted to the enneaiodide by treatment with KI_3 solution or powdered iodine.

Enneaiodide ($C_5H_{14}ON \cdot I \cdot I_8$): Green needles, soluble in alcohol but very insoluble in water; loses iodine rapidly in air and goes over to the hexaiodide.

Mercuric chloride double salt ($C_5H_{14}ON \cdot Cl \cdot 6 \ HgCl_2$): Melts at 249 to 251°,[15] 242 to 243°;[22] insoluble in cold water and very insoluble in alcohol.

Chloroaurate ($C_5H_{14}ON \cdot Cl \cdot AuCl_3$): Melts at 243 to 244° (slow heating), 259° (rapid heating),[97] 257°[98] 267 to 270°;[21] deep yellow needles from hot alcohol or octahedra and cubes from dilute alcohol; sparingly soluble in water, and very insoluble in alcohol.

Chloroplatinate ($C_5H_{14}ON \cdot Cl)_2PtCl_4$: Quickly decomposes on heating at 241 to 242°;[65] dimorphous; crystallizes in cubes and octahedra from hot alcohol and water (1:1), but in six-sided pyramids or monoclinic rhombic

[93] G. Bischoff, W. Grab, and J. Kapfhammer, *Hoppe-Seyler's Z. physiol. Chem.* **200**, 153 (1931).

[94] E. Strack and H. Schwaneberg, *Hoppe-Seyler's Z. physiol. Chem.* **245**, 11 (1936).

[95] H. Paal, *Biochem. Z.* **211**, 244 (1929).

[96] F. H. Shaw, *Biochem. J.* **32**, 1002 (1938).

[97] J. Smorodinzew, *Hoppe-Seyler's Z. physiol. Chem.* **80**, 218 (1912).

[98] C. Reuter, *Hoppe-Seyler's Z. physiol. Chem.* **78**, 167 (1912).

crystals from water; both forms of crystals are orange-red in color; very insoluble in alcohol but moderately soluble in water.

Bromoplatinate $(C_5H_{14}ON\ Br)_2PtBr_4$: Melts at 240° (decomp.); large dark-red prisms or octahedra; sparingly soluble in water.[99]

Picrate $(C_5H_{14}ON \cdot C_6H_2O_7N_3)$: Melts at 240°; readily soluble in water and alcohol.[100]

Complex with uranium $[C_5H_{14}ON \cdot UO_2(NO_3)_2]_2$: Yellow, non-hygroscopic crystals insoluble in ethanol and ether and sparingly soluble in water; aqueous solution fluoresces in ultraviolet light.[101]

III. Industrial Preparation

WENDELL H. GRIFFITH and JOSEPH F. NYC

The reaction between trimethylamine and either ethylene chlorohydrin[1, 2] or ethylene oxide[3] is used commonly in the manufacture of choline.

$$(CH_3)_3N + ClCH_2CH_2OH \rightarrow (CH_3)_3N^+CH_2CH_2OH + Cl^{1}$$

$$(CH_3)_3N + CH_2\!\!-\!\!CH_2 + H_2O \rightarrow (CH_3)_3N^+CH_2CH_2OH + [OH]^{1}$$
$$\diagdown\!\diagup$$
$$O$$

In Hopf and Vierling's modification of the first reaction[2] gaseous trimethylamine is passed through ethylene chlorohydrin at 80°. In Körner's procedure[3] trimethylamine and ethylene oxide react in the presence of water and carbon dioxide and the resulting choline is transformed to other salts by treatment with various acids.

Choline has been prepared more recently by a two-step synthesis.[4] The quarternary salt, 2-(ethoxymethoxy)ethyltrimethylammonium formate, is formed by heating 2-(ethoxymethoxy)ethyldimethylamine with an excess of methyl formate at 140 to 150° under a pressure of 250 p.s.i. The quarternary salt is then refluxed in a mixture of ethyl alcohol and hydrochloric acid, and the reaction mixture is taken to dryness at a reduced pressure. The crude choline chloride remaining in the residue is purified by crystallization from isobutyl alcohol.

[99] A. B. Weinhagen, *Hoppe-Seyler's Z. physiol. Chem.* **105**, 249 (1919).

[100] U. Suzuki, T. Shimamura, and S. Odake, *Biochem. Z.* **43**, 89 (1912).

[101] C. Soye, *Compt. rend.* **228**, 1228 (1949).

[1] R. R. Renshaw, *J. Am. Chem. Soc.* **32**, 128 (1910).

[2] H. Hopff and K. Vierling, German Pat. 801,210 (December 28, 1950).

[3] F. Körner, French Pat. 736,107 (April 29, 1932).

[4] W. F. Gresham, U. S. Pat. 2,457,226 (December 28, 1948).

IV. Biochemical Systems

WENDELL H. GRIFFITH and JOSEPH F. NYC

A. ENZYMES AND COENZYMES

Studies on choline and its derivatives have emphasized the biochemical importance of these compounds as structural components of tissues, as intermediates in vital metabolic reactions, and as specific chemical reactants of marked biological potency. On the other hand, evidence for the participation of choline or of its derivatives in a specific manner as cofactors in enzymatic systems is meager, although a few reports have linked it or its phosphoric acid ester with phosphatases. Caution is needed in questioning the importance of choline as a component of coenzymes, because relatively little definite information is at hand regarding the functions and properties of the lipoproteins that contain choline phospholipids.

Kielley and Myerhof[1] believe that a magnesium-activated adenosine-triphosphatase (ATPase) of muscle may consist of a lipoprotein with a choline-containing phospholipid as a constituent. The compound was devoid of myosin and actomyosin, and there was no indication that it was another form of myosin ATPase. Its pH optimum was 6.8, and it was strongly inhibited by calcium. Inactivation of the enzyme and hydrolysis of the phospholipid portion by lecithinase of *Clostridium welchii* paralleled each other. The occurrence of the pyrophosphoric acid ester of choline in the prosthetic groups of acid and alkaline phosphatases has been reported.[2] Other workers[3] have noted that this ester contains a labile phosphate group, hydrolyzable by crude and not by purified muscle pyrophosphatase, but they are not of the opinion that it is a coenzyme of a phosphatase. Alkyl nitrogen-substituted derivatives of aminoethanol and of choline activate alkaline phosphomonoesterases.[4] Activation of an ATPase system in rat submaxillary gland by acetylcholine in vitro has been reported.[5]

B. CHOLINE ACETYLASE AND ACETYLCHOLINESTERASE

Coenzyme A (CoA) appears to be a common coenzyme for most, if not all, of the acetyl-transferring systems, including the acetylation of choline. The constituents of one form, at least, of this important thermostable compound include adenosine-2′(or 3′)-phosphate,[6, 7] pyrophosphate,[6] panto-

---

[1] W. W. Kielley and O. Myerhof, *J. Biol. Chem.* **176,** 591 (1948); **183,** 391 (1950).

[2] W. Kutscher and H. Sieg, *Naturwissenschaften* **37,** 451 (1950).

[3] J. Roche, N.-V. Thoai, and N.-V. Thiem, *Compt. rend. soc. biol.* **145,** 168 (1951).

[4] R. Granger and J. Fraux, *Trav. soc. pharm. Montpellier* **5,** 48 (1945–1946); **6,** 93 93 (1946–1947).

[5] K. P. DuBois and V. R. Potter, *J. Biol. Chem.* **148,** 451 (1943).

[6] F. Lipmann, N. O. Kaplan, G. D. Novelli, and L. C. Tuttle, *J. Biol. Chem.* **186,** 235 (1950).

thenic acid,[6] and β-mercaptoethylamine.[6, 8, 9] It is probable that the nucleoside is joined to the terminal alcoholic hydroxyl of the pantothenate by a pyrophosphate bridge and that the sulfur component forms an acid amide linkage with the carboxyl of the β-alanine moiety of the pantothenate. The pantothenic acid-mercaptoethylamine complex can be obtained from CoA by hydrolysis by intestinal phosphatase[10, 11] and is identical with Snell's *Lactobacillus bulgaricus* growth factor (LBF or pantetheine).[9, 11]

The free-SH group is the principal site of reactivity in the CoA molecule, and it is readily acetylated to acetyl CoA (CoA—S—CO—CH₃) in the presence of ATP. A partially purified preparation of acetyl CoA has been obtained from baker's yeast by Lynen *et al.*[12] This molecule, formerly designated "active acetate," serves as a donor of acetyl groups in the presence of specific apoenzymes. Energy in the form of ATP is required for its formation, and it is of considerable interest that its acyl-mercaptide linkage is an energy-rich bond.[13-15] CoA may exist in the disulfide form (CoA—S—S—CoA), and mixed disulfides with other sulfhydryl compounds have complicated its isolation.

The application of these findings to the metabolism of choline is illustrated by the system which transfers acetyl from citrate to choline. Ochoa *et al.*[16] have isolated a condensing enzyme from heart muscle which catalyzes reversibly the reaction between acetyl CoA and oxalacetate to give CoA and citrate. If choline and a second acetyl-transferring enzyme (acetylase) are present in addition to Ochoa's condensing enzyme plus citrate and CoA, acetylcholine is formed.[14]

The probable identity of the factor (presumably CoA) required in the acetylation of sulfanilamide and of choline was indicated in 1946.[17] Subsequently, Nachmansohn obtained a fraction termed acetylkinase from pigeon liver and demonstrated that both sulfanilamide and choline were acetylated

[7] J. Baddiley and E. M. Thain, *J. Chem. Soc.* **1951**, 3421.

[8] W. H. DeVries, W. M. Govier, J. S. Evans, J. D. Gregory, G. D. Novelli, M. Soodak, and F. Lipmann, *J. Am. Chem. Soc.* **72**, 4838 (1950).

[9] E. E. Snell, G. M. Brown, V. J. Peters, J. A. Craig, E. L. Wittle, J. A. Moore, V. M. McGlohon, and O. D. Bird, *J. Am. Chem. Soc.* **72**, 5349 (1950).

[10] G. D. Novelli, N. O. Kaplan, and F. Lipmann, *Federation Proc.* **9**, 209 (1950).

[11] G. M. Brown, J. A. Craig, and E. E. Snell, *Arch. Biochem.* **27**, 473 (1950).

[12] F. Lynen, E. Reichert, and L. Rueff, *Ann.* **574**, 1 (1951).

[13] F. Lynen, E. Reichert, *Angew. Chem.* **63**, 47 (1951).

[14] J. R. Stern, B. Shapiro, E. R. Stadtman, and S. Ochoa, *J. Biol. Chem.* **193**, 703 (1951).

[15] E. R. Stadtman, *J. Biol. Chem.* **196**, 535 (1952).

[16] S. Ochoa, J. R. Stern, and M. C. Schneider, *J. Biol. Chem.* **193**, 691 (1951).

[17] F. Lipmann and N. O. Kaplan, *J. Biol. Chem.* **162**, 743 (1946).

in the presence of the enzyme, ATP, and acetate.[18] It may be assumed that the fraction contained CoA as well as acetylkinase. Choline acetylase was inhibited or inactivated by iodoacetate.[19] Thiolacetate would replace the ATP and acetate in this system and in acetylating systems prepared from brain and from *Escherichia coli* extracts, but not in the system obtained from ganglia from the head of the squid.[20] Surprisingly, dimethylaminoethanol was esterified at the same rate as was choline whereas neither aminoethanol nor monomethylaminoethanol was active. It is of interest that the acetic acid ester of dimethylaminoethanol bears no resemblance in biological activity to the corresponding trimethyl compound, acetylcholine. Although revisions may be necessary in the present understanding of phosphorylations during the acetylation of choline, it is reasonable to assume that a failure to find changes in concentrations of either inorganic phosphate or in ATP[21] may be ascribed to the presence of acetyl CoA or, possibly, of a substance such as thiolacetate.

The recognition of the indispensable role of a derivative of pantothenic acid in the metabolism of acetate involves this vitamin in the over-all synthesis of fatty acids from carbohydrate and, hence, in the production of fatty livers. The same possibility is recognized in the case of thiamine because of the role of diphosphothiamine in pyruvate metabolism.[22, 23] The role of the vitamins of the B complex in choline-deficient animals is discussed in Section IV, p. 33.

The extreme physiological activity of acetylcholine makes it understandable that rapid inactivation is essential as part of the mechanism controlling its concentration in tissues. Acetylcholine is hydrolyzed at various rates by miscellaneous tissue esterases and at a rapid rate by pseudocholinesterase and by cholinesterase. An attempt at differentiation on the basis of substrate specificity has been made[24] and reports have appeared on the localization in tissues[25] and on inhibitors[26, 27] of a specific acetylcholinesterase. A more satisfactory definition of a specific acetylcholinesterase and its description must await the isolation and characterization of such an enzyme.

[18] D. Nachmansohn, J. B. Wilson, S. R. Korey, and R. Berman, *J. Biol. Chem.* **195**, 25 (1952).

[19] D. Nachmansohn and A. L. Machado, *J. Neurophysiol.* **6**, 397 (1943).

[20] S. R. Korey, B. de Braganza, and D. Nachmansohn, *J. Biol. Chem.* **189**, 705 (1951).

[21] N.-V. Thoai, L. Chevillard, and S. Mayer, *Compt. rend.* **229**, 254 (1949).

[22] R. A. Peters and J. R. O'Brien, *Ann. Rev. Biochem.* **7**, 305 (1938).

[23] E. S. G. Barron, C. M. Lyman, M. A. Lipton, and J. M. Goldinger, *J. Biol. Chem.* **141**, 957 (1941).

[24] K. Augustinsson and D. Nachmansohn, *Science* **110**, 98 (1949).

[25] G. B. Koelle, *J. Pharmacol. Exptl. Therap.* **103**, 153 (1951).

[26] M. G. Ord and R. H. S. Thompson, *Biochem. J.* **46**, 346 (1950).

[27] W. N. Aldridge, *Biochem. J.* **46**, 451 (1950).

C. MECHANISM OF ACTION OF CHOLINE

1. DERIVATIVES OF PHOSPHORYLCHOLINE

In so far as participation in the intermediary metabolism of phospholipids is concerned, it is important to determine the relative activities of choline and its phosphorylated derivatives. Of these phosphorylcholine and glycerylphosphorylcholine (GPC) have received special attention. Riley determined the rate of utilization of radioactive phosphorylcholine (P^{32}) in rats and found no evidence of its preferential use in phospholipid metabolism[28] or in bone metabolism.[29] Severe choline deficiency did not alter the uptake of P^{32} by the femur to any marked degree.[30] Schmidt *et al.*[31] have

TABLE II

AMOUNTS OF FREE CHOLINE AND OF GLYCERYLPHOSPHORYLCHOLINE (GPC) IN SOME MAMMALIAN TISSUES[31]

	Choline, mg./g. moist tissue	
	As choline	As GPC
Beef heart, skeletal muscle, and brain, fresh	Negligible	Negligible
Beef spleen, fresh	Negligible	34
Beef pancreas, fresh	22	53
Beef pancreas, incubated	32	169
Lamb testicle, fresh	5.3	6.4
Lamb kidney, fresh	22	48
Lamb liver, fresh frozen	Negligible	75, 123, 126
Rabbit liver, fresh	Negligible	35
Rat liver, adult, fresh frozen	Negligible	Negligible
Rat liver, weanling, fresh frozen	Negligible	Negligible
Human bile, fresh	Negligible	Negligible

analyzed tissues for free choline and GPC and have made the surprising observation that GPC may make up a relatively large fraction of the total free and combined tissue choline. This was true particularly in lamb liver whereas beef and rat livers contained only negligible quantities of either free choline or GPC (Table II). The incubation of ground beef pancreas increased free choline slightly and GPC markedly. Neither compound occurred in rat intestine in more than traces, but incubation of ground intestine at pH 5.2 resulted in liberation of GPC whereas incubation at pH 8.2 yielded free choline. Schmidt *et al.* believe that their findings suggest the

[28] R. F. Riley, *J. Biol. Chem.* **153,** 535 (1944).

[29] R. F. Riley, B. McCleary, and R. E. Johnson, *Am. J. Physiol.* **143,** 677 (1945).

[30] W. F. Neuman and R. F. Riley, *J. Biol. Chem.* **168,** 545 (1947).

[31] G. Schmidt, L. Hecht, P. Fallot, L. Greenbaum, and S. J. Thannhauser, *J. Biol. Chem.* **197,** 601 (1952).

general importance of GPC as an intermediary in the phospholipid metabolism of mammals.

Baccari[32] has compared the hydrolysis of phosphorylcholine and of glycerophosphoric acid by phosphatases in pancreas, intestinal mucosa, and brain. Phlorizin and fluoride inhibited both hydrolyses. Hydrolysis of the glycerophosphate but not of phosphorylcholine was greatly accelerated by magnesium chloride.

The direct phosphorylation of choline by adenosine triphosphate in the presence of extracts from brewer's yeast and preparations from liver, brain, intestine, and kidney of several species has been reported by Wittenberg and Kornberg.[32a] The enzyme, choline phosphokinase, also catalyzed the phosphorylation of aminoethanol and of the mono- and dimethyl (and ethyl) aminoethanols. It was suggested that these phosphorylated derivatives may be activated precursors of the respective phosphatides even though previous attempts to demonstrate such a conclusion have been unsuccessful.

Reference has been made previously to the occurrence of sphingosylphosphorylcholine. It is oxidized more rapidly by minced liver, kidney, and brain than by other tissues of the guinea pig.[33]

2. CHOLINE AND TRANSMETHYLATION

The first intimation that the dietary supply of choline might have nutritional significance resulted from survival studies on depancreatized dogs subsequent to the discovery of insulin by Banting and Best. Both Fisher[34] and Allan et al.[35] observed fatty and severely degenerated livers in the animals deprived of the pancreas but supplied with insulin. In the latter study, survival was reported in the case of one animal that received raw pancreas in its diet. Six years passed before it was reported that the protective action of raw pancreas in depancreatized dogs was duplicated by the feeding of lecithin.[36-38] At this time Best et al.[39] observed that fatty livers resulted from feeding rats mixed grains and fat and that dietary lecithin was lipotropic, i.e., it prevented the accumulation of hepatic fat

[32] V. Baccari, *Boll. soc. ital. biol. sper.* **20**, 397, 398 (1945).

[32a] J. Wittenberg and A. Kornberg, *J. Biol. Chem.* **202**, 430 (1953).

[33] M. Aloisi, *Atti accad. nazl. Lincei, Rend. Classe sci. fis. mat. e nat.* **2**, 98 (1947).

[34] N. F. Fisher, *Am. J. Physiol.* **67**, 634 (1924).

[35] F. N. Allan, D. J. Bowie, J. J. R. Macleod, and W. L. Robinson, *Brit. J. Exptl. Pathol.* **5**, 75 (1924).

[36] J. M. Hershey, *Am. J. Physiol.* **93**, 657 P (1930).

[37] J. M. Hershey and S. Soskin, *Am. J. Physiol.* **98**, 74 (1931).

[38] C. H. Best and J. M. Hershey, *J. Physiol. (London)* **75**, 49 (1932).

[39] C. H. Best, J. M. Hershey, and M. E. Huntsman, *J. Physiol. (London)* **75**, 56 (1932).

under these conditions. Best and coworkers soon noted that the effective component in lecithin was choline.[40-42] Betaine was also found to have lipotropic activity in rats.

The use of the rat as a test animal in place of the depancreatized dog facilitated greatly the extension of the investigations that comprised the first phase of the study of the role of choline as a dietary essential. During the next few years the study of the relation of dietary factors to choline-preventable fatty livers in rats was pursued vigorously. Best *et al.* noted the protective action of choline in diets containing added cholesterol[43, 44] and the protective effect of protein.[45-48] Channon and coworkers examined the effect of protein and of amino acids.[49-52] Following the demonstration of the antilipotropic effect of dietary cystine by Beeston and Channon,[51] Tucker and Eckstein[53] noted that supplements of methionine had an opposite effect and were lipotropic. This similarity in the anti-fatty liver action of choline and of methionine was the first observation in the second phase of studies of the nutritional importance of choline, a phase that was to place choline in a unique position in metabolism as a source of labile methyl groups as well as a component of biochemically important tissue constituents.

In 1932 Jackson and Block[54] presented the first evidence of a mammalian requirement of methionine in experiments in which growth was improved in rats by the addition of this amino acid to a diet low in sulfur amino acids. In the same year Butz and du Vigneaud[55] prepared homocystine, a de-methylated product of methionine, by the action of strong sulfuric acid on methionine, and du Vigneaud *et al.*[56] showed that homocystine supported the growth of rats on a cystine-poor diet. Later, Womack *et al.*[57] found that

[40] C. H. Best, J. M. Hershey, and M. E. Huntsman, *Am. J. Physiol.* **101**, 7P (1932).

[41] C. H. Best and M. E. Huntsman, *J. Physiol.* (*London*) **75**, 405 (1932).

[42] C. H. Best, G. C. Furguson, and J. M. Hershey, *J. Physiol.* (*London*) **79**, 94 (1933).

[43] C. H. Best and J. H. Ridout, *J. Physiol.* (*London*) **78**, 415 (1933).

[44] C. H. Best, H. J. Channon, and J. H. Ridout, *J. Physiol.* (*London*) **81**, 409 (1934).

[45] C. H. Best and M. E. Huntsman, *J. Physiol.* (*London*) **83**, 255 (1935).

[46] C. H. Best and H. J. Channon, *Biochem. J.* **29**, 2651 (1935).

[47] C. H. Best, R. Grant, and J. H. Ridout, *J. Physiol.* (*London*) **86**, 337 (1936).

[48] C. H. Best and J. H. Ridout, *J. Physiol.* (*London*) **87**, 55P (1936).

[49] H. J. Channon and H. Wilkinson, *Biochem. J.* **29**, 350 (1935).

[50] A. W. Beeston, H. J. Channon, and H. Wilkinson, *Biochem. J.* **29**, 2659 (1935).

[51] A. W. Beeston and H. J. Channon, *Biochem. J.* **30**, 280 (1936).

[52] A. W. Beeston, H. J. Channon, J. V. Loach, and H. Wilkinson, *Biochem. J.* **30**, 1040 (1936).

[53] H. F. Tucker and H. C. Eckstein, *J. Biol. Chem.* **121**, 479 (1937).

[54] R. W. Jackson and R. J. Block, *J. Biol. Chem.* **98**, 465 (1932).

[55] L. W. Butz and V. du Vigneaud, *J. Biol. Chem.* **99**, 135 (1932).

[56] V. du Vigneaud, H. M. Dyer, and J. Harman, *J. Biol. Chem.* **101**, 719 (1933).

[57] M. Womack, K. S. Kemmerer, and W. C. Rose, *J. Biol. Chem.* **121**, 403 (1937).

cystine was not an indispensable amino acid as had been believed since the evidence of its supplementary potency presented by Osborne and Mendel over twenty years earlier.[58] The experiments in Rose's laboratory showed the essential character of the methionine requirement[57] and that this amino acid was a precursor of cystine *in vivo*.[59] It was evident also that cystine could spare the methionine requirement in so far as cystine was needed by the animal.[60]

The demonstration of growth-stimulating activity of homocystine in rats on a methionine-poor diet was difficult to understand, inasmuch as cystine was ineffective.[61] The explanation of the methionine-like action of homocystine was soon found to depend upon the presence of choline in the diet. Homocystine replaced methionine as a growth factor in young rats if the water-soluble vitamins were provided in the form of concentrates of milk and rice bran but not if purified vitamins were used.[62] In the latter instance markedly fatty livers were observed and the addition of choline to the mixture of purified vitamins permitted homocystine to function as a source of methionine.[63] Choline was isolated from the concentrates of milk and rice bran vitamins.

The concept of transmethylation or transfer of intact methyl groups was established by du Vigneaud and his collaborators in a series of experiments in which isotopically labeled compounds were employed. Choline containing deuterium-labeled methyl was isolated from the carcasses of rats fed a choline-deficient diet supplemented with methionine containing deuterium in the sulfur methyl.[64] By the same procedure the methyl of creatine was shown to come from methionine.[65] In addition, the transfer of methyl from choline to creatine[65] and to methionine[66] occurred if labeled choline and homocystine replaced methionine in the diet. The transfer of methyl to guanidoacetic acid to form creatine, however, was irreversible.[67, 67a] This impressive evidence of transfer of intact methyls was given additional support by the experiment in which choline was isolated after feeding rats doubly

[58] T. B. Osborne and L. B. Mendel, *J. Biol. Chem.* **20,** 351 (1915).
[59] W. C. Rose and T. R. Wood, *J. Biol. Chem.* **141,** 381 (1941).
[60] M. Womack and W. C. Rose, *J. Biol. Chem.* **141,** 375 (1941).
[61] A. White and E. F. Beach, *J. Biol. Chem.* **122,** 219 (1937).
[62] V. du Vigneaud, H. M. Dyer, and M. W. Kies, *J. Biol. Chem.* **130,** 325 (1939).
[63] V. du Vigneaud, J. P. Chandler, A. W. Moyer, and D. M. Keppel, *J. Biol. Chem.* **131,** 57 (1939).
[64] V. du Vigneaud, M. Cohn, J. P. Chandler, J. R. Schenck, and S. Simmonds, *J. Biol. Chem.* **140,** 625 (1941).
[65] V. du Vigneaud, *Biol. Symposia* **5,** 234 (1941).
[66] S. Simmonds, M. Cohn, J. P. Chandler, and V. du Vigneaud, *J. Biol. Chem.* **149,** 519 (1943).
[67] V. du Vigneaud, J. P. Chandler, and A. W. Moyer, *J. Biol. Chem.* **139,** 917 (1941).
[67a] S. Simmonds and V. du Vigneaud, *Proc. Soc. Exptl. Biol. Med.* **59,** 293 (1945).

labeled methionine. Within experimental error the same ratio of C^{14} to deuterium was found in choline and creatine methyls as in the sulfur methyl of the administered methionine.[68]

At the time these studies were in progress there was no reason to doubt the supposed inability of the animal organism to synthesize so-called labile methyl, the methyl of choline and of methionine. The ease with which either choline or methionine deficiency was produced and the ease of prevention of these deficiencies by methionine or by choline and homocystine, respectively, made the concept of a dietary deficiency of labile methyl very plausible. More recent findings, however, have made it necessary to revise this concept. Discussions to follow indicate that the animal organism does have the ability to synthesize the methyls found in choline or methionine but only if the diet is otherwise adequate. Furthermore, under the best circumstances the rate of the synthetic process may be limited.

This conclusion has been reached in three types of experiments: (1) diets containing homocystine but devoid of methionine and of other known sources of labile methyl have supported the growth of rats;[63, 69, 70] (2) deuterium-labeled choline methyl was found in the tissues of germ-free rats supplied deuterium-labeled water;[71, 72] and (3) C^{14}-labeled choline and methionine methyls have been found after the incubation of tissue preparations with C^{14}-labeled formate.[73] Although there is nothing in the present evidence that questions the reality of metabolic transfer of intact methyl groups under certain conditions, it is necessary to distinguish carefully between methylation due to transmethylation and methylation due to synthesis of a methyl from formate. The term transmethylation will be used for the reactions in which intact methyls participate. The general designation, formate transfer, and the more descriptive terms, formate-to-methyl and methyl-to-formate transfer, will be employed for those reactions in which there is synthesis or degradation of a methyl group. In these instances a carbon-oxygen linkage replaces the carbon-hydrogen bonding, or the reverse, in addition to transfer of the carbon.

In many instances the experimental data are insufficient to permit an unequivocal differentiation between the two types of methylation. Particularly disturbing is the difficulty in describing the series of reactions in which a formate carbon becomes a labile methyl carbon. It is not possible to state

[68] E. B. Keller, J. R. Rachele, and V. du Vigneaud, *J. Biol. Chem.* **177**, 733 (1949).
[69] M. A. Bennett, G. Medes, and G. Toennies, *Growth* **8**, 59 (1944).
[70] M. A. Bennett, *J. Biol. Chem.* **163**, 247 (1946); **187**, 751 (1950).
[71] V. du Vigneaud, C. Ressler, and J. R. Rachele, *Science* **112**, 267 (1950).
[72] V. du Vigneaud, C. Ressler, J. R. Rachele, J. A. Reyniers, and T. D. Luckey, *J. Nutrition* **45**, 361 (1951).
[73] V. du Vigneaud and W. G. Verly, *J. Am. Chem. Soc.* **72**, 1049 (1950).

with certainty whether the first appearance of the newly synthesized methyl is in methionine, thetin, or choline. The bulk of evidence supports the hypothesis that three successive methylations convert aminoethanol into choline. If this is the pathway of reactions for formate-to-methyl synthesis, an alternative reaction must exist for the direct formation of choline by transmethylation. Otherwise, an explanation of the appearance of doubly labeled methyl (C^{14} and deuterium) in tissue choline following the administration in rats of similarly labeled methionine is obscure.[68] In general, the quantitative aspects of formate-to-methyl synthesis have been difficult to assess and the isotopic data may be misleading in this respect. *In vivo* experiments in which growth is the criterion show only that some methylation other than transmethylation has occurred. In no instance has optimum growth of rats or chicks been demonstrated in the complete absence of recognized dietary sources of labile methyl. For this reason, it will be assumed in the following paragraphs that the requirements for growth or for tissue repair may create demands for methyl that, in the absence of adequate dietary sources, exceed the rate of production by one or more of the reactions in the formate-to-methyl transfer with resulting evidences of deficiency. Other nutrients, possibly folacin and B_{12}, appear to influence the formate-to-methyl transfer and, possibly, transmethylation also.

Clarification of the roles of choline, betaine, methionine, and thetin must await the recognition and isolation of the numerous enzymes and cofactors concerned with the fascinating mechanisms of methyl synthesis and methyl transfer. Although current findings are subject to different interpretations and present a most complex picture, they are discussed below on the basis of a relatively simple hypothesis in which certain arbitrary and provisional assumptions are made. This possible oversimplification of the problem is justified by the emphasis placed on phases that particularly require further investigation. The tentative scheme distinguishes between transmethylation and formate-to-methyl transfer as follows:

(a) *Methionine* in its active form is the principal methyl donor for transmethylations resulting in the synthesis of creatine from guanidoacetic acid, of choline from dimethylaminoethanol, of trigonelline and N^1-methylnicotinamide from nicotinic acid and its amide, respectively, and of many other methyl-containing metabolites.

(b) *Homocysteine* is converted to methionine by accepting labile methyl from betaine, only one of the three methyls of which is labile.

(c) *Homocysteine* is also converted to methionine by a reaction involving formate-to-methyl synthesis, possibly with a thetin as an intermediate. These and other relationships are illustrated in Fig. 1.

3. Nature of Methyl Donors in Transmethylation

The process of transmethylation involves demethylation of a methyl donor and methylation of a methyl acceptor. Donors of intact methyl groups appear to be limited to methylated quaternary nitrogen and sulfo-

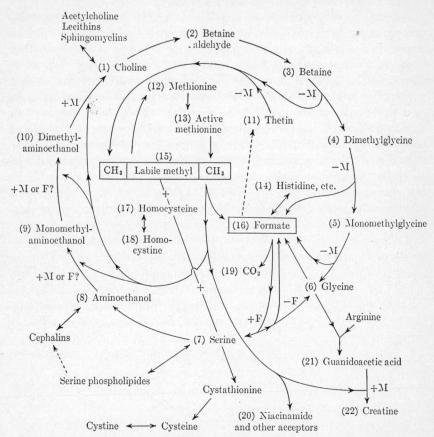

Fig. 1. Schematic representation of pathways of transmethylation, of formate-to-methyl synthesis, and of methyl-to-formate oxidation. Letters M and F represent labile methyl and active formate, respectively. Directions of reactions are indicated, but reacting compounds are not shown with the exception of the reaction of homocysteine with methyl to yield methionine and with serine to yield cystathionine. A distinction is indicated between the methyls of methionine and of active methionine. The use of formate in the synthesis of thetin, shown by the dash line, is hypothetical.

nium compounds. It is reasonable to relate lability of a methyl to its attachment to a nitrogen or sulfur atom which has acquired an additional covalent bond and positive charge. The main nitrogen compounds in this category, in addition to choline and choline-containing compounds, are betaine aldehyde and betaine. Betaine was observed to be lipotropic in the early experiments of Best,[41] and du Vigneaud[63, 74, 75] showed that it yielded methyl to homocysteine to form methionine. Welch found betaine aldehyde as well as betaine lipotropic in rats[76] and mice.[77]

The known sulfur compounds that are methyl donors in transmethylation are dimethylthetin, propio-β-dimethylthetin, and active methionine. The first, an analog of betaine (sulfobetaine), was first shown to be lipotropic by Welch (cited by du Vigneaud et al.[77a, 78]), and its part in transmethylation was demonstrated by du Vigneaud and coworkers.[78] Propio-β-dimethylthetin has been isolated from a marine alga, *Polysiphonia fastigiata*, by Challenger and Simpson.[79] It supports rat growth with homocystine and is, therefore, a source of methyl.[80, 81] The activity of methionine as a methyl donor appeared to be an exception until it was shown by Cantoni that it probably is converted to a sulfonium compound prior to its demethylation. Barrenscheen[82] had concluded previously that the sulfoxide of methionine was the first intermediate in transmethylation. The formula provisionally assigned to active methionine, S-adenosylmethionine, by Cantoni, is as follows:[83]

$$\text{Adenine—ribose—}\overset{+}{\text{S}}\text{—CH}_2\text{—CH}_2\text{—CH—C}=\text{O}$$
$$\underset{\text{CH}_3}{|} \qquad\qquad \underset{\text{NH}_2}{|}\ \underset{\text{O}_-}{|}$$

Presumably, substrate specificity is also involved because certain betaines[63, 84] and the sulfur analog of choline, sulfocholine,[85] do not donate methyl to homocysteine.

It cannot be assumed that choline serves directly as a methyl donor. Present evidence suggests strongly that it must be oxidized to betaine first and that dimethylglycine rather than dimethylaminoethanol is a prod-

[74] V. du Vigneaud, J. P. Chandler, and A. W. Moyer, *J. Nutrition* **19,** 11 (1940).

[75] V. du Vigneaud, S. Simmonds, J. P. Chandler, and M. Cohn, *J. Biol Chem.* **165,** 639 (1946).

[76] A. D. Welch, *J. Nutrition* **40,** 113 (1950).

[77] A. D. Welch and M. S. Welch, *Proc. Soc. Exptl. Biol. Med.* **39,** 7 (1938).

[77a] A. W. Moyer and V. du Vigneaud, *J. Biol. Chem.* **143,** 373 (1942).

[78] V. du Vigneaud, A. W. Moyer, and J. P. Chandler, *J. Biol. Chem.* **174,** 477 (1948).

[79] F. Challenger and M. I. Simpson, *Biochem. J.* **41,** xl (1947).

[80] G. A. Maw and V. du Vigneaud, *J. Biol. Chem.* **174,** 381 (1948).

[81] G. A. Maw and V. du Vigneaud, *J. Biol. Chem.* **176,** 1037 (1948).

[82] H. K. Barrenscheen and T. von Valy-Nagi, *Hoppe-Seyler's Z. physiol. Chem.* **283,** 91 (1948).

[83] G. L. Cantoni, *J. Am. Chem. Soc.* **74,** 2942 (1952).

[84] H. E. Carter and D. B. Melville, *J. Biol. Chem.* **133,** 109 (1940).

[85] G. A. Maw and V. du Vigneaud, *J. Biol. Chem.* **176,** 1029 (1948).

uct of the demethylation. The role of choline oxidase in this regard is described below.

The significance of the thetins in methyl metabolism is not clear. Neither has been detected as a naturally occurring intermediate in animal tissues. The very active dimethylthetin is the most potent known donor of methyl to homocysteine in *in vitro* experiments. However, evidence that it supplies methyl for creatine synthesis has not been presented. Clarification of the function of methylated sulfonium compounds of this type can be confidently expected because of the presence in tissues of a dimethylthetin transmethylase.

4. Methyl Acceptors, Transmethylation, and Formate-to-Methyl Synthesis

The early studies on labile methyl quickly brought to light three prime examples of methyl acceptors—homocysteine, guanidoacetic acid, and niacinamide. Each of these has been widely used experimentally, and the first two, at least, give rise by methylation to highly important metabolites, methionine and creatine, respectively. It may well be that N^1-methylniacinamide also is more than a urinary end product and that it represents some unrecognized function of the antipellagric vitamin.

The formation of choline by the methylation of a carbon-nitrogen precursor is obviously an indispensable reaction, but the exact nature of the precursor has not been as evident as in the case of the three acceptors named above. Whether the methylation of the precursor is an obligatory reaction is also uncertain. Presumably, the substance in question is aminoethanol, a molecule readily synthesized by animal tissues.

The synthesis of choline in animals by transmethylation of the methyl of methionine has been mentioned previously.[64, 65, 68] Production of choline by methylation involving formate-to-methyl synthesis is also well-established, but these observations do not exclude the possibility that the formation of choline is secondary to the appearance of the new methyl in methionine or in a thetin.

The fact of synthesis of choline *de novo* has been established by du Vigneaud *et al.*[71, 72] in experiments in which labeled choline was isolated from tissues of germ-free rats fed heavy water. Other evidence for this conclusion has been reported by Bennett[69, 70] and by Stekol and Weiss[86] on the basis of rat growth on diets lacking obvious sources of labile methyl and containing homocystine and a suitable vitamin supplement.

Production of choline by methylation of a carbon-nitrogen precursor by means of formate-to-methyl synthesis is well established. The amount of

[86] J. A. Stekol and K. W. Weiss, *J. Biol. Chem.* **186**, 343 (1950).

radioactivity in the methyl groups of choline or of methionine isolated from tissues of rats after the administration of C^{14} precursors indicates that an appreciable transfer of carbon from methanol,[73, 87, 88] formaldehyde,[87, 89, 90] formic acid,[87-89, 91, 92] acetone,[93] and serine[92, 94] occurs. Formate is not the only precursor of the β-carbon of serine, according to Kruhøffer.[95] In his studies rat liver homogenates transferred glycine but not formate to serine, although the conversion of formate to serine did occur with liver slices. Although no evidence has been presented for the transmethylation of the intact methyl group of methanol,[87] the administration of sodium deuterio-C^{14}-formate subcutaneously in the rat was followed by the isolation of tissue choline containing C^{14}-labeled methyl with no detectable loss of deuterium.[96] This finding suggests that in the formate-to-methyl synthesis one hydrogen, at least, remains attached to carbon in the intermediate forms. The incorporation of C^{14} into the β-carbon of serine occurs more rapidly from formaldehyde than from formate or methanol,[90] but this is not necessarily evidence that formaldehyde is the precursor of the methyl group. Jonsson and Mosher[94] found the C^{14} label in both the carbon chain and in the methyl of liver choline after the administration of β-C^{14}-labeled serine in the rat.

Reid and Landefeld[97] and Toporek et al.[98, 99] have presented evidence that histidine is an important dietary source of the carbon of methyl groups of choline and creatine. L-Histidine-2-C^{14} was fed to rats, and the labeled carbon was found not only in tissue choline and creatine methyls but also in the aminoethanol portion of choline. In the work of Toporek et al.,[99] the transfer to choline was enhanced in choline deficiency both in the intact animal and in isolated perfused cirrhotic livers of rats with chronic choline deficiency. Interestingly, these authors have calculated the histidine content of diets used by Griffith and Mulford[100] and by Rose et al.[101] and have concluded that this amino acid played an important role in their experi-

[87] V. du Vigneaud, W. G. Verly, J. E. Wilson, J. R. Rachele, C. Ressler, and J. M. Kinney, J. Am. Chem. Soc. **73**, 2782 (1951).

[88] H. R. V. Arnstein, Biochem. J. **48**, 27 (1951).

[89] V. du Vigneaud, W. G. Verly, and J. E. Wilson, J. Am. Chem. Soc. **72**, 2819 (1950).

[90] L. Siegel and J. Lafaye, Proc. Soc. Exptl. Biol. Med. **74**, 620 (1950).

[91] W. Sakami and A. D. Welch, J. Biol. Chem. **187**, 379 (1950).

[92] P. Siekevitz and D. M. Greenberg, J. Biol. Chem. **186**, 275 (1950).

[93] W. Sakami, J. Biol. Chem. **187**, 369 (1950).

[94] S. Jonsson and W. A. Mosher, J. Am. Chem. Soc. **72**, 3316 (1950).

[95] P. Kruhøffer, Biochem. J. **48**, 604 (1951).

[96] C. Ressler, J. R. Rachele, and V. du Vigneaud, J. Biol. Chem. **197**, 1 (1952).

[97] J. C. Reid and M. O. Landefeld, Arch. Biochem. and Biophys. **34**, 219 (1951).

[98] M. Toporek, Federation Proc. **11**, 299 (1952).

[99] M. Toporek, L. L. Miller, and W. F. Bale, J. Biol. Chem. **198**, 839 (1952).

[100] W. H. Griffith and D. J. Mulford, J. Nutrition **21**, 633 (1941).

[101] R. H. McCoy and W. C. Rose, J. Biol. Chem. **117**, 581 (1937).

ments. The conversion of carbon 2 of histidine into choline methyls, presumably by way of formate, is supported by the finding of Soucy and Bouthillier[102] that approximately one-fourth of the radioactivity of an hydrolyzate of liver protein was in the form of serine after feeding rats labeled histidine. The reverse reaction, the synthesis of histidine from precursors that include formate, has been demonstrated by Coon and Levy.[103, 104] These observations are not unexpected in view of the earlier discovery by Edlbacher[105, 106] of the enzyme, histidase, in liver and its disruption of the imidazole ring to give a product yielding formate on acid hydrolysis.

It is significant that satisfactory proof is lacking for a methyl donor function for mono- and dimethylaminoethanol.[88] As in the case of the reported transmethylation of methyl from sarcosine,[107] unequivocal proof would require double labeling of the methyl to rule out intermediary formate formation, i.e., oxidation and reduction of the carbon in question. Du Vigneaud[108] has shown that deuterium-methyl-labeled dimethylaminoethanol is converted in the rat into choline. This final methylation, yielding choline, is apparently an irreversible reaction, inasmuch as Muntz[109] found dimethylglycine rather than dimethylaminoethanol after the incubation of rat liver homogenate with added choline and homocysteine. Substantial support for the conclusion that oxidation of choline to betaine is necessary before transmethylation occurs is provided by the observations of Dubnoff[110] and others on choline oxidase (Section IV, p. 33).

The methylation *in vivo* of homocysteine, following its administration as such or as homocystine, is discussed in Section IV, p. 19. Similarly, the requirement of methionine in chicks is satisfied by homocystine plus choline[111] or betaine.[112] These metabolic reactions undoubtedly spare the requirement of methionine, and there is no reason to doubt that the methionine-homocysteine reaction may account for repeated transfers of intact methyl. Nevertheless, it is pertinent to emphasize the fact that homocysteine and its disulfide form are not known to occur naturally and that their presence in the body is dependent on the methionine intake except in

[102] R. Soucy and L. P. Bouthillier, *Rev. can. biol.* **10**, 290 (1951).
[103] M. J. Coon and L. Levy, *Federation Proc.* **10**, 174 (1951).
[104] L. Levy and M. J. Coon, *J. Biol. Chem.* **192**, 807 (1951).
[105] S. Edlbacher and J. Kraus, *Hoppe-Seyler's Z. physiol. Chem.* **191**, 225 (1930); **195**, 267 (1931).
[106] S. Edlbacher, *Ergeb. Enzymforsch.* **9**, 131 (1943).
[107] V. du Vigneaud, S. Simmonds, and M. Cohn, *J. Biol. Chem.* **166**, 47 (1946).
[108] V. du Vigneaud, J. P. Chandler, S. Simmonds, A. W. Moyer, and M. Cohn, *J. Biol. Chem.* **164**, 603 (1946).
[109] J. A. Muntz, *J. Biol. Chem.* **182**, 489 (1950).
[110] J. W. Dubnoff, *Arch. Biochem.* **24**, 251 (1949).
[111] A. A. Klose and H. J. Almquist, *J. Biol. Chem.* **138**, 467 (1941).
[112] H. J. Almquist and C. R. Grau, *J. Nutrition* **27**, 263 (1944).

so far as either is added to the diet as a synthetic product. It is not known definitely if any one molecule of methionine can serve the dual function of supplying both methyl for transmethylation and sulfur for cysteine formation.[113]

Borsook and Dubnoff[114] first demonstrated the *in vitro* synthesis of methionine from homocysteine and choline by rat liver slices, homogenates, and lyophilized preparations. Betaine was superior to choline as a methyl donor, and homocysteine to homocysteinethiolactone or homocystine as a methyl acceptor. The reaction was independent of oxygen and of inhibitors of cellular oxidative reactions. These workers[115] subsequently compared the methyl-donating capacities of choline, betaine, dimethylthetin, and propio-β-dimethylthetin in rat liver slice preparations under anaerobic conditions and in the presence of added homocysteine. Both sulfur derivatives were more effective than betaine, and dimethylthetin was ten to twenty times as effective. An enzyme was isolated in a partially purified state which transferred one methyl from the thetins. The enzyme was present in the liver and kidney of rat, guinea pig, and hog but was absent from muscle, pancreas, and spleen.

It appears quite reasonable to believe that methylation of homocysteine may involve the direct transfer of methyl from the betaine formed by the oxidation of choline. However, there is no certainty that homocysteine is methylated directly by formate-to-methyl synthesis, although this is a plausible conclusion. Using inhibition and dilution studies in which a labeled methionine methyl appeared after incubation of guinea pig liver slices with homocysteine and C^{14}-formate, Berg concluded that neither choline nor betaine methyl was an intermediate.[116] In subsequent studies with a cell-free extract of pigeon liver the chromatographic separation of the incubation mixture yielded evidence for an unidentified product formed from C^{14}-labeled formate and homocysteine.[117] Reference has already been made to active methionine studied by Cantoni.[83] It is again emphasized that such a compound as adenosylmethionine may represent the methyl donor structure of methionine[118, 119] without necessarily being the molecule in which methyl first appears as a result of formate-to-methyl synthesis. Methionine sulfoxide has been reported to be the first intermediate in transmethylation.[82]

Stetten fed N^{15}-labeled aminoethanol to rats and determined the N^{15} in

[113] D. J. Mulford and W. H. Griffith, *J. Nutrition* **23,** 91 (1942).
[114] H. Borsook and J. W. Dubnoff, *J. Biol. Chem.* **169,** 247 (1947).
[115] J. W. Dubnoff and H. Borsook, *J. Biol. Chem.* **176,** 789 (1948).
[116] P. Berg, *J. Biol. Chem.* **190,** 31 (1951).
[117] P. Berg, *Federation Proc.* **11,** 186 (1952).
[118] G. L. Cantoni, *J. Biol. Chem.* **189,** 745 (1951).
[119] G. L. Cantoni, *Federation Proc.* **11,** 330 (1952).

the aminoethanol and choline isolated from the respective phospholipids.[120] The data indicated that choline was formed from the precursor without hindrance even though the diet was sufficiently low in sources of methyl to cause deposition of extra liver fat. It is reasonable to accept this finding as evidence of the conversion of aminoethanol to choline, but it does not distinguish between methylation by transmethylation and methylation by formate-to-methyl synthesis. The latter type of synthesis of choline has been reported by Steensholt[121, 121a] and by Barrenscheen and Skudrzyk[121b] in experiments in which various tissue preparations were incubated with aminoethanol and either methionine or methionine sulfoxide. Steensholt also concluded that D-methionine is a more efficient methyl donor than the natural isomer.[121a] According to Veitch and Zweig,[121c] caution is needed in the interpretation of tissue experiments in which evidence of the synthesis of choline by transmethylation consists of a decrease in the methionine content of the medium or in the appearance of an otherwise unidentified reineckate. These workers noted that a D-amino acid oxidase in the tissues used by Steensholt and by Barrenscheen decreased the level of methionine during the incubation period without formation of choline. They showed, in addition that a reineckate of aminoethanol was actually formed under the conditions[121b] in which choline reineckate was presumed to have been isolated.

The methylation *in vivo* of guanidoacetic acid (GA) by transmethylation from choline and from methionine was demonstrated in rats by du Vigneaud and his associates.[65, 66] The irreversibility of the reaction has been confirmed by a number of investigators.[67, 67a, 122-124] The apparent inability of the animal organism to avoid methylation of a part of a dietary supplement of GA makes it possible to use this means of decreasing available methyl groups in the whole animal.[125]

Borsook and Dubnoff reported the *in vitro* formation of creatine from GA and methionine by rat liver slices and noted that choline was ineffective as a donor of methyl unless homocystine was provided.[126-128] Adenosine-

[120] D. Stetten, Jr., *J. Biol. Chem.* **142**, 629 (1942).

[121] G. Steensholt, *Acta Physiol. Scand.* **10**, 333 (1945); **11**, 294 (1946); **14**, 340 (1947).

[121a] G. Steensholt, *Acta Physiol. Scand.* **17**, 276 (1949).

[121b] H. K. Barrenscheen and I. Skudrzyk, *Hoppe-Seyler's Z. physiol. Chem.* **284**, 228 (1949).

[121c] F. P. Veitch and G. Zweig, *J. Am. Chem. Soc.* **74**, 1921 (1952).

[122] K. Bloch, R. Schoenheimer, and D. Rittenberg, *J. Biol. Chem.* **138**, 155 (1941).

[123] K. Bloch and R. Schoenheimer, *J. Biol. Chem.* **131**, 111 (1939).

[124] W. H. Griffith and D. J. Mulford, *J. Am. Chem. Soc.* **63**, 929 (1941).

[125] D. Stetten, Jr., and G. F. Grail, *J. Biol. Chem.* **144**, 175 (1942).

[126] H. Borsook and J. W. Dubnoff, *J. Biol. Chem.* **132**, 559 (1940).

[127] H. Borsook, *J. Biol. Chem.* **134**, 635 (1940).

[128] H. Borsook and J. W. Dubnoff, *J. Biol. Chem.* **160**, 635 (1945).

triphosphate was indispensable for the methylation of GA by methionine if homogenized liver preparations were employed.[129, 130] In this case, oxygen was also essential, and the reaction was affected by inhibitors of oxidative mechanisms. Cohen[131, 132] showed that homogenized liver preparations of many species, including cattle, sheep, swine, chickens, hamsters, and rabbits, formed little or no creatine in the presence of GA, methionine, ATP, and oxygen. Similar preparations from adult guinea pigs were active, but those obtained from embryonic specimens were active only if a member of the Kreb's cycle, such as fumarate, was added to the medium. Homogenized rat liver required a pteridine derivative in addition to fumarate. Surprisingly, 10-formylfolic acid, aminopterin, and A-methopterin were almost as potent as folic acid. Attempts to replace methionine as the methyl donor by choline, betaine, sarcosine, formate, and other compounds were unsuccessful. Cohen prepared soluble enzyme systems by centrifugation of homogenized rat and guinea pig liver and observed that the creatine-forming activity of these preparations in the presence of GA, ATP, methionine, and either oxygen or nitrogen was not enhanced by additions of folic acid or of fumarate. It was evident, therefore, that the latter were not required under these conditions for the methylation of GA. Inasmuch as appropriate additions of mitochondria to the soluble enzyme system restored the need of folic acid, fumarate, and oxygen, it appeared that the maintenance of a high level of ATP in the presence of mitochondria was dependent on an aerobic process involving folic acid or another pteridine.

Menne[133, 134] studied the formation of creatine in pulped muscle. Muscle extracts were found to contain a myosin-like apoenzyme and a heat-stable, water-soluble coenzyme. Atrophic and dystrophic muscles were unable to synthesize creatine. Conditions for creatine synthesis in muscle were also examined by Barrenscheen.[135, 136] According to this author creatine is formed in muscle by methylation directly from methionine and indirectly from choline with trimethylamine oxide as an intermediate. The pherase acting on methionine was cyanide-sensitive whereas the cholinepherase was cyanide-insensitive. Vignos and Cantoni[130] prepared partially purified fractions of a guanidoacetic acid methylpherase which were free of the enzyme necessary for the synthesis of active methionine.

[129] H. Borsook and J. W. Dubnoff, *J. Biol. Chem.* **171**, 363 (1947).
[130] J. Vignos, Jr., and G. L. Cantoni, *Federation Proc.* **11**, 399 (1952).
[131] S. Cohen, *J. Biol. Chem.* **193**, 851 (1951).
[132] S. Cohen, *Federation Proc.* **11**, 197 (1952); *J. Biol. Chem.* **201**, 93 (1953).
[133] F. Menne, *Hoppe-Seyler's Z. physiol. Chem.* **273**, 269 (1942).
[134] F. Menne, *Z. ges. exptl. Med.* **112**, 38 (1943).
[135] H. K. Barrenscheen and J. Pany, *Hoppe-Seyler's Z. physiol. Chem.* **283**, 78 (1948).
[136] H. K. Barrenscheen and M. Pantlitschko, *Hoppe-Seyler's Z. physiol. Chem.* **284**, 250 (1949).

Binkley and Watson[137] observed that methylphosphate was active in the formation of creatine from GA by liver homogenates and extracts but inactive in so far as growth of rats was concerned on diets containing homocystine in place of methionine. To what extent this ambiguous finding is related to the toxicity of the methylphosphate is not known.

Trigonelline and N^1-methylniacinamide may be excreted in the urine following the administration of niacin and niacinamide, respectively. Considerable species variability exists in so far as the formation and elimination of these substances are concerned, and the significance of the methylations is not known. Rats, but not rabbits or guinea pigs, excrete N^1-methylniacinamide after administration of niacinamide.[138] Growth in rats on protein-low and methyl-poor diets is affected by the amide if a sufficient quantity is fed, a result doubtless explained in part by loss of methyl from the body.[139] Perlzweig et al.[140] demonstrated the synthesis of N^1-methylniacinamide by rat liver slices and noted that the process was strictly aerobic, that intact cells were required, and that niacin was unaffected by the system in which the amide served as a methyl acceptor. These findings were confirmed by Ellinger,[141] who noted in addition that niacin was amidated by kidney and brain tissue and by liver tissue if supplementary glutamine was provided. This work was extended by Cantoni,[142] who was able to show that the methylation of niacinamide does occur in cell-free preparations of rat liver under anaerobic conditions in the presence of methionine, magnesium ions, and a source of energy-rich phosphate such as ATP. The enzyme system, for which the name nicotinamide methylkinase was suggested, was partially purified.

Epinephrine represents a product of transmethylation, according to Keller et al.[143] Following the administration of C^{14}-methyl-labeled methionine in rats, this substance, formed presumably by the methylation of norepinephrine, was isolated from the adrenals.

The methylations of dimethylaminoethanol, of homocysteine, of guanidoacetic acid, and of niacinamide by transmethylation appear to be of two types which differ on the basis of the methyl donor and according to the need of energy-rich phosphate bond compounds. Apparently, the presence of methyl-containing quaternary nitrogen or ternary sulfur groups is essential, and, for such substances, transmethylation proceeds in the absence

[137] F. Binkley and J. Watson, J. Biol. Chem. **180,** 971 (1949).
[138] P. Handler, J. Biol. Chem. **154,** 203 (1944).
[139] P. Handler and W. J. Dann, J. Biol. Chem. **146,** 357 (1942).
[140] W. A. Perlzweig, F. Bernheim, and M. L. C. Bernheim, J. Biol. Chem. **150,** 401 (1943).
[141] P. Ellinger, Biochem. J. **40,** Proc. xxxi (1946); **42,** 175 (1948).
[142] G. L. Cantoni, J. Biol. Chem. **189,** 203 (1951).
[143] E. B. Keller, R. A. Boissonnas, and V. du Vigneaud, J Biol. Chem. **183,** 627 (1950)

of ATP. On the other hand, methionine must also be converted to a form having ternary sulfur in order to serve as a methyl donor. For its formation ATP is necessary, and the reaction consists in the addition of adenosine to methionine with the splitting out of 3 moles of H_3PO_4.[83] Active methionine, or S-adenosylmethionine, is believed to be the donor of methyl to guanidoacetic acid, to niacinamide, and, probably, to aminoethanol. According to the hypothesis presented earlier, homocysteine is remethylated with methyl from betaine, the oxidation product of choline, or with methyl from thetin.

Little is known of the mechanisms and of the energetics of formate-to-methyl synthesis. Because of the original concept of labile methyl as an indispensable dietary factor, emphasis has been largely on the proof of a metabolic origin of methyl groups. The evidence for this is satisfactory from a qualitative viewpoint. However, whether the intermediate is formate, formaldehyde, a phosphorylated derivative of a one-carbon molecule, or, possibly, folinic acid, is unknown. Of utmost importance is the identification of the formate acceptor, for instance, in the reaction that yields monomethylaminoethanol. Does reduction of the carbon occur before or after its addition to the amino nitrogen atom? If before, is thetin the formate acceptor? Answers to these questions will mark a significant milestone in the progress of intermediary metabolism.

5. CHOLINE OXIDASE AND THE CHOLINE-BETAINE-GLYCINE RELATIONSHIP

a. Choline Oxidase

The demonstrated transfer of labeled methyl *in vivo* from choline to homocysteine gives no clue to the intermediate steps between the original donor and the final acceptor. Several lines of investigation have supported the hypothesis that the methyl of choline becomes a labile methyl only after the oxidation of the alcohol, choline, to the acid, betaine. The presence of an oxidizing enzyme, a choline oxidase, in tissues was first suggested by Bernheim and Bernheim,[144] who observed an increase in oxygen uptake when acetylcholine was added to liver and kidney extracts of rat and cat. Guinea pig liver was found to be inactive in this respect. The fact that choline was oxidized by tissues was confirmed by Trowell,[145] using liver slices. Mann and Quastel[146] isolated the oxidation product of choline as the reineckate and identified it as betaine aldehyde. Some evidence was obtained that betaine aldehyde was also oxidized by rat liver slices and rat liver or kidney extracts, though at a much slower rate than choline. It was suggested that the oxidation product in this case was betaine.

[144] F. Bernheim and M. L. C. Bernheim, *Am. J. Physiol.* **104**, 438 (1933); **121**, 55 (1938).
[145] O. A. Trowell, *J. Physiol.* (*London*) **85**, 356 (1935).
[146] P. J. G. Mann and J. H. Quastel, *Biochem. J.* **31**, 869 (1937).

Bernheim and Bernheim[144] prepared a choline oxidase extract of rat liver and showed that it was distinct from the enzyme which oxidized ethyl alcohol. The oxygen uptake and the properties of the end products indicated that at pH 6.7 choline was oxidized to betaine aldehyde with the uptake of one atom of oxygen. At this pH betaine aldehyde was oxidized further at a very slow rate, whereas at pH 7.8 the aldehyde was oxidized rapidly to betaine, presumably by another enzyme system. The above workers found the oxidase system in the liver and kidney of the rat but failed to find it in blood, brain, or muscle.

Klein and Handler[147] were able to show that the oxidation of betaine aldehyde required diphosphopyridine nucleotide, but that of choline did not. In the presence of the nucleotide, betaine aldehyde was also oxidized by preparations of rat kidney, brain, and muscle, the activities of these tissues compared to liver being 0.33, 0.13, and 0.10, respectively.

Mann and his coworkers[148] observed that arsenocholine, like choline, is oxidized to the corresponding aldehyde by the choline oxidase of rat liver. The substitution of nitrogen by arsenic reduces the affinity of the enzyme for the substrate. According to these authors the choline oxidase system consists partly of a dehydrogenase. This was shown by the fact that rat liver extracts, in the presence of choline or arsenocholine, rapidly reduce sodium ferricyanide under anaerobic conditions. It was also observed that choline oxidase in the presence of choline or arsenocholine reduces cytochrome c at room temperature.

An apparent phosphate requirement for choline oxidase activity was observed by Angel and Miller.[149] When rat liver homogenates were prepared with phosphate, veronal, and citrate buffers at pH 7.8, the choline oxidase activities of the suspensions in citrate and veronal buffers were 18 % and 50 %, respectively, of that in the phosphate buffer. Addition of phosphate to citrate and veronal suspensions stimulated the oxidase activity by 25 to 50 %, respectively. The phosphate continued to stimulate the choline oxidase activity in the presence of dinitrophenol (10^{-3} M).

The requirements of the rat liver choline oxidase system in whole liver homogenates have been studied by Williams et al.,[150] who investigated the effect of pH on the oxidation of choline by homogenates of rat liver. Only small differences were observed in the activities at pH 6.8, 7.3, and 7.8. The oxidation of choline at pH 6.8 and 7.8 gave sigmoidal oxygen consumption curves if allowed to run for 2 hours, while the pH 7.3 homogenate gave maximum activity during the first 10-minute period, with a gradual decrease

[147] J. R. Klein and P. Handler, *J. Biol. Chem.* **144**, 537 (1942).
[148] P. J. G. Mann, H. E. Woodward, and J. H. Quastel, *Biochem. J.* **32**, 1024 (1938).
[149] C. Angel and O. N. Miller, *Federation Proc.* **11**, 435 (1952).
[150] J. N. Williams, Jr., G. Litwack, and C. A. Elvehjem, *J. Biol. Chem.* **192**, 73 (1951).

in activity thereafter. From data obtained by these workers on 10-minute incubations it appeared that, if two enzyme systems with different pH optima for their activities were involved, the over-all activity in whole rat liver homogenates was the same for the three pH values employed. Since Williams and his coworkers[150] were interested in developing an assay system for total rat liver homogenates, they also studied the product inhibition of the choline oxidase system. It was noted that the oxidation of betaine aldehyde to betaine occurred at a much slower rate than the oxidation of choline alone and that betaine aldehyde apparently inhibited the oxidation of choline. Although betaine aldehyde was a potent inhibitor of choline oxidase, betaine had no effect upon the oxidation of choline. Further experiments showed that for the first 10 to 12 minutes oxidation of choline proceeded linearly and that, as betaine aldehyde concentrations increased, the rate of choline oxidation gradually decreased. Therefore, the first 10-minute interval can be used as a measure of choline oxidase activity without interference from the inhibitory action of betaine aldehyde or its slower rate of oxidation. The requirements of the system for added cytochrome c and for diphosphopyridine nucleotide were investigated also, and it was concluded that for adequate assay no additional cofactors were necessary. On the basis of the above findings Williams et al.[150] described an assay system for measuring choline oxidase activity in total liver extracts. Their data showed that rat liver choline oxidase is remarkably constant for comparable animals. Niacinamide strongly inhibited the activity of the oxidase system under all conditions. Both niacinamide and diphosphopyridine nucleotide inhibited the activity of the oxidase system in total liver extracts.

Further studies by Williams [151] on the mechanism of the metabolism of choline and betaine aldehyde have shown that the latter metabolite can be converted to betaine either aerobically or anaerobically, whereas choline oxidase appears to be an oxygen-requiring system.

Early studies on the intracellular distribution of the components of the choline oxidase system were made by Lan,[152, 153] who failed to find any appreciable amount of the oxidase activity in isolated nuclei of rat liver cells. Kensler and Langemann found 78 % of the oxidase activity in the mitochondrial fraction of rat liver preparations and also demonstrated that the addition of succinate greatly reduced the oxidation of choline by tissue homogenates, presumably because of saturation of proton and electron acceptors.[154, 155] Concentration of choline oxidase activity in mitochondria was confirmed

[151] J. N. Williams, Jr. Proc. Soc. Exptl. Biol. Med. 78, 202 (1951).
[152] T. H. Lan, J. Biol. Chem. 151, 171 (1943).
[153] T. H. Lan, Cancer Research 4, 37, 42 (1944).
[154] C. J. Kensler and H. Langemann, J. Biol. Chem. 192, 551 (1951).
[155] H. Langemann and C. J. Kensler, Federation Proc. 11, 366 (1952).

in extensive studies by Williams.[156] A potent heat labile inhibitor of choline oxidase was found in the supernatant fraction. These studies also showed that the betaine aldehyde oxidase activity of the supernatant fraction can be considerably increased if diphosphopyridine nucleotide is added. The nuclei and microsomes are unaffected by addition of this nucleotide.

Although choline oxidase activity has been found in the livers and kidneys of rats, chicks, rabbits, dogs, and monkeys,[157] most of the *in vitro* studies on this enzyme system have used tissues of the rat. It has been shown that choline oxidase in the rat liver is cyanide-sensitive and that it is readily inhibited by copper and phenylhydrazine.[158] Barron and Singer[159] have classified it in the group of sulfhydryl enzymes. Choline oxidase loses its activity at a fairly rapid rate if partially purified. The rate of loss, which is that of a first-order reaction, is more rapid at pH 6.7 than at 7.8. Cystine and semicarbazide increase the rate of inactivation both in presence and absence of choline. Nickel, cobalt, and iron salts not only increase the inactivation rate of the enzyme but also combine reversibly with a group on the enzyme to inhibit it.[160] Halogenated alkylamines are powerful inhibitors for choline oxidase.[161] Among these is the nitrogen mustard, methylbis-(β-chloroethyl)amine, which irreversibly inhibits choline oxidase. Colter and Quastel[162] observed that benzedrine, ephedrine, tyramine, methylamine, aminoethanol, and histamine not only reversibly inhibit choline oxidase but also prevent the irreversible inhibition by the nitrogen mustard.

The enzyme in rat liver which oxidizes choline was named choline dehydrogenase by Bargoni and Di Bella.[163] Its activity was ascribed to free amino and carbonyl rather than to mercapto groups. The enzyme shows no color with nitroprusside nor with Grote's reagent and is inhibited by cyanide but not by malonate. The dehydrogenation system involves the oxidation of reduced cytochrome c.

At pH values below 7.0, stearic, palmitic, and oleic acids at 0.004 M concentrations inhibit choline oxidase activity 61 %, 41 %, and 29 %, respectively. Fats and mixtures of cephaline and lecithin are without effect. It has been suggested[164] that the fatty acids in liver may determine to some degree how much free choline can be oxidized and how much can be used for synthesis of phospholipids.

[156] J. N. Williams, Jr., *J. Biol. Chem.* **194,** 139 (1952); **195,** 37 (1952); **197,** 709 (1952).

[157] J. S. Dinning, C. K. Keith, and P. L. Day, *Arch. Biochem.* **24,** 463 (1949).

[158] F. Bernheim, *J. Biol. Chem.* **133,** 485 (1940).

[159] E. S. G. Barron and T. P. Singer, *Science* **97,** 356 (1943).

[160] G. S. Eadie and F. Bernheim, *J. Biol. Chem.* **185,** 731 (1950).

[161] E. S. G. Barron, G. R. Bartlett, and Z. B. Miller, *J. Exptl. Med.* **87,** 489 (1948).

[162] J. S. Colter and J. H. Quastel, *Nature* **166,** 773 (1950).

[163] N. Bargoni and S. Di Bella, *Atti accad. sci. Torino* **84,** 149 (1949–1950).

[164] F. Bernheim, *J. Biol. Chem.* **133,** 291 (1940).

Evidence was presented by Williams[165] demonstrating a positive connection between the choline oxidase system of rat liver and the probable precursors of the *Leuconostoc citrovorum* factor (LCF) as well as LCF itself. It was shown that when ascorbic acid and folic acid were incubated with rat liver homogenate small but significant stimulation of the choline oxidase system was observed. This effect was more pronounced in rats fed aminopterin. Since aminopterin is believed to inhibit the conversion of folic acid to LCF,[166] Williams[165] postulated that the stimulatory effect of the folic acid and ascorbic acid added *in vitro* was due to the enzymatic conversion of these substances to LCF, which was actually responsible for stimulation of the enzyme system. In work that followed, Williams[167] studied various combinations of factors related to LCF, e.g., folic acid, ascorbic acid, vitamin B_{12}, and synthetic LCF itself in relation to choline oxidase. This work was done with a modified enzyme system containing homocysteine which amplified the effects of the above factors. The results of this investigation showed that folic acid, *Leuconostoc citrovorum* factor, vitamin B_{12}, and ascorbic acid individually or in combination markedly stimulate choline oxidation in the liver homogenates of rats fed aminopterin. Only ascorbic acid and folic acid were found to stimulate choline oxidation in normal rat liver homogenates. The stimulation by these factors was observed to be much more marked in aminopterin-fed rats.

Williams *et al.*[167a] subsequently noted that folic and folinic acids in whole liver and in isolated mitochondria were markedly decreased in folic acid deficiency in rats. Aminopterin-fed animals showed a similar decrease in folinic acid, but there was no effect on the folic acid content of the liver or of the mitochondrial fraction. The loss in choline oxidase activity in the latter fraction paralleled the disappearance of folinic acid, and it was concluded that this substance rather than folic acid was involved in the maintenance of choline oxidase activity.

The influence of several dietary factors on tissue choline oxidase has been reported. The removal of folic acid from the diet of the monkey or the administration of aminopterin to this animal eliminated most of the choline oxidase activity from the liver and kidney.[157] Further studies disclosed that aminopterin-treated chickens did not exhibit the choline oxidase activity normally found in bone marrow,[168] and that livers from folic acid-deficient chicks oxidized choline at a reduced rate.[169] Chick kidney choline oxidase was not found to be significantly reduced in folic acid deficiency.

[165] J. N. Williams, Jr., *J. Biol. Chem.* **191,** 123 (1951).

[166] C. A. Nichol and A. D. Welch, *Proc. Soc. Exptl. Biol. Med.* **74,** 52, 403 (1950).

[167] J. N. Williams, Jr., *J. Biol. Chem.* **192,** 81 (1951).

[167a] J. N. Williams, Jr., A. Sreenivasan, Shan-Ching Sung, and C. A. Elvehjem, *J. Biol. Chem.* **202,** 233 (1953).

[168] J. S. Dinning, C. K. Keith, P. L. Davis, and P. L. Day, *Arch. Biochem.* **27,** 89 (1950).

Williams[170] observed that rats fed aminopterin exhibit a concentration of liver ascorbic acid which is less than 50 % normal, suggesting that folic acid is probably involved in ascorbic acid synthesis in the rat. His work indicated that, whereas high levels of ascorbic acid in liver extracts stimulate the choline oxidase system, low levels of this vitamin added *in vitro* actually inhibit the oxidation of choline. On the basis of these observations Williams postulated that the low ascorbic acid concentration in the liver of rats fed aminopterin may help to explain some of the previous observations on the low choline oxidase activity of livers of those rats.

Choline oxidase activity was greatly depressed in the fatty liver of rats on a low methionine diet.[171] It was suggested that the oxidase inhibition may be due to the increased lipid content of the liver, since fatty acids have been shown to be inhibitory to the system.[164] The importance of the choline oxidase system in the development of fatty livers caused by choline deficiency is suggested by the observations that guinea pigs which lack the enzyme system cannot be made to develop fatty livers very readily[172] and that hamsters which have some enzyme but much less than rats do not accumulate as much liver fat on a deficient diet as do rats.[173] A lack of the enzyme system can be considered an advantage when minimal amounts of choline are present for fat transport and metabolism, and the suggestion has been advanced that it is the diminished choline oxidase activity which permits the existence of a normal hepatic choline concentration (as phospholipid) despite a dietary choline deficiency.[171, 174] The work of Dubnoff[110] and Muntz[109] showed that the choline oxidase system also plays an important role in transmethylation reactions. However, a mechanism must exist in the guinea pig for the catabolism of choline. Dubnoff injected C^{14}-methyl-labeled choline and betaine intraperitoneally into this animal and found that both contributed to labeled expired carbon dioxide as well as to labeled tissues but the ratio of utilization of betaine methyl to choline methyl was 4.6.[175]

Liver choline oxidase was decreased by a riboflavin deficiency in rats.[176, 177] The B_2-deficient rat livers showed a reduced activity of about 20 to 30 % of the control levels.[177] Atabrine, which has been known to inhibit flavin enzyme systems, *in vitro* was found to bring about an inhibition

[169] J. S. Dinning, C. K. Keith, and P. L. Day, *J. Biol. Chem.* **189,** 515 (1951).
[170] J. N. Williams, Jr., *Proc. Soc. Exptl. Biol. Med.* **77,** 315 (1951).
[171] P. Handler and F. Bernheim, *J. Biol. Chem.* **144,** 401 (1942).
[172] P. Handler, *Proc. Soc. Exptl. Biol. Med.* **70,** 70 (1949).
[173] P. Handler and F. Bernheim, *Proc. Soc. Exptl. Biol. Med.* **72,** 569 (1949).
[174] H. P. Jacobi and C. A. Baumann, *J. Biol. Chem.* **142,** 65 (1942).
[175] J. W. Dubnoff, *Arch. Biochem.* **22,** 474 (1949).
[176] W. Hess and G. Voillier, *Helv. Chim. Acta* **31,** 381 (1948).
[177] B. Kelley, *Federation Proc.* **11,** 238 (1952).

of choline oxidase activity.[177] The oxidase system was not influenced by a deficiency of vitamin B_{12} in the chick[178] or by thiamine,[179] vitamin E,[180] or histidine[181] deficiency in the rat. Intraperitoneal injection of urethane as well as x-irradiation of mature hens reduced the bone marrow choline oxidase.[182] Whole body x-irradiation of adult male rats with a dosage of 200 r. appeared to decrease liver choline oxidase activity, but the effect was uncertain in view of the marked increase in endogenous respiration.[183] The enzyme was poisoned by high oxygen tensions, probably due to its dependence on its sulfhydryl groups.[184] The injection of thyroxine had no effect on the oxidase activity of the rat.[185]

Swendseid et al.[185a] showed that the feeding of ethionine (S-ethylhomocysteine) to rats decreased the choline and sarcosine oxidases but not the succinoxidase of the liver. This possible antagonist of methionine also inhibited choline and sarcosine oxidases in vitro in homogenized preparations, but the effect was absent if the preparation was dialyzed before its addition. Neither methoxinine nor methionine sulfoximine inhibited choline oxidase in the in vitro studies.

In summarizing the discussion of "choline oxidase," it is pertinent to emphasize that, with few exceptions, the term has not referred specifically to either of the dehydrogenases that convert choline to betaine aldehyde and the aldehyde to betaine but has included the system responsible for the transport of protons and electrons through the cytochromes to oxygen. The two dehydrogenases appear to be different enzymes, although both occur in liver mitochondria. They may be separated on the basis of the greater solubility of the betaine aldehyde dehydrogenase.[185b] Each is estimated by the anaerobic reduction of ferricyanide in the presence of the respective substrate, choline or betaine aldehyde. Strength et al.[185b] believe that both enzymes are DPN-linked, although the necessity of DPN for the action of choline dehydrogenase has been questioned.[150] Folinic acid[170] and riboflavin[176, 177] appear essential for the dehydrogenation of choline. Ebisuzaki and Williams[185c] demonstrated the importance of flavin adenine dinucleotide (FAD) for liver choline oxidase activity, especially in prepara-

[178] M. B. Gillis and R. J. Young, Poultry Sci. 30, 468 (1951).

[179] E. Egana, Publs. lab. med. exptl. clin. med. Univ. Chile 1, 127 (1946).

[180] E. L. Hove and J. O. Hardin, Proc. Soc. Exptl. Biol. Med. 78, 858 (1951).

[181] J. W. Bothwell and J. N. Williams, Jr., J. Biol. Chem. 191, 129 (1951).

[182] J. S. Dinning, I. Meschan, C. K. Keith, and P. L. Day, Proc. Soc. Exptl. Biol. Med. 74, 776 (1950).

[183] H. O. Kunkel and P. H. Phillips, Arch. Biochem. and Biophys. 37, 366 (1952).

[184] F. Dickens, Biochem. J. 40, 171 (1946).

[185] R. L. Smith and H. G. Williams-Ashman, Nature 164, 457 (1949).

[185a] M. E. Swendseid, A. L. Swanson, and F. H. Bethell, J. Biol. Chem. 201, 803 (1953).

[185b] D. R. Strength, J. R. Christensen, and L. J. Daniel, J. Biol. Chem. 203, 63 (1953).

[185c] K. Ebisuzaki and J. N. Williams, Jr., J. Biol. Chem. 200, 297 (1953).

tions from riboflavin-deficient rats. These workers believe that FAD functions in the hydrogen transport system prior to the participation of cytochrome c.

b. The Choline-Betaine-Glycine Relationship

The evidence appears indisputable that choline serves as a source of labile methyl by irreversible oxidation to either betaine aldehyde or to betaine. Whether the aldehyde or the acid is the methyl donor is unknown, although in Fig. 1 it is assumed that it is betaine which is demethylated initially. If it is not, its reduction to the aldehyde must occur with great rapidity. In any event, glycine is the product of the complete demethylation of the choline molecule, and the di- and monomethyl derivatives of glycine are logical intermediates in addition to glycine.

Stetten administered N^{15}-labeled ethanolamine, choline, glycine, and betaine singly to rats and later isolated the first three compounds from tissues. On the basis of the extent of labeling in the isolated materials he concluded that glycine and ethanolamine were intermediates between betaine and choline[186] and that the major route of demethylation is the conversion of betaine to glycine, a precursor of ethanolamine.[187] Definite evidence that choline is not demethylated was the finding of methionine and labeled dimethylglycine, not dimethylaminoethanol, after incubation of a rat liver homogenate containing homocysteine and N^{15}-labeled choline.[109]

The proof of the transfer of one intact methyl group, at least, from the product of oxidation of choline, either betaine aldehyde or betaine, is impressive. Following the feeding of deuteriomethyl-labeled choline to rats, methionine and creatine containing deuteriomethyl groups were isolated from tissues.[66] This transmethylation occurred regardless of a dietary need of methionine, indicating that the reaction was one of those characterized by Schoenheimer as an "automatic and non-interruptable biochemical process."[188] That betaine is a source of labile methyl in the sense commonly ascribed to the choline methyl has long been known.[41, 77, 124, 189, 190] Significantly, betaine is not a complete replacement for choline in the chick which is unable to form monomethylaminoethanol from aminoethanol. It is not antiperotic, for instance, a function which appears to depend upon the incorporation of choline or of a similar molecule, such as arsenocholine, into phospholipids.[191]

[186] D. Stetten, Jr., *J. Biol. Chem.* **138,** 437 (1941).
[187] D. Stetten, Jr., *J. Biol. Chem.* **140,** 143 (1941).
[188] A. R. Moss and R. Schoenheimer, *J. Biol. Chem.* **135,** 415 (1940).
[189] A. P. Platt, *Biochem. J.* **33,** 505 (1939).
[190] J. P. Chandler and V. du Vigneaud, *J. Biol. Chem.* **135,** 223 (1940).
[191] T. H. Jukes, *J. Nutrition* **20,** 445 (1940).

The series of reactions pictured in Fig. 1 indicates that only one methyl of betaine takes part in true transmethylation, the remaining two being converted to formate. Needless to say, the nitrogen is no longer quaternary after the first demethylation. High radioactivity in the β-carbon was found in serine isolated from livers of rats after the administration of choline with C^{14}-labeled methyl groups, thus demonstrating the conversion of one methyl, at least, to formate.[192] The *in vitro* production of formate from the methyls of choline has been demonstrated by Siekevitz and Greenberg in experiments in which rat liver slices were incubated with similarly labeled choline.[92] These authors concluded that the nitrogen-methyl carbons of choline and the α-carbon of glycine are specific formate donors in the synthesis of serine from glycine.

The contrast in the roles of betaine and of dimethylglycine in transmethylation is clearly illustrated in the experiments of du Vigneaud et al. in which N^{15}-deuteriomethyl-labeled betaine and deuteriodimethylglycine were fed to rats.[75] Negligible labeling of tissue choline and creatine occurred in the latter instance, whereas significant labeling with deuterium did occur after the administration of betaine. Little of the nitrogen of betaine appeared in choline and creatine, showing that there had been no direct reduction of betaine to choline. Oginsky[193] found more methionine formed from homocystine and betaine by a rat liver homogenate than from homocystine and choline.

The degradation of monomethylglycine, or sarcosine, has been studied in several laboratories. Conversion to glycine was noted by Abbot and Lewis in rabbits which excreted increased amounts of hippuric acid following feeding of sarcosine and benzoic acid.[194] The failure to observe a similar effect of dimethylglycine and of betaine may be due possibly to a slower rate of demethylation of these substances to the monomethyl derivative. Bloch and Schoenheimer observed glycine formation in rats fed N^{15}-labeled sarcosine,[195] and Handler et al. demonstrated the conversion of dimethylglycine and of sarcosine to glycine and formaldehyde in rat liver homogenates.[196] Mackenzie isolated C^{14}-formaldehyde as the dimedon derivative from preparations containing rat liver homogenates or slices and labeled sarcosine.[197] Labeled formic acid and carbon dioxide were also identified. According to this worker formaldehyde from methyl carbons of betaine is a normally occurring metabolite, as is sarcosine.

The formation of serine by the addition of formate to glycine, with the

[192] W. Sakami, *J. Biol. Chem.* **179,** 495 (1949).
[193] E. L. Oginsky, *Arch. Biochem.* **26,** 327 (1950).
[194] L. D. Abbot, Jr. and H. B. Lewis, *J. Biol. Chem.* **131,** 479 (1939).
[195] K. Bloch and R. Schoenheimer, *J. Biol. Chem.* **135,** 99 (1940).
[196] P. Handler, M. L. C. Bernheim, and J. R. Klein, *J. Biol. Chem.* **138.** 211 (1941).
[197] C. G. Mackenzie, *J. Biol. Chem.* **186,** 351 (1950).

formate becoming the β-carbon of the new serine molecule, appears definitely established. In *in vitro* experiments with rat liver homogenates, Winnick *et al.*[198] isolated carboxyl-labeled serine after addition of C^{14}-carboxyl-labeled glycine and serine labeled in the α- and β-carbons after addition of C^{14}-α-carbon-labeled glycine. Following the feeding of C^{13}-carboxyl-labeled glycine and radioformate (C^{14}) to rats, Sakami[199] isolated serine from liver tissue and found C^{13} in the serine carboxyl group and C^{14} in the β position. Confirmatory evidence for the formation of serine from glycine was supplied by Greenberg and his coworkers as a result of *in vivo* studies in rats[200] and *in vitro* experiments with rat liver slices.[201] Ehrensvärd *et al.*[202] noted a rapid conversion of C^{13}-carboxyl-labeled glycine to serine by yeast.

Serine is also a source of formate, possibly by reversal of the reaction in which formate is added to glycine. Shemin[203] isolated hippuric acid after the administration of benzoic acid and C^{13}-carboxyl-labeled, N^{15}-labeled serine in rats and guinea pigs and found the same $N^{15}:C^{13}$ ratio in the glycine component as in the serine. C^{14}-formate is produced from C^{14}-β-carbon-labeled serine by rat liver in *in vitro* experiments.[192]

The mechanisms of the glycine-serine reactions are not known. Shemin[203] suggested the possibility of a removal of two hydrogens from the β-position of serine with the formation of α-amino-β-ketopropionic acid as the immediate precursor of glycine and formic acid. On the other hand, a serine dehydrase has been reported in mouse[204] and rat liver.[205] In the latter instance α-aminoacrylic acid was postulated as the product of the removal of water from the β-carbon of serine. Ratner *et al.*[206] have prepared a glycine oxidase from liver and kidney of several species. Its prosthetic group is flavin adenine dinucleotide, and the enzyme converts glycine to glyoxylic acid plus ammonia and sarcosine to glyoxylic acid plus methylamine. Paretsky and Werkman[207] concluded that formaldehyde is an intermediate in the dissimiliation of glycine by *Achromobacter*.

The evidence is clear-cut also for the decarboxylation of serine to amino-

198 T. Winnick, I. Moring-Claesson, and D. M. Greenberg, *J. Biol. Chem.* **175**, 127 (1948).

199 W. Sakami, *J. Biol. Chem.* **176**, 995 (1948).

200 P. D. Goldsworthy, T. Winnick, and D. M. Greenberg, *J. Biol. Chem.* **180**, 341 (1949).

201 P. Siekevitz and D. M. Greenberg, *J. Biol. Chem.* **180**, 845 (1949).

202 G. Ehrensvärd, E. Sperber, E. Saluste, L. Reio, and R. Stjernholm, *J. Biol. Chem.* **169**, 759 (1947).

203 D. Shemin, *J. Biol. Chem.* **162**, 297 (1946).

204 F. Binkley, *J. Biol. Chem.* **150**, 261 (1943).

205 E. Chargaff and D. B. Sprinson, *J. Biol. Chem.* **151**, 273 (1943).

206 S. Ratner, V. Nocito, and D. E. Green, *J. Biol. Chem.* **152**, 119 (1944).

207 D. Paretsky and C. H. Werkman, *Arch. Biochem.* **25**, 288 (1950).

ethanol. Stetten[208] fed N^{15}-labeled serine to rats and found the N^{15} in tissue phospholipids and proteins, in cystine, and in aminoethanol. Levene and Tarver[209] observed a rapid uptake of C^{14}-β-carbon-labeled serine in tissue proteins and the appearance of the C^{14} in aminoethanol in rats fed the labeled serine. Similiar evidence has been presented by other workers.[71, 88, 94, 210] In the experiments of Weissbach et al.,[210] rats fed serine, doubly labeled by C^{14} in the β-carbon and by N^{15}, converted the amino acid into choline-containing C^{14} in the alcoholic carbon and N^{15}. This would be expected by the decarboxylation of serine to aminoethanol and by the methylation of the latter.

In so far as the carbon chain of choline is concerned, the evidence is strong for a cycle as described in Fig. 1. In theory at least, the nitrogen-carbon combination of choline might remain in the cycle indefinitely, but with each complete series of reactions a new second carbon would enter the cycle, entering as the β-carbon and leaving as carbon dioxide from the carboxyl carbon of serine. As far as is known the glycine-serine reaction is the only reversible reaction of consequence among those concerned with the carbon chain of choline (compounds 1 to 10, Fig.1).

6. OXIDATION OF METHYL CARBONS

The rapid appearance of radioactive carbon dioxide in the expired air of rats after the feeding of C^{14}-methyl-labeled methionine clearly demonstrated the oxidizability of the labile methyl group.[211] A similar result followed the intraperitoneal injection of C^{14}-labeled choline, betaine, dimethylthetin, and dimethylpropiothetin.[212-214] In each of the latter experiments the highest level of radioactivity of carbon dioxide was found in the first 4-hour period. Less choline was oxidized, but this may only have been a reflection of its normal use in lecithins and in other metabolites. Reference has already been made to the appearance of the labeled β-carbon of serine after administration of methyl-labeled choline or methionine. For this reason, it is reasonable to assume, as indicated in Fig. 1, that formate is an intermediate in the catabolism of a labile methyl and that the formate car-

[208] D. Stetten, Jr., J. Biol. Chem. **144**, 501 (1942).
[209] M. Levine and H. Tarver, J. Biol. Chem. **184**, 427 (1950).
[210] A. Weissbach, D. Elwyn, and D. B. Sprinson, J. Am. Chem. Soc. **72**, 3316 (1950).
[211] C. G. Mackenzie, J. P. Chandler, E. B. Keller, J. R. Rachele, N. Cross, D. B. Melville, and V. du Vigneaud, J. Biol. Chem. **169**, 757 (1947).
[212] C. G. Mackenzie, J. P. Chandler, E. B. Keller, J. R. Rachele, N. Cross, and V. du Vigneaud, J. Biol. Chem. **180**, 99 (1949).
[213] C. G. Mackenzie, J. R. Rachele, N. Cross, J. P. Chandler, and V. du Vigneaud, J. Biol. Chem. **183**, 617 (1950).
[214] M. F. Ferger and V. du Vigneaud, J. Biol. Chem. **185**, 53 (1950).

bon may be completely oxidized or built into serine or any other formate-accepting anabolic product depending on a diversity of metabolic factors. The demonstration of the loss of labile methyl groups by oxidation makes understandable the continuous need of the organism for replacement methyls.

7. OTHER ASPECTS OF METHYL TRANSFER AND OXIDATION

Dimethylsulfone has been isolated from beef blood[215] and adrenal cortex[216] and from the plants *Equisetum palustre, E. arvenue,* and *E. hyemale.*[217, 218] Inasmuch as so little is known about the intermediate steps in the oxidation of sulfur, it cannot be said that this compound is not a normal intermediate. However, it appears most unlikely that it is important in transmethylation. Smythe demonstrated the formation of hydrogen sulfide from cysteine by liver slices and suggested that it might be a precursor of the sulfone.[219]

The chemical mobility of one methyl group in betaine, at least, was observed by Willstätter at the beginning of the century.[220] If heated to 300° it is converted in part to the methyl ester of dimethylaminoacetic acid. Challenger *et al.* extended this observation to include the transfer of methyl from betaine under the influence of heat with the formation of dimethyl derivatives of selenium, tellurium, and sulfur from selenite, tellurite, and sulfite, respectively.[221, 222] It was also demonstrated that the heating of betaine with aromatic primary amines such as aniline, *p*-toluidine, or β-naphthylamine resulted in a transfer of methyl and the formation of the corresponding monomethyl derivatives. Dimethylthetin also yielded the methyl ester of thiomethylacetic acid on heating.[223]

Methylation of selenides and tellurides in the animal organism has been the subject of much controversy since the original report by Hofmeister in 1894.[224] The excretion in expired air of a volatile selenide or telluride has not been questioned, but proof that the substance in question was a methyl derivative has been unsatisfactory. However, McConnell and Portman have

[215] J. J. Pfiffner and H. B. North, *J. Biol. Chem.* **134,** 781 (1940).
[216] L. Ruzicka, M. W. Goldberg, and H. Meister, *Helv. Chim. Acta* **23,** 559 (1940).
[217] P. Karrer and C. H. Eugster, *Helv. Chim. Acta* **32,** 957 (1949).
[218] P. Karrer, C. H. Eugster, and D. K. Patel, *Helv. Chim. Acta* **32,** 2397 (1949).
[219] C. V. Smythe, *J. Biol. Chem.* **142,** 387 (1942).
[220] R. Willstätter, *Ber.* **35,** 584 (1902).
[221] F. Challenger and C. Higginbottom, *Biochem. J.* **29,** 1757 (1935).
[222] F. Challenger, P. Taylor, and B. Taylor, *J. Chem. Soc.* **1942,** 48.
[223] F. Challenger and P. Fothergill, *Biochem. J.* **45,** xxvii (1949).
[224] F. Hofmeister, *Arch. exptl. Pathol. Pharmakol.* **33,** 198 (1894).

identified dimethylselenide and measured its excretion following the administration in rats of sodium selenate containing radioselenium.[225]

V. Specificity of Action

WENDELL H. GRIFFITH and JOSEPH F. NYC

The following discussion deals with specificity of action of choline in the animal organism. Certain aspects of this problem in microorganisms are included in the section on biogenesis (Section VI).

Inasmuch as choline can be synthesized *in vivo*, the recognition of a choline-like action in another compound depends in large part on whether or not the compound in question is used with greater facility than choline can be synthesized. The characteristic effects of choline are its role as a potential source of labile methyl and its complex function as a constituent of phospholipids. These properties are measured, respectively, by the rate of growth of rats on diets containing homocystine but devoid of methionine and by the prevention of increases of hepatic lipids in rats deprived of choline. Presumably this latter property may be ascribed to phospholipids such as lecithin which may also be responsible for the prevention of renal lesions in young rats and of perosis in chicks and turkey poults and for stimulation of growth in the young fowl. Although the specificity of choline as a source of labile methyl or of phospholipid is high, it shares these properties to a limited extent. Pertinent data are shown in Tables III to VI which are expanded from the material reported by Moyer and du Vigneaud.[1]

As indicated earlier (Section IV, p. 19), the lability of a methyl is related to its attachment to a nitrogen or sulfur atom which has acquired an additional covalent bond and positive charge. In addition to compounds containing preformed choline that may be liberated by hydrolysis (Table III) and to compounds with sulfur methyls and "onium" sulfur (Table IV), the only substances known to be in this category are betaine and dimethyl-ethyl-β-hydroxyethylammonium hydroxide or monoethylcholine (Tables V and VI). This represents a high degree of specificity, indeed, and it appears that conversion to glycine betaine or to a very similar structure is a prerequisite for choline activity in substances of this type. It is clearly evident, however, that the presence of a methylated quaternary nitrogen in betaine is not the sole factor governing specificity because betaines of

[225] K. P. McConnell and O. W. Portman, *J. Biol. Chem.* **195,** 277 (1952).
[1] A. W. Moyer and V. du Vigneaud, *J. Biol. Chem.* **143,** 373 (1942).

TABLE III
BIOLOGICAL ACTIVITY OF CHOLINE AND OF SOME OF ITS DERIVATIVES

Compound	Perosis	Prevention of Renal lesion	Prevention of Fatty liver	Fowl growth	Growth with homocystine
Choline	+[2,3]	+[4]	+[5]	+[2,3,6]	+[7]
Phosphorylcholine			+[8]		+[1]
Lecithin	+[9]		+[5]	+[9]	+[1]
Choline sulfate		−[10]			
Arsenocholine	+[2,3]	+[10,11]	+[12,13]	+[3,14]	−[15]
Phosphocholine		+[10]	+[8]		
Sulfocholine		+[16]	+[16]		−[16]
Monoethylcholine	+[3,14]	+[10,11]	+[1]	+[3,14]	+[1]
Diethylcholine	+[3,14]	+[10,11]	+[11]	−[3,14]	−[15]
Triethylcholine	−[3,14]	+[10,11]	+[17,18]	−[3,14]	−[7]
Tripropylcholine		−[10]	−[10,18]		
Homocholine			+[18]		−[1]
Trimethyl-β-hydroxypropyl-ammonium hydroxide		−[10]	−[19]		
Diethylmethyl-β-γ-dihydroxypropylammonium chloride					−[1]
Choline methyl ether			−[20]		
β-Methylcholine	±[3]	±[10]	−[8]	−[3]	−[15]
β-Methylcholine ethyl ether			−[8]		
α,α-Dimethylcholine	−[3]			−[3]	−[21]
α-Methyl-β-phenylcholine			−[8]		

[2] T. H. Jukes, *J. Nutrition* **20,** 445 (1940).

[3] T. H. Jukes and A. D. Welch, *J. Biol. Chem.* **146,** 19 (1942).

[4] W. H. Griffith and N. J. Wade, *Proc. Soc. Exptl. Biol. Med.* **41,** 188 (1939).

[5] C. H. Best, J. M. Hershey, and M. E. Huntsman, *Am. J. Physiol.* **101,** 7P (1932).

[6] A. A. Klose and H. J. Almquist, *J. Biol. Chem.* **138,** 467 (1941).

[7] V. du Vigneaud, J. P. Chandler, A. W. Moyer, and D. M. Keppel, *J. Biol. Chem.* **131,** 57 (1939).

[8] A. D. Welch and M. S. Welch, *Proc. Soc. Exptl. Biol. Med.* **39,** 7 (1938).

[9] T. H. Jukes, *Poultry Sci.* **20,** 251 (1941).

[10] A. D. Welch, *J. Nutrition* **40,** 113 (1950).

[11] A. D. Welch, cited by T. H. Jukes, ref. 14.

[12] A. D. Welch and R. L. Landau, *J. Biol. Chem.* **144,** 581 (1942).

[13] A. D. Welch, *Proc. Soc. Exptl. Biol. Med.* **35,** 107 (1936).

[14] T. H. Jukes, Proc. Am. Inst. Nutrition, *J. Nutrition* **21,** *Suppl.* 13 (1941).

[15] A. D. Welch, *J. Biol. Chem.* **137,** 173 (1941).

[16] G. A. Maw and V. du Vigneaud, *J. Biol. Chem.* **176,** 1029 (1948).

[17] H. J. Channon and J. A. B. Smith, *Biochem. J.* **30,** 115 (1936).

[18] H. J. Channon, A. P. Platt, and J. A. B. Smith, *Biochem. J.* **31,** 1736 (1937).

[19] C. H. Best and J. H. Ridout, *Can. Med. Assoc. J.* **39,** 188 (1938).

[20] A. P. Platt, *Biochem. J.* **33,** 505 (1939).

[21] A. D. Welch, cited by A. W. Moyer and V. du Vigneaud, ref. 1.

TABLE IV

BIOLOGICAL ACTIVITY OF METHIONINE, OF DIMETHYLTHETIN, AND OF SOME OTHER S-ALKYL COMPOUNDS

| Compound | Perosis | Prevention of | | Fowl growth | Growth with homocystine |
		Renal lesion	Fatty liver		
Methionine	−22	+4	+23	−22	
Methionine sulfoxide			+24		
Homomethionine					−1
Ethionine					
Dimethylthetin		+10	+10, 21		+25
Methylethylthetin		+10, 25	+25		+25
Diethylthetin		−10, 25	−10, 25		−25
Dimethylpropiothetin		+25	+25		+25
S-Methylcysteine			+24, 26		−1, 15
S-Ethylcysteine			+24		
S-Methylthioglycolic acid		−25			−25

TABLE V

BIOLOGICAL ACTIVITY OF BETAINE AND OF SOME OF ITS DERIVATIVES

| Compound | Perosis | Prevention of | | Fowl growth | Growth with homocystine |
		Renal lesions	Fatty liver		
Betaine	−2, 3	+10, 11, 27	+28	−2 ±3	+7
Arsenobetaine		−10	−8		−1
Phosphobetaine		−10	−8		
Triethylbetaine			−22		
Betaine aldehyde	−3	+10	+8	±3, 29	
Betaine aldehyde acetol			+8		
α-Alanine betaine		−23	−10		−1
β-Alanine betaine					Toxic[1]
Cystine betaine			+24		−1
Glutamic betaine		−21	−21		
Serine betaine		−23	−30		−1
Threonine betaine			−30		
Allothreonine betaine			−30		
Ergothioneine			−31		−7
Stachydrine					−1
Trigonelline			−1		−1

[22] T. H. Jukes, *J. Nutrition* **22**, 315 (1941).
[23] H. F. Tucker and H. C. Eckstein, *J. Biol. Chem.* **121**, 479 (1937).
[24] S. A. Singal and H. C. Eckstein, *J. Biol. Chem.* **140**, 27 (1941).
[25] G. A. Maw and V. du Vigneaud, *J. Biol. Chem.* **176**, 1037 (1948).
[26] H. J. Channon, M. C. Manifold, and A. P. Platt, *Biochem. J.* **34**, 866 (1940).
[27] W. H. Griffith and D. J. Mulford, *J. Am. Chem. Soc.* **63**, 929 (1941).

other amino acids appear unable to serve as methyl donors (Table V). Furthermore, sulfocholine is also negative in this respect, despite the great activity of similar sulfur methyl groups in the thetins.

As far as is known, the attribute of being a methyl donor also confers on a molecule the function of serving as a precursor of the methyl portion

TABLE VI

BIOLOGICAL ACTIVITY OF VARIOUS N-ALKYL AND RELATED COMPOUNDS

Compound	Perosis	Prevention of Renal lesions	Prevention of Fatty liver	Fowl growth	Growth with homocystine
Trimethylamine oxide			— [8]		
Trimethylammonium chloride			— [32]		
Trimethylethylammonium chloride			Toxic[32]		
Tetramethylammonium chloride			Toxic[32]		
Trimethylphenylammonium chloride			Toxic[32]		
Tetra-β-hydroxyethylammonium chloride			— [23]		
Monomethylaminoethanol	+[a, 33]			[a, 33]	
Dimethylaminoethanol	+[b, 33]	+[10, 34]	+[10, 34]	[b, 33]+	
Monomethylglycine			— [35]		— [7]
Dimethylglycine		— [34]	— [34]		— [1]
Dimethylglycine methyl ester					— [1]
Creatine	— [22]		— [20]	±[22]	— [35]
Creatinine			— [35]		— [7]
Caffeine			— [1]		— [7]
Methanol			— [1]		— [7]
Neurine					Toxic[1]

[a] In presence of betaine and B_{12}.
[b] In presence of B_{12}.

of choline. On the other hand, derivatives of choline are known that may be used in the synthesis of lecithin but lack the methyl donor characteristic

[28] C. H. Best and M. E. Huntsman, *J. Physiol. (London)* **75**, 405 (1932).
[29] T. H. Jukes, cited by A. W. Moyer and V. du Vigneaud, ref. 1.
[30] H. E. Carter and D. B. Melville, *J. Biol. Chem.* **133**, 109 (1940).
[31] C. H. Best and J. H. Ridout, *Ann. Rev. Biochem.* **8**, 349 (1939).
[32] M. E. H. Mawson and A. D. Welch, *Biochem. J.* **30**, 417 (1936).
[33] A. E. Schaefer, W. D. Salmon, and D. R. Strength, *J. Nutrition* **44**, 305 (1951).
[34] V. du Vigneaud, S. Simmonds, J. P. Chandler, and M. Cohn, *J. Biol. Chem.* **165**, 639 (1946).
[35] V. du Vigneaud, J. P. Chandler, and A. W. Moyer, *J. Biol. Chem.* **139**, 917 (1941).

completely. In this category are arsenocholine, phosphocholine, and triethylcholine. Following the administration of the arsenic and phosphorus analogs of choline, Welch[10] noted lipotropic activity and, in the case of arsenocholine, demonstrated its presence in tissue phospholipid.[12, 13] Similar findings for triethylcholine were reported by McArthur.[36, 37] It is natural to ascribe the lipotropic effect of these compounds to their corresponding phospholipid forms, but the certainty of such an assumption remains to be proved. Caution in this respect is required because of the possibility of unrecognized biological properties of acetycholine or of other derivatives of choline. That triethylcholine, for instance, may exhibit activity as an antagonist of choline has been reported.[38]

VI. Biogenesis

WENDELL H. GRIFFITH and JOSEPH F. NYC

The biogenesis of choline in the animal organism, discussed in a preceding section, depends on dietary sources of vitamins such as folic acid and B_{12} which may be required as cofactors in its enzymatic formation. Limited synthesis occurs under advantageous dietary conditions in the rat and chick, the two species used most commonly in choline studies. Severe deficiencies result on diets low in labile methyl and in the vitamins in question even though the diet may appear quite adequate in other respects. On the other hand, unlimited synthesis characterizes the growth of most microorganisms and plants.

Pneumococci[1, 2] and artificially produced mutant strains of *Neurospora*[3, 4] are the only forms known to require external supplies of choline for normal growth. Choline and homocystine can replace methionine for the growth of *L. casei*[5] but not of *E. coli.*[6] In preliminary experiments designed to develop a microbiological assay for choline, Badger[2] found that aminoethanol would support the growth of a strain of pneumococcus in the absence of choline. Other compounds which are related to choline and aminoethanol were then tested for their activity in promoting growth of

[36] C. S. McArthur, *Science* **104**, 222 (1946).

[37] C. S. McArthur and C. C. Lucas, *Biochem. J.* **46**, 226 (1950).

[38] A. S Keston and S. B. Wortis, *Proc. Soc. Exptl. Biol. Med.* **61**, 439 (1946).

[1] L. Rane and Y. SubbaRow, *J. Biol. Chem.* **134**, 455 (1940).

[2] E. Badger, *J. Bacteriol.* **47**, 509 (1944); *J. Biol. Chem.* **153**, 183 (1944).

[3] N. H. Horowitz and G. W. Beadle, *J. Biol. Chem.* **150**, 325 (1943).

[4] N. H. Horowitz, D. Bonner, and M. B. Houlahan, *J. Biol. Chem.* **159**, 145 (1945).

[5] R. J. Evans, *Arch. Biochem.* **16**, 357 (1948).

[6] M. N. Green and M. G. Sevag, *Arch. Biochem.* **9**, 129 (1946).

this organism. It was found that the active compounds contained N—C—C—OH and N—C—C—C—OH linkages. Substitution of, or through, the hydroxyl group resulted in complete inactivation of the molecule. Aminoethanol, monomethylaminoethanol, and dimethylaminoethanol were among these substances supporting the growth of the organism. The activity of triethylcholine, diethylaminoethanol, and similar compounds plus the inactivity of betaine, methionine, and other compounds containing labile methyl groups indicated that the role of choline in pneumococcal metabolism is not that of transmethylation. The fact that aminoethanol is required in ten times the concentration of choline for equivalent growth suggested that choline is not demethylated to give ethanolamine.

In contrast to the pneumococcus, two genetically different strains of *Neurospora crassa* are unable to utilize aminoethanol in place of choline.[4] These mutants are designated as strain 34486, or *cholineless-1*, and strain 47904, or *cholineless-2*. Each strain is believed to carry a mutation of a different single gene concerned with the synthesis of choline,[4] and each strain attains a growth rate comparable to that of the wild type in choline-supplemented media. The following compounds show some activity for both mutants: choline, dimethylaminoethanol, monomethylaminoethanol, acetylcholine, arsenocholine, phosphorylcholine, dimethylethylhydroxyethylammonium chloride, diethylmethylhydroxyethylammonium chloride, triethylcholine, and methionine. The following compounds are inactive for both mutants: aminoethanol, betaine, creatine, sarcosine, neurine, diethylaminoethanol, dimethylamine, trimethylamine, and tetramethylammonium chloride.[3, 4, 7, 8] The work of Horowitz[9] showed that an inherent difference exists between the two cholineless mutants of *Neurospora* in their ability to utilize monomethylaminoethanol and dimethylaminoethanol. The results suggested that the gene-controlled deficiency in *cholineless-2* may be concerned with the methylation of a mono- or dimethylated precursor of choline, whereas that in *cholineless-1* blocks a prior step in the synthesis. It was observed that *cholineless-2* produces a substance which is inactive for itself but which promotes the growth of *cholineless-1*. The substance has been isolated from the cultures of *cholineless-2* and identified as monomethylaminoethanol. This substance is therefore a normal intermediate in the synthesis of choline in *Neurospora*. According to Horowitz, in *cholineless-1* the genetic block precedes monomethylaminoethanol, so that the mutant cannot synthesize this intermediate but can utilize it for choline synthesis if an exogenous supply is available. In *cholineless-2* a partial block exists between monomethylaminoethanol and choline. This mutant

[7] T. H. Jukes, A. C. Dornbush, and J. J. Oleson, *Federation Proc.* 4, 157 (1945).

[8] T. H. Jukes and A. C. Dornbush, *Proc. Soc. Exptl. Biol. Med.* 58, 142 (1945).

[9] N. H. Horowitz, *J. Biol. Chem.* 162, 413 (1946).

can synthesize monomethylaminoethanol but is unable to convert it to choline at the normal rate; as a result, the intermediate accumulates in the culture. Hypothetical intermediates are bracketed, and vertical dotted lines indicate points of blocking in the following scheme proposed by Horowitz.

$$
\begin{bmatrix} NH_2 \\ | \\ CH_2 \\ | \\ CH_2 \\ | \\ OH \end{bmatrix}
\xrightarrow[\text{cholineless-1}]{}
\begin{matrix} HN \cdot CH_4 \\ | \\ CH_2 \\ | \\ CH_2 \\ | \\ OH \end{matrix}
\xrightarrow[\text{cholineless-2}]{}
\begin{bmatrix} N \cdot (CH_3)_2 \\ | \\ CH_2 \\ | \\ CH_2 \\ | \\ OH \end{bmatrix}
\rightarrow \text{Choline}
$$

Challenger and coworkers[10-12] showed that trimethylarsine is one of the volatile odorous products evolved from mold cultures containing arsenious acid. The mold *Scopulariopsis brevicaulis* not only methylates arsenite but also converts selenite[13] and tellurite[14] to the respective dimethyl derivatives. Challenger and Higginbottom[10] suggested that choline or betaine might supply methyl for these methylations. A means of separation and identification of aminoethanol, devised by Simons,[15] failed to show an accumulation of this possible demethylation product of choline in a culture of *S. brevicaulis* containing added choline and arsenite. No evidence was obtained for the methylation of sulfur compounds by this organism except by fission of dialkyl disulfides.[16, 17] However, dimethyl sulfide was isolated as a product of the fungus *Schizophyllum commune Fr.*[18] Smith and Schlenk observed that thiomethyladenosine accumulated in yeast grown in a medium containing an excess of methionine but not of sulfate, homocystine, cysteine, or glutathione. The nucleoside was used by the yeast as a source of sulfur if added to a deficient medium.[19]

Although the *Neurospora* studies suggest similarity in the biogenesis of choline between animals and microorganisms, there is little evidence that degradation of choline proceeds along the same pathways. Trimethylamine is the usual product, and its formation has been noted in choline-containing

[10] F. Challenger and C. Higginbottom, *Biochem. J.* **29**, 1757 (1935).

[11] F. Challenger, C. Higginbottom, and L. Ellis, *J. Chem. Soc.* **1933**, 95.

[12] F. Challenger and A. A. Rawlings, *J. Chem. Soc.* **1936**, 264.

[13] F. Challenger and H. E. North, *J. Chem. Soc.* **1934**, 68.

[14] M. L. Bird and F. Challenger, *J. Chem. Soc.* **1939**, 163; **1942**, 571, 574.

[15] C. Simons, *Biochem. J.* **35**, 749 (1941).

[16] F. Challenger and S. Blackburn, *J. Chem. Soc.* **1938**, 1872.

[17] F. Challenger and P. T. Charlton, *J. Chem. Soc.* **1947**, 424.

[18] J. H. Birkinshaw, W. P. K. Findlay, and R. A. Webb, *Biochem. J.* **36**, 526 (1942).

[19] R. L. Smith and F. Schlenk, *Federation Proc.* **11**, 289 (1952); *Arch. Biochem. and Biophys.* **38**, 159, 167 (1952).

cultures of *Bacillus prodigiosus*,[20] *Shigella alkalescens*,[21] *Proteus vulgaris*,[22] and many other organisms.

There is a wide distribution of choline phospholipids throughout the plant world. Ducet[23, 24] examined seedlings of soybean, barley, and pea and other young plants and concluded that synthesis of choline occurs in rapidly growing tissues, such as leaf buds. He believed that glycerylphosphorylcholine is an intermediate in the synthesis of lecithin. The occurrence of small amounts of free choline was ascribed to the presence of lecithinase.

VII. Estimation

WENDELL H. GRIFFITH and JOSEPH F. NYC

A. CHEMICAL PROCEDURES

Chemical procedures for the quantitative determination of choline in biological materials have been extensively treated in various publications.[1-4] The method based on the precipitation of choline as the periodide has been one of the preferred chemical procedures. Earliest studies on the precipitation of choline periodide were made by Staněk,[5] who proposed the use of potassium triiodide as the reagent for the quantitative precipitation of choline. In 1923, Sharpe[6] published a quantitative chemical method, based on the original work of Staněk, in which choline was precipitated with iodine as the periodide which was washed free of excess reagent with ice-cold water and decomposed with dilute nitric acid. The liberated iodine was extracted with chloroform and estimated using a standard solution of sodium thiosulfate.

Roman[7] and Maxim[8] investigated the original Staněk method and, as a

[20] D. Ackermann and H. Schütze, *Zentr. Physiol.* **24,** 210 (1910).

[21] A. J. Wood and F. E. Keeping, *J. Bacteriol.* **47,** 309 (1944).

[22] G. N. Cohen, B. Nisman, and M. Raynaud, *Compt. rend.* **225,** 647 (1947).

[23] G. Ducet, *Compt. rend.* **227,** 871 (1948).

[24] G. Ducet, *Ann. agron.* **19,** 184 (1949).

[1] C. H. Best and C. C. Lucas, *Vitamins and Hormones* **1,** 1 (1943).

[2] P. Handler, *Biol. Symposia* **12,** 361 (1947).

[3] P. György and S. H. Rubin, *in* Vitamin Methods, Vol. 1, p. 243. Academic Press, New York, 1950.

[4] Association of Vitamin Chemists, Inc., Methods of Vitamin Assay, 2nd ed., p. 287. Interscience Publishers, New York, 1951.

[5] V. Staněk, *Hoppe-Seyler's Z. physiol. Chem.* **46,** 280 (1905); **47,** 83 (1906); **48,** 334 (1906).

[6] J. S. Sharpe, *Biochem. J.* **17,** 41 (1923).

[7] W. Roman, *Biochem. Z.* **219,** 218 (1930).

[8] M. Maxim, *Biochem. Z.* **239,** 138 (1931).

result of their findings, described the first microchemical method for the estimation of choline. Roman obtained reproducible results within a range of 5 γ to 5 mg. of choline with a maximum error of 5 %.

Erickson and her collaborators[9] improved the periodide micromethod of Roman by using immersion filter sticks which facilitated washing the labile choline iodide precipitate with minimum disturbance. The introduction of this step in the procedure was desirable because the greatest source of error in the periodide method was the volatile and unstable nature of the choline precipitate. A further improvement was the introduction of bromine oxidation to convert the iodine to iodate preceding titration with standard sodium thiosulfate. The latter modification offered the advantages of ready solubility of the precipitate in the bromine solution and a sixfold increase in the final titration value.

Potassium periodide yields precipitates with dimethylamine, trimethylamine, betaines, certain cyclic bases, and many alkaloids.[10] The presence of these substances in plants makes it impossible to relate the results obtained by the periodide method to a definite constituent in a plant extract. Reifer[10] claimed that the greatest part, if not all, of the periodide-precipitable substances in plant extracts, with the exception of choline, were removed by lead acetate and Norit.

At the present time the most widely used method for the quantitative determination of choline appears to be by precipitation as reineckate. Among the first to employ the reineckate method for the determination of choline were Kapfhammer and Bischoff,[11] who washed the choline reineckate with ether and determined it gravimetrically. This method required fairly large amounts of choline and, therefore, was not easily adaptable for general use. A more sensitive method described by Beattie[12] consisted of the precipitation of choline with a freshly prepared solution of ammonium reineckate, solution of the precipitate in acetone, and comparison of the bright red color imparted to the solvent with that of a standard solution. Using a visual colorimeter, quantities of the order of 0.3 mg. of choline in a concentration of 0.003 % were estimated by this procedure with an error of not more than 3 %. The use of photoelectric colorimetry greatly increased the sensitivity of the method.[13-16] According to the procedure of Jacobi et al.,[15] the ground sample was extracted with boiling 1:1 alcohol-

[9] B. N. Erickson, I. Avrin, D. M. Teague, and H. H. Williams, *J. Biol. Chem.* **135,** 671 (1940).

[10] I. Reifer, *New Zealand J. Sci. Tech.* **22B,** iii (1941).

[11] J. Kapfhammer and C. Bischoff, *Hoppe-Seyler's Z. physiol. Chem.* **191,** 179 (1930).

[12] F. J. R. Beattie, *Biochem. J.* **30,** 1554 (1936).

[13] R. W. Engel, *J. Biol. Chem.* **144,** 701 (1942).

[14] D. Glick, *J. Biol. Chem.* **156,** 643 (1944).

[15] H. P. Jacobi, C. A. Baumann, and W. J. Meek, *J. Biol. Chem.* **138,** 571 (1941).

[16] M. H. Thornton and F. K. Broome, *Ind. Eng. Chem. Anal. Ed.* **14,** 39 (1942).

ether mixture and the residue of this extract was saponified for 2 hours at 80° with baryta. The choline, precipitated as the reineckate, was dissolved in acetone and the color intensity was measured, using a light filter which transmits at 520 mμ.

Engel[13] advised more exhaustive extraction of biological samples with methanol and hydrolysis of extracts with baryta for 2 hours at 100° rather than at 80°, as recommended by Jacobi et al. Glick[14] further improved the reineckate method by showing that interference due to many compounds which form insoluble reineckates is circumvented by precipitating the choline reineckate in an alkaline medium. Propanol was found to be the most suitable solvent for washing the reineckate. The maximum light absorption for choline reineckate, as determined spectrophotometrically by Glick, is near 526 mμ. Glick's reineckate method and the more recently published modification by Willstaedt et al.[17] are in wide use today.

The development of a brown color, by adding an iodine reagent to an aqueous solution of choline reineckate, was used as the basis of a method by Shaw.[18] Still another modification of the reineckate method was proposed by Marenzi and Cardini.[19] It is based on the oxidation of the chromium of choline reineckate to the chromic state by means of alkaline hydrogen peroxide, followed by colorimetric determination of the chromate by means of the violet-red color produced in an acid solution with diphenylcarbazide (Cazeneuve's reaction). The authors claim that this method will allow the estimation of as little as 15 γ of choline. Winzler and Meserve[20] increased the sensitivity of the reineckate method by making use of the very great absorption of acetone solutions of choline reineckate at 327 mμ. This method has an accuracy of $\pm 5\%$ with samples containing 50 to 400 γ of choline hydrochloride.

Lintzell and Fomin[21] introduced a new micromethod for choline estimation based on the oxidative degradation of choline to trimethylamine and titration of the latter. Neither the original method nor the modifications of it[22, 23] appears to have gained general acceptance.

Less well-known methods for the determination of choline are those of Ambo and Aoki[24] and of Eagle,[25] who based their procedures on the volumetric determination of mercury in the mercuric salt of choline. A simple

[17] H. Willstaedt, M. Borggard, and H. Lieck, Z. Vitaminforsch. 18, 25 (1946).
[18] F. H. Shaw, Biochem. J. 32, 1002 (1938).
[19] A. D. Marenzi and C. E. Cardini, J. Biol. Chem. 147, 363 (1943).
[20] R. J. Winzler and E. R. Meserve, J. Biol. Chem. 159, 395 (1945).
[21] W. Lintzel and S. Fomin, Biochem. Z. 238, 438 (1931).
[22] G. Klein and H. Linser, Biochem. Z. 250, 220 (1932).
[23] W. Lintzel and G. Monasterio, Biochem. Z. 241, 273 (1931).
[24] H. Ambo and T. Aoki, Trans. Japan. Pathol. Soc. 21, 171 (1931).
[5] E. Eagle, J. Lab. Clin. Med. 27, 103 (1941).

gravimetric procedure for the assay of choline chloride in pharmaceutical products, based on the precipitation of choline from absolute ethanol with phosphotungstic acid, has been described by Gakenheimer and Reguera.[26] A recent gravimetric method[27] consists of precipitating the cadmium chloride complex of choline from an alcoholic solution. This method can be used for the assay of pharmaceutical products but has not been studied with biological samples.

B. MICROBIOLOGICAL PROCEDURES

A microbiological method for the determination of choline by the use of a mutant of *Neurospora crassa* was described by Horowitz and Beadle.[28] The mutant (34486) had been produced by ultraviolet irradiation of a normal "wild type" strain. As a result of the induced mutation this organism fails to grow on an unsupplemented basal medium but grows if choline is supplied. Combined choline, as in lecithin, is also utilized by the test organism, but less efficiently than free choline. For this reason the choline in samples must be liberated by hydrolysis prior to assay. Methionine has a sparing action on choline and, when present in appreciable amounts, must be removed from the sample. Jukes and Dornbush[29] have shown that dimethylaminoethanol is also active for the mutant.

A second cholineless strain (47904) which differs genetically from strain 34486, was described by Horowitz *et al.*,[30, 31] and this mutant may also be used in the bioassay of choline. The growth of both cholineless mutants is stimulated by such compounds as acetylcholine, phosphorylcholine, monomethylaminoethanol and dimethylaminoethanol. The following compounds were found to be inactive for both mutants: betaine, creatine, sarcosine, aminoethanol, neurine, diethylaminoethanol, dimethylamine, trimethylamine, and tetramethylammonium chloride.

The procedure for the *Neurospora* assay has been described in several texts.[2, 3, 32] According to the original method[28] the sample for assay is autoclaved with 3 % sulfuric acid for 2 hours at 15 pounds pressure to liberate choline from its combined forms, and the solution is neutralized with barium hydroxide. The solution is passed through a column containing Permutit in order to separate the choline from methionine, and the ab-

[26] W. C. Gakenheimer and R. M. Reguera, *J. Am. Pharm. Assoc. Sci. Ed.* **35**, 311 (1946).

[27] W. Seaman, J. J. Hugonet, and W. Leibmann, *Anal. Chem.* **21**, 411 (1949).

[28] N. H. Horowitz and G. W. Beadle, *J. Biol. Chem.* **150**, 325 (1943).

[29] T. H. Jukes and A. C. Dornbush, *Proc. Soc. Exptl. Biol. Med.* **58**, 142 (1945).

[30] N. H. Horowitz, D. Bonner, and M. B. Houlahan, *J. Biol. Chem.* **159**, 145 (1945).

[31] N. H. Horowitz, *J. Biol. Chem.* **162**, 413 (1946).

[32] B. C. Johnson, Methods of Vitamin Determination, p. 95. Burgess Publishing Co., Minneapolis, 1948.

sorbed choline is then eluted from the column with 5 % sodium chloride. Aliquots of the solution and of standard choline solutions are added to flasks containing the basal medium, and these are inoculated and incubated for about 3 days at 25°. The response of the mold to the added supplements is determined by weighing the dried mycelium. Siegel[33] has recommended the removal of the mycelium from the culture fluid by filtration through a tared, sintered glass filter of medium porosity which is then dried and weighed. Dry weights from duplicate flasks agree within about 5 %, and choline values determined on different amounts of the same solution agree within 10 %. Standard curves must be run with each assay.

Luecke and Pearson[34] have used the method for the determination of free choline in plasma and urine and for the estimation of free choline in animal tissues. Comparative determinations on the same samples showed that the microbiological values were in excellent agreement with those obtained by chemical methods. Hodson[35] used a modification of the above procedure in the assay of milk products. The results obtained with the *Neurospora* procedure indicate that this method is considerably more sensitive and more specific than the chemical methods investigated to date.[36] The various analogs that support growth of the organism do not appear in appreciable quantities in most biological materials or, as in the case of methionine, can be separated by use of adsorbents.

Special attention has been given the determination of choline-containing phospholipids in blood, liver, and other tissues by workers in the laboratories of Thannhauser,[37-39] Chaikoff,[40-42] Chargaff,[43, 44] and McKibbin.[45, 46]

[33] L. Siegel, *Science* **101**, 674 (1945).

[34] R. W. Luecke and P. B. Pearson, *J. Biol. Chem.* **153**, 259 (1944); **155**, 507 (1944).

[35] A. Z. Hodson, *J. Biol. Chem.* **157**, 383 (1945).

[36] F. J. Bandelin, *J. Am. Pharm. Assoc.* **38**, 304 (1949).

[37] G. Schmidt, L. Hecht, P. Fallot, L. Greenbaum, and S. J. Thannhauser, *J. Biol. Chem.* **197**, 601 (1952).

[38] S. J. Thannhauser, J. Benotti, and H. Reinstein, *J. Biol. Chem.* **129**, 709 (1939).

[39] S. J. Thannhauser, J. Benotti, A. Walcott, and H. Reinstein, *J. Biol. Chem.* **129**, 717, (1939).

[40] C. Entenman, A. Taurog, and I. L. Chaikoff, *J. Biol. Chem.* **155**, 13 (1944).

[41] A. Taurog, C. Entenman, B. A. Fries, and I. L. Chaikoff, *J. Biol. Chem.* **155**, 19 (1944).

[42] C. Entenman and I. L. Chaikoff, *J. Biol. Chem.* **160**, 377 (1945).

[43] E. Chargaff, M. Ziff, and D. Rittenberg, *J. Biol. Chem.* **138**, 439 (1941); **144**, 343 (1942).

[44] E. Chargaff, C. Levine, and C. Green, *J. Biol. Chem.* **175**, 67 (1948).

[45] J. M. McKibbin and W. E. Taylor, *J. Biol. Chem.* **178**, 17, 29 (1949).

[46] W. E. Taylor and J. M. McKibbin, *J. Biol. Chem.* **188**, 677 (1951).

Kahane and Lévy worked out procedures for the estimation of free choline, total water-soluble choline, and total choline.[47-49]

C. BIOLOGICAL ASSAYS

The first determination of choline by biological assay was based on its acetylation to acetylcholine and on the estimation of the latter by virtue of its pharmacological action on tissues. An extensive discussion of this procedure has been published by Chang and Gaddum.[50] The most satisfactory tissues for the test are the rectis abdominis muscle of the frog, the isolated intestine of the rabbit, and the longitudinal muscle of the leech. The method was used by Abdon[51] for the determination of acetylcholine and its precursor in tissues and by Fletcher et al.[52] in the analysis of a number of foodstuffs for total choline. Accuracy is difficult because of interfering substances such as histamine, potassium salts, and many other physiologically active constituents of tissues.

Attempts have been made to develop a biological assay procedure for the determination of the total choline in foods and in other biological materials by comparison of the degree of prevention of renal pathology by the test substance and by choline in young rats on a choline-deficient diet.[13, 53] The method is not particularly sensitive and the interpretation of results is complicated by variations in food consumption and in the composition of the ration.

D. PHYSICAL ESTIMATION

The ultraviolet absorption spectrum of choline[54, 55] is not useful as an analytical tool although advantage is taken of the spectrum of choline reineckate. It has not been possible to utilize other physical properties of choline in its estimation.

[47] G. Ducet and E. Kahane, *Bull. soc. chim. biol.* **28**, 794 (1946).
[48] E. Kahane and J. Lévy, *Compt. rend.* **207**, 642 (1938).
[49] E. Kahane, J. Lévy, and O. Libert, *Bull. soc. chim. biol.* **27**, 65 (1945).
[50] H. C. Chang and J. H. Gaddum, *J. Physiol. (London)* **79**, 255 (1933).
[51] N. O. Abdon and K. Ljungdahl-Ostberg, *Acta Physiol. Scand.* **8**, 103 (1944).
[52] J. D. Fletcher, C. H. Best, and O. M. Solandt, *Biochem. J.* **29**, 2278 (1935).
[53] W. H. Griffith and D. J. Mulford, *J. Am. Chem. Soc.* **63**, 929 (1941).
[54] A. Castille and M. Ruppal, *Bull. acad. roy. méd. Belg.* **56**, 263 (1926).
[55] W. Graubner, *Z. ges. exptl. Med.* **63**, 527 (1928).

VIII. Standardization of Activity

WENDELL H. GRIFFITH and JOSEPH F. NYC

Choline is a fairly stable chemical that participates directly and indirectly in metabolic reactions. The factors that control its synthesis by transmethylation and by formate-to-methyl synthesis are not known definitely. Standardization of activity in the usual sense is, therefore, not feasible.

IX. Occurrence

WENDELL H. GRIFFITH and JOSEPH F. NYC

The total choline present in typical foods (Tables VII and VIII) has been determined by Engel,[1] and the amount in common meat cuts (Table IX) by McIntire et al.[2] Grains and milled wheat products were also analyzed by Glick[3] (Table X). The examination of foodstuffs in India[4] and in Sweden[5] has given values similar to those in the tables. Egg yolk, glandular meats, and brain are the richest animal sources, and the germ of cereals, legumes, and seed-oil meals are the best plant sources. Of interest is the relatively high level in patent flour.

The choline content of fresh and of processed milk has been studied in several laboratories.[6-8] According to Hodson[6] little loss occurs in the preparation of dried milk, although Marquez[7] reported that in both raw and pasteurized milk no choline was present after standing 48 hours at room temperature. Most of the choline of milk is found in the aqueous rather than the cream layer.[8]

Sadhu[9] noted a slight positive correlation between the choline content of the brain and the lactose content of the milk of nine species of mammals whereas a high correlation was found between the lactose level and the brain cerebrosides. He suggested that sphingosine can react reversibly

[1] R. W. Engel, J. Nutrition 25, 441 (1943).

[2] J. M. McIntire, B. S. Schweigert, and C. A. Elvehjem, J. Nutrition 28, 219 (1944).

[3] D. Glick, Cereal Chem. 22, 95 (1945).

[4] H. Chattopadhyay and S. Banerjee, Food Research 16, 230 (1591).

[5] N. E. Borglin, Acta Pharmakol. Toxicol. 3, Suppl. 1 (1947).

[6] A. Z. Hodson, J. Nutrition 29, 137 (1945).

[7] V. M. Marquez, School Hyg. and Publ. Health, Biochem. Dept., Johns Hopkins University (Separate), March 1942.

[8] E. Kahane and J. Lévy, Bull. soc. chim. biol. 27, 72 (1945); Compt. rend. 220, 97 (1945).

[9] D. P. Sadhu, J. Dairy Sci. 31, 347 (1948).

TABLE VII

TOTAL CHOLINE CONTENT OF ANIMAL PRODUCTS[1]

Product	Choline chloride, mg./g.		Product	Choline chloride, mg./g.	
	Fresh	Dry		Fresh	Dry
Pig			Beef		
Adrenals	5.88	18.35	Veal liver	6.52	22.72
Liver	5.52	13.67	Beef liver	6.30	20.47
Spinal cord	4.27	18.20	Veal kidney	3.48	15.00
Brain	3.75	12.60	Beef kidney	3.33	16.32
Pancreas	3.29	14.10	Veal rib roast	1.13	3.44
Kidney, No. 1	3.17	13.06	Beef roundsteak	0.95	3.53
Kidney, No. 2	2.56	17.38	Beef rib roast	0.82	2.44
Ovary	2.78	11.16	Milk		
Heart	2.31	10.01	Skim milk powder	1.59	1.63
Spleen	2.08	14.86	Whole milk powder	1.07	1.10
Small intestine	1.65	5.41	Cheddar cheese	0.48	0.70
Tongue, No. 1	1.39	4.86	Fresh milk	0.147	1.14
Tongue, No. 2	1.36	2.29	Commercial casein	—	<0.05
Shoulder, No. 1	1.05	2.03	Butter	—	<0.05
Shoulder, No. 2	0.86	2.00	Fish		
Ham	0.88	1.81	Fish meal	3.29	3.47
Chops	0.77	<0.05	Trout muscle	0.87	4.89
Lard	—		Red snapper muscle	0.84	4.12
Chicken			Cod liver oil	—	<0.05
Egg yolk	17.13	32.81	Miscellaneous		
Liver	3.42	12.50	Liver extract	15.93	16.36
Heart	2.36	10.40	Extracted liver residue	4.39	4.50
Kidney	2.23	11.32	Liver sausage	2.67	5.52
Egg albumen	—	<0.05	Tankage	2.31	2.65
Lamb			Meat meal, No. 1	1.62	1.73
Kidney	3.60	17.82	Meat meal, No. 2	1.30	1.42
Shoulder	1.19	3.07	Bologna sausage	0.71	2.38
Chops	1.07	3.27			

TABLE VIII
Total Choline Content of Plant Products[1]

Product	Choline chloride, mg./g.		Product	Choline chloride, mg./g.	
	Fresh	Dry		Fresh	Dry
Cereal grains			**Other seeds**		
Defatted wheat germ	4.23	4.53	Cottonseed meal No. 1 (7.0% fat)	3.50	3.76
Raw wheat germ, No. 1	4.10	4.40	Cottonseed meal No. 2 (7.5% fat)	3.25	3.51
Raw wheat germ, No. 2	4.03	4.32	Soybean meal (2.5% fat)	3.45	3.75
Raw corn germ stock	1.60	1.78	Mature soybeans (19.5% fat)	3.40	3.58
Rolled oats	1.51	1.63	Cottonseed kernels (36% fat)	2.98	3.19
Wheat shorts	1.48	1.63	Edible peanut meal	2.35	2.52
Wheat bran	1.43	1.56	Peanut meal (6% fat)	2.26	2.44
Barley	1.39	1.55	Peanuts (Spanish) (43% fat)	1.67	1.74
Rice polish	1.26	1.36	Peanuts (Runner) (45.5% fat)	1.57	1.65
Oats	0.94	1.00	Peanut butter	1.45	1.48
Wheat	0.92	1.01	Pecans	0.50	0.53
Polished rice	0.88	1.02			
Molasses (blackstrap)	0.86	—	**Root crops (sun-dried)**		
Wheatena	0.62	0.68	Irish potatoes	1.06	1.31
White flour	0.52	0.57	Carrots	0.95	1.12
Corn meal (unbolted)	0.42	0.47	Turnips	0.94	1.11
Yellow corn	0.37	0.41	Sweet potatoes	0.35	0.36
Corn meal (bolted)	0.10	0.11			
			Leafy material (sun-dried)		
Non-leafy vegetables (sun-dried)			Mustard tops	2.52	2.77
Snapbeans	3.40	3.81	Young cabbage	2.51	2.90
Green soybeans	3.00	3.32	Turnip tops	2.45	2.69
English peas	2.63	2.90	Spinach	2.38	2.75
Cowpeas	2.57	2.84	Rape	2.30	2.86
Asparagus	1.28	1.47	Pokeweed	2.28	2.64
			Alfalfa leaf meal, No. 1	1.43	1.55
Vegetable oils			Alfalfa leaf meal, No. 2	1.22	1.31
Hydrogenated cocoanut oil	—	<0.05			
Oleomargarine	—	<0.05			
Refined corn oil	—	<0.05			
Refined soybean oil	—	<0.05			

with galactose or choline phosphoric acid to form either cerebrosides or sphingomyelins.

The choline content of various biological fluids has been reported by

TABLE IX
Total Choline Content of Meats[2]

| Sample | Choline, mg./100 g. | | | |
| | Fresh | | Dry | |
	Range	Avg.	Range	Avg.
Veal				
Leg	95–108	102	366–432	389
Roast leg	125–141	132	338–392	360
Shoulder	83–100	93	268–373	337
Roast shoulder	133–143	139	310–376	343
Sirloin chop	87–105	96	242–404	317
Braised chop	128–157	140	242–342	285
Shoulder chop	92–101	97	307–422	376
Braised chop	149–156	154	317–400	366
Stew meat	94–100	96	336–400	367
Cooked stew	137–149	142	360–378	370
Lamb				
Leg	75– 92	84	262–317	290
Roast	122–124	123	284–295	290
Sirloin chop	75– 77	76	179–198	189
Broiled chop	100–126	113	204–252	228
Stew meat	76– 82	79	222–230	226
Cooked stew	116–128	122	247–291	269
Pork				
Ham	101–129	120		
Cured ham	98–129	122		
Beef				
Liver	470–570	510		
Round	65– 70	68		
Tongue	108	108		
Heart	170	170		
Braised heart	200–275	238		
Kidney	240–284	262		
Brain	399–420	410		
Miscellaneous				
Bologna	60	60		
Frankfurters	57	57		
Pork links	48	48		
Canadian bacon	80	80		

Eagle[10] (Table XI), and Schmidt *et al.*[11] have recorded data on the occurrence of glycerylphosphorylcholine in tissues (Table II).

TABLE X
TOTAL CHOLINE CONTENT OF GRAINS AND OF GRAIN PRODUCTS
(expressed as milligrams of choline chloride per 100 g. on a moisture-free basis)[3]

Variety		Milled fractions	
Hard spring wheat	91	Whole wheat	102
Hard winter wheat	79	Germ	354
Soft winter wheat	88	Bran	153
Soybeans	237	Low-grade flour	69
Oats	114	Bleached low-grade flour	69
Barley	110	Clear flour	61
Flax	107	Bleached clear flour	62
		Patent flour	70
		Bleached patent flour	69

TABLE XI
FREE CHOLINE IN BIOLOGICAL FLUIDS[10]

Material	No. of samples	Choline, mg./l.	
		Average	Range
Human saliva, male[a]	12	11.6	8.6– 14.4
Human saliva, male[b]	7	6.5	4.7– 9.9
Human saliva, female[a]	75	16.9	6.2– 36.4
Human blood, male[c]	8	13.2	10.3– 17.1
Human blood, male[d]	10	13.5	8.5– 22.8
Human blood, female[d]	19	14.6	9.4– 21.8
Human blood, pregnancy	62	13.1	9.9– 19.9
Human semen	17	341.0	234.0–477.0
Bladder bile, dog	7	250.0	78.0–380.0
Lymph, dog	3	18.2	14.2– 23.5

[a] Collected while chewing paraffin.
[b] Collected by use of dental siphon.
[c] Normal.
[d] Outpatients.

X. Effects of Deficiency

A. GENERAL MANIFESTATIONS

WENDELL H. GRIFFITH and JOSEPH F. NYC

The specific recognition of sources of labile methyl is accomplished by the *in vivo* administration of a suitably labeled, possible methyl donor or

[10] E. Eagle, *J. Lab. Clin. Med.* **27**, 103 (1941).
[11] G. Schmidt, L. Hecht, P. Fallot, L. Greenbaum, and S. J. Thannhauser, *J. Biol. Chem.* **197**, 601 (1952).

by its addition to an *in vitro* system followed by the isolation of methyl-containing products and estimation of the isotopic carbon and hydrogen. More general procedures include measurements of effectiveness in the prevention of fatty livers and of renal lesions in rats, of growth of rats on homocystine-containing, methionine-poor diets, of stimulation of growth and prevention of perosis in chicks or turkey poults, and of extent of conversion of homocysteine and of guanidoacetic acid to methionine and creatine, respectively, in *in vitro* tissue systems. Choline, with at least one labile methyl group after oxidation to betaine and with one or more carbons that may participate in formate-to-methyl synthesis under the proper conditions, reacts positively in each of these procedures. It is particularly effective in reactions in which it serves directly, presumably as a constituent of phospholipids or of acetylcholine, rather than as a source of methyl. This appears to be the case in so far as its lipotropic activity is concerned and, possibly, its antihemorrhagic and antiperotic activities also. Obviously, it is not always possible to distinguish with certainty between evidences of a deficiency of methyl and of choline in experiments on animals. It is important, nevertheless, that deficiency symptoms, prevented by choline, may be produced without difficulty in several animal species.

B. RAT

WENDELL H. GRIFFITH and JOSEPH F. NYC

1. RENAL LESION

The rat has been the principal test animal in investigations of choline. The recognition of the lipotropic action of choline in adult rats by Best has been described earlier (Section IV C 2). The importance of this substance in the nutrition of the young rat was demonstrated by Griffith *et al.*, who showed that choline was essential in weanling rats not only for the prevention of the fatty liver but also for the maintenance of tissue structure and even for survival.[1-4]

The feeding of low choline diets to male rats, 20 to 26 days of age, results in a spectacular series of effects which reach a crisis within 6 to 8 days. This critical period may terminate fatally, or it may be followed by a rapid, partial recovery. Recovery on the same diet that produces severe degeneration of tissues is highly interesting and as yet an unexplained phenomenon. A marked increase in liver fat occurs within 48 hours and is maximal after 4 to 6 days. Renal lesions, named hemorrhagic degeneration, develop between the sixth and eighth days; the animals become noticeably

[1] W. H. Griffith and N. J. Wade, *Proc. Soc. Exptl. Biol. Med.* **41**, 188 (1939).

[2] W. H. Griffith and N. J. Wade, *J. Biol. Chem.* **131**, 567 (1939).

[3] W. H. Griffith, *J. Nutrition* **19**, 437 (1940).

[4] W. H. Griffith, *Biol. Symposia* **5**, 193 (1941).

sick, and there is a marked elevation of blood non-protein nitrogen (Fig. 2). Severely affected rats show an extensive regression of the thymus, and

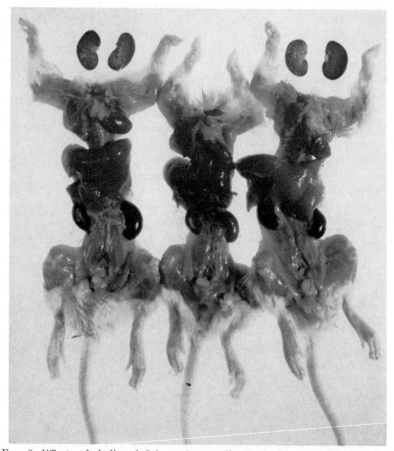

FIG. 2. Effects of choline deficiency in weanling rats after an 8-day period with choline (center) and without choline. The photograph illustrates the enlarged yellowish fatty liver, the enlarged kidneys with hemorrhagic degeneration, and the partial regression of the thymus. The sectioned kidneys above the deficient animals emphasize the cortical congestion which is evident in Fig. 3 and which, with or without subcapsular hemorrhage, is responsible for the dark-red appearance of the kidneys.

ocular hemorrhage is frequently observed. The renal changes develop over a 24- to 48-hour period and are characterized grossly by an increase in size and weight and by hemorrhagic discoloration. Proteinuria but not hematuria occurs. Recovery is noteworthy because of the rapidity with which the renal function improves, evident also in the gross appearance of the kidneys. The recovered kidneys are enlarged and pale brown in color and are frequently rough and scarred with a white incrustation, the so-called frosted kidney.

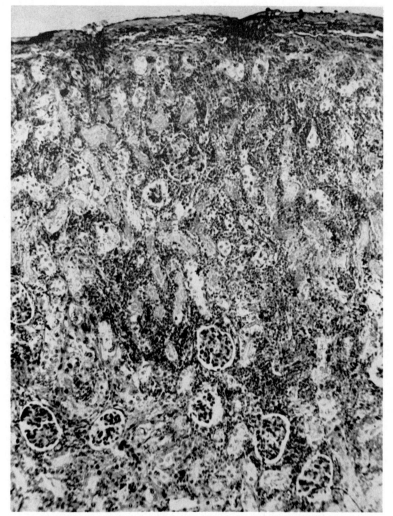

FIG. 3. Section from cortex of kidney of a choline-deficient rat similar to those illustrated in Fig. 2. Prominent changes include vascular congestion and tubular degeneration.

Christensen has described the course of the involution of the thymus[5] and the renal pathology[6] which is summarized as follows (Fig. 3). The

[5] K. Christensen and W. H. Griffith, *Endocrinology* **30**, 574 (1942).
[6] K. Christensen, *Arch. Pathol.* **34**, 633 (1942).

primary vascular change during the acute stage is congestion of the peripheral cortical capillaries and capsular blood vessels and, sometimes, of the glomerular blood vessels; hemorrhage, if present, occurs only in the capsule and at the periphery of the cortex; peripheral cortical tubules undergo necrosis or granular or hyaline droplet degeneration; hyaline casts are always abundant in tubules of the inner zone of the cortex and of the outer zone of the medulla; and calcification of degenerated peripheral tubules occurs in the most severely affected kidneys.

Hartroft and Best[7-10] have emphasized the role in this syndrome of small droplets of stainable fat which appear in the epithelial cells of the proximal convoluted tubules of the cortex. Concomitantly, generalized swelling of the affected nephrons occurs, with obstruction of the intervening capillary plexus in the cortex. Tubular ischemia and necrosis are followed by engorgement of the proximal cortical vessels which may rupture into and beneath the capsule. Choline feeding has relatively little effect on the total renal lipids.[11] That the acute renal lesion is an effect of a deficiency of choline has been repeatedly confirmed[12-16]. Conditions for producing a uniformly fatal outcome were described by Engel[13, 17]. Handler showed that the lesion occurred in adult rats after unilateral nephrectomy if the animals were placed immediately on the deficient diet.[14] The observations of Olsen and Deane[16] included changes in the adrenal cortex which is enlarged during the acute phase with definite evidence of hyperactivity of the zona fasciculata and zona glomerulosa, especially the latter.

The prevention of hemorrhagic degeneration is relatively specific for choline, although methyl-sparing compounds, such as methionine or betaine, and certain other compounds are effective. Substances which resemble choline sufficiently to be built by anabolic processes into lecithin-like molecules without obviously serving as inhibitors, such as arsenocholine or triethylcholine, have more or less activity.[18-20] It may be that certain of these compounds will be found later not to be antihemorrhagic. The onset

[7] W. S. Hartroft and C. H. Best, *Science* **105**, 315 (1947).
[8] W. S. Hartroft, *Brit. J. Exptl. Pathol.* **29**, 483 (1948).
[9] C. H. Best and W. S. Hartroft, *Federation Proc.* **8**, 610 (1949).
[10] W. S. Hartroft, *Proc. 1949 Milbank Mem. Fund* p. 144 (1950).
[11] G. Gualandi and S. M. Tamburello, *Boll. soc. ital. biol. sper.* **26,** 945 (1950).
[12] P. György and H. Goldblatt, *J. Exptl. Med.* **72,** 1 (1940).
[13] R. W. Engel and W. D. Salmon, *J. Nutrition* **22,** 109 (1941).
[14] P. Handler, *J. Nutrition* **31,** 621 (1946).
[15] F. I. Dessau and J. J. Oleson, *Proc. Soc. Exptl. Biol. Med.* **64,** 278 (1947).
[16] R. E. Olson and H. W. Deane, *J. Nutrition* **39,** 31 (1949).
[17] R. W. Engel, *Proc. Soc. Exptl. Biol. Med.* **50,** 193 (1942).
[18] A. D. Welch, *J. Nutrition* **40,** 113 (1950).
[19] A. D. Welch, cited by T. H. Jukes, Proc. Am. Inst. Nutrition, *J. Nutrition* **21,** *Suppl.* 13 (1941).
[20] J. M. Patterson and E. W. McHenry, *J. Biol. Chem.* **145,** 207 (1942).

of this syndrome, as is the magnitude of fatty infiltration, is influenced by the intake of food and, in particular, by the adequacy of the caloric intake.[21] McArthur and Lucas emphasized the inhibitory effect of triethylcholine on appetite,[22] and Strength *et al.* suggested that this compound was not only not a substitute for choline but that it functioned as an antimetabolite.[23] No obvious explanation can be given for the protective action of atabrine against hemorrhagic degeneration,[24] unless it spares choline by inhibition of choline oxidase.[25]

Results do not permit an unequivocal conclusion regarding the mechanism of this choline effect in the kidney of the rat. Jacobi *et al.* were not able to demonstrate any lack of choline in affected kidneys,[26, 27] but Patterson and McHenry found a significant decrease in renal phospholipids.[28, 29] The lesion has been reported to be associated with a low activity of alkaline and acid phosphatase in the renal tubules.[30]

Hemorrhagic manifestations in weanling rats on low choline diets have been described in the eyes,[2, 4, 13, 31] heart muscle,[13] liver,[32] adrenals,[13] and brain,[33] as well as in the kidneys. The observation by Jervis[33] that hemorrhagic lesions of the cerebellum occurred in young rats of mothers fed a low choline diet after the eighth day of pregnancy followed the report of György and Goldblatt that the young of mothers on choline-deficient diets developed a fatal paralysis.[12] This finding cannot be ascribed to changes in the brain phospholipids, according to Foa *et al.*[34]

2. FATTY LIVER

MacLean and Best described the histological picture of the rat liver loaded with fat because of choline deficiency,[35] and this has been amplified by Hartroft[36, 37] with particular reference to the development of experi-

[21] D. J. Mulford and W. H. Griffith, *J. Nutrition* **23**, 91 (1942).
[22] C. S. McArthur and C. C. Lucas, *Biochem. J.* **46**, 226 (1950).
[23] D. R. Strength, E. A. Schaefer, and W. D. Salmon, *J. Nutrition* **45**, 329 (1951).
[24] D. M. Hegsted, J. M. McKibbin, and F. J. Stare, *J. Nutrition* **27**, 149 (1944).
[25] B. Kelley, *Federation Proc.* **11**, 238 (1952).
[26] H. P. Jacobi, C. A. Baumann, and W. J. Meek, *J. Biol. Chem.* **138**, 571 (1941).
[27] H. P. Jacobi and C. A. Baumann, *J. Biol. Chem.* **142**, 65 (1942).
[28] J. M. Patterson, N. B. Keevil, and E. W. McHenry, *J. Biol. Chem.* **153**, 489 (1944).
[29] J. M. Patterson and E. W. McHenry, *J. Biol. Chem.* **156**, 265 (1944).
[30] M. Wachstein, *Arch. Pathol.* **38**, 297 (1944).
[31] J. G. Bellows and H. Chinn, *Arch. Ophthalmol.* (*Chicago*) **30**, 105 (1943).
[32] P. György, *Ann. N. Y. Acad. Sci.* **49**, 525 (1948).
[33] G. A. Jervis, *Proc. Soc. Exptl. Biol. Med.* **51**, 193 (1942).
[34] P. P. Foa, H. R. Weinstein, and B. Kleppel, *Arch. Biochem.* **19**, 209 (1948).
[35] D. L. MacLean and C. H. Best, *Brit. J. Exptl. Pathol.* **15**, 193 (1934).
[36] W. S. Hartroft, *Rept. Ann. Meeting and Proc. Roy. College Phys. Surg.* (*Canada*) p. 120 (Nov. 25–26, 1949).
[37] W. S. Hartroft, *Anat. Record* **106**, 61 (1950).

mental cirrhosis. Droplets of stainable lipid appear in the hepatic cells surrounding the central veins within 24 hours after rats are placed on a diet low in choline and in its precursors. Large intracytoplasmic masses of fat are formed from smaller droplets during the first week, and the parenchymal cells are expanded to twice the original size. The fat content cf the liver in this stage may be increased ten times, but it rapidly disappears if choline is administered to the rat. If the choline-deficient diet is continued for 1 to 2 months, distended cell walls rupture and large fatty masses, called lipodiastemata, form by fusion of several cells. These and the fatty liver cells compress the sinusoids in the center of lobules where the intravascular pressure is lowest, with resulting interference with the oxygen supply. The partial anoxia is believed by Hartroft to be an important factor in the ensuing atrophy and regression of liver cells which are followed by disappearance of the fat and by the growth of fibrous tissue.

The rapidity and extent of the increase in liver lipids in choline deficiency as well as their removal following administration of choline suggest strongly that the effectiveness of choline as a lipotropic agent depends on some function of choline-containing phospholipids in fat metabolism. Definite evidence of an influence of choline on phospholipid activity in the form of data on the turnover of P^{32} has been presented, but the correlation of the appearance or disappearance of liver fat with changes in lecithin levels is not at all satisfactory. The accelerating effect of aminoethanol and of its mono- and dimethyl derivatives in certain aspects of phospholipid activity together with the lipotropic activity of betaine and methionine indicate that the maintenance of choline in one or another of its combined forms is a complex function of considerable importance. Actually, the choline requirement in weanling male rats given an adequate supply of protein was found by Griffith and Mulford[38] to be 2 and 5.5 mg. of choline chloride per day for the prevention of renal lesions and of fatty livers, respectively. The nature of the compounds sharing the lipotropic activity of choline is indicated in Section V, p. 45.

The quantity and nature of the dietary fat influences the fatty liver but is not the determining factor because accumulation of liver lipids occurs on low choline diets that are low in fat.[39, 40] Barrett et al.[41] fed deuterium-labeled fatty acids and were unable to demonstrate the presence of the isotope in the liver fat. There appears little question but that the bulk of the excess fat in a fatty liver of this type is formed in the liver from carbohydrate. Nevertheless, Channon and Wilkinson[42] found variations due to the nature

[38] W. H. Griffith and D. J. Mulford, *J. Am. Chem. Soc.* **63,** 929 (1941).

[39] C. H. Best and M. E. Huntsman, *J. Physiol.* (*London*) **83,** 255 (1935).

[40] W. H. Griffith, *J. Biol. Chem.* **132,** 639 (1940).

[41] H. M. Barrett, C. H. Best, and J. H. Ridout, *J. Physiol.* (*London*) **93,** 367 (1938).

[42] H. J. Channon and H. Wilkinson, *Biochem. J.* **30,** 1033 (1936).

of the dietary fat, as follows, in the liver fat of adult rats fed a low choline diet containing 5 % casein and 40 % fat: butterfat, 30.7 %; beef fat, 27.1 %; olive oil, 15.6 %; and cod liver oil, 7.2 %. The proportion of saturated fatty acids containing 14 to 18 carbons in the diet appeared to increase the deposition of fat more so than unsaturated fatty acids, including the solid unsaturated acid, elaidic acid.[43] Stetten and Salcedo [44, 45] fed ethyl esters of fatty acids in low choline diets and found the degree of the fatty liver to increase as the chain length decreased from 18 to 14. No severe fatty livers occurred if the dietary fatty acid contained less than 12 carbons. Ethyl laurate, however, was extremely toxic and caused death within a few days with symptoms resembling those of an acute deficiency of potassium. The fatal myocarditis was not related to a lack of tissue potassium, however, and the syndrome was prevented by choline.

Raman[46] compared the liver and carcass lipids resulting from feeding a fat-free and a high fat diet with and without choline. The dietary fat was highly saturated and fed at a 30 % level. The proportion of saturated fatty acids and the degree of unsaturation of the unsaturated fatty acids of liver phospholipids increased in choline-deficient rats on both diets. The carcass fat of animals on the high fat ration was increased by choline from 1.5 to 2.8 % of carcass weight. Carcass fat on the fat-free diet was much higher (12 % of carcass weight) and was unaffected by choline. It was evident that choline had little, if any, effect on the character of depot fat synthesized and stored in rats fed the fat-free ration. The usual lipotropic action of choline on liver lipids was observed in these experiments.

The feeding of cholesterol brings about the deposition of neutral fat and of cholesterol esters in livers of rats fed low choline diets containing added cholesterol. Choline prevents the fatty liver and partly reduces the level of the sterol esters.[47, 48] Similar results were obtained by supplements of casein[49, 50, 51] and of methionine.[52] Choline deficiency was aggravated by dietary cholesterol in weanling rats.[40] Choline was protective over the critical 8-day period but not over a 30-day period in surviving animals.[53] Inositol was not more effective than choline upon cholesterol esters.[54]

[43] H. J. Channon, S. W. F. Hanson, and P. A. Loizides, Biochem. J. 36, 214 (1942).
[44] D. Stetten, Jr., and J. Salcedo, Jr., J. Nutrition 29, 167 (1945).
[45] H. D. Kesten, J. Salcedo, Jr., and D. Stetten, Jr., J. Nutrition 29, 171 (1945).
[46] C. S. Raman, Biochem. J. 52, 320 (1952).
[47] C. H. Best and J. H. Ridout, J. Physiol. (London) 78, 415 (1933).
[48] C. H. Best, H. J. Channon, and J. H. Ridout, J. Physiol. (London) 81, 409 (1934).
[49] C. H. Best and J. H. Ridout, J. Physiol. (London) 87, 55P (1936).
[50] A. W. Beeston, H. J. Channon, and H. Wilkinson, Biochem. J. 29, 2659 (1935).
[51] A. W. Beeston, H. J. Channon, and A. P. Platt, J. Soc. Chem. Ind. 56, 292 (1937).
[52] H. J. Channon, M. C. Manifold, and A. P. Platt, Biochem. J. 32, 969 (1938).
[53] W. H. Griffith and D. J. Mulford, J. Nutrition 21, 633 (1941).
[54] C. H. Best, C. C. Lucas, J. M. Patterson, and J. H. Ridout, Biochem. J. 48, 452 (1951).

Little is known of the details of the synthesis of lecithin, for instance, in the animal organism. In an attempt to clarify certain aspects of this problem, Tolbert and Okey[55] injected P^{32}-labeled phosphate and C^{14}-methyl-labeled choline simultaneously in rats and determined the specific activity of various liver fractions after time intervals ranging from 3 to 96 hours. Similar renewal rates for phospholipid choline and phospholipid phosphate seemed likely because of the similarity in the rates of decrease in the specific activities of the two labeled fractions after reaching their initial maximum concentrations. Glycerophosphate satisfied the criteria for an immediate precursor of phospholipid.

Artom has investigated thoroughly the effect of choline and of related compounds on the phospholipid content of livers of rats 2 to 3 months old and fed diets low in protein and in sources of labile methyl. Significant decreases were found in the total and in the choline-containing phospholipids.[56] These decreases were only partly prevented by supplements of choline administered at the start of the experiment and not prevented at all if fatty infiltration was allowed to exist for 7 or more days prior to the addition of choline to the diet.[57] The absence of an effect of choline in the latter experiments was not prevented by simultaneous administration of various vitamins and amino acids, including methionine. In the case of diets varying in fat content, the addition of choline after the development of the fatty liver did restore the phospholipid level if 20 % or more of fat was present in the ration.[58] Choline was more effective also if lactose replaced dietary sucrose.[59] The phospholipid turnover in intestinal mucosa after the injection of P^{32} and the feeding of choline with and without fat was less if the choline and fat were administered separately.[60] The conclusion seemed clear that choline increased phospholipid formation in the intestine and did so especially during the digestion and absorption of fat. Liver phospholipids were affected similarly.[61] Aminoethanol and mono-methyl- and dimethylaminoethanol stimulated the formation of total phospholipids in both intestine and liver as much as did choline. The increase with choline was limited to the choline-containing phospholipids, whereas both choline-containing and non-choline-containing phospholipids were increased by aminoethanol and by its methylated forms.[62]

Artom's demonstration of the inadequacy of choline for the complete

[55] M. E. Tolbert and R. Okey, *J. Biol. Chem.* **194,** 755 (1952).
[56] C. Artom and W. H. Fishman, *J. Biol. Chem.* **148,** 405, 415, 423 (1943).
[57] W. H. Fishman and C. Artom, *J. Biol. Chem.* **154,** 117 (1941).
[58] W. H. Fishman and C. Artom, *J. Biol. Chem.* **164,** 307 (1946).
[59] C. Artom and W. H. Fishman, *J. Biol. Chem.* **170,** 587 (1947).
[60] C. Artom and W. E. Cornatzer, *J. Biol. Chem.* **165,** 393 (1946).
[61] C. Artom and W. E. Cornatzer, *J. Biol. Chem.* **171,** 779 (1947).
[62] C. Artom and W. E. Cornatzer, *J. Biol. Chem.* **176,** 949 (1948).

restoration of the decrease in choline-containing phospholipids caused by choline deficiency in 2- to 3-month-old rats is particularly interesting because he was able to show that choline was largely effective in weanling rats[56] and that this effect was not duplicated by aminoethanol, methionine, serine, or glycine.[63] He has interpreted these data as evidence for the participation with choline of a factor essential in phospholipid syntheses and present in weanling rats to a greater extent than in older animals. Artom and Fishman[56] have emphasized the fact that older rats were used in previous experiments which failed to demonstrate an effect of choline on total liver phospholipids[48, 64, 65] or an effect on the choline content of livers,[27, 48] whereas weanling rats were used in studies in which total phospholipids[20, 66] or total choline-containing phospholipids[66-68] were reported to be increased by administration of choline.

Brante[69] found a significant increase in liver cephalin in rats maintained for several months on a choline-deficient, high fat diet. The level of choline-containing phospholipids in the liver was the same in rats with and without choline. No difference in the total choline content of liver and kidneys of rats on control and low choline diets was noted by Kahane et al.,[70] but the amount in the rest of the body was somewhat less in the deficient group. Muscle creatine levels were not affected by an existing deficiency of choline that permitted development of fatty livers.[71]

Kensler et al.[72] have made the very significant observation that the choline oxidase activity of the liver and kidneys of young rats increases sharply during the age period in which they are particularly susceptible to acute choline deficiency. Of interest in this connection is the finding that the severe renal lesions of choline deficiency were less frequently fatal in 20-day-old rats than in those 21 to 27 days of age.[3]

Chaikoff investigated the rate of phospholipid metabolism in rat liver as measured by phosphorus turnover studies following the administration of radioactive phosphorus (P^{32}). Choline and betaine[73] and cystine and methionine[74] accelerated the turnover of phosphorus, the effect of a single

[63] W. H. Fishman and C. Artom, J. Biol. Chem. **154**, 109 (1944).

[64] J. H. Channon and H. W. Wilkerson, Biochem. J. **28**, 2026 (1934).

[65] F. Cedrangolo and V. Baccari, Arch. sci. biol. (Italy) **24**, 311 (1938).

[66] R. W. Engel, J. Biol. Chem. **144**, 701 (1942).

[67] D. Stetten, Jr., and G. F. Grail, J. Biol. Chem. **144**, 175 (1942).

[68] P. Handler and W. J. Dann, J. Biol. Chem. **146**, 357 (1942).

[69] G. Brante, Acta Physiol. Scand. **6**, 291 (1943).

[70] E. Kahane, J. Lévy, and O. Tanguy, Arch. sci. physiol. **4**, 185 (1950).

[71] E. Roberts and H. C. Eckstein, J. Biol. Chem. **154**, 377 (1944).

[72] C. J. Kensler, M. Rudden, E. Shapiro, and H. Langemann, Proc. Soc. Exptl. Biol. Med. **79**, 39 (1952).

[73] I. Perlman and I. L. Chaikoff, J. Biol. Chem. **127**, 211 (1939); **130**, 593 (1939).

[74] I. Perlman, N. Stillman, and I. L. Chaikoff, J. Biol. Chem. **133**, 651 (1940).

supplement lasting 6 or more hours. Betaine was less effective than choline. The latter substance was particularly active in rats fed cholesterol.[75] There was little indication in these experiments of variations in the total phospholipid content of the liver. A slight increase in this fraction of liver lipids following the administration of choline or methionine was noted by Horning and Eckstein, but this was not correlated necessarily with lipotropic activity.[76]

Artom and Swanson observed that slices from livers of rats previously fed a low choline, low protein diet incorporated P^{32} into phospholipids at a slower rate than slices from rats fed high protein diet or a stock diet. Prior administration of choline *in vivo* reversed the fatty infiltration but did not restore the ability of the isolated liver to synthesize phospholipids. In fact, the addition of choline *in vitro* inhibited phospholipid formation.[77] Boxer and Stetten fed N^{15}-labeled choline to rats and found the rate of replacement of phospholipid choline in the liver to be 3.9 mg. per rat per day. With cessation of the labeled choline supplement, new, non-isotopic choline replaced the isotopic fraction at a rate of 1.3 mg. per day while fatty livers developed. They concluded that the fatty livers were due to a decrease in the rate of incorporation of choline into tissue phospholipids.[78] The administration of choline and of aminoethanol increased the rates of formation of lecithin and of cephalin, respectively, in fasted and fed rats previously given radioactive phosphate.[79] Partial hepatectomy impaired the formation of intestinal and hepatic phospholipids,[80, 81] but choline was ineffective in preventing the resulting fatty liver.[82]

Deposition of excess lipids in the liver may result from many and diverse causes, and, in certain instances, choline is without effect as a lipotropic agent. Best has summarized the pertinent facts in this field.[83] Of particular significance is the distribution of accumulating fat, in the center of liver lobules if due to hypolipotropism and in the periphery if due to the activity of the anterior pituitary or to extracts of this gland. The administration of anterior pituitary extract in fasting guinea pigs, rats, and mice mobilized body fat in the liver.[84, 85] Inasmuch as this result did not occur if the adrenals were removed, MacKay concluded that the effect was mediated

[75] I. Perlman and I. L. Chaikoff, *J. Biol. Chem.* **128**, 735 (1939).
[76] M. G. Horning and H. C. Eckstein, *J. Biol. Chem.* **166**, 711 (1946).
[77] C. Artom and M. A. Swanson, *J. Biol. Chem.* **193**, 473 (1951).
[78] G. E. Boxer and D. Stetten, Jr., *J. Biol. Chem.* **153**, 617 (1944).
[79] A. P. Platt and R. R. Porter, *Nature* **160**, 905 (1947).
[80] E. Chargaff, *J. Biol. Chem.* **128**, 587 (1939).
[81] E. Chargaff, K. B. Olson, and P. F. Partington, *J. Biol. Chem.* **134**, 505 (1940).
[82] E. M. MacKay and H. O. Carne, *Proc. Soc. Exptl. Biol. Med.* **38**, 131 (1938).
[83] C. H. Best, *Federation Proc.* **9**, 506 (1950).
[84] C. H. Best and J. Campbell, *J. Physiol.* (*London*) **86**, 190 (1936); **92**, 91 (1938).
[85] J. Campbell and C. C. Lucas, *Biochem. J.* **48**, 241 (1951).

through the adrenals.[86] That depot fat was the probable source of the mobilized fat was indicated by the use of deuterium as a means of distinguishing newly synthesized triglycerides.[41, 87] Liver fat was increased by both growth hormone and by ACTH,[88, 89] presumably the active materials in the original pituitary extract employed by Best and Campbell.[84] On the other hand, the administration of cortisone in rats fed a low choline diet failed to prevent the deposition of liver fat, although considerable protection against hemorrhagic degeneration was afforded.[90] Olson and Deane[16] described changes in the adrenal cortex during the acute phase of hemorrhagic degeneration but believed the alterations to be secondary to the renal lesions. Neither desoxycorticosterone acetate nor whole adrenal extract influenced the course of the acute phase of choline deficiency. The marked hyperactivity of the zona glomerulosa at the time of the renal lesion was ascribed to altered electrolyte balance.

The feeding of choline-deficient diets to adult rats removed the elevated blood pressure resulting from partial nephrectomy in the experiments of Handler and Bernheim. ACTH restored temporarily the hypertensive state in these animals although it was without effect in normal controls, and it was suggested that secretion of ACTH is impaired in choline-deficient rats.[91] Adrenalectomy partially prevented fatty livers in male rats on a choline-deficient diet, but there was little effect in females.[92]

Shipley et al. noted increased liver fat in female rats but not in males after castration.[92] Testosterone propionate aggravated both renal and hepatic lesions in female rats and hepatic lesions in male rats fed a low choline, high fat diet.[93] Male rats had been found more susceptible than females to severe, acute choline deficiency.[3] Castration of male rats caused a marked reduction in blood lipid phosphorus in rats on a hypolipotropic diet.[94]

Shipley reported that thyroidectomy prevented fatty livers in male and female rats on a choline-deficient diet.[92] Handler, on the other hand, found that removal of the thyroid or the feeding of thiouracil caused a small increase in neutral fat and a marked increase of cholesterol in livers of both control and choline-deficient rats.[95]

[86] E. M. MacKay and R. H. Barnes, Am. J. Physiol. **118**, 525 (1937); **120**, 361 (1937).

[87] D. Stetten, Jr. and J. Salcedo, Jr., J. Biol. Chem. **156**, 27 (1944).

[88] L. L. Bennett, R. E. Kreiss, C. H. Li, and H. M. Evans, Am. J. Physiol. **152**, 210 (1948).

[89] C. H. Li, M. E. Simpson, and H. M. Evans, Arch. Biochem. **23**, 51 (1949).

[90] E. A. Sellers, R. W. You, J. H. Ridout, and C. H. Best, Nature **166**, 514 (1950).

[91] P. Handler and F. Bernheim, Am. J. Physiol. **162**, 375 (1950).

[92] R. A. Shipley, E. B. Chudzik, and P. György, Arch. Biochem. **16**, 301 (1948).

[93] W. J. Emerson, P. C. Zamecnik, and I. T. Nathanson, Endocrinology **48**, 548 (1951).

[94] R. Honorato and M. Modak, Bol. soc. biol. Santiago Chile **4**, 24 (1947).

[95] P. Handler, J. Biol. Chem. **173**, 295 (1948).

The lipotropic effect in rats of exposure to cold constitutes a striking exception to the usual correlation between severity of choline deficiency and the metabolic level. Sellars and You found an average liver fat of 7.2 ± 1.24 % in animals maintained at 2.5° whereas controls fed the same low choline diet and maintained at 25° had an average liver fat of 24.8 ± 4.90 %. The "cold" animals consumed 50 % more food.[96] The choline-like effect of cold was not a temporary phenomenon and continued through a 15-week experimental period; it occurred in animals acclimatized to cold prior to the feeding of the hypolipotropic diet; and it was not prevented by thyroidectomy and subsequent administration of a daily maintenance dose of thyroxin.[97] However, exposure to cold was only partially lipotropic if the diet contained 50 % fat. Stimulation of the adrenals was not believed a primary factor because cortisone failed to prevent the development of the fatty liver in rats on a low choline diet.[90] The study of the increased metabolism in "cold" rats under various conditions has not permitted a satisfactory explanation of the lipotropism due to the lowered environmental temperature.[98] Although both thyroid and adrenal hormones were believed necessary for the mechanism involved, hyperactivity of either gland was not considered an essential factor.[99, 100]

The administration of low molecular weight halogenated hydrocarbons by injection or by inhalation in rats on low choline, low protein diets causes severe fatty infiltration and degeneration of the liver. Heppel et al. found methionine considerably more protective than choline, although the latter with cystine increased the resistance of animals exposed to ethylene and propylene dichloride.[101, 102] Calder concluded that choline plus a thermolabile factor in yeast, which was not thiamine, decreased the liver damage caused by chloroform in rats.[103] Carbon tetrachloride caused anemia as well as hepatic pathology in rats.[104] The former responded to methionine, but neither methionine nor choline prevented the fatty degeneration. Coulson and Brazda tested pyridine, quinoline, and a number of pyridine derivatives and found choline relatively ineffective as a protective agent.[105]

Reference has been made previously to the degenerative changes in the

[96] E. A. Sellars and R. W. You, *Science* **110**, 713 (1949).
[97] E. A. Sellars and R. W. You, *Biochem. J.*, **51**, 573 (1952).
[98] E. A. Sellars and S. S. You, *Am. J. Physiol.* **163**, 81 (1950).
[99] E. A. Sellars, S. S. You, and N. Thomas, *Am. J. Physiol.* **165**, 481 (1951).
[100] E. A. Sellars and R. W. You, *J. Nutrition* **44**, 513 (1951).
[101] L. A. Heppel, P. A. Neal, F. S. Daft, K. M. Endicott, M. L. Orr, and V. T. Porterfield, *J. Ind. Hyg. Toxicol.* **27**, 15 (1945).
[102] L. A. Heppel, B. Highman, and V. T. Porterfield, *J. Pharmacol.* **87**, 11 (1946).
[103] R. M. Calder, *J. Pathol. Bacteriol.* **54**, 355 (1942).
[104] H. Benard and M. Gajdos-Torok, *Compt. rend. soc. biol.* **141**, 122 (1947).
[105] R. A. Coulson and F. G. Brazda, *Proc. Soc. Exptl. Biol. Med.* **65**, 1 (1947); **69**, 480 (1948).

liver that predispose to experimental cirrhosis in rats and to the fact that hypolipotropic diets usually result in hepatic fibrosis that starts in the centrolobular region. This type of liver pathology is prevented by lipotropic agents, particularly by choline and methionine. Extent of curative effects depends on the degree of damage that has occurred. This experimental cirrhosis must be distinguished from the hemorrhage and necrosis or necrotic degeneration that occurs in rats if fed certain deficient diets, especially diets low in cystine and vitamin E, and from the pathology caused by an excess of dietary cystine. These various conditions have been described by many workers.[106-118]

A characteristic feature of cirrhotic livers due to a deficiency of lipotropic factors is an acid-fast and sudanophilic pigment named "ceroid" by Lillie et al.[111] Victor and Pappenheimer reported that ceroid was associated with vitamin E deficiency,[112] a conclusion supported by Hartroft,[36] who suggested the possibility that the deposit was a mixture of lipids and some component of erythrocytes.[119]

Liver damage caused by the excessive administration of ethanol in rats affords an excellent illustration of the protective role of lipotropic substances such as choline.[109, 120] Ashworth reported, however, that alcohol exerted an effect unrelated to lipotropic factors.[121] Best et al.[122] and Hartroft[36] found increased fibrous tissue formation in nearly 50 % of rats fed a low protein, low choline diet and given 15 % alcohol as drinking water. Pair-fed controls developed the same degree of damage only if the total caloric intake was

[106] A. C. Curtis and L. H. Newburgh, Arch. Internal Med. 39, 828 (1927).
[107] P. György and H. Goldblatt, J. Exptl. Med. 70, 185 (1939); 75, 355 (1942); 90, 73 (1949).
[108] H. Blumberg and E. V. McCollum, Science 93, 598 (1941).
[109] F. S. Daft, W. H. Sebrell, and R. D. Lillie, Proc. Soc. Exptl. Biol. Med. 48, 228 (1941); 50, 1 (1942).
[110] D. P. Earle and J. Victor, J. Exptl. Med. 73, 161 (1941); 75, 179 (1942).
[111] R. D. Lillie, L. L. Ashburn, W. H. Sebrell, F. S. Daft, and J. V. Lowry, Publ. Health Repts. (U.S.) 57, 502 (1942).
[112] J. Victor and A. M. Pappenheimer, J. Exptl. Med. 82, 375 (1945).
[113] J. Green and A. Brunschwig, Proc. Soc. Exptl. Biol. Med. 61, 348 (1946).
[114] P. Handler and I. N. Dubin, J. Nutrition 31, 141 (1946).
[115] P. Handler and R. H. Follis, Jr., J. Nutrition 35, 669 (1948).
[116] C. A. Hall and V. A. Drill, Proc. Soc. Exptl. Biol. Med. 69, 3 (1948).
[117] L. E. Glynn, H. P. Himsworth, and O. Lindan, Brit. J. Exptl. Pathol. 29, 1 (1948).
[118] K. Schwarz, Proc. Soc. Exptl. Biol. Med. 77, 818 (1951).
[119] W. S. Hartroft, Science 113, 673 (1951).
[120] J. V. Lowry, L. L. Ashburn, and W. H. Sebrell, Jr., Quart. J. Studies Alc. 6, 271 (1945).
[121] C. T. Ashworth, Proc. Soc. Exptl. Biol. Med. 66, 382 (1947).
[122] C. H. Best, W. S. Hartroft, C. C. Lucas, and J. H. Ridout, Brit. Med. J. II, 1001 (1949).

made equivalent to the alcohol intake by isocaloric amounts of sucrose. It was concluded that the effect of alcohol on the livers of rats in experiments of this type was due to a deficiency of lipotropic factors, especially of choline.

Kaufman *et al.* were unable to produce experimental hemochromatosis in rats by feeding a diet low in lipotropic factors and containing a moderately toxic level of copper.[123] The combination of copper and choline in this diet decreased the body weight of the animals.

3. Effect of Sulfur Amino Acids

In 1935, Best and Huntsman reported that casein exhibited lipotropic activity,[39] a result confirmed by Channon and Wilkinson[124] and extended to egg white and beef protein, but not to gelatin, by Best *et al.*[125] In a survey of the effect of various amino acids, Beeston and Channon found one, cystine, with a marked antilipotropic activity.[126] In subsequent experiments, negative results for most of the other amino acids were confirmed,[127, 128] and cysteine and homocystine were found to resemble cystine in augmenting the deposition of fat in the livers of rats fed the low choline, 5 % protein, and 40 % fat diets that were commonly used.[129, 130] The explanation of the puzzling lipotropic character of many proteins was indicated by the important observation of Tucker and Eckstein that a supplement of methionine reduced markedly the liver fat of rats on the experimental diets and, in this respect, acted oppositely to cystine.[131] The choline-like property of methionine has been confirmed repeatedly.[52, 132-135] It is pertinent that Best called attention to the significant fact that methionine rarely reduced the level of liver lipids to normal values even though it was highly effective in preventing excessively fatty livers.[132] The participation of methionine in transmethylation as a methyl donor with synthesis or sparing, at least, of choline offers a reasonable explanation of the lipotropic property (Section

[123] N. Kaufman, J. A. Cartaya, P. L. White, D. M. Hegsted, and T. D. Kinney, *J. Nutrition* **46,** 433 (1952).

[124] H. J. Channon and H. Wilkinson, *Biochem. J.* **29,** 350 (1935).

[125] C. H. Best, R. Grant, and J. H. Ridout, *J. Physiol. (London)* **86,** 337 (1936).

[126] A. W. Beeston and H. J. Channon, *Biochem. J.* **30,** 280 (1936).

[127] S. A. Singal and H. C. Eckstein, *J. Biol. Chem.* **140,** 27 (1941).

[128] A. W. Beeston and A. P. Platt, *J. Soc. Chem. Ind.* **56,** 292 (1937).

[129] S. A. Singal and H. C. Eckstein, *Proc. Soc. Exptl. Biol. Med.* **41,** 512 (1939).

[130] H. J. Channon, M. C. Manifold, and A. P. Platt, *J. Soc. Chem. Ind.* **57,** 600 (1938).

[131] H. F. Tucker and H. C. Eckstein, *J. Biol. Chem.* **121,** 479 (1937).

[132] C. H. Best and J. H. Ridout, *J. Physiol. (London)* **97,** 489 (1940).

[133] W. H. Griffith and N. J. Wade, *J. Biol. Chem.* **132,** 627 (1940).

[134] C. R. Treadwell, *J. Biol. Chem.* **176,** 1141 (1948).

[135] J. M. R. Beveridge, C. C. Lucas, and M. K. O'Grady, *J. Biol. Chem.* **160,** 505 (1945).

IV). The similar behavior of most proteins depends on their content of this amino acid inasmuch as it is the only one of these units commonly present in proteins for which significant lipotropic activity has been demonstrated.[136-139]

The effect of cystine and its apparent antagonism to methionine have intrigued many investigators. Beeston and Channon noted that the cystine effect was not proportional to the level of the cystine supplement,[126] and this may explain the minimal influence of additions of the amino acid to low choline, low protein diets in which the protein was gliadin[137] or albumin,[140] both relatively richer in cystine than casein. Attempts to compare the lipotropic activity of free methionine with equivalent amounts in various proteins have not yielded uniformly consistent results.[132, 135, 137, 140-143] This is not surprising in view of differences in strains and in the age of experimental rats, of changes in the nutritional state of the animals in those instances in which a deficiency of protein was superimposed on a deficiency of methyl, of variations in the supply of cystine, and of the unrecognized presence in some diets of nutrients, such as B_{12}, which are now believed to influence favorably the utilization of methionine.

Somewhat more consistent results have been obtained in studies of the cystine effect in weanling rats. Griffith and Wade noted clear evidence of the aggravating effect of added cystine on both renal lesions and deposition of liver fat on diets ordinarily considered adequate in total protein.[133] Cox et al. had observed this result before choline was recognized as a dietary factor.[144] In line with data obtained on older rats,[126] the maximum cystine effect in weanling rats fed a diet containing 0.05 % choline chloride and 18 % casein resulted if 0.1 to 0.2 % additional cystine was added. Cystine supplements up to 2 % had no additional effect.[21] These data emphasized the physiological role of a small supplement of cystine and removed any basis for an explanation of the cystine effect because of toxicity. Mulford and Griffith demonstrated that the addition of extra cystine to the 18 % casein diet supplemented with sufficient choline to prevent fatty livers resulted in improved growth of the rats as measured by increased body weight and length and efficiency of utilization of food. Accordingly, it was concluded

136 H. J. Channon, J. V. Loach, P. A. Loizides, M. C. Manifold, and G. Soliman, *Biochem. J*. **32**, 976 (1938).

137 H. F. Tucker and H. C. Eckstein, *J. Biol. Chem*. **126**, 117 (1938).

138 W. H. Griffith, *J. Nutrition* **21**, 291 (1941).

139 M. G. Horning and H. C. Eckstein, *J. Biol. Chem*. **155**, 49 (1944).

140 H. J. Channon, M. C. Manifold, and A. P. Platt, *Biochem. J*. **34**, 866 (1940).

141 C. R. Treadwell, M. Groothuis, and H. C. Eckstein, *J. Biol. Chem*. **142**, 653 (1942).

142 J. M. R. Beveridge, C. C. Lucas, and M. K. O'Grady, *J. Biol. Chem*. **154**, 9 (1944).

143 H. F. Tucker, C. R. Treadwell, and H. C. Eckstein, *J. Biol. Chem*. **135**, 85 1940).

144 G. J. Cox, C. V. Smythe, and C. F. Fishback, *J. Biol. Chem*. **82**, 95 (1929).

that the phenomenon involving cystine was related to its improvement of the nutritive value of the diet, i.e., the removal of the existing sulfur deficiency. The resulting increased metabolic level raised the choline requirement and exaggerated the deficiency signs in the absence of a supply of the required extra choline. This explanation made unnecessary any hypothesis based on a specific antagonism or competition between the sulfur amino acids, methionine and cystine.

The fact that weanling rats develop severe evidences of deficiency on low choline diets, even on diets adequate in protein, made it possible to study protein effects without the risk of protein deficiency. Griffith fed mixtures of casein, lactalbumin, fibrin, edestin, and gelatin with and without supplements of methionine and cystine and found that dietary choline was not required for the prevention of hemorrhagic degeneration if the food mixture provided 0.8 % or more methionine, regardless of whether this level was attained by use of proteins or by methionine supplements.[138] Renal lesions and fatty livers occurred on low choline diets providing 10 to 25 % casein,[133] and 30 % casein was required to prevent the cystine effect in the absence of added choline.[21] The latter observation was the basis for the conclusion that a single molecule of methionine is not simultaneously a source of both labile methyl and cystine sulfur, inasmuch as 22 to 24 % casein supplies the optimum level of sulfur if dietary choline is provided.[21]

The relation between the general adequacy of the diet for growth, except for its choline content, and the deposition of liver fat was emphasized in the first report on choline deficiency in weanling rats. With diets only moderately deficient in choline, the deposition of liver fat was intensified in those permitting the better rates of growth.[2] The concept that nutritionally adequate diets involve increased needs of choline, and the converse, that choline requirements are less if the food mixture or the food intake does not allow growth, were supported by the results of caloric restriction in weanling rats fed a choline-deficient diet. The development of renal lesions and of fatty livers was completely prevented by removal of part of the carbohydrate and fat of the diet.[21] Similar conclusions regarding the nature of the diet and the requirement of choline have been reached by Beveridge et al.[135, 142] Salmon,[145] Handler,[146] and Best.[122, 147]

Handler prevented growth in young rats by feeding them a diet deficient in choline and in the mineral component of the ration. After 4 weeks these animals had not grown and the values for liver lipids were nearly normal whereas rats restricted to the same amount of food containing the mineral component grew slowly and had markedly fatty livers.[146]

[145] W. D. Salmon, *J. Nutrition* **33**, 155 (1947).
[146] P. Handler, *J. Biol. Chem.* **149**, 291 (1943).
[147] C. H. Best, C. C. Lucas, J. H. Ridout, and J. M. Patterson, *J. Biol. Chem.* **186**, 317 (1950).

Salmon concluded that weanling rats on diets containing 18 % or less casein were subject to methyl deficiency unless supplemental choline or methionine was supplied.[145] This deficiency was intensified by cystine and by fat. Such animals also required supplementary nicotinic acid or additional tryptophan unless the diet was high in fat. It was not possible to demonstrate a deficiency of cystine unless the methyl and nicotinic acid deficiencies were remedied. In contrast is the surprising observation of Tyner et al. that the cystine effect was abolished if generously adequate levels of niacin or of tryptophan were provided.[148]

Treadwell and coworkers have also studied the cystine effect in both young and adult rats.[134, 149-151] The intensification of renal lesions in weanling rats by supplements of cystine was confirmed, but the explanation based on the increased demand for choline because of the otherwise improved food mixture was questioned.[134] Treadwell suggested that the metabolism of cystine may require methyl groups or that extra cystine may depress the demethylation of methionine by a mass action effect.[149] Neither possibility explains the similarity of lipotropism in diets supplemented with 0.1 and 2.0 % cystine.[21] The failure of cystine to induce growth on low casein diets, as noted by Treadwell[149] and by Salmon,[145] is not surprising. Griffith and Nawrocki found that threonine increased the need of choline in cystine-supplemented 8 % casein diets and concluded that at this casein level cystine (or methionine) and threonine were the first and second limiting amino acids, respectively.[152]

The synthesis of choline in rats fed diets containing methionine as the main methyl donor requires a suitable carbon-nitrogen moiety to serve as the methyl acceptor and whatever cofactors are necessary for the enzymatic systems involved. There appears to be little difficulty in the provision of the dietary essentials for these mechanisms. Rose et al. found no statistically significant effect on the growth of weanling rats as a result of the omission of glycine, serine, cystine, and most of the choline from a standard diet containing a mixture of highly purified amino acids as the source of nitrogen.[153] The same omissions caused a slight but significant retardation of growth in similar diets in which the methionine level was decreased from 0.8 to 0.5 % (as DL-methionine) and the threonine level from 0.7 to 0.4 % (as L-threonine) and in which the liver extract, a possible source of B_{12}, was also omitted.

Ethionine (S-ethyl-DL-homocysteine) is a homolog of methionine and is,

[148] E. P. Tyner, H. B. Lewis, and H. C. Eckstein, J. Biol. Chem. 187, 651 (1950).
[149] C. R. Treadwell, J. Biol. Chem. 176, 1149 (1948).
[150] C. R. Treadwell, H. C. Tidwell, and J. H. Gast, J. Biol. Chem. 156, 237 (1944).
[151] C. R. Treadwell, J. Biol. Chem. 160, 601 (1945).
[152] W. H. Griffith and M. F. Nawrocki, Federation Proc. 7, 288 (1948).
[153] W. C. Rose, W. W. Burr, Jr., and H. J. Sallach, J. Biol. Chem. 194, 321 (1952).

therefore, a potential antagonist of the natural amino acid. It was found to inhibit methyl transfer from methionine to choline but not to creatine.[154] Fatty livers occurred rapidly after its injection into female rats but not in male rats, and this antilipotropic effect was opposed by methionine.[155] Evidence has been provided for its incorporation *in vivo* into an abnormal type of tissue protein.[156] Stekol showed that ethionine was deethylated in the rat[157] and that its inhibitory action on rat growth was prevented by the administration of either choline or methionine.[158] In similar experiments with triethylcholine, choline was more efficient than methionine in the prevention of a deleterious effect on growth.[159] These data suggest the participation and interference of ethionine in transmethylation.

4. Effect of Other Nutrients

A lipotropic action of inositol was first reported by Gavin and McHenry[160] and studied further by MacFarland and McHenry.[161] Rats, 90 to 100 g. in weight, were depleted of fat and of B vitamins for 3 weeks on a fat-free, high carbohydrate diet; during a fourth week test substances were administered and the livers were analyzed for lipids. In such experiments a crude beef liver fraction, a liver extract, or a biotin plus folic acid supplement with extra thiamine, riboflavin, pantothenate, and nicotinic acid produced fatty livers resistant to choline and responsive to inositol. McHenry emphasized particularly the effectiveness of inositol in reducing the level of liver cholesterol. A supplementary action of inositol with choline was described by Engel[162] and confirmed by Forbes.[163] Beveridge noted that the inositol effect was absent if the diet contained corn oil.[164, 165] The favorable influence of inositol was also observed by Handler,[166] but both Handler[14] and Best *et al.*[167] reported that in the absence of choline renal lesions were intensified

[154] S. Simmonds, E. B. Keller, J. P. Chandler, and V. du Vigneaud, *J. Biol. Chem.* **183**, 191 (1950).

[155] D. Jensen, I. L. Chaikoff, and H. Tarver, *J. Biol. Chem.* **192**, 395 (1951).

[156] M. Levine and H. Tarver, *J. Biol. Chem.* **192**, 835 (1951).

[157] J. A. Stekol, K. W. Weiss, and S. Weiss, *J. Am. Chem. Soc.* **72**, 2309 (1950).

[158] J. A. Stekol and K. W. Weiss, *Proc. Soc. Exptl. Biol. Med.* **77**, 213 (1951); *J. Biol. Chem.* **179**, 1049 (1949); **185**, 577 (1950).

[159] J. A. Stekol and K. W. Weiss, *J. Biol. Chem.* **185**, 585 (1950).

[160] G. Gavin and E. W. McHenry, *J. Biol. Chem.* **139**, 485 (1941); **141**, 619 (1941).

[161] M. L. MacFarland and E. W. McHenry, *J. Biol. Chem.* **159**, 605 (1945); **176**, 429 (1948).

[162] R. W. Engel, *J. Nutrition* **24**, 175 (1942).

[163] J. C. Forbes, *Proc. Soc. Exptl. Biol. Med.* **54**, 89 (1943).

[164] J. M. R. Beveridge, *Science* **99**, 539 (1944).

[165] J. M. R. Beveridge and C. C. Lucas, *J. Biol. Chem.* **157**, 311 (1945).

[166] P. Handler, *J. Biol. Chem.* **162**, 77 (1946).

[167] C. H. Best, C. C. Lucas, J. M. Patterson, and J. H. Ridout, *Science* **103**, 12 (1946).

by inositol. Best *et al.* have reinvestigated the lipotropic activity of inositol and have found that the analysis for liver lipids at the end of the 7-day test subsequent to the depletion period may not be representative of values existing earlier or later.[54] They concluded that inositol has no unique lipotropic properties and that it is inferior to choline in the reduction of either liver fat or cholesterol esters. Its supplementary action with choline in fat-free diets was confirmed. No explanation has been brought forward for the influence of inositol on liver lipids other than its possible role in an inositol-containing phospholipid.

In 1933 Blatherwick *et al.* reported the occurrence of fatty livers in rats fed large amounts òf whole liver.[168] This result was confirmed by Beeston and Wilkinson, who were unable to demonstrate a lipotropic action of choline.[169] McHenry, using the depletion procedure referred to above, found marked increases in liver fat and cholesterol following the feeding of a liver fraction[170] and biotin.[160, 161] The term "biotin fatty liver" was applied, and it was believed that inositol was more effective than choline in this condition. The concept of a special type of fatty liver due to biotin was attacked by Best *et al.*[171] and by Handler.[166] These workers were unable to find satisfactory evidence for an unusual effect of inositol or for a special role of biotin other than the effect to be expected as a result of changes in food intake and utilization.

McHenry noted a marked increase in liver fat in rats following the addition of thiamine to a low choline, thiamine-deficient diet.[172] Choline, but not inositol, was found to be lipotropic for this so-called "thiamine fatty liver." Somewhat similar results were observed by Engel and Phillips, who concluded that thiamine therapy caused a temporary pathological state as a result of disruption of cells by excessive production of fat.[173] The hydropic degeneration and fatty changes were not prevented by choline, but desiccated thyroid was effective. McHenry had suggested earlier that thiamine might be essential for the synthesis of fat from carbohydrate.[174] The probability of such an origin of the extra liver lipids in choline deficiency was supported by the exclusion of increased absorption from the intestine[175] and of increased mobilization of tissue fat[41] as possible sources. Regardless of

[168] N. R. Blatherwick, E. M. Medlar, P. J. Bradshaw, A. L. Post, and S. D. Sawyer, *J. Biol. Chem.* **103,** 93 (1933).

[169] A. W. Beeston and H. Wilkinson, *Biochem. J.* **30,** 121 (1936).

[170] E. W. McHenry and G. Gavin, *Science* **91,** 171 (1940).

[171] C. H. Best, C. C. Lucas, J. M. Patterson, and J. H. Ridout, *Biochem. J.* **40,** 368 (1946).

[172] E. W. McHenry, *J. Physiol. (London)* **89,** 287 (1937).

[173] R. W. Engel and P. H. Phillips, *J. Nutrition* **18,** 329 (1939).

[174] E. W. McHenry, *Science* **86,** 200 (1937).

[175] H. E. Longenecker, G. Gavin, and E. W. McHenry, *J. Biol. Chem.* **134,** 693 (1940).

the relation of thiamine to the synthesis of fat, it is doubtful if the deposition of extra fat resulting from the supplementation of the deficient diet has any different explanation from that which explains satisfactorily the effects of biotin,[171] cystine,[4] and minerals.[146] This conclusion is given solid support by the findings of Boxer and Stetten, who caused labeling of newly synthesized fat by the administration of D_2O in rats, produced fatty livers on a low choline diet with and without dietary thiamine, and noted that the decrease in the synthesis of fat in the thiamine-deficient animals was paralleled by that in the animals supplied thiamine but restricted to the same food intake as the thiamine-deficient group.[176]

By way of contrast to thiamine, it is of interest that pyridoxine has been reported to be necessary for the prevention of fatty livers. Rats deficient in vitamin B_6 developed fatty livers to a greater extent than controls,[177] and necrosis of the kidney cortex was noted more frequently as a symptom of choline deficiency.[178] The feeding of a very high casein diet after depletion of fat and of B vitamins resulted in an additional weight loss and in the development of fatty livers unless pyridoxine was supplied.[179] According to Engel, pyridoxine and essential fatty acids must be present for the normal functioning of choline as a lipotropic agent in rats.[162]

Niacin and its derivatives have been linked with lipotropism in rats in a variety of experiments. Niacinamide and, under certain conditions, the diphosphopyridine nucleotide inhibited choline oxidase in *in vitro* studies.[180] Growth of rats on low protein, methyl-poor diets containing niacinamide was affected adversely, presumably because of further depletion of methyl due to the formation and excretion of N^1-methylniacinamide.[68] The cystine effect was absent in young rats unless nicotinic acid was present in the diet,[145] and the cystine effect was abolished in older animals in the presence of generously adequate levels of this vitamin.[148] Forbes found that the addition of niacin to a low choline diet increased the cholesterol content of fatty livers and decreased the responsiveness of the animals to the lipotropic effect of choline.[181] It is not possible to conclude that any of these effects represent direct relations between the metabolism of choline and of niacin *in vivo* except the changes introduced by the methylation of the vitamin. Many of these results may be explicable on the basis of non-specific effects on food intake and utilization. Handler showed that dietary niacinamide (2 %) resulted in a greater loss of weight in partially hepatectomized rats

[176] G. E. Boxer and D. Stetten, Jr., *J. Biol. Chem.* **153**, 607 (1944).
[177] N. Halliday, *J. Nutrition* **16**, 285 (1938).
[178] P. György and R. E. Eckardt, *Biochem. J.* **34**, 1143 (1940).
[179] E. W. McHenry and G. Gavin, *J. Biol. Chem.* **138**, 471 (1941).
[180] J. N. Williams, Jr., G. Litwack, and C. A. Elvehjem, *J. Biol. Chem.* **192**, 73 (1951).
[181] J. C. Forbes, *J. Nutrition* **22**, 359 (1941).

than in controls.[182] Fatty livers on low choline diets were prevented by niacinamide or by a deficiency of thiamine. These results were believed due to an impairment of the metabolism of the rat rather than to a specific defect involving niacin or thiamine.

It is not possible to discuss the many investigations that indicate important relationships of folic acid, folinic acid, and B_{12}, or their derivatives, to choline and to methyl metabolism. That certain of these factors may be involved in transmethylation, in formate-to-methyl synthesis, or in the betaine-glycine-aminoethanol system appears highly probable. In so far as the rat is concerned, observations up to the present time have demonstrated that its ability to synthesize the methyl and the aminoethanol portions of choline depends on one or more of these newer vitamins. Schaefer et al.[23, 183-185] have demonstrated that the requirement of choline for the prevention of renal lesions and for the maintenance of normal liver lipids in young rats on a diet low in choline and in methionine may be decreased as much as one-half by the addition of B_{12} and folic acid. These nutrients appeared to increase the utilization of betaine and methionine in the methylation of aminoethanol to choline and of betaine in the methylation of homocystine to methionine. In general, B_{12} was effective alone if present in adequate amounts. If present at a subnormal level, its value was improved by folic acid. The latter was believed ineffective in the absence of B_{12}. Hale and Schaefer noted that weanling rats of the Sprague-Dawley strain had a lower choline requirement for protection against renal hemorrhage and a higher requirement for prevention of fatty livers than young of the Alabama Experiment Station strain.[186] Lipotropic activity was ascribed to B_{12} in the experiments of György[187, 188] and to B_{12} and folic acid in the studies of Drill[116, 189] and of Fischer.[190] Growth of rats on diets devoid of labile methyl and containing B_{12} and folic acid was reported by Bennett,[190a] by Stekol,[190b] and by du Vigneaud.[190c]

See p. 67
23 ref.

[182] P. Handler and F. Bernheim, J. Biol. Chem. 148, 649 (1943).

[183] A. E. Schaefer, W. D. Salmon, and D. R. Strength, Proc. Soc. Exptl. Biol. Med. 71, 193 (1949).

[184] A. E. Schaefer, W. D. Salmon, D. R. Strength, and D. H. Copeland, J. Nutrition 40, 95 (1950).

[185] A. E. Schaefer and J. L. Knowles, Proc. Soc. Exptl. Biol. Med. 77, 655 (1951).

[186] O. M. Hale and A. E. Schaefer, Proc. Soc. Exptl. Biol. Med. 77, 633 (1951).

[187] P. György ahd C. S. Rose, Proc. Soc. Exptl. Biol. Med. 73, 372 (1950).

[188] C. S. Rose, T. E. Machella, and P. György, Proc. Soc. Exptl. Biol. Med. 64, 352 (1947); 67, 198 (1948).

[189] H. M. McCormick and V. A. Drill, Proc. Soc. Exptl. Biol. Med. 74, 626 (1950).

[190] M. A. Fischer and G. D. Hall, Federation Proc. 11, 211 (1952).

[190a] M. A. Bennett, J. Biol. Chem. 163, 247 (1946); 187, 751 (1950).

[190b] J. A. Stekol and K. W. Weiss, J. Biol. Chem. 186, 343 (1950).

[190c] V. du Vigneaud, C. Ressler, J. R. Rachele, J. A. Reyniers, and T. D. Luckey, J. Nutrition 45, 361 (1951).

Many observations support the view that folic acid or a derivative influences formate metabolism in the rat and thereby affects the formation of aminoethanol from serine and glycine and the formate-to-methyl synthesis which may be involved in the conversion of aminoethanol to choline. Totter *et al.* noted a favorable effect of folic acid on the metabolism of glycine which was manifested by an increased excretion of porphyrins, believed to indicate improved synthesis of hemoglobin, and by a neutralization of the symptoms of glycine deficiency produced by the administration of sodium benzoate.[191] Elwyn and Sprinson found that the conversion of N^{15}-L-serine to glycine and the subsequent excretion of N^{15}-benzoylglycine were reduced markedly in folic acid-deficient rats.[192] Stekol *et al.* reported that the deficiency impaired the use of the β-carbon of serine and, to a lesser extent, of the γ-carbon of glycine in choline formation.[193, 194] The incorporation of C^{14}-formate into serine of liver proteins was greatly increased by the treatment of deficient rats with folic acid,[195] and the synthesis of the choline methyl from methanol was improved by either folic acid or leucovorin.[196, 197] In confirmation of his own results[198, 199] and of those of others,[200] Williams found in *in vitro* studies that symptoms of folic acid deficiency in rats caused by feeding the antagonist, aminopterin, included an inhibition of the liver oxidases that convert choline and betaine aldehyde to betaine and of the enzymes that methylate homocystine.[201] In contrast to the slight influence of a synthetic citrovorum factor, leucovorin, folic acid was necessary for the optimal formation of N^1-methylnicotinamide from administered nicotinamide in rats.[202]

As in the case of folic acid, B_{12} has been involved in both methyl and formate metabolism. Oginsky found B_{12}-deficient rats less able to form methionine from homocystine and either choline or betaine.[203] The deficiency had no appreciable effect on the formation of choline methyl from methanol[196] or from the β-carbon of serine.[204] Arnstein and Neuberger,[204] how-

[191] J. R. Totter, E. S. Amos, and C. K. Keith, *J. Biol. Chem.* **178**, 847 (1949).

[192] D. Elwyn and D. B. Sprinson, *J. Biol. Chem.* **184**, 475 (1950).

[193] J. A. Stekol, S. Weiss, and K. W. Weiss, *Arch. Biochem. and Biophys.* **36**, 5 (1952).

[194] J. A. Stekol, S. Weiss, B. Hsu, and P. Smith, *Federation Proc.* **11**, 292 (1952).

[195] G. W. E. Plaut, J. J. Betheil, and H. A. Lardy, *J. Biol. Chem.* **184**, 795 (1950).

[196] W. G. Verly, J. E. Wilson, J. M. Kinney, and J. R. Rachele, *Federation Proc.* **10**, 264 (1951).

[197] W. G. Verly, J. M. Kinney, and V. du Vigneaud, *J. Biol. Chem.* **196**, 19 (1952).

[198] J. N. Williams, Jr., *J. Biol. Chem.* **191**, 123 (1951).

[199] J. N. Williams, Jr., *J. Biol. Chem.* **192**, 81 (1951).

[200] J. S. Dinning, C. K. Keith, P. L. Davis, and P. L. Day, *Arch. Biochem.* **27**, 89 (1950).

[201] J. N. Williams, Jr., *Proc. Soc. Exptl. Biol. Med.* **78**, 206 (1951).

[202] L. S. Dietrich, W. J. Monson, and C. A. Elvehjem, *J. Biol. Chem.* **199**, 2 (1952).

[203] E. L. Oginsky, *Arch. Biochem.* **26**, 327 (1950).

[204] H. R. V. Arnstein and A. Neuberger, *Biochem. J.* **48**, ii (1951).

ever, considered their data evidence for a role of B_{12} in the reactions which result in the formation of serine from glycine, and Stekol *et al.* arrived at the same conclusion.[193, 194] Choline prevented depletion of B_{12} in the livers of rats, but not of mice, on choline-deficient diets containing sulfasuxidine and iodinated casein.[205] The decrease in the epinephrine content of the adrenals of rats on a low B_{12} diet containing desiccated thyroid or iodinated casein was partially prevented by B_{12}, and it was suggested that B_{12} may function in the formation of the methyl group of epinephrine.[206] The sarcosine oxidase content of livers of hyperthyroid rats deficient in folic acid was unaffected but was reduced in B_{12}-deficient animals.[207] B_{12}, however, was ineffective in restoring the enzyme content.

Williams *et al.*[207a, 207b] compared the effect of a deficiency of B_{12} on liver xanthine oxidase and betaine-homocysteine transmethylase levels and concluded that the decreased xanthine oxidase activity was an indirect metabolic effect, whereas the data indicated that the transmethylase may require B_{12} as a cofactor or as a precursor of a cofactor. Hawk and Elvehjem[207c] found no evidence of a choline-sparing action of B_{12f}, a biologically different form of B_{12} recently described by Lewis *et al.*[207d] Stekol *et al.*[207e] observed no effect of B_{12} deficiency on the transmethylation that yields choline from methionine although the incorporation of methyl into choline was diminished in both folic acid-deficient and pyridoxine-deficient animals. It was suggested that B_{12}, folic acid, and pyridoxine may be more concerned with the synthesis of methyl acceptors than with transmethylation itself.

Dubnoff has made the interesting suggestion that one of the functions of a B_{12} derivative is the reduction of homocystine to homocysteine, believed to be the actual acceptor of methyl.[208] A B_{12} concentrate increased the sulfhydryl content of rat liver slices, and this effect was particularly noticeable in experiments on B_{12}-deficient rats. The activity was associated with the B_{12} color after paper chromatography, although crystalline B_{12} and B_{12a} were negative. In subsequent observations Dubnoff demonstrated that homocysteine or homocystine plus a reducing agent replaced B_{12} or methionine

[205] J. J. Travers and L. R. Cerecedo, *Federation Proc.* **11**, 457 (1952).

[206] A. D'Iorio and G. W. E. Plaut, *Arch. Biochem. and Biophys.* **41**, 153 (1952).

[207] M. E. Swendseid, A. L. Swanson, and F. H. Bethell, *Arch. Biochem. and Biophys.* **41**, 138 (1952).

[207a] J. N. Williams, Jr., W. J. Monson, A. Sreenivasan, L. S. Dietrich, A. E. Harper, and C. A. Elvehjem, *J. Biol. Chem.* **202**, 151 (1953).

[207b] J. N. Williams, Jr., W. J. Monson, A. E. Harper, and C. A. Elvehjem, *J. Biol. Chem.* **202**, 607 (1953).

[207c] E. A. Hawk and C. A. Elvehjem, *J. Nutrition* **49**, 495 (1953).

[207d] U. J. Lewis, D. V. Tappan, and C. A. Elvehjem, *J. Biol. Chem.* **194**, 539 (1952); **199**, 517 (1952).

[207e] J. A. Stekol, S. Weiss, P. Smith, and K. W. Weiss, *J. Biol. Chem.* **201**, 1 (1953).

[208] J. W. Dubnoff, *Arch. Biochem.* **27**, 466 (1950).

for the growth of an *Escherichia coli* mutant (No. 113-3), a form which requires either B_{12} or methionine.[209] The growth-promoting value of homocysteine was enhanced by a trace of B_{12}, by a methyl donor such as dimethyl-β-propiothetin, or by catalytic amounts of p-aminobenzoic acid. Dubnoff suggested that B_{12} is necessary for the maintenance of homocysteine in the reduced state and that it may also be required for the synthesis of p-aminobenzoic acid which may be involved in the synthesis of methyl groups. According to Shive, p-aminobenzoic acid, folic acid, and B_{12} are involved in the metabolism of formate in microorganisms.[210] Ling and Chow reported that B_{12} corrected the decreased sulfhydryl content of blood of B_{12}-deficient rats.[211]

Although the dog has been used in most of the investigations on lipocaic, believed by Dragstedt to be a pancreatic hormonal anti-fatty liver factor,[212] studies on rats also have been conducted and with varying results. Data have been presented which support the view that the lipotropic activity of preparations of lipocaic is explained completely by their content of choline and of protein.[213-216] In contrast to these results are findings which indicate that the potency of lipocaic cannot be explained on the basis of its content of choline, methionine, or inositol.[217-221] More recently, successful ligation of the pancreatic duct has been reported to result in fatty livers in rats on a choline-deficient diet.[222] As in the experiments on dogs to be discussed later, this result appears due to the lack of a proteolytic factor in the external secretion of the pancreas that normally releases a choline precursor, presumably methionine, from dietary protein. Choline and the anti-fatty liver factor of the pancreas were reported to have opposing effects on the excretion of urinary ketones.[223]

Rats fed a protein-free diet showed an accumulation of liver glycogen and fat after one month, and the increase in lipid was only partially pre-

[209] J. W. Dubnoff, *Arch. Biochem. and Biophys.* **37**, 37 (1952).
[210] W. Shive, *Ann. N. Y. Acad. Sci.* **52**, 1272 (1950).
[211] C.-T. Ling and B. F. Chow, *Federation Proc.* **11**, 249 (1952).
[212] L. R. Dragstedt, *J. Am. Med. Assoc.* **114**, 29 (1940); **115**, 454 (1940).
[213] F. X. Aylward and L. E. Holt, Jr., *J. Biol. Chem.* **121**, 61 (1937).
[214] E. M. MacKay and R. H. Barnes, *Proc. Soc. Exptl. Biol. Med.* **38**, 410 (1938).
[215] C. H. Best and J. H. Ridout, *Am. J. Physiol.* **122**, 67 (1938).
[216] A. N. Wick and E. Laurence, *Arch. Biochem.* **20**, 113 (1949).
[217] H. J. Channon, J. V. Loach, and G. R. Tristram, *Biochem. J.* **32**, 1332 (1938).
[218] G. Gavin, J. M. Patterson, and E. W. McHenry, *J. Biol. Chem.* **148**, 275 (1943).
[219] D. E. Clark, M. L. Eilert, and L. R. Dragstedt, *Am. J. Physiol.* **144**, 620 (1945).
[220] M. L. Eilert and L. R. Dragstedt, *Am. J. Physiol.* **147**, 346 (1946).
[221] M. J. Raymond and C. R. Treadwell, *Proc. Soc. Exptl. Biol. Med.* **70**, 43 (1949).
[222] G. H. A. Clowes, Jr. and L. B. Macpherson, *Am. J. Physiol.* **165**, 628 (1951).
[223] V. Baccari and A. Guerritore, *Boll. soc. ital. biol. sper.* **24**, 842 (1948).

vented by choline.[224] Extremely fatty livers resulted in choline-deficient rats fed at 20 % protein diet for one week following 7 days of fasting or 21 days of protein depletion, although choline was effective in these experiments.[225] Prolonged feeding of diets low in protein and in choline resulted in severe nutritional anemia and edema in rats.[226, 227] Both were prevented by choline, and Engel suggested that choline was a more important factor than dietary protein in the development of these abnormalities. The edematous condition was associated with hepatic fatty infiltration and subsequent cirrhosis. Anemia was also observed by Diaz *et al.* in rats fed a choline-deficient ration.[228]

Weanling rats fed diets low in protein or in riboflavin or containing iodinated casein consistently showed decreased levels of liver and kidney choline oxidase.[229] Ebisuzaki and Williams observed a parallelism between the flavin adenine dinucleotide and the choline oxidase levels of riboflavin-deficient rats. The latter workers concluded that the riboflavin-containing enzyme system was a part of the hydrogen transport mechanism involved in the oxidation of choline by choline oxidase.[230]

Singal *et al.* produced fatty livers in young rats fed low protein or low amino acid rations deficient in essential amino acids such as lysine and threonine but containing 0.2 % choline.[231] Normal liver lipid levels resulted from supplementation with the missing amino acid. High levels of choline were lipotropic in the animals on the deficient diets but only partly so in those fed the inadequate amino acid mixture. B_{12} had no lipotropic action in these experiments. As observed by Eckstein,[232] threonine was without effect in the absence of dietary choline. The rate of turnover of liver phospholipids was increased by the administration of threonine to threonine-deficient animals, although no such effect was noted in the turnover rate in the kidneys or in the small intestine. These results are of unusual interest in view of the observation that supplements of threonine in a low protein, choline-deficient diet aggravated symptoms in young rats during the period in which the acute phase of the deficiency occurred.[152]

[224] C. F. Wang, D. M. Hegsted, A. Lapi, N. Zamcheck, and M. B. Black, *J. Lab. Clin. Med.* **34**, 953 (1949).

[225] O. M. Hale and A. E. Schaefer, *J. Nutrition* **46**, 479 (1952).

[226] R. W. Engel, *J. Nutrition* **36**, 739 (1948).

[227] H. D. Alexander and R. W. Engel, *J. Nutrition* **47**, 361 (1952).

[228] C. J. Diaz, H. Castro-Mendoza, G. Paniagua, and F. Vivanco, *Bull. Inst. Med. Research, Univ. Madrid* **1**, 101 (1948).

[229] D. A. Richert and W. W. Westerfeld, *J. Biol. Chem.* **199**, 2 (1952).

[230] K. Ebisuzaki and J. N. Williams, Jr., *J. Biol. Chem.* **200**, 297 (1953).

[231] S. A. Singal, S. J. Hazan, V. P. Sydenstricker, and J. M. Littlejohn, *J. Biol. Chem.* **200**, 867 (1952).

[232] H. C. Eckstein, *J. Biol. Chem.* **195**, 167 (1952).

Morgan and Lewis noted the absence of fatty livers in rats on diets lacking both choline and pantothenic acid.[233] They concluded that fat metabolism was seriously deranged in these animals because of a depression of adrenal activity resulting from the lack of pantothenic acid.

Honorato and his associates suggested that choline plays a role in the antihemorrhagic activity of 2-methyl-1,4-naphthoquinone and reported that the latter showed lipotropic activity.[234] An antagonism between heparin and choline with inactivation of the former[235] was not confirmed.[236] Lecoq et al. observed that the effect of dietary cystine on chronaxie of rats was corrected by vitamin K plus choline.[237]

5. OTHER EFFECTS

In the preceding discussion, emphasis has been placed on the renal and hepatic changes that appear in choline-deficient rats. Many other effects of the deficiency syndrome have been recognized, some traceable directly to previous abnormalities in the kidneys and liver. Of unusual interest has been the observation of Best and Hartroft,[9, 238] confirmed by others,[239, 240] that hypertension developed in rats 4 to 7 months after the onset of acute choline deficiency even though fed a normal diet subsequent to the acute episode. It had been demonstrated previously by Sobin and Landis that hypertension did not result from a prolonged chronic deficiency of choline,[241] and Handler et al. noted that hypertension in partially nephrectomized rats disappeared if a choline-deficient diet was fed.[91] A partial solution of this anomalous situation in which damage occurred as a result of restoration of a normal diet was afforded by the demonstration that the hypertension following acute deficiency was prevented by decapsulation of the kidneys.[242] This suggested that the damaged capsule restricted the increase in size of the recovering kidney as it developed on the normal diet and that hypertension was the ultimate result as in the case of animals in which hypertension was induced by coating the kidney with cellophane or other restrictive materials.

In studies on the carcinogenic action of p-dimethylaminoazobenzene

[233] A. F. Morgan and E. M. Lewis, J. Biol. Chem. 200, 839 (1952).
[234] C. R. Honorato and H. Molina, Rev. soc. argentina biol. 18, 431 (1942).
[235] V. A. Cabezas and C. R. Honorato, Bol. soc. biol. Santiago Chile 2, 26 (1944).
[236] G. W. Howe and C. L. Spurr, Proc. Soc. Exptl. Biol. Med. 71, 429 (1949).
[237] R. Lecoq, P. Chauchard, and H. Mazoué, Compt. rend. soc. biol. 141, 220 (1947).
[238] W. S. Hartroft and C. H. Best, Brit. Med. J. I, 423 (1949).
[239] C. Moses, G. M. Longabaugh, and R. S. George, Proc. Soc. Exptl. Biol. Med. 75, 660 (1950).
[240] P. Handler and F. Bernheim, Am. J. Physiol. 162, 189 (1950).
[241] S. S. Sobin and E. M. Landis, Am. J. Physiol. 148, 557 (1947).
[242] P. Handler and F. Bernheim, Proc. Soc. Exptl. Biol. Med. 76, 338 (1951).

(DAB), or butter yellow, demethylation prior to fission of the azo linkage[243, 244] and methylation of the resulting p-monomethylaminoazobenzene[244] were demonstrated in rats. This observation appeared to support the conclusion of Jacobi and Baumann that DAB was a methyl donor because it prevented the development of renal lesions in young rats on a choline-deficient diet.[245] Later, Baumann was of the opinion that the protection against renal lesions must have had another explanation[246] in view of the failure of choline or of choline deficiency to affect the incidence of tumors following DAB administration.[247-250] Subsequently, it was shown by the feeding of C-14-methyl-labeled DAB that the tagged carbon appeared quickly as carbon dioxide in the expired air and that none was found in the methyls of tissue choline or creatine.[251] Choline in drinking water did not affect the induction of tumors in rats following the injection of 1,2,5,6-dibenzanthracene[252] or the lesions of bone marrow produced by nitrogen mustards.[253]

Using a strain of rats with a high choline requirement,[254, 255] Engel et al. observed that over one-half of chronically deficient animals developed neoplasms of various types whereas no lesions appeared in control animals.[256, 257] A similar finding was reported by Viollier.[258] Aloisi and Bonetti described lesions in the muscles of rats suffering from a prolonged deficiency of methyl donors.[259] The abnormality differed from the experimental dystrophy due to a deficiency of vitamin E, but it was not possible to separate the direct effect of a lack of methyl from the secondary influence of the hepatic pathology.

Malignant tumors of the human brain contained elevated levels of free

[243] E. S. Stevenson, K. Dobriner, and C. P. Rhoads, *Cancer Research* **2**, 160 (1942).

[244] J. A. Miller, E. C. Miller, and C. A. Baumann, *Cancer Research* **5**, 162 (1945).

[245] H. P. Jacobi and C. A. Baumann, *Cancer Research* **2**, 175 (1942).

[246] C. A. Baumann, *Trans. 2nd Conf. on Biol. Antioxidants, New York*, p. 114 (Oct. 9–10, 1947).

[247] E. C. Miller and C. A. Baumann, *Cancer Research* **6**, 289 (1946).

[248] P. N. Harris, M. E. Krahl, and G. H. A. Clowes, *Cancer Research* **7**, 162 (1947).

[249] J. White and J. E. Edwards, *J. Natl. Cancer Inst.* **3**, 43 (1942).

[250] H. M. Dyer, *J. Natl. Cancer Inst.* **11**, 1073 (1951).

[251] R. A. Boissonnas, R. A. Turner, and V. du Vigneaud, *J. Biol. Chem.* **180**, 1053 (1949).

[252] J. W. Cook and R. Schoental, *Brit. J. Cancer* **3**, 557 (1949).

[253] J. Domokos and E. Kelemen, *Intern. Z. Vitaminforsch.* **21**, 443 (1950).

[254] R. W. Engel, *Proc. Soc. Exptl. Biol. Med.* **52**, 281 (1943).

[255] D. H. Copeland, *Proc. Soc. Exptl. Biol. Med.* **57**, 33 (1944).

[256] D. H. Copeland and W. D. Salmon, *Am. J. Pathol.* **22**, 1059 (1946).

[257] R. W. Engel, D. H. Copeland, and W. D. Salmon, *Ann. N. Y. Acad. Sci.* **49**, 49 (1947).

[258] H. Staub, G. Viollier, and A. Werthemann, *Experientia* **4**, 233 (1948).

[259] M. Aloisi and E. Bonetti, *Arch. sci. biol. (Italy)* **36**, 206 (1952).

and combined choline,[260] and increased concentrations were also found in transplanted epidermal carcinomas in mice.[261] In the latter studies the increase appeared to be due to phospholipids.

The passage of fat through the intestinal mucosa during absorption was accelerated by feeding choline with the fat, according to Frazer.[262] Tidwell presented evidence for the view that choline played a chemical role and did not influence absorption because of an effect on emulsification.[263] This view is in line with the favorable influence of choline on phospholipid synthesis.[28, 60, 264] Directly or indirectly, choline affected the intestinal absorption and distribution of vitamin A. Rats on a choline-deficient diet containing liberal amounts of carotene developed fatty livers poor in vitamin A although the kidneys were rich in the vitamin.[265] The addition of choline to solutions of vitamin A in olive oil yielded higher levels of liver vitamin A after oral administration in normal rats.[266]

Choline and pyridoxine were protective against the hyperplasia and ulcerations that appeared in the forestomach of rats fed a diet containing white flour and cystine as the sources of nitrogen.[267] Sharpless suggested that regurgitated bile might be an important cause of the lesions and that choline prevented regurgitation by stimulation of the smooth muscle of the intestine.[268]

Abdon and Borglin reported that an impairment of oxidative metabolism was an early symptom of choline deficiency in rats. The *in vitro* oxygen consumption of minced muscle tissue from deficient rats was not increased by choline or methionine but was returned to a normal value by an acetone-insoluble preparation of splenic tissue.[269] Olson and Deane noted decreased respiration of kidney slices during the acute phase of hemorrhagic degeneration.[16]

Dinning *et al.* demonstrated that leucopenia was present in rats maintained for 65 days on a diet low in methionine (0.27 %) and in B_{12} and containing a moderate level of choline (0.1 %). The interference with leucocyte formation was prevented by supplemental methionine with or without folic

[260] D. Vincent, S. Daum, and M. Bouchet, *Trav. membres soc. chim. biol.* **23,** 1363 (1941).

[261] M. G. Ritchey, L. F. Wicks, and E. L. Tatum, *J. Biol. Chem.* **171,** 51 (1947).

[262] A. C. Frazer, *Nature* **157,** 414 (1946).

[263] H. C. Tidwell, *J. Biol. Chem.* **182,** 405 (1950).

[264] H. D. Friedlander, I. L. Chaikoff, and C. Entenman, *J. Biol. Chem.* **158,** 231 (1945).

[265] H. Popper and H. Chinn, *Proc. Soc. Exptl. Biol. Med.* **49,** 202 (1942).

[266] A. Pederzini, *Boll. soc. ital. biol. sper.* **24,** 1146 (1948).

[267] G. R. Sharpless, *Proc. Soc. Exptl. Biol. Med.* **45,** 487 (1940).

[268] G. R. Sharpless and M. Sabol, *J. Nutrition* **25,** 113 (1943).

[269] N. O. Abdon and N. E. Borglin, *Nature* **158,** 793 (1946); **159,** 272 (1947); *Acta Pharmacol. Toxicol.* **3,** 73 (1947).

acid and B_{12}, or by additional choline or betaine with supplements of folic acid and B_{12}.[270] Later it was shown that leukemic mice excreted larger quantities of creatine and allantoin than normal animals[271] and that this was the result of increased synthesis of creatine.[272] Kelley et al. caused marked leucocytosis in rats by feeding excessive levels of glycine (10 %) and choline (2 %). Riboflavin and folic acid were essential for this effect.[273]

Chèvremont concluded that choline was responsible for spontaneous transformation of cells of cultures of skeletal muscle or of subcutaneous connective tissue into histiocytes.[274] The change of muscle cells into histiocytes, believed to be caused by high concentration of choline, was observed also by Firket and Cornil.[275]

Abdon and Borglin observed bradycardia in choline-deficient rats, which disappeared quickly following intravenous administrations of choline.[276] Choline restored to normal an increased level of pseudocholinesterase in male rats and a decreased level in female rats.[277]

Guggenheim and Olson determined the specific activity of tissue fatty acids after administration of carboxyl-labeled acetate and were unable to find evidence of impaired lipogenesis in choline-deficient rats.[278] Deuel et al. showed that the lipotropic activity of choline was not due to an increased rate of oxidation of fat.[279] The deposition of vitamin A in the livers of depleted rats was not affected by choline deficiency or by the presence of a fatty liver.[280] Impaired metabolism of carbohydrate and of fat, as well as functional damage to liver cells, decreased the hepatic synthesis of choline.[281] Elevated environmental temperature increased the choline requirement of rats.[282] The report that choline deficiency resulted in a loss of contractility of the uterus and partial atrophy of both uterus and ovaries in rats[283] has not

[270] J. S. Dinning, L. D. Payne, and P. L. Day, Arch. Biochem. 27, 467 (1950); J. Nutrition 43, 525 (1951).
[271] J. S. Dinning and L. D. Seager, Science 114, 2967 (1951).
[272] J. S. Dinning, L. D. Seager, L. D. Payne, and J. R. Totter, Science 116, 121 (1952).
[273] B. Kelley, M. Northrup, and P. D. Hurley, Proc. Soc. Exptl. Biol. Med. 76, 804 (1951).
[274] M. Chèvremont, J. Morphol. 76, 139 (1945).
[275] J. Firket and A. Cornil, Compt. rend. soc. biol. 139, 51 (1945).
[276] N. O. Abdon and N. E. Borglin, Acta Pharmacol. Toxicol. 2, 247 (1946).
[277] R. D. Hawkins and M. T. Nishikawara, Biochem. J. 48, 276 (1951).
[278] K. Guggenheim and R. E. Olson, J. Nutrition 48, 345 (1952).
[279] H. J. Deuel, Jr., S. Murray, L. F. Hallman, and D. B. Tyler, J. Biol. Chem. 120, 277 (1937).
[280] L. S. Bentley and A. F. Morgan, J. Nutrition 31, 333 (1946).
[281] H. K. Barrenscheen and D. Papadopoulou, Hople-Seyler's Z. physiol. Chem. 284, 236 (1949).
[282] C. A. Mills, Proc. Soc. Exptl. Biol. Med. 54, 265 (1943).
[283] M. Peet and M. M. Sampson, Science 107, 548 (1948).

been confirmed.[284] Sure concluded that choline was indispensable for lactation and growth in rats.[285] Rustiness of the hair was produced by omission of either choline or pantothenic acid from the diet.[286] On the other hand, so-called bronzing of the hair in young rats was ascribed to the choline intake and was prevented by dietary yeast or by the presence of dextrin in the ration.[287] Dietary choline prevented toxic effects of excess methionine.[288]

6. Fate of Choline

The data of Luecke and Pearson may be cited as confirmatory evidence of the conclusion of earlier investigators[289, 290] that administered choline and betaine disappear rapidly.[291] Of 10 to 20 g. of choline administered to sheep, only 1 % was recovered in the urine during a 48-hour period, an equal amount was found in the feces, and no accumulation was detected in liver, kidney, or blood. Similar results were found in dogs. No excretion of betaine followed the ingestion of 20 g. of this substance in a sheep. Davies showed that 14 to 43 % of the nitrogen of choline and of betaine in the diet of cows was excreted as trimethylamine oxide.[292] Small amounts of trimethylamine and traces of the di- and monomethylamines were found. Davies noted that cattle fed sugar beet by-products consumed as much as 100 g. of betaine daily without the excretion of detectable amounts. It is probable that trimethylamine is the result of the action of intestinal microorganisms on choline or betaine,[293] inasmuch as many organisms are known to have this effect.[294-296] Whether or not animal tissues also form trimethylamine needs further study. This substance was identified as a product of *in vitro* metabolism in liver slices, but the sterility of the system was not demonstrated.[297] The rapid disappearance of repeated sublethal doses of choline in rats and mice was reported by Kahane *et al.*[298]

[284] C. P. Kraatz and C. M. Gruber, *Science* **109**, 310 (1949).
[285] B. Sure, *J. Nutrition* **19**, 71 (1940).
[286] H. S. Owens, M. Trautman, and E. Woods, *Science* **93**, 406 (1941).
[287] G. M. Higgins, O. R. Joneson, and F. C. Mann, *Proc. Staff Meetings Mayo Clinic* **20**, 320 (1945).
[288] J. S. Roth and J. B. Allison, *J. Biol. Chem.* **183**, 173 (1950).
[289] M. Guggenheim and W. Löffler, *Biochem. Z.* **74**, 208 (1916).
[290] H. Fuchs, *Z. Biol.* **98**, 473 (1938).
[291] R. W. Luecke and P. B. Pearson, *J. Biol. Chem.* **158**, 561 (1944).
[292] W. L. Davies, *J. Dairy Sci.* **7**, 14 (1936).
[293] E. R. Norris and G. J. Benoit, Jr., *J. Biol. Chem.* **158**, 443 (1945).
[294] D. Ackermann and H. Schütze, *Zentr. Physiol.* **24**, 210 (1910).
[295] A. J. Wood and F. E. Keeping, *J. Bacteriol.* **47**, 309 (1944).
[296] G. N. Cohen, B. Nisman, and M. Raynaud, *Compt. rend.* **225**, 647 (1947).
[297] C. Artom and M. Crowder, *Arch. Biochem.* **29**, 227 (1950).
[298] E. Kahane, J. Lévy, R. Bourgeois, and O. Tanguy, *Arch. sci. physiol. (Italy)* **4**, 173 (1950).

A most extensive study of the urinary excretion of choline in rats and in man has been carried out by Borglin.[299] The output in the urine of rats varied with the intake and amounted to 0.27 to 0.44 % of the choline in the food. The dietary choline was the principal factor governing excretion, the presence or absence of other sources of methyl, of protein, and of fat having relatively little effect.

The oxidation of methyl groups of choline to carbon dioxide has been noted previously, and it is reasonable to assume that the nitrogen of the demethylated choline or betaine is excreted as urea. There is some question regarding the fate of administered trimethylamine. Davies reported the quantitative excretion of this compound and of its oxide as the oxide in the cow.[292] Langley, however, recovered only 20 % of the trimethylamine given to rabbits; the remainder of the nitrogen was believed to be excreted as urea.[300]

C. AVIAN SPECIES

WENDELL H. GRIFFITH and JOSEPH F. NYC

The primary effects of a deficiency of choline in chicks are interference with growth and the appearance of perosis or "slipped tendon disease." This characteristic abnormality is influenced by multiple factors but, if caused by a lack of choline, is prevented readily by supplements of choline or of compounds with specific choline activity. There is gross enlargement of the tibial-metatarsal joint, twisting or bending of the distal portion of the tibia and of the proximal end of the metatarsus, and slipping of the gastrocnemius tendon from its condyles. If this occurs in severe form, the chick is incapacitated. Until 1940 a lack of manganese was considered the principal cause of perosis.[301] In this year Jukes demonstrated that in certain diets, adequate in manganese, choline was an effective antiperotic and growth-stimulating agent.[302] This unexpected finding was soon confirmed in a number of laboratories.[303-305]

An understanding of the relation of choline to the prevention of perosis is complicated by the fact that the abnormality is aggravated by creatine,[306]

[299] N. E. Borglin, *Acta Pharmacol. Toxicol.* **3** *Suppl.* **1** (1947).

[300] W. D. Langley, *J. Biol. Chem.* **84,** 561 (1929).

[301] H. S. Wilgus, L. C. Norris, and G. F. Heuser, *J. Nutrition* **14,** 155 (1937).

[302] T. H. Jukes, *J. Nutrition* **20,** 445 (1940).

[303] A. G. Hogan, L. R. Richardson, H. Patrick, and H. L. Kempster, *J. Nutrition* **21,** 327 (1941).

[304] D. M. Hegsted, R. C. Mills, C. A. Elvehjem, and E. B. Hart, *J. Biol. Chem.* **138,** 459 (1941).

[305] P. R. Record and R. M. Bethke, *Poultry Sci.* **21,** 271 (1942).

[306] T. H. Jukes, *Proc. Soc. Exptl. Biol. Med.* **46,** 155 (1941).

by glycine,[307, 308] and by gelatin.[302, 307, 309] Briggs showed that 10 % gelatin in chick diets increased the need of niacin and might cause niacin deficiency.[310] This effect was counteracted by either niacin or tryptophan. Perosis caused by egg white injury[311] was prevented by biotin.[312] In so far as choline is concerned, its antiperotic effect does not necessarily depend on the same deficiency state in which its growth-stimulating action is evident. In choline-deficient chicks neither methionine[305, 307] nor betaine[302, 307] was antiperotic unless the diet contained mono- or dimethylaminoethanol. This is due to the fact that the chick is practically unable to convert aminoethanol into monomethylaminoethanol.[313, 314] On the other hand, arsenocholine is strongly antiperotic and growth-promoting,[302, 315] even though it does not cause the methylation of homocystcinc.[316] This analog of choline is known to be incorporated into the lecithin molecule,[317] and it is a fair assumption that this occurs in the chick also. From the data in Tables III to VI it is evident that antiperosis in choline-deficient chicks is a function of choline, possibly in phospholipid form, and not a general function of sources of labile methyl. In this connection it should be noted that 4 and 9 %, respectively, of the tagged methyl of C^{14}-methyl-labeled methionine were found in tissue choline isolated from 2 chicks 48 hours after the feeding of amino acid.[318] This is not conclusive evidence of transmethylation, even at a relatively slow rate, because the labeled choline may have resulted from the methylation of dietary dimethylaminoethanol through C^{14}-formate resulting from the partial oxidation of the labeled methionine methyl.

For normal growth chick rations must contain 1.1 % of methionine, one-half of which may be replaced by cystine.[319] Homocystine can be substituted for cystine and for methionine also if the supply of methyl donors is adequate. Choline and betaine are suitable donors.

The requirement of chicks for choline has been reported as 150 and 100 mg. %, respectively, for a diet of natural foodstuffs[305] and for a purified diet.[304] The allowance recommended by the Committee on Animal Nutri-

[307] T. H. Jukes, J. Nutrition 22, 315 (1941).
[308] T. H. Jukes, and E. L. R. Stokstad, J. Nutrition 43, 459 (1951); 48, 209 (1952).
[309] H. L. Lucas, L. C. Norris, and G. F. Heuser, Poultry Sci. 25, 93 (1946).
[310] G. M. Briggs, J. Biol. Chem. 161, 749 (1945).
[311] L. W. McElroy and T. H. Jukes, Proc. Soc. Exptl. Biol. Med. 45, 296 (1940).
[312] T. H. Jukes and F. H. Bird, Proc. Soc. Exptl. Biol. Med. 49, 231 (1942).
[313] A. E. Schaefer, W. D. Salmon, and D. R. Strength, J. Nutrition 44, 305 (1951).
[314] T. H. Jukes, J. J. Oleson, and A. C. Dornbush, J. Nutrition 30, 219 (1945).
[315] T. H. Jukes and A. D. Welch, J. Biol. Chem. 146, 19 (1942).
[316] H. J. Almquist and T. H. Jukes, Proc. Soc. Exptl. Biol. Med. 51, 243 (1942).
[317] A. D. Welch and R. L. Landau, J. Biol. Chem. 144, 581 (1942).
[318] K. A. Burke, R. F. Nystrom, and B. C. Johnson, J. Biol. Chem. 188, 723 (1951).
[319] C. R. Grau and H. J. Almquist, J. Nutrition 26, 631 (1943).

tion of the National Research Council is 130 mg. %.[320] For diets containing homocystine in place of methionine, 60 mg. % of betaine-irreplaceable and 140 mg. % of betaine-replaceable choline are required, according to Almquist.[321] Minimum levels of methionine and of irreplaceable choline were reported as 500 and 100 mg. %, respectively, by McKittrick.[322] West et al. found 100 mg. % of choline adequate if ample methionine was provided.[323] The growth-depressing action of excess methionine in chick diets was counteracted by guanidoacetic acid and by serine but not by decreasing dietary cystine. Excess homocystine did not depress growth unless choline was also present. McKittrick also noted that betaine was a satisfactory replacement of part but not of all the choline requirement.

Although the significance of betaine-replaceable choline in the chick is not readily apparent in view of the reported failure of betaine to show antiperotic activity, the distinction between the two parts of the choline requirement has emphasized the role of B_{12} in this phase of avian metabolism. Patton et al. noted a beneficial growth effect of fish meal in chick diets composed mainly of corn and soybean oil meal.[324] Choline, betaine, and methionine were also reported to have an interchangeable supplementary effect in the improvement of the corn-soybean ration.[325, 326] Gillis and Norris found liver paste superior to supplements of choline or betaine and later obtained similar results with B_{12} in place of liver paste.[327] Schaefer et al. reported that both folic acid and B_{12} decreased the choline requirement for growth.[184, 328] Jukes and Stokstad demonstrated that B_{12} spared the choline requirement for growth but not for prevention of perosis.[308] The response to homocystine in the presence of B_{12} was augmented by the addition of either choline or betaine. However, a supplement of methionine has been reported to decrease the B_{12} requirement of chicks on a diet lacking animal protein.[329] Methyla-

[320] W. W. Cravens, H. J. Almquist, R. M. Bethke, L. C. Norris, and H. W. Titus, Recommended Nutrient Allowances for Poultry, National Research Council (U.S.), Washington, D. C., 1944, revised 1946.

[321] H. J. Almquist, Science 103, 722 (1946).

[322] D. S. McKittrick, Arch. Biochem. 15, 133 (1947); 18, 437 (1948).

[323] J. W. West, C. W. Carrick, S. M. Hauge, and E. T. Mertz, Poultry Sci. 30, 880 (1951).

[324] A. R. Patton, J. P. Marvel, H. G. Petering, and J. Waddell, J. Nutrition 31, 485 (1946).

[325] J. A. Marvel, C. W. Carrick, R. E. Roberts, and S. M. Hauge, Poultry Sci. 23, 294 (1944).

[326] D. H. Mishler, C. W. Carrick, and S. M. Hauge, Poultry Sci. 28, 24 (1949).

[327] M. B. Gillis and L. C. Norris, J. Biol. Chem. 179, 487 (1949); Poultry Sci. 28, 749 (1949).

[328] A. E. Schaefer, W. D. Salmon, and D. R. Strength, Proc. Soc. Exptl. Biol. Med. 71, 202 (1949).

[329] G. M. Briggs, E. G. Hill, and M. J. Giles, Poultry Sci. 29, 723 (1950).

tion of mono-and dimethylaminoethanol in chicks fed betaine did not occur unless B_{12} was present.[313]

Contrary to the results of others, McGinnis *et al.* found methionine and betaine effective antiperotic agents in certain diets, but this result was not obtained if more highly purified diets were employed.[330] In later experiments, Gillis and Norris observed the same stimulation of growth by betaine and by choline if the B_{12} stores were normal but inferior growth with choline if the B_{12} stores were low.[331] The absence of an effect of B_{12} on the utilization of betaine was also demonstrated by the equal stimulation of growth of B_{12}-deficient chicks by methionine and by homocystine plus betaine.[332]

Thus, the interrelationships of choline, betaine, and B_{12} in the chick are not clear. Gillis and Norris do not believe that B_{12} is concerned with the conversion of choline to betaine by choline oxidase because no evidence was found of a decreased content of this enzyme in the livers of B_{12}-deficient chicks.[331] They concluded that at least one mechanism by which the chick uses choline is impaired by a deficiency of B_{12} whereas betaine remains effective under the same conditions.

The depression of choline oxidase in the bone marrow[200] and liver[333] of chicks deficient in folic acid and the reduction of this enzyme in the bone marrow of hens exposed to x-irradiation[334] have been mentioned previously. Choline oxidase in the livers of chick embryos was decreased by folic acid fed to the mother hen whereas much less reduction occurred if folic acid was injected directly into the egg during or prior to incubation.[335] Conflicting evidence has been presented regarding the need of dietary choline by pullets and older hens. Abbott and DeMasters reported increased egg production with dietary choline,[336] but no significant differences in this respect or in hatchability, fertility, or body weight were noted by Lucas *et al.*[337] Hatchability was not improved in the study of Bethke *et al.*[338] Ringrose and Davis likewise found no change in egg production with added choline. It was noted in the latter experiments that twice as much choline was present in the egg yolks as was present in the diet.[339] Total blood cholesterol and cholesterol ester and the levels of these components of aorta, heart

---

[330] J. McGinnis, L. C. Norris, and G. F. Heuser, *Proc. Soc. Exptl. Biol. Med.* **56**, 197 (1944).

[331] M. B. Gillis and L. C. Norris, *J. Nutrition* **43**, 295 (1951).

[332] M. B. Gillis and L. C. Norris, *Proc. Soc. Exptl. Biol. Med.* **77**, 13 (1951).

[333] J. S. Dinning, C. K. Keith, and P. L. Day, *J. Biol. Chem.* **189**, 515 (1951).

[334] J. S. Dinning, I. Meschan, C. K. Keith, and P. L. Day, *Proc. Soc. Exptl. Biol. Med.* **74**, 776 (1950).

[335] J. N. Williams, Jr., M. L. Sunde, W. W. Cravens, and C. A. Elvehjem, *J. Biol. Chem.* **185**, 895 (1950).

[336] O. D. Abbott and C. U. DeMasters, *J. Nutrition* **19**, 47 (1940).

[337] H. L. Lucas, L. C. Norris, and G. F. Heuser, *Poultry Sci.* **25**, 373 (1946).

[338] R. M. Bethke, D. C. Kennard, and V. D. Chamberlin, *Poultry Sci.* **25**, 579 (1946).

[339] R. C. Ringrose and H. A. Davis, *Poultry Sci.* **25**, 646 (1946).

muscle, and liver have been reported by Herrmann to be reduced by supplements of 0.5 g. of choline chloride daily in the diet of old laying hens.[340]

Ducklings require choline for growth and for prevention of perosis[341, 342] and of fatty infiltration of the liver.[342] Betaine was not found to be antiperotic or growth-stimulating, nor was methionine lipotropic in this species.[342]

Young turkeys require choline, and the effects of a deficiency are similar to those in the chick. Perosis is produced more easily, severe symptoms appearing without the presence in the diet of aggravating materials such as creatine, gelatin, or glycine. The antiperotic requirement of choline in poults is greater than the requirement for growth.[302, 343-347] Methionine has no activity, although it is indispensable in the ration of the turkey.[348] As in the chick, arsenocholine is antiperotic, but betaine[302] and creatine[348] have been reported ineffective. Scott[347] and McGinnis,[349] however, have observed that betaine has a considerable degree of antiperosis if some choline is present in the diet. Scott also found that creatine and sarcosine are as active as betaine. This is an interesting finding in view of the demonstration that choline was never completely effective as an antiperotic agent in diets lacking animal protein unless either betaine or relatively high levels of glycine and B_{12} were provided. According to Kratzer the effectiveness of choline for growth was increased by B_{12} but its antiperotic activity was decreased, and the possibility was suggested that more choline was used in growth and less in antiperosis in the presence of B_{12}.[350] Betaine caused only a small increase in growth and did not prevent perosis on a low choline diet. Biotin and an unidentified organic substance[351] and niacin[352] are believed to be the contributing factors which with choline prevent perosis in the poult.

D. DOG

WENDELL H. GRIFFITH and JOSEPH F. NYC

Choline is important in canine nutrition although it may be partly dispensable in certain diets containing adequate levels of factors such as B_{12},

[340] G. R. Herrmann, *Proc. Soc. Exptl. Biol. Med.* **61,** 302 (1946).
[341] A. Roos, D. M. Hegsted, and F. J. Stare, *J. Nutrition* **32,** 473 (1946).
[342] R. Bernard and J. M. Demers, *J. Cancer Research* **27E,** 281 (1949).
[343] T. H. Jukes, *J. Biol. Chem.* **134,** 789 (1940).
[344] M. Rhian, *Wash. Agr. Expt. Sta. Bull.* **410,** 33 (1941).
[345] R. J. Evans, M. Rhian, and C. I. Draper, *Poultry Sci.* **22,** 88 (1943).
[346] R. J. Evans, *Poultry Sci.* **22,** 266 (1943).
[347] M. L. Scott, *J. Nutrition* **40,** 611 (1950).
[348] T. H. Jukes, *Poultry Sci.* **20,** 251 (1941).
[349] J. McGinnis, *Poultry Sci.* **25,** 91 (1946).
[350] F. H. Kratzer, *J. Nutrition* **48,** 201 (1952).
[351] H. Patrick, R. V. Boucher, R. A. Dutcher, and H. C. Knandel, *J. Nutrition* **26,** 197 (1943).
[352] G. M. Briggs, *J. Nutrition* **31,** 79 (1946).

as appears to be the case in the rat. Fouts produced a severe deficiency in
dogs which was characterized by loss of weight, anemia, dermal and peptic
ulcers, fatty cirrhotic livers, and death, and which responded to the combined administration of choline and liver extract.[353] It was also apparent
that choline is one of the nutrients essential for growth and for hemoglobin
production in young dogs.[354, 355] Hough *et al.* observed a decrease in hepatic
dye clearance and an elevation of serum phosphatase in puppies and in
adult dogs on choline-deficient diets.[356] Both manifestations of impaired
liver function were prevented or reversed by choline. McKibbin *et al.* developed a ration which produced fatal choline deficiency in 3 weeks or less
in puppies.[357, 358] In addition to decreased bromosulfalein elimination and
increased plasma phosphatase, a fall in plasma cholesterol and in its ester,
and increase in prothrombin time, and decreases in hemoglobin, hemato-
crit, and plasma proteins were noted. Total lipids in the liver increased
markedly. In an extensive analysis of the tissues of normal and choline-
deficient puppies,[359] little or no change was found in the lipids of the cerebrum, spleen, pancreas, kidney, heart, and lungs, but a marked shift in
the pattern of the liver and plasma lipids was evident. In the liver this was
characterized by a decrease in choline and by an increase in sphingosine and
in other undetermined nitrogenous components of lipids, although the total
phospholipids were unchanged. In the plasma there was a marked decrease
in total phospholipids. The data suggested that sphingomyelins were replacing lecithins, but the percentage of choline phospholipids in the plasma
remained the same. Schaefer *et al.* were able to produce chronic choline deficiency in dogs which was characterized by cirrhotic livers, edema, and
duodenal ulcers.[360] The protective level of choline was halved by administration of B_{12}. Burns and McKibbin also observed this effect of B_{12} and
noted that liver impairment in some puppies was prevented completely
by B_{12} alone.[361]

Chaikoff and coworkers have studied the mechanisms by which choline
exerts its lipotropic activity in dogs by means of determinations of the

[353] P. J. Fouts, *J. Nutrition* **25,** 217 (1943).
[354] W. R. Ruegamer, L. Michaud, C. A. Elvehjem, and E. B. Hart, *Am. J. Physiol.*
145, 23 (1945).
[355] A. E. Schaefer, J. M. McKibbin, and C. A. Elvehjem, *Proc. Soc. Exptl. Biol. Med.*
47, 365 (1941).
[356] V. H. Hough, E. P. Monahan, T. W. Li, and S. Freeman, *Am. J. Physiol.* **139,** 642
(1943).
[357] J. M. McKibbin, S. Thayer, and F. J. Stare, *J. Lab. Clin. Med.* **29,** 1109 (1944).
[358] J. M. McKibbin, R. M. Ferry, Jr., S. Thayer, E. G. Patterson, and F. J. Stare,
J. Lab. Clin. Med. **30,** 422 (1945).
[359] J. M. McKibbin and W. E. Taylor, *J. Biol. Chem.* **185,** 357 (1950).
[360] A. E. Schaefer, D. H. Copeland, and W. D. Salmon, *J. Nutrition* **43,** 201 (1951).
[361] M. M. Burns and J. M. McKibbin, *J. Nutrition* **44,** 487 (1951).

turnover rate of phosphorus-containing compounds after the administration of P^{32}. Single feedings of choline increased the activity of the choline-containing phospholipids.[362] Measurements on samples of blood and on liver biopsy specimens after the administration of choline and of P^{32} led to the conclusion that the removal of liver fat under the influence of choline does not involve increased transport of fat from liver to peripheral tissues via plasma phospholipids.[363] No increase in the calculated turnover rates of plasma lecithin or sphingomyelin was found, contrary to a previous conclusion on this point.[264] However, determinations of rates of disappearance of these two phospholipids from plasma showed that the turnover rate of lecithin was five times as great as that of sphingomyelin.[364] It was suggested that choline acts on the utilization of fat within the liver itself and that glycerylphosphoric acid is a precursor of lecithin.[363] The greater activity of liver lecithin phosphorus than that of cephalin rules out the possibility of synthesis of lecithin by the methylation of cephalin.

Liver lipids were unchanged after hypophysectomy even though the dogs were observed as long as 32 months.[365] Thyroidectomy, however, resulted in fatty livers. The increase in lipids was more rapid and of greater magnitude in force-fed dogs if both thyroid and hypophysis were removed. The hepatic changes were prevented for the most part by choline, but this substance did not prevent an increase in blood lipids.

Davis has reported a depression of cobalt-induced polycythemia in dogs by choline[366] and has extended his findings to the involvement of choline in an experimental anemia and in pathological changes in the nervous system related to changes observed in pernicious anemia.[367, 368] This effect of choline, ascribed by Davis to a vasodilator action on bone marrow arterioles with a resulting decrease in hematopoiesis,[369] has not been confirmed.[370] Choline was ineffective in reducing arteriosclerotic lesions in dogs fed a diet containing added cholesterol and thiouracil.[371] A limited beneficial action of choline was observed in dogs with fat emboli produced by bone marrow curettage.[372] The latter study was prompted by the finding that the

[362] C. Entenman, I. L. Chaikoff, and H. D. Friedlander, *J. Biol. Chem.* **162**, 111 (1946).
[363] D. B. Zilversmit, C. Entenman, and I. L. Chaikoff, *J. Biol. Chem.* **176**, 193 (1948).
[364] D. B. Zilversmit, C. Entenman, and I. L. Chaikoff, *J. Biol. Chem.* **176**, 209 (1948).
[365] C. Entenman, I. L. Chaikoff, and F. L. Reichert, *Endocrinology* **42**, 210 (1948);
      C. Entenman, I. L. Chaikoff, F. L. Reichert, and T. Gillman, *ibid.* **42**, 215 (1948).
[366] J. E. Davis, *Am. J. Physiol.* **127**, 322 (1939); *J. Pharmacol.* **70**, 408 (1940).
[367] J. E. Davis and D. E. Fletcher, *J. Pharmacol.* **88**, 246 (1946).
[368] J. E. Davis, *Science* **105**, 43 (1947).
[369] J. E. Davis, *Am. J. Physiol.* **142**, 65 (1944).
[370] M. F. Clarkson and C. H. Best, *Science* **105**, 622 (1947).
[371] J. D. Davidson, W. Meyer, and F. E. Kendall, *Circulation* **3**, 332 (1951).
[372] E. M. Monson and C. Dennis, *Proc. Soc. Exptl. Biol. Med.* **70**, 330 (1949).

fat content of human bone marrow was decreased markedly following the intravenous administration of choline.[373]

Interest in choline as an anti-fatty liver factor originated with the first experiments designed to test whether the administration of insulin was sufficient to replace the internal secretion of the pancreas in depancreatized dogs.[374, 375] The manner in which these studies led to the recognition of the lipotropic activity of choline has been described in Section IV, p. 19. In 1936 Dragstedt and coworkers published the first of a series of papers on lipocaic, a factor believed to be a true hormonal product of the pancreas and involved in lipid metabolism in the liver.[212, 376-379] Fatty infiltration and degeneration, the hepatic changes in depancreatized dogs, were not observed in animals after ligation of the pancreatic ducts or after preparation of total pancreatic fistulae. Pancreatic juice was ineffective, if administered orally. Choline was not believed to be the main protective agent because the potency of raw pancreas was considered much greater than its content of choline. For these reasons Dragstedt concluded that the external digestive secretion of the pancreas was not an important factor. This latter finding has not been confirmed. Ralli et al. were unable to find any difference between the fatty changes in the livers of dogs after pancreatectomy and after ligation of the ducts,[380] and Best and Ridout could find no satisfactory evidence for lipocaic as a second pancreatic hormone.[215] This problem was reinvestigated by Chaikoff and coworkers, who arrived at the following conclusions: (a) a fraction can be prepared from the pancreas which is more protective than can be accounted for on the basis of its content of choline, although sufficient choline is as effective as the pancreatic fraction;[381] (b) ligation of the ducts does result in a fatty liver, and the liver changes are prevented by the oral administration of pancreatic juice;[382] (c) the fatty

[373] F. B. Moosnick, E. M. Schleicher, and W. E. Peterson, J. Clin. Invest. 24, 228 (1945).
[374] N. F. Fisher, Am. J. Physiol. 67, 634 (1924).
[375] F. N. Allan, D. J. Bowie, J. J. R. Macleod, and W. L. Robinson, Brit. J. Exptl. Pathol. 5, 75 (1924).
[376] J. Van Prohaska, L. R. Dragstedt, and H. P. Harms, Am. J. Physiol. 117, 166, 175 (1936).
[377] W. C. Goodpasture, C. W. Vermeulen, P. B. Donovan, and L. R. Dragstedt, Am. J. Physiol. 124, 642 (1938).
[378] O. C. Julian, D. E. Clark, J. Van Prohaska, C. Vermeulen, and L. R. Dragstedt, Am. J. Physiol. 138, 264 (1942–43).
[379] J. G. Allen, C. Vermeulen, F. M. Owens, Jr., and L. R. Dragstedt, Am. J. Physiol. 138, 352 (1942–43).
[380] E. P. Ralli, S. H. Rubin, and C. H. Present, Am. J. Physiol. 122, 43 (1938).
[381] C. Entenman and I. L. Chaikoff, J. Biol. Chem. 138, 477 (1941).
[382] I. L. Chaikoff, C. Entenman, and M. L. Montgomery, J. Biol. Chem. 160, 387 (1945).

changes that occur in the livers of pancreatectomized or of duct-ligated dogs can be prevented by the feeding of pancreas, pancreatic extracts, methionine, choline, or merely by substituting hydrolyzed casein for the casein of the basal diet;[383] and, (d) trypsin is a possible factor that ensures the liberation of methionine from dietary protein.[384] In view of this solution of the problem it is of interest that Ralli and Rubin had noted earlier that pancreatectomized dogs fed extracted meat powder did not develop fatty livers whereas those fed the untreated raw meat did so, a difference believed due to the greater digestibility of the meat powder.[385] Haanes and György have extended the results of Chaikoff by showing that a highly lipotropic pancreatic fraction without proteolytic activity actually contained trypsin and trypsin inhibitor and that the inhibitor was overcome by enterokinase in duodenal juice.[386] Even though these data represent substantial support for the enzymatic nature of lipocaic, it is possible that other lipotropic substances may occur in pancreas. Schilling et al. have reported the presence in preparations of lipocaic of a non-enzymatic, heat-stable lipotropic material.[387, 388]

E. OTHER SPECIES

WENDELL H. GRIFFITH and JOSEPH F. NYC

An increase in liver fat and an abnormality of gait without retardation of growth were reported in swine after the feeding of a low choline ration.[389] Choline has been found necessary, in addition to pantothenic acid and pyridoxine, for protection of pigs from locomotor incoordination resulting from nerve degeneration.[390] Poor reproduction, lactation, and survival of young resulted from feeding sows a choline-deficient ration.[391] Baby pigs fed a synthetic diet low in choline but containing 0.8 % methionine showed gross symptoms of unthriftiness, were short-legged and pot-bellied, lacked coordination of movements and the normal rigidity of joints, and exhibited fatty infiltration of the liver, characteristic renal glomerular occlusion, and

[383] I. L. Chaikoff, C. Entenman, and M. L. Montgomery, J. Biol. Chem. **168,** 177 (1947).
[384] M. L. Montgomery, C. Entenman, I. L. Chaikoff, and H. Feinberg, J. Biol. Chem. **185,** 307 (1950).
[385] E. P. Ralli and S. H. Rubin, Am. J. Physiol. **138,** 42 (1942–1943).
[386] M. L. Haanes and P. György, Am. J. Physiol. **166,** 441 (1951).
[387] K. Schilling, 1st Intern. Congr. Biochem. Abstr. Communs. (Cambridge, Engl.) p. 15 (1949).
[388] P. Bruun, H. Dam, and K. Schilling, Acta Physiol. Scand. **20,** 319 (1950).
[389] M. M. Wintrobe, M. H. Miller, R. H. Follis, Jr., H. J. Stein, C. Mushatt, and S. Humphreys, J. Nutrition **24,** 345 (1942).
[390] N. R. Ellis, L. L. Madsen, and C. O. Miller, J. Animal. Sci. **2,** 365 (1943).
[391] M. E. Ensminger, J. P. Bowland, and T. J. Cunha, J. Animal Sci. **6,** 409 (1947).

some tubular epithelial necrosis.[392, 393] No growth effect was noted if the food intake was equalized. Doubling of the methionine content of the artificial milk was effective in the prevention of these symptoms,[394] and it is evident that the pig does not lack the ability to methylate aminoethanol if labile methyl is available in diets otherwise adequate.

The need of choline by newborn calves fed a choline-deficient, artificial milk was demonstrated by Johnson et al.[395] After 7 days an acute syndrome developed which was characterized by marked weakness, labored or rapid breathing, and anorexia. Certain of the calves showed evidences of renal hemorrhage and fatty liver. These effects were prevented by choline, although subsequent removal of the choline supplement was not injurious. Earlier studies by Waugh et al.[396] had emphasized the importance to the calf of the relatively high concentration of choline in colostrum and the relation of this fact to the level of choline in the blood of the calf. A decrease in blood choline was noted in calves, 5 weeks of age, following the removal of milk from the diet, although restoration of the choline level was not obtained by dietary supplements of choline.

Evidence of choline deficiency in rabbits is lacking, but experiments on the young have not yet been reported. Hypercholesteremia and aortic atherosclerosis were not prevented by choline in the study by Firstbrook,[397] but others have concluded that choline does have a beneficial effect in the prevention or removal of this induced abnormality in rabbits.[398-400] Sprunt concluded that subcutaneously administered choline inhibited the susceptibility of the rabbit to infection with vaccinia,[401] and a transitory decrease in red cells has been observed following the administration of choline in rabbits rendered polycythemic by cobalt.[402] Transmethylation occurs in this species as evidenced by the isolation of labeled choline, creatine, anserine, and creatinine, after the feeding of deuteriomethionine.[403]

A deficiency of choline or of methyl has not been demonstrated in the

[392] B. C. Johnson and M. F. James, J. Nutrition 36, 339 (1948).

[393] A. L. Neumann, J. L. Krider, M. F. James, and B. C. Johnson, J. Nutrition 38, 195 (1949).

[394] R. O. Nesheim and B. C. Johnson, J. Nutrition 41, 149 (1950).

[395] B. C. Johnson, H. H. Mitchell, J. A. Pinkos, and C. C. Morrill, J. Nutrition 43, 37 (1951).

[396] R. K. Waugh, S. M. Hauge, and W. A. King, J. Dairy Sci. 30, 457, 641 (1947).

[397] J. B. Firstbrook, Proc. Soc. Exptl. Biol. Med. 74, 741 (1950).

[398] L. M. Morrison and A. Rossi, Proc. Soc. Exptl. Biol. Med. 69, 283 (1948).

[399] A. Steiner, Arch. Pathol. 45, 327 (1948).

[400] C. Moses and G. M. Longabaugh, Arch. Pathol. 50, 179 (1950).

[401] D. H. Sprunt, Proc. Soc. Exptl. Biol. Med. 51, 226 (1942).

[402] M. Saviano and V. Baccari, Arch. fisiol. 43, 243 (1943).

[403] J. R. Schneck, S. Simmonds, M. Cohn, C. M. Stevens, and V. du Vigneaud, J. Biol. Chem. 149, 355 (1943).

guinea pig, and this is correlated with the observation that the turnover of choline is relatively slow, owing presumably to the absence of choline oxidase in the liver of this species.[404] Handler found no accumulation of fat in the livers of guinea pigs fed seven different diets that did cause fatty livers in rats, even though guanidoacetic acid was added to the guinea pig diets.[405] Dubnoff and Borsook have reported the presence of an enzyme in the liver and kidney of this animal, as well as in these organs of the rat and hog, that transfers methyl from thetin to homocysteine.[406] The metabolism of choline in the guinea pig may differ only quantitatively from that in the rat inasmuch as Dubnoff has noted some methyl lability in guinea pigs following the administration of C^{14}-methyl-labeled choline.[407]

The mouse appears more resistant to choline deficiency than the rat, and it has been used relatively little in studies of transmethylation. The production of fatty livers was noted in Best's laboratory,[41] but the development of renal lesions in weanling mice has been found to occur only if a choline-deficient diet is eaten prior to weaning.[408] The presence or absence of choline did not affect the rate of disappearance of deuterium from either liver or depot fatty acids.[409]

Some evidence has been presented that choline decreases the acute liver destruction that occurs in rhesus monkeys inoculated with yellow fever virus.[410] Choline was required for normal lactation in the hamster.[411] Trout fed a choline-deficient diet showed renal degeneration and intestinal hemorrhage.[412] The omission of choline from an otherwise adequate synthetic diet resulted in complete growth failure and death in the cockroach, *Blatella germanica* L.[413, 414] Betaine was practically as effective as choline in the prevention of the deficiency. Choline is stated to be essential for the development of larvae of *Aedes aegypti*.[415]

[404] F. Bernheim and M. C. L. Bernheim, *Am. J. Physiol.* **104**, 438 (1933); **121**, 55 (1938).
[405] P. Handler, *Proc. Soc. Exptl. Biol. Med.* **70**, 70 (1949).
[406] J. W. Dubnoff and H. Borsook, *J. Biol. Chem.* **176**, 789 (1948).
[407] J. W. Dubnoff, *Arch. Biochem.* **22**, 474 (1949).
[408] E. A. White and L. R. Cerecedo, *Proc. Am. Chem. Soc.* **23B**, (1946).
[409] D. Stetten, Jr. and G. F. Grail, *J. Biol. Chem.* **148**, 509 (1943).
[410] A. W. Sellards and W. S. McCann, *U. S. Naval Med. Bull.* **43**, 420 (1944).
[411] J. W. Hamilton and A. G. Hogan, *J. Nutrition* **27**, 213 (1944).
[412] B. A. McLaren, E. B. Keller, D. J. O'Donnell, and C. A. Elvehjem, *Arch. Biochem.* **15**, 169 (1947).
[413] J. L. Noland and C. A. Baumann, *Proc. Soc. Exptl. Biol. Med.* **70**, 198 (1949).
[414] J. L. Noland, J. H. Lilly, and C. A. Baumann, *Ann. Entomol. Soc. Amer.* **42**, 154 (1949).
[415] W. Trager, *Proc. 29th Ann. Meeting New Jersey Mosquito Exterm. Assoc.*, p. 46 (1942).

F. MAN

W. STANLEY HARTROFT, COLIN C. LUCAS, and CHARLES H. BEST

Direct evidence of disease in man due to choline deficiency is still lacking, although two decades have elapsed since Best and Huntsman[416] demonstrated the lipotropic action of choline in the experimental animal. It has been suggested that, in such deficiency states as kwashiorkor, infantile cirrhosis, and related conditions in parts of the world where the nutritional status of much of the population is low, a deficiency of the lipotropic factors as well as of other vitamins, coupled with a low intake of poor protein, may be responsible in part for the lesions in liver, pancreas, and kidney. There are many references to this question in the recent literature,[417-421] but such a complex problem will not be discussed here. The clinician must await more direct evidence based on controlled therapeutic trials before he can properly assess the role of the lipotropic factors in these perplexing diseases. Experimental research in this field has now progressed sufficiently to justify attempts by physicians to provide clinical data to answer their own questions.

In contrast to our ignorance concerning the etiology of those hepatic disorders which are endemic in countries with extremely low standards of living, there is considerable evidence that the cirrhosis frequently encountered in cases of chronic alcoholism is the direct result of choline deficiency induced by the replacement of a large portion of the individual's food intake by alcohol—an alipotropic source of abundant calories. This conclusion is based on data obtained from animal experiments and also from a few clinical trials, which are understandably limited and incompletely controlled. In experiments conducted in this laboratory[422] an adequate supplement of choline prevented the development of fatty and fibrotic hepatic changes that occurred in rats given alcohol (15 %) in their drinking water. This confirmed the earlier investigations of Sebrell and his associates in the U. S. Public Health group.[423] In addition it was shown that in comparable paired-fed animals given an amount of sugar isocaloric with the alcohol consumed, identical lesions (Figs. 4 and 5) developed unless equal amounts of choline

[416] C. H. Best and M. E. Huntsman, *J. Physiol.* (*London*) **83**, 255–274 (1934–1935).

[417] J. N. P. Davies, *Trans. 9th Conf. Liver Injury, New York* pp. 151–200 (1950); *Lancet* **I**, 317–320 (1948).

[418] J. C. Waterlow, *Med. Research Council* (*Brit.*) *Spec. Rept. Ser.* **263**, 78 (1948).

[419] J. Gillman and T. Gillman, *Lancet* **I**, 169 (1948).

[420] V. Ramalingaswami, P. S. Menon, and P. S. Venkatachalam, *Indian Physician* **7**, 229–237 (1948).

[421] Kenneth R. Hill, *Trans. 10th Conf. Liver Injury, New York* pp. 263–320 (1951).

[422] C. H. Best, W. S. Hartroft, C. C. Lucas, and J. H. Ridout, *Brit. Med. J.* **II**, 1001–1006 (1949).

[423] F. S. Daft and W. H. Sebrell, *Publ. Health Repts.* (*U.S.*) **56**, 1255–1258 (1941).

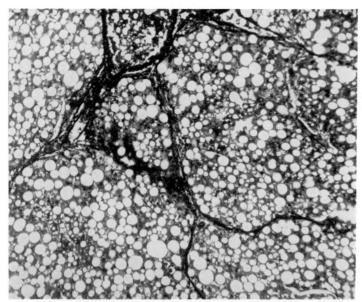

Fig. 4. Early fibrosis in the liver of a rat in which large amounts of fat had accumulated as a result of inducing a relative deficiency of choline by replacing the drinking water with 15% alcohol (see text). Paraffin section; hematoxylin and eosin stain; ×200. (Compare with Fig. 5.)

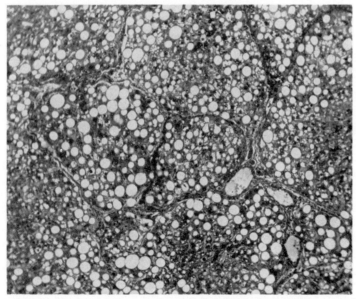

Fig. 5. Early fibrosis in the liver of a rat in which large amounts of fat had accumulated as a result of inducing a relative deficiency of choline by adding an amount of sucrose to the basal diet, isocaloric with the alcohol consumed by the group of rats illustrated in Fig. 4 (see text). Technical data as for Fig. 4.

or its precursors were added to the diet to compensate for the additional calories supplied by this amount of sucrose. These experiments indicate that the ratio of lipotropic factors to the total caloric intake must be above a certain critical level to protect the liver from harmful degrees of fat storage and its almost inevitable successor, fibrosis. If the caloric intake be raised by any means without a simultaneous increase in the lipotropes, the resulting disturbance of liver function may eventually produce as grievous

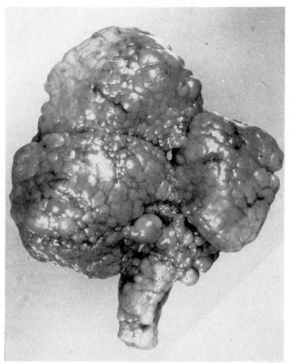

Fɪɢ. 6. Gross appearance of the liver of rat which had been maintained on a choline-deficient diet for approximately one year.

a result as the operation of an engine without adequate lubrication. Such an imbalance has been produced in animals by choline-deficient caloric increments supplied not only as carbohydrate and alcohol but also as fat or methionine-poor protein. Persistent addiction to excessive amounts of alcohol in man constitutes a fairly close clinical duplication of these experimental conditions, and it is a reasonable working hypothesis that cirrhosis of this type is due to choline deficiency.[424] It is possible also that the fatty

[424] It must be recognized, of course, that the alcoholic patient is probably suffering from multiple dietary deficiencies, involving not only the vitamins but also minerals and particularly proteins.

and fibrotic livers frequently associated with obesity[425] should be included in this category. Cases of gross obesity induced by chronic overindulgence in candy, desserts, and starchy foods are possibly due to a lowered choline/calorie ratio, but dietary histories are too inadequate to warrant more than a suggestion at present. Investigators are hampered by the fact that the glutton, like the drunkard, is frequently untruthful about his habitual overindulgence.

The hypothesis that alcoholic cirrhosis in man is the clinical counterpart

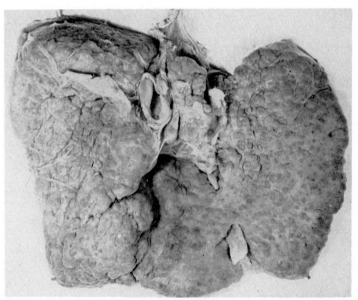

Fig. 7. Gross appearance of the liver of a man aged 39 years who had been addicted to alcohol for several years before his death. If one allows for the difference in size of this liver and that illustrated in Fig. 6, the characteristics of the cirrhotic lesions are remarkably similar.

of cirrhosis in choline-deficient animals might be less tenable if the histopathology of the two conditions were not essentially identical. The gross appearances of the livers are certainly remarkably similar (Figs. 6 and 7), but, although this is accepted by all investigators, there is lack of agreement concerning the similarity of the microscopic characteristics. It has been stated[426] that "This peculiar experimental hepatic cirrhosis of rats has no counterpart in the usually described varieties of hepatic cirrhosis in man,"

[425] S. Sherlock, A. G. Bearn, and B. Billing, *Trans. 10th Conf. Liver Injury, New York* pp. 205–262 (1951).
[426] R. D. Lillie, L. L. Ashburn, W. H. Sebrell, F. S. Daft, and J. V. Lowry, *Publ. Health Repts. (U.S.)* **57**, 502–508 (1942).

and that "This experimental cirrhosis is not identifiable with any of the previously described experimental toxogenic cirrhoses nor with any of the usual varieties of hepatic cirrhosis in man." If these statements were supported by the available facts, it would indeed be rash to assume that choline-deficiency cirrhosis in rats bears any true relation to alcoholic cirrhosis in man. But there is evidence that differences in the histopathology of the two lesions are more apparent than real, and that in fact they can be regarded as minor variants of a fundamentally identical pattern. The importance of this question in any discussion of the pathology of choline deficiency in man is self-evident, and it will therefore be considered in some detail.

Cirrhosis in choline-deficient rats has been said to differ from that in human alcoholics in the following essentials: (a) Usually there are abundant amounts of stainable fat in the cirrhotic rat's liver, whereas frequently little can be demonstrated in the alcoholic patient's liver at autopsy. (b) Ceroid is often deposited in the livers of choline-deficient rats,[426] whereas this pigment is absent or present in only small amounts in alcoholic cirrhosis.[426-429] (c) The cirrhosis of alcoholism is described as "portal"; that in choline-deficient rats as "non-portal." These points will be considered in turn.

1. STAINABLE FAT

Stainable fat in cirrhotic livers of alcoholics, although a common finding, is not constantly present at autopsy. This has been responsible for the concept that this type of cirrhosis may not have been preceded by fatty parenchymal change. Although stainable fat may be absent from the liver of an alcoholic at autopsy, there is much to suggest that abundant lipid might have been demonstrable at an earlier, more actively progressive stage in the development of the lesion. The fat content of cirrhotic livers at autopsy and in the animal experiments has been shown to be inversely proportional to the degree of fibrosis.[430, 431] This is true also for the experimental cirrhosis produced in rats by a dietary deficiency of choline.[432] In fact a stage may be reached in the rat where, even though the animal has been maintained continuously on the low choline diet, microscopic examination fails to reveal more than very small amounts of stainable fat in a liver that is grossly cirrhotic (see Fig.10). This indicates that much of the abnormal lipid that accumulates in the liver must eventually escape or disappear even in the absence of choline. The pathways by which this occurs may be abnormal and involve the biliary and vascular systems.[433]

[427] A. M. Pappenheimer and J. Victor, *Am. J. Pathol.* **22**, 395–412 (1946).
[428] H. Popper, P. György, and H. Goldblatt, *Arch. Pathol.* **37**, 161–168 (1944).
[429] W. S. Hartroft, *Proc. Roy. College Phys. Surg. (Canada)* pp. 120–138 (1949).
[430] C. L. Connor, *Am. J. Pathol.* **14**, 347–364 (1938).
[431] I. L. Chaikoff, C. L. Connor, and G. R. Biskind, *Am. J. Pathol.* **14**, 101–110 (1938).
[432] C. C. Lucas, J. H. Ridout, and W. S. Hartroft, Unpublished data (1952).
[433] W. S. Hartroft and J. H. Ridout, *Am. J. Pathol.* **27**, 951–990 (1951).

The accumulation of fat in non-portal regions of the livers of choline-deficient rats may become so great that it can no longer be stored in *intra-cellular* form but eventually bursts the cells, thus permitting the fat to escape from the confines of the cell membrane. Single tenuous septa are formed by the compression and stretching exerted on cell membranes of adjacent cells distended by large fat spherules. These septa are frequently the sites of ruptures when fat accumulation in the cells becomes excessive.

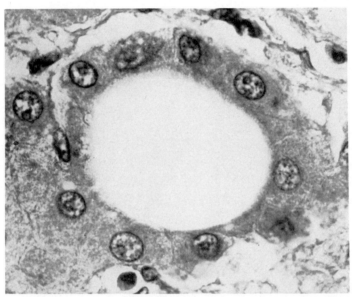

FIG. 8. A large fatty cyst in the liver of a male alcoholic (39 years old). In this single, random section (5 μ), the nuclei of nine parenchymal cells which form the wall of the cyst may be seen. The greatest diameter of the cyst in this section is over 90 μ. If the cyst had been followed through serial sections, it is likely that the total number of cells in its wall would be found to total almost 50. Cells in walls of cysts are usually more stretched and thinned than those illustrated here. Paraffin section; hematoxylin and eosin stain; ×800.

This rupture permits the adjacent fat spherules from each cell to fuse and so become enclosed by the conjoined parent cells. As a result, the latter actually form a small two-celled epithelial cyst (Fig. 8), and these *fatty cysts*[433, 434] are the cytometaplastic links between the fatty and fibrotic lesions of choline deficiency. Once formed, cysts may further increase in size by fusing with other cysts or with fat-laden cells in the same manner as the cysts were originally formed from individual cells. Eventually, large cysts rupturing may cause damage to surrounding biliary or vascular channels, and when this occurs fat may escape into the lumina of the latter

[434] W. S. Hartroft, *Anat. Record.* **106,** 61–87 (1950).

and so leave the liver. Cell remnants of disrupted cysts may survive for some time, as their nuclei are not often damaged. Condensation of these atrophic parenchymal cells (along with their reticular stroma) produces the so-called "fibrous" trabeculae of the cirrhotic lesion (Fig. 9). The condensation is responsible for the annular surface depressions, while parenchymal hyperplasia (compensatory in nature) in the portal regions produces the nodular, raised areas.

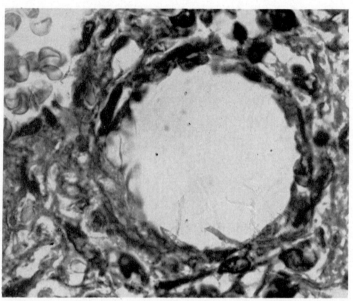

Fig. 9. The cells in the wall of this fatty cyst are thinned and stretched. The surrounding stroma is condensed, and the cyst is enmeshed in a trabecula. A portion of a radicle of an hepatic vein is shown in the upper left corner. Liver of a rat fed a choline-deficient diet for 6 months; paraffin section; hematoxylin and eosin stain; ×800.

The fact that the natural sequence of events is the formation, rupture, and dissolution of fatty cysts[434] with consequent escape of their contents from the liver explains why the amount of fat in the liver decreases as the fibrosis increases. For, with the rupture of each additional cyst, more fat escapes from the liver and condensation of the cellular and stromal elements of the torn cyst adds to the growth of trabeculae. The loss of parenchyma incident to the eventual destruction of each cyst (a large one may consist of as many as 60 cells) stimulates compensatory hyperplasia in portal areas. This region commonly exhibits only a moderate degree of fat storage which is almost entirely intracellular in nature. Intracellular fat is very rapidly mobilized when the deficiency in lipotropic factors is corrected. This may be effected in a variety of ways, as, for example, decreased growth of the animal (thus sparing more methionine for lipotropic use), reduced food intake, or the addition of choline to the diet. The result is a cirrhotic liver without obvious fatty change (Fig. 10). This sequence has been observed repeatedly in experimental animals. The clinical counterpart of this presumably occurs when a cirrhotic alcoholic in hospital is denied access to his alcohol and is given a well-balanced diet (with or without therapeutic

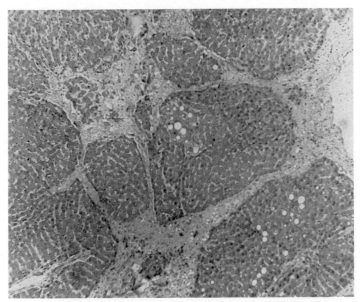

FIG. 10. Almost all the stainable fat in this cirrhotic liver of a choline-deficient rat has disappeared. That which remains is chiefly contained within persistent fatty cysts. This demonstrates the small amount of abnormal fat which may be present in a liver in which fibrosis has become severe. Liver of a rat fed a choline-deficient diet for over a year. Paraffin section; hematoxylin and eosin stain; ×100.

adjuvants of choline or methionine). If, in addition, the patient's caloric intake drops sharply owing to terminal complications such as ascites or ruptured esophageal varices, his death may be preceded by a significant loss in weight (which may be masked by ascites or edema). This should mobilize all intracellular fat from his liver and even much of the extracellular lipid. Experiments with rats have demonstrated[435, 436] that most of the extracellular fat in cysts will be resorbed eventually if the deficiency of lipotropes is relieved. The only evidences of previous fatty change that can then be found in liver sections are occasional remnants of cysts within the

[435] W. S. Hartroft and E. A. Sellers, *Am. J. Pathol.* **28,** 387–399 (1952).
[436] C. H. Best, W. S. Hartroft, and E. A. Sellers, *Gastroenterology* **20,** 375–384 (1952).

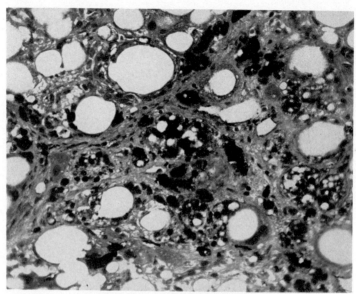

Fig. 11. Many of the fatty cysts illustrated in this field are undergoing involutionary changes, since they are losing their contained lipid. The surrounding stroma is condensed around the atrophic cysts. (Black material is ceroid pigment.) Liver of a rat fed a choline-deficient diet for 6 months. Paraffin section; Ziehl-Neilson stain; ×400.

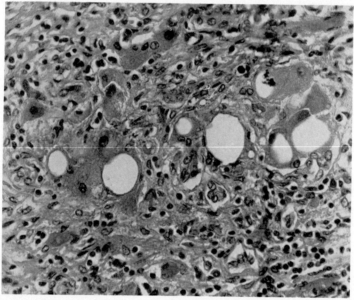

Fig. 12. Atrophic cysts in an area of reticular condensation in the liver of a human alcoholic (male). A few of the cells in the walls of the cysts (center left) retain sufficient characteristics so that they can still be identified as parenchymal. Compare with Fig. 11. Paraffin section; hematoxylin and eosin stain. ×400.

trabeculae (Fig. 11), and for these the pathologist may have to search assiduously. If such a search is successful, the clinical pathologist is well rewarded in cases of cirrhosis in which the pathogenesis may be shrouded in obscurity,[437] for fatty cysts at any stage imply, by their very existence, that at one time liver cells had been distended to the bursting point by fat and this finding may provide an important clue to the etiology (Fig. 12).

The foregoing should serve to establish that the presence of large amounts of stainable fat in cirrhotic livers is not a criterion for determining whether or not the lesions were initiated by an excess accumulation of fat. Although stainable fat is usually demonstrated with ease in experimental cirrhosis of dietary origin, such animals are most frequently sacrificed before they become moribund and while their food intake is still within normal limits. Consequently the investigator commonly observes this type of cirrhosis at the height of active progression of lesions when fat is abundant. This is in sharp contrast to the clinical situation. Patients have usually been treated by withdrawal of their alcohol, and terminal complications may have produced significant degrees of weight loss, both of which are potent factors in clearing hepatic cells of stainable fat. These considerations may well explain the frequent absence of stainable fat in livers of alcoholics at death.

2. CEROID

In the trabeculae of cirrhotic, choline-deficient rats, abundant amounts of an orange-brown pigment may be demonstrated. This material, which was named ceroid by Lillie et al.,[426] is sudanophilic, acid-fast, and insoluble in alcohol, xylol, and other common fat solvents. It is most easily and certainly identified by staining paraffin sections (from which all soluble lipids have been removed by the dehydrating agents) with any of the dyes which demonstrate fat (Sudan, Oil Red O, etc.). Ceroid in cases of cirrhosis in man is absent or scanty;[426-429] at most, only small amounts can be demonstrated in alcoholics.

Deposition of ceroid in cirrhotic rats can be greatly reduced by either supplementing their diet with large amounts of α-tocopherol, or replacing unsaturated fats in the diet with hydrogenated vegetable oils such as Crisco or Primex.[434, 438-440] Both in vitro and in vivo experiments[441] have now demonstrated the possibility that ceroid is the product of the oxidation of unsaturated fatty acids into an insoluble polymer, which, however, retains the characteristic of sudanophilia. Tocopherol may act to inhibit this reaction by virtue of its role as an antioxidant. Small hemorrhages frequently occur

[437] W. S. Hartroft, Federation Proc. 11, 417 (1952).
[438] J. Victor and A. M. Pappenheimer, J. Exptl. Med. 82, 375–383 (1945).
[439] P. György and H. Goldblatt, J. Exptl. Med. 89, 245–268 (1949).
[440] P. György and H. Goldblatt, J. Exptl. Med. 90, 73–84 (1949).
[441] W. S. Hartroft, Science 113, 673–674 (1951).

in ruptured fatty cysts,[433] with the result that red cells are bathed in liver fat. Much of the ceroid that is found in experimental cirrhosis could be explained as the polymerization of unsaturated fats which coat the surface of erythrocytes in hemorrhagic fatty cysts. This explanation is supported not only by direct observation of transition forms between red cells and ceroid aggregates in sections and by the experiments cited above, but also by the fact that, in livers that contain ceroid, hemosiderin is scanty or absent. In cirrhotic livers of rats fed a diet designed to repress ceroid formation, hemosiderin deposits were demonstrated.[442] This finding suggests that, if red cells become coated with ceroid, their disintegration, with release of histochemically demonstrable iron, is prevented.

Hemosiderin pigment can usually be demonstrated in cirrhotic livers of human alcoholics. The sequence of pathologic events responsible for this finding may be fundamentally similar to those which produce ceroid in choline-deficient rats, since manipulation of the diet of the latter will diminish ceroid deposition in the animals' livers and favor hemosiderin release.[442] The chain of evidence will not be complete until alcoholics have been encountered in which the converse has occurred—i.e., prevention of hemosiderin formation by coating of red cells with ceroid. Although examples of such prevention have not been reported to date, there are sufficient data at hand to suggest that it is unlikely that the presence of ceroid deposits in experimental cirrhosis indicates any fundamental etiological variant.

3. Portal versus Non-Portal Cirrhosis

The classical concept of cirrhosis associated with alcoholism in man is that it is portal in distribution. Orginally this term was also applied to cirrhosis in choline-deficient rats.[443] It was only after careful and detailed studies by the U. S. Public Health group in Bethesda[444] that the locus of the initial sites of formation of the trabeculae in these animals was realized to be, in fact, non-portal. This finding has now been independently confirmed.[434, 445] It is in line with the lobular distribution of abnormal fat in choline deficiency, which is also initially and primarily non-portal.[436] Thus portal alcoholic cirrhosis and non-portal experimental cirrhosis appear to differ fundamentally in their cytoarchitecture.

The initial observers of dietary cirrhosis in rats based their conclusion regarding its portal distribution on careful inspection of microsections of

[442] W. S. Hartroft, *Trans. 9th Conf. Liver Injury, New York* pp. 109–150 (1950).
[443] P. György and H. Goldblatt, *J. Exptl. Med.* **70,** 185–192 (1939).
[444] J. L. Asburn, K. M. Endicott, F. S. Daft, and R. D. Lillie, *Am. J. Pathol.* **23,** 159–171 (1947).
[445] L. E. Glynn, H. P. Himsworth, and O. Lindan, *Brit. J. Exptl. Pathol.* **29,** 1–9 (1948).

livers in an advanced stage of the lesion. These are more comparable to those usually seen in human alcoholics at autopsy than are the earlier stages of experimental cirrhosis. It is evident that conclusions concerning the nature of the lesions in the two conditions should be based only on comparisons of material at similar stages in their development. Early cases of alcoholic cirrhosis in man are not encountered at autopsy frequently

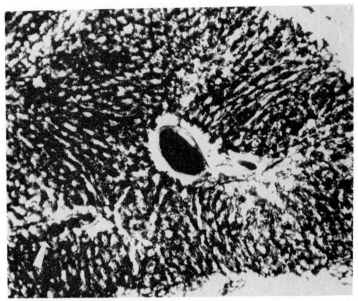

FIG. 13. Thick (100 μ) cleared slice of the liver of a rat injected with India ink at the time of sacrifice. In the center of the field is a large *conducting* (see text) branch of the portal vein, and to the right is a small branch of the hepatic artery. Note that the surrounding sinusoids do not communicate with this large vein. The white arrow in the lower left corner points to a small *distributing* (see text) branch of the portal vein which is breaking up into sinusoids. ×250.

enough to permit careful comparison with beginning fibrosis in choline-deficient rats. The fallacy of comparing early phases of cirrhosis in rats (nonportal) with late phases in alcoholics (portal) is demonstrated by the fact that late phases even in the rats were described as portal by expert pathologists when material from this stage only was available. Though it is well established that the distribution of the initial lesions in rats is non-portal, this should not be taken as evidence that experimental cirrhosis differs fundamentally from that in man, until it is possible to conduct equally complete and intensive studies of the early stages of cirrhosis in man.

Several questions arise from the foregoing. How does it happen that

initially non-portal trabeculae in cirrhotic rats eventually assume characteristics which are at least pseudoportal? Is it possible that the trabecular
distribution of advanced cases of alcoholic cirrhosis is also only pseudoportal? Is there in fact any essential difference in the histopathology of the

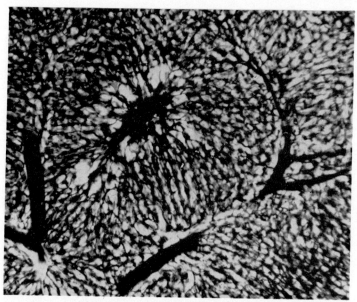

FIG. 14. Preparation (similar to that shown in Fig. 13), of a rat which had received a single oral dose of carbon tetrachloride 24 hours before it was sacrificed.
Central veins (radicles of the hepatic vein) can be easily identified in such a specimen
as they are surrounded by partially ischemic zones in which liver cells have swollen
as a result of the toxin. A radicle of the hepatic vein occupies the center of the field.
The branch of the portal vein below and to the right is a terminal *distributing* vessel
(see text) and is breaking up into sinusoids. The surrounding parenchyma is *functionally* periportal, whereas that illustrated around the *conducting* branch of the
portal vein in Fig. 13 is periportal only in a geographical sense. In livers of both
choline-deficient rats and alcoholic man, fibrosis develops around large branches of
the portal vein such as that in Fig. 13, but rarely and only in very advanced cases is
fibrosis found around these terminal branches illustrated here. ×250.

end stages of the two types of cirrhosis? An attempt to answer these questions will be made by surveying the general architecture of the hepatic
vasculature and relating it to the pathological anatomy of experimental
and alcoholic cirrhosis.

Large branches of the portal vein, like other large afferent vessels of the
body, rarely give off direct branches of sinusoidal or capillary dimensions.
Before supplying the bulk of the parenchyma, branches of this vessel, of

the order of veins, divide into small terminals of the order of *venules*, and
it is from the latter that blood enters the hepatic sinusoids (Figs. 13 and
14). These *terminal venules* ("distributors") of the portal vein should be
regarded as the most significant landmarks for orientation of lesions in
relation to the functional lobular units of the liver. Unhappily, in micro-

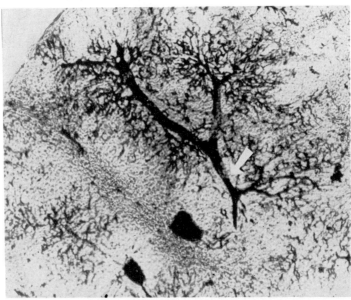

FIG. 15. Cleared and injected (India ink) slice (100 μ) of liver of a rat fed a choline-
deficient diet for approximately one year. The white arrow (right center) points to
a large branch of the portal vein. Fibrosis in non-portal regions has destroyed the
sinusoidal patterns except for small trees at the ends of the terminal venules of the
portal vein. Note the manner in which the trabeculae (clear areas in illustration)
embrace the *conducting* portion of the portal vein as indicated by the position of the
arrow. Fibrosis at this site is periportal in an anatomical sense only. In functionally
periportal positions around the terminal portal venules, the sinusoidal pattern is
relatively intact. ×100.

sections, these venules, with their accompanying bile radicles and hepatic
arterioles, are small and insignificant. Each venule supplies a parenchymal
unit which is many times its diameter in section (about 10 μ and several
hundred microns, respectively), and therefore thin random sections of the
unit frequently fail to include its small afferent vessels. In contrast, the
large, *non-terminal veins* ("conductors") of the portal system readily attract
the attention of the morphologist by virtue of their large diameter and their
lengthy course as they pass through many parenchymal units to which they
are not *directly* related in a functional sense. The relation of the latter

to such large vessels is analogous to that of houses at the edge of a highway which must be approached circuitously by way of secondary sideroads and streets. To reach such a house, the traveler would have to traverse as great a distance after leaving the highway as if the building were not located near any main route at all. In the liver, parenchymal cells beside large *conducting* portal veins (in contrast to cells around terminal, *distributing*

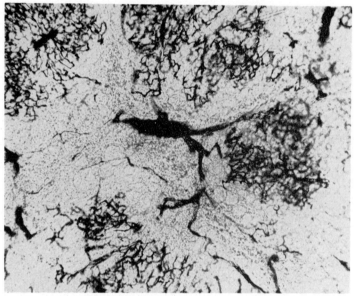

FIG. 16. Similar preparation to that shown in Fig. 15. A portion of a large *conducting* branch of the portal vein occupies the center of the field and is surrounded by fibrosis (clear area). Branches from this extend toward the small trees of intact sinusoids in which *terminal* branches of the portal vein link with the sinusoids and are free of encircling trabeculae (upper left corner). Although there is periportal fibrosis around the large portal venous branches, the small distributing portal venules are not directly involved and from a *functional* standpoint the distribution of the trabeculae is non-portal.

venules) are no more periportal in a physiological sense than cells in other, more obvious, non-portal regions. Cells adjacent to non-terminal portal canals are therefore periportal only in a limited regional sense. In terms of blood supply, with reference to the entry of blood into a parenchymal unit, these portions of the parenchyma are non-portal, since to reach them blood must first traverse sinusoids for some distance. Lesions, such as fibrosis around *conducting* portal triads, are therefore periportal in a geographical sense only. To be periportal from a functional standpoint, the lesions should involve parenchymal cells adjacent to the proximal end of the sinusoidal plexus. However, cells bordering junctions between sinusoids and terminal portal venules obviously have prior access to any essential food factors (including choline). Actually it is cells more remote from these favored sites that would first develop evidence of deficiency when the amount of an essential substance reaching the liver is insufficient to supply all parts of the organ. Cells adjacent to large conducting (but not distributing) portal

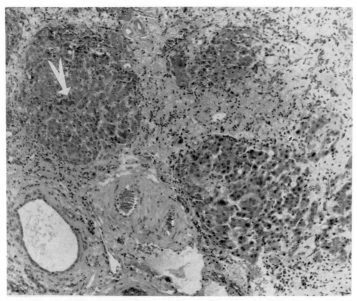

Fig. 17. This is a paraffin section of the liver of a rat comparable to the preparation illustrated in Figs. 15 and 16. The lower left portion of the field is occupied by a large bile duct, branches of the hepatic artery, and a small portion of a large branch of the portal vein. These structures are encircled by trabeculae, and to this extent the fibrosis is periportal. But the small terminal branches of the portal vessels are free of fibrosis, and in this functional sense the distribution of the trabeculae is non-portal. The white arrow indicates a small terminal portal area which is enlarged in Fig. 18. Hematoxylin and eosin stain. ×200.

vessels are in a position which is no more favorable for obtaining metabolites that may be in short supply than cells in other non-portal regions equally remote from the site at which blood enters the parenchymal unit.

Both fatty and fibrotic lesions in choline-deficient rats make their initial appearance and reach their most advanced stages in those portions of the hepatic lobule which are farthest from the sites at which blood leaves terminal portal venules to enter the sinusoids of each parenchymal unit. The most non-portal areas of the liver are those which surround the radicles of the hepatic vein, and these pericentral regions are the first sites of both fat storage and fibrosis. From here, trabeculae can extend only in directions toward neighboring central veins or *conducting* portal veins; otherwise they would encroach more directly on portal regions (Figs. 15 and 16). Thus, extension of trabeculae in accordance with the non-portal principle eventually results in fibrotic replacement in regions around large portal triads which are *anatomically*, but not functionally, periportal. By this process, considerable areas along large portal veins become surrounded, often in

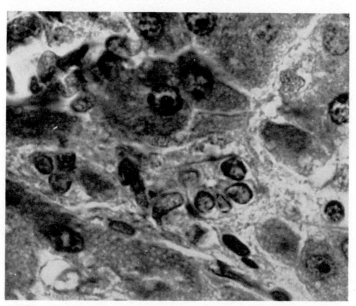

Fig. 18. The field immediately below the white arrow in Fig. 17 is enlarged in this photomicrograph. A small bile duct is shown in cross section, and below it, but less clearly shown, is a small terminal portal venule containing one or two red cells. There is no fibrosis present, and with regard to these functionally periportal regions, the fibrosis is non-portal. ×800.

eccentric fashion (Fig. 16), by trabeculae of condensed hepatic stroma. But even in relatively advanced stages of cirrhosis in rats, the terminal portal venules at the points where they ramify into sinusoids remain almost completely free of fibrosis. This may not be readily appreciated in thin microsections, for these venules are small and often missed by the plane of the section. Furthermore, if the parenchyma surrounding them be fatty, they are even more difficult to find under the lower powers of the microscope. If the observer is not aware of their importance as landmarks in orienting the lobular distribution of lesions, he may completely overlook these small vessels. By contrast, he may be readily misled by the large conducting portal vessels which are always easily found and are rendered even more conspicuous when partially surrounded by bands of fibrosis (Figs. 17 and 18). All these features have been followed in the rat through the various stages of the development of cirrhotic lesions, and they offer a reasonable explanation for the apparent disagreement between observers studying different stages of the same condition. When cases of human alcoholic

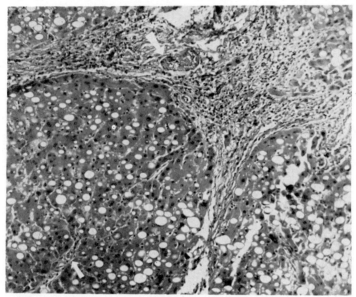

FIG. 19. Paraffin section of the cirrhotic liver of an alcoholic man. At the top of the field a large branch of the hepatic artery (indicated by the upper white arrow) is enmeshed by fibrous tissue. The portal area so identified is fibrotic and to this extent the distribution of the lesion is periportal. But, as in the rat, there is no fibrosis around terminal portal vessels (indicated by the white arrow at the lower left). This region is enlarged in Fig. 20. Hematoxylin and eosin stain; ×200.

cirrhosis are reexamined with these considerations in mind, similar features are encountered.

In studying sections of livers from cases of so-called portal cirrhosis in alcoholic men, we have been able to demonstrate repeatedly that fibrosis is rarely present around the terminal portal venules, but of course is abundant around many portions of the large conducting veins (Figs. 19 and 20).

In the latter sense only is this cirrhosis portal. But if this is accepted as the definition of the term, then so must it be employed with reference to the choline-deficient rat. By this standard, the cirrhosis in choline-deficient rats is as much portal as that in human alcoholics. Conversely the cirrhosis of alcoholism is as much non-portal as that of choline deficiency. It must therefore be conceded that the architectures of both lesions are essentially similar. The distinction of portal from non-portal cirrhotic lesions has been heightened by the anatomical nomenclature employed, but is apparently only one of degree.

If the validity of these arguments is accepted, evidence based on dietary studies would strongly suggest that alcoholic cirrhosis in man is indeed due

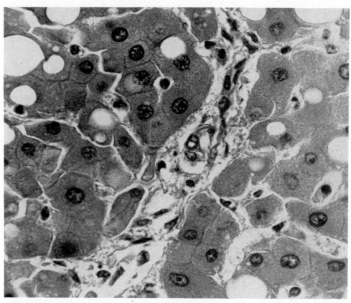

FIG. 20. The field indicated by the white arrow in the lower left portion of Fig. 19 is enlarged in this photomicrograph. A small bile duct occupies the center of the field, and at the bottom a terminal portal venule is seen in tangential section. There is no fibrosis present. As in the rat, with regard to these functionally periportal areas, the fibrosis is non-portal. ×800.

in large part to the dietary deficiency of the lipotropic agents. Clinicians might be richly rewarded were they to accept this as a working hypothesis on which to base well-controlled studies designed to test its validity. The results may well necessitate modification of the views presented in this chapter, for it is quite possible that toxic substances, both organic and inorganic, in commercial spirits may play an important role in the effects of alcohol-containing drinks on man.

There is no evidence at present that extrahepatic lesions involving the kidney, the eye, or the cardiovascular system of choline-deficient animals have any clinical counterparts, despite some suggestions to the contrary.

There are strong anatomical and histological parallelisms between the various forms of renal damage that develop in rats on low choline diets, and lesions in some types of nephrotic conditions and in subacute and chronic stages of Bright's disease. But any assumption that choline deficiency may play a part in the production of these conditions or that their treatment with lipotropic factors might produce favorable results is completely without either experimental or clinical foundation.

XI. Pharmacology

W. STANLEY HARTROFT, COLIN C. LUCAS, and CHARLES H. BEST

Choline given parenterally causes a fall in blood pressure (due to dilatation of peripheral vessels and slowing of the heart); it increases peristalsis of stomach and intestines and increases salivation. Some variability of response has been noted. Choline generally lowers the blood pressure,[1] but sometimes there is, instead, a rise. It has been claimed that in cats a rise generally follows the fall.[2] The variable response does not depend upon impurities,[3] as was suggested at one time. Choline acts powerfully upon the autonomic (involuntary, vegetative, or visceral) nervous system. Choline and most other quaternary ammonium compounds possess in varying degrees three distinct types of pharmacological action: the so-called "muscarinic," the "nicotine-like," and the "curariform" effects.

Muscarine, a powerful drug occurring in the poisonous mushroom Amanita muscaria, stimulates by direct action (not via the nerve endings) smooth muscles and glands innervated by postganglionic parasympathetic fibers. It causes cardiac slowing, peripheral vasodilation with consequent fall in blood pressure, increased peristalsis (with vomiting and defecation), bronchial constriction, salivation, sweating, and miosis. The similarity of the responses of the heart, smooth muscle, and glands to choline (or acetylcholine) and muscarine led to the adoption of the term "muscarinic action" to describe these effects. Nicotine has long been known to stimulate autonomic ganglia before paralyzing them. Choline and acetylcholine produce similar effects. Furthermore, both choline and nicotine have a similar effect (stimulation, then inhibition) on skeletal muscle. For this reason the stimulatory action of choline (and other quaternary ammonium compounds) on ganglia and voluntary muscles has been called "nicotine-like."

[1] F. W. Mott and W. D. Halliburton, J. Physiol. (London) 21, xvii–xx (1897).

[2] J. Pal, Z. exptl. Pathol. Therap. 9, 191–206 (1911).

[3] R. R. Renshaw, F. P. Underhill, and L. B. Mendel, J. Pharmacol. Exptl. Therap. 3, 457–458 (1912).

(This expression is to be preferred to the older term "nicotinic," to avoid confusion with the effects of nicotinic acid, now a product of therapeutic importance.) Curare, a powerful alkaloid derived from several South American species of *Strychnos*, acts as blocking agent on skeletal muscles and autonomic ganglia, causing muscular weakness ending eventually in paralysis as the muscle becomes completely flaccid. Choline and other quaternary ammonium salts in higher concentrations have a *"curariform"* effect.

Efforts to establish clearly the distinction between the *muscarinic* action (peripheral effects on glands and smooth muscle cells) and the *nicotine-like* action (on ganglion cells and skeletal muscles) evoked much study of the esters of choline and of related phosphonium, arsonium, stibonium, and sulfonium bases.

Hunt and Taveau[4, 5] reported upon the circulatory effects and relative toxicities of a large series of choline derivatives. Substitution of the hydrogen atom of the alcoholic OH group by acid radicals usually increases the physiological activity, from 500 to many thousand times, depending upon the substituent and the particular response observed.[6, 7] Acetylcholine, for example, is about 100,000 times more active than choline in causing a fall in blood pressure. Replacing the hydroxyl group by a carboxyl (betaine) leads to a product which is practically inert physiologically. Acetyl-β-methylcholine (mecholyl) resembles acetylcholine except that it produces practically no nicotine-like action. Carbaminoylcholine (carbachol, doryl, lentine), on the other hand, has a greater nicotine-like effect than acetylcholine.[8]

In comparison with many of its esters and many other quaternary ammonium compounds the toxicity of choline is relatively low. Given as chloride or citrate by mouth, choline has very low toxicity; it is considerably more toxic by subcutaneous, intraperitoneal, or intravenous injection. The relatively low (acute) toxicity of choline chloride may be illustrated by a statement of Mott and Halliburton[9] in 1899 that "We have never succeeded in killing an animal by injection of choline or choline hydrochloride." Others had succeeded, however. In 1885 Boehm[10] found that 0.05 g. of choline chloride injected subcutaneously would kill a small frog, and 0.1 g. a large one.

The minimum lethal dose, so-called, of choline chloride, for rabbits was

[4] R. Hunt and R. De M. Taveau, *Brit. Med. J.* **II**, 1788–1791 (1906).

[5] R. Hunt and R. De M. Taveau, *Hyg. Lab. Bull.* (*U. S.*) **73** (1911).

[6] H. H. Dale, *J. Pharmacol. Exptl. Therap.* **6**, 147–190 (1914).

[7] G. A. Alles, *Physiol. Revs.* **14**, 276–307 (1934).

[8] H. Molitor, *J. Pharmacol. Exptl. Therap.* **58**, 337–360 (1936).

[9] F. W. Mott and W. D. Halliburton, *Trans. Roy. Soc.* (*London*) **B191**, 211–267 (1899); see p. 223.

[10] R. Boehm, *Arch. exptl. Pathol. Pharmakol.* **19**, 87–100 (1885).

found by subcutaneous injection to be between 0.5 and 1.0 g. per kilogram.[11, 12] Dreyfus[13] reported that rabbits are killed by 1 g. per kilogram given rectally or subcutaneously but that only 0.11 g. per kilogram is required intravenously. Cats are killed by 24 mg. of choline chloride per kilogram given intravenously.[14] The rate of administration is, of course, important. Arai[15] found that if the drug was injected slowly cats could tolerate 15 mg. of choline chloride per kilogram given intravenously without any observable toxic effect; 30 mg. given slowly produced a reversible arrest of respiration but 35 mg., even if injected slowly, was lethal. As choline is rapidly destroyed (see below), about 0.8 to 0.9 mg. per kilogram per minute may be injected practically indefinitely into a cat if the concentration is between 0.2 and 0.4%. The MLD for mice (subcutaneously) is 0.7 g. per kilogram.[15]

The acute toxicity of choline chloride for both mice and rats has been determined in recent years by using larger numbers of animals and by applying the technique of probit analysis to the data. This permits a more accurate estimate of the dose needed to kill one-half of a given population, i.e., the so-called LD_{50}. Hodge and Goldstein[16] injected mice (weighing 18 to 26 g.) intraperitoneally with different volumes of 2% solution of choline chloride. The LD_{50} was 6.4 mg., or about 300 to 320 mg. per kilogram. The importance of the strength of the solution was shown by Neumann and Hodge[17] when they found the LD_{50} in rats given choline chloride by stomach tube to be of the order of 3.4 g. per kilogram when concentrated solutions (670 mg. or 500 mg. per milliliter) were given, but 6.1 g. per kilogram when weaker solutions (400 or 200 mg. per milliliter) were used. McArthur and Lucas[18] obtained a value for the LD_{50} (oral) of choline chloride in rats weighing 150 g. of about 760 mg., i.e., about 5.1 g. per kilogram when the drug was administered in 2 ml. By intraperitoneal or intravenous injection the LD_{50} in rats is very much less (one-tenth to one-fiftieth, according to preliminary tests, i.e., of about the same order as was found in mice).

Prolonged ingestion of choline has not revealed any chronic toxicity. Many investigators of lipotropic phenomena have fed rations containing 0.1 up to 2% of choline chloride to rats for periods of from several weeks to

[11] Brieger, Ueber Ptomaine. Hirschwald, Berlin, 1885–1886.
[12] Karl Vogt, Sitzber. Abhandl. naturforsch. Ges. (Rostock), New Ser. I, 1 (1909): quoted by Arai in ref. 15.
[13] L. Dreyfus, Compt. rend. soc. biol. 83, 481–483 (1920).
[14] A. Lohmann, Pflügers Arch. ges. Physiol. 118, 215–227 (1907).
[15] K. Arai, Pflügers Arch. ges. Physiol. 193, 359–395 (1922).
[16] H. C. Hodge and M. R. Goldstein, Proc. Soc. Exptl. Biol. Med. 51, 281–282 (1942).
[17] N. W. Neumann and H. C. Hodge, Proc. Soc. Exptl. Biol. Med. 58, 87–88 (1945).
[18] C. S. McArthur and C. C. Lucas, Biochem. J. 46, 226–231 (1950).

several months with no evidence of any toxic effects, other than some slight decrease in food intake at the higher concentrations.

Hodge[19] administered relatively large amounts of choline chloride to rats for a period of 4 months, to some in their food, to others in the drinking water. Prolonged consumption of diets or drinking water containing 1 % choline chloride produced no evidence of toxicity. Food intake was low and growth poor when the diet contained over 2.7 %; no deaths occurred in those given 5 % choline chloride in the ration. Those given 10 % lost weight, and three out of five died, but no histological evidence of damage was detectable. When the drinking water contained 2.7 % choline chloride a 40 % reduction in growth occurred; when it was increased to 4 % no growth took place and all the rats (five out of five) died within 3 months.

Davis[20] has claimed that administration of choline chloride to dogs by stomach tube (10 mg. per kilogram of body weight, once or twice daily) produces hyperchromic anemia. However, when Clarkson and Best[21] maintained dogs on a good ration under controlled conditions for a period sufficient to stabilize the blood picture (satisfactorily constant basal values for red cell counts and hemoglobin concentrations) and then added to the diet extra choline chloride (up to 30 mg. per kilogram of body weight per day), no evidence whatever of macrocytic anemia could be detected. On the contrary, the condition of the dogs given choline chloride, either in the diet or by stomach tube, improved steadily, probably owing to the general excellence of the diet rather than to the added choline.

Roth and Allison[22] fed rats of the Sherman strain a diet containing 1.35 % choline chloride for 20 days. The rats were fed the same weight of food as was consumed by another group given an excess (4.8 %) of methionine in the diet. The animals in both groups lost about 35 % of their body weight in the 20-day period. Although the food intake is not given, it would appear from the data for ingested nitrogen that the rats (250 g.) obtained only 6.7 g. of the ration (12 % casein) per day. Restriction of food intake rather than toxicity of choline chloride appears to explain the loss in weight observed in this study.

The fate of choline in the organism has not been fully elucidated. Choline is destroyed in the body with considerable speed.[23] When injected it dis-

[19] H. C. Hodge, *Proc. Soc. Exptl. Biol. Med.* **58**, 212–215 (1945).

[20] J. E. Davis, *Am. J. Physiol.* **142**, 213–215, 402–406 (1944); **147**, 405–411 (1946); *Science* **105**, 43–44 (1947); J. E. Davis and D. E. Fletcher, *J. Pharmacol. Exptl. Therap.* **88**, 246–253 (1946); J. E. Davis and J. B. Gross, *Am. J. Physiol.* **144**, 444–446 (1945).

[21] M. F. Clarkson and C. H. Best, *Science* **105**, 622–623 (1947).

[22] J. S. Roth and J. B. Allison, *J. Biol. Chem.* **183**, 173–178 (1950).

[23] H. von Hoesslin, *Beitr. chem. Physiol. Pathol.* **8**, 27–37 (1906); quoted by Fuchs, ref. 31.

appears rapidly from the blood stream[24] but does not increase appreciably the amount in the urine.[25-27]

When Luecke and Pearson[26] fed large doses of choline chloride (10, 20 and 40 g. to sheep and 5 g. to dogs), no significant increase resulted in the free or total choline in plasma, liver, or kidney and only a very small fraction (0.5 to 2.5%) was recovered in the urine (24-hour collection). Before treatment normal sheep excreted in the urine about 2 mg. of choline per 24 hours; after 40 g. daily for a period of 6 days the output increased significantly to between 300 and 500 mg. daily in one animal and to between 600 and 1050 mg. in the other (0.7 to 2.5% of the intake). Johnson et al.[27] found that equally small proportions (0.7 to 1.5%) of the choline intake were excreted as such in the urine by human subjects.

Choline is not destroyed by blood in vitro.[28] The destruction probably occurs largely in the liver. In some species (rat and hamster, but not guinea pig) a specific enzyme, choline oxidase, is found in the liver and kidney[29, 30] which oxidizes the alcohol group to give betaine aldehyde. A second enzyme continues the oxidation to betaine. Only negligible amounts of choline, trimethylamine, or its oxide could be found in the urine of a large dog given 20 g. of choline chloride during a 6-day period.[31] Possibly the methyl groups are oxidized in some species by another enzyme via formic acid to CO_2 and water.

The methyl groups of choline appeared to be labile in certain physiological environments, but recent studies suggest that they become labile only after conversion to compounds such as betaine aldehyde or betaine.[32-34]

Popper[35, 36] has reported that in normal human beings about two-thirds of orally administered doses of choline chloride appear in the urine as trimethylamine (mainly in the form of its oxide). Since the proportion so excreted is greatly reduced after treatment of the patient with antibiotics and is even smaller when the choline chloride is administered intravenously,

[24] R. Hunt, J. Pharmacol. Exptl. Therap. 7, 301–337 (1915).

[25] M. Guggenheim and W. Löffler, Biochem. Z. 74, 208–218 (1916).

[26] R. W. Luecke and P. B. Pearson, J. Biol. Chem. 158, 561–566 (1945).

[27] B. C. Johnson, T. S. Hamilton, and H. H. Mitchell, J. Biol. Chem. 159, 5–8 (1945).

[28] F. Wrede, E. Strack, and E. Bornhofen, Hoppe-Seyler's Z. physiol. Chem. 183, 123–132 (1929).

[29] F. Bernheim and M. L. C. Bernheim, Am. J. Physiol. 104, 438–440 (1933).

[30] F. Bernheim and M. L. C. Bernheim, Am. J. Physiol. 121, 55–60 (1938).

[31] H. Fuchs, Z. Biol. 98, 473–478 (1938).

[32] J. W. Dubnoff, Federation Proc. 8, 195 (1949).

[33] J. W. Dubnoff, Arch. Biochem. 24, 251–262 (1949).

[34] J. A. Muntz, J. Biol. Chem. 182, 489–499 (1950).

[35] H. Popper, in Discussion, Trans. 10th Conf. Liver Injury, New York (1951).

[36] J. de la Huerga and H. Popper, J. Clin. Invest. 30, 463–470 (1951).

it would appear that intestinal bacteria are responsible for the breakdown observed. In rats about 40 % of orally administered choline chloride is excreted in the urine as trimethylamine or its oxide.[37]

XII. Requirements

A. REQUIREMENTS OF ANIMALS

WENDELL H. GRIFFITH and JOSEPH F. NYC

Requirements of choline in the rat, chick, and turkey poult have been stated for specific dietary conditions in the preceding discussion. Requirements cannot be described otherwise at the present time because of the multiplicity of factors that govern the dietary need of this substance. There is experimental support for the provisional conclusion that choline is indispensable in the diet of chicks. This conclusion may need revision if it is shown that mono- and dimethylaminoethanol can be methylated by formate-to-methyl synthesis or by transmethylation at a rate sufficiently rapid to meet the chick's demand for choline. In the event that such a finding is established, the effect would be merely the transfer of dietary indispensability from choline to monomethylaminoethanol. There is no evidence of wide and ample distribution of the latter compound in natural foods. In so far as the rat and other animal species are concerned, there appears little question concerning the ability to produce methyl groups. Whether or not the rate of formation by this means is ever adequate for growth, reproduction and lactation on diets completely devoid of choline but otherwise of reasonable composition remains to be determined.

Among the dietary factors that influence the requirement of preformed choline are (1) those that are involved in the enzymatic reactions of transmethylation and of formate-to-methyl synthesis, (2) those that provide labile methyl, and (3) those that affect metabolism generally. In the first category are folic acid and B_{12} without which the choline requirement is definitely increased. In the second category are methyl donors other than choline, such as methionine, betaine, and the thetins. Of these, only methionine occurs widely in nature, and the quantity and composition of dietary protein are, therefore, important factors in determining how much choline should be contained in the ingested food. In the third category are any modifications of the food mixture, including a decrease in the amount consumed, that may lower the requirement of choline by depression of

[37] H. Popper, J. de la Huerga, and D. Koch-Weser, *J. Lab. Clin. Med.* **39,** 725–736 (1952).

the rate of growth or of the level or character of metabolism. In this group are fasting and inhibition of appetite due to a deficiency of thiamine or of other nutrients.

Undoubtedly there are many ways in which the metabolism of lipids is affected with a concomitant change in the rate of turnover of choline-containing phospholipids and in the rate of utilization of choline. Furthermore, the demand for methyl groups in the synthesis of creatine and of other methylated metabolites may divert part of the dietary supply of choline to such uses. On the other hand, choline may spare methionine as a source of methyl and thus allow additional amounts of this amino acid to be used in protein synthesis, directly or after conversion of its sulfur to cystine. Certainly, the need of choline is increased during growth.

The position of choline among dietary essentials is unique and at the same time anomalous. Clear-cut evidence for activity as a biocatalyst is lacking, but there can be no question regarding its nutritional importance in very fundamental biochemical systems in association with vitamins and other indispensable nutrients.

B. REQUIREMENTS OF HUMAN BEINGS

W. STANLEY HARTROFT, COLIN C. LUCAS, and CHARLES H. BEST

Although some data are available which make possible a rough estimate of the choline requirement of the rat, dog, and poultry, there are no comparable data for man. The daily choline intake of adults eating average mixed diets was determined in Toronto[1] by actual analysis of representative servings. The values found (ranging from 250 to 600 mg.) are in good agreement with calculated values of 300 to 500 mg. reported from Sweden by Borglin.[2] The choline intake of young men on a constant, adequate diet was determined in the United States by Johnson et al.[3] for a 5-day period; it varied from 624 to 899 mg., with a mean value of 737 mg., or about 150 mg. per day.

Borglin[2] found the excretion of choline by adults to vary normally between 2 and 4 mg. per day, i.e., 0.5 % to 1 % of the intake. He noted that, when the intake was reduced (e.g., starvation, ulcer diet) the amount excreted fell. Dietary factors (e.g., fat, methyl acceptors) which increase the requirement for choline reduced the choline excretion. Conversely, diets rich in lipotropic agents (protein, methionine, betaine) increased the excretion of choline, obviously indicating a lessened requirement for choline. These findings in human subjects paralleled those made during his investi-

[1] J. H. Ridout, C. C. Lucas, J. M. Patterson, and C. H. Best, *Biochem. J.* **52**, 79–83 (1952).

[2] N. E. Borglin, *Acta Pharmacol. Toxicol.* **3** *Suppl.* **1**, 1–123 (1947).

[3] B. C. Johnson, T. S. Hamilton, and H. H. Mitchell, *J. Biol. Chem.* **159**, 5–8 (1945).

gations in animals. Negligible excretion of choline has also been reported by others[4] even after giving extra choline.[5-8] Thus "loading tests" are of no value in determining the choline requirement.

[4] T. Z. Csáky, J. Möllerström, and O. V. Sirek, *Arch. Internal Med.* **84,** 730–737 (1949).

[5] H. Castro Mendoza, C. Jiménez Díaz, and J. del Río, *Bull. Inst. Med. Research* (*Madrid*) **1,** 7–17 (1948).

[6] J. de la Huerga and H. Popper, *J. Lab. Clin. Med.* **36,** 816 (1950).

[7] J. de la Herga, H. Popper, and F. Steigmann, *J. Lab. Clin. Med.* **38,** 904–910 (1951).

[8] R. Busset, *Rev. méd.* (*Liége*) **6,** 60–64 (1951).

Chapter 6

VITAMIN D GROUP

I. Nomenclature and Formulas

ROBERT S. HARRIS

Accepted names: Vitamin D_2 (or calciferol) from ergosterol by irradiation; ergocalciferol

                Vitamin D_3 (or activated 7-dehydrocholesterol) from 7-dehydrocholesterol by irradiation; cholecalciferol

Obsolete names: Rachitamin

                Rachitasterol

                Antirachitic vitamin

Empirical formulas: Vitamin D_2: $C_{28}H_{44}O$

                    Vitamin D_3: $C_{27}H_{44}O$

Chemical names: Vitamin D_2

                Vitamin D_3

Structure:

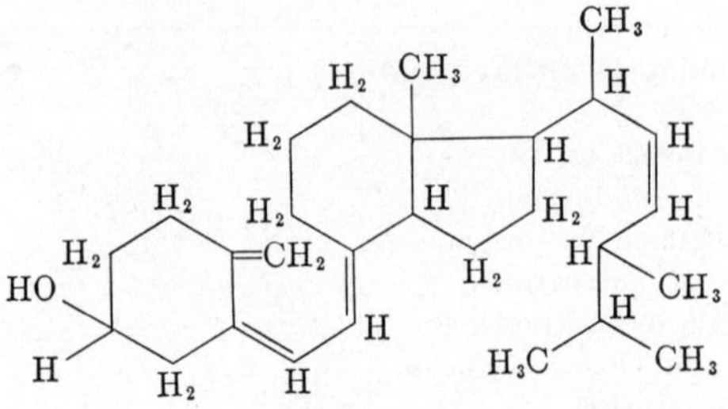

Vitamin D_2

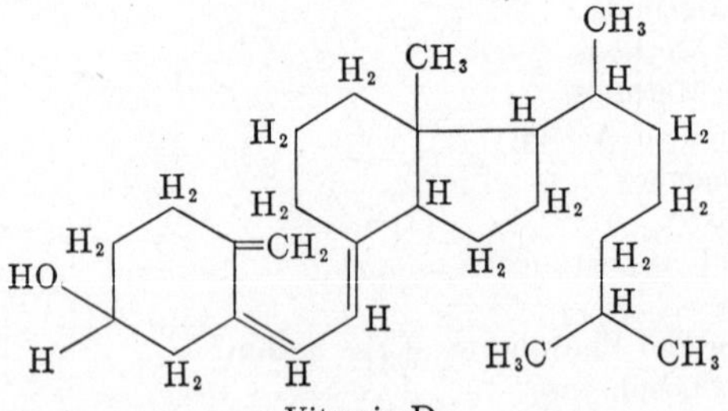

Vitamin D_3

II. Chemistry

CHARLES E. BILLS

The term vitamin D is applied to several antiricketic[1] substances derived from, or associated with, the sterols. The existence of the vitamin was first

---

[1] The English word rickets, which probably derives from wrygates (crooked goings),

indicated in experiments by Mellanby,[2] who found that rickets in puppies is a deficiency disease, and that cod liver oil contains a factor which prevents it. In 1922 the vitamin was recognized as a substance distinct from vitamin A by McCollum et al.[3] These workers bubbled air through heated cod liver oil until the antixerophthalmic factor, vitamin A, was destroyed, leaving the antiricketic factor which they later[4] termed vitamin D. Zucker et al.[5] found that vitamin D appears in the unsaponifiable, or sterol, fraction of cod liver oil, and they suggested that "it may be a sterol related to cholesterol or a cholesterol derivative."

Proof of the relationship to sterols followed the discovery in 1924 of the antiricketic activation of foods. It was found by Steenbock[6] and Hess and Weinstock[7] that numerous foods acquire vitamin D activity when exposed to ultraviolet rays. In 1925 further experiments by Hess et al.,[8] Steenbock and Black,[9] and Rosenheim and Webster[10] demonstrated that in foods it is the sterol content which is activated. Extension of this work led in a few years to the preparation of calciferol, or vitamin D_2, in the pure state, and it is noteworthy that this was accomplished before any form of the vitamin had been isolated from natural sources.

A. THE STEROLS

The literature of the sterols is voluminous, and the subject complex; only the facts most pertinent to vitamin D will be given here. Bills' review of the physiology of the sterols[11] will be drawn upon for early material of a biochemical nature. The organic chemistry of vitamin D, particularly in its three-dimensional aspects, has been covered by Lettré and Inhoffen,[11a]

antedates the unrelated classical coinage, rachitis (inflammation of the spine), and is more accurately descriptive of the disease. Hence the terms rickets, ricketic and antiricketic appear preferable to rachitis, rachitic, and antirachitic.

[2] E. Mellanby, *Med. Research Council (Brit.) Spec. Rept. Ser.* **61**, (1921).

[3] E. V. McCollum, N. Simmonds, J. E. Becker, and P. G. Shipley, *J. Biol. Chem.* **53**, 293 (1922).

[4] E. V. McCollum, N. Simmonds, J. E. Becker, and P. G. Shipley, *J. Biol. Chem.* **65**, 97 (1925).

[5] T. F. Zucker, A. M. Pappenheimer, and M. Barnett, *Proc. Soc. Exptl. Biol. Med.* **19**, 167 (1922).

[6] H. Steenbock, *Science* **60**, 224 (1924); U. S. Pat. 1,680,818 (1928).

[7] A. F. Hess and M. Weinstock, *J. Biol. Chem.* **62**, 301 (1924).

[8] A. F. Hess, M. Weinstock, and F. D. Helman, *J. Biol. Chem.* **63**, 305 (1925).

[9] H. Steenbock and A. Black, *J. Biol. Chem.* **64**, 263 (1925).

[10] O. Rosenheim and T. A. Webster, *Lancet* **I**, 1025 (1925).

[11] C. E. Bills, *Physiol. Revs.* **15**, 1 (1935).

[11a] H. Lettré and H. H. Inhoffen, Über Sterine, Gallensäuren und verwandte Naturstoffe. Ferdinand Enke, Stuttgart, 1936.

Sobotka,[12] Strain,[13] Rosenberg,[14] Fieser and Fieser,[15] Shoppee,[16] and Deuel,[17] and will not be repeated in detail. It is to be noted that the nomenclature and symbolism of sterol chemistry are in a state of flux, the most recent usage being that of Fieser and Fieser and of Shoppee. The book by Reed et al.[18] emphasizes the physiological and therapeutic aspects of vitamin D.

The sterol skeleton is shown in Fig. 1. This is a perhydro-1,2-cyclopentenophenanthrene ring system, with methyl groups at positions 10 and 12 and a side chain at position 17. The conventional numbering of the carbon atoms and the lettering of the rings are as indicated. The evidence leading to this structural concept is briefly reviewed by Heilbron et al.[19] Several routes to the synthesis of the ring system have been described,[20] and recently Woodward et al.[21] have achieved the total synthesis of cholesterol.

The hydrocarbon skeleton common to the sterols is one of the largest ring systems with which living cells have to deal. It occurs not only in the common sterols, but also in the sex and cortical hormones, bile acids, cardiac glucosides, toad poisons, and some carcinogens. But in vitamin D the nucleus is broken in ring B, so that the structure is no longer a sterol in the strictest sense. The several forms of vitamin D are sometimes classed with the steroids in recognition of their origin, but properly they are not sterols.

As an introductory convenience, the student of vitamin D may narrow the field to three types of naturally occurring sterols, differing in the degree of saturation in their ring system. In any of these types the side chain may or may not be saturated, and always there are possibilities of structural and steric isomerism.

1. The cholesterol type, characterized by just one double bond in the ring

[12] H. Sobotka, Chemistry of the Steroids. Williams and Wilkins Co., Baltimore, 1938.

[13] W. H. Strain, in Organic Chemistry, 2nd ed., Vol. II, Chapter 19. John Wiley and Sons, New York, 1943.

[14] H. R. Rosenberg, Chemistry and Physiology of the Vitamins. Interscience Publishers, New York, 1945.

[15] L. F. Fieser and M. Fieser, Natural Products Related to Phenanthrene, 3rd ed. Reinhold Publishing Corp., New York, 1949.

[16] C. W. Shoppee, Vitamins and Hormones 8, 255 (1950).

[17] H. J. Deuel, Jr., The Lipids. Interscience Publishers, New York, 1951.

[18] C. I. Reed, H. C. Struck, and I. E. Steck, Vitamin D. University of Chicago Press, 1939.

[19] I. M. Heilbron, J. C. E. Simpson, and F. S. Spring, J. Chem. Soc. 1933, 626.

[20] J. W. Cook and C. L. Hewett, J. Soc. Chem. Ind. 52, 451 (1933); J. Chem. Soc. 1933, 1098; L. Ruzicka, L. Ehmann, M. W. Goldberg, and H. Hösli, Helv. Chim. Acta 16, 833 (1933); G. A. R. Kon, J. Chem. Soc. 1933, 1081; A. Koebner and R. Robinson, ibid. 1938, 1994; C. K. Chuang, C. M. Ma, Y. L. Tien, and Y. T. Huang, Ber. 72, 949 (1939).

[21] R. B. Woodward, F. Sondheimer, and D. Taub, J. Am. Chem. Soc. 73, 3548 (1951).

system, always at C-5. Examples: cholesterol, sitosterol, stigmasterol, brassicasterol, campesterol, fucosterol, and others (Fig. 2).

2. The saturated ring type, in which there is no double bond in the ring system. Examples: dihydrocholesterol (cholestanol), dihydrositosterol (sitostanol), etc. (Fig. 3).

3. The ergosterol, or provitamin, type, characterized by two double bonds in the ring system, always at C-5 and C-7. Examples: ergosterol (provitamin D_2), 7-dehydrocholesterol (provitamin D_3), and the incompletely identified provitamins D of mollusks (Fig. 4).

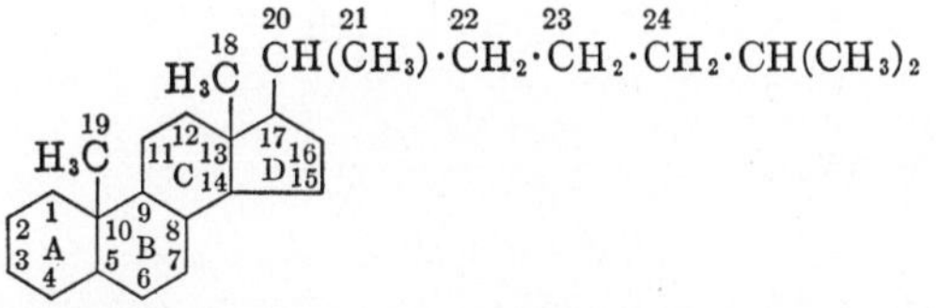

FIG. 1. The sterol ring structure, with a typical side chain at C-17. Rings A, B, C, and D are sometimes designated I, II, III, and IV.

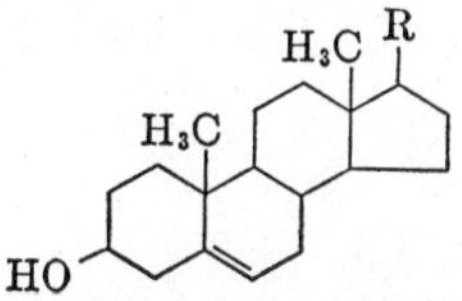

Cholesterol	R =	$-CH(CH_3) \cdot CH_2 \cdot CH_2 \cdot CH_2 \cdot CH(CH_3)_2$
β-Sitosterol	R =	$-CH(CH_3) \cdot CH_2 \cdot CH_2 \cdot CH(C_2H_5) \cdot CH(CH_3)_2$
Stigmasterol	R =	$-CH(CH_3) \cdot CH=CH \cdot CH(C_2H_5) \cdot CH(CH_3)_2$
Brassicasterol	R =	$-CH(CH_3) \cdot CH=CH \cdot CH(CH_3) \cdot CH(CH_3)_2$
Campesterol	R =	$-CH(CH_3) \cdot CH_2 \cdot CH_2 \cdot CH(CH_3) \cdot CH(CH_3)_2$
Fucosterol	R =	$-CH(CH_3) \cdot CH_2 \cdot CH_2 \cdot CH=C(CH_3) \cdot CH(CH_3)_2$

FIG. 2. Examples of cholesterol-type sterols.

Cholesterol (Fig. 2) is the principal sterol of the higher animals, or vertebrates. It is abundant in nerve tissue, fats, and skin, and present to some extent in all bodily structures. It is usually accompanied by traces of other sterols, which in a few instances have been identified as dihydrocholesterol (cholestanol) and 7-dehydrocholesterol.

In the invertebrates cholesterol is partly or wholly replaced by mixtures of other sterols, and in these mixtures 7-dehydrocholesterol and other provitamins D may be present in considerable amounts. The sterols of mollusks are of particular interest in connection with vitamin D, and among these it is to be noted that the sterols of the Pelecypoda (bivalves, such as clams and oysters) differ from those of the Gastropoda (snails). Examples are given in Table I, taken from Bergmann.[22] The bivalves may exhibit some cholesterol, but chiefly their sterols are difficultly separable mixtures of C_{28} and C_{29} sterols, with di-unsaturated C-24 epimers of C_{28} sterols predominating.[22, 23] The snails, however, show chiefly cholesterol, like the higher animals, but with small amounts of phytosterol-like sterols.

The sterols of plants, especially the higher plants, or phanerogams, are collectively known as phytosterols. By far the commonest phytosterol is sitosterol, a sterol which exists in three isomeric forms designated α, β, and γ, which are so difficultly separable that they are usually considered as one.

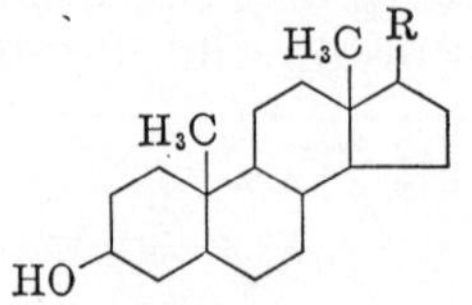

Cholestanol   R = —$CH(CH_3) \cdot CH_2 \cdot CH_2 \cdot CH_2 \cdot CH(CH_3)_2$
β-Sitostanol   R = —$CH(CH_3) \cdot CH_2 \cdot CH_2 \cdot CH(C_2H_5) \cdot CH(CH_3)_2$

FIG. 3. Examples of saturated-ring sterols.

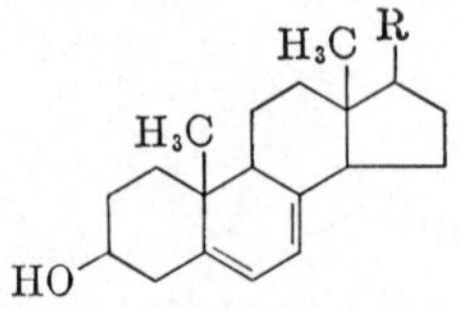

Ergosterol   R = —$CH(CH_3) \cdot CH{=}CH \cdot CH(CH_3) \cdot CH(CH_3)_2$
7-Dehydrocholesterol R = —$CH(CH_3) \cdot CH_2 \cdot CH_2 \cdot CH_2 \cdot CH(CH_3)_2$

FIG. 4. Ergosterol and 7-dehydrocholesterol, commonest examples of provitamins D.

Sitosterol is usually accompanied by traces of dihydrositosterol (sitostanol) and a provitamin which might be expected to be 7-dehydrositosterol but which is probably ergosterol. Other sterols occurring with sitosterol in the higher plants are campesterol, brassicasterol, stigmasterol, and spinasterol. In the lower plants, or cryptogams, sitosterol appears in the green algae, but in the brown algae it is replaced by fucosterol. In the fungi the principal sterol is ergosterol, accompanied by small amounts of 5-dihydroergosterol and traces of several other sterols not of interest in connection with vitamin D.

From the structural formulas it can be seen that the sterols which predominate in the higher forms of life differ only in their side chains. Their

[22] W. Bergmann, J. Marine Research (Sears Foundation) 8, 137 (1949).
[23] W. Bergmann and E. M. Low, J. Org. Chem. 12, 67 (1947).

ring systems are identical and exhibit but one double bond, located at C-5. These sterols and the dihydro derivatives which accompany them in traces lack any system of conjugated double bonds and hence do not show absorption bands in the ultraviolet region when examined spectrographically.

TABLE I

Sterols of Mollusks (Bergmann[22])

Class and species	Melting point of steryl acetate, °C.	Principal sterol
Pelecypoda		
Tapes phillippinarum	137	
Corbicula leana	126–127	Corbi-, brassicasterol
Cristaria plicata	137–138	
Meretrix meretrix	137–138	Meretristerol
Ostrea gigas	136–137	Conchasterol
Ostrea virginica	134–135	Ostreasterol
Mya arenaria	131	
Volsella modiolus	127–128	
Tridacna gigas	156–157	Shakosterol
Venus mercenaria	131	
Modiolus modiolus	131	
Modiolus demissus	156–157	Brassicasterol
Gastropoda		
Haliotis gigantea	117	Cholesterol
Turbo cornutus	116	Cholesterol
Rapana thomasiana	120	Cholesterol
Cellana nigrolineata	115	Cholesterol
Tegula xanthostigma	118	Cholesterol
Fulgur (Sp.)	117	Cholesterol
Buccinum undatum		Cholesterol
Littorina littorea		Cholesterol
Nerita peleronta		Cholesterol
Nassa obsoleta		Cholesterol
Cephalopoda		
Sepia officinalis		Cholesterol
Octopus vulgaris		Cholesterol

On the other hand, the sterols which are most characteristic of the lower forms of life and which occur in traces with the sterols of the higher forms (ergosterol, 7-dehydrocholesterol) have double bonds at C-5 and C-7. As would be expected on theoretical grounds, these sterols with conjugated double bonds exhibit ultraviolet absorption bands. With these principles in mind, one can look back understandingly on the development of the provitamin theory.

B. THE PROVITAMIN THEORY AND SYNTHESES

1. HISTORY

When it became evident that in foodstuffs the sterol fraction contains the acceptor of the activating rays, investigators tried to explain chemically the changes induced in the sterols by irradiation. Hess and Weinstock[24] introduced the use of the quartz spectrograph for investigating the chemistry of activation. They found that ordinary cholesterol and wheat phytosterol (sitosterol) were somewhat opaque to ultraviolet light, and that irradiation decreased their opacity. On the other hand, dihydrocholesterol and dihydrositosterol, which were not activatable, were practically transparent. Unfortunately, a mercury arc was used as the light source for the spectrograms. Since this gives a discontinuous spectrum, nothing could be learned of the spectral structure in the region of absorption.

Schlutz and Morse,[25] with better spectrographic technique, determined that the absorption spectrum of ordinary cholesterol is banded. They recognized two maxima of absorption, at approximately 294 and 283 mμ and were thus the first to record the provitamin absorption spectrum. They noticed that after brief irradiation the inflections gave way to general absorption, and, considering Beer's law, they postulated that either the cholesterol had been at least half metamorphosed, or else "the substance in which the absorption spectrum is changed may be a small amount of impurity in the cholesterol which is not removed by repeated crystallizations from alcohol, and which is exceedingly absorptive."

Rosenheim and Webster[26] found that cholesterol which had been regenerated from cholesterol dibromide was so pure that it no longer showed the characteristic absorption spectrum and was no longer activatable. Heilbron et al.[27] reported that fractional crystallization of cholesterol led to the accumulation, in the least soluble fraction, of the substance responsible for the characteristic absorption spectrum. They recognized a third absorption maximum, λ 269 mμ. Irradiation destroyed the three bands, leaving only general absorption. Pohl,[28] by the technique of photoelectric photometry, also detected three absorption bands in cholesterol, which faded upon irradiation. With the knowledge that complete disappearance of the bands corresponded to the destruction of only a trivial fraction of the cholesterol, he concluded that the absorbing substance was present only in minute

[24] A. F. Hess and M. Weinstock, *J. Biol. Chem.* **64**, 181 (1925); **64**, 193 (1925).

[25] F. W. Schlutz and M. Morse, *Am. J. Diseases Children* **30**, 199 (1925).

[26] O. Rosenheim and T. A. Webster, *J. Soc. Chem. Ind.* **45**, 932 (1926); *Biochem. J.* **21**, 127 (1927).

[27] I. M. Heilbron, E. D. Kamm, and R. A. Morton, *J. Soc. Chem. Ind.* **45**, 932 (1926); *Biochem. J.* **21**, 78 (1927).

[28] R. Pohl, *Nachr. Ges. Wiss. Göttingen, Math. physik. Kl.* 142 (1926).

amounts. He found that cholesterol purified via the dibromide, or via allo-cholesterol, and sitosterol purified via the dibromide, did not show the usual absorption.

These studies made it plain that an impurity present in ordinary cholesterol and sitosterol is responsible for at least the greater part of the anti-ricketic activity conferred upon the sterols by irradiation. The impurity, or provitamin, was presently identified as ergosterol, a sterol which Rosenheim and Webster[29] had previously found to be activatable, but with which they had made no quantitative studies. Pohl[30] found that the three known absorption bands of ordinary cholesterol are also exhibited by ergosterol, but in vastly greater intensity. Additional chemical studies and a biological assay were made by Windaus and Hess,[31] who found that, as expected, the antiricketic potency of irradiated ergosterol was far greater than that of irradiated cholesterol. Rosenheim and Webster[32] also conducted chemical and biological studies and concluded that the precursor of vitamin D "is ergosterol, or a highly unsaturated sterol of similar constitution."

Bills et al.[33] confirmed these studies in a way which supported the view that ergosterol was the contaminant provitamin. By the use of a continuous light source they discovered that ordinary cholesterol exhibits a fourth absorption band, λ 260 mμ. The same band was shown by ergosterol, making the series $\lambda\lambda$ 293.5, 282, 270, and 260 mμ, with four points of identity instead of three. Moreover, the spectra faded at the same rate when acetone solutions of ordinary cholesterol and of provitamin-free cholesterol plus added ergosterol were oxidized with permanganate.

In spite of all the evidence, it turned out that the identification of the provitamin of cholesterol as ergosterol was incorrect, yet it was so convincing that it was generally accepted from 1927 to 1934. However, there was during that period a growing knowledge of the multiple nature of vitamin D, which has been reviewed elsewhere in some detail.[34] In particular, Massengale and Nussmeier[35] observed that activated ergosterol is much less effective than cod liver oil, rat unit for rat unit, in the prevention of rickets in chicks. They offered no explanation of this phenomenon, but their work provided an important tool, the chick-rat efficacy ratio, for future studies on the D vitamins.

It remained for Waddell[36] to demonstrate that the provitamin D of

[29] O. Rosenheim and T. A. Webster, Biochem. J. 20, 537 (1926).
[30] R. Pohl, Nachr. Ges. Wiss. Göttingen, Math. physik. Kl. 185 (1927).
[31] A. Windaus and A. Hess, Nachr. Ges. Wiss. Göttingen, Math. physik. Kl. 175 (1927).
[32] O. Rosenheim and T. A. Webster, Lancet I, 306 (1927); Biochem. J. 21, 389 (1927).
[33] C. E. Bills, E. M. Honeywell, and W. A. MacNair, J. Biol. Chem. 76, 251 (1928).
[34] C. E. Bills, Cold Spring Harbor Symposia Quant. Biol. 3, 328 (1935).
[35] O. N. Massengale and M. Nussmeier, J. Biol. Chem. 87, 423 (1930).
[36] J. Waddell, J. Biol. Chem. 105, 711 (1934).

cholesterol is not ergosterol. He compared irradiated cholesterol with irradiated ergosterol on chicks and rats in a series of experiments designed to be free from alternative interpretations. His findings proved beyond question that the vitamin D from the provitamin of cholesterol is different from the vitamin D from ergosterol, and therefore the provitamin of cholesterol is not ergosterol.

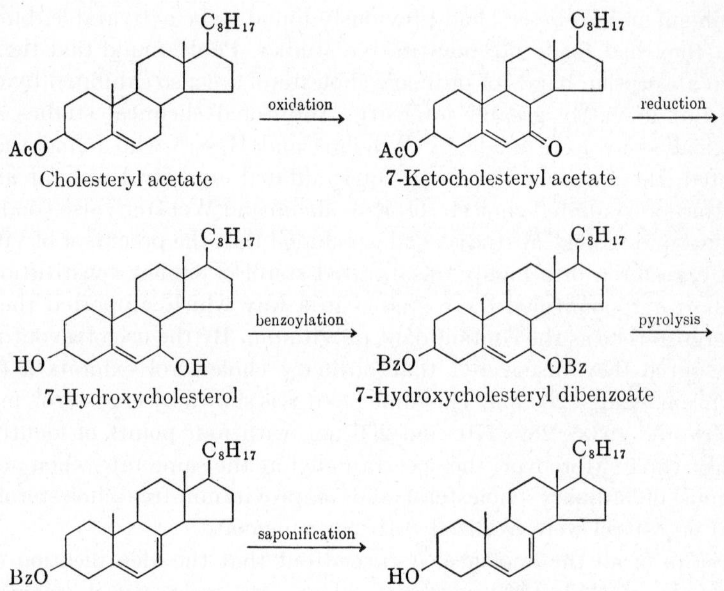

Cholesteryl acetate → 7-Ketocholesteryl acetate → 7-Hydroxycholesterol → 7-Hydroxycholesteryl dibenzoate → 7-Dehydrocholesteryl benzoate → 7-Dehydrocholesterol

FIG. 5. Synthesis of 7-dehydrocholesterol (method of Windaus *et al.*[38]).

2. SYNTHESES

A few months before the appearance of Waddell's paper, Callow[37] suggested, on theoretical grounds, that there might exist in nature a provitamin D which "is a cholesterol derivative with the double bonds in the critical position, a demethyl-dihydro-ergosterol." This substance, now usually known as 7-dehydrocholesterol, was synthesized by Windaus *et al.*[38] in the following manner (Fig. 5). Cholesteryl acetate was oxidized by chromic acid to 7-ketocholesteryl acetate. This was reduced by aluminum isopropylate to 7-hydroxycholesterol, the dibenzoate of which gave upon strong heating *in vacuo* the benzoate of 7-dehydrocholesterol. The latter was saponified to the free provitamin. 7-Dehydrocholesterol is highly acti-

[37] R. K. Callow, *Sci. J. Roy. Coll. Sci.* 4, 41 (1934).
[38] A. Windaus, H. Lettré, and F. Schenck, *Ann.* **520**, 98 (1935).

vatable and exhibits ultraviolet absorption bands in practically the same position and intensity as ergosterol. It also shares the property of being somewhat unstable. These facts account for the original misidentification of the provitamin in cholesterol.

By reactions analogous to the ones used in the synthesis of 7-dehydrocholesterol, the corresponding 7-dehydro derivatives of several other natural sterols have been made, namely, 7-dehydrositosterol,[39] 7-dehydrostigmas-

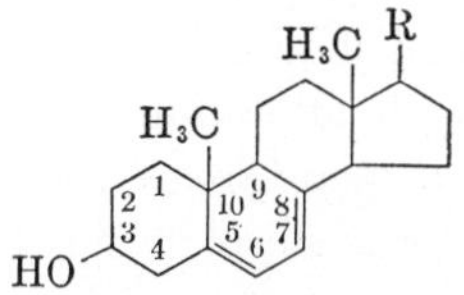

Activatability	Sterol	Side chain
+	Ergosterol	
+	Epiergosterol	
+	Lumisterol	20 21 22 23 24
−	Pyrocalciferol	$R = -CH(CH_3) \cdot CH=CH \cdot CH(CH_3) \cdot CH(CH_3)_2$
−	Isopyrocalciferol	
+	22,23-Oxidoergosterol	O
+	22-Dihydroergosterol	$R = -CH(CH_3) \cdot CH \cdot CH \cdot CH(CH_3) \cdot CH(CH_3)_2$
+	7-Dehydrocampesterol	
?	7-Dehydroclionasterol	$R = -CH(CH_3) \cdot CH_2 \cdot CH_2 \cdot CH(C_2H_5) \cdot CH(CH_3)_2$
?	7-Dehydrositosterol	
?	7-Dehydrostigmasterol	$R = -CH(CH_3) \cdot CH=CH \cdot CH(C_2H_5) \cdot CH(CH_3)_2$
+	7-Dehydrocholesterol	$R = -CH(CH_3) \cdot CH_2 \cdot CH_2 \cdot CH_2 \cdot CH(CH_3)_2$
+	7-Dehydroepicholesterol	
?	$\Delta^{5,7,22}$-Cholestatriene-3-ol	$R = -CH(CH_3) \cdot CH=CH \cdot CH_2 \cdot CH(CH_3)_2$
?	$\Delta^{5,7}$-Norcholestadiene-3-ol	$R = -CH(CH_3) \cdot CH_2 \cdot CH_2 \cdot CH_2 \cdot CH_2 \cdot CH_3$
?	3-Hydroxy-$\Delta^{5,7}$-choladienic acid	$R = -CH(CH_3) \cdot CH_2 \cdot CH_2 \cdot COOH$
?	3,17-Dihydroxyandrostadiene	$R = -OH$

FIG. 6. The provitamins D and related sterols with double bonds at C-5 and C-7. The sign + means that the sterol becomes antirachetic upon irradiation, the sign − means that the irradiation product exhibits no antirachetic action, and the sign ? means that the sterol has not been adequately tested for activatability.

terol,[40] 7-dehydrocampesterol,[41] and 7-dehydroclionasterol.[42] The structures of these and other sterols unsaturated in the critical C-5 and C-7 positions are shown in Fig. 6.

A provitamin D of special theoretical interest is 22-dihydroergosterol, which is intermediate in structure between ergosterol and 7-dehydrocholesterol, and epimeric on C-24 with 7-dehydrocampesterol. This provitamin was prepared by Windaus and Langer[43] by saturating the double bond in

[39] W. Wunderlich, *Hoppe-Seyler's Z. physiol. Chem.* **241,** 116 (1936).
[40] O. Linsert, *Hoppe-Seyler's Z. physiol. Chem.* **241,** 125 (1936).
[41] W. L. Ruigh, *J. Am. Chem. Soc.* **64,** 1900 (1942); U. S. Pat. 2,378,435 (1945).
[42] W. Bergmann, A. M. Lyon, and M. J. McLean, *J. Org. Chem.* **9,** 290 (1944).
[43] A. Windaus and R. Langer, *Ann.* **508,** 105 (1933).

the side chain of ergosterol. To do this, ergosteryl acetate was heated with maleic anhydride to form an addition product in which the two double bonds in ring B were saturated. The double bond at C-22 was then hydrogenated, after which the maleic anhydride was thermally split from the molecule, thus restoring the double unsaturation in ring B which is essential for activation. The free provitamin was obtained by saponification of the ester.

Ten other sterols with double bonds at C-5 and C-7 are also known. Their structures are included in Fig. 6. Epiergosterol is prepared by the reduction of ergosterone with aluminum isopropylate.[44] It has not been obtained pure, but has been made free from ergosterol. Lumisterol is the initial irradiation product of ergosterol.[45, 46] It has not been found in nature, but it undoubtedly occurs in natural products where vitamin D is being formed by insolation. Pyrocalciferol and isopyrocalciferol are thermal transformation products of calciferol.[45] 22,23-Oxidoergosterol has been prepared, but the details of its synthesis were not disclosed.[47] Rosenberg[14] surmises that it was made by treating the maleic anhydride addition product of an ergosterol ester with a mild oxidizing agent to form the 22,23-oxido compound, which upon thermal decomposition would yield the 22,23-oxido-ergosterol ester. 7-Dehydroepicholesterol has been made by applying the reactions in Fig. 5 to epicholesterol,[48] and also, in poor yield, by reducing dehydrocholestenone with aluminum isopropylate.[49] $\Delta^{5,7,22}$-Cholestatriene-3-ol has been identified[50] indirectly as one of the provitamins of *Mytilus edulis*; it has not been prepared synthetically. $\Delta^{5,7}$-Norcholestadiene-3-ol has been made by a series of reactions from the oxidation products of sitosterol.[51] 3-Hydroxy-$\Delta^{5,7}$-choladienic acid is obtained by the pyrolysis of the dibenzoate of methyl 3,7-dihydroxy-Δ^5-cholenate in dimethylaniline.[52] 3,17-Dihydroxyandrostadiene is made from androstenediol by reactions analogous to those in Fig. 5.[53]

Besides the chemically definite provitamins cited in the preceding paragraphs, there are provitamins of unknown structure which will be considered under the heading, Provitamins D of Invertebrates. There are also

[44] A. Windaus and K. Buchholz, *Ber.* **72**, 597 (1939).
[45] A. Windaus, A. Lüttringhaus, and P. Busse, *Nachr. Ges. Wiss. Göttingen, Math. physik. Kl., Fachgruppe* **III**, 150 (1932).
[46] A. Windaus, K. Dithmar, and E. Fernholz, *Ann.* **493**, 259 (1932).
[47] K. Dimroth and J. Paland, *Ber.* **72**, 187 (1939).
[48] A. Windaus and J. Naggatz, *Ann.* **542**, 204 (1939).
[49] A. Windaus and O. Kaufmann, *Ann.* **542**, 218 (1939).
[50] J. van der Vliet, *Rec. trav. chim.* **67**, 246, 265 (1948).
[51] C. G. Alberti, B. Camerino, and L. Mamoli, *Helv. Chim. Acta* **32**, 2038 (1949); **33**, 229 (1950).
[52] G. A. D. Haslewood, *J. Chem. Soc.* **1938**, 224.
[53] A. Butenandt, E. Hausmann, and J. Paland, *Ber.* **71**, 1316 (1938).

several vaguely recognized bodies from which antiricketic materials have been obtained by irradiation or other treatment; these will be discussed under Minor and Obscure Forms of Vitamin D.

3. CHEMICAL STRUCTURE AND ACTIVATABILITY

a. The Hydroxyl Group at C-3

It has long been established that certain esters of crude cholesterol, i.e., of 7-dehydrocholesterol, are made antiricketic by irradiation. These include the acetate,[29, 54, 55] benzoate,[55] isobutyrate,[55] palmitate,[29] and phosphate (monocholesteryl).[56] Ergosterol esters undergo the chemical changes of activation as readily as the free sterol. However, the esters of calciferol which are formed by the irradiation of the corresponding esters of ergosterol are not uniformly effective when administered to rats. Irradiated ergosteryl acetate,[57, 58] irradiated ergosteryl ethyl carbonate,[58] and irradiated diergosteryl phosphate[59] are as effective as irradiated ergosterol. The irradiated benzoate was at first claimed to be as effective[57] as irradiated ergosterol but later was found to be considerably less effective.[58, 59a] The palmitate is also less effective.[59a, 60] The allophanate, cinnamate, diphenylacetate, oxalate, α-naphthylurethane, and phenylurethane are inactive at the usual curative levels.[59a] The differences in antiricketic effectiveness are due merely to differences in the assimilability of the esters, for by saponification the full effectiveness of the vitamin D in any of the esters can be brought out. This phenomenon has also been observed in the natural vitamin D esters of fish oils.[60]

When the hydroxyl group in 7-dehydrocholesterol is replaced by halogens, the molecule is considerably stabilized. The chloride and bromide of this provitamin D undergo changes upon exposure to ultraviolet rays which indicate spectrographically that the corresponding halides of vitamin D_3 are formed. These halides, which are resistant to saponification, are devoid of antiricketic action when fed to rats and chicks, even in large doses.[61] Compounds such as these, where the structure is present but the activity hidden, raise the poser: "When is a vitamin not a vitamin?"

[54] A. F. Hess, M. Weinstock, and E. Sherman, J. Biol. Chem. **67**, 413 (1926).

[55] C. E. Bills and F. G. McDonald, J. Biol. Chem. **72**, 13 (1927).

[56] H. von Euler and A. Bernton, Ber. **60**, 1720 (1927).

[57] O. Rosenheim and T. A. Webster, Lancet **II**, 622 (1927).

[58] R. K. Callow, Biochem. J. **25**, 79 (1931).

[59] H. von Euler, A. Wolf, and H. Hellström, Ber. **62**, 2451 (1929).

[59a] A. Windaus and O. Rygh, Nachr. Ges. Wiss. Göttingen, Math. physik. Kl. 202 (1928).

[60] B. E. Bailey, J. Fisheries Research Board Can. **6**, 103 (1943).

[61] S. Bernstein, J. J. Oleson, H. B. Ritter, and K. J. Sax, J. Am. Chem. Soc. **71**, 2576 (1949).

By replacing the hydroxyl group with a thiol group, Strating and Backer[62] and Bernstein and Sax[63] have recently prepared 7-dehydrothiocholesterol (7-dehydrocholesteryl mercaptan or cholestadiene-5,7-thiol-3). This compound exhibits an absorption spectrum similar to that of the provitamins D and undergoes similar spectral changes upon irradiation, but the thiol isostere of vitamin D_3 which apparently resulted was not antiricketic for chicks, even at generous doses.

Strating and Backer[64] have also prepared the compound, "7-dehydro-3-homocholesterol," in which the hydroxyl group is replaced by the $HOCH_2$ group, i.e., 3-hydroxymethyl-cholestadiene-5,7. This exhibits the typical provitamin D absorption spectrum, but no studies on its activatability have been reported.

The C-3 position is a center of asymmetry. Sterols which differ from normal only in the steric arrangement of substitutions on C-3 are defined as episterols.[48] They are not precipitable by digitonin. The epi configuration is exhibited by epiergosterol and 7-dehydroepicholesterol. Both are highly activatable, 7-dehydroepicholesterol acquiring about one-tenth as much activity as is acquired by 7-dehydrocholesterol under similar exposure to ultraviolet light.[44, 48]

b. Orientations at C-9 and C-10

Isopyrocalciferol is the C-9 epimer of ergosterol, and except for this difference the two are identical in structure. The fact that isopyrocalciferol does not become antiricketic upon irradiation is evidence that the normal configuration at C-9 is essential for activation. Lumisterol differs from ergosterol only in the epimerization of its substituent methyl group at C-10. The fact that it is fully activatable is evidence that the configuration at C-10 is not a determinant of activatability. Pyrocalciferol differs from ergosterol in the spatial arrangements at both C-9 and C-10, and it is not activatable.

c. The Side Chain

The sex hormone, 3,17-dihydroxyandrostadiene, differs structurally from ergosterol and 7-dehydrocholesterol only in the absence of a side chain, the substitution at C-17 being an hydroxyl group. This compound, when irradiated, undergoes the spectral changes indicative of vitamin D formation (Fig. 7), but the product shows no antiricketic activity.[47]

The cholanic acid analog of ergosterol and 7-dehydrocholesterol, known as 3-hydroxy-$\Delta^{5,7}$-choladienic acid, differs from the activatable provita-

[62] J. Strating and H. J. Backer, *Rec. trav. chim.* **69,** 909 (1950).
[63] S. Bernstein and K. J. Sax, *J. Org. Chem.* **16,** 685 (1951).
[64] J. Strating and H. J. Backer, *Rec. trav. chim.* **70,** 389 (1951).

mins only in having a short side chain terminating in a carboxyl group. It is nevertheless not activatable.[65]

The sterol, $\Delta^{5,7}$-norcholestadiene-3-ol, differs from 7-dehydrocholesterol in that its side chain is unbranched and has one fewer CH_2 group. Although it is described as "a new provitamin D," no study of its antiricketic activatability has appeared.

The natural compound, $\Delta^{5,7,22}$-cholestatriene-3-ol, or 22-dehydro-7-dehydrocholesterol, differs from 7-dehydrocholesterol only in having a double

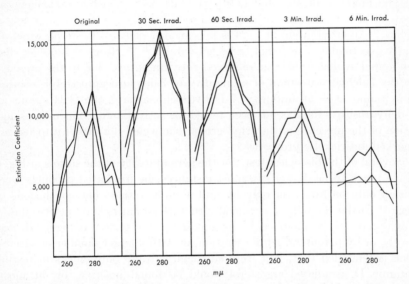

Fig. 7. Spectral changes during the irradiation, under identical conditions, of ergosterol (upper curves) and 3,17-dihydroxyandrostadiene (lower curves). (After Dimroth and Paland.[47])

bond at C-22. It has not been isolated in sufficient purity for direct studies to be made on its activatability, but as a component of the provitamin D mixture occurring in *Mytilus edulis* it probably contributes to the vitamin D potency of the irradiated mixture.[50] One would expect it to be activatable, because the double bond at C-22 is known (in ergosterol) not to prevent the formation of an effective vitamin D.

7-Dehydrocholesterol and 7-dehydroepicholesterol have identical side chains, the shortest and simplest found in any provitamin D of unquestioned activatability. A double bond at C-22, as in ergosterol, is favorable to activation, but not essential for it, because when it is saturated, as in 22-dihydroergosterol, activation can still occur, although the vitamin D

[65] G. A. D. Haslewood, *Biochem. J.* **33,** 454 (1939).

produced is of lesser potency.[66, 67] When the double bond is replaced by an oxido group, as in 22,23-oxidoergosterol, the activatability is sharply reduced.[47]

7-Dehydrocampesterol is a C-24 epimer of 22-dihydroergosterol.[68, 69] It is about one-tenth as activatable as ergosterol, being in this respect somewhat inferior to 22-dihydroergosterol. Thus it appears that the difference in antiricketic activity due to stereoisomerism on C-24 is somewhat greater than the difference caused by the double bond at C-22.

The presence of an ethyl group at C-24, as in 7-dehydrostigmasterol, instead of a methyl group as in ergosterol, apparently destroys activatability.[65] An ethyl group at C-24 is present in 7-dehydrositosterol, which in early experiments was found to be activatable.[39, 67] Ruigh,[69] however, has presented evidence that the observed activatability is due to the presence in the 7-dehydrositosterol of a quantity of 7-dehydrocampesterol or other provitamin D as an impurity. 7-Dehydroclionasterol, the C-24 epimer of 7-dehydrositosterol, has not been tested for activatability, but in consideration of the presence of the ethyl group, one would not expect it to acquire marked antiricketic properties.

Several of the biological tests for the activatability of the sterols in Fig. 6 leave much to be desired. In most instances the irradiated products were tested only on rats, and only by oral administration. The conclusions in regard to the relation of chemical structure to antiricketic activatability might have to be modified if the products were tested at higher dosage levels, or by parenteral administration, or with a larger number of species. One is reminded that, if it were customary to use only chicks in testing vitamin D, irradiated ergosterol would be found inactive, or, at most, feebly active, in comparison with irradiated 7-dehydrocholesterol. The question mark is therefore applied to some sterols in Fig. 6, even though the best reported tests have indicated that their irradiation products do not cure rickets.

4. Newer Synthetic Methods

The provitamins D, especially 7-dehydrocholesterol, are so important commercially that much effort has been applied to improving the original synthesis[38] and to devising new procedures for dehydrogenating common sterols. Windaus and Schenck[70] patented the original procedure as applied to cholesterol, sitosterol, and stigmasterol and offered zirconium and magnesium alcoholates as alternatives to aluminum isopropylate for the re-

[66] F. G. McDonald, *J. Biol. Chem.* **114**, *Proc.* lxv (1936).

[67] W. Grab, *Hoppe-Seyler's Z. physiol. Chem.* **243**, 63 (1936).

[68] E. Fernholz and W. L. Ruigh, *J. Am. Chem. Soc.* **63**, 1157 (1941).

[69] W. L. Ruigh, *J. Am. Chem. Soc.* **64**, 1900 (1942).

[70] A. Windaus and F. Schenck, U. S. Pat. 2,098,984 (1937).

duction of the keto to the hydroxy sterols. They also obtained a product patent[71] on 7-hydroxycholesterol. Barr *et al.*[72] made 7-hydroxycholesterol by oxidizing cholesteryl hydrogen phthalate with permanganate. Haslewood[73] found that better yields of the monobenzoate of the dehydro sterols were obtained when the dibenzoate of the 7-hydroxy sterols was treated with boiling dimethylaniline instead of being heated dry *in vacuo*. Rosenberg[74] patented the use of organic bases in general for this purpose. Wintersteiner and Ruigh[75] discovered that the dibenzoate, when treated at room temperature with sodium methylate in methanol, undergoes an unexpected partial hydrolysis, the acyl group at position 3 being removed, while the acyl group at position 7 remains. The resulting 7-monobenzoate of the hydroxy sterol can then be heated in dimethylaniline to give the desired 7-dehydro sterol in superior yield and purity.

Wintersteiner[76] made 7-hydroxy sterols by treating stabilized colloidal solutions of the original sterol with molecular oxygen, and Wintersteiner and Bergström[77] obtained good yields of 7-ketocholesterol and 7-hydroxycholesterol by this means. Krámli[78] prepared 7-ketocholesteryl acetate by anodic oxidation, reduced it to 7-hydroxycholesterol with sodium methylate in methanol-benzene, and dehydrated the product to 7-dehydrocholesterol by boiling with concentrated oxalic acid solution. The dehydration procedure was admittedly open to improvement, and the product was not well characterized. Horváth and Krámli[79] obtained, among other products, 7-dehydrocholesterol from cholesterol by the action of *Azotobacter* and[80] a good yield of 7-hydroxycholesterol by the action of *Proactinomyces roseus*.

Milas and Heggie[81] have patented the dehydrogenation of cholesterol and similar sterols by treatment with a wide variety of agents. Their examples were confined to cholesteryl acetate, which they dehydrogenated with quinone, chloranil, sulfur, diphenyl sulfide, benzaldehyde, methylene blue in the presence of light, and the succinodehydrogenase of beef heart. Their best example (with quinone) showed a yield of 20 % of provitamin. Mazza

[71] A. Windaus and F. Schenck, U. S. Pat. 2,098,985 (1937).
[72] T. Barr, I. M. Heilbron, E. G. Parry, and F. S. Spring, *J. Chem. Soc.* **1936,** 1437.
[73] G. A. D. Haslewood, *J. Chem. Soc.* **1938,** 224; *Biochem. J.* **33,** 454 (1939).
[74] H. R. Rosenberg, U. S. Pat. 2,209,934 (1940).
[75] O. Wintersteiner and W. L. Ruigh, *J. Am. Chem. Soc.* **64,** 1177 (1942); U. S. Pat. 2,411,177 (1946).
[76] O. Wintersteiner, U. S. Pat. 2,400,380 (1946).
[77] O. Wintersteiner and S. Bergström, *J. Biol. Chem.* **137,** 785 (1941); S. Bergström and O. Wintersteiner, *ibid.* **141,** 597 (1941); **145,** 309, 327 (1942).
[78] A. Krámli, *Arch. Biol. Hung.* **17,** 337, 343 (1947).
[79] J. Horváth and A. Krámli, *Nature* **160,** 639 (1947).
[80] A. Krámli and J. Horváth, *Nature* **162,** 619 (1948); **163,** 219 (1949).
[81] N. A. Milas and R. Heggie, *J. Am. Chem. Soc.* **60,** 984 (1938); U. S. Pat. 2,260,085 (1941).

and Migliardi[82] dehydrogenated cholesteryl acetate with quinone in boiling acetic acid during exposure to filtered light (to activate the quinone) and obtained a yield of 7-dehydrocholesterol amounting to 30 %. Sah[83] made the provitamin by heating cholesteryl acetate with ordinary quinone and several homologs and analogs thereof.

A new semisynthesis of provitamin D, based on the selective bromination of sterols at position 7 by means of N-bromosuccinimide, has been described by Henbest et al.,[84] Bide et al.,[85] and Buisman et al.[86] Cholesteryl acetate gives 7-bromocholesteryl acetate, and this, when heated in diethylaniline, splits off hydrogen bromide, leaving 7-dehydrocholesteryl acetate, from which the free provitamin is obtained by saponification. Yields up to 30 % have been claimed. Schaaf[87] has patented some technical details of the reaction, claiming yields up to 40 %. Redel and Gauthier[88] bring about the dehydrobromination by heating with collidine, and Ruigh and Gould[89] use quinaldine, which they claim gives 50 % better yields than diethylaniline. Schaaf[90] effects a further improvement in yield by employing quinaldine diluted with aromatic hydrocarbons.

C. THE PROVITAMINS D IN NATURE

1. ISOLATION

Only rarely does a provitamin D occur in such abundance, or so free from other sterols, that it can be obtained in fair purity simply by the recrystallization of unsaponifiable extracts. The exceptions are ergosterol in certain fungi, and the new provitamin D_m in the ribbed mussel, Modiolus.[91] Usually it is necessary to employ special techniques, such as digitonin precipitation to concentrate the sterol fraction, esterification with suitable agents for the double purpose of protecting the provitamin from destruction and enhancing fractionation, and above all, chromatographic separation of the provitamin or its esters. Esterification with 3,5-dinitrobenzoyl chloride in pyridine is a characterization procedure borrowed

---

[82] F. P. Mazza and C. Migliardi, Quaderni nutriz. 8, 86 (1941).

[83] P. P. T. Sah, Rec. trav. chim. 59, 454 (1940).

[84] H. B. Henbest, E. R. H. Jones, A. E. Bide, R. W. Peevers, and P. A. Wilkinson, Nature 158, 169 (1946); E. R. H. Jones and R. W. Peevers, British Pat. 574,432 (1946).

[85] A. E. Bide, H. B. Henbest, E. R. H. Jones, R. W. Peevers, and P. A. Wilkinson, J. Chem. Soc. 1948, 1783.

[86] J. A. K. Buisman, W. Stevens, and J. van der Vliet, Rec. trav. chim. 66, 83 (1947).

[87] K. H. Schaaf, U. S. Pat. 2,542,291 (1951).

[88] J. Redel and B. Gauthier, Bull. soc. chim. France 15, 607 (1948).

[89] W. L. Ruigh and D. H. Gould, U. S. Pat. 2,546,787 (1951).

[90] K. H. Schaaf, U. S. Pat. 2,546,788 (1951).

[91] H. G. Petering and J. Waddell, J. Biol. Chem. 191, 765 (1951).

TABLE II
Occurrence of the Provitamins D in Plants and Animals[a]

Source	Provitamin D, parts per thousand of total sterol
Phanerogams	
Cottonseed oil	28*
Rye grass	15
Scopolia root	14
Spinach	10
Wheat germ oil	10*
Cocksfoot grass	8
Horse chestnut	8
Rutabaga	2.8
Carrot	1.7
Bean	1.0
Cabbage	0.5
Cryptogams	
Mold, *Aspergillus niger*	≐ 1000
Mushroom, *Cortinellus shiitake*	≐ 1000
Ergot, *Claviceps purpurea*	900
Yeast, *Saccharomyces cerevisiæ*	800*
Mold, *Penicillium puberulum*	280
Alga, seaweed, *Fucus vesiculosus*	0.8
Vertebrates	
Skin, pig	46*
Skin, chicken feet	25*
Skin, rat	19*
Skin, wild pig	16
Skin, mouse	9
Skin, calf	7
Skin, human adult	4.2
Skin, human infant	1.5
Skin, cow	1.8
Skin, deer	1.6
Skin, eel	1.2
Skin, chicken trunk	0.06*
Liver, tuna, Japanese	11
Liver, cod, Atlantic	4.4
Liver, shark	1.0
Liver, tuna	1.0
Liver, pig	1.0
Liver, cod, Japanese	0.90
Liver, halibut	0.60*
Liver, tuna, bluefin	0.40
Liver, whale	0.12
Brain, rabbit	0.70
Brain, lumpfish	0.50
Brain, human fetus	0.50*

TABLE II—*Continued*

Source	Provitamin D, parts per thousand of total sterol
Vertebrates—*Continued*	
Brain, sheep	0.40
Brain, deer	0.33
Brain, human infant	0.20*
Brain, horse	0.19
Brain, cow	0.13*
Brain, human adult	0.06*
Eggs, duck, Chinese	60*
Eggs, duck, Dutch	13
Eggs, cod (roe)	5.5
Eggs, herring (roe)	2.4*
Eggs, hen	1.6*
Eggs, cormorant	1.0
Eggs, mire crow	1.0
Eggs, silver gull	1.0
Eggs, lumpfish (roe)	0.3
Body of frog	8.8
Venom of toad	4.6*
Wool fat, sheep	3.9*
Milk, cow	2.3
Placenta, cow	1.8
Pancreas, beef	1.8
Blood serum, cow	1.5
Spinal cord, beef	1.2
Mice, gutted carcasses	0.80
Colostrum, cow	0.70
Thymus, cow	0.70
Bile, ox	0.50
Herring oil	0.50
Spleen, cow	0.45
Milt, herring	0.40
Heart, calf	0.32
Lymph, dog	0.30
Rats, gutted carcasses	0.30
Gallstones, man	0.25*
Lung, calf	0.25
Blood, dog	0.10
Sclerotic aortas, man	Nil
Invertebrates	
Poriferans	
Commercial species of sponges	20
Cliona celata, sponge	<10
Spheciospongia vesparia, loggerhead sponge	<10
Halychondria panicea, sponge	6

TABLE II—*Continued*

Source	Provitamin D, parts per thousand of total sterol
Invertebrates—*Continued*	
Coelenterates	
Metridium dianthus, sea clove	86
Actinoloba dianthus, sea anemone	52*
Actinia equina, sea anemone	50
Urticina crassicornis, sea anemone	45
Pennatula quadrangularis, sea pen	42
Alcyonium digitatum, sea finger	34
Anemonia sulcata, sea anemone	17
Commercial species of corals	10
Australian species of sea anemones	9
Unidentified species of sea anemones	trace
Bryozoan	
Flustra securifrons, sea mat	65*
Annelids	
Tubifex (Sp.), waterworm	210*
Lumbricus terrestris, earthworm	170*
Arenicola marina, lugworm, sandworm	55*
Hirudo medicinalis, leech	39*
Nereis virius, ragworm	16*
Arthropods	
Tenebrio molitor, mealworm	120*
Melolontha vulgaris, cockchafer grubs	89
Gyronomus (Sp.), gnat	61
Dytiscus marginalis, diving beetle	40
Carausius morosus, locust eggs	25
Aleurobius farinae, meal mite	25
Eriocheir sinensis, wool hand crab	23*
Blatta orientalis, cockroach	23
"Kieferspinnerraupe," pine caterpillar	22
Cantharis vesicatoria, Spanish fly	22
Cancer pagurus, common crab	15*
Bombyx mori, silkworm eggs	8.9*
Daphnia (Sp.), waterflea	7.5
Musca domestica, housefly	7.0
Melolontha vulgaris, cockchafer, May beetle	5.0
Apis mellifica, honeybee	4.5
Crangon vulgaris, shrimp	3.8*
Munida bamffica, crustacean	3.5
Homarus vulgaris, lobster	2.5
Mollusks	
Modiolus demissus, ribbed mussel	370*
Arion empiricorum, slug, red road snail	220*
Buccinum undatum, whelk, wave horn snail	180*
Littorina littorea, periwinkle	170*
Archidoris tuberculata, sea snail	150

TABLE II—*Concluded*

Source	Provitamin D, parts per thousand of total sterol
Invertebrates—*Continued*	
Ostrea (Sp.), Australian oyster	130
Arion (Sp.), black road snail	120
Mytilus edulis, sea mussel	100*
Helix pomatia, edible snail, vineyard snail	97*
Anodonta cygnea, swan mussel	80
Ostrea virginica, oyster	80
Pecten (Sp.), Australian scallop	65
Mytilus planulatus, Australian mussel	62*
Cardium edule, cockle, sand shell	50*
Cardium tenuicostatum, Australian cockle	41*
Ostrea edulis, oyster	34*
Limax agrestis, earth snail	32
Sepia (Sp.), cuttlefish, squid	12*
Echinoderms	
Astropecten irregularis, little sea aster	4.5
Asterias rubens, starfish, big sea aster	3.8

[a] Data from Windaus,[94] Gillam and Heilbron,[95] van derVliet,[96] and others. Figures marked (*) are the average of two or more determinations.

from the organic chemists by Callow,[92] who first applied it to vitamin D work in the isolation of calciferol from irradiated ergosterol. It has proved useful in the identification of both the vitamins and provitamins D, to which latter purpose it was first applied by Boer *et al.*[93] Boer was also the first to adapt chromatography to the isolation of a provitamin D, and he gave a good working account of this procedure.

The unsaponifiable fractions of the fats of nearly all plant and animal tissues (Table II) exhibit the provitamin D absorption spectrum, but the quantity of provitamin D present is usually so small that its isolation is a task of considerable magnitude.[97] Isolation has been achieved in only a few instances, leaving great territories unexplored. The following examples constitute most of the published work to date.

[92] R. K. Callow, Chemistry at the Centenary (1931) Meeting of the British Association for the Advancement of Science, p. 149. Heffer, Cambridge, 1932.

[93] A. G. Boer, E. H. Reerink, A. van Wijk, and J. van Niekerk, *Proc. Koninkl. Akad. Wetenschap. Amsterdam* **39**, 622 (1936); A. G. Boer, J. van Niekerk, E. H. Reerink, and A. van Wijk, Dutch Pat. 45,849 (1939).

[94] A. Windaus, *Nachr. Ges. Wiss. Göttingen, Math. physik. Kl., Fachgruppe* **III** 185 (1936).

[95] A. E. Gillam and I. M. Heilbron, *Biochem. J.* **30**, 1253 (1936).

[96] J. van der Vliet, *Chem. Weekblad* **39**, 271 (1942).

[97] A. Windaus and O. Stange, *Hoppe-Seyler's Z. physiol. Chem.* **244**, 218 (1936).

2. ERGOSTEROL

Tanret[98] discovered ergosterol in ergot, and Gérard[99] noted its occurrence generally in the fungi. Heiduschka and Lindner[100] compared the ergosterol content of ten fungi, including yeasts, finding from 0.29 to 1.17 % of ergosterol in the dry substance. The ergosterol content of twenty-nine species and strains of yeast, grown under similar conditions, was determined spectrographically by Bills et al.[101] and found to vary from a trace to as high as 2.0 % of the dry material. The ergosterol of commerce is obtained from baker's yeast, i.e., strains of *Saccharomyces cerevisiae* grown in aerated wort. Part of the supply was formerly obtained from *Aspergillus niger*,[102] but this source has been abandoned in favor of yeast. Savard and Grant[103] cited previous studies on the occurrence of ergosterol in several species of *Penicillium* and isolated some ergosterol from the mycelium of *P. notatum* grown in submerged culture. Although available in quantity from the antibiotics industry, *Penicillium* has not become a commercial source of ergosterol, because the yield is comparatively low.

Windaus and Stange[94, 97] isolated ergosterol from the sterol of hens' eggs. Its presence there, in association with cholesterol, was surprising but explainable on the basis that it had been transferred from the feed of the hens (cf. grass, grains, and earthworms, below). It is known[104] that hens, unlike mice, rats, rabbits, or dogs, absorb small amounts of fed ergosterol. The finding of ergosterol in eggs does not preclude the possibility that other provitamins D were also present but less readily isolated by the chromatographic technique which was employed.

Bock and Wetter[105] studied the sterols of the vineyard snail, *Helix pomatia*, the red road snail, or slug, *Arion empiricorum*, and the common earthworm, *Lumbricus terrestris*. In these the major sterols were cholesterol and some phytosterol-like substances, but the only provitamin isolated from the mixtures was ergosterol. The coexistence of other provitamins was not precluded, and almost certainly others were present, for Boer et al.[106, 107]

[98] C. Tanret, *Ann. chim. et phys.* Ser. 5, **17,** 493 (1879); *Compt. rend.* **108,** 98 (1889); *Ann. chim. et phys.* Ser. 6, **20,** 289 (1890); Ser. 8, **15,** 313 (1908).

[99] E. Gérard, *Compt. rend.* **114,** 1544 (1892); **121,** 723 (1895); **126,** 909 (1898); *J. pharm. chim. Ser.* 6, **1,** 601 (1895).

[100] A. Heiduschka and H. Lindner, *Hoppe-Seyler's Z. physiol. Chem.* **181,** 15 (1929).

[101] C. E. Bills, O. N. Massengale, and P. S. Prickett, *J. Biol. Chem.* **87,** 259 (1930).

[102] A. Zimmerli, U. S. Pat. 1,893,317 (1933).

[103] K. Savard and G. A. Grant, *Science* **104,** 459 (1946).

[104] R. Schönheimer and H. Dam, *Hoppe-Seyler's Z. physiol. Chem.* **211,** 241 (1932); W. Menschick and I. H. Page, *ibid.* **211,** 246 (1932).

[105] F. Bock and F. Wetter, *Hoppe-Seyler's Z. physiol. Chem.* **256,** 33 (1938).

[106] A. G. Boer, J. van Niekerk, E. H. Reerink, and A. van Wijk, U. S. Pat. 2,163,659 (1939).

[107] A. G. Boer, J. van Niekerk, E. H. Reerink, and A. van Wijk, U. S. Pat. 2,266,674 (1941).

have ascribed to the "spectroscopically pure" provitamin of earthworms physical constants different from those of ergosterol and have further described the earthworm provitamins as a "chicken provitamin D." Indeed, van der Vliet[96] ascribes to earthworm provitamin D, activated, an efficacy ratio of 100.

Pollard[108] found ergosterol in cocksfoot grass, and Windaus and Bock identified it in wheat germ oil,[109] cottonseed oil, and scopolia root sterols.[110] The 7-dehydro derivatives of sitosterol, stigmasterol and campesterol, which might have been expected in these sources, were not found and, in fact, have never been found in nature.

The foregoing chemical studies are supported and extended by chick-rat assays on irradiated vegetable materials. Thus Bethke et al.[111] found the low efficacy ratio characteristic of irradiated ergosterol in irradiated specimens of cottonseed oil, wheat middlings, and alfalfa leaf, as well as in yeast and Aspergillus. Haman and Steenbock[112] found the low ratios in irradiated coconut, peanut, and wheat germ oils, and Black and Sassaman[113] got similar results with alfalfa unsaponifiables and maize oil phytosterol. Koch and Koch,[114] however, reported that irradiated maize oil phytosterol showed a somewhat higher efficacy ratio than irradiated ergosterol. On the whole, it appears that, with one exception, no provitamin D but ergosterol has yet been identified in the vegetable kingdom. The exception is 22-dihydroergosterol, which Santos Ruíz[115] has separated chromatographically from the minor sterols of ergot.

3. 7-Dehydrocholesterol

In only three instances has 7-dehydrocholesterol been isolated from a natural source. Boer et al.[93] obtained it from a sample of duck egg cholesterol containing 4.5 % of provitamin D. That ducks' eggs should contain a different provitamin D from hens' eggs is remarkable and doubtless reflects a difference in diet, perhaps a predominantly fish diet in the case of the ducks. Windaus and Bock[116] isolated 7-dehydrocholesterol from pigskin, and Bock and Wetter[105] obtained it from the wave horn snail, or whelk, Buccinum undatum. It is noteworthy that this snail yielded 7-dehydrocholesterol, whereas the two other snails studied by the same investigators gave ergosterol.

[108] A. Pollard, Biochem. J. 30, 382 (1936).
[109] A. Windaus and F. Bock, Hoppe-Seyler's Z. physiol. Chem. 256, 47 (1938).
[110] A. Windaus and F. Bock, Hoppe-Seyler's Z. physiol. Chem. 250, 258 (1937).
[111] R. M. Bethke, P. R. Record, and O. H. M. Wilder, J. Biol. Chem. 112, 231 (1935).
[112] R. W. Haman and H. Steenbock, J. Biol. Chem. 114, 505 (1936).
[113] A. Black and H. L. Sassaman, Am. J. Pharm. 108, 237 (1936).
[114] E. M. Koch and F. C. Koch, J. Biol. Chem. 116, 757 (1936).
[115] A. Santos Ruíz, Anales real acad. farm. 3, 201 (1941).
[116] A. Windaus and F. Bock, Hoppe-Seyler's Z. physiol. Chem. 245, 168 (1937).

It is assumed, on the basis of chick-rat assays, that the provitamin D in the cholesterol of all mammalian sources is 7-dehydrocholesterol. Commercial cholesterol, such as was used in Waddell's work,[36] comes from the spinal cords of cattle. Bethke et al.[111] found that activated samples of butter, lard, and brain exhibit the same high efficacy ratio as cod liver oil or irradiated ordinary cholesterol. Haman and Steenbock[112] reported high efficacy ratios for irradiated lard and chicken fat.

4. PROVITAMINS D OF INVERTEBRATES

The phenomenal abundance of provitamin D in the sterols of the invertebrates has been demonstrated by a number of workers,[91, 94-96, 105-107, 117-121] whose findings are included in Table II. In several instances provitamins have been isolated, which, although "pure" by spectrographic tests, do not correspond in other properties to any known form of provitamin D. Some of these have considerable commercial, as well as theoretical, importance.

Four provitamins were described in the patents of Boer et al.[106, 107, 117] The one from the earthworm, Lumbricus terrestris, has already been discussed and shown to be a mixture of ergosterol with at least one other, unidentified, provitamin. The one from the waterworm, Tubifex, has not been further investigated chemically, but in view of the findings on Lumbricus it seems unlikely that it is a single substance. In biological tests[96] it has been found to have an efficacy ratio of 100 when activated. The one from the common sea mollusk, Mytilus edulis, has been reinvestigated by van der Vliet,[50] who considers it to be a mixture of three main components, 7-dehydrocholesterol, ergosterol, and a provitamin tentatively identified as 22-dehydro-7-dehydrocholesterol (i.e., $\Delta^{5,7,22}$-cholestatriene-3-ol). These sterols were not isolated, but their presence indicated indirectly by fractionations, degradations, and efficacy ratios. The presence of ergosterol could account for the somewhat low efficacy ratio of 71% reported[120] for the mixture. It has been suggested that the provitamin D of the periwinkle, Littorina littorea, may be impure 7-dehydroclionasterol.[122] After irradiation it is said[96] to exhibit an efficacy ratio of 100%. Such effectiveness seems inconsistent with the presence of an ethyl group in the side chain.

Van der Vliet[96] has determined the chick-rat efficacy ratios of several other invertebrate provitamins D which have not been examined

[117] A. G. Boer, J. van Niekerk, E. H. Reerink, and A. van Wijk, U. S. Pat. 2,216,719 (1940).
[118] P. Fantl, Australian J. Exptl. Biol. Med. Sci. 20, 55 (1942).
[119] W. S. Calcott, J. Waddell, and H. R. Rosenberg, U. S. Pat. 2,383,446 (1945).
[120] H. R. Rosenberg and J. Waddell, J. Biol. Chem. 191, 757 (1951).
[121] H. Rosenberg, U. S. Pat. 2,475,917 (1949).
[122] C. A. Kind and S. C. Herman, J. Org. Chem. 13, 867 (1948).

chemically. After irradiation, the provitamins of the mealworm, *Tenebrio molitor*, the sea mussel, *Mytilus edulis*, the starfish, *Asterias rubens*, and the sponge, *Halychondria panicea*, exhibited efficacy ratios of about 100 %, which indicates the absence of much ergosterol. But the activated provitamin of the leech, *Hirudo medicinalis*, showed only 65 % effectiveness, and that of the crab, *Cancer pagurus*, only 10 %. These must have contained ergosterol, or some other provitamin of low efficacy ratio.

The richest of all known animal sources of provitamin D is the ribbed mussel, *Modiolus demissus*,[91, 119, 120] in which the provitamin content amounts to from 35 % to 50 % of the total sterol. The crude provitamin appears to be a mixture of provitamins D, according to Rosenberg and Waddell,[120] who noted differences in chick-rat efficacy ratios of specimens made from mussels from different environments. From the crude sterols Petering and Waddell [91] isolated a provitamin which they tentatively called provitamin D_m (m for *Modiolus*). This appears to be a single substance, with 29 carbon atoms, which in the activated form exhibits an efficacy ratio 10 % to 20 % higher than cod liver oil.[119]

5. Biogenesis

Plants differ from animals in having no mechanism for the translocation of lipoids. Therefore, in plants, the provitamin D, like all sterols, must originate and accumulate in the cells where it is found, whereas in animals its origin may be remote from the site of accumulation.

In plants ergosterol is the predominant provitamin D. In some of the lower species it comprises up to 95 % of the total sterol, and hence it would seem to be a primary metabolic product. Sumi[123] observed that the formation of ergosterol in the mushroom, *Cortinellus shiitake*, can occur at any stage of the life cycle, and that the percentage of ergosterol steadily rises as the plant grows older.

It would seem that in plants ergosterol is synthesized from simple compounds of carbon. Thus ergosterol has been produced in *Penicillium glaucum* from sucrose and tartaric acid,[124] in *Mucor mucedo* from lactose,[125] in *Penicillium puberulum*,[126] *Aspergillus fischeri*,[127] and many other fungi[128] from dextrose as the carbon sources.

[123] M. Sumi, *Sci. Papers Inst. Phys. Chem. Research Tokyo*, **20**, 254 (1933).
[124] E. Gérard, *Compt. rend.* **114**, 1544 (1892).
[125] E. Gérard, *Compt. rend.* **121**, 723 (1895); *J. pharm. chim. Ser.* 6, **1**, 601 (1895).
[126] J. H. Birkinshaw, R. K. Callow, and C. F. Fischmann, *Biochem. J.* **25**, 1977 (1931).
[127] L. M. Pruess, W. H. Peterson, and E. B. Fred, *J. Biol. Chem.* **97**, 483 (1932).
[128] L. M. Preuss, W. H. Peterson, H. Steenbock, and E. B. Fred, *J. Biol. Chem.* **90**, 369 (1931).

Massengale *et al.*[129] demonstrated that the yeast *Saccharomyces cerevisiae* elaborated widely different amounts of ergosterol, according to the sugar which supplied the carbon to the basal medium. This work contributes one of the few bits of information available on the mechanism of sterol formation. Seven fermentable sugars were used, with the finding that di- and trihexoses occasioned the synthesis of greater amounts of ergosterol than did the monohexoses (singly or in admixture) into which they are hydrolyzed. The amounts of ergosterol produced bore no relation to the protein or fat content of the yeast cells. It is a reasonable inference, therefore, that the monohexoses which are split from the higher sugars by the yeast enzymes exist at the instant of cleavage in forms particularly suitable for synthesis into sterol. According to this concept, ergosterol is primarily a product of carbohydrate metabolism.

In this connection, an experiment by Maclean and Hoffert[130] is significant. It was found that the presence of sulfite in the sugar solution in which the yeast was incubated resulted in a marked decrease in ergosterol production but in little or no interference with the elaboration of fatty acid. The argument was advanced that in the formation of sterol, but not of fatty acid, an aldehyde removable by sulfite comes into the picture between the hexose and the final product. The action of the sulfite might have been better explained as that of an oxygen remover. Actually, the production of ergosterol is enhanced by the presence of oxygen carriers such as methylene blue and various inorganic per-salts.[131]

Halden and his associates,[132] who maintain that there is a biogenetic relationship between fats and sterols, have succeeded in increasing the ergosterol production of yeast ten- to fortyfold by keeping it in a state of semidehydration and supplying alcohol and air. Under these conditions the normal processes of budding and fermenting are repressed, while the production of fat and sterol, especially the latter, is augmented to an extraordinary degree. Halden's papers contain a valuable review of ergosterol production in yeast.

In the higher plants even less is known about the origin of the ubiquitous ergosterol. Heilbron and Sexton[133] suggested that it arises from the simultaneous oxidation and reduction (dehydrogenation and hydrogenation) of sitosterol, which at the time (1929) was believed to have 27 carbon atoms, the same as ergosterol. This would relate the known wide occurrence of

[129] O. N. Massengale, C. E. Bills, and P. S. Prickett, *J. Biol. Chem.* **94,** 213 (1931).
[130] I. Smedley Maclean and D. Hoffert, *Biochem. J.* **20,** 343 (1926).
[131] W. G. Bennett, U. S. Pat. 2,059,980 (1936).
[132] W. Halden, *Hoppe-Seyler's Z. physiol. Chem.* **225,** 249 (1934); Austrian Pat. 140,190 (1934); M. Sobotka, W. Halden, and F. Bilger, *Hoppe-Seyler's Z. physiol. Chem.* **234,** 1 (1935).
[133] I. M. Heilbron and W. A. Sexton, *Nature* **123,** 567 (1929).

dihydrositosterol and ergosterol to the commonest vegetable sterol, but, unfortunately for this hypothesis, sitosterol and ergosterol were later found to contain 29 and 28 carbon atoms, respectively.[134] If ergosterol is the 7-dehydro derivative of anything, it would be of brassicasterol, but this sterol is much less widely distributed than sitosterol. Also, against the hypothesis of origin by oxidation-reduction is the fact that no provitamin except ergosterol (and 22-dihydroergosterol) has been found in the vegetable kingdom. Until a better explanation is offered, it will have to suffice to regard ergosterol as a primary metabolic product of the higher plants, as well as of the lower.

In animals the provitamins D are partly absorbed from food and partly formed within the body. The ergosterol in hens' eggs is a clear example of an exogenous provitamin. The ergosterol of worms, snails, and bivalves is probably also derived from the food, but the 7-dehydrocholesterol of these species may be endogenous. In carnivorous and omnivorous animals it is probable that some of the 7-dehydrocholesterol is absorbed along with the cholesterol of their prey. In a word, it appears that all ergosterol originates in plants, and all 7-dehydrocholesterol in animals; almost nothing is known about the origin of the still unidentified provitamins of the invertebrates.

Herbivorous mammals, which normally never ingest cholesterol after weaning, and also the herbivorous lower animals, apparently must synthesize their 7-dehydrocholesterol as well as their cholesterol, and it is probable that all animals do this to some extent. It is not known whether total synthesis from simple compounds of carbon or partial synthesis from cholesterol takes place. There is no evidence of total synthesis other than the analogy of the well-established fact that animals synthesize cholesterol itself.[11, 134a]

There is considerable evidence that 7-dehydrocholesterol can be formed *in vivo* from cholesterol. Schoenheimer[135] in 1931 applied Wieland's dehydrogenation theory to the explanation of the ubiquitous occurrence of dehydrocholesterol and dihydrocholesterol in cholesterol. According to this view, dehydrogenation and hydrogenation of cholesterol occur simultaneously as a general biological process in which cholesterol functions as hydrogen acceptor. (It is immaterial that Schoenheimer spoke of ergosterol as the provitamin in this system, for at that time ergosterol was thought to have the same number of carbon atoms as cholesterol; his argument applies equally well to 7-dehydrocholesterol). In keeping with this theory are the observations that dehydrogenation of cholesterol can be brought about *in vitro* by an enzyme[81] and by bacterial action.[79] The constant forma-

[134] A. Windaus, F. von Werder, and B. Gschaider, *Ber.* **65,** 1006 (1932).
[134a] K. Bloch and D. Rittenberg, *J. Biol. Chem.* **145,** 625 (1942).
[135] R. Schoenheimer, *Science* **74,** 579 (1931).

tion of traces of 7-dehydrocholesterol by some sort of oxidation-reduction mechanism may also explain the reported presence of the unstable provitamin D in roughly normal amount in the cholesterol from the brain of a mummy 1400 years old.[136]

It may be that the biosynthesis of 7-dehydrocholesterol occurs in steps, rather than as a dehydrogenation-hydrogenation reaction. Bergström and Wintersteiner[137] have shown that position 7 in cholesterol is extremely susceptible to attack by molecular oxygen. Haslewood[138] and others have detected 7-hydroxycholesterol in the animal body, and although this was possibly an artifact, the ease with which it is formed from cholesterol in stabilized colloidal solutions points to a possible route of synthesis, since only the dehydration step is needed to convert it to 7-dehydrocholesterol. 7-Ketocholesterol, which precedes 7-hydroxycholesterol in the laboratory synthesis, has also been found in the animal body.[137, 139]

Whatever the reactions involved, the fact of conversion of cholesterol to 7-dehydrocholesterol appears to be established by the experiments of Scott et al.[140] These workers found provitamin D in the lining of the small intestine of guinea pig, rat, and ox in amounts as large or larger than in the skin, usually regarded as the site of the greatest concentration. It persisted in the gut wall despite fasting for 24 hours or the feeding of a low-sterol diet. When spectroscopically pure cholesterol was fed to fasted guinea pigs the amount of provitamin in the small intestine increased during the period of absorption but returned to normal when absorption was completed. Since during the same cycle the amount of provitamin in the liver increased progressively, it follows that the provitamin was formed in the gut wall and stored in the liver. The concentration of provitamin was greatest in the duodenum and was associated largely with the mucosa and lamina propria.

Partially supporting this work is a note by Rosenberg,[141] who found in clams feeding on algae a much higher concentration of provitamin in the viscera than in the body. The kind of provitamin was not determined, but the efficacy ratio was the same for the visceral as for the body material, and it was much higher than would be expected of a vegetable source. It would seem that in these clams provitamin D was being elaborated in the gut wall, from nutrients in the process of absorption, but whether the synthesis was a total one or merely a dehydrogenation is not clear.

[136] H. King, O. Rosenheim, and T. A. Webster, *Biochem. J.* **23,** 166 (1929).
[137] S. Bergström and O. Wintersteiner, *J. Biol. Chem.* **141,** 597 (1941).
[138] G. A. D. Haslewood, *Biochem. J.* **33,** 709 (1939); *Nature* **154,** 29 (1944).
[139] V. Prelog, L. Ruzicka, and P. Stein, *Helv. Chim. Acta* **26,** 2222 (1943).
[140] M. Scott, J. Glover, and R. A. Morton, *Nature* **163,** 530 (1949).
[141] H. R. Rosenberg, *Nature* **164,** 795 (1949).

D. THE VITAMINS D

1. Occurrence and Origin

In contrast to the almost universal occurrence of provitamin D, vitamin D itself is very limited in its distribution.[142] In the vegetable kingdom it is especially rare and never found in high concentration. Occasional specimens of coconut oil show antiricketic activity, but the potency here is not natural; it is man-made in the primitive process of drying the copra under the sun. It is historically interesting to note that what was probably the first therapeutic use of an irradiated material was made a century ago by Thompson,[143] who, writing on the anemia of tuberculosis, stated that "the use of almond-oil and of olive-oil was not followed by any remedial effect, but from cocoa-nut oil results were obtained almost as decided as from the oil of the liver of the Cod . . ."

Yeast normally never contains vitamin D, but it can be activated to a potency of 10,000 I.U. per gram by exposing it in powdered form to sunlight under controlled conditions.[144] Clover hay when cured in the dark is inactive, but when cured in the sun it acquires a slight antiricketic activity.[145] Cocoa shell, as obtained from fermented beans dried in the sun, has been reported to contain 28 I.U. of vitamin D per gram, part of which may have originated in the surface fungi known to be present.[146] The antiricketic activity of ergot[147] is probably due to something other than vitamin D, because the active substance cannot be extracted from the unsaponifiable fraction with petroleum ether.

Marine vegetation being the ultimate food of fishes, much interest attaches to the possible occurrence of vitamin D in the plant life of the ocean.[9] Leigh-Clare[148] observed that the marine diatom, *Nitzschia closterium*, fails to effect any genesis of vitamin D, when cultured under conditions of maximum insolation. Drummond and Gunther[149] found little or no vitamin D in mixed phytoplankton taken from the ocean. Johnson and Levring[150]

[142] E. P. Daniel and H. E. Munsell, *U. S. Dept. Agr. Misc. Publ.* **275** (1937); L. E. Booher, E. R. Hortzler, and E. M. Hewston, Vitamin Values of Foods. Chemical Publishing Co., Brooklyn, 1942.

[143] T. Thompson, *Proc. Roy. Soc. (London)* **7**, 41 (1854).

[144] O. N. Massengale, C. E. Bills, and P. S. Prickett, *J. Biol. Chem.* **94**, 213 (1931); C. E. Bills, U. S. Pat. 1,877,382 (1932).

[145] H. Steenbock, E. B. Hart, C. A. Elvehjem, and S. W. F. Kletzien, *J. Biol. Chem.* **66**, 425 (1925).

[146] A. W. Knapp and K. H. Coward, *Analyst* **59**, 474 (1934).

[147] E. Mellanby, E. Surie, and D. C. Harrison, *Biochem. J.* **23**, 710 (1929).

[148] J. L. Leigh-Clare, *Biochem. J.* **21**, 368 (1927).

[149] J. C. Drummond and E. R. Gunther, *Nature* **126**, 398 (1930); *J. Exptl. Biol.* **11**, 203 (1934).

[150] N. G. Johnson and T. Levring, *Svenska Hydrograf.-Biol. Komm. Skrifter*, Ser. 3, **1**, No. 3, 7 pp. (1947) [*C. A.* **45**, 236 (1951)].

found no vitamin D in two species of higher algae, *Enteromorpha intestinalis* and *Laminaria saccharina*, but in *Fucus vesiculosus* they reported slight activity. They found provitamin D, but no vitamin D, in phytoplankton oil.

Darby and Clarke[151] investigated the floating brown alga, *Sargassum*, in the area of its origin near the Tortugas Islands. Here in clear water under the tropical sun enormous quantities of the weed develop. Masses of it break away and drift into the Gulf Stream, in which it floats as far as Iceland. As it drifts along it becomes heavily infested with mollusks, shrimps, and other invertebrates, and thus indirectly it is a major food of fish. *Sargassum* free of foreign matter contains about 3 % of oil on the dry basis, and this oil was reported to have an antiricketic potency of the same order as some of the poorer fish liver oils.

An especially interesting example of the natural occurrence of vitamin D in the vegetable kingdom is found in the work of Scheunert *et al.*[152] with edible mushrooms. Four species were studied, and they showed a vitamin D content of 0.21 to 1.25 I.U. per gram when grown in the absence of strong light. One species, the common *Agaricus campestris*, exhibited 0.21 I.U. per gram when grown in a cellar, and three times as much when grown in a meadow where light presumably was a factor. In these ergosterol-rich plants, a minute fraction of the provitamin apparently is activated without the agency of light.

There is no evidence that vitamin D plays any role in plant physiology, and it is not difficult to understand why it is seldom found in live plant tissues. The lower, non-pigmented, non-photosynthesizing plants, which contain much ergosterol, thrive in dark places and perish in the light. The higher plants, containing relatively little provitamin, possess pigments which presumably filter out the activating rays at the short end of the solar spectrum. Even if the vitamin could be formed in the superficial layers, plants could not store it, unprovided as they are with any system for the translocation of lipoids.

In the animal kingdom vitamin D is less rare than in plants, but it is abundant only in certain fishes. In mammals it is found principally in the milk and liver, and in birds in the liver and egg yolks.[142] These foods contain from a fraction of a unit to several units per gram—only enough to make them marginal sources of vitamin D for human nutrition. The amount can be substantially increased by irradiating the animals or adding vitamin D to their food.[142]

The fact that mammals and birds are subject to rickets is proof that they cannot synthesize vitamin D. Except for occasional amounts gained by eating

[151] H. H. Darby and H. T. Clarke, *Science* **85**, 318 (1937).
[152] A. Scheunert, M. Schieblich, and J. Reschke, *Hoppe-Seyler's Z. physiol. Chem.* **235**, 91 (1935).

such foods as fish and eggs, the vitamin must normally be obtained by exposure of the body surface to the sun (the "sunshine vitamin"). Since sunshine is variable, both daily and seasonally, the amounts obtained by insolation vary widely. The body has two mechanisms for adjustment to the variable supply. Excess vitamin D is stored, principally in the liver, where it may be held and released over long periods of time. This is the basis of the "Stosstherapie" method of preventing rickets in children, which consists in administering massive doses of vitamin D at intervals of several months.[153, 154] Prolonged insolation results in tanning, a process of temporary pigmentation which presumably has the effect of filtering out the activating rays received in superabundance. It is well known that Negroes and other dark-skinned people are more susceptible to rickets than white people, and this difference appears to be due at least in part to pigmentation.[155, 156] The picturesque suggestion has been made that in human evolution vitamin D played a role in the appearance of blonde races in the cold countries, where they have an advantage over dark races in the absorption of the limited sunlight.

That man and animals are well adapted to a variable supply of vitamin D is clearly shown in the phenomenally wide margin which exists between the therapeutic and the toxic doses of this substance.[11] For rats, doses 1000 times the antiricketic dose, administered daily for months, are just perceptibly harmful, and much larger single doses can be tolerated. For man, the margin appears to be somewhat less, but still enormous. Probably no other potent therapeutic agent exhibits such a wide margin of safety, but if it were not wide, animal life could not have survived the fluctuations in solar activity and vitamin D formation to which it has always been subjected in nature.

The formation of vitamin D on the body surface has been thoroughly studied. Sunshine, like fish oil, is an old remedy for rickets. In 1919 Huldschinsky[157] clearly demonstrated, by means of radiographs, the healing action of sunlight and of the light from the quartz mercury arc. Hess et al.[158] determined that the effective wavelengths of light are the shorter ultraviolet waves of the solar spectrum, or the still shorter waves of artificial

[153] G. O. Harnapp, *Wien. klin. Wochschr.* **53**, 698 (1940).

[154] H. Uflacker, *Z. Kinderheilk.* **67**, 350 (1949).

[155] A. F. Hess, Rickets, Osteomalacia and Tetany, p. 92. Lea and Febiger, Philadelphia, 1929.

[156] M. M. Eliot and E. A. Park, *in* Brennemann's Practice of Pediatrics, Vol. 1, Chapter 36, pp. 3, 12. W. F. Prior Co., Hagerstown, Md., 1948.

[157] K. Huldschinsky, *Deut. med. Wochschr.* **45**, 712 (1919); *Z. orthopäd. Chir.* **39**, 426 (1920).

[158] A. F. Hess, A. M. Pappenheimer, and M. Weinstock, *Proc. Soc. Exptl. Biol. Med.* **20**, 14 (1922).

sources. Goldblatt and Soames[159] discovered that the livers of irradiated rats, when fed to non-irradiated rats, convey some of the virtue of irradiation to the animals which eat them. Hess et al.[8] found that lanolin, the fat of wool, is activatable, and Hess and Weinstock[24] discovered that skin itself becomes antiricketic upon irradiation and that irradiated cholesterol is effective when administered subcutaneously.

Rekling[160] found that irradiation did not protect rats from rickets when they were prevented from licking their fur. Hou and Tso[161] found that the skin of normal rabbits was slightly antiricketic, the dorsal skin more so than the ventral, but that the skin of rickety rabbits or of normal rabbits reared indoors was without protective action. Hou[162] noted that the effectiveness of ultraviolet irradiation for curing rickets in rabbits was almost lost when the skin had been previously washed with ether. Rowan[163] observed that birds of prey on a meat diet developed rickets, and that the addition of feathers to the diet supplied protection. He suggested that the preen gland is concerned with the formation of vitamin D. Hou[164] made an elaborate study of the formation of vitamin D in birds. In brief, his findings were as follows. Birds differ from mammals in having only one gland of a sebaceous nature. This is the *glandula uropygialis*, or preen gland. Preen gland oil contains provitamin D, which birds, by preening, distribute over their feathers and effectively expose to sunlight. The vitamin D is either ingested by swallowing the feathers, or absorbed by the skin from the feathers. The feathers and skin of normal birds were shown to be antiricketic, but in rickety birds, or birds whose preen glands had been removed, the feathers and skin had little, if any, antiricketic action. Removal of the preen gland made the birds susceptible to rickets, and rickety birds without the gland were not benefited by exposure to ultraviolet radiation or sunshine.

Thus Hou[165] was led to see that " . . . vitamin D or its precursor is principally derived from the oil secretion rather than from the diet. This may be more or less true for all birds. For although nocturnal birds, and the carnivorous animals which prey upon other forms of 'feather and fur,' may derive their vitamin D supply mainly from their victims, yet the source of the vitamin in the prey would appear to lie in the oil secretion. This may explain the absence of oil gland in some species of birds . . . and the necessity of adding rabbits or small birds with the fur or feather intact, to the diet

[159] H. Goldblatt and K. M. Soames, *Biochem. J.* **17,** 446 (1923).
[160] E. Rekling, *Strahlentherapie* **25,** 568 (1927).
[161] H. C. Hou and E. Tso, *Chinese J. Physiol.* **4,** 93 (1930).
[162] H. C. Hou, *Chinese J. Physiol.* **4,** 345 (1930).
[163] W. Rowan, *Nature* **121,** 323 (1928).
[164] H. C. Hou, *Chinese J. Physiol.* **2,** 345 (1928); **3,** 171 (1929); **4,** 79 (1930); **5,** 11 (1931).
[165] H. C. Hou, *Chinese J. Physiol.* **3,** 171 (1929).

of young carnivora in captivity to ensure their successful development . . .
Further, it is commonly known that if herbivora, e.g., horses, are scrubbed
thoroughly with soap and water, they do not thrive. It may thus be inferred
that the sebaceous secretion of the preen gland of birds . . . is an important
source of vitamin D in the mammal."

Hou[166] found that rickety chickens with preen glands removed could be
cured by irradiating the feet, even though irradiation of the body or of the
head was ineffective. In this case the substance activated was obviously
neither preen gland oil nor circulating blood, but something in the tissues
of the feet which was directly absorbed.

Evidence enough has been presented to show that the higher animals obtain vitamin D in at least three ways, the relative importance of which
must vary with the habits, requirements, and opportunities: (1) by eating
such foods as eggs, fish, whole furred or feathered animals, and insolated
dead vegetable tissues; (2) by ingesting insolated sebaceous matter in the
process of neatening the body—licking and preening; and (3) by directly
absorbing the products of insolation formed on or in the skin.

The occurrence of vitamin D in fishes is a phenomenon of great biochemical, as well as practical, interest. Nearly all fish oils contain vitamin D,
but the amount varies prodigiously with the species (Table III) and other
factors. Both free and esterified forms are present.[60, 169]

The principal fat storage depots of fish are the muscle tissue and the
liver. Some fat is also found in the viscera and head. Species which store
much oil in the muscle, such as salmon, have small livers which contain
little oil. Species which store little oil in the muscle, such as cod, have large
livers which contain much oil. The amount of oil which is stored in muscle
or liver depends on the abundance of food and the demands of spawning

The occurrence of vitamin D in fish body oils was first noted by Bills[170]
in experiments with commercial menhaden oil. In most physicochemical
characteristics the liver and body oils of a given species are similar, but the
concentration of vitamin D is generally higher in the liver oil. In some
species, such as the tunas, the liver oil may contain several thousand times

[166] H. C. Hou, *Chinese J. Physiol.* **5**, 11 (1931).

[167] C. E. Bills, F. G. McDonald, O. N. Massengale, M. Imboden, H. Hall, W. D. Hergert, and J. C. Wallenmeyer, *J. Biol. Chem.* **109**, Proc. vii (1935).

[168] D. S. Jordan, B. W. Evermann, and H. W. Clark, Check List of the Fishes and
Fishlike Vertebrates of North and Middle America North of the Northern Bound-
ary of Venezuela and Columbia. Report of the U. S. Commissioner of Fisheries
for the Fiscal Year 1928 with Appendixes, Part 2. Gov't Printing Office, Washington, 1930.

[169] K. C. D. Hickman, *Ind. Eng. Chem.* **29**, 1107 (1937); K. C. D. Hickman and E. L.
Gray, *ibid.* **30**, 796 (1938).

[170] C. E. Bills, Studies on the Antiricketic Vitamin: Dissertation. Johns Hopkins
Press, Baltimore, 1924.

TABLE III

DISTRIBUTION OF VITAMINS D AND A IN THE LIVER OILS OF 100 SPECIES OF FISH[a]

Common name of fish	Scientific name	Zoological order	Vitamin D, I.U./g.	Vitamin A, I.U./g.
Oriental tuna*	*Thunnus orientalis*	Percomorphi	45,000	170,000
Frigate mackerel*	*Auxis thazard*	Percomorphi	44,000	30,000
California bluefin tuna*	*Thunnus saliens*	Percomorphi	42,000	65,000
Striped tuna*	*Katsuwonus pelamis*	Percomorphi	42,000	36,000
Meji tuna*	*Parathunnus sibi*	Percomorphi	38,000	22,000
Bonito*	*Sarda lineolata*	Percomorphi	35,000	57,000
Yellowtail*	*Seriola dorsalis*	Percomorphi	25,000	67,000
Red snapper	*Lutianus campechanus*	Percomorphi	22,000	61,000
Atlantic tuna	*Thunnus secundodorsalis*	Percomorphi	16,000	80,000
Albacore*	*Thunnus germo*	Percomorphi	13,000	12,000
Yellowfin tuna*	*Neothunnus macropterus*	Percomorphi	12,000	35,000
White sea-bass*	*Cynoscion nobilis*	Percomorphi	11,000	92,000
Jewfish*	*Stereolepis gigas*	Percomorphi	9,000	500,000
Ishinagi*	*Stereolepis ishinagi*	Percomorphi	7,000	500,000
Swordfish*	*Xiphius gladius*	Percomorphi	7,000	130,000
Black perch	*Embiotoca jacksoni*	Holconoti	7,000	6,000
Broadfin sole	*Lepidopsetta bilineata*	Heterosomata	6,800	13,000
Oriental mackerel*	*Scomber japonicus*	Percomorphi	6,300	59,000
Corsair rockfish	*Sebastomus rosaceus*	Cataphracti	5,800	75,000
Mackerel scads	*Decapturus muroadsi*	Percomorphi	5,800	5,900
Grouper	*Epinephelus morio*	Percomorphi	4,800	24,000
Barracuda*	*Sphyræna argentea*	Percomorphi	4,700	67,000
Starry rockfish	*Sebastomus constellatus*	Cataphracti	4,500	89,000
Yellowtail rockfish	*Sebastosomus flavidus*	Cataphracti	4,000	82,000
Red rockfish	*Rosicola miniatus*	Cataphracti	2,600	14,000
Totuava*	*Eriscion macdonaldi*	Percomorphi	2,500	190,000
Jack smelt	*Atherinopsis californiensis*	Percomorphi	2,400	96,000
Spearfish*	*Makaira mitsukurii*	Percomorphi	2,300	120,000
Bastard halibut*	*Paralichthys californicus*	Heterosomata	2,300	69,000
Sardine (pilchard)	*Sardinia cærulea*	Isospondyli	2,300	16,000
Rockfish	*Pteropodus vexillaris*	Cataphracti	2,200	49,000
Red rockfish	*Sebastopyr ruberrimus*	Cataphracti	2,100	100,000
Snoek*	*Thyristes atun*	Percomorphi	2,000	23,000
Bocaccio	*Sebastodes paucispinis*	Cataphracti	1,800	77,000
Yellowbacked rockfish	*Pteropodus maliger*	Cataphracti	1,800	32,000
Pacific hake	*Merluccius productus*	Anacanthini	1,500	50,000
Black rockfish	*Sebastosomus mystinus*	Cataphracti	1,500	37,000
China rockfish	*Pteropodus nebulosus*	Cataphracti	1,400	110,000
Fringe sole	*Psettichthys melanostictus*	Heterosomata	1,400	10,000
Halibut*	*Hippoglossus hippoglossus*	Heterosomata	1,200	75,000
Shad	*Alosa sapidissima*	Isospondyli	1,200	17,000
Striped bass	*Roccus saxatilis*	Percomorphi	1,200	4,500
Orange rockfish	*Rosicola pinniger*	Cataphracti	1,100	86,000
Green spotted rockfish	*Sebastomus chlorostictus*	Cataphracti	1,100	47,000
Rockfish	*Acutomentum entomelas*	Cataphracti	1,100	8,000
Wall-eyed perch	*Hyperprospon argenteus*	Holconoti	1,100	3,500
Rabbitfish	*Cyclichthys schœpfi (?)*	Plectonathi	1,100	2,200
Starry flounder	*Platichthys stellatus*	Heterosomata	1,000	8,200
Striped rockfish	*Hispaniscus elongatus*	Cataphracti	990	74,000
Ainame	*Hexagrammos otakaii*	Cataphracti	950	3,900
Ling cod*	*Ophiodon elongatus*	Cataphracti	920	160,000
Striped perch	*Tæniotoca lateralis*	Holconoti	900	4,300
Rubberlip perch	*Rhacochilus toxotes*	Holconoti	890	9,300
Rockfish black bass	*Sebastosomus melanops*	Cataphracti	830	49,000
Spanish flag rockfish	*Hispaniscus rubrivinctus*	Cataphracti	810	32,000

TABLE III—*Concluded*

Common name of fish	Scientific name	Zoological order	Vitamin D, I.U./g.	Vitamin A, I.U./g.
Boston mackerel	*Scomber scombrus*	Percomorphi	750	31,000
California mackerel*	*Pneumatophorus diego*	Percomorphi	730	45,000
Pufferfish	*Sphœroides maculatus*	Plectonathi	570	1,500
Cabezon	*Scorpænichthys marmoratus*	Cataphracti	530	16,000
Round-nose sole*	*Eopsetta jordani*	Heterosomata	520	76,000
Nibe	*Sciæna mitsukurii*	Percomorphi	500	5,400
Pacific white perch	*Phanerodon furcatus*	Holconoti	460	6,400
Fork-tail perch	*Damalichthys argyrosomus*	Holconoti	410	2,700
Black cod*	*Anoplopoma fimbria*	Cataphracti	310	42,000
Chili-pepper	*Sebastodes goodei*	Cataphracti	270	150,000
Cabrilla*	*Epinephelus analogus*	Percomorphi	260	160,000
Newfoundland turbot	*Reinhardtius hippoglossoides*	Heterosomata	260	7,000
Pacific cod*	*Gadus macrocephalus*	Anacanthini	190	4,800
Atlantic salmon	*Salmo salar*	Isospondyli	180	12,000
Rock cod	*Sebastolobus alascanus*	Cataphracti	150	6,400
Rex sole	*Errex zachirus*	Heterosomata	140	8,200
Pointed sole	*Parophrys vetulus*	Heterosomata	140	6,100
Sculpin	*Scorpæna guttata*	Cataphracti	140	3,000
Sand dab	*Citharichthys sordida*	Heterosomata	120	3,700
Atlantic hake*	*Urophycis* (Sp.)	Anacanthini	120	2,300
California turbot	*Pleuronichthys decurrens*	Heterosomata	110	8,200
Menuke*	*Sebastodes baramenuke*	Cataphracti	100	120,000
Atlantic cod*	*Gadus morrhua*	Anacanthini	100	1,400
Yellow sole	*Pseudopleuronectes dignabilis*	Heterosomata	87	17,000
Widowfish	*Acutomentum ovale*	Cataphracti	82	73,000
Tinker mackerel	*Pneumatophorus grex*	Percomorphi	77	9,300
Atlantic pollack*	*Pollachius virens*	Anacanthini	70	2,300
Pacific pollack*	*Theragra chalcogramma*	Anacanthini	67	8,300
Sheepshead	*Pimelometopon pulcher*	Pharyngognathi	62	6,600
California flying fish	*Cypselurus californicus*	Synentognathi	51	35,000
Corbina	*Menticirrhus undulatus*	Percomorphi	51	11,000
Rosefish*	*Sebastes marinus*	Cataphracti	33	26,000
Common skate of California	*Raja inornata*	Batoidei	25	9,800
Abura karei	*Hippoglossoides dubius*	Heterosomata	25	5,100
Big skate of California*	*Raja binoculata*	Batoidei	24	4,100
Kichiji	*Sebastolobus macrochir*	Cataphracti	22	4,900
Wolffish	*Anarhichas lupus*	Jugulares	19	1,300
Pacific dogfish*	*Squalus suckleyi*	Tectospondyli	13	13,000
Same karei	*Clidoderma asperrimum*	Heterosomata	12	4,900
Thresher shark	*Alopias vulpinus*	Euselachii	9	2,400
Basking shark	*Cetorhinus maximus*	Euselachii	6	<100
Atlantic dogfish	*Squalus acanthias*	Tectospondyli	3	1,700
Ratfish	*Hydrolagus colliei*	Chimæroidei	2	180
Gray sole	*Glyptocephalus cynoglossus*	Heterosomata	<2	8,900
Sturgeon	*Acipenser fulvescens*	Glaniostomi	<1	600

a From Bills *et al.*[167] with revisions; nomenclature from Jordan *et al.*[168] wherever possible. The species marked (*) are represented by more than one assay.

as much vitamin D per gram as the body oil. Different species show differences in the physicochemical constants of the oil, but these differences yield no clue as to the amount of vitamin D in the oil or how it got there.

The vitamin D values given in Table III represent average figures for the more important species, and occasional figures for the less common ones.

Within any species, however, great variations in potency are noted when the oils of individual livers are assayed. Hess *et al.*[171] found that the vitamin D potency of the oils from individual cod livers varies inversely with the oil content, and as much as 1000 times. Similar inverse ratios were noted for haddock and pollack.

Bills *et al.*[172] investigated the commercial halibut catch of Seattle at weekly intervals. In January the oil content of the pooled livers was at the lowest point, 12 %, and the vitamin D content of the liver oil was highest, 1400 I.U. per gram. In August the oil content reached its highest point, 25 %, and the vitamin D potency was lowest, 900 I.U. per gram. Thus, although the decline in vitamin D potency was a little less than can be accounted for by dilution with inactive new oil, it was about what one would expect from dilution with oil containing a little vitamin D. Nevertheless this explanation is not wholly satisfactory, for it was noted that the vitamin A content of the liver oil varied with the vitamin D content, but several times more widely. It declined from 240,000 I.U. per gram in January to 35,000 in August, thus reaching a low point which was much lower than could have resulted merely from dilution. It is possible, of course, that the two vitamins are so different in origin and metabolism that comparisons have no significance.

Pugsley[173] observed that the content of both vitamins D and A in the liver oil and intestinal oil of the Alaska cod, *Gadus macrocephalus*, varied inversely with the fatness of the livers. Pugsley *et al.*[174] found that the vitamins D and A of the liver oil of the Atlantic cod, *Gadus morrhua*, varied inversely with the oil content, but remained constant when figured as units per gram of body weight for fish of a given age group. However, the vitamin content of the liver oil increased with the age of the fish in years. Bailey[175] reported that the vitamin D potency of commercial pilchard oil, made from the whole fish including stomach contents, varied inversely with the oil yield, and Pugsley[173] noted that the inverse relationship held for both vitamins D and A in this species.

Hess *et al.*[176] reported that the milt and roe of cod and other species contain vitamin D, but the fry were "practically devoid of this factor, which evidently had been used up in the course of the development of the larvae." Thus it appears that fish begin life with little vitamin D, and as they grow

[171] A. F. Hess, C. E. Bills, and E. M. Honeywell, *J. Am. Med. Assoc.* **92**, 226 (1929).
[172] C. E. Bills, M. Imboden, and J. C. Wallenmeyer, *J. Biol. Chem.* **105**, Proc. x (1934).
[173] L. I. Pugsley, *J. Fisheries Research Board Can.* **4**, 405 (1939).
[174] L. I. Pugsley, C. A. Morrell, and J. T. Kelly, *Can. J. Research* **F23**, 243 (1945).
[175] B. E. Bailey, *Biol. Board Can. Pacific Progr. Repts.* **23**, 11 (1935).
[176] A. F. Hess, C. E. Bills, M. Weinstock, E. Honeywell, and H. Rivkin, *Proc. Soc. Exptl. Biol. Med.* **25**, 652 (1928).

up they somehow accumulate it, at times losing part of their supply for spawning, but on balance always gaining more.

The function of the vitamin D in fish is unknown. If it is related to bone calcification, the questions remain why different species require widely different amounts of it, and why most species store much greater quantities than do the marine mammals, such as seals and whales, which consume them. Several investigators[177] have associated a low vitamin D content in the liver oil with imperfect bone formation in the so-called cartilaginous fishes—elasmobranchs and cyclostomes—including representative sharks, dogfish, skates, rays, chimeras, and lampreys. It is well established that in these species the liver oil seldom contains as much as 100 I.U. of vitamin D per gram, and usually much less. Examples are given in Table III. It is evident, however, that *some* cartilaginous fishes store more vitamin D than *some* fishes with hard bones; also that sturgeons, which are usually classified as true fishes in spite of their skeletal softness, have the lowest vitamin D content of all.

The studies on the cartilaginous fishes marked the first correlation between zoological classification and vitamin D content. They were followed by the work of Bills *et al.*,[178] who made a taxonomic study of the distribution of vitamins D and A in 100 species of fish (Table III). This work revealed that several fishes of the order Percomorphi exhibit extraordinary concentrations of vitamin D in their livers (tunas, basses, and swordfish). On the other hand, livers of fishes of the order Heterosomata, which includes the halibuts, flounders, and other flatfish, were comparatively poor in vitamin D, though rich in vitamin A. Livers of fishes of the order Cataphracti, the rockfishes, were better than average sources of both vitamins.

After Massengale and Nussmeier[35] in 1930 demonstrated that irradiated ergosterol is less effective than cod liver oil, per rat unit for chicks, many writers, especially in the medical field, were given to distinguishing the two forms as "synthetic" and "natural." The implication was that the natural vitamin D of fish oils was a single definite substance. That this is not so was first shown in 1934 by Bills *et al.*[179] who found that a specimen of bluefin tuna liver oil exhibited a chick-rat efficacy ratio of about 15, whereas the ratio for cod liver oil was 100 and that for irradiated ergosterol was 1. (The tuna species was described as *Thunnus thynnus*, the designation some-

[177] E. Poulsson, *Strahlentherapie* 34, 648 (1929); S. Schmidt-Nielsen and S. Schmidt-Nielsen, *Hoppe-Seyler's Z. physiol. Chem.* 189, 229 (1930); R. K. Callow and C. F. Fischmann, *Biochem. J.* 25, 1464 (1931); E. André and R. Lecoq, *Compt. rend.* 194, 912 (1932).

[178] C. E. Bills, F. G. McDonald, O. N. Massengale, M. Imboden, H. Hall, W. D. Hergert, and J. C. Wallenmeyer, *J. Biol. Chem.* 109, *Proc.* vii (1935).

[179] C. E. Bills, O. N. Massengale, and M. Imboden, *Science* 80, 596 (1934).

times applied to all bluefins; this was later corrected[180] to *T. saliens*, the California bluefin, in accordance with the Jordan classification.[168])

Confirmation of this work appeared in the studies of Haman and Steenbock[112] and Black and Sassaman.[113] It was shown[112] that a commercial, mixed-species tuna liver oil was "somewhat less effective" on chickens, per rat unit, than other oils which were compared. Repeated trials[113] with three Japanese species of tuna (bluefin, striped, and yellowfin) showed that the liver oils were only from 40 % to 63 % as effective, rat unit for rat unit, as cod liver oil on chickens. Bills *et al.*[180] extended the work with the oils of twenty-five species of fish. They found conspicuously low efficacy ratios for albacore, striped tuna, totuava, and California bonito, as well as for the original California bluefin tuna. Several other species, especially white sea bass and Pacific dogfish, appeared to have efficacy ratios that were distinctly above par.

It is true, nevertheless, that most fish oils have an efficacy ratio of around 100, the value characteristic of cod liver oil and activated 7-dehydrocholesterol (vitamin D_3). Thus sardine (pilchard) body oil, which Bills [180a] in 1927 found similar to cod liver oil in assays with rats, has for many years been successfully used in poultry raising. Rygh[181] could recognize no significant differences in the efficacy ratios of the liver oils of seventeen species of fish. Haman and Steenbock[112] found that sardine body oil, halibut liver oil, and burbot liver oil had about the same efficacy ratio as cod liver oil. Black and Sassaman[113] found that the liver oils of cod, halibut, swordfish, and Japanese mackerel were about the same in efficacy ratios. In the work of Rygh[181] and especially of Dols,[182] the vitamin D of tuna liver oil was found to have the same efficacy ratio as cod liver oil; the tuna was the European bluefin, *Thunnus thynnus*, a species distinct from the California and Japanese forms.

The fact that cod liver oil and many other fish oils exhibit the efficacy ratio of vitamin D_3 is no proof that this is the one and only form of vitamin D which these oils contain. It is possible that other forms are present which are equally effective for rats and chicks, or that forms of higher and lower efficacy ratio are present in admixture. Hickman and Gray[169] utilized the technique of molecular distillation in an investigation of the vitamin D of several fish oils. They found at the outset that about 70 % of the vitamin D of cod liver oil occurs as esters, and so it was necessary to conduct the short path distillations with saponified material. Cod liver oil exhibited a complex elimination curve indicative of two major, two minor, and two

[180] C. E. Bills, O. N. Massengale, M. Imboden, and H. Hall, *J. Nutrition* **13**, 435 (1937).
[180a] C. E. Bills, *J. Biol. Chem.* **72**, 751 (1927).
[181] O. Rygh, *Nature* **136**, 552 (1935).
[182] M. J. L. Dols, *Z. Vitaminforsch.* **5**, 161 (1936).

trace forms of vitamin D. The vitamin D of tuna liver oil was so unstable that good curves could not be obtained. White sea bass liver oil gave an unusually pure curve, indicative of a preponderance of one form of vitamin D. Spearfish liver oil gave a fairly good curve, with a somewhat higher elimination maximum, suggesting a vitamin D of higher molecular weight. Albacore liver oil had chiefly one form of vitamin D, with lesser amounts of higher and lower boiling forms. The most volatile vitamin D of cod liver oil was one of the minor forms, and this, when assayed[183] with rats and chicks, exhibited an efficacy ratio of between 25 % and 50 %.

In two instances the vitamin D of fish oils has been isolated. The vitamin D from halibut liver oil[184] was identified as vitamin D_3, and that from tuna liver oil[185] was vitamin D_3 with an admixture of vitamin D_2. It is therefore established, by efficacy ratio studies, by molecular distillation, and by actual isolation, that more than one kind of vitamin D occurs in fish oils, and it seems probable that several kinds may be present. Whether or not the oil of any given species always contains the same kind or mixture is not known, but it would be reasonable to assume that some qualitative variation, as well as quantitative, occurs as a result of differences in food and other environmental factors.

Little but conjecture can be written about the origin of vitamin D in fish oils. Steenbock and Black,[9] in one of their early papers on the activation of foods, emphasized the suggestion that vitamin D is formed by the insolation of plankton, which is ingested by little fish, and these in turn by larger fish, and so on. So far as green phytoplankton is concerned, this hypothesis has received no experimental support, but the discovery of vitamin D in the brown alga, *Sargassum*, renews interest in it.[151] Furthermore, since ergosterol is a vegetable sterol, it seems more likely than not that the activated ergosterol (vitamin D_2) found in tuna liver oil originated in the vegetable kindgom, although it could be that the ergosterol was absorbed as such and activated in a mollusk or fish. On the other hand, the activated 7-dehydrocholesterol (vitamin D_3) which was the only form of vitamin D identified in halibut liver oil and the predominant one in tuna liver oil, almost certainly originated in an animal, because cholesterol is never found in the vegetable kindgom.

Marine animal life other than fish does not exhibit much vitamin D. Drummond and Gunther[149] found a small amount in zooplankton oil. Belloc *et al.*[186] found that zooplankton collected in the spring contained provita-

[183] C. E. Bills, O. N. Massengale, K. C. D. Hickman, and E. L. Gray, *J. Biol. Chem.* **126,** 241 (1938).

[184] H. Brockmann, *Hoppe-Seyler's Z. physiol. Chem.* **245,** 96 (1937).

[185] H. Brockmann and A. Busse, *Naturwissenschaften,* **26,** 122 (1938); *Hoppe-Seyler's Z. physiol. Chem.* **256,** 252 (1938).

[186] G. Belloc, R. Fabre, and H. Simonnet, *Compt. rend.* **191,** 160 (1930).

min D but no vitamin D, whereas that taken in midsummer showed both provitamin and vitamin. Their data are interesting in view of the July change in vertical distribution of zooplankton described by Russell.[187] Copping[188] demonstrated the presence of small amounts of vitamin D in copepods collected in summer. Of the larger marine invertebrates, it may be noted that the body oil of squid showed about 6 I.U. of vitamin D per gram in a test reported by Bills.[180a]

Clear sea water is sufficiently transparent for the activating rays of the sun to reach a depth of about one meter.[189, 190] It is therefore possible, and in view of Belloc's work even probable, that in the smaller zooplankton where the body area is large in relation to the volume, some vitamin D is formed by insolation. It is unlikely that any significant amount of vitamin D is formed by the insolation of fish or of the larger invertebrates, for most of these species do not inhabit the top meter of the sea. The basking shark, *Cetorhinus maximus*, is an exception in that it basks for hours at the surface, feeding on little fish and plankton; yet its liver oil is poor in vitamin D, even for an elasmobranch.[191] The common goldfish, *Carassius auratus*, which feeds in shallow pools, accumulates hardly a trace of vitamin D in its body oil.[191a] River catfish, *Ictalurus punctatus*, when experimentally irradiated, proved very sensitive to ultraviolet rays, but even after many exposures did not accumulate more vitamin D than catfish not irradiated.[180a]

The suggestion that vitamin D may be synthesized by fish was first made by Bills[180a] in 1927. He observed that during the first four weeks of the summer fattening season the cod of the Newfoundland shore fisheries gorged themselves on a little fish called capelin, *Mallotus villosus*, and that during this time the oil content of their livers doubled without diminution of vitamin D potency. It was roughly estimated that the capelin eaten could not account for all the vitamin D accumulated, and the balance was attributed to synthesis. In view of the later work of Pugsley and others, the original premises may have been faulty, in that they did not contemplate the possibility that the cod population may have involved different

[187] F. S. Russell, *Nature* **126,** 472 (1930).

[188] A. M. Copping, *Biochem. J*. **28,** 1516 (1934).

[189] W. R. G. Atkins and H. H. Poole, *Trans. Roy. Soc.* (*London*) **B222,** 129 (1933); H. H. Darby, E. R. F. Johnson, and G. W. Barnes, *Carnegie Inst. Wash. Publ.* **475,** 191 (1937).

[190] N. G. Jerlov, *Nature* **166,** 111 (1950). Jerlov's claim that effective radiations penetrate to a depth of 20 meters was based on the use of light filters centering on 310 mμ. One suspects that the radiations detected at this depth represented leakage at the long wave side of the pass band.

[191] S. Schmidt-Nielsen and S. Schmidt-Nielsen, *Hoppe-Seyler's Z. physiol. Chem.* **189,** 229 (1930).

[191a] C. E. Bills, unpublished observation.

age groups. But the work did inspire further attempts to demonstrate the synthesis of vitamin D under controlled conditions.

Bills[180a] kept young catfish in darkened aquaria for six months on a diet of veal muscle, which contained no detectable amount of vitamin D. At the end of this period the fish had doubled in weight, and their visceral oil deposits had increased. The visceral oil of these fish contained at least as much vitamin D per gram as the oil of fish assayed at the beginning. Although this experiment was not conclusive, it strongly suggested that synthesis had occurred. Hess *et al.*[171] tried to demonstrate synthesis by allowing cod livers to digest with added ergosterol, but the findings were negative. In another experiment,[192] captive codfish were given ergosterol by mouth, and also intramuscularly, but there was no indication that any of it was converted to vitamin D.

Fish feed extensively on mollusks, such as whelk,[193] and thereby ingest quantities of various provitamins D, yet the chief sterol of fish is cholesterol containing only the traces of provitamin which are characteristic of the higher animals. To associate the ingestion of much provitamin D with the accumulation of much vitamin D implies a synthesis, for which there is considerable evidence but as yet no proof. An up-to-date version of the experiments of Hess and Bills would comprise the digesting of 7-dehydrocholesterol with the intestinal tissue or with the enzyme-rich pyloric cecum of species known to be good accumulators of vitamin D, such as the tunas.

2. ISOLATION FROM NATURAL SOURCES

Isolation of vitamin D is a task beset with difficulties. In the first place, the amount of vitamin D present, even in such rich sources as fish oils, is small. Assuming that the vitamin D of cod liver oil has the same potency as vitamin D_3, it can be figured that a ton of oil contains only 2 or 3 g. of vitamin. But this vitamin, according to the evidence of molecular distillations,[169] exists in several forms. Furthermore, when taken out of its protecting esters and oily vehicle, it is unstable. It is thus understandable that vitamin D has only once been obtained in the crystalline state from a natural source.

The crystalline preparation was isolated from tuna liver oil by Brockman and Busse.[185] The procedure, in brief, consisted in the following steps: (1) saponification and separation of the unsaponifiable fraction of the oil, (2) partial separation of vitamin D from vitamin A by partitioning between

[192] A. F. Hess, C. E. Bills, M. Weinstock, and M. Imboden, *Proc. Soc. Exptl. Biol. Med.* **29**, 1227 (1932).

[193] A. H. Cooke, *in* Cambridge Natural History, Vol. 3, p. 59. Macmillan, London, 1913.

[194] H. Brockmann, *Hoppe-Seyler's Z. physiol. Chem.* **241**, 104 (1936); H. Brockmann and A. Busse, *ibid.* **249**, 176 (1937).

hydrocarbons and alcohols, (3) chromatographic adsorption on alumina gel, aided at certain stages by an indicator dye, (4) removal of sterols by crystallization from methanol and precipitation with digitonin, (5) esterification to the 3,5-dinitrobenzoate, (6) chromatographic purification of the crude esters, (7) recrystallization of esters, (8) saponification of purified ester to free vitamin, and (9) crystallization of the free vitamin.

The product thus obtained consisted of vitamin D_3 with an admixture of vitamin D_2 to the extent of about 10 %. Previously Brockmann had made from tuna liver oil[194] and halibut liver oil[184] preparations of vitamin D which were crystallized as dinitrobenzoates but not as free vitamin. They were regarded at the time as pure vitamin D_3 esters, but in the light of the later work they must be considered as somewhat less than pure. However, in view of the known high efficacy ratio of halibut liver oil, it seems unlikely that any vitamin D_2 was present in this preparation. Zucker et al.[195, 196] obtained the vitamin D of tuna liver oil in the form of its 3,5-dinitrobenzoate and allophanate, and that of cod liver oil as allophanate. Apparently these products were about three-quarters pure. Haslewood and Drummond[197] also have worked with tuna liver oil, obtaining the allophanate of the vitamin in semipure condition.

In the isolation techniques the importance of the exclusion of air is emphasized, even of air dissolved in solvents. Oxygen-free nitrogen and carbon dioxide gases are used to replace air in apparatus and liquids. Numerous modifications of the procedure of isolation described above are possible. Alternative methods of removing vitamin A from vitamin D include the reacting of the vitamin A with maleic anhydride.[198] Presumably, citraconic anhydride would react similarly.[199] An alternative method of separating vitamin D from hydrocarbon oils is to esterify the vitamin D with phthalic anhydride, leaving the hydrocarbons behind.[195] An alternative method of purifying vitamin D by adsorption consists in the use of tricalcium phosphate instead of alumina gel.[200]

3. Physics of Activation

Since the absorption spectra of the several provitamins D are almost identical in shape and position and not much different in height, it will

[195] E. J. H. Simons and T. F. Zucker, J. Am. Chem. Soc. 58, 2655 (1936).
[196] T. F. Zucker, E. J. Simons, H. C. Colman, and B. Demarest, Naturwissenschaften 26, 11 (1938).
[197] G. A. D. Haslewood and J. C. Drummond, J. Soc. Chem. Ind. (London) 55, 598 (1936).
[198] O. Dalmer, F. von Werder, and T. Moll, Hoppe-Seyler's Z. physiol. Chem. 224, 86 (1934).
[199] A. Windaus, O. Linsert, A. Lüttringhaus, and G. Weidlich, Ann. 492, 226 (1932).
[200] S. E. Miller, U. S. Pat. 2,179,560 (1939).

suffice to show the absorption spectrum of ergosterol (Fig. 8). The location of the maxima at 262, 271, 282, and 293.5 mμ are based on recent determinations with the Beckman spectrophotometer, and they are probably a bit more accurate than earlier data obtained photographically. The absorption minima at 263, 277, and 289.5 mμ are also shown in the figure.

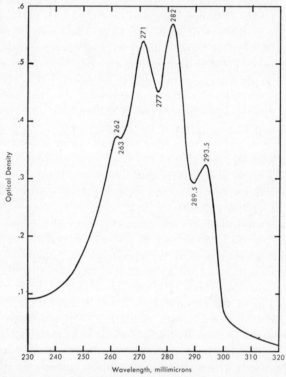

FIG. 8. Absorption spectrum of ergosterol in alcohol 1:50,000 w./v. Ergosterol monohydrate recrystallized from alcohol-benzene 2:1. (Courtesy of the Sulphite Pulp Manufacturers' Research League.)

Other maxima, detectable in more concentrated solutions, will be discussed in the section on the chemistry of activation.

The wavelengths which affect ergosterol must be among those which it absorbs. Ergosterol absorbs strongly from 300 mμ to 230 mμ in the far ultraviolet region, but it exhibits some absorption beyond these limits in both directions. The shortest effective wavelength has not been ascertained, but it is known that 230 mμ activates ergosterol readily.[201] Wavelengths as long as 313 mμ are known to activate ergosterol slightly [202] and this

[201] A. L. Marshall and A. Knudson, *J. Am. Chem. Soc.* **52**, 2304 (1930).
[202] R. W. Haman and H. Steenbock, *Ind. Eng. Chem. Anal. Ed.* **8**, 291 (1936).

wavelength also appears to be the upper limit for 7-dehydrocholesterol.[203-205] There is reason to believe that still longer waves play a part in the decomposition of ergosterol and/or of its irradiation products.[206] The predominance of these longer waves may explain the relatively feeble effect of sunlight in activation. White light in the presence of optical sensitizers produces chemical changes in ergosterol, such as peroxide and pinacol formation, but it does not produce vitamin D.[207]

Ergosterol in the form of vapor, spray, powder, or solution can be activated by a high-frequency oscillating discharge, with or without electrodes.[208-210] High-voltage direct current has also been claimed to be effective.[209] Some activation is induced by cathode rays[209, 210a] and by radium emanation.[211] X-rays apparently do not activate it.[212]

In an early (1927) study of the disappearance of ergosterol during irradiation in dilute solution, Morton et al.[213] concluded that the time-disappearance curve is a straight line. They measured the disappearing ergosterol spectrographically and did not know at the time of the existence of the intermediate products of irradiation which contribute irrelevant absorption to the system. Bourdillon et al.[214] measured the disappearance by digitonide precipitation and found that the rate slows down as the irradiation proceeds. The problem was finally resolved by Dasler[215] in 1938. He found that the time-disappearance curve had the shape of a first-order curve. The reaction involving the disappearance was, however, apparently a zero-order reaction, because the half-life of the ergosterol was directly proportional to the initial ergosterol concentration. The first-order character of the curve was explained by the fact that increasing amounts of light were filtered out by the piling up of light-absorbing irradiation products.

Before the structure of vitamin D was known, Pohl[28] suggested that

[203] J. W. M. Bunker, R. S. Harris, and L. M. Mosher, J. Am. Chem. Soc. **62**, 508 (1940).
[204] A. F. Hess and W. T. Anderson, Jr. J. Am. Med. Assoc. **89**, 1222 (1927).
[205] C. Sonne and E. Rekling, Strahlentherapie **25**, 552 (1927).
[206] Lahousse and Gonnard, J. phys. radium, Ser. 6, **10**, 114S (1929).
[207] A. Windaus, P. Borgeaud, and J. Brunken, Nachr. Ges. Wiss. Göttingen, Math. physik. Kl. 313 (1927); A. Windaus and P. Borgeaud, Ann. **460**, 235 (1928); A. Windaus and J. Brunken, Ann. **460**, 225 (1928).
[208] N. A. Milas, U. S. Pat. (Reissue) 22,038 (1942).
[209] I. G. Farbenindustrie, Austrian Pat. 119,210 (1930).
[210] C. C. Whittier, U. S. Pats. 2,106,779, 2,106,780, 2,106,781, 2,106,782 (1938); W. Dasler and C. D. Bauer, J. Biol. Chem. **167**, 581 (1947).
[210a] A. Knudson and C. N. Moore, J. Biol. Chem. **81**, 49 (1929).
[211] R. B. Moore and T. DeVries, J. Am. Chem. Soc. **53**, 2676 (1931).
[212] H. Goldblatt, Ergebn. allg. Pathol. u. pathol. Anat. **2**. Abt. 25, 58 (1931).
[213] R. A. Morton, I. M. Heilbron, and E. D. Kamm, J. Chem. Soc. **1927**, 2000.
[214] R. B. Bourdillon, C. F. Fischmann, R. G. C. Jenkins, and T. A. Webster, Proc. Roy. Soc. (London) **B104**, 561 (1929).
[215] W. Dasler, Summaries of Doctoral Dissertations Univ. Wisconsin **3**, 219 (1938).

activation may involve the addition of energy to the sterol molecule through an electron displacement. This is an oversimplification of what happens, although it is true that energy is required for the rupture of ring B with the formation of a fourth double bond for the vitamin molecule.

Estimations of the energy requirements of activation have been made by several investigators,[201-204, 216-221] most recently by Harris *et al.*[217] The latter workers[217] found that 7.5×10^{13} quanta were required to produce one U.S.P. unit of vitamin D_2 from ergosterol. The U.S.P. unit official at the time (1938) was nominally identical with the international unit, but experienced bioassayers were aware that the U.S.P. Reference Cod Liver Oil was weak in terms of the international standard. Arnold[222] found the U.S.P. unit to be 20% weak (49.7 U.S.P.U. = 40 I.U.), a conclusion with which the present author closely agrees. Nelson[223] recognizes a deficiency of 6.6%, but this probably refers to a later and improved batch of reference oil. Applying Arnold's correction, one figures that 9.3×10^{13} quanta are required to produce one international unit of vitamin D_2 from ergosterol.

Bunker *et al.*[220] found no significant differences in quantum efficiency for the wavelengths within the region where ergosterol absorbs strongly, but they got some slight evidence that wavelength 302.5 mμ, which is near the edge of the region of absorption, is less efficient. Haman and Steenbock[202] had earlier found that line 313, where absorption is still less, is distinctly less efficient.

In the activation of the provitamin D of cholesterol, Hess and Anderson[204] demonstrated as early as 1927 that the efficiency of line 313 is very low. Bunker *et al.*,[203] working with 7-dehydrocholesterol itself, observed no activation by line 313. They reported that wavelengths 248.3, 253.7, 265.2, 280.4, and 302.5 mμ are substantially uniform per quantum of energy applied. But they claimed[203, 220] that line 296.7 is a little more efficient than the others, an observation which is difficult to reconcile with the fact that the absorption spectra of 7-dehydrocholesterol and ergosterol are practically identical.

The production of vitamin D directly in animals by irradiation may be regarded as a special instance of the activation of 7-dehydrocholesterol. It is complicated by the presence in the skin of substances exhibiting general absorption, a form of light-filtering which usually becomes more and more

[216] S. K. Kon, F. Daniels, and H. Steenbock, *J. Am. Chem. Soc.* **50,** 2573 (1928).
[217] R. S. Harris, J. W. M. Bunker, and L. M. Mosher, *J. Am. Chem. Soc.* **60,** 2579 (1938).
[218] A. Knudson and F. Benford, *J. Biol. Chem.* **124,** 287 (1938).
[219] J. R. Owen and A. Sherman, *J. Am. Chem. Soc.* **59,** 763 (1937).
[220] J. W. M. Bunker, R. S. Harris, and L. M. Mosher, *J. Am. Chem. Soc.* **62,** 1760 (1940).
[221] J. W. M. Bunker and R. S. Harris, *New Engl. J. Med.* **216,** 165 (1937).
[222] A. Arnold, *Proc. Soc. Exptl. Biol. Med.* **63,** 230 (1946).
[223] E. M. Nelson, *J. Assoc. Offic. Agr. Chemists* **32,** 801 (1949).

manifest, the shorter the wavelength involved. Hence it is to be expected
that the longer wavelengths in the critical region will exhibit greater over-all
efficiency than the shorter ones. This is borne out experimentally. Bunker
and Harris[221] found that line 296.7 was the most effective for producing
vitamin D in depilated rats. Knudson and Benford[218] also used rats, but
under the conditions of their experiment line 280.4 was the most efficient.
The findings with animals represent a special situation, which has little
bearing on the physics of activation *in vitro*.

The uniformity in quantum efficiencies for the production of vitamin D
is especially noteworthy, when it is considered that the conversion is not
a single step, but an over-all effect involving the production of several
substances in succession, of which vitamin D is not the last (Fig. 9). No

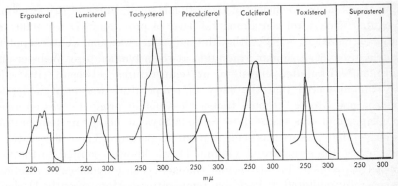

FIG. 9. Absorption spectra of ergosterol and its irradiation products. (After
Windaus *et al.*[45] and Velluz *et al.*[223a])

studies have been reported on the energy requirements of the intermediate
reactions, but it is assumed that the requirements are less uniform than
for the over-all activation.

Before the energy relations in activation were understood, the suggestion
was occasionally advanced[224, 224a] that the yield of vitamin D might be
improved by the use of filtered light or of light sources predominating in
certain wavelengths. The goal was a light which would activate provitamin
D, but not destroy the vitamin D produced. Why this has never been
reached is evident from the spectra in Fig. 9, which show that ergosterol
and calciferol, as well as the intermediate products, absorb light over
essentially the same range, 230 mμ to 300 mμ. There are, however, some
differences in the absorption maxima, which may account for the fact that

[223a] L. Velluz, G. Amiard, and A. Petit, *Bull. soc. chim. France* **16**, 501 (1949).
[224] T. A. Webster and R. B. Bourdillon, *Biochem. J.* **22**, 1223 (1928).
[224a] I. M. Heilbron, E. D. Kamm, and R. A. Morton, *Nature* **120**, 617 (1927).

the composition of the crude irradiation product varies with the wavelength used.[225] In particular, it has been demonstrated that long waves favor the accumulation of lumisterol, and short waves of tachysterol, each at the expense of the other.[226]

The light sources used for irradiation are principally the quartz mercury arc and the cored carbon arc, carbons for the latter containing compounds of iron, magnesium, or other metals. A favorite experimental source in the early years was the magnesium spark.[28, 30, 226-230] Light filters have not come into general use, but for special studies the Corning[24] or Jena[226, 228, 230] glasses or Vitaglass[224a] have been employed, or filter cells containing benzene,[227, 231] xylene,[226, 231-233] diphenyl,[231] carbon disulfide,[234] chlorine,[224, 227] bromine,[204] chlorine-bromine,[24, 204, 232] tartrazine,[228] salicylic acid,[228] lead acetate,[235] potassium nitrate,[227] nickel sulfate,[232] or alcoholic cobalt chloride.[224]

The temperature coefficient of activation is small. Bills and Brickwedde[236] found that cholesterol containing 1.2 parts of provitamin D per 1000 was readily activated at $-183°$, although the product was somewhat less potent than the product of similar irradiation at room temperature. Webster and Bourdillon[224] irradiated ergosterol at temperatures between $-195°$ and $+78°$ and observed that the effect of temperature was only moderate. Knudson and Moore[210a] noted that a "less potent product" was obtained when ergosterol was exposed to cathode rays at liquid air temperature than when the exposure was made at room temperature. These observations, made before the structure of vitamin D was known, pointed to the fact that activation is an intramolecular change, because bimolecular reactions are generally inhibited at very low temperatures. More recently Dasler[215] has stated that temperature has "no effect upon the time-disappearance curve of ergosterol nor upon the time-activation curve of ergosterol." The fact that activation is best conducted in boiling solvents is not contra-

[225] E. H. Reerink and A. van Wijk, *Biochem. J.* **23,** 1294 (1929); A. Windaus, *Nachr. Ges. Wiss. Göttingen, Math. physik. Kl.* 36 (1930); F. A. Askew, R. B. Bourdillon, H. M. Bruce, R. G. C. Jenkins, and T. A. Webster, *Proc. Roy. Soc. (London)* **B107,** 91 (1930).

[226] P. Setz, *Hoppe-Seyler's Z. physiol. Chem.* **215,** 183 (1933).

[227] E. H. Reerink and A. van Wijk, *Biochem. J.* **23,** 1294 (1929).

[228] A. Windaus, *Nachr. Ges. Wiss. Göttingen, Math. physik. Kl.* 36 (1930).

[229] A. Smakula, *Nachr. Ges. Wiss. Göttingen, Math. physik. Kl.* 49 (1928).

[230] A. Windaus, *Deut. med. Wochschr.* **57,** 678 (1931).

[231] I. G. Farbenindustrie, German Pat. 565,900 (1932).

[232] F. A. Askew, R. B. Bourdillon, H. M. Bruce, R. G. C. Jenkins, and T. A. Webster, *Proc. Roy. Soc. (London)* **B107,** 91 (1930).

[233] E. H. Reerink and A. van Wijk, *Biochem. J.* **25,** 1001 (1931).

[234] N. V. Philips' Gloeilampenfabrieken, British Pat. 385,626 (1932).

[235] G. Sperti, R. J. Norris, R. B. Withrow, and H. Schneider, U. S. Pat. 1,982,029 (1934).

[236] C. E. Bills and F. G. Brickwedde, *Nature* **121,** 452 (1928).

dictory to the conclusion that the temperature coefficient of activation is small; it merely reflects the better exposure of molecules in agitated solution and perhaps also the driving of the precalciferol $\rightleftarrows$ calciferol equilibrium to the right (see below).

Ergosterol can be activated in the solid state, in the vapor phase, or in solution. When it is irradiated in the solid state the first irradiation products which form on the exposed surfaces act as filters which prevent light from reaching the under layers until the surface products are destroyed. The degree of antiricketic potency attainable by the irradiation of solid ergosterol is therefore relatively low, and under practical conditions generally not more than 10% of that attained in solution. Few studies have been made of activation in the vapor phase, a procedure which is handicapped by the fact that the melting point of ergosterol is higher than the temperature at which calciferol begins to undergo transformation into its inactive pyro-isomers.

Irradiation in quiet solutions is less effective than in agitated solutions,[237] because agitation breaks up the formation of strata of irradiation products like those on the surface of crystals and promotes uniform exposure of all portions of the liquid. Thus it is that in commercial practice the solutions are always agitated by stirring, flowing, or boiling during exposure to the activating rays.

Apart from any light-filtering action of solvents, and from any role which they may play as carriers of dissolved oxygen, there appears to be what Bills et al.[238] termed a specific solvent effect on activation. This was revealed by parallel spectrographic and biologic examinations on the course of activation in three transparent solvents—alcohol, cyclohexane, and ether. The importance of the specific solvent effect was shown by the fact that the time required for the attainment of maximum potency in ether was longer than the time required for the entire sequence of activation and destruction in alcohol (Fig. 10). The maximum potency reached in ether was higher than in alcohol or cyclohexane, but certain spectral changes (see below) were more conspicuous in alcohol. Dasler[215] reported that the maximum potency obtained by the irradiation of ergosterol in alcohol represented a 30% conversion of ergosterol to calciferol, while the maximum potency obtained in ether represented a 70% conversion.

4. Chemistry of Activation

When a provitamin D is exposed to ultraviolet light of suitable wavelength, the transformation into the corresponding vitamin D begins at once.

[37] A. Windaus, K. Westphal, F. von Werder, and O. Rygh, *Nachr. Ges. Wiss. Göttingen, Math. physik. Kl.* 45 (1929).
[38] C. E. Bills, E. M. Honeywell, and W. M. Cox, Jr., *J. Biol. Chem.* **92,** 601 (1931).

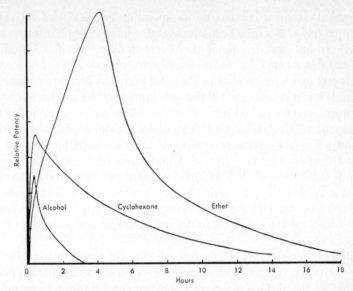

FIG. 10. Time-potency curves of the activation of ergosterol in alcohol, cyclo-hexane, and ether. An example of the specific solvent effect. (After Bills *et al.*[238])

However, the provitamin, even under the most favorable conditions, never gives a 100 % yield of vitamin. The transformation proceeds in overlapping steps, with the formation of a series of products of which vitamin D is not the last. The series has received special study by Windaus *et al.*[45] and Setz,[226] whose conclusions, modified in the light of other work, can be expressed in the following scheme. Here is illustrated the transformation of ergosterol into calciferol (vitamin D_2), but with other provitamins the changes which take place are analogous.

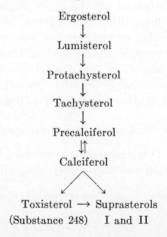

Ergosterol
↓
Lumisterol
↓
Protachysterol
↓
Tachysterol
↓
Precalciferol
⇅
Calciferol

Toxisterol → Suprasterols
(Substance 248)   I and II

The quantity of any one irradiation product present after a given period varies with the conditions of exposure, and correspondingly there is a variation in the spectral picture of the total mixed products. As explained above, the wavelength is a factor, particularly important in the accumulation of lumisterol and tachysterol. Temperature appears to be important in the accumulation of precalciferol. The specific solvent effect is a factor in the accumulation of toxisterol.

The presence of dissolved oxygen in the solvent markedly affects the spectral picture of activation.[238a] It does so by altering the by-products of

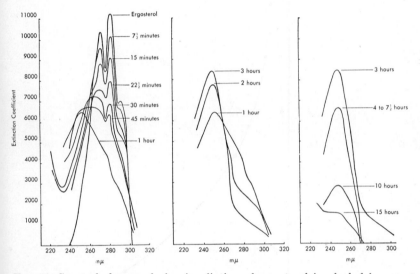

Fig. 11. Spectral changes during irradiation of ergosterol in alcohol by quartz mercury lamp. Compare Fig. 12. (After Bills et al.[239])

activation, rather than by affecting to any large extent the formation or destruction of vitamin D.[239] In one study,[240] extreme freedom from oxygen during the irradiation of ergosterol did not occasion any enhancement of antiricketic potency. The products of oxidation make difficult the crystallization of vitamin D,[241] and are therefore especially to be avoided when

[238a] A. Smakula, Nachr. Ges. Wiss. Göttingen, Math. physik. Kl. 49 (1928); C. E. Bills, E. M. Honeywell, and W. M. Cox, Jr., J. Biol. Chem. 80, 557 (1928); E. H. Reerink and A. van Wijk, Biochem. J. 23, 1294 (1929).

[239] C. E. Bills, E. M. Honeywell, and W. M. Cox, Jr., J. Biol. Chem. 80, 557 (1928).

[240] H. H. Beard, R. E. Burk, H. E. Thompson, and H. Goldblatt, J. Biol. Chem. 96, 307 (1932).

[241] T. C. Angus, F. A. Askew, R. B. Bourdillon, H. M. Bruce, R. K. Callow, C. F. Fischmann, J. St. L. Philpot, and T. A. Webster, Proc. Roy. Soc. (London) B108, 340 (1931).

the production of crystalline calciferol is desired. It has been shown[225, 241, 242] that vitamin D, either in crystalline form or as the crude resin, is decidedly more stable to oxidation than some of the non-vitamin substances which are formed with it in irradiation. It is, however, somewhat less stable than ergosterol itself.[243]

By following the course of activation both spectrographically and biologically, curves can be constructed which illustrate the absorption spectra of the mixed irradiation products from time to time, and the corresponding

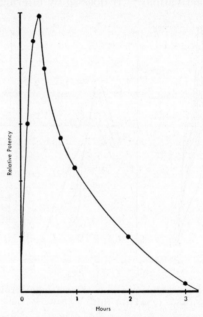

FIG. 12. Potency changes during irradiation of ergosterol in alcohol by quartz mercury lamp. Compare Fig. 11. (After Bills *et al.*[239])

rise and fall of vitamin D potency (Figs. 11 and 12). The illustrations depict the changes observed when an alcoholic solution of ergosterol at room temperature is exposed to the unfiltered radiations of a water-cooled quartz mercury vapor lamp. As explained above, different conditions give different curves. Early expectations that the study of the crude absorption spectra would yield useful information on the products of irradiation have not materialized. It has been necessary to isolate the products and examine them individually.

[242] C. E. Bills, F. G. McDonald, L. N. BeMiller, G. E. Steel, and M. Nussmeier *J. Biol. Chem.* **93,** 775 (1931).
[243] A. L. Bacharach, E. L. Smith, and S. G. Stevenson, *Analyst* **58,** 128 (1933).

a. Ergosterol

Usual, or hydrated, form, $C_{28}H_{44}O \cdot H_2O$, molecular weight 414.648; anhydrous, $C_{28}H_{44}O$, molecular weight 396.632. Three double bonds. Melting point about 165°, unsharp, varies with conditions. *In vacuo*, sublimation occurs at 180°,[58] heavy vapors at 185°,[244] and distillation with slight decomposition at 198°.[58] Principal absorption maxima at 262, 271, 282, and 293.5 mμ (in alcohol). Absorption minima at 263, 277, and 289.5 mμ. Molecular extinction coefficient at 282 mμ = 11,500. $[\alpha]_D^{20}$ = −135°, and $[\alpha]_{5461}^{20}$ = −174° (anhydrous ergosterol in chloroform). Heat of combustion (anhydrous), 9,950 calories$_{15}$ per gram.[242] Specific gravity (anhydrous), 1.040.[244] Ratio of digitonide to sterol, 4.0:1.[245]

Crude ergosterol as obtained from the unsaponifiable matter of the fat of fungi contains other sterols in varying amounts. Tanret[246] was the first to prepare ergosterol of high purity. He made it from the crude sterols of ergot by fractional crystallization in ether. The ergosterol of yeast is accompanied by a number of minor sterols to the extent of about 20 %.[247, 248] Bills and Honeywell[249] obtained from yeast a purified product identical with Tanret's by recrystallizing the crude sterols from 95 % alcohol-benzene 2:1. Alternatively, the same degree of purification was attained by converting the ergosterol into ergosteryl isobutyrate, which forms massive crystals easy to purify. The ester was saponified, and the ergosterol recovered. Callow[58] purified ergosterol via the benzoate, and by this means eliminated, along with other impurities, an exceptionally persistent contaminant, 5-dihydroergosterol, which may be present to the extent of about 5 %.[250] This ergosterol, hydrated, showed $[\alpha]_D^{20}$ = −128.7°, and anhydrous, $[\alpha]_D^{20}$ = −135° (in chloroform). Huber *et al.*[251] crystallized ergosterol from 95 % alcohol-benzene 1:2 (not 2:1, as used by Bills and Honeywell). They obtained hydrated ergosterol which had $[\alpha]_D$ = −133° (in chloroform). Although the ambient temperature was not stated, it would seem that this value represented a sample of exceptional purity.

Ergosterol forms snow-white crystals, the gross appearance of which varies with the solvent. From 95 % alcohol it crystallizes in leaflets, and from ether, chloroform, and acetone in fine needles.[246] Larger crystals are obtained from ether-acetone 1:3.[249, 252] The presence of a little water in

[44] C. Tanret, *Compt. rend.* **108,** 98 (1889); *Ann. chim. et phys.* Ser. 6, **20,** 289 (1890).
[45] H. Pénau and Z. Hardy, *J. pharm. chim.* Ser. 8, **9,** 145 (1929).
[46] C. Tanret, *Ann. chim. et phys.* Ser. 8, **15,** 313 (1908).
[47] A. Castille and E. Ruppol, *Bull. acad. roy. med. Belg.* Ser. 5, **13,** 48 (1933).
[48] W. Halden, *Hoppe-Seyler's Z. physiol. Chem.* **225,** 249 (1934).
[49] C. E. Bills and E. M. Honeywell, *J. Biol. Chem.* **80,** 15 (1928).
[50] R. K. Callow, *Biochem. J.* **25,** 87 (1931).
[51] W. Huber, G. W. Ewing, and J. Kriger, *J. Am. Chem. Soc.* **67,** 609 (1945).
[52] C. E. Bills, U. S. Pat. 1,775,548 (1930).

ethyl acetate-alcohol or in benzene-alcohol mixtures promotes the formation of large crystals.[253] Under the microscope ergosterol crystals are found to be elongated six-sided prisms, the angles adjacent to the long sides measuring about 127°, and the angles between the short sides 106°. The extinction is parallel, the sign positive, and the plane of the optical axes transverse to the length. The needles differ from the leaflets only in exaggeration of length. It is somewhat uncertain whether the crystals are monoclinic or orthorhombic, but examination in convergent light suggests that they are monoclinic.[246, 249]

Ergosterol usually contains one molecule of water of crystallization.[58, 243, 246, 251] It retains this water so tenaciously that drying at room temperature over sulfuric acid or calcium chloride removes only part of it.[58, 246] Tanret[246] apparently felt that ergosterol can be completely dehydrated without decomposition by heating to 105° in a vacuum or in carbon dioxide (time not specified, but presumably brief). The product thus obtained regains its original weight after a few hours of exposure to air, but this is not the case if it has become discolored. Callow[58] warns that the water "is difficult to remove completely without decomposition." Bacharach et al.[243] state that "attempts to remove the water of crystallization by ordinary methods involve some decomposition of the sterol."

Tanret[244, 246] noted that ergosterol oxidizes readily, especially in solution or under the influence of warmth and light; it becomes yellow and odorous and its melting point and optical rotation are lowered. Callow[58] observed that anhydrous ergosterol oxidizes more readily than does the hydrated form. However, hydrated ergosterol, kept over calcium chloride and exposed to air occasionally, took up five atoms of oxygen in the course of a year, arriving at practically constant weight. The oxygen uptake curve was that of an autocatalytic oxidation. The destruction of ergosterol is very noticeable in hot solutions,[246, 249, 251] and it is probable that some damage occurs whenever an ergosterol solution is heated, unless extraordinary precautions are taken to exclude oxygen.

To preserve ergosterol, Tanret[246] recommended that it be kept in a vacuum or under carbon dioxide. Callow[58] reported that in sealed tubes it remains unchanged for long periods. Bills and Honeywell[249] found that ergosterol, kept in the dark at 0°, remained colorless for a year, even though exposed to air. However, Bacharach et al.[243] observed yellowing in a sample kept in the dark at "a low temperature." It is the experience of industrial users that ergosterol can be kept indefinitely in well-sealed bottles, which have been gassed and stored in a cool, dark place.

The melting point, or melting range, of ergosterol has never been satisfactorily established. Callow[58] reported that the purest ergosterol, partially dehydrated, melted in sealed capillaries at 160° to 163°. The circumstances of heating were not stated, nor was it made clear whether any precautions against oxidation were taken. Tanret[246] found that purified hydrated ergosterol in sealed capillaries melted from 4° to 6° lower than in capillaries filled with carbon dioxide or than it did on the Maquenne block,[254] which minimizes oxidation by rapid heating. He gave the melting point as 165°. Bacharach et al.[243] emphasized the importance of rapid heating. They found melting points between 162° and 164° for commercial hydrated ergosterol in open capillaries. Huber et al.[251] reported the same range, 162° to 164°, for a purified sample of hydrated ergosterol, but did not specify how the determinations were made. Bills and Honeywell[249] observed that the point at which molten purified ergosterol in sealed capillaries becomes clear depends upon the water content. The clearing points (in distinction from the liquefying points given by others) ranged from 166° to 183°, according to the degree of hydration.

The turbidity associated with moisture may be related to the phenomenon of mesomorphism described by Friedel[255] and noted by Gaubert[256, 257] in ergosterol complexes ("liquid crystals"). Certainly it makes difficult the observation of the true melting point, for it lengthens the apparent melting range, thus more or less offsetting the depressing effects of oxidation. All facts considered, one must conclude that the melting point of ergosterol should be taken in the open to facilitate the escape of water, and rapidly to minimize oxidation. Tanret's value of 165° on the Maquenne block is perhaps the best determination so far recorded.

The melting points of thirty ergosterol esters are given in Table IV. Many of these esters, and others studied by Gaubert,[256] exhibit melting point anomalies associated with mesomorphism. It is probable, moreover, that the single melting points ascribed to certain other esters in the table represent only the final, or clearing, points, the authors having neglected to note earlier phases. Thus, Tanret[246] gave the melting point of ergosteryl butyrate simply as 129.5°, whereas Gaubert, working later with the same specimen of this ester, recorded a spread of 28° between the liquefying and clearing points (100° to 128°). Besides the esters, there are several loose combinations of ergosterol with glycerol, orcinol, urea, and substituted ureas, which exhibit more or less extended turbid phases in their melting.[256, 257] It is well known that mesomorphic states are exhibited by numerous esters and complexes of cholesterol and other sterols, as well as ergosterol. However, with the ergosterol compounds, the viscous, or smectic,

[54] L. Maquenne, Bull. soc. chim. France Ser. 2, 48, 771 (1887).
[55] G. Friedel, Ann. phys. Ser. 9, 18, 273 (1922).
[56] P. Gaubert, Bull. soc. franç. minéral. 32, 62 (1909).
[57] P. Gaubert, Compt. rend. 149, 608 (1909).

TABLE IV
ERGOSTEROL ESTERS

Ester, reference	Melting point, °C.	Rotation (in CHCl₃)
Ergosteryl acetate[249]	179 turbid 181 clear	$[\alpha]_D^{25} = -90°$
Ergosteryl allophanate[59a]	250	
Ergosteryl β-anthraquinone carbonate[257a]	195–200	
Ergosteryl benzoate[58]	169–171.5	$[\alpha]_{5461}^{20} = -88.3°$
Monoergosteryl esters of n-butane-1,2,3,4-tetracarboxylic acid:		
the more soluble isomer[260]	168 decomp.	
the less soluble isomer[260]	230 decomp.	
Ergosteryl butyrate[246]	100–129.5	$[\alpha]_D = -73°$
Ergosteryl 2-chloro-3,5-dinitrobenzoate[134]	203–204	$[\alpha]_D^{25} = -38°$
Ergosteryl cinnamate[59a]	175 turbid 190 clear	$[\alpha]_D^{19} = -50.8°$
Ergosteryl 3,5-dinitrobenzoate[110]	202	
Ergosteryl 3,5-dinitrobenzoate[251]	198–199	$[\alpha]_D = -40.8°$
Ergosteryl 3,5-dinitro-4-methylbenzoate[134]	213–214	$[\alpha]_D^{20} = -49°$
Ergosteryl diphenylacetate[59a]	186	$[\alpha]_D^{17} = -60°$
Ergosteryl ethyl carbonate[58]	150–153.5	$[\alpha]_{5461}^{20} = -111.1°$
Ergosteryl formate[246]	161.5	$[\alpha]_D = -97.9°$
Ergosteryl isobutyrate[249]	148 viscous, turbid 159 thin, turbid 162 clear	$[\alpha]_D^{25} = -84°$
Ergosteryl isovalerate[249]	138 viscous, turbid 157 thin, turbid 160 clear	$[\alpha]_D^{25} = -82°$
Ergosteryl β-naphthoate[257a]	175	
Ergosteryl α-naphthylurethane[59a]	186	$[\alpha]_D^{16} = -55°$
Ergosteryl 3-nitrobenzoate[258]	151	$[\alpha]_D = -71°$
Ergosteryl 4-nitrobenzoate[258]	182	$[\alpha]_D = -49.5°$
Ergosteryl 3-nitro-4-methylbenzoate[251]	191–193	$[\alpha]_D = -47.2°$
Diergosteryl oxalate[59a]	255	$[\alpha]_D^{20} = -76.4°$
Ergosteryl palmitate[59a]	107–108	$[\alpha]_D^{18} = -50.9°$
Ergosteryl phenylurethane[59a]	185	$[\alpha]_D^{16} = -63.1°$
Diergosteryl [β-chloroethyl] phosphate[59]	165–167	
Diergosteryl phosphate[59]	180–182	
Monoergosteryl phosphite[59]	146	
Monoergosteryl phthalate[258, 259]	169	$[\alpha]_D = -51°$
Diergosteryl propionate[246]	147.5	$[\alpha]_D = -77°$
Monoergosteryl succinate[259]	162	

phase is more pronounced, while the color play frequent with other sterols is usually absent.

Ergosterol is insoluble in water,[246] but the presence of 0.2 % of water in ethyl acetate is claimed[253] to increase its solubility in the latter solvent. Weak aqueous colloidal solutions can be made by means of a mutual solvent such as acetone, or by the action of supersonic waves, or with the aid of dispersing agents. Better colloidal solutions can be made by dissolving the sodium, potassium, or ammonium salts of ergosteryl acid esters, e.g., the monoergosteryl esters of phthalic,[258, 259] succinic,[259] and especially n-butane-1,2,3,4-tetracarboxylic[260] acids.

Ergosterol is sparingly soluble in methyl formate and in methanol, which makes these low-boiling liquids useful for washing ergosterol crystals in analytical procedures, and for recovering unconverted ergosterol from crude irradiation resin. Ergosterol is soluble in most organic solvents and in oils and fats. Examples of its solubility in certain solvents are given in Table V.

The stability of ergosterol in different solvents varies. Alcoholic solutions keep for several weeks if stored in a dark place. Pyridine favors decomposition and oxidation.[58] Ethylene dichloride is unsuitable because of the difficulty of keeping it free from traces of hydrogen chloride,[58] to which ergosterol is very sensitive. Chloroform, which is so widely used for the determination of the specific rotations of organic compounds that it may be said to be the solvent of first choice, must be used with caution for ergosterol. Hydrated ergosterol dissociates in chloroform, giving the unstable anhydrous sterol and a quantity of free water sometimes sufficient to create turbidity and optical unfitness.[246] Moreover, a solution of ergosterol in chloroform discolors in a week, and if exposed to daylight it becomes brown in a few hours.[243, 246] Chloroform intended for optical test solutions should be tested for traces of hydrogen chloride, which might induce isomerization.[251] Any solvent subject to peroxide formation, such as acetone or ether, should, on general principles, be removed from ergosterol crystals to prevent the possible initiation of destructive changes.

Ergosterol is strongly levorotatory, more so, in fact, than any sterol likely to be associated with it. Consequently its rotation is a reliable index of purity. On this basis it would seem that the preparations of Callow[58] and Huber et al.[251] are the purest ever described. Ergosterol does not exhibit mutarotation (in chloroform).[249] Its rotation is more influenced than that of sugars by the wavelength employed, and it is also greatly influenced by the solvent. Data on these factors, obtained by Bacharach et al.[243] with

[257a] M. Sumi, Sci. Papers Inst. Phys. Chem. Research Tokyo 30, 252 (1936).
[258] H. Emerson and F. W. Heyl, J. Am. Chem. Soc. 52, 2015 (1930).
[259] F. Hoffmann-La Roche and Co., German Pat. 495,450 (1930).
[260] R. Schönheimer and F. Breusch, Hoppe-Seyler's Z. physiol. Chem. 211, 19 (1932).

a commercial sample of hydrated ergosterol, are shown in Table VI. From the table it appears that the ratio $[\alpha]_{5461}:[\alpha]_D$ is 1.27 at 20° and is practically independent of the solvent. The specific rotations, however, vary

TABLE V
SOLUBILITIES OF ERGOSTEROL

A. Data from Tanret[246]

Solvent	Temperature, °C.	Parts of solvent to dissolve 1 part
Acetone	20	200
Acetone	Boiling	32
Alcohol, 95%	Cold	526
Alcohol, 95%	Boiling	36
"Benzine"	16	94
Chloroform	18	50
Chloroform	Hot	Few
Ether, anhydrous	20	50
Ether, anhydrous	Boiling	28
Ether, hydrated	20	112
Ether, hydrated	Boiling	50
Water		Insol.

B. Data from Honeywell and Bills[260a]

Solvent	Temperature, °C.	Milliliters of boiling solvent to dissolve 1 g.
Acetone	56	27
Alcohol, 96%	78	50
Benzene	80	4.6
Ether, U.S.P.	35	70
Ethyl acetate	77	6.5
Hexane	65–70	24
Isopropyl alcohol	82	10
Methanol	65	280
Methyl acetate	54	35
Methylcyclohexane	101	<2

widely with the solvent, being highest in chloroform, $[\alpha]_D^{20} = -125.25°$, and lowest in acetone, $[\alpha]_D^{20} = -92.0°$. From the data of Bills and Honeywell,[249] it appears that the ratio is only slightly influenced by temperature, being 1.30 at 20° and 1.27 at 25°. The values themselves, however, showed considerable temperature effect. From the data of Callow,[58] it appears that

[260a] E. M. Honeywell and C. E. Bills, *J. Biol. Chem.* **99,** 71 (1932).

the ratio is essentially the same for hydrated ergosterol, 1.30, as for anhydrous ergosterol, 1.29.

The specific rotations of twenty-one ergosteryl esters are given in Table
IV. In several instances the values seem anomalous, in that they are widely
different from what would be expected on the basis of differences in molecular weight. This does not necessarily indicate contamination or error, for
similar anomalies have been observed in cholesterol esters.[261]

The absorption spectrum of ergosterol, Fig. 8, reveals the four commonly
recognized bands with maxima at 262, 271, 282 and 293.5 mμ. In addition
to these, there are four other bands, or inflections, which can be seen clearly
only in more concentrated solutions. Smakula[229] reported a band at 232
mμ, and Sumi[264] noted an inflection at 250 mμ. Hogness et al.[265] located the

TABLE VI
OPTICAL ROTATION OF ERGOSTEROL[a]

Solvent	$[\alpha]_{5461}^{20}$	$[\alpha]_{D}^{20}$	Ratio
Chloroform	−158.5°	−125.25°	1.27
Benzene	−156.0°	−124.0°	1.26
Ethyl acetate	−120.0°	−95.0°	1.26
Ether	−120.0°	−94.0°	1.27
Alcohol (absolute)	−119.0°	−93.0°	1.28
Acetone	−118.0°	−92.0°	1.28
		Average value of ratio =	1.27

[a] Data from Bacharach et al.[243] on a commercial grade of ergosterol.

latter band at 252 mμ and found two more at 325 and 337.5 mμ. The fact
that ergosterol absorbs, even slightly, these longer waves, probably accounts
for the otherwise unexplained destructive effect of subdued daylight.

Hogness et al.[265] and Huber et al.[251] compared the absorption spectra of
ergosterol in several solvents. The wavelengths of the maxima were essentially the same in alcohol, hexane, and isoöctane. The extinction coefficients
were highest in alcohol and hexane, and a little lower in isoöctane. In
chloroform the extinction was considerably lower, and the position of the
maxima shifted 3 mμ toward the visible region.

Sterol color reactions depend on the double bond systems and hence are

[261] R. L. Shriner and L. Ko, J. Biol. Chem. **80,** 1 (1928).
[262] C. Liebermann, Ber. **18,** 1804 (1885).
[263] F. A. Askew, R. B. Bourdillon, H. M. Bruce, R. K. Callow, J. St. L. Philpot, and
T. A. Webster, Proc. Roy. Soc. (London) **B109,** 488 (1932).
[264] M. Sumi, Biochem. Z. **204,** 397 (1929).
[265] T. R. Hogness, A. E. Sidwell, Jr., and F. P. Zscheile, Jr., J. Biol. Chem. **120,** 239
(1937).

specific only as to classes. Reactions of interest in the study of ergosterol and/or other provitamins D include the following: the Tanret or reversed Salkowski reaction,[244, 246] the Liebermann-Burchard reaction,[100, 246, 262] the Tortelli-Jaffé reaction,[243, 266, 267, 268] the Rosenheim reactions (trichloroacetic acid or chloral hydrate),[243, 269] the Rosenheim-Callow reaction,[243, 270] the Tschugajeff reaction,[14, 271] and the antimony trichloride reaction.[243, 266, 267] A modification of the trichloroacetic acid reaction, notable for its extreme sensitivity, is described by Christiani and Anger.[272] Most of these reactions distinguish the provitamins D from sterols of the cholesterol-phytosterol class. Some distinguish provitamins from their esters,[269, 272] and oxidized from fresh specimens of provitamin.[243, 246, 250]

For the quantitative estimation of ergosterol, three general methods are available: (1) color reactions, (2) digitonide precipitation, and (3) spectrophotometric measurement. No method is known which will distinguish minute amounts of ergosterol from other provitamins D, but when sufficient material is on hand, the esters and oxidation products can sometimes be identified. The color reactions have the advantage of being applicable to minute quantities, but they are subject to considerable error. Heiduschka and Lindner[100] used the Liebermann-Burchard reaction for the determination of ergosterol in yeast, a questionable procedure because this reaction is given not only by ergosterol but (more slowly) by sterols with a single double bond.[246] Bilger et al.[273] used the Liebermann-Burchard reaction for the total sterols of yeast, and a modification of the Rosenheim trichloroacetic acid reaction for the ergosterol. Page[274] applied a modification of the Rosenheim reaction to the estimation of "ergosterol" in animal tissues; see, however, the comments of Bilger. The more recent (1939) Christiani-Anger[272] modification, in which the chloroform solution of the unknown is treated with trichloroacetic acid and lead tetraacetate, deserves a quantitative development. In spot tests it detects as little as 0.1 γ of ergosterol, and it distinguishes esters from free sterols.

Ergosterol, like all sterols of normal steric configuration, gives with digitonin a precipitate of low solubility which lends itself to gravimetric estimation. The digitonin reaction is accurate but time-consuming. It does not take place with esters, and thus when applied to tissue extracts before

[266] E. P. Häussler and E. Brauchli, Helv. Chim. Acta 12, 187 (1929).

[267] I. M. Heilbron and F. S. Spring, Biochem. J. 24, 133 (1930).

[268] U. Westphal, Ber. 72, 1243 (1939).

[269] O. Rosenheim, Biochem. J. 23, 47 (1929).

[270] O. Rosenheim and R. K. Callow, Biochem. J. 25, 74 (1931).

[271] L. Tschugajeff, Chem. Z. 24, 542 (1900); Z. angew. Chem. 13, 618 (1900).

[272] A. F. v. Christiani and V. Anger, Ber. 72, 1124, 1482 (1939).

[273] F. Bilger, W. Halden, and M. K. Zacherl, Mikrochemie 15, 119 (1934).

[274] I. H. Page, Biochem. Z. 220, 420 (1930).

and after saponification, it provides a means of determining the percentages of free and esterified total sterols. Digitonin does not give a precipitate with any form of vitamin D. The critical details of conducting an analysis with digitonin are given by Pénau and Hardy,[245] Castille and Ruppol,[247] and Bilger *et al.*[273]

With the availability of modern apparatus, the spectrophotometric method of determining ergosterol and other provitamins D is usually the method of choice. The characteristic spectrum (Fig. 8) is shown by the free provitamins and also by their esters, provided that the acid radical does not itself absorb in the critical region.[59a, 251] If the unknown is free of "ultraviolet dirt," it is only necessary to compare the optical density at the 282 mμ maximum with that of pure provitamin D. To prove that the unknown is not dirty, it is usually sufficient to measure the absorption at the nearby minimum, 277 mμ; the relation of this to the maximum should be 0.8. If irrelevant absorption cannot be avoided, one may resort to the procedure employed by Castille and Ruppol[247] in studies with yeast. This consists in precipitating the total sterols with digitonin, dissolving the washed and dried digitonides in absolute alcohol, and making the spectral measurement on the resulting solution. In this case it is desirable to use as the standard a preparation of pure ergosterol digitonide.

The accepted formula of ergosterol is the work of many chemists. Tanret[244] in 1889 recognized the single hydroxyl group and the molecule of water of crystallization, and he presented analyses corresponding to the formula $C_{26}H_{40}O \cdot H_2O$. In 1908 he[246] revised the formula to $C_{27}H_{42}O \cdot H_2O$, which remained accepted until 1932, when Windaus *et al.*,[134, 275] by the analysis of halogenated nitrobenzoic esters and other complex derivatives, established the empirical formula as $C_{28}H_{44}O \cdot H_2O$. The structural formula (Fig. 4) was established by Windaus *et al.*[276] in 1934. Confirmation of details followed in papers by Fernholz and Chakravorty[277] and Dimroth and Trautmann.[278] The complicated proofs of structure of ergosterol and related sterols are reviewed by Rosenberg[14] and Fieser and Fieser.[279]

b. Lumisterol

$C_{28}H_{44}O$. Three double bonds. Melting point 118°. Principal absorption maxima at 265 and 279 mμ. Molecular extinction coefficient at 279 mμ = 8500.[280] $[\alpha]_D^{19} = +192°$, and $[\alpha]_{5461}^{19} = +235°$ (in acetone).

[275] A. Windaus and A. Lüttringhaus, *Nachr. Ges. Wiss. Göttingen, Math. physik Kl., Fachgruppe* III 4 (1932).
[276] A. Windaus, H. H. Inhoffen, and S. von Reichel, *Ann.* **510,** 248 (1934).
[277] E. Fernholz and P. N. Chakravorty, *Ber.* **67,** 2021 (1934).
[278] K. Dimroth and G. Trautmann, *Ber.* **69,** 669 (1936).
[279] L. F. Fieser and M. Fieser, Natural Products Related to Phenanthrene, 3rd ed. Reinhold Publishing Corp., New York, 1949.
[280] I. M. Heilbron, G. L. Moffet, and F. S. Spring, *J. Chem. Soc.* **1937,** 411.

Lumisterol, the initial phototransformation product of ergosterol, was isolated by Windaus et al.[281] and Askew et al.[263] in 1932. From acetone-methanol it crystallizes in fine needles. It is easily soluble in chloroform, ether, and acetone, somewhat difficultly soluble in methanol. In air it oxidizes "only slowly." Like ergosterol, it is isomerized by hydrogen chloride. It gives the color reactions of ergosterol with minor differences. It does not give a precipitate with digitonin. It is physiologically inert but is activated by irradiation. It forms a molecular addition compound with calciferol, this complex being the old vitamin D_1 of the German school.

The structure of lumisterol has been the subject of many studies, which are critically reviewed by Rosenberg,[14] with the conclusion that the only

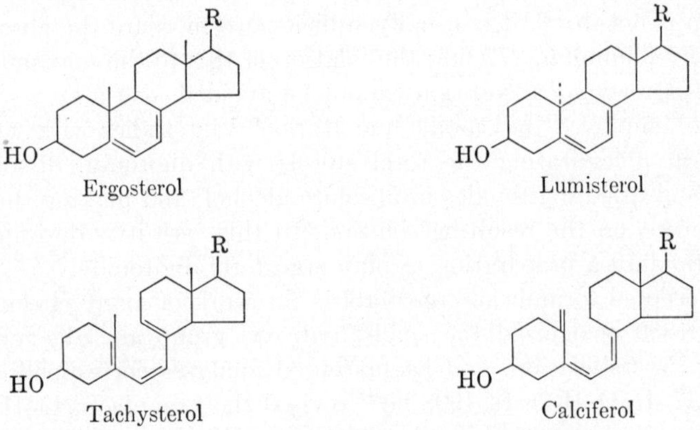

FIG. 13. Ergosterol irradiation products of known structure.

difference between lumisterol and ergosterol is an epimerization of the methyl group at C-10. It is conventional to indicate such steric differences by a dotted bond line, as shown in Fig. 13.

c. Protachysterol

In 1931, before much was known about the individual products of irradiation, Windaus and Auhagen[282] made a remarkable study of the stability of irradiated ergosterol. A solution of ergosterol in dioxane-petroleum 1:9 was irradiated, the unconverted ergosterol frozen out and filtered off, and the filtrate stored and examined polarimetrically and spectroscopically—all in a closed system practically devoid of oxygen. It was found that, over a period of 50 days at room temperature, the specific rotation changed from −17° to a constant value at +7°, and the absorption spectrum at 280 mμ

[281] A. Windaus, K. Dithmar, and E. Fernholz, Ann. **493**, 259 (1932).
[282] A. Windaus and E. Auhagen, Hoppe-Seyler's Z. physiol. Chem. **196**, 108 (1931).

showed a substantial increase. These changes were not accompanied by any significant loss of vitamin D potency.

To explain the observed spectral change, Windaus et al.[45] postulated the existence of an unstable "protachysterol" which changes into tachysterol, the intermediate characterized by intense absorption at 280 mμ. This explanation does not account for the change in specific rotation, which was opposite to what would be expected if tachysterol were being formed. Interpretation of this dark reaction is further complicated by the subsequent discovery of precalciferol, described below.

d. Tachysterol

$C_{28}H_{44}O$. Four double bonds. Melting point of 3,5-dinitro-4-methyl benzoate 154° to 155°. Absorption maximum at 280 mμ, minor bands at 268 and 294 mμ. Molecular extinction coefficient at 280 mμ = 24,000. $[\alpha]_D^{18}$ = −70°, and $[\alpha]_{5461}$ = −86.3° (in "Normalbenzin").

Tachysterol was isolated from activation resin by Windaus, Lüttringhaus and Busse[45] in 1932, and its preparation and properties were described in detail by Windaus, von Werder, and Lüttringhaus.[283] It got its name in recognition of the speed (Gr. tachys) with which it reacts with maleic or citraconic anhydride to form an adduct useful in its separation. Tachysterol has not been obtained in crystalline form, although tachysteryl acetate-citraconic anhydride and tachysteryl 3,5-dinitro-4-methyl benzoate form good crystals. Tachysterol is a source of trouble in the separation of irradiation products, because, besides failing to crystallize, it exhibits an exceptional affinity for oxygen, and the oxidation of calciferol is promoted by its presence.[45] It is insoluble in water, but easily soluble in the common organic solvents, including methanol. It does not give a precipitate with digitonin. It gives in modified form the color reactions of ergosterol.

The structure of tachysterol (Fig. 13) has been elucidated largely through the work of Müller[284] and Grundmann,[285] supported by von Werder.[286] In tachysterol ring B is ruptured, with the formation of a fourth double bond. Thus, like calciferol, it does not, in the strict sense, possess the sterol ring structure. Its similarity to calciferol is further shown by the fact that, upon reduction with sodium in alcohol, both compounds yield the same dihydro derivative.[284] Tachysterol is converted into calciferol by irradiation,[283] and calciferol is converted into tachysterol by the introduction and removal of an atom of iodine.[286a]

[283] A. Windaus, F. von Werder, and A. Lüttringhaus, Ann. 499, 188 (1932).
[284] M. Müller, Hoppe-Seyler's Z. physiol. Chem. 233, 223 (1935).
[285] W. Grundmann, Hoppe-Seyler's Z. physiol. Chem. 252, 151 (1938).
[286] F. von Werder, Hoppe-Seyler's Z. physiol. Chem. 260, 119 (1939).
[286a] P. Meunier and G. Thibaudet, Compt. rend. 223, 172 (1946).

Tachysterol exhibits considerable pharmacological activity. It is about one-half as toxic as calciferol in producing kidney tubule calcification in the mouse.[283] For calcifying bone it is greatly inferior to calciferol although still a potent agent. Windaus et al.[283] observed no antiricketic activity from doses of 1 γ daily to rats, but higher doses were not explored. Meunier and Thibaudet[286a] observed healing at the 10-γ level. This is about 500 times the requirement of calciferol. Probably the antiricketic action was not due to contamination with calciferol, for it was the same in samples of tachysterol prepared the usual way and by the deiodination of iodocalciferol.

e. Precalciferol

$C_{28}H_{44}O$. Probably four double bonds. Melting point of 3,5-dinitrobenzoate 103° to 104°. $[\alpha]_D$ of 3,5-dinitrobenzoate $= +45°$ in chloroform and $+30°$ in benzene, with mutarotation. Absorption maximum (of free form, by graphic subtraction), at 265 mμ. Molecular extinction coefficient at 265 mμ $= 9600$. In solution, transforms into calciferol.

In 1948–1949, when the irradiation series had come to be regarded as a closed book, a renewed interest in the dark reaction came out of the studies of Velluz and his associates.[287] Ergosterol in ether was irradiated under nitrogen, the ether distilled off, the unconverted ergosterol frozen out of alcohol, and the alcohol removed—all at a temperature below 25°. Without heating, the resin was converted into 3,5-dinitrobenzoates, and the product fractionated on alumina. The least strongly adsorbed fraction was crystallized from ligroin, giving yields of precalciferyl 3,5-dinitrobenzoate which amounted to as much as 50% of the resin taken. That such an abundant product should have been so long overlooked is surprising but understandable because it transforms itself into calciferol in solution, especially when warmed.

Precalciferyl 3,5-dinitrobenzoate crystallizes from ligroin in fine pale-yellow needles, m.p. 103° to 104°, obviously different from the bright yellow massive crystals of calciferyl 3,5-dinitrobenzoate, m.p. 158° to 159°. The ester upon saponification gives a non-crystalline free form of precalciferol, which does not precipitate with digitonin and which gives the calciferol color reactions of Pesez[288] in reduced intensity. The absorption spectrum of precalciferol is strikingly similar to that of calciferol, except that it is only about half as intense. The curve (Fig. 9) shows no evidence of admixture of other precursors of calciferol. When a benzene solution of precal-

[287] L. Velluz, A. Petit, G. Michel, and G. Rousseau, Compt. rend. **226**, 1287 (1948); L. Velluz, A. Petit, and G. Amiard, Bull. soc. chim. France **15**, 1115 (1948); L. Velluz and G. Amiard, Compt. rend. **228**, 692, 853 (1949); L. Velluz, G. Amiard, and A. Petit, Bull. soc. chim. France **16**, 501 (1949).

[288] M. Pesez, Bull. soc. chim. France **16**, 507 (1949).

ciferol or precalciferyl 3,5-dinitrobenzoate is held at 60° for several hours in the dark, the dextrorotation increases to almost that of calciferol or calciferyl 3,5-dinitrobenzoate, and the latter products can be isolated. Conversely, solutions of calciferol or calciferyl 3,5-dinitrobenzoate produce some precalciferol or precalciferyl 3,5-dinitrobenzoate. In any of these solutions, calciferol always predominates at equilibrium. The relationship of the two isomers is presumed to be a phenomenon of transitory cyclization. The increasing dextrorotation in the Windaus and Auhagen[282] experiment, heretofore unexplained, was probably due to the precalciferol-calciferol transformation, which was overshadowed spectrally by the simultaneously occurring protachysterol-tachysterol transformation. Thus it appears that there are two dark reactions in the activation series.

Mention should be made of the claim by Raoul et al.[289] that, in ionizing solutions, calciferol and tachysterol are interchangeable. It was found that in an ionizing agent such as symmetrical dichloroethane, activated with 1 % glycerol dichlorohydrin, calciferol undergoes a change, its optical properties simulating those of tachysterol. If the ionization is checked before it has continued too long, the product reverts to calciferol, but if it has been prolonged, the change back to calciferol can be brought about only by irradiation. That the product into which the calciferol changed was really tachysterol may be questioned, since it was reported that an attempt to prepare the 3,5-dinitro-4-methylbenzoate of tachysterol resulted only in the formation of the corresponding ester of calciferol.

f. Calciferol. Vitamin D_2. Ergocalciferol

$C_{28}H_{44}O$. Four double bonds. Melting point 121°.[290] Distils, with decomposition, at 150° in high vacuum.[241] Broad absorption band with maximum at 265 mμ; molecular extinction coefficient = 19,400 in alcohol ($E_{1\ cm}^{1\%}$ = 490).[290, 290a] $[\alpha]_D^{20}$ = +106°, $[\alpha]_{5461}^{20}$ = +125° (in absolute alcohol).[243]

In 1930–1931 the English and German teams of investigators succeeded in isolating pure vitamin D from the irradiation resin of ergosterol. An ingenious method for the distillation and fractional condensation of the resin in a high vacuum was described by Askew et al.[291] Small amounts of potent crystals were obtained. The method was improved, and a detailed study of the active crystals was reported by Angus et al.[241] The name, calciferol, was given to the crystalline substance. A few months later, in 1931, Askew et al.[263] discovered that the original calciferol was a mixture,

[289] Y. Raoul, J. Chopin, P. Meunier, and N. Le Boulch, Compt. rend. 228, 1064 (1949).
[290] H. Pénau and G. Hagemann, Helv. Chim. Acta 29, 1366 (1946).
[290a] S. K. Crews and E. L. Smith, Analyst 64, 568 (1939).
[291] F. A. Askew, R. B. Bourdillon, H. M. Bruce, R. G. C. Jenkins, and T. A. Webster, Proc. Roy. Soc. (London) B107, 76 (1930).

separable via the 3,5-dinitrobenzoate into pure calciferol and two inactive sterols. One of these, pyrocalciferol, was merely a thermal transformation product, produced during the distillation. The other, "sterol X" (lumisterol), had come over from the original irradiation product. By the new esterification technique calciferol could be obtained directly from the resin, without distillation.

While the isolation of calciferol was in progress in England, Windaus and his associates in Germany were developing a different technique to the same end. Windaus[292] and Windaus et al.[293] reviewed their preliminary studies on activation and announced that a crystalline vitamin D was obtained by removing the inactive components of the resin by means of maleic or citraconic anhydride. Presently Linsert[294] in 1931 obtained another crystalline preparation somewhat different in its properties from the first. For a few weeks Windaus and Lüttringhaus[295] regarded these two preparations as distinct forms of vitamin D, and called them vitamin D_1 and vitamin D_2, respectively. Soon, however, it was realized by Windaus et al.[199] that the Linsert preparation was essentially identical with Bourdillon's pure calciferol, while the first German preparation was an addition compound of calciferol with lumisterol.

The name vitamin D_1 has been abandoned, but the name calciferol has been retained, so that vitamin D_2 and calciferol are now synonyms for the pure product. The Commission on Nomenclature of Biological Chemistry of the International Union of Pure and Applied Chemistry[296] has adopted the name ergocalciferol as another synonym, for the purpose of making clearer the distinction from vitamin D_3, which they call cholecalciferol.

Callow's[92] procedure of purifying calciferol via the 3,5-dinitrobenzoate works so well that the properties and constants of calciferol are known with better agreement than those of ergosterol.

Calciferol crystallizes from methanol in clusters of colorless needles,[263] and from acetone in long prisms.[199] It is very soluble in most organic solvents, but less so in methanol than in acetone.[263] The solubility in acetone amounts to 1 g. in 14 ml. at 7°.[199] At 26° 100 ml. of acetone dissolves 25 g., 100 ml. of absolute alcohol 28 g., and 100 ml. of ethyl acetate 31 g. of calciferol.[290]

The stability of calciferol has been reviewed and studied by Huber and Barlow.[297] Calciferol is even more unstable than ergosterol. Samples kept under ordinary laboratory conditions show signs of decomposition in 2 or

[292] A. Windaus, Proc. Roy. Soc. (London) B108, 568 (1931).
[293] A. Windaus, A. Lüttringhaus, and M. Deppe, Ann. 489, 252 (1931).
[294] O. Linsert, cited, in a footnote, by A. Windaus, A. Lüttringhaus, and M. Deppe, Ann. 489, 252 (1931); U. S. Pat. 1,902,785 (1933).
[295] A. Windaus and A. Lüttringhaus, Hoppe-Seyler's Z. physiol. Chem. 203, 70 (1931).
[296] A. M. Patterson, Chem. Eng. News 30, 104 (1952).
[297] W. Huber and O. W. Barlow, J. Biol. Chem. 149, 125 (1943).

3 days. Inert gases or low temperatures greatly diminish, but do not prevent, the decomposition. In the author's experience, a sample stored for 6 years in the dark at 0° in a closed but not hermetically sealed bottle, retained its crystalline form but became deep yellow, and shortly after warming to room temperature it mildly exploded. Huber and Barlow found that samples sealed under vacuum in amber ampules and kept in the refrigerator, showed no change up to 9 months. The esters of calciferol (Table VIII, page 204) with various nitrobenzoic acids are remarkably stable and provide a means of storage as well as of characterization. They remain unchanged over a period of years if a slight photodecomposition is avoided by keeping them in amber bottles.[297] Fresh calciferol can then be had at any time, merely by applying a simple saponification procedure which avoids recrystallization and its attendant hazards to purity. Solutions of calciferol in edible oils or in propylene glycol, and dispersions of it in canned milk, have excellent keeping qualities, even under severe conditions.[297]

The melting point data on commercial calciferol are reviewed by Anderson et al.[297a] The melting point is close to 116°, values between 115° and 117° being the usual range. Perhaps because of slight thermal decomposition, the actual melting point is unsharp. Highly purified calciferol melts at 121°, according to Pénau and Hagemann.[290]

Calciferol is strongly dextrorotatory, although less so than lumisterol; the presence of the latter as an impurity can be determined quantitatively by a procedure described by Setz.[226] The positive rotation decreases markedly with increasing temperature; in alcohol this decrease amounts to 0.515° per degree of temperature rise.[297a] The dextrorotation of calciferyl 3,5-dinitrobenzoate, on the other hand, increases with increasing temperature. The specific rotations of both calciferol and its 3,5-dinitrobenzoate increase substantially with the concentration of the test solution. The effects of solvents on the specific rotation are even greater than for ergosterol, but in a generally reversed order, as shown in Table VII in comparison with Table VI. Since the specific rotation of calciferol is highest in absolute alcohol, and also because calciferol is extremely sensitive to traces of hydrogen chloride,[251] it is customary to determine the specific rotation in alcohol, rather than in chloroform.

The absorption spectra of calciferol and several of its substituted nitrobenzoic acid esters have been studied by Huber et al.[251] The curve for calciferol is smoother than some previously published and shows no evidence of inflections other than the one broad band at 265 mμ. Identical values were obtained in alcohol and hexane, and the curves were also identical with those of vitamin D_3 in the same solvents. The molecular extinction coefficient of 18,200 is in good agreement with previously re-

[297a] F. W. Anderson, A. L. Bacharach, and E. L. Smith, Analyst 62, 430 (1937).

ported values, but inferior to the value 19,400 ($E_{1\,cm.}^{1\%}$ = 490) found by Pénau and Hagemann[290] and Crews and Smith.[290a]

Calciferol gives no precipitate with digitonin. In the well-known color reactions, it generally gives weaker and less well-defined colors than ergosterol. These responses are described by Askew et al.,[263] Windaus et al.,[199] and Bacharach et al.[243] Color reactions of special interest in connection with vitamin D are described by Pesez,[288] Banchetti,[298] Schaltegger,[299] Villar Palasí,[300] and De Witt and Sullivan.[301]

The structural formula of calciferol (Fig. 13) was established by Windaus and Thiele[302] in 1935 and by Heilbron et al.[303] in 1936. Their published work

TABLE VII

OPTICAL ROTATION OF CALCIFEROL[a]

Solvent	$[\alpha]_{5461}^{20}$	$[\alpha]_{D}^{20}$	Ratio
Alcohol (absolute)	+125.0°	+106.25°	1.18
Ethyl acetate	+113.25°	+ 95.0°	1.19
Ether	+105.5°	+ 88.75°	1.19
Benzene	+102.12°	+ 87.5°	1.17
Acetone	+ 99.5°	+ 83.5°	1.19
n-Hexane	+ 66.5°	+ 56.25°	1.18
Chloroform	+ 61.75°	+ 52.25°	1.18
		Average value of ratio =	1.18

[a] Data from Bacharach et al.[243] on commercial lots of refined material.

was the culmination of a long series of attacks on the problems of structure which are reviewed by Fieser and Fieser[279] and by Rosenberg.[14] The correctness of the formula has been confirmed, and detailed stereochemical relations of the atoms within the molecule established, by Crowfoot and Dunitz[304] through a study of the X-ray diffraction pattern of calciferyl 4-iodo-5-nitrobenzoate.

g. Toxisterol. Substance 248

$C_{28}H_{44}O$. Melting point about 50°.[305] Narrow absorption band with maximum at 248 mμ; molecular extinction coefficient = 18,300.[45] $[\alpha]_D^{22}$ = −16° (in chloroform).[305]

[298] A. Banchetti, Ann. chim. appl. **38**, 394 (1948).

[299] H. Schaltegger, Helv. Chim. Acta **29**, 285 (1946).

[300] V. Villar Palasí, Nature **160**, 88 (1947).

[301] J. B. De Witt and M. X. Sullivan, Ind. Eng. Chem. Anal. Ed. **18**, 117 (1946).

[302] A. Windaus and W. Thiele, Ann. **521**, 160 (1935).

[303] I. M. Heilbron, R. N. Jones, K. M. Samant, and F. S. Spring, J. Chem. Soc. **1936**, 905.

[304] D. Crowfoot and J. D. Dunitz, Nature **162**, 608 (1948).

[305] O. Linsert, U. S. Pat. 2,030,377 (1936).

In 1927 Morton *et al.*,[213] extending the work of Pohl,[30] showed that when ergosterol is irradiated its characteristic absorption bands disappear, and a single new band of great intensity develops at 247 or 248 mμ, which in turn fades away to weak general absorption in the far ultraviolet region. With inadequate biological evidence, the assumption was easily made that this new band represented vitamin D. Smakula,[229] however, concluded that substance 248 was not the vitamin. Bills *et al.*[239] showed that the appearance of the band at 248 mμ coincided not with the development, but with the destruction, of antiricketic potency. They, and also van Wijk and Reerink,[306] associated substance 248 with isoergosterol. Cox and Bills[307] contributed further evidence of relationship to the isoergosterols, but noted a point of difference, namely, that substance 248 does not precipitate with digitonin.

Bills *et al.*[239] found that irradiation products withdrawn for examination at the moment when substance 248 was at its maximum concentration still contained some vitamin D. Further irradiation totally eliminated antiricketic activity, while only a small amount of substance 248 was destroyed. Laquer and Linsert[308] attributed a toxic quality to substance 248, and proposed the name Toxisterin (toxisterol). The product which they investigated still contained some vitamin D, but not enough to account for the relatively great toxicity. It was evidently a mixture similar to the one which Hoyle[309] obtained by limited overirradiation and which he reported to have toxic-calcifying properties all out of proportion to the antiricketic potency. Such a mixture, unfortunately, seems to have been the "vitamin D" of the I. G. Farbenindustrie patent[310] of 1928 (the old Vigantol of toxic repute). The claims of this patent, and of the corresponding American patent,[311] call for the irradiation of ergosterol to be continued just until the absorption spectrum of what is now recognized as toxisterol attains its maximum! The mistake was clearly the result of assuming, in the absence of proper bioassays, that the spectrographically most conspicuous irradiation product was the vitamin. There is considerable evidence, both spectrographic and toxicologic, that toxisterol is formed most readily when alcohol is the solvent in which the ergosterol is irradiated.[238, 239, 306, 309, 312]

The purest described preparation of toxisterol is that of the Linsert (Farbenindustrie) patent[305] for isolating, from the irradiation products of

306 A. van Wijk and E. H. Reerink, *Nature* **122,** 648 (1928).
307 W. M. Cox, Jr., and C. E. Bills, *J. Biol. Chem.* **88,** 709 (1930).
308 F. Laquer and O. Linsert, *Klin. Wochschr.* **12,** 753 (1933).
309 J. C. Hoyle, *J. Pharmacol. Exptl. Therap.* **40,** 351 (1930).
310 I. G. Farbenindustrie Aktiengesellschaft, British Pat. 296,093 (1928).
311 W. Zimmermann and W. Frankenburger, U. S. Pat. 1,896,191 (1933).
312 W. E. Dixon and J. C. Hoyle, *Brit. Med. J.* **2,** 832 (1928); L. J. Harris and T. Moore, *Biochem. J.* **22,** 1461 (1929); J. C. Hoyle and H. Buckland, *ibid.* **23,** 558 (1929); R. Kern, M. F. Montgomery, and E. U. Still, *J. Biol. Chem.* **93,** 365 (1931).

vitamin D, a "product which is essentially characterized by its increasing action on the level of blood calcium." According to the example, crystalline vitamin D, made from ergosterol, is irradiated in heptane in the absence of oxygen until its absorption maximum at 265 mμ substantially disappears. The product is converted into the 3,5-dinitrobenzoate, which is crystallized free of the suprasterols. Saponification of the dinitrobenzoate, which is dextrorotatory, $[\alpha]_D^{22} = +33°$ in acetone, m.p. 130°, gives the free drug as a whitish powder which is levorotatory, $[\alpha]_D^{22} = -16°$ in chloroform. (A similar anomalous difference in sign of rotation between dinitrobenzoate and free sterol is noted in tachysterol$_3$[313]).

The exceptionally low melting point, about 50°, casts some doubt on the purity of the preparation, but the product is stated to be "practically antirachitically inactive." It is worth noting that the patent description of this drug, which was one of a series of blood calcium raising substances then under investigation by the I.G. (following the Vigantol episode), makes no mention of the term toxisterol and no reference to the absorption spectrum of the product by which it could be identified as substance 248. Although the isolation of toxisterol has never been described elsewhere than in this patent and its European counterparts, the German workers appear to have been familiar with toxisterol to the extent of publishing its absorption spectrum showing the extinction coefficient.[45]

h. Suprasterol I

$C_{28}H_{44}O$. Three double bonds. General absorption below 250 mμ. $[\alpha]_D^{18} = -76°$ in chloroform. Melting point 104°.

Suprasterol II

$C_{28}H_{44}O$. Three double bonds. General absorption below 250 mμ. $[\alpha]_D^{19} = +63°$ in chloroform. Melting point 110°.

The products of extreme overirradiation, the end products of the series, were designated Suprasterine by Windaus et al.[314] in 1930. They recognized two isomers, suprasterol I and suprasterol II, which they separated by taking advantage of differences in the solubility of the allophanic acid esters. The designations I and II do not refer to sequence of formation, but to the order in which the two allophanates crystallize out of solution. The suprasterols, especially suprasterol II, are much more soluble in organic solvents than ergosterol. They are unaffected by irradiation. They can be distilled unchanged at 190° *in vacuo*. They do not precipitate with digitonin. Of their color reactions, the most conspicuous is the intense red violet which they give with chloral hydrate. They show no antiricketic activity at dosage

[313] A. Windaus, M. Deppe, and W. Wunderlich, *Ann.* **533,** 118 (1937).

[314] A. Windaus, J. Gaede, J. Köser, and G. Stein, *Ann.* **483,** 17 (1930).

levels several times higher than the usual dose for calciferol. They are only slightly toxic.

Suprasterol I crystallizes in fine needles from acetone, and suprasterol II in dense prisms from acetone or methanol. Suprasterol I is less sensitive to oxidation than ergosterol or calciferol, but slowly yellows in contact with air; suprasterol II was not observed in this connection.

From the work of Windaus et al.[314] and other studies reviewed and extended by Müller,[284] it appears that the suprasterols have three double bonds and are therefore tetracyclic, but the ring structure may not be that of the sterols. In other words, the ring closure suffered by calciferol in the formation of the suprasterols may not be at the point of rupture of the original ring B of ergosterol and lumisterol. Certainly the double bonds are no longer in conjugated position, for the suprasterols show no absorption bands.

i. 7-Dehydrocholesterol. Provitamin D_3

$C_{27}H_{44}O \cdot H_2O$. Molecular weight 402.638. Two double bonds. Melting point 149° to 150°.[70] Principal absorption maxima at 262.5, 271, 281.5, and 293 mμ.[251, 265] Molecular extinction coefficient at 281.5 mμ = 10,920 (in alcohol).[251] $[\alpha]_D^{20}$ = −124° (in chloroform).[70]

The series of irradiation products which stem from 7-dehydrocholesterol is in every respect analogous to the ergosterol series, but it has not been studied in quite as much detail. Windaus et al.[313] have proposed a nomenclature for these products, according to which the names of the ergosterol series are retained, but a subscript number 3 is added; thus lumisterol₃ and tachysterol₃ are the 7-dehydrocholesterol products corresponding to lumisterol and tachysterol. Similarly, for the 22-dihydroergosterol series the subscript 4 is used.

7-Dehydrocholesterol crystallizes in slender platelets from ether-methanol.[38] It is difficultly soluble in methanol, and readily soluble in ether.[70] The crystals contain one mole of water[251] which cannot be completely removed.[38] 7-Dehydrocholesterol forms a precipitate with digitonin.[38] It also gives the color reactions of ergosterol with minor differences.[38] Its specific rotation is a little less strongly levorotatory than that of ergosterol.[70] Its absorption spectrum is practically identical with that of ergosterol,[251, 265] and besides the four major bands, minor inflections are exhibited at 252, 321, and 336 mμ.[265]

7-Dehydrocholesterol is much more unstable than ergosterol.[38, 251, 315] It shows yellowing in less than 2 days when exposed to air at room temperature, even in the dark. However, when it is crystallized together with cholesterol, a remarkable stabilization results, depending upon the amount of

[315] H. R. Rosenberg and W. W. Woessner, U. S. Pat. 2,434,015 (1948).

cholesterol. Thus a sample containing 59% cholesterol showed no change after 5 weeks under the above conditions.[315] The presence of much cholesterol may be presumed to have been a factor in the survival of the provitamin found in the brain of the mummy, mentioned above in another connection. The substituted nitrobenzoates of 7-dehydrocholesterol are also stable. Huber et al.[251] have recommended converting the provitamin into its 3,5-dinitrobenzoate, both as a means of purifying it and preserving it, so that fresh samples of the free provitamin can be had at any time merely by subjecting the ester to a simple saponification.

j. Lumisterol₃

$C_{27}H_{44}O$. Dimorphous: needles from acetone, melting point 87° to 88°; mixed forms from methanol, melting point 63° to 64°. $[\alpha]_D^{18} = +197°$ in chloroform. Absorption spectrum almost the same as that of lumisterol₂.

The initial irradiation product of 7-dehydrocholesterol is lumisterol₃, isolated by Windaus et al.[313] in 1937. It is distinguished from lumisterol₂ by the fact that it does not form a molecular addition compound with its corresponding vitamin D.

k. Tachysterol₃

$C_{27}H_{44}O$. Melting point of 3,5-dinitro-4-methyl benzoate 137°. Free form has $[\alpha]_D^{21} = -11.5°$ in "Normalbenzin," but the ester is dextrorotatory. Absorption spectrum like that of tachysterol₂, but somewhat less intense.

From the irradiation products of 7-dehydrocholesterol, tachysterol₃ was isolated by Windaus et al.[313] in 1937. Like tachysterol₂, it does not crystallize, but forms crystallizable esters.

l. Precalciferol₃

$C_{27}H_{44}O$. Melting point of 3,5-dinitrobenzoate 110° to 111°. $[\alpha]_D^{18}$ of 3,5-dinitrobenzoate $= +52°$ in chloroform and $+38.5°$ in benzene, with mutarotation.

Velluz et al.[316] in 1949 obtained precalciferol₃ in the form of its 3,5-dinitrobenzoate, which crystallizes in pale yellow, thread-like needles not exhibiting the dimorphism of the corresponding ester of vitamin D₃. The free form does not crystallize. The free (or ester) form exists in solution in equilibrium with the corresponding free (or ester) form of vitamin D₃, with the vitamin (or ester) predominating.

m. Vitamin D₃. Calciferol₃. Cholecalciferol

$C_{27}H_{44}O$. Three double bonds. Melting point 84° to 85°.[251, 297] Broad absorption band with maximum at 265 mμ; molecular extinction coefficient $= 18,200$ in alcohol or hexane.[251] $[\alpha]_D^{20} = +84.8°$ in acetone.[297]

[316] L. Velluz and G. Amiard, *Compt. rend.* **228**, 1037 (1949); L. Velluz, G. Amiard, and A. Petit, *Bull. soc. chim. France* **16**, 501 (1949).

Vitamin D_3 was obtained in crystalline form by Schenck[317] in 1937. The isolation procedure was essentially the same as for calciferol, i.e., purification via the 3,5-dinitrobenzoate, followed by saponification. Vitamin D_3 is more difficult to crystallize than D_2, and the yields are inferior.[297, 313, 318] There has been described a double compound of the vitamin with cholesterol (or with cholestanol or coprosterol), which crystallizes in good yield and represents the most economical way to obtain a preparation of uniform purity.[297, 319] The constants of the esters of vitamin D_3 are shown in Table VIII.

Pure crystalline vitamin D_3 is slightly more stable than D_2, and much more stable than its precursor, 7-dehydrocholesterol. Considerable deterioration occurs in 72 hours when the vitamin is exposed to air at room temperature, even in brown bottles. Deterioration is negligible after 12 months' storage in evacuated amber ampules at refrigerator temperature.[297] The complex with cholesterol is less stable than the pure vitamin.[297] As with calciferol, the various nitrobenzoic acid esters of vitamin D_3 are remarkably stable. They remain unchanged for at least 5 years with no special precautions other than the avoidance of light. Solutions of vitamin D_3 in edible oils or in propylene glycol and dispersions of it in canned milk have excellent keeping qualities, even under severe conditions.[297]

Vitamin D_3 is sensitive to hydrogen chloride.[251] It does not give a precipitate with digitonin.[317] It gives a yellow color in the antimony trichloride reaction.[317] In these respects, as well as in optical properties and chemical reactions, it reveals its similarity to calciferol. The similarity in most non-biological properties and reactions of these two forms of vitamin D supports the quip that only a bird can tell them apart.

5. Minor and Obscure Forms

The number of steroids which exhibit antiricketic action is considerable, but many of them are so vaguely characterized that an exact count is impossible. In attempting to enumerate them, one is confronted with the inadequacy of many reported animal tests and with the probability that, if tests were conducted differently, the number of recognized vitamins D would be larger. There is also the problem of contamination, which has confused investigators ever since the first crude cholesterol was irradiated and which now is involved in the so-called vitamin D_5, or activated 7-dehydrositosterol. Lastly, there is the factor of the occasional bad assay, which, according to the statisticians, appears even in the best-regulated laboratories at unpredictable times.

[317] F. Schenck, *Naturwissenschaften* **25,** 159 (1937); A. Windaus and F. Schenck, U. S. Pat. 2,099,550 (1937).

[318] A. Windaus, F. Schenck, and F. von Werder, *Hoppe-Seyler's Z. physiol. Chem.* **241,** 100 (1936).

[319] O. Linsert, U. S. Pat. 2,264,320 (1941).

TABLE VIII
Vitamin D Esters

Ester, reference	Melting point, °C.	Specific rotation
Calciferyl (Vitamin D_2) acetate[290]	86	$[\alpha]_{5790} = +38°$ acetone
Calciferyl allophanate[226]	194–195	$[\alpha]_D^{20} = +50.4°$ chloroform
Calciferyl anisate[226]	99.5–101	$[\alpha]_D^{21} = +120°$ chloroform
Calciferyl benzoate[290]	92	$[\alpha]_{5790} = +100°$ acetone
Monocalciferyl esters of n-butane-1,2,3,4-tetracarboxylic acid (unseparated isomers)[260]	90–100 decomp.	
Calciferyl chaulmoograte[290]	53	$[\alpha]_{5790} = +52°$ chloroform
Calciferyl 2-chloro-3,5-dinitrobenzoate[134]	132	$[\alpha]_D^{22} = +60°$ acetone
Calciferyl 3,5-dinitrobenzoate[263, 297a]	147–149	$[\alpha]_{5461}^{20} = +69°$ benzene
Calciferyl 3,5-dinitrobenzoate[297]	146–147	$[\alpha]_D^{20} = +91.5°$ chloroform
Calciferyl 3,5-dinitrobenzoate[297]		$[\alpha]_D^{20} = +86.5°$ acetone
Calciferyl 3,5-dinitro-4-methylbenzoate[297]	116–117	$[\alpha]_D^{20} = +95.8°$ chloroform
Calciferyl β-naphthoate[257a]	132	$[\alpha]_D^{20} = +150°$ chloroform
Calciferyl 4-nitrobenzoate[297]	94.5–95	$[\alpha]_D^{20} = +105.2°$ chloroform
Calciferyl 3-nitro-4-methylbenzoate[297]	119–120	$[\alpha]_D^{20} = +106.8°$ chloroform
Calciferyl oleate[290]	Liquid	$[\alpha]_{5790} = +18.7°$ chloroform
Calciferyl phenylurethane[226]	122	$[\alpha]_D^{19} = +49.2°$ chloroform
Calciferyl propionate[290]	77	$[\alpha]_{5790} = +37.6°$ acetone
Vitamin D_3 anisate[313]	114	$[\alpha]_D^{21} = +127°$ chloroform
Vitamin D_3 3,5-dinitrobenzoate (dimorphous)		
From benzene-methanol[297]	132	$[\alpha]_D^{20} = +97.9°$ chloroform
From ether[297]	141	
Leaflets[316]	142	$[\alpha]_D^{20} = +97°$ chloroform
Needles[316]	150	
Vitamin D_3 3,5-dinitro-4-methylbenzoate[297]	128–129	$[\alpha]_D^{20} = +106.6°$ chloroform
Vitamin D_3 4-nitrobenzoate[297]	125–126	$[\alpha]_D^{20} = +114.6°$ chloroform
Vitamin D_4 3,5-dinitrobenzoate[321]	127–128	$[\alpha]_D^{22} = +93.2°$ acetone
Vitamin D_m 3,5-dinitrobenzoate[119]	128–128.5	$[\alpha]_D = +92°$ chloroform

(1) Of the minor forms, the best known is vitamin D_4, produced by the irradiation of 22-dihydroergosterol. Windaus and Trautmann[320] in 1937 prepared this vitamin in crystalline form. Windaus and Güntzel[321] repeated the preparation, and also isolated other members of the irradiation series, namely, lumisterol₄, tachysterol₄, and suprasterol II₄. Vitamin D_4 crystallizes out of acetone in long needles, m.p. 96° to 98°, $[\alpha]_D^{21} = +85.7°$ in acetone, spectrum similar to that of calciferol.[321] The potency of the crystalline vitamin amounts to 20,000 to 30,000 I.U. per milligram for the rat[320] (50 % to 75 % of the value of D_2 or D_3). The chick-rat efficacy ratio of vitamin D_4 may be estimated, from the findings of McDonald[66] and Grab,[67] at about 20 %, which places it between D_2 (1 %) and D_3 (100 %), quite in keeping with its structure. Vitamin D_4 ranks as a minor form only because it has received no practical application.

(2) The vitamins D produced by the irradiation of mollusk provitamins are obscure forms chemically but important commercially because they are widely used in poultry feeding. As indicated in the discussion headed Provitamins D of Invertebrates, the provitamins of different mollusks, even when "pure" spectrographically, differ from each other and from any chemically known form of provitamin D. They are probably mixtures, perhaps containing some 7-dehydrocholesterol and occasionally a little ergosterol, but predominantly composed of other sterols, such as the provitamin D_m of Petering and Waddell[91] which appears to have 29 carbon atoms. The vitamin D obtained from provitamin D_m is notable for exhibiting a chick-rat efficacy ratio somewhat above 100 %. [119, 120] It has been crystallized in the form of its 3,5-dinitrobenzoate, m.p. 128° to 128.5°, $[\alpha]_D = +92°$ in chloroform.[119] Even though this may not be a pure substance, there is no doubt but that it represents an obscure vitamin D characterized by high efficacy and high molecular weight.

(3) In the discussion of vitamin D in fish oils, it was shown that several forms are present, although only D_2 and D_3 have been identified. One of the minor forms detected in cod liver oil by Hickman and Gray[169] exhibited a boiling point in molecular distillation so low as to suggest the absence of any side chain in the molecule at C-17. This form, in a chick-rat assay, was found to have an efficacy ratio of between 25 % and 50 %. It must be regarded as a distinct form of vitamin D.

(4) It has been amply demonstrated by Waddell,[36] Bills et al.,[180] Remp and Marshall,[322] and others that, rat unit for rat unit, vitamin D_3 and cod liver oil are about equally effective for chicks. From this has come the un-

[320] A. Windaus and G. Trautmann, *Hoppe-Seyler's Z. physiol. Chem.* **247,** 185 (1937); A. Windaus, U. S. Pat. 2,128,199 (1938).

[321] A. Windaus and B. Güntzel, *Ann.* **538,** 120 (1939).

[322] D. G. Remp and I. H. Marshall, *J. Nutrition* **15,** 525 (1938).

warranted deduction, occasionally seen in medical literature, that vitamin D_3 is the vitamin D of cod liver oil. It has been shown by Matterson et al.[323] and by Waddell and Kennedy[324] that, when vitamin D_3 and cod liver oil are standardized with chicks kept on a diet in which most of the phosphorus is inorganic (e.g., the A.O.A.C. diet), and then again assayed with chicks or turkey poults kept on a diet in which most of the phosphorus is phytic, the vitamin D_3 is found to be much more effective than the vitamin D of cod liver oil. This can mean only that vitamin D_3 is not the dominant vitamin D of cod liver oil and that the dominant form (or forms) of vitamin D in cod liver oil is something different from any recognized form.

(5) In determining the efficacy ratios of the liver oils of twenty-five species of fish, Bills et al.[180] found a few oils with a ratio much above 100. The extreme example was the liver oil of the white sea bass, *Cynoscion nobilis*, which had a ratio of about 300. This oil, when subjected to molecular distillation,[169] showed an exceptionally pure elimination curve, indicative of a preponderance of one form of vitamin D. If the assays can be confirmed, it will be established that white sea bass liver oil contains a new form of vitamin D characterized by the highest known efficacy ratio.

(6) Windaus and Trautmann[320] and Dimroth and Paland[47] briefly mention the irradiation product of 22,23-oxidoergosterol. Described only as a feebly active product, this is presumably 22,23-oxidocalciferol.

(7) Windaus and Buchholz[325] have prepared an oily ketone of vitamin D_2 which was probably uncontaminated with traces of the vitamin, and which exhibited about $\frac{1}{300}$ of the potency of the vitamin in tests with rats.

(8) McDonald [326] has found that by the irradiation of 7-hydroxycholesterol (or an impurity associated therewith) a slight antiricketic potency is developed. Conceivably, the irradiation causes dehydration, with the formation of traces of 7-dehydrocholesterol, in which case the vitamin produced would not be a new form, but merely D_3.

(9) Weinhouse and Kharasch[327] claim to have produced a form of vitamin D by irradiating the heated reaction product of 7-ketocholesteryl acetate and isobutyl magnesium bromide.

(10) In the section headed Chemical Structure and Activatability, mention was made of the vitamin D from 7-dehydrocampesterol. Corresponding to the structure of its precursor, this vitamin can be regarded as the C-24 epimer of vitamin D_4.

(11) The vitamin D from epiergosterol is, presumably, epicalciferol.

[323] L. D. Matterson, H. M. Scott, and E. P. Singsen, *J. Nutrition* **31**, 599 (1946).
[324] J. Waddell and G. H. Kennedy, *J. Assoc. Official Agr. Chemists* **30**, 190 (1947).
[325] A. Windaus and K. Buchholz, *Hoppe-Seyler's Z. physiol. Chem.* **256**, 273 (1938).
[326] F. G. McDonald, cited by C. E. Bills, The Vitamins, Chapter xxiii. American Medical Association, Chicago, 1939.
[327] S. Weinhouse and M. S. Kharasch, *J. Org. Chem.* **1**, 490 (1936).

(12) The vitamin D from 7-dehydroepicholesterol is, by the same analogy, epicalciferol₃.

(13) The compound dihydrotachysterol, better known under its trade names A. T. 10 (anti-tetany compound No. 10) and Hytakerol, possesses some antiricketic activity, in addition to its useful property of elevating blood calcium in parathyroid tetany. It was obtained by von Werder[328] in 1939 by the reduction of tachysteryl 3,5-dinitro-4-methylbenzoate with sodium and alcohol, followed by saponification and chromatographic purification. This drug should not be confused with its isomer, 22-dihydrotachysterol (tachysterol₄), which is a product of the irradiation of 22-dihydroergosterol or of the reduction of tachysteryl acetate adduct with hydrogen. The side-chain double bond in dihydrotachysterol is intact, the reduction being effected in ring A. With the reduction there occurs a migration of the remaining double bonds into the alignment characteristic of calciferol. Thus, although the product is genetically dihydrotachysterol, it is chemically a dihydrocalciferol, differing structurally from the latter only in that the methylene group at C-19 is reduced. With this simple change, the compound loses most of its antiricketic activity, while retaining a relatively large proportion of its blood calcium-elevating activity.

Dihydrotachysterol, $C_{28}H_{46}O$, crystallizes in colorless needles from 90 % methanol. It is easily soluble in organic solvents. It has m.p. 125° to 127°, $[\alpha]_D^{22} = +97.5°$ in chloroform, strong absorption maxima at wavelengths 242, 251, and 261 mμ.[328] Somewhat varying reports on its antiricketic effectiveness has been made by von Werder,[328] Correll,[329] McChesney,[330] Motzok,[331] and others. It appears to have a potency of about 90 I.U. per milligram for rats, which is between $\frac{1}{400}$ and $\frac{1}{500}$ of the potency of calciferol and the same as the potency of tachysterol itself. When compared with cod liver oil or vitamin D_3 with rats and chicks, it shows an efficacy ratio of 400 to 750 %. Willgeroth et al.[332] claim that it is somewhat more effective on turkey poults than on chicks.

(14) In 1928 Bills et al.,[33] repeating the work of the English and German workers in destroying the provitamin D in ordinary cholesterol, found that treatment with charcoal or bromine never resulted in a total, but only in a relative (to about $\frac{1}{30}$), reduction of activatability. Samples so treated, when examined spectrographically in sufficiently high concentrations, still showed the characteristic provitamin bands, and, also, two new bands at

[328] F. von Werder, Hoppe-Seyler's Z. physiol. Chem. 260, 119 (1939); U. S. Pat. 2,228,491 (1941).
[329] J. T. Correll and E. C. Wise, J. Nutrition 23, 217 (1942).
[330] E. W. McChesney, J. Nutrition 26, 81, 487 (1943).
[331] I. Motzok, D. C. Hill, and H. D. Branion, Poultry Sci. 25, 644 (1946).
[332] G. B. Willgeroth, J. L. Halpin, H. R. Halloran, and J. C. Fritz, J. Assoc. Official Agr. Chemists 27, 289 (1944).

wavelengths 304 and 315 mμ. Heilbron *et al.*[333] suggested that the extra bands might be those of cholesterilene, which is non-activatable and hence irrelevant. Other studies with specially purified cholesterol are discussed in the author's review of the multiple nature of vitamin D.[34] It will suffice here to note that Hathaway and Lobb[334] performed chick-rat assays on the irradiation product of cholesterol which had been purified via the dibromide. They found that its efficacy ratio was very low, in a class with that of irradiated ergosterol. Since no known cholesterol derivative has a low efficacy ratio, and since ergosterol could not have survived bromination and could not have been formed anew from a sterol of lower molecular weight, it must be concluded that the irradiated purified cholesterol contained a new form of vitamin D. Presumably the provitamin was the substance which showed the absorption bands in the Bills preparation, and which originated during or after the debromination of the cholesterol dibromide.

Koch *et al.*,[335] in a series of papers summarized[336] in 1935, found that by strongly heating highly purified cholesterol in the presence of traces of oxygen, the provitamin D activity could be enhanced 100 times. The typical provitamin spectrum was not observed, but it may have been present and obscured by a strong general absorption. Waddell[337] found that by heating the cholesterol in the presence of water, the provitamin D activity could be enhanced 100 to 150 times. The vitamin D from heat-treated cholesterol was found by Hathaway and Lobb[334] and Waddell[337] to have a high efficacy ratio in chick-rat assays. This fact, together with the later work on the synthesis of provitamins D, makes it seem probable that the provitamin formed by heating cholesterol is 7-dehydrocholesterol. Unless this assumption is disproved, one cannot regard the vitamin D from irradiated heat-treated cholesterol as a new form.

(15) Meunier and Thibaudet[338] have prepared a monoiodocalciferol, m.p. 150°, which is at least as potent as the parent substance. Removal of the iodine with hyposulfite yielded tachysterol.

(16) Bills and McDonald[339] treated ergosterol with ethyl nitrite, and then treated the product with isopropylamine, obtaining a substance which showed a trivial antiricketic action with rats. Since the conventional forms

[333] I. M. Heilbron, R. A. Morton, and W. A. Sexton, *Nature* **121**, 452 (1928).

[334] M. L. Hathaway and D. E. Lobb, *J. Biol. Chem.* **113**, 105 (1936).

[335] F. C. Koch, E. M. Koch, and I. K. Ragins, *J. Biol. Chem.* **85**, 141 (1929); E. M. Koch, F. C. Koch, and H. B. Lemon, *ibid.* **85**, 159 (1929); M. L. Hathaway and F. C. Koch, *ibid.* **108**, 773 (1935).

[336] E. M. Koch and F. C. Koch, *Science* **82**, 394 (1935).

[337] J. Waddell, U. S. Pat. 2,028,364 (1936).

[338] P. Meunier and G. Thibaudet, *Compt. rend.* **223**, 172 (1946).

[339] C. E. Bills and F. G. McDonald, cited by C. E. Bills, *Cold Spring Harbor Symposia Quant. Biol.* **3**, 328 (1935).

of vitamin D are destroyed by nitrites, this active substance must be different from any known form of vitamin D.

(17) The oldest of the minor forms is the antiricketic product which Bills and McDonald[340] made in 1926 by treating cholesterol with fuller's earth. Its potency was trivial, but interesting at the time in view of the irradiated cholesterol which had been discovered the year before. The preparation was repeated by Kon et al.[216] and later the reaction was investigated by Yoder,[341] who identified the product as a sulfonated cholesteriline which resulted from dehydration followed by sulfonation attributed to traces of sulfur trioxide in the preheated acid clay. In a series of experiments Yoder and his associates[342] worked out the details of "antiricketic sulfonation" and found that a considerable family of hydroxy steroids can be activated by this means. One of the treatments was essentially the Liebermann reaction. The potency attained was never high by irradiation standards, and the healing action on rats was often accompanied by weight loss. Yoder and Thomas[343] have reported that the product from cholesterol has an exceptionally high chick-rat efficacy ratio.

According to Raoul et al.[344] the action of sulfuric acid on cholesterol in the Liebermann and Salkowski reactions results in the formation of an "ether-oxide" of "tachysterol" (meaning ditachysteryl₃ ether?), which, in an ionizing solvent, and without irradiation, transforms itself into "vitamin D." The French authors state, "These experiments teach that it is not sulfonation which is the cause of the transformation of cholesterol into an antiricketic product. There is really formed a vitamin D by the intermediary of tachysterol under the sole influence of ionizations of various origins (acetyl chloride, acetic anhydride, sulfuric acid) as two of us envisaged in 1947." The claim that vitamin D can be made from cholesterol by a simple chemical treatment is most interesting, but the description of what happens is unclear and lacks explanation of the required dehydrogenation step. In a later paper, Raoul et al.[345] admit that the antiricketic compound formed is not vitamin D_3. It seems well established that Yoder's active preparations are monosulfonated unsaturated hydrocarbons, but it may be that products of the type studied by Raoul are also formed in the same reactions.

[340] C. E. Bills and F. G. McDonald, J. Biol. Chem. **67,** 753 (1926).
[341] L. Yoder, J. Biol. Chem. **116,** 71 (1936).
[342] J. C. Eck, B. H. Thomas, and L. Yoder, J. Biol. Chem. **117,** 655 (1937); J. C. Eck and B. H. Thomas, ibid. **119,** 621, 631 (1937); **128,** 257 (1939); L. Yoder and B. H. Thomas, ibid. **178,** 363 (1949); Ind. Eng. Chem. **41,** 2286 (1949).
[343] L. Yoder and B. H. Thomas, Arch. Biochem. and Biophys. **32,** 14 (1951).
[344] Y. Raoul, J. Chopin, P. Meunier, A. Guérillot-Vinet, and N. Le Boulch, Compt. rend. **229,** 259 (1949); Y. Raoul, J. Chopin, P. Meunier, N. Le Boulch, and A. Guérillot-Vinet, ibid. **232,** 1154 (1951).
[345] Y. Raoul, N. Le Boulch, P. Meunier, J. Chopin, and A. Guérillot-Vinet, Compt. rend. **232,** 1258 (1951).

III. Industrial Preparation

CHARLES E. BILLS

The patent index in Rosenberg's[1] book bears witness to the effort and ingenuity which have been applied to the industrial development of vitamin D. The index includes 242 titles and short abstracts of the more important United States and foreign patents through 1941.

The preparation of fish oils is described in Tressler and Lemon's[2] "Marine Products of Commerce" and especially in Brocklesby's[3] "Chemistry and Technology of Marine Animal Oils." The ancient method of rendering fish liver oils by the natural disintegration of livers began to be replaced by steam cooking about the middle of the nineteenth century.[4] With technical improvements, steaming sufficed for most vitamin oil production until about 1933, when interest developed in the production of high-potency oils from low-yield livers.

Nearly all high-potency fish liver oils are manufactured by a process based on the liquefaction of the liver with alkali. This process was worked out independently and at about the same time by Young and Robinson[5] and Wallenmeyer.[6] Sufficient alkali is added to the livers so that, with heating, they go into solution, but the amount of alkali is limited so that substantial saponification of the oil does not occur. The oil is then separated centrifugally from the aqueous liquor, washed, and refined as desired. The vitamin D in liver oils is remarkably stable, but in consideration of the less stable vitamin A, the oils are usually stored under inert gas or in tanks with floating tops.

The patent literature contains many references to equipment designed for the antiricketic activation of foods under the basic Steenbock[7] patent. The common aim in these inventions is the brief exposure of a shallow, moving layer to the rays of a mercury or carbon arc. Milk, because of its suitability for treatment, and its importance to infants and children, has been most extensively activated. A representative apparatus for irradiating milk is shown in Fig. 14. Direct activation of milk is practiced less now than formerly; instead, fortification with vitamin D is accomplished by the

[1] H. R. Rosenberg, Chemistry and Physiology of the Vitamins. Interscience Publishers, New York, 1945.

[2] D. K. Tressler and J. McW. Lemon, Marine Products of Commerce. Reinhold Publishing Corp., New York, 1951.

[3] H. N. Brocklesby, Chemistry and Technology of Marine Animal Oils with Particular Reference to Those of Canada. Fisheries Research Board of Canada, Ottawa, 1941.

[4] C. E. Bills, *Chem. Revs.* **3**, 425 (1927).

[5] F. H. Young and H. D. Robinson, U.S. Pat. 2,136,481 (1938).

[6] J. C. Wallenmeyer, Mexican Pat. 35,140 (1934).

[7] H. Steenbock, *Science* **60**, 224 (1924); U.S. Pat. 1,680,818 (1928).

addition of concentrated fatty emulsions or propylene glycol solutions of vitamin D_2 or D_3. Milk can also be fortified by irradiating the cow or feed-

Fig. 14. Irradiating unit for milk and other aqueous fluids. From the regulating chamber at the left, the milk enters the annular top trough, flows over the weir, and cascades down the wall of the tank to the bottom trough. Carbon arc lamp and fume exit shown swung out of position. Forced air for ventilation enters at bottom. (Courtesy of National Carbon Co.)

ing the cow irradiated yeast. The vitamin D in irradiated milk, or milk from irradiated cows, presumably is vitamin D_3; in milk from cows fed irradiated yeast it is vitamin D_2.

Concentrated preparations of vitamins D_2, D_3, and D_m are produced in a much greater total unitage than fish oils for medicinal use and animal feeding. The manufacture of fish oils has continued at a high level because of their importance as a source of vitamin A, but since 1950, with the advent of synthetic vitamin A at low cost, the trend to replacement by synthetics has been accelerated. The end use, as well as the source, of vitamin D has undergone great change. In 1925 vitamin D, then almost solely in the form of cod liver oil, was used principally to *cure* rickets in children. By 1950 florid rickets had become a rarity, thanks to the use of vitamin D in many forms to *prevent* it. During the same period, the use of vitamin D in poultry raising expanded from the experimental stage to the principal field for this vitamin.

The first synthetic vitamin D manufactured in the United States was produced by pumping a peanut oil solution of ergosterol through the cooling jacket of a quartz mercury vapor lamp and then through a heat exchanger, cyclically, until the desired conversion was effected.[8] A more efficient unit, employing the carbon arc, and designed to activate provitamins D in transparent solvents, is shown in Fig. 15. This unit, still in use after more than twenty years, has a daily capacity of the equivalent of 8 metric tons of cod liver oil. In a different arrangement, shown in Fig. 16, the solution flows through a series of activating units, each containing a water-cooled Hanovia lamp and an outer quartz chamber for the provitamin D solution.

In commercial practice, ether is usually the preferred solvent. The irradiation is continued until a certain percentage of the provitamin is transformed, the exact amount being determined for optimum vitamin yield under the conditions of exposure, particularly the type of light source and the kind of provitamin. Usually not over 50 % transformation is allowed. The unchanged provitamin is recovered by evaporating the solvent, taking up the resin in methanol, and freezing out. After the methanol is removed, the resin is either dissolved without further treatment in an edible oil, or it is converted into 3,5-dinitrobenzoate for the preparation of crystalline vitamin D.

Some manufacturers use light filters, and others do not. The advantages in yield gained by using light of about λ 280 mμ are more or less offset by the loss of light, but filtered light is probably advantageous when minimal accumulation of tachysterol is desired, as in the production of crystalline vitamin D. Some choice of wavelengths is available to users of carbon arcs, for carbons can be purchased with different core materials, and large users can even have them made to order. The hot mercury arc differs spectrally from the cold, but both are rich in the shorter waves, the cold especially so.

It is customary to exclude oxygen during irradiation, either by using

8 C. E. Bills, U.S. Pats. 1,808,760 (1931); 1,848,305 (1932).

Fig. 15. Apparatus for the activation of ergosterol. The light source is an alternating current carbon arc operating at 40 volts, 40 amperes across the terminals. By the use of a constant current (floating secondary) transformer and a system of relays sensitive to voltage changes, the automatic feeding of the carbons is closely regulated. Equidistant from the arc four fused quartz flasks are located, each of 1 liter bulb capacity. The neck of each is greatly extended, so as to form the inner tube of a reflux condenser. Refrigerated water is circulated through the insulated jacket. 40 g. of ergosterol and 3600 cc. of purified ether constitute a charge. CO_2 is passed through the solution to expel air, and immediately the open end of the condenser is capped with a toy balloon. Thus in the "breathing" incident to irregular boiling, the system is compelled to breathe its own breath, and ingress of air is prevented. (After Bills et al.[12])

213

closed systems or by replacing the air over solutions with inert gas. Ether used as a solvent should be peroxide-free. Stabilizers added to the solution are claimed to greatly increase the yield of vitamin. Among these, various sugar amines have been employed.[9] The most effective stabilizers appear to be the non-provitamin D sterols, such as cholesterol or the inactivatable fraction of mollusk sterols. Waddell and Woessner[10] claim that in the activa-

FIG. 16. Irradiating units in series for vitamin D production. Each unit consists of a vertical quartz mercury lamp surrounded by two cylindrical chambers through which water circulates for cooling. The solution of ergosterol or other provitamin D is circulated through a third cylindrical chamber. (Courtesy of E. R. Squibb and Sons.)

tion of 7-dehydrocholesterol the presence of an equal amount of cholesterol increases the vitamin yield almost 40 %, besides enhancing the recovery of unconverted provitamin. The highly unstable provitamins D of mollusks are protected by the non-provitamin D sterols which naturally accompany them. When, in the course of repeated irradiations, the protecting sterols of the mollusk sterol mixture accumulate excessively, they can be removed and converted into provitamins by reactions analogous to those employed in the synthesis of 7-dehydrocholesterol.[11] The stabilization of provitamins

[9] H. W. Elley and J. Waddell, U.S. Pat. 2,234,554 (1941).

[10] J. Waddell and W. W. Woessner, U.S. Pat. 2,410,254 (1946).

[11] H. R. Rosenberg, U.S. Pat. 2,475,917 (1949).

by other sterols occurs not only in activation by irradiation, but in the less widely practiced activation in the vapor phase by a high-frequency electrical discharge.[12]

IV. Estimation

CHARLES E. BILLS

Vitamin D is the only one of the better-known vitamins for which physical or chemical methods of estimation have not largely replaced biological methods. The reason for this is plain: vitamin D is so potent that even in the richer sources its concentration is usually minute. Conversely, the substances which interfere with physical or chemical determination of it are likely to be present in relatively overwhelming amounts. In biological assays, however, rats or chicks show measurable responses to vitamin D when it is present in their diet in amounts as little as 1 part in several hundred million. Interference with the biological response occurs only when comparatively gross quantities of materials such as phosphates are encountered.

With the publication of György's "Vitamin Methods,"[1] the art of estimating vitamins is presented in two volumes. Therefore, the techniques will be presented here only in outline, in order to guide the reader to the more detailed sources of information.

A. PHYSICAL METHODS

In very concentrated forms, vitamin D can be estimated by purely physical means. Thus Pirlot[2] recommends infrared spectrophotometry for determining calciferol in the irradiation products of ergosterol. For calciferol itself, or concentrated oily solutions thereof, Pénau and Hagemann[3] employed ultraviolet spectrophotometry. The estimation, based on the extinction at λ 265 mμ, is straightforward, provided that the absorption curve is normal. If there is displacement of the maximum, accentuated asymmetry, or other abnormality, the presence of impurities or degradation products is indicated. Concentrated oily solutions are diluted with choloroform and absolute alcohol to make a 0.0015 % solution of calciferol. The extinction is determined, and correction is made for the oil, if known. If the oil is unknown, the unsaponifiable fraction is separated, and allowance is made for saponification loss, which usually amounts to about 7.5 %.

[12] C. E. Bills, F. G. McDonald, L. N. BeMiller, G. E. Steel, and M. Nussmeier, *J. Biol. Chem.* **93,** 775 (1931).

[1] P. György, Vitamin Methods. Academic Press, New York, 1950–1951.

[2] G. Pirlot, *Anal. Chim. Acta* **2,** 744 (1948) [*C.A.* **43,** 7997 (1949)].

[3] H. Pénau and G. Hagemann, *Helv. Chim. Acta* **29,** 1366 (1946).

B. CHEMICAL METHODS

A drawback to direct spectrophotometric estimation is the fact that the absorption maximum of vitamin D lies at 265 mμ, a region where ultraviolet dirt is especially likely to show up. Accordingly, in the devising of chemical methods of estimation, it has been sought to form strong and stable colors in the visible range, less susceptible to irrelevant absorption, and, of course, as nearly as possible specific to the vitamin.

The most widely used color reaction is that given by antimony trichloride and first applied to pure vitamin D$_2$ by Askew et al.[4] A deep yellow color is developed, with the absorption maximum at 500 mμ. Nield et al.[5] increased the sensitivity of the reaction to the point where they could measure the color given by 0.2 γ of calciferol, and they also increased the permanence of the color. Milas et al.[6] applied modifications of the reaction to the assay of fish liver oils. In one procedure they made interference corrections for sterols and vitamin A, and in their preferred method they first removed the interfering substances by coupling them with maleic anhydride and then measured the color developed at 500 mμ. They were able to get fairly good agreement with bioassays in the case of fish oils containing 10,000 units or more of vitamin D per gram.

Details of the antimony trichloride reaction were worked out by Vacher et al.,[7] Shantz,[8] Nielsen,[9] and others. The important step of chromatographic purification was introduced and improved successively by Ewing et al.,[10] De Witt and Sullivan,[11] Müller,[12] Ewing et al.,[13] and Fujita and Aoyama.[14] Under favorable conditions the pigment generated in this reaction from vitamin D$_2$ or D$_3$ shows $E_{1\text{ cm.}}^{1\%} = 1800$ at 500 mμ.[5] This is an intense absorption, nearly four times as great as that of the vitamin itself at 265 mμ, and comparable with that of strongly absorbing dyes such as fuchsin. Hence it seems unlikely that efforts to find a better color reaction will substantially improve upon this one with regard to intensity of color, although there is

[4] F. A. Askew, R. B. Bourdillon, H. M. Bruce, R. K. Callow, J. St. L. Philpot, and T. A. Webster, *Proc. Roy. Soc. (London)* **B109**, 488 (1932).

[5] C. H. Nield, W. C. Russell, and A. Zimmerli, *J. Biol. Chem.* **136**, 73 (1940).

[6] N. A. Milas, R. Heggie, and J. A. Raynolds, *Ind. Eng. Chem. Anal. Ed.* **13**, 227 (1941).

[7] M. Vacher, Y. Lortie, and H. Colson, *Bull. soc. chim. biol.* **26**, 206 (1944).

[8] E. M. Shantz, *Ind. Eng. Chem. Anal. Ed.* **16**, 179 (1944).

[9] P. B. Nielsen, *Nutrition Abstracts & Revs.* **19**, 57 (1949).

[10] D. T. Ewing, G. V. Kingsley, R. A. Brown, and A. D. Emmett, *Ind. Eng. Chem. Anal. Ed.* **15**, 301 (1943).

[11] J. B. De Witt and M. X. Sullivan, *Ind. Eng. Chem. Anal. Ed.* **18**, 117 (1946).

[12] P. B. Müller, *Helv. Chim. Acta* **30**, 1172 (1947).

[13] D. T. Ewing, M. J. Powell, R. A. Brown, and A. D. Emmett, *Anal. Chem.* **22**, 317 (1948).

[14] A. Fujita and M. Aoyama, *J. Biochem. (Japan)* **37**, 113 (1950).

room for improvement with regard to permanence and specificity. In its more highly developed forms, the antimony trichloride reaction and its associated steps of purification are complicated procedures, which give fairly reliable estimations with oily solutions containing 5000 or 10,000 I.U. per gram or more of vitamin D.

Another color reaction has been described by Sobel et al.[15] With a chloroform solution of dichlorohydrin and acetyl chloride, vitamin D gives a green color with peak absorption at 625 mμ. The color is more stable and more nearly specific than that of the antimony trichloride reaction. Rouir and Pirlot,[16] applying Sobel's reaction to pharmaceuticals, stressed the importance of correcting for oil. Campbell[17] increased the sensitivity of the reaction twentyfold, which makes it only five times less sensitive than the antimony trichloride reaction. He found that by measuring the absorption at 410 mμ, instead of 625 mμ, the interferences given by maize oil, fish oil, ergosterol, and 7-dehydrocholesterol were minimized. The reaction deserves further study with high-potency oils.

A third promising color reaction is that of Schaltegger.[18] Carbenium salts produced by treating vitamin D with perchloric acid are reacted with aldehydes, giving colors of improved specificity. Banchetti,[19] using vanillin as the aldehyde in the reaction, was able to detect 50 γ of vitamin D in the presence of two hundred times as much of other sterols. The possibilities of this reaction have not been explored.

Investigators of color reactions should note the report of McMahon et al.,[20] in which is described the separation and identification of vitamin D from other sterols by partition paper chromatography, the sterol spots being developed by spraying with antimony pentachloride in chloroform.

A chemical method for estimating vitamin D, which is not a color reaction in the usual sense, was described by Green[21] in 1951. It is based on the liberation of iodine in the reaction between vitamin D and iodine trichloride in carbon tetrachloride. A comprehensive study was made of methods for separating vitamin D from interfering substances by means of differential solubility, digitonin precipitation, and chromatography on Floridin. Highly efficient purification is claimed, and the purified product can be reacted stoichiometrically with the reagent. The older techniques of condensation with maleic or citraconic anhydride, and of selective ultraviolet irradiation

[15] A. E. Sobel, A. M. Mayer, and B. Kramer, *Ind. Eng. Chem. Anal. Ed.* **17**, 160 (1945)·
[16] E. V. Rouir and G. Pirlot, *Bull. soc. chim. biol.* **29**, 1005 (1947).
[17] J. A. Campbell, *Anal. Chem.* **20**, 766 (1948).
[18] H. Schaltegger, *Helv. Chim. Acta* **29**, 285 (1946).
[19] A. Banchetti, *Ann. chim. appl.* **38**, 394 (1948).
[20] J. M. McMahon, R. B. Davis, and G. Kalnitsky, *Proc. Soc. Exptl. Biol. Med.* **75**, 799 (1950).
[21] J. Green, *Biochem. J.* **49**, 36, 45, 54 (1951).

for the separation of vitamin A from vitamin D, are not, in Green's opinion, good ones, for considerable losses of vitamin D may be encountered.

C. BIOLOGICAL METHODS

The author has elsewhere[22] presented a chapter on the use of the rat in the estimation of vitamin D, and Waddell and Kennedy[23] have published a companion chapter on the use of the chick for this purpose. New workers in the field of bioassay are advised first of all to absorb the wisdom in Coward's[24] "Biological Standardization of the Vitamins." The practical, theoretical, and statistical aspects of this subject are also covered by György,[1] and in particularly fine detail.

The official method of estimating vitamin D in medicinal oils is described in U.S. Pharmacopeia (14th revision). It is essentially a 7-day curative technique, observations being made by the line test on rats previously rendered ricketic. The official procedure for estimating vitamin D in milk is given in the A.O.A.C. "Methods of Analysis."[25] It is similar to the U.S.P. method but requires the feeding of skim milk powder to the reference rats in amounts equivalent to the milk given the test animals, thus to counter-balance the interfering action of milk *per se*. The A.O.A.C. method for estimating vitamin D intended for poultry use is a 21-day prophylactic technique with baby chicks, observations being made on the percentage of ash in the tibiae. These are all pass-or-fail tests, useful in quality control, but not otherwise very informative as to the amount of vitamin present. To gain quantitative information, one must either repeat the assays at numerous levels or, better, interpret the findings by means of response curves.

To illustrate the use of response curves, two are shown in Fig. 17. Let us consider the cod liver oil curve, bearing in mind that it portrays the typical, or ideal, response of chicks to graded doses of vitamin D *under an established set of conditions.* (With a different basal diet, or with chicks of different age or different breed, the curve would be different.) Under the prescribed conditions, 10 I.U. of cod liver oil vitamin D will produce, on the average, a bone ash of 43 %. Now suppose that an assay is conducted with two groups of chicks. The reference group is given 10 I.U. of vitamin D per 100 g. of diet in the form of a reference cod liver oil (the curve was made when cod

[22] C. E. Bills, *Biol. Symposia* **12,** 409 (1947).

[23] J. Waddell and G. H. Kennedy, *Biol. Symposia* **12,** 435 (1947).

[24] K. H. Coward, The Biological Standardization of the Vitamins, 2nd ed. Williams and Wilkins, Baltimore, 1947.

[25] Methods of Analysis, 7th ed. Association of Official Agricultural Chemists, Washington, 1950.

liver oil was the official standard of reference, but vitamin D_3 gives responses not very different). At the end of the assay the reference group

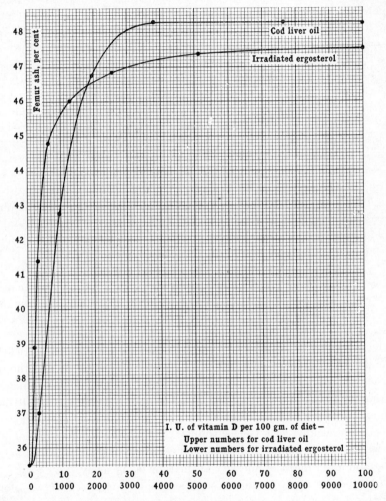

FIG. 17. Response of chicks to graded doses of cod liver oil and irradiated ergosterol assayed with rats, showing that efficacy ratios vary with the dose. (After Massengale and Bills.[26])

shows a bone ash of, say, 42.3 %. The assay group has been given an unknown
cod liver oil, the amount by weight being the same as that of the reference
oil. This group shows a bone ash of, say, 44 %. On the pass-or-fail basis, and
without reference to the curve, it can be said that the unknown oil contains

more vitamin D than the reference oil. But how much more? By the curve, it is seen that 44% ash corresponds to 11.6 I.U. However, the reference group in this assay showed only 42.3% ash, which corresponds to 9 I.U. Apparently, then, the chicks, for some unknown reason, are responding a little low, and a correction is called for: $X:11.6::10:9$, or $X = 12.9$. Thus the unknown oil is found to be supplying 12.9 I.U. of vitamin D per 100 g. of the diet.

The example given above is a practical, everyday illustration of the use of response curves, and it introduces the important subject of error. For a discussion of error, the reader is referred to the paper by Massengale and Bills[26] from which Fig. 17 was taken, and especially to the more professional discussions of statistical methods given by Coward[24] and Bliss.[27] Suggestions on means of minimizing error are given in the technical articles previously mentioned,[22, 23] and the chapter by Guerrant in the second volume of György's book.[1]

In 1951 a method for the determination of vitamin D with radiophosphorus was described by Snyder et al.[28] Applied as yet only to the rat, it would appear to be adaptable also to the chick. This method is the fifth satisfactory means of measuring the response of animals to vitamin D, the others being the line test, x-ray, bone ash, and growth methods. The new method is claimed to give results comparable in accuracy to the other methods, and it has the advantages of requiring distinctly less time and labor, and covering an extraordinarily wide span of units (0.5 to 50 units) in one test.

The procedure is as follows. Young (21-day) rats are placed on ricketogenic diet, and, after 16 days, are given by mouth a single dose of the test solution of vitamin D. Forty-eight hours later a solution containing approximately 20 μc. of P^{32} is injected intraperitoneally. After another 10 days without further treatment, the forepaws of the still-living rats are located beneath the window of a Geiger counter. The observed radiation count is interpreted by means of a response curve established from points at the upper and lower limits of linearity at the time of the assay.

In the course of twelve series of experiments over a year it was noted that the slope of the response curves varied considerably. This is another way of saying that the response of animals, or even of groups of animals, is variable, as is well known. It is because of this variability that it is

[26] O. N. Massengale and C. E. Bills, *J. Nutrition* **12**, 429 (1936).

[27] C. I. Bliss, *in* Vitamin Methods, Vol. 2, p. 445. Academic Press, New York, 1951.

[28] R. H. Snyder, H. J. Eisner, and H. Steenbock, *J. Nutrition* **45**, 305 (1951).

necessary to check response curve interpretations by the use of reference (positive control) groups, as described on the preceding page.

V. Standardization of Activity

CHARLES E. BILLS

The present international standard for vitamin D, adopted by the World Health Organization[1] in 1949, is pure vitamin D_3. The international unit (I.U.) is defined as the vitamin D activity of 0.025 γ of the standard. The U.S. Pharmacopeial unit is also now defined in terms of vitamin D_3 and is identical with the international unit. The former A.O.A.C. chick unit is now replaced by the international chick unit, which also represents 0.025 γ of vitamin D_3. Four of the A.O.A.C. units equal three international chick units. A review of the development of the international unit is given by Coward,[2] and a brief account of the recent changes is given by Nelson.[3]

The original international unit of vitamin D was defined[4] "as the vitamin D activity of 1 mg. of the international standard solution of irradiated ergosterol." Parenthetically, and not as a part of the definition, it was noted that "the international standard solution has been prepared to have such potency that approximately 1 mg. thereof given daily to a rachitic rat for eight successive days will produce a wide line of calcium deposits in the metaphysis of the proximal ends of the tibiae and of the distal ends of the radii."

The original international standard solution was an olive oil solution of ergosterol irradiation products, prepared under defined conditions and issued from the National Institute for Medical Research, London. Solutions of similar composition and potency had served, since 1927, as the Pharmaceutical Society's standard, and, since 1930, as the official standard of the Medical Research Council of Great Britain.[2, 5] At the second international conference on vitamin standardization, 1934, the definition of the unit was broadened to read, "the Vitamin D activity of 1 milligram of the international standard solution of irradiated ergosterol, which has been found equal to that of 0.025 microgram of crystalline vitamin D." Provision was made

[1] World Health Organization: Expert Committee on Biological Standardization, *Chronicle World Health Org.* **3,** 147 (1949).

[2] K. H. Coward, *J. Pharm. Pharmacol.* **1,** 737 (1949).

[3] E. M. Nelson, *J. Assoc. Offic. Agr. Chemists* **32,** 801 (1949).

[4] Report of the Conference on Vitamin Standards, No. C.H. 1055 (1). League of Nations, Geneva, 1931.

[5] K. H. Coward, F. J. Dyer, and B. G. E. Morgan, *Analyst* **57,** 368 (1932).

for future lots of the international standard solution to be made from crystalline vitamin D_2 of specified physical constants.[6] The 1949 decision to use crystalline vitamin D_3, rather than D_2, was prompted by the knowledge that D_3, which exhibits approximately the same potency as D_2 for the rat, has the additional feature of being also effective for chicks.

The U.S.P. unit of vitamin D, officially adopted[7] in 1934, was "equal, in antirachitic potency for the rat, to one International Unit of Vitamin D as defined and adopted by the Conference of (*sic*) Vitamin Standards of the Permanent Commission on Biological Standardisation of the League of Nations in June of 1931." An official reference cod liver oil of declared potency was issued, and this remained the standard of reference in the

TABLE IX

VITAMIN D CONTENT OF AVERAGE COD LIVER OIL IN TERMS OF VARIOUS SYSTEMS OF UNITS. (ADAPTED FROM BILLS[9])

Unit system	Potency
International, since 1931 (see text)	100 units/g.
U.S.P., since 1934 (see text)	100 units/g.
Medical Research Council, 1930[2, 10]	100 units/c.c.
Steenbock, 1930[11]	37 units/g.
American Drug Manufacturers' Association, 1931[12]	350 units/g.
Oslo, 1928 (Poulsson and Lövenskiold[13])	110 units/g.[a]
Oslo, 1933 (Poulsson and Ender[14])	160 units/g.[a]
German, 1929 (rat unit)[15]	15 units/c.c.
German (clinical unit)[15]	0.15 unit/c.c.
American Medical Association, 1931[16]	2.8 "D" potency

[a] Vaguely defined.

United States until the new vitamin D reference standard of vitamin D_3 in oil became official in 1950.[8]

[6] *Quart. Bull. Health Organization League Nations* **3**, extract 15 (1934).
[7] U.S. Pharmacopeia, 10th revision, Interim Revision Announcement No. 2, 1934.
[8] U.S. Pharmacopeia, 14th revision, Easton, 1950.
[9] C. E. Bills, *Physiol. Revs.* **15**, 1 (1935).
[10] Medical Research Council, *Lancet* II, 503 (1930).
[11] H. Steenbock, E. B. Hart, F. Hanning, and G. C. Humphrey, *J. Biol. Chem.* **88**, 197 (1930).
[12] A. D. Holmes, *J. Am. Pharm. Assoc.* **20**, 588 (1931).
[13] E. Poulsson and H. Lövenskiold, *Biochem. J.* **22**, 135 (1928).
[14] E. Poulsson and E. Ender, *Skand. Arch. Physiol.* **66**, 92 (1933).
[15] A. Scheunert and M. Schieblich, *Biochem. Z.* **209**, 290 (1929); F. Holtz and E. Schreiber, *Hoppe-Seyler's Z. physiol. Chem.* **191**, 1 (1930); F. Holtz, F. Laquer, H. Kreitmair, and T. Moll, *Biochem. Z.* **237**, 247 (1931).
[16] New and Nonofficial Remedies, p. 414. Council on Pharmacy and Chemistry, American Medical Association, 1931.

The older literature contains many references to assays reported in terms of vitamin D units no longer in use. The values of the various systems are compared in Table IX.

VI. Effects of Deficiency

A. IN ANIMALS

JAMES H. JONES

The over-all effect of a deficiency of vitamin D in the higher animals is known as rickets. According to Park,[1] Jost and Koch have stated that rickets is a common disturbance among puppies, pigs, lambs, and kids but occurs less frequently among colts, calves, and rabbits. However, from at least four different Agricultural Experiment Stations in this country have come reports of either spontaneous or experimental rickets in calves,[2-5] and poultry should also be added to the above list. Rodents, such as the rat, are not so susceptible to rickets as the higher mammals and poultry. Rickets in this type of animal can be produced only if the diet is abnormal with respect to calcium or phosphorus as well as deficient in vitamin D.

McCollum et al.,[6] Sherman and Pappenheimer,[7] and Steenbock and Black[8] have developed diets which will produce rickets in rats. All these diets are composed principally of cereals and are high in calcium and moderately low in phosphorus. Part of the phosphorus in these diets is in the form of phytic acid, and the high calcium increases the unavailability of this form of phosphorus.[9] The above diets are all of the low phosphorus –high calcium type, but if the phosphorus is sufficiently low, rickets in rats can be produced without increasing the calcium to unusually high levels.[10]

The low phosphorus type of rickets in rats simulates rickets in humans,

[1] E. A. Park, *Physiol. Revs.* **3,** 106 (1923).
[2] S. I. Bechdel, K. G. Landsburg, and O. J. Hill, *Penna. Agr. Expt. Sta. Bull.* **291** (1933).
[3] I. W. Rupel, G. Bohstedt, and E. B. Hart, *Wis. Agr. Expt. Sta. Research Bull.* **115** (1933).
[4] H. E. Bechtel, E. T. Hallman, C. F. Huffman, and C. W. Duncan, *Mich. Agr. Expt. Sta. Tech. Bull.* **150** (1936).
[5] J. W. Hibbs, W. E. Krauss, C. F. Monroe, and W. D. Pounden, *Bimonthly Bull. Ohio Expt. Sta.* **30,** No. **232** (1945).
[6] E. V. McCollum, N. Simmonds, P. G. Shipley, and E. A. Park, *Bull. Johns Hopkins Hosp.* **33,** 31 (1922).
[7] H. C. Sherman and A. M. Pappenheimer, *J. Exptl. Med.* **34,** 189 (1921).
[8] H. Steenbock and A. Black, *J. Biol. Chem.* **64,** 263 (1925).
[9] H. M. Bruce and R. K. Callow, *Biochem. J.* **28,** 517 (1934).
[10] J. H. Jones, *J. Nutrition* **28,** 7 (1944).

but the low calcium type of rickets with either moderate or low levels of phosphorus also has been studied in the rat.[11] Experimental rickets has also been produced in mice,[12] hamsters,[13] foxes,[14] and sheep.[15] In the last two cases the diets contained ample calcium and phosphorus.

One of the first investigators to study experimental rickets in animals was Findlay,[16] who worked with pups. Mellanby likewise used pups in his early work on rickets.[17] From this work he concluded that rickets was due to a deficiency of a specific dietary factor. These results aroused considerable interest and led to a very large number of investigations in this field during the following decade.

The signs of rickets in animals are not particularly different from those in humans, and those of spontaneous rickets are essentially the same as in experimental rickets. In the latter case, however, the condition may be allowed to go to a more advanced state than in spontaneous rickets. Below are discussed the various signs of rickets in animals. Most of the cases discussed are experimental in type.

1. EXTERNAL APPEARANCE

Numerous investigators have described (either by photographs or words) the outward signs of rickets in various animals. The signs in the calf have been described very well by Bechtel et al.[4] as follows: " ... the skeletal changes included bowing of the forelegs either forward or to the side, swelling of the knee and hock joints, straightening of the pasterns, occasional ring-like swellings on the pasterns, and humping of the back. Posterior paralysis occurred in cases of fractured vertebrae. Fractured femora sometimes occurred. Other symptoms frequently observed were stiffness of gait, dragging of the rear feet, standing with the rear legs crossed, irritability, tetany, rapid respiration, bloat, anorexia for grain and roughages but not for milk, weakness and inability to stand for any length of time, and finally the retardation or complete cessation of growth in body weight."

Similar signs are seen in other types of animals but with some variations, depending on the anatomy of the animal and on the severity of the disease. Bowing of the forelegs, enlargement of the hock and the knee joints, and a tendency to drag the hind legs are very characteristic of all animals suffering from severe rickets. Another common sign is the enlargement of the costochondral junctions or beading of the ribs. Deformities of the thorax are

[11] A. T. Shohl, *J. Nutrition* **11,** 275 (1936).
[12] C. Foster, J. H. Jones, W. Henle, and S. A. Brenner, *J. Infectious Diseases* **85,** 173 (1949).
[13] J. H. Jones, *J. Nutrition* **30,** 143 (1945).
[14] L. E. Harris, C. F. Bassett, and C. F. Wilke, *J. Nutrition* **43,** 153 (1951).
[15] J. Duckworth, W. Godden, and W. Thomson, *J. Agr. Sci.* **33,** 190 (1943).
[16] L. Findlay, *Brit. Med. J.* **II,** 13 (1908).
[17] E. Mellanby, *Lancet* **I,** 407 (1919).

also common if the disease is in an advanced state. In the rat, enlargement of the carpal joint appears to be rather characteristic.

2. GROWTH

As mentioned above, Bechtel et al.[4] found decreased growth in ricketic calves, and Steenbock and Black[18] used the increase in weight of rats over the ricketic controls as a criterion for the activity of antiricketic substances. Hart et al.[19] have demonstrated the marked effect of sunlight on the growth of chicks on a synthetic diet which contained ample calcium and phosphorus but was low in vitamin D. The vitamin A was supplied by fresh ground clover. One group was given the basal ration without sunlight, and the other received the same diet but was exposed to summer sunlight one-half hour each day. At the end of 6 weeks on the experimental diets the two remaining ricketic fowls weighed 80 and 90 g., respectively, and the two controls weighed 145 and 180 g. The authors present radiographs of one bird from each diet which show a pronounced difference in the degree of calcification, especially of the long bones. Evidence that the lack of vitamin D also markedly inhibits the growth of pups has been presented by Steenbock et al.[20] Steenbock has repeatedly emphasized the essential requirement of vitamin D for growth.

The relation of rickets to growth has also been discussed by Rosenberg.[21] He believes that this effect is of primary significance and not secondary to other factors such as anorexia.

3. CALCIUM AND PHOSPHORUS OF THE SERUM

One of the most consistent changes in the composition of the blood during rickets is a decrease in the level of inorganic phosphate, which was first noted by Howland and Kramer[22] while working with children. In Table X are given the calcium and inorganic phosphorus in the serum of two ricketic litter-mate pups as well as the calcium and phosphorus in the serum of three other members of the same litter which were on the identical basal diet but received vitamin D in addition.[20] The level of these blood constituents is given at 6 and 9 weeks after the pups were put on the experimental diet. Both the calcium and inorganic phosphorus are considerably lower in the serum of the ricketic than control animals. The calcium, although low, is about the same at 6 weeks and 9 weeks on the diet, but the phosphorus is considerably lower at the later period than it was earlier. Bechtel et al.[4]

[18] H. Steenbock and A. Black, J. Biol. Chem. **61,** 405 (1924).

[19] E. B. Hart, H. Steenbock, S. Lepkovsky, and J. G. Halpin, J. Biol. Chem. **58,** 33 (1923–1924).

[20] H. Steenbock, J. H. Jones, and E. B. Hart, J. Biol. Chem. **58,** 383 (1923–1924).

[21] H. R. Rosenberg, Chemistry and Physiology of the Vitamins. Interscience Publishers, New York, 1942.

[22] J. Howland and B. Kramer, Am. J. Diseases Children **22,** 105 (1921).

report that the first detectable signs of rickets in calves is a decrease in the level of inorganic phosphorus in the serum. The same investigators also found a low calcium content of the serum of their animals which was accompanied in some cases by tetany. Previously, Steenbock and associates[20] had observed tetany in ricketic pups. The same laboratory has also found low calcium and low phosphorus in the serum of chicks[23] and low phosphorus in swine[24] during rickets. In the later case, no calcium studies were reported, but Loeffel et al.[25] observed low calcium and low inorganic phosphorus in the sera from their ricketic pigs.

When rickets is produced in rodents by means of low phosphorus diets, the phosphorus of the serum is, as expected, considerably below normal. If

TABLE X
EFFECT OF RICKETS IN PUPS ON CALCIUM AND PHOSPHORUS IN SERUM AND ON FEMUR ASH[20]

| | | Serum | | | | Femur ash | |
| | | Calcium, mg./100 ml. | | Phosphorus, mg./100 ml. | | | |
Dog No.	Ration	6 wk. on ration	9 wk. on ration	6 wk. on ration	9 wk. on ration	Grams	%
35	Basal	7.59	7.99	4.96	2.23	1.69	28.28
36	Basal	7.99	7.32	4.60	1.67	1.91	28.86
37	Saponified cod liver oil	11.32	11.72	7.88	8.57	6.27	46.45
38	Saponified cod liver oil	10.87	12.98	7.67	9.75	5.46	45.59
39	Cod liver oil	11.12	12.25	7.07	9.00	5.75	47.61

the calcium in the diet is high,[6-8] the serum calcium is either normal or slightly elevated. The rat, for instance, never develops tetany on this type of diet.

4. BLOOD PHOSPHATASE

Kay[26] and Bodansky and Jaffe[27] have reported high serum phosphatase (alkaline) during rickets in children, and Common[28] found the same to be true during rickets in chicks.

[23] H. Steenbock, E. B. Hart, J. H. Jones, and A. Black, *J. Biol. Chem.* **58**, 59 (1923–1924).

[24] H. Steenbock, E. B. Hart, and J. H. Jones, *J. Biol. Chem.* **61**, 775 (1924).

[25] W. J. Loeffel, R. R. Thalman, F. C. Olson, and F. A. Olson, *Nebr. Agr. Expt. Sta. Research Bull.* **58** (1931).

[26] H. D. Kay, *J. Biol. Chem.* **89**, 249 (1930).

[27] A. Bodansky and H. L. Jaffe, *Am. J. Diseases Children* **48**, 1268 (1934).

[28] R. H. Common, *J. Agr. Sci.* **26**, 492 (1936).

Sure *et al.*,[29] on the other hand, failed to observe a marked increase in blood phosphatase during rickets in rats. Dikshit and Patwardhan[30] not only found no increase in the phosphatase of the blood of rats during rickets but observed a pronounced fall as the disease progressed. Truhlar *et al.*[31] found no change in the phosphatase content in the lung, liver, kidney, and heart of ricketic rats.

In the above work on rats the diets were low in phosphorus and high in calcium. Whether this accounts for the lower phosphatase in rickets in rats as compared to the human or the chick, or whether it is a species difference, apparently is not clear. Rupel *et al.*[3] have reported an increase in serum phosphatase in ricketic calves. Here, again, the rise was not pronounced, and the diet contained ample calcium and phosphorus.

5. X-Ray Examination

Owing to the failure to deposit calcium salts in the skeleton of ricketic animals, the bone is less impervious to the roentgen ray. It is thus possible to detect rickets by means of the x-ray.

Steenbock and others[20] have presented the roentgenograms of the right rear leg of a ricketic pup and of two normal controls. The ricketic pup was on a basal diet free from vitamin D but containing sufficient calcium and phosphorus. The controls received the same diet, but, in addition, the non-saponifiable fraction of cod liver oil was given to one control and whole cod liver oil was supplied to the other. Calcification in general was considerably less in the bones from the ricketic dog than in those from either of the two controls. The patella and the condyles in the former are barely visible, and the cortices of the tibia are thin and less opaque. The diameter of the tibia is enlarged, and the distance between the diaphysis and the epiphysis is increased. In the controls the line of demarcation between the diaphysis and the epiphysis is distinct and sharp but narrow, whereas that in the ricketic animal is indistinct and irregular.

Roentgenograms of the costochrondal junction of ricketic calves have been presented by Bechtel *et al.*[4] Here again the junction of diaphysis and cartilage in the ricketic animals is irregular and indefinite and in places shows areas of incomplete calcification.

Hart and associates[19] published radiographs of the complete bony structure of a ricketic chick and of a normal control. In the ricketic animal there was very little differentiation between cortex and marrow cavity, and the whole skeleton was almost devoid of any dense bone.

[29] B. Sure, M. C. Kik, and K. S. Buchanan, *Proc. Soc. Exptl. Biol. Med.* **35**, 209 (1936–1937).

[30] P. K. Dikshit and V. N. Patwardhan, *Indian J. Med. Research* **35**, 91 (1947).

[31] J. Truhlar, L. Drekter, G. McGuire, and K. G. Falk, *J. Biol. Chem.* **127**, 345 (1939).

Pappenheimer *et al.*[32] have presented roentgenograms of the rear leg of a ricketic rat which shows the same lack of calcification and the wide area of uncalcified cartilage at the junctions of the diaphyses and epiphyses.

6. Calcium and Phosphorus Balance

Some of the early work on the influence of the antiricketic factor on the excretion or retention of calcium and phosphorus was reported in a series of publications by Hart, Steenbock, and their associates.[33] They found that lactating cows and goats on a diet of grains and timothy hay had a pronounced negative calcium balance, and frequently the balance of phosphorus was also negative. It was possible to bring the milking goats into a positive calcium and phosphorus balance by giving alfalfa hay or cod liver oil or by irradiating the animals with ultraviolet light. More difficulty was encountered when an attempt was made to bring about a retention of calcium and phosphorus in the lactating cow. The best results were obtained with alfalfa hay, and the green plant was better than the dried hay. The giving of as much as 10 ml. of cod liver oil per day caused the cows to lose their appetite.

Nicolaysen[34] found that vitamin D decreased the amount of calcium excreted in the feces of rats and increased the excretion in the urine. The absorption of calcium from an isolated intestinal loop was also augmented by vitamin D.

Bergeim[35] has made a more detailed study of the absorption of calcium and phosphorus from the intestinal tract. He found that in the normal animal calcium is absorbed in the upper part of the intestines and a portion of it is re-excreted in the lower part of the tract. In rickets the absorption is normal, but a larger proportion is re-excreted.

Phosphorus, on the other hand, is excreted into the upper portion of the intestine and reabsorbed from the lower part. In rickets this reabsorption is below normal. The administration of cod liver oil resulted in a positive balance of calcium and phosphorus. Cohen and Greenberg,[36] also with the rat, found only a slight increase in the intestinal absorption of radioactive phosphorus, although there was a marked improvement in the deposition of phosphorus in the bone when vitamin D was administered.

In contrast to phosphorus, Greenberg[37] found a definite increase in the

[32] A. M. Pappenheimer, G. F. McCann, and T. F. Zucker, *J. Exptl. Med.* **35,** 421 (1922).

[33] E. B. Hart, H. Steenbock, E. C. Teut, and G. C. Humphrey, *J. Biol. Chem.* **84,** 367 (1929).

[34] R. Nicolaysen, *Biochem. J.* **31,** 122, 323 (1937).

[35] O. Bergeim, *J. Biol. Chem.* **70,** 51 (1926).

[36] W. E. Cohn and D. M. Greenberg, *J. Biol. Chem.* **130,** 625 (1939).

[37] D. M. Greenberg, *J. Biol. Chem.* **157,** 99 (1945).

intestinal absorption of radioactive calcium following the administration of vitamin D to ricketic rats. Shohl and Bennett[38] observed a decrease in calcium retention, but at no time did the balance become negative in ricketic pups. Phosphorus was still less positive in respect to the control animals than was the calcium, and in some cases the phosphorus balance was negative. The authors state that even on a diet high in phosphorus and low in calcium the most marked deficiency lies in the phosphorus retention.

7. Acidity of Intestinal Contents

Zucker and Matzner[39] were the first to show that the pH of the feces of rats becomes higher as the animals develop rickets, and falls again when cod liver oil is fed. Similar results have been obtained with rats by Jephcott and Bacharach[40] and Heller and Caskey.[41]

Abrahamson and Miller,[42] Yoder,[43] and Redman et al.[44] observed a higher pH of the intestinal contents of ricketic rats than in non-ricketic controls. This difference appeared to be constant through the small and large intestines. When cod liver oil was given to the ricketic animals the hydrogen ion concentration of the intestinal contents increased. Grayzel and Miller[45] have made similar observations on the dog, and Kline and associates[46] have shown that irradiation of ricketic chicks decreases the pH of the proximal part of the intestines but not of the distal portion.

The significance of this change in acidity of feces and intestinal contents and its relation to the cure of rickets is not clear at the present. According to Shohl and Bing,[47] the change in acidity of feces did not occur when rats, made ricketic on the Steenbock-Black diet, were cured by irradiation of the food or by the addition of alkaline phosphates. Oser[48] reports that the effect of vitamin D on increasing the acidity of the intestinal contents and feces of rats is inconsistent and non-specific, and Jones[49] found that increasing the acidity of the intestinal contents by other means did not cause a

[38] A. T. Shohl and H. B. Bennett, J. Biol. Chem. **76**, 633 (1928).

[39] T. F. Zucker and M. J. Matzner, Proc. Soc. Exptl. Biol. Med. **21**, 186 (1923–1924).

[40] H. Jephcott and A. L. Bacharach, Biochem. J. **20**, 1351 (1926).

[41] V. G. Heller and C. Caskey, J. Nutrition **2**, 59 (1929–1930).

[42] E. M. Abrahamson and E. G .Miller, Jr., Proc. Soc. Exptl. Biol. Med. **22**, 438 (1924–1925).

[43] L. Yoder, J. Biol. Chem. **74**, 321 (1927).

[44] T. Redman, S. G. Willimott, and F. Wokes, Biochem. J. **21**, 589 (1927).

[45] D. M. Grayzel and E. G. Miller, Jr., Proc. Soc. Exptl. Biol. Med. **24**, 668 (1926–1927).

[46] O. L. Kline, J. A. Keenan, C. A. Elvehjem, and E. B. Hart, J. Biol. Chem. **98**, 121 (1932).

[47] A. T. Shohl and F. C. Bing, J. Biol. Chem. **79**, 269 (1928).

[48] B. L. Oser, J. Biol. Chem. **80**, 487 (1928).

[49] J. H. Jones, J. Biol. Chem. **142**, 557 (1942).

comparable increase in calcification. According to Friedman,[50] the increase in acidity during the healing of rickets is caused by a change in bacterial flora of the intestinal tract, from non-acid-forming bacteria to acid formers.

8. BONE ASH

In his early work on rickets in pups Mellanby[17] observed a decrease in the calcium content of the skeleton of his animals. Telfer[51] found a very low bone ash in his ricketic pups. The percentage of ash in the dry limb bones decreased from 44.9 in the normal controls to 17.7 in the deficient animals. Steenbock and associates[20] made comparable observations. Table X gives the percentages of ash in the dry, fat-free femurs of their ricketic and control pups. The decrease in ash content as reported by Steenbock was somewhat less than that given by Telfer.

McCollum and associates[52] found a low ash in the bone of ricketic rats. Bethke et al.[53] as well as Dutcher et al.[54] have made detailed studies of the changes of the bone ash of ricketic rats and correlated the percentages of bone ash with the level of serum phosphorus. Dutcher and coworkers report a bone ash of 62 % in the dry, fat-free bones from normal rats; in rickets it fell as low as 24 % with an average percentage of 26.5.

A reduction in the percentage of ash in long bones or ricketic pigs has been reported by Elliot et al.[55] and Loeffel et al.[25] In a like manner, there is less ash in the bones of ricketic calves than in the normal controls,[2, 3, 56] and the same is true for ricketic fowls.[23] The official method for determining vitamin D in poultry feed[57] is based on the increase in the ash of bones of chicks when vitamin D is supplied to animals previously made ricketic. According to Chick et al.,[58] the best criterion of defective calcification is given by the value of the ratio of the amount of ash to the amount of organic material contained in the fat-extracted bone. This is essentially the same as the percentage of ash in the dry, fat-free bone which has been used more frequently.

[50] H. Friedman, J. Nutrition 12, 165 (1936).

[51] S. V. Telfer, Quart. J. Med. 16, 63 (1922–1923).

[52] E. V. McCollum, N. Simmonds, E. M. Kinney, and C. J. Grieves, Bull. Johns Hopkins Hosp. 33, 202 (1922).

[53] R. M. Bethke, H. Steenbock, and M. T. Nelson, J. Biol. Chem. 58, 71 (1923–1924).

[54] R. A. Dutcher, M. Creighton, and H. A. Rothrock, J. Biol. Chem. 66, 401 (1925).

[55] W. E. Elliot, A. Crichton, and J. B. Orr, Brit. J. Exptl. Pathol. 3, 10 (1922).

[56] C. F. Huffman and C. W. Duncan, J. Dairy Sci. 18, 511 (1935).

[57] Official Methods of Analysis, 7th ed., p. 792. Association of Official Agricultural Chemists, 1950.

[58] H. Chick, V. Korenchevsky, and M. H. Roscoe, Biochem. J. 20, 622 (1926).

9. HISTOLOGICAL CHANGES IN THE RICKETIC BONE

The following description of the microscopic changes of the costochondral junction and adjoining areas of the ricketic rat is condensed from the discussion by Pappenheimer.[59]

The zone of proliferating cartilage does not differ greatly from the normal in extent or in arrangement of its cells. It is difficult, however, to define the boundaries of this zone, owing to the lack of calcification in severely ricketic bones. When there is lateral swelling of the cartilage the columns of cells are separated by an excessive amount of matrix.

In the zone of preparatory calcification are found the most pronounced changes. There is a complete lack of calcification, and the depth of this zone is greatly increased. In the normal rib there is little variation in the depth, and it seldom exceeds four or five cells, whereas in the ricketic rib the depth may be fifty cells or more. The extent to which this zone is enlarged depends upon the length of time that the animals have been on the ricketogenic diet and the extent of growth. If no growth has taken place during the time on the experimental diet, there is but little enlargement of this zone. In general, the more the animal grows, the greater the depth of this zone, but usually this enlargement is one of the most dependable characteristics of rickets. It has been frequently observed that ricketic lesions are more severe in animals that do show definite growth during the period on the ricketogenic diet. This is true in spite of the fact that vitamin D is necessary for continued growth, as previously discussed. The arrangement of the cartilage cells in the columns is usually maintained in the basal portion of the zone of preparatory calcification, but toward the diaphysis this arrangement of the cells is entirely lost, and there is considerable variation in the size and shape of the cells. The uncalcified matrix takes on the appearance of osteoid tissue which forms a considerable portion of the metaphysis, particularly surrounding the perforating vessels.

After 4 weeks on the ricketogenic diet there is formed an excessive amount of calcium-free osteoid tissue in the region of the primary spongiosa. The arrangement of the trabeculae is no longer orderly, but instead they are broad, convoluted masses of osteoid several times thicker than normal trabeculae. Their relation to the original trabeculae is completely obscured. Some of the osteoid masses contain a core of calcified tissue, but many others show no trace of calcification. The osteoid is usually homogeneous and stains evenly and deeply with eosin. The demarcation between osteoid and calcified tissue is always very sharp.

The perichondral osteoid of the ricketic rib is entirely free from calcifica-

[59] A. M. Pappenheimer, *J. Exptl. Med.* **36**, 335 (1922).

tion, and it forms a large mass which contributes largely to the swelling of the junction.

Both the endosteal and periosteal surfaces of the calcified cortex are covered by osteoid tissue. It is most extreme near the epiphysis but extends the entire length of the shaft. At times the osteoid may be so abundant as to decrease the diameter of the marrow cavity. The calcified portion of the cortex is considerably reduced in thickness, and in places calcium salts appear to be entirely lacking.

The blood vessels are not dilated, and hyperemia is not pronounced.

Bechtel et al.[4] have given a detailed description of the microscopic changes in the bones of ricketic calves which for the most part agrees with the findings of Pappenheimer.

B. IN PATHOLOGY OF HUMAN BEINGS

BENJAMIN KRAMER and ABRAM KANOF

The pathological changes in human beings resulting from deficiency of vitamin D are almost entirely confined to the skeleton. Here there develops a distortion of bone growth which gives rise to the clinical picture which we designate as rickets. The primary disturbance responsible for this distortion is a failure to mineralize newly formed osteoid tissue and cartilage matrix. Hence, the unusual softness of the bone which under the stress and strain of weight bearing and locomotion gives rise to the characteristic deformities of the disease. To understand these changes it is important to review the process of normal bone development and growth.[60, 61]

From the point of view of embryologic development there are two types of bone. The first is membranous bone, occurring in the vault of the skull, the lower jawbone, and part of the clavicle. The first step in the formation of these bones in the blastoderm is a condensation of the mesodermal cells which soon develop into fibrous membrane. Between the cells of this membrane a dense intercellular substance accumulates, and when the proper stage of development of this substance is reached calcium is deposited into it. The property of calcifiability is conferred upon the transformed connective tissue by the osteoblasts. Osteoblasts arise in the early embryo by direct transformation from mesenchymal cells. In the adult they arise from fibroblasts and reticular cells. It is through the activity of these osteoblasts on the fibrous sheath that the bone attains increasing thickness, as additional layers of periosteum are laid down and ossified without the inter-

[60] A. Robinson, Cunningham's Textbook in Anatomy. William Wood and Co., New York, 1923.

[61] A. A. Maximow and W. Bloom, A Textbook of Histology. W. B. Saunders and Co., Philadelphia, 1948.

mediate formation of cartilage.[62] What is originally membrane thus becomes cortex of the new bone.

The second type of bone, which includes all the bones not listed above, is known as cartilage bone. In this type of bone, growth takes place with the intermediation first of cartilage formation and then destruction of the cartilage before bone can be formed. In the prenatal formation of these bones there is first an aggregation or condensation of mesodermal cells at the location of the future bone. This aggregation of cells becomes demarcated from the surrounding mesoderm and forms a rudimentary model of the future bone. In the area of the future shaft the peripheral cells become fibroblasts and form the periosteum, while at the ends of the future bone the cells form the periochondrium.

In the region of the shaft, where the membranous periosteum has formed, bone formation proceeds in the manner described for membranous bone. Elongation of the bone takes place at its ends, where the condensation of mesenchymal cells has resulted in the formation of a cartilaginous plate which during childhood remains distinct from the shaft, and is called the epiphysis. The flattened cells in this cartilaginous plate are normally arranged in columns. Each cell in the column is separated from its fellow by a thin bridge of matrix, while the adjacent columns are separated by wider, parallel bands of matrix material. The epiphysis is attached to the diaphysis by a number of calcified prongs remaining from those destroyed which form a bridge between epiphysis and diaphysis.

As one proceeds from the relatively quiescent epiphysis toward the zone of ossification, the appearance of the individual cells changes. The rows of cells most distant from the shaft are composed of cells hardly differentiable from the ordinary cartilage, and they form the zone of resting cartilage. As we proceed in the direction of the shaft or diaphysis toward the second layer, the cells begin to show evidence of degeneration. The mitochondria appear rod-like, and later shrink; vacuoles containing fat and glycogen appear, and the cell nucleus shrinks. This zone, the zone of proliferating cartilage, varies in depth, depending on the rate of bone growth. In the third layer, the zone of preparatory calcification, the process of cell disintegration is complete. Here we find clumps of degenerated cells, or only lacunae from which the cells have disappeared. At the same time, if there are adequate concentrations of calcium and phosphate in the blood plasma, the matrix around the cells undergoes a notable change. There is a precipitation of calcium salts which results in the matrix walls' becoming calcified. Immediately to the shaft side of this area of preparatory calcification, the final stage of actual ossification takes place. This process is due to the activity of the osteoblasts and blood vessels of the bone marrow. The cells

---

[62] E. A. Park, Personal communication.

known as osteoblasts are fibroblast derivatives which possess the double function of bone formation and bone destruction. Although it is in both instances the same cell, the term osteoblast is applied to those cells which are producing bone, and the term osteoclast is applied to those in the process of bone resorption. As death of cartilaginous cells proceeds, there is an invasion of the matrix by capillaries proceeding upward from the diaphysis. These invade the empty lacunae. Some of the matrix trabeculae are resorbed by activity of the osteoblasts, giving rise to an increasing size of the marrow space and a reduction in the number but an increase in size of the trabeculae. Into the enlarged lacunae the blood vessels grow, continuously carrying with them connective tissue, osteoblasts, and osteoclasts. Upon the larger trabeculae the osteoblasts lay down true bone. Between the osteoblasts and the cartilage matrix, a new layer of tissue appears, gradually thickens, and surrounds the contours of the cartilage projections. It is this tissue which under favorable conditions begins to calcify as it is deposited and thus becomes bone. Physiologically, there is a lag in calcification, resulting in formation of an uncalcified osseous material known as osteoid. This appears in a limited degree under physiological conditions but becomes enlarged when there is local failure to supply calcium and phosphate. When this failure is marked and generalized, there is an increase in the width of the osteoid border. This is a picture typical of diaphyseal rickets and of osteomalacia. By this complex process (bone formation and bone resorption) the bones become more hollow because of the increase in size of the marrow spaces, and stronger because of the widening and ossification of the trabeculae and the increased strengthening of the cortex.

Although the morphological changes associated with endochondral bone formation have been carefully studied and adequately described, the chemical changes related to this process are not so well understood. Mineralization of bone matrix and osteoid consists of the deposition of calcium and phosphate, plus, to a lesser degree, carbonates, fluorides, and perhaps other anions combined with small amounts of calcium, sodium, magnesium, and potassium. The nature of the mineral deposit has been the subject of much investigation and controversy. The most acceptable concept has been that the mineral matter of bone has a crystalline structure resembling that of the apatite minerals, and that dissolved in this, perhaps as an adsorbate or as a solid solution, are the calcium salts hydroxide, fluoride, carbonate, etc. It seems clear that an adequate concentration of calcium and inorganic phosphorus both in the bone matrix and the tissue fluid is essential for this process, but the exact level at which calcification occurs is as yet poorly defined, and the mechanism itself is not clear.

Studies on calcification of endochondral cartilage *in vitro* have added much to our knowledge of this subject. Inhibition of this process may occur in a variety of ways, and the explanation for such inhibition has been that the inhibiting agent in some way affects an enzymic process, the ultimate aim of which is the liberation of inorganic phosphorus from phosphoric acid esters. The source of this inorganic phosphorus has been a stumbling block in any theory of calcification. Shipley et al.[63] produced in vitro calcification with artificial serum ultrafiltrates containing an adequate concentration of both calcium and inorganic phosphorus. Robison[64] demonstrated the presence of alkaline phosphatase in the hypertrophic cartilage cells and produced calcification in vitro using solution of calcium and hexosephosphoric acid. The latter was hydrolyzed by alkaline phosphatase, thus liberating inorganic phosphorus. However, Shipley et al. pointed out that plasma and presumably tissue fluid contain only traces of organically bound phosphorus. Furthermore, preparatory cartilage cells contain only minute amounts of organic phosphorus although rich in glycogen and phosphorylase. The problem of finding a source of organic phosphorus seemed to constitute an unsurmountable obstacle until Gutman[65] suggested the process of phosphylative glycogenolysis as a possible source of inorganic phosphorus and produced confirmatory evidence in the finding that substances which interfered with this process inhibited in vitro calcification.

Glycogen, like alkaline phosphatase, may be demonstrated in the cartilage cells of the hypertrophic cartilage, just before and during calcification, only to disappear as the process of calcification becomes complete. That glycogen may play an important role in endochondral calcification is indicated by the fact that in vitro calcification will not take place if the glycogen is removed with ptyaline.

The role of phosphatase in calcification has received the most intense study.[66] It is presumed to play an important role for the following reasons.

1. It is present in the preliminary stages wherever tissue is about to be calcified, i.e., in cartilage matrix, in osteoid, and at the site of metastatic calcification.

2. Substances that inhibit phosphatase activity inhibit in vitro calcification. Some of these substances are potassium cyanide, hydrocyanic acid, and fluoride.

3. In vitro calcification takes place in living cartilage in the presence of phosphatase when phosphoric acid esters represent the only source of inorganic phosphorus.

On the other hand, calcification in vitro can definitely occur in the ab-

[63] P. G. Shipley, B. Kramer, and J. Howland, Biochem. J. 20, 379 (1926).
[64] R. Robison, Biochem. J. 35, 304 (1924).
[65] A. B. Gutman and T. F. Yu, Trans. 2nd Conf. Metabolic Interrelations p. 167, 1950.
[66] R. H. Follis, Jr., Bull. Johns Hopkins Hospital 85, 360 (1949).

sence of phosphatase or in tissue heated to a temperature which destroys it. Moreover, the optimal pH for phosphatase activity is much beyond the pH of normal tissue fluids. Third, calcification *in vitro* will fail to occur when cells are poisoned, although such substances may not affect phosphatase activity.

Endochondral calcification takes place in the presence of an adequate concentration of plasma calcium and inorganic phosphorus. Deficiency of inorganic phosphorus in rickets apparently cannot be made up by the local action of alkaline phosphatase or phosphorylative glycogenolysis in the hypertrophic cartilage cells under the same conditions.

Since all tissue fluids presumably have the same concentration of calcium and inorganic phosphorus, there still remains the question of why certain tissues can be mineralized whereas this occurs in others only under abnormal conditions or not at all. Rubin and Howard[67] have demonstrated the presence of a mucopolysaccharide resembling chondroitin sulfate in tissues potentially capable of undergoing calcification. This metachromic staining material seems to form a combination with calcium and this may be the first step in the process of calcium salt deposition. During the course of this process the mucopolysaccharide seems to disappear and the tissue loses its peculiar staining characteristics. This has been cited as a point against its importance in primary calcification by Sobel,[65] but Rubin and Howard[67] have shown that the polysaccharide does not disappear during calcification but can be stained and its presence thus proved, if the section is decalcified before staining.

Although much has been learned concerning the mechanism of mineral salt deposition, little is known regarding the morphology, the chemical composition, including the enzyme content, and the metabolism of the organic matter of bone, including the cartilage matrix and osteoid upon which the calcium salts are deposited. Much has been added to our knowledge by the use of special dyes and the ordinary light microscope, and this information has been broadened and extended with the aid of the wide-angle diffraction pattern and the electron microscope. The use of special dyes that react specifically with certain constituents of the cell and the application of enzymes that are specific cytoplasmic components afford further insight into the functioning of osteoid and cartilage cells. Studies dealing with the effects of vitamin C deprivation on osteoid structure and composition in animals has thrown light on the mechanism of protein synthesis of cell cytoplasm that may have far-reaching implications for cells in general.[68]

Cartilage matrix which under the ordinary light microscope and with the

---

[67] P. S. Rubin and J. E. Howard, *Trans. 2nd Conf. Metabolic Interrelations* p. 155 (1950).

[68] R. H. Follis, Jr., *Trans. 4th Conf. Metabolic Interrelations* p. 11 (1952).

usual tissue fixation and staining appears quite homogeneous is found to show a fibrillar network lying in a homogeneous matrix; this network is made up chiefly of a protein, collagen, and the matrix itself contains a polysaccharide, probably chondroitic sulfuric acid. The collagen fibers show a definite periodicity of bands in their structure with finer bands within the periods. These collagen fibers resemble those found in skin, where the chemical composition has been studied extensively and fascinating theories concerning the arrangement of their chemical groups have been proposed that may account for some of their physical properties.

The homogeneous matrix is also being studied and among other properties shows the property of metachromasia. This is present in the cartilage matrix and seems concentrated about the hypertrophic cartilage cells; it is probably due to the peculiar effect of the polysaccharides upon the specific dye (polymerization).

The osteoblasts have been shown to contain lipids, glycogen, phosphatase, and lecithinase. Cytochromic oxidase has been demonstrated in the osteoblasts in addition to ribonucleic acid and its enzyme, ribonuclease. Less is known about the chemical composition of cartilage cells, but alkaline phosphatase, phosphorylases, glycogen, lipoids, and lecithinase have been demonstrated in these cells as well as some oxidases.

The reactivation of dormant osteoblasts in the scorbutic animal treated with vitamin C has yielded valuable information concerning the mechanism of synthesis of cell cytoplasm. Under the influence of vitamin C cell cytoplasm is synthesized: alkaline phosphatase reappears, protein synthesis is accelerated, and cells become filled with ribonucleic acid and ribonuclease and glycogen.

The electron microscope has revealed the location and orientation of mineral crystals on the collagen fibers as well as their configuration.[69]

The mechanism of bone resorption remains as obscure as ever, although the local application of parathormone can initiate and maintain such resorption by stimulating osteoclastic activity. Osteoclasts can bring about the resorption of both calcified and uncalcified cartilage matrix as well as osteoid tissue. Just how the mineral matter is made to disappear during the process of reabsorption of calcified trabeculae is not clear. Inorganic crystals have been demonstrated in the osteoclasts. This is very rare, however, and the mechanism of action of both osteoblasts as well as osteoclasts in the absorption of bone is quite obscure. Tension seems to affect enzyme activity, a fact to bear in mind in explaining the effect of tension in molding bone.

The chief consequence of vitamin D deficiency is the disruption of the orderly processes of bone formation which we have briefly described. In the

---

[69] R. A. Robinson, *Trans. 3rd Conf. Metabolic Interrelations* pp. 271–289 (1951); R. A. Robinson, *Trans. 5th Conf. Metabolic Interrelations* 1953 (In press).

shafts of the long bones, and in the membranous bones, there is produced instead of endosteal and periosteal bone an excessive amount of uncalcified bone, called osteoid. This osteoid is the framework of bone, without lime salt addition, so that it is both soft and radiotranslucent. The amount of this osteoid laid down varies at different points, increasing at areas of stress and strain, but decreasing at points of tension. An example of the former, is the excessive osteoid at the tendinous insertions into the bone, within the angles of a fracture, and on the concave side of bone generally.

When this soft bone is subjected to various and changing stresses and pressures such as those that occur in walking, sitting, etc., many types of deformities result. The deformities depend on the severity and extent of the disease process, its duration, the age of the child,[70] and the stresses and strains the bones are subject to. The age is important because it influences other factors. The first of these is the rapidity of growth of the various bones: the more active the growth, the greater the liability to damage. Second, the child's age and stage of development will determine which of the bones are particularly subjected to strain and stress. For example, during the first few months, the child lies on its back, and the stresses on the bones during these early months are those of gravity. During that period also the head and chest are growing most rapidly. For these two reasons, ricketic deformities encountered in the earliest period of life are most conspicuous in these two anatomic structures.

Changes in the skull are thus among the earliest manifestations of rickets. First there is flattening of the occipital bones from the pull of gravity. The lack of calcification in circumscribed areas of the skull (craniotabes) is due to the failure of calcification in portions of this membranous bone. In the areas where the bending of the bone is most pronounced, on the parietal and frontal bones, there are accumulations of osteoid tissue which give rise to the bossae which are typical of this disease.

Deformity of the chest and consequent physiological inadequacy of the respiratory organs represent some of the most dramatic and serious consequences of severe rickets.[71] In the advanced case, as the child lies in bed, the front of the chest is seen as a blunt wedge protruding forward, with the sternum and adjacent ends of the ribs corresponding to the prow of a ship. The anterolateral portions of the ribs, corresponding to the costochondral junctions, have sunk inward, producing the depressions running the vertical length of the chest. The clavicles are exceedingly prominent and bowed, giving undue prominence to the manubrium sternum. Often there are multiple fractures of the ribs. When these fractures are anterior, they form small mounds of callus; if posterior, they tend to eliminate the

---

[70] M. M. Eliot and E. A. Park, Brennemann's Practise of Pediatrics. W. F. Prior Co., Hagerstown, Md., 1950.

[71] E. A. Park and J. Howland, *Bull. Johns Hopkins Hosp.* **32**, 101 (1921).

rounded character of the rib angle. Most important of all is what happens at the costochondral junction. Normally, the cartilage and rib shaft are accurately and rigidly joined end to end. In rickets, they are separated by the soft metaphysis, which has little or no rigidity and permits of considerable movement during respiration. The metaphysis soon gives way to the negative intrathoracic pressure, the ribs become more and more bent inward, until finally the rib ends lie internal to the cartilage, and the enlargement of the costochondral junction is within the chest and compresses the adjacent lung. Thus the lung is divided into an anterior emphysematous portion and a posterior portion which is partly emphysematous and partly atelectatic separated by a longitudinal zone of complete atelectasis.

As one watches such a child breathe, he observes that with inspiration almost every one of these deformities becomes exaggerated. The moment inspiration ends, the chest in early cases springs into the expiratory position. Observation, or measurement, will reveal that the inspiration has barely, if at all, increased the chest circumference. Moreover, it appears that life is maintained not by the awkward and inefficient movement of the rib cage, but by the exertions of the diaphragm. Later the elasticity of the thoracic cage is lost and even the diaphragm is partly relaxed during rest.

The essential difficulty physiologically is the loss of thoracic rigidity. As this process progresses, the linear depressions which at first were present only during inspiration tend to persist in expiration. As the efficiency of each respiration is diminished by the chest collapse and the intrusion of costochondral junctions and the rib ends into the chest cavity, there is an attempt at compensation by increasing the frequency of respiration. But the greater and more frequent the force applied, the greater is the collapse. The diaphragm pulls its attachments further inward, and the accessory muscles of respiration draw the bones out of position without stabilizing the chest as a whole. As there is progressive decrease in chest capacity, there develops increasing atelectasis, the pressure in the pulmonary circulation rises, the right heart hypertrophies, and cyanosis may appear. The dyspnoea is extreme, the respirations rising to 60 and 100 times a minute. There may also appear dilatation of the nostrils, a grunt and a cough. If, now, an additional burden, such as an infection, is superimposed, the mechanism and its compensations may fail, the vital capacity becomes equal to or less than the tidal air, and permanent cyanosis is the result. Sudden death may follow.

On the other hand, if the child does not die, he may improve. As the rickets heals and lime salts are deposited in the bone, the chest regains its rigidity. Despite the persistence of deformities, the efficiency of respiration improves and then may gradually return to normal.

In neo-natal rickets, the pelvis becomes flattened, by virtue of the pull of gravity on the soft structure. After a few months the child begins to spend much of his time in the sitting position. The pelvis must now support the weight of the head and trunk, and as a result of this new stress a dorsal kyphosis appears. When the child stands up, and later when he begins to walk, the strain on the spine changes again. Now the dorsal kyphosis changes to a sharp lumbar lordosis, and the spine pushes forward at the promontory of the sacrum, thus further decreasing the anterior-posterior diameter of the pelvis. In the severest cases, the head of the femur may push up the acetabulum, thus further encroaching upon the pelvic space.

In the period during which the child begins to sit up, various deformities of the long bones may develop. The severely ricketic child sits cross-legged and supports the weight of his body by extending his hands to the table or floor. In this position the upper of the two crossed legs is bent by gravity as it extends over the lower shin which acts as a fulcrum. At the same time the wrists against which the weight of the body rests may also bend. This pressure against soft and rapidly growing bones results in bending deformities. Occasionally, the bending may progress to actual angulation of the epiphyses which is then bent towards the diaphysis. As the growth of the diaphysis in the original axis continues, however, the bend is accentuated. The process of growth may carry the bend some distance from the epiphysis so that its real nature may not be easily recognized. Such deformities occur, particularly at the lower ends of the tibiae and fibulae, and in the lower ends of the radius and ulna. They occur particularly when the rickets is severe at about the age of 2 years, when growth in these areas is particularly rapid. Bending deformities may also be due to fractures which occur chiefly in the severer forms of the disease. In addition to the actual bone involvement, there is great relaxation of the tendons in rickets, and this looseness seems to initiate or accentuate many of the deformities.

To summarize, curvatures of the shaft may result from bending of softened bone, tilting and dislocation of the epiphysis, and as a result of fractures. Posture may suffer from tendon relaxation. The typical deformities of the lower extremities which occur as a result of these forces are bowlegs (genu varum), knock-knees (genu valgum), and saber shin deformity. The curvatures of the arms are much less marked than those in the leg. Outward bowing of the humerus and exaggeration of the normal curvatures of the radius and the ulna may be seen.

The type of rickets we have been describing is the moderately severe type. Park has pointed out that rickets may vary in degree. Both he and Follis have described cases in adults and in children in which the only evidence of the disease is a slight to moderate increase in the osteoid seam around the trabeculae. This may be limited even to one aspect or side of the trabeculum, with or without minimal changes at the chondro-osseous junction in the form of localized defects of cartilage matrix calcification. Such cases show no change clinically or roentgenologically, and may or may not show changes in the blood calcium or inorganic phosphorus. In contrast, the process may be so severe that the bones are almost translucent and difficult to differentiate on x-ray examination from the surrounding soft parts.

Since endochondral ossification ceases with the closure of the epiphysis, deficiency of vitamin D in older people results only in shaft or diaphyseal changes, and the disease characterized by this process is called osteomalacia. Pathologically, we see only the superabundance of osteoid around the trabeculae and a certain amount of osteoporosis. All the complications of soft bones, which we have already described, can then occur. Severe osteomalacia occurs rarely in the western world except during exceptional times of great stress. An endemic of this disease occurred in Germany during the allied blockade in the first world war and in the subjugated countries subjected to German genocide methods during the second world war. It is sometimes seen following dietary restrictions either self-imposed or imposed as a therapeutic measure. It also occurs in India, in Japan, and in northern China, among women, where prolonged lactation, with its drain on the calcium reserves, may result in a negative calcium balance. It also occurs among women of the higher classes, who practice purdah and are therefore kept confined indoors away from the sun.[72]

At the epiphyseal end of the bones where the process of endochondral bone formation normally results in elongation of the bone, rickets manifests itself by a disruption of the orderly processes which we have already described for that area.[73] The progressive steps in that disruption may be listed as follows:

1. Failure of calcium salt deposition in the cartilage matrix.

2. Failure of the cells to mature, making them impervious to invasion and therefore leading to their accumulation rather than their destruction.

3. Compression of the proliferating cartilage cells.

4. Elongation, swelling, and degeneration of the proliferative cartilage.

5. Abnormal pattern of invasion of the cartilage by tufts of capillaries.

There is some difference of opinion as to what is the very first change from normal when the child is deprived of vitamin D. Park believes that failure of calcium deposition in the matrix is the first deviation (Figs. 18 and 19). Because of this failure, the guiding influence of the calcified matrix is absent when the invading blood vessels approach, and these vessels,

[72] A. F. Hess, Rickets Including Osteomalacia and Tetany. Lea and Febiger, Philadelphia, 1929.

[73] E. A. Park, *Harvey Lectures* 157 (1938–1939).

instead of taking a parallel course, are diverted and the cartilage is broken up into uneven tongues. Park points out that in the earliest cases the histologist will find only in the fastest growing bone some thinning of an occasional spicule, and an area here and there where calcification is entirely absent from one of the main partitions in the cartilage.[73]

As a result of the total or partial failure of the calcification in the matrix substance of the cartilage, there is failure of support for the large cartilage cells lying nearest the shaft. There results, therefore, the phenomenon of compression of these cells which may be flattened out, or in severe cases

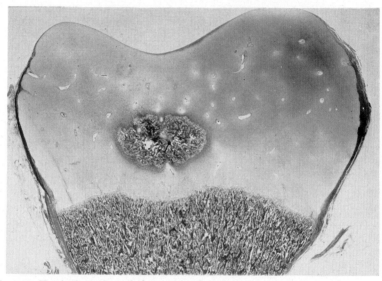

Fig. 18. Vertical section of the proximal end of tibia, showing early changes at the chondro-osseus junction. Focal defects in the calcification of the zone of preliminary calcification.

actually ruptured. Such compression is generally distributed in a spotty manner and is severe and generalized only in bones where there is rapid growth, and in a child with severe rickets. In a severe case the spicules surrounding the cells are bent and buckled so that they may actually lie on their sides. Occasionally, the fractured spicules may be driven into the cartilage.

The continued proliferation of cartilage cells, without concomitant mineralization and ossification, results in the lengthening of the cartilage plate and in swelling of individual cells. The increase in size of the cartilaginous plate is not due to an increased production of cartilage cells, as proposed by Ziegler.[74] There is a normal production of these cells, but they fail to

[74] E. Ziegler, *Lehrbuch der Allg. Pathol. Anat.* **2,** 179 (1898).

undergo normal senescence and they accumulate, thereby causing a widening of the cartilage plate in the proliferative zone (Fig. 20). If the rickets
persists, however, the rate of proliferation of these cells diminishes, so that
in extreme cases dwarfism may result. Besides this basic cause of dwarfism
in extreme rickets, shortness of stature may be due to a bending of the

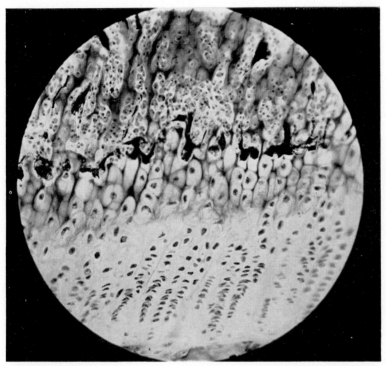

FIG. 19. High power of Fig. 18, showing first maturation of cartilage cells with
disappearance of some of the cells at the chondro-osseus junction. Beginning irregularity of the blood vessels. Deficient, almost absent calcification in the zone of provisional calcification.

soft long bones, and accompanying fractures with shortening, and also to
squashing of the metaphysis.

The pattern of capillary invasion into the growing cartilage becomes
abnormal in two ways. In the normal bone, vessels invade the cartilage by
extension from the shaft only. In the ricketic bone, in addition to invasion
from the shaft, tiny blood vessels penetrate also from the epiphyseal end
and from the sides. The second abnormality is the type and formation of
the invading blood vessels. In the normal cartilage the capillaries are seen
extending up from the shaft and penetrating the matrix walls between the
cell columns, and by depositing lime salts on to these partitions they create

calcified fasicles. These calcified matrix columns in due time become transformed into true bone. In rickets, the blood vessels attack several fasicles together, and invade the very thick partitions. In severe cases an entire bush of capillaries, branching from large arteries and attacking widespread areas of the cartilage matrix, may cause gross defects in some parts of the cartilage plate, while in other, perhaps adjoining areas, there may be a mass of cartilage cells. Only the heaviest partitions remain, and the osteoblasts settle upon these and cover them with osteoid.

Wolbach[75] explained the occurrence of this abnormal calcification and

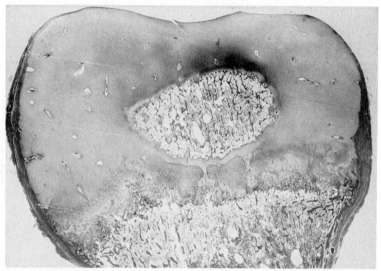

Fig. 20. Advanced rickets. Marked widening and irregularity of epiphyseal line irregular vascular invasion, and defective calcification and ossification at chondro-osseus junction. Osteoporotic appearance of metaphyseal region.

these changes at the chondro-osseus junction as follows: The capillaries invade those regions which are uncalcified or soft, and after their penetration grow into large vessels, drawing away the circulation from the calcified areas. Park believes, however, that the compressed cartilage cells we have already described form the chief obstruction to the advancing capillaries.

The abnormal penetration of the blood vessels results in a variable blood supply to the different parts of the cartilage, and the sections suffering from insufficient blood may develop abnormally. Aside from the change of the cartilage into osteoid rather than bone, there appear also bizarre, degenerative forms of cartilage cells. The cells may vary greatly in size and shape, with occasional appearance of double nuclei. At first these cells stain heavily

[75] S. B. Wolbach, J. Am. Med. Assoc. 108, 7 (1937).

with hematoxylin, but later, as the degenerative process continues, they lose their staining ability entirely.

The degeneration of cartilage cells may progress to the formation of actual areas of necrosis. Although found most frequently in rats, such areas, hemispherical and circumscribed, have also been described in humans. Occasionally such degenerative and necrotic areas may dominate the pathologic picture.

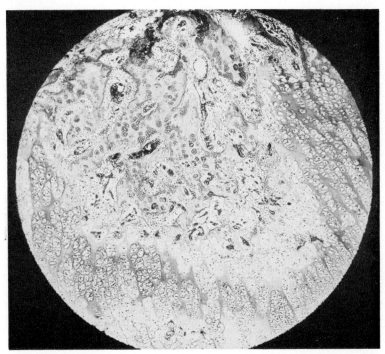

Fig. 21. Large capillary tuft invading the cartilage. Severe rickets. Calcium deficiency; large masses of uncalcified osteoid; connective tissue marrow.

We have already noted that during the ricketic process the proliferation of new cartilage cells continues while the formation of bone is retarded or stopped. This, together with the invasion of this zone by large vascular tufts (Fig. 21), results in the formation of a wide zone, soft and radiotranslucent, between the shaft of the bone and the epiphysis. This zone, known as the metaphysis, is an entirely abnormal area in which are scattered all the elements of the pathologic picture of rickets, including large vascular clumps, which enter the area from all sides, masses of cartilage broken up into cartilaginous and osteoid trabeculae, bizarre cartilage cells, occasional mineral salt deposits representing evanescent attempts at healing, and foci of complete degeneration (Fig. 22). In this region we may note evidence of the operation of mechanical forces on the newly and poorly formed bone. Groups of cells may be compressed, a trabeculum may be bent or doubled up on itself, the cartilage column at the periphery may fan out to extreme angles, and there may even be a displacement of the upper metaphysis against the bone shaft so that the long axis of both structures form an angle (Fig. 23). Moreover, since the human being seldom suffers from complete absence of vitamin D, one finds evidence of transient periods of healing, followed by recurrence of the ricketic process. To add

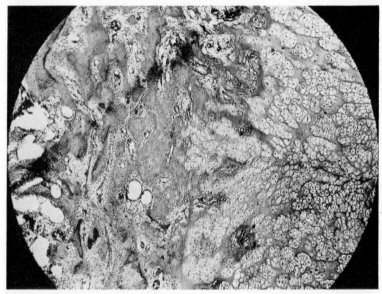

Fig. 22. Metaphyseal area. Irregular masses of cartilage cells, some swollen, some compressed; compressed trabeculae of uncalcified osteoid tissue; irregular invasion of cartilage by blood vascular marrow which shows early fibrous changes; some degenerated cartilage and ghost cells; osteoid surrounding the invading marrow.

to the complexity of the picture, one may find evidence also of other vitamin deficiency such as deficiency of vitamin C, or, less often, deficiency of vitamin A and vitamins of the B complex. Deficiency of vitamin C may lead to hemorrhage, osteoblastic degeneration, and fractures of newly calcified trabeculae.

This variable and unpredictable histologic appearance is reflected in the roentgenographs of the bones. Cupping and enlargement of the space between the epiphysis and the end of the shaft due to the transparency and swelling of the metaphysis is most obvious. Cortical spurs or linear extensions of the cortex which hug the proliferative cartilage may be an early sign. Frayings, consisting of thread-like shadows extending from the end of the shaft into the transparent cartilage, are seen. In early rickets the individual threads are short, thin, and hard to see; in moderate and advanced cases the threads are long and coarse. In the shaft, the cortex may appear thickened and composed of longitudinal, slightly curved interlacing lamellae. The bone shadow may be slightly or moderately diminished. In the severe forms, there is marked translucency of the entire shaft. If present,

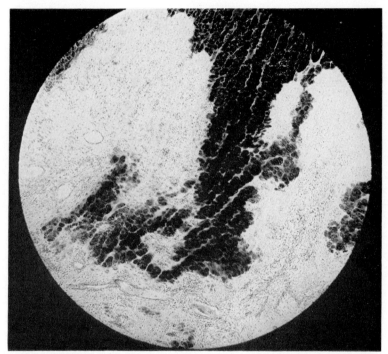

FIG. 23. Cartilage mass which has been compressed projecting into metaphysis. Predominantly connective tissue marrow.

the x-ray will always show these distortions and fractures as described, especially after healing has begun.

Whether or not the condition of the teeth is influenced by the lack of vitamin D is still an open question. It seems that primary dentition may be delayed in rickets, and when the teeth do appear they may do so in an abnormal order. The permanent teeth also show defects attributable to rickets.[76, 77] The teeth which are developing at the time when the rickets is most active may, when they erupt, show a hypoplasia of the enamel.

[76] M. M. Eliot, S. P. Southner, B. A. Anderson, and S. Arnim, *Am. J. Diseases Children* **46**, 458 (1933).

[77] A. F. Hess and H. Abramson, *Dental Cosmos* **73**, 849 (1931).

This condition is characterized by a symmetrical distribution of thinning and pitting defects in the dental enamel. Although the relationship of rickets to the incidence of caries has still not been established, it is generally recognized that rickets results in enamel defects in the teeth which in turn predispose to caries. This disabling disorder may be best prevented by the ingestion of a calorically adequate and well-balanced diet, along with adequate amounts of vitamin D.[78, 79]

VII. Chemical Pathology and Pharmacology

BENJAMIN KRAMER and ABRAM KANOF

The chemical pathology of vitamin D deficiency is concerned with the role which lack of this vitamin plays in preventing or delaying calcification. In the last analysis rickets prevention depends upon the maintenance of a normal concentration of calcium and inorganic phosphorus in the plasma and presumably in the tissue fluids, thus in a large measure ensuring a constant and adequate supply of these elements for mineralization of newly formed cartilage matrix and osteoid. Exceptions to this rule are seen in the very rapidly growing premature or newborn or in chronic nephritis or hyperparathyroidism. An understanding of the mechanism of rickets prevention therefore involves an understanding of the mechanism of calcium and inorganic phosphorus, homeostasis. There are four facets to this problem: (1) the mechanism of absorption of calcium and inorganic phosphorus from the gastrointestinal tract; (2) the factors determining the level of these elements in the blood; (3) the role of the kidneys in calcium and phosphorus homeostasis; and (4) the factors which determine deposition of calcium salts in the cartilage and osteoid, and the resolution of these same materials (the local factor).

Just how calcium and inorganic phosphorus are absorbed from the gastrointestinal tract is unknown. We do know that soluble salts of calcium are more readily absorbed than the less soluble combinations. A shift of the pH of the intestinal contents to the acid side favors absorption, probably through conversion of the less soluble alkaline salts to the more soluble acid forms. The presence of large amounts of fats, especially the higher fatty acids, gives rise to highly insoluble calcium salts, while an excess of carbohydrate, by increasing fermentation, shifts the pH of the intestinal contents to the acid state and may give rise to the more volatile and more soluble lower fatty acids.

[78] M. C. Agnew, R. C. Agnew, and F. F. Tisdall, *J. Am. Dent. Assoc.* **20**, 193 (1933).
[79] A. F. Hess, H. Abramson, and J. M. Lewis, *Am. J. Diseases Children* **47**, 477 (1934).

We have noted that the formation of insoluble salts of calcium such as oxalate, tartrate, and alkaline phosphates, for example, tends to interfere with absorption. Much of this interference with the absorption of calcium can be overcome by inclusion of vitamin D in the diet, or by adequate irradiation with ultraviolet rays of the correct wavelength. Thus, in the absence of vitamin D, less than 20 % of ingested calcium is absorbed from the gastrointestinal tract; if there is an adequate vitamin D intake, 50 % to 80 % may be absorbed.

In the case of phosphate, which constitutes the most important anion component of the calcium salts, the situation is rather more complicated, for phosphorus plays an important role in innumerable enzymic processes within the cells and is a constituent of many cellular components, e.g., nucleic acid, phosphatides, phosphoproteins, creatine phosphate, hexose phosphates, ATP, ADP, etc. Phosphorus must be available at all times for basic chemical processes.

It is therefore not surprising that the absorption of phosphorus from the gut is in large measure independent of vitamin D intake, and that such inefficiency of absorption as is observed in rickets is secondary to the failure of calcium absorption. Moreover, such improvement of phosphorus absorption as is obtained by feeding vitamin D to the ricketic patient is a consequence of improvement of calcium absorption.[1] The degree of phosphorus absorption can be influenced by the pH of the intestinal tract. Administration of cations, such as iron, aluminum, or beryllium which form insoluble phosphates will interfere with the absorption of phosphate.[2]

The level of calcium and phosphorus in the blood is not entirely dependent upon the amount of these elements absorbed from the gut. Physicochemical as well as endocrine factors play a part. The relationship between the plasma calcium and inorganic phosphorus concentration is reciprocal, as is that of the ions of any slightly soluble salt in a saturated solution, and, presumably, the maximum concentration of either in the presence of the other determines the magnitude of the solubility product. When the solubility product falls below a certain critical value, lime salt deposition becomes irregular, and if this is sufficient to interfere with the normal sequences of organic bone growth and mineralization of these tissues, rickets develops. The magnitude of this solubility product in the human varies with age, decreasing as the rate of bone growth diminishes. It can increase to a higher level following fractures, or it may drop to a lower level with infection. Both endocrine and physicochemical factors determine the satura-

[1] R. Nicolaysen, *Biochem. J.* **31**, 122 (1937).

[2] F. Albright, and E. C. Reifenstein, The Parathyroid Glands and Metabolic Bone Disease, Williams & Wilkins Co., Baltimore, 1948, p. 38.

tion level. The attainment of the normal level in the otherwise normal individual depends chiefly on an adequate intake of vitamin D.[3]

The availability of calcium to the plasma does not in itself determine its level in the plasma, since introduction of calcium to the plasma in hypoparathyroidism results only in a temporary rise in the plasma calcium concentration with a rapid re-establishment of the previous low calcium level. In the ricketic child with hypocalcemia the administration of soluble calcium salts in the absence of vitamin D will restore the normal serum calcium level, but there will follow a simultaneous drop in inorganic phosphorus concentration. In the presence of adequate vitamin D intake, normal calcium level is restored while normal inorganic phosphorus remains unchanged, thus establishing a higher calcium phosphorus product. Only toxic doses of vitamin D will raise this product still further. This indicates the existence of a homeostatic mechanism which tends to keep both ion concentrations at a level which is constant for the age group. Vitamin D therefore influences the concentration of calcium in at least two ways: by increasing absorption from the gastrointestinal tract, and by raising the solubility product of calcium phosphate in the plasma, and perhaps by regulating renal loss of calcium and phosphate either directly or through the parathyroid glands. The mechanism seems to be as follows: the vitamin D produces a rise in the serum calcium, which in turn depresses parathyroid activity. Since the action of the parathyroids is to diminish the renal threshold for phosphorus, their suppression raises the threshold and elevates the serum phosphorus level.[4]

Under normal conditions bone acts as a reservoir for blood calcium. Hastings[5] has demonstrated a rapid restoration of plasma calcium after removal of calcium from the blood and the return of such decalcified blood to the circulation. Presumably this is accomplished by solublizing calcium from bone. It is possible that the parathyroid glands play an important role in this process. It is postulated that bone mineral forms the solid phase of a bone-tissue fluid blood plasma system which is normally in equilibrium. A reduction of plasma calcium concentration disturbs this equilibrium, and

---

[3] For a given animal there would seem to be two products, one that is maintained in the absence of vitamin D, and another, higher one when adequate vitamin D is available. The former may be attained with a normal calcium level and a low inorganic phosphorus concentration or a low calcium with a normal inorganic phosphorus. The level of one ion is at the mercy of the amount of the other that enters the plasma. With adequate vitamin D the total product as well as the concentration of the individual components are stabilized, and if disturbed by excessive ingestion of one, equilibrium is rapidly re-established at the normal level.

[4] F. Albright and E. C. Reifenstein, The Parathyroid Glands and Metabolic Bone Disease, p. 127. Williams & Wilkins Co., Baltimore, 1948.

[5] A. B. Hastings, *New Engl. Med. J.* **216,** 377 (1937).

bone calcium is mobilized to restore the normal concentration of the liquid phase. Just how this is accomplished is not clear, since calcium in bone is presumably tied up with structural materials in bone, and resolution of calcium salts usually goes on parallel with organic bone destruction.

The amount of phosphorus required is in excess of the amount needed for bone mineralization alone, since phosphorus participates in most chemical processes in the cell. In addition it is an important buffer in maintaining the normal reaction of blood plasma and in enabling the kidneys to excrete large amounts of inorganic and organic acids within the normal span of urinary pH. Although the mechanism of excretion of calcium and perhaps the mechanism of its resorption by the kidney has not as yet received sufficient attention, the problem of renal clearance of inorganic phosphorus has received considerable study. These studies have concerned themselves not only with normal subjects but also with individuals suffering from various bone diseases, as well as other conditions such as acidosis, diabetes, and parathyroid disturbances. When vitamin D is not available in the animal with intact parathyroid, inorganic phosphate clearance seems to be increased by virtue of a diminution in tubular resorption, a result of the unopposed activity of parathyroid hormone. This may explain the normal plasma calcium level in most cases of rickets, in spite of defective calcium absorption from the bowel. The hypophosphatemia in rickets is presumably in part due to this defect. It is possible that the parathyroids play a part in this process, since in experimental rickets these glands are found to be enlarged. This may also explain the presence of a normal or only slightly reduced calcium level in rickets due to vitamin D deficiency where absorption of calcium from the gastrointestinal tract is minimal. This increased parathyroid activity has a twofold effect, the protection of the organism against tetany by maintaining a normal calcium ion level in the face of decreased calcium absorption from the gastrointestinal tract and an excessive inorganic phosphorus clearance by the kidney with resulting hypophosphatemia. In this way the ricketic condition is aggravated while the child is protected from the possibly fatal convulsions of tetany.

The action of vitamin D differs in the parathyroidectomized animal as compared to animals with intact parathyroids. It is possible that with intact parathyroids adequate intake of vitamin D depresses parathyroid activity, resulting in a greater resorption of phosphorus by the renal tubules, although the actual amount of phosphorus excreted in the urine exceeds that found during active rickets (vitamin D deficiency). In parathyroidectomized animals or human beings, vitamin D actually increases renal loss of phosphorus.

The action of vitamin D in the ricketic animal is threefold: (1) It restores the normal capacity of the gastrointestinal tract to absorb calcium. (2) It restores the normal phosphorus absorption which was secondarily impaired by defective calcium absorption and the formation of slightly soluble phosphates of calcium. (3) It increases urinary phosphorus excretion, although phosphorus clearance actually is decreased because of increased tubular resorption of phosphorus. This is accomplished presumably by the inhibitory effect of increased plasma calcium upon parathyroid hormone secretion. In the absence of the parathyroids phosphorus clearance is actually increased by vitamin D intake.

Thus with more calcium and inorganic phosphorus available from exogenous sources and improved phosphorus resorption by the kidney, normal levels of both elements are maintained, and normal mineralization of bone is restored. Whether parathyroid hormone acts not only through the kidneys but also directly on the bone itself is not known.

In the serum of normal children the concentration of calcium is remarkably constant, at about 10 ± 1.5 mg. %. The inorganic phosphorus content of the serum is also fairly constant and in normal children is usually about 6 ± 1 mg. %. In the newborn infant the calcium content of the blood serum may vary between 7.0 mg. and 11.0 mg. per 100 ml. The inorganic phosphorus content of the blood in premature and newborn full-term infants is 5.0 to 6.0 mg. %; it is slightly lower after 3 years of age, and still lower in adults. It has been demonstrated that, whereas in tetany there is regularly a marked reduction in the calcium of the serum, the drop in rickets is infrequent and may be caused by other factors than the vitamin D deficiency. There is, however, a constant and sometimes marked decrease in the concentration of inorganic phosphorus with patients suffering from rickets. Howland and Kramer[6] and Iverson and Lenstrup[7] independently made observations with respect to inorganic and acid-soluble phosphorus in patients with rickets and found that it varied from 0.6 to 3.2 mg. per 100 ml., the average being 2.0 mg., or less than 50 % of the normal serum content. Howland and Kramer showed that the administration of cod liver oil in therapeutic doses had no effect on the calcium concentration but did result in a marked increase of the phosphorus level.

We may say, therefore, that there is a fairly constant and a clinically significant deficiency of the inorganic phosphorus of the plasma in rickets. Howland and Kramer developed a mathematical formula which determines the chemical requirements for normal bone deposition.[8] They found that in most cases of uncomplicated rickets if the product of calcium concentration in milligrams per cent and the inorganic phosphorus concentra-

[6] J. Howland and B. Kramer, *Am. J. Diseases Children* **22**, 105 (1921).

[7] P. Iverson and E. Lenstrup, *Forhandlingerne Ved. Forste Nordiske Kongres for Pediatri.* 1920.

. Howland and B. Kramer, *Trans. Am. Pediat. Soc.* **34**, 204 (1922).

tion in milligrams per cent is less than 30, rickets exists; if it is above 40, rickets is not present or is healing. Studies on *in vitro* calcification indicate that the blood of the normal child is slightly undersaturated with respect to secondary calcium phosphate, and that equilibration experiments with bone and artificial sera, as well as similar experiments using either tertiary calcium phosphate or hydroxyapatite as the substrate, all point to the fact that the determining factor in precipitation is the solublity product of this compound (secondary calcium phosphate). Since both components entering into this product are represented by the first power, it follows that there must be some relationship between the actual ion product and the product expressed in this simple non-chemical way in terms of milligrams of each component in 100 ml. of serum.

It must be emphasized, however, that the product is not the only factor determining calcification. In rapidly growing premature infants osteoid formation may proceed so rapidly that calcium salts deposition fails to keep pace although the Ca × P product is normal.

Obviously the Ca × P product is only one basic essential for calcification. Only certain tissues will calcify, although all are bathed presumably with the same tissue fluid having its origin in the same plasma. Local processes probably bring about a further increase of the product, presumably by increasing the anion level. The many factors which may play a role in this complicated process have already been discussed. Alkaline phosphatase is the only one of the enzymes involved which can be readily measured. The number of units reported in a particular case represents the number of milligrams of inorganic phosphorus liberated by the amount of enzyme in 100 ml. of serum. The normal plasma values for children vary between 5 and 15 units. In active rickets this value is increased, and it is diminished during healing. As the excess tissue either becomes calcified or resorbed, the phosphatase concentration in the plasma tends to return to normal.

VIII. Requirements

A. OF ANIMALS

JAMES H. JONES

So many factors influence the requirements for vitamin D that it is difficult to express quantitatively the need of animals for this vitamin unless the environment and diet are known. The most important of these factors is sunlight. It is well recognized that exposure to sufficient summer sunshine makes the giving of vitamin D unnecessary. Consequently, the determination of the requirements of any species for vitamin D is done under conditions which exclude the actinic rays.

The amount and ratio of calcium and phosphorus in the diet also influence the need of the animal for vitamin D. As discussed previously, it is impossible to produce rickets in rats and other rodents which have been studied unless the diet is low in either phosphorus or calcium. However, even with larger mammals and fowls which develop rickets on diets containing ample amounts of calcium and phosphorus, the demand for vitamin D is increased if the ratio of calcium to phosphorus is far removed from that required by the animal, and/or the calcium or phosphorus in the diet is deficient.

The availability of phosphorus (and also calcium) is another factor in the requirements of animals for vitamin D. Most of the common ricketogenic diets contain approximately 0.3 to 0.4 % of phosphorus. If this were all available, these diets would not produce rickets in rats, but they are composed largely of cereals which contain considerable phytic acid. The phosphorus of phytic acid is not available until the acid is hydrolyzed by the phytase of the intestinal secretions. When a large amount of calcium is added to the diet, the phytic acid is precipitated as the calcium salt. The acid cannot be hydrolyzed, and the phosphorus cannot be made available. Mellanby[1] discussed the chemistry of phytic acid and its salts and their relation to rickets. If the diet contains inorganic phosphates, it is probable that here again the high calcium makes some of the phosphorus unavailable by precipitating it as an insoluble calcium phosphate.

Still another factor which influences the requirements of animals for vitamin D is the acidity of the diet. As the acidity is increased, the less ricketogenic the diet becomes.[2] The effect, in all probability, is due to an increased solubility of the calcium and phosphorus. Shohl *et al.*,[3] however, found little difference among acid, neutral, and alkaline phosphates in their effects on rickets in rats.

In the following discussion on the requirements of farm animals, it is assumed that the animals are away from direct sunlight, but that the supply of calcium and phosphorus is adequate, and the ratio of these two elements to each other is not far from that demanded by the animals.

Recently the Committee on Animal Nutrition of the National Research Council has issued several reports giving the recommended nutrient allow-

[1] E. Mellanby, A Story of Nutritional Research. Williams and Wilkins Co., Baltimore, 1950.

[2] T. F. Zucker, W. C. Johnson, and M. Barnett, *Proc. Soc. Exptl. Biol. Med.* **20**, 20 (1922–1923).

[3] A. T. Shohl, H. B. Bennett, and K. L. Weed, *J. Biol. Chem.* **78**, 181 (1928).

ances for domestic animals.[4] The following data dealing with the recommendations for vitamin D are taken from these reports.

In Table XI are given the recommended daily amounts in international units of vitamin D for the maintenance of chickens of various weights and for laying and breeding. The recommended amounts of vitamin D per pound of feed for starting chicks (0 to 8 weeks), growing chicks (8 to 18 weeks) laying hens, and breeding hens are 180, 180, 450, and 450 A.O.A.C. units, respectively. For turkey poults, growing turkeys, and breeding turkeys, 800 A.O.A.C. units of vitamin D per pound of feed is recommended.

The recommended daily amounts of vitamin D, in international units, for various weights of market swine and for breeding stock are given in

TABLE XI[a]

RECOMMENDED DAILY ALLOWANCES[b] OF VITAMIN D FOR CHICKENS

| Body weight, lb. | Maintenance | | | | | | | | | Laying | Breeding |
	0.5	1.0	1.5	2.0	2.5	3.0	4.0	4.5	5.5?		
White Leghorns and similar breeds	11.88	18.5	23.2	26.1	28.3	31.1	28.4			92.7	92.7
Heavy breeds	12.6	18.7	25.7	30.1		36.0		34.2	36.0?	111.6	111.6

[a] Adapted from Recommended Nutrient Allowances for Poultry: A Report of the Committee on Animal Nutrition, National Research Council.
[b] International units per animal.

Table XII The quantity of vitamin D per pound of feed recommended for all types of swine is 50 I.U.

The daily allowances of vitamin D for dairy cattle are again based on body weight. For heifers weighing 50, 100, 150, and 200 pounds, the recommended amounts are 200, 400, 600, and 800 I.U., respectively. The allowances per pound of feed for dairy heifers weighing 50, 100, 150, and 200 pounds should be 220, 200, 150, and 130 I.U., respectively. No recommendations are made for heavier animals.

No general recommendations are made regarding the needs of beef cattle for vitamin D. It is pointed out that usually these animals receive suffi-

[4] Committee on Animal Nutrition, Recommended Nutrient Allowances for Domestic Animals: No. I, Recommended Nutrient Allowances for Poultry (Revised 1950); No. II, Recommended Nutrient Allowances for Swine (Revised 1950); No. III, Recommended Nutrient Allowances for Dairy Cattle (Revised 1950); No. IV, Recommended Nutrient Allowances for Beef Cattle (Revised 1950); No. V, Recommended Nutrient Allowances for Sheep (Revised 1949); No. VI, Recommended Nutrient Allowances for Horses (1949).

cient sunlight to make a dietary source of vitamin D unnecessary. However, the report on the nutritive recommendations quote Bechtel et al.[5] as finding the vitamin D requirements of young beef calves to be about 300 I.U. per 100 pounds of live weight.

Sheep, like beef cattle, also spend considerable time on the range and probably need no dietary source of vitamin D. Lambs away from sunlight should be given this vitamin, and the Committee on Animal Nutrition recommends a daily allowance of 250 to 300 I.U. of vitamin D per 100 pounds of live weight. In a similar manner, the working horse in all probability needs no dietary source of vitamin D because it is exposed to direct sunlight for hours at a time. Where horses are confined away from the light of the sun, it is recommended that the daily allowance be 300 I.U. per 100 pounds of live weight. There is no experimental information available on

TABLE XII[a]

RECOMMENDED DAILY ALLOWANCES[b] OF VITAMIN D FOR SWINE

| | | | | | | Breeding stock | | | |
| | | | | | | Pregnant females and breeding boars | | Lactating females | |
	Market stock					Young	Adults	Gilts	Adults
Live weight, lb.	50	100	150	200	250	300	500	350	450
Vitamin D	150	265	340	375	415	300	375	550	625

[a] Adapted from Recommended Nutrient Allowances for Swine: A Report of the Committee on Animal Nutrition, National Research Council.
[b] International units per animal.

the horse, but the recommendations are based on knowledge concerning other animals.

It is to be remembered that these recommendations are not minimal quantities, but a rather liberal allowance has been made for a margin of safety.

Harris et al.[6] found that for foxes on a basal diet which contained 0.82 I.U. of vitamin D per gram the addition of 200 I.U. per kilogram of body weight "was not above the limit for best physiological efficiency." They[7] have also studied the requirements of minks for vitamin D, and they found that 0.82 I.U. per gram of food was sufficient, provided that the calcium to phosphorus ratio was between 0.75:1.00 and 1.70:1.00.

[5] H. E. Bechtel, E. T. Hallman, C. F. Huffman, and C. W. Duncan, Mich. Agr. Expt. Sta. Tech. Bull. 150 (1936).
[6] L. E. Harris, C. F. Bassett, and C. F. Wilke, J. Nutrition 43, 153 (1951).
[7] C. F. Bassett, L. E. Harris, and C. F. Wilke, J. Nutrition 44, 433 (1951).

B. OF HUMAN BEINGS

BENJAMIN KRAMER and ABRAM KANOF

In general terms the amount of vitamin D required by any human being is the amount needed to permit normal growth and mineralization of the bones and teeth during infancy and childhood and to maintain these structures during later life, as well as to meet the increased demands of infection, pregnancy, and lactation. Specifically, the determining factors for vitamin D requirement are the varying capacity of people of various ages to absorb and retain calcium, the rate of growth of the individual, and the adequacy of the diet as regards not only the absolute amounts of calcium and inorganic phosphorus but also the ratio of the elements to each other in the diet. The nature of the compound of calcium or phosphorus may determine the availability of the element for absorption by the intestine or utilization by the tissues. Thus the less soluble calcium salts are more poorly absorbed than are the more soluble ones. In phytin the phosphorus is almost completely unavailable. Inorganic phosphorus is better absorbed than organic phosphorus from the gastrointestinal tract even in osteomalacia.

However, a high Ca/P ratio means poor phosphorus absorption, whereas a very low ratio means poor calcium absorption, especially where the intestinal contents are alkaline in reaction. Similarly, any cation such as aluminum or Fe which tends to form poorly soluble phosphorus compounds will interfere with phosphorus absorption. The proportions of protein, fat, and carbohydrate in the diet influence calcium and phosphorus absorption through their effect on the reaction of the intestinal contents. Little is known regarding the mechanism of absorption of calcium salts, but the less favorable the condition for calcium and phosphorus absorption the more vitamin D will be required to ensure optimal utilization of available materials.

Roughly, the daily need for calcium is 0.1 g. throughout infancy,[8] 0.3 g. during childhood, and 0.5 g. during adolescence.[9] The actual amount required by an individual will depend directly on his rate of growth, hence the tendency of the rapidly growing infant to develop rickets under conditions in which the adult will be free of disease. The prematurely born infant is born with a minimal store of calcium and phosphorus, and in addition under proper conditions his rate of growth is greater than that of the fullterm infant. He then suffers from a double handicap, namely, a greater need of bone-forming minerals and vitamin D, with a decreased capacity for absorption of these substance. The fetal need for calcium during the last

[8] White House Conference Reports: II Nutrition, p. 196. Century Co., New York, 1932.
[9] I. Leitch, *Nutrition Abstr. & Revs.* **6**, 533 (1937).

month of gestation is 0.3 g. daily. A newborn premature infant simply cannot ingest enough calcium to enable him to retain this amount plus the extra amount needed for his rapid growth. Such an infant will need large doses of vitamin D to prevent rickets.[10]

The infant fed on the usual cow's milk dilutions ingests an enormous amount of calcium and inorganic phosphorus per square meter of body surface as compared to the adult or the breast-fed infant. However, the Ca/P ratio of cow's milk is far from optimal and at times may be dangerous, whereas the breast-fed infant, although receiving a much smaller amount of bone-forming elements, ingests these materials in a more optimal ratio and in amounts which do not tax the calcium and inorganic phosphorus homeostatic mechanism of the kidney. It is perhaps this which explains the lower incidence of rickets and ricketic tetany in breast-fed infants. More than 95 % of ingested calcium goes to form bone. For this purpose an amount of phosphorus equal to about 50 % of retained calcium is needed. Since phosphorus plays an important role in all intracellular chemical processes, an additional amount of phosphorus is needed by the cells. In addition to this factor, it seems also that the requirement of a breast-fed infant for phosphorus is generally less than that of one fed on cow's milk.

Infections may be associated with deficiency of blood calcium and inorganic phosphorus, even when ordinarily adequate amounts of vitamin D are ingested.

For a clearer understanding of the problem of vitamin D dosage in the human being, it is important to differentiate between the prevention and the cure of vitamin D deficiency (rickets) and also to determine whether we are dealing with an organism that is initially normal or one suffering from visceral or other disease or immaturity of vital organs. For practical reasons, an adequate preventive dose of vitamin D is one that will prevent all clinical and radiographic evidence of rickets whereas a therapeutic dose is one that will re-establish normal calcification and bone growth and in due time correct most of the deformities of the disease. Some telltale radiographic evidence may persist in spite of adequate dosage, and occasionally gross changes may require surgical intervention or other forms of therapy. A dose of vitamin D that will cure rickets is also adequate to prevent the disease.

For the prevention of rickets in the average normal infant 1000 units of vitamin D given daily orally either as a concentrated fish oil or as vitamin D dispersed in water will suffice. Vitamin D-enriched milk containing 400 U.S.P. units per liter is now widely used either with fresh cow's milk, evaporated, or dried milk. The advantage of vitamin D-enriched milk is that

[10] P. C. Jeans and G. Stearns, The Vitamins, p. 493. American Medical Association, Chicago, 1939.

calcium and phosphorus are ingested simultaneously and in a fixed ratio to each other and to vitamin D. When concentrated forms of vitamin D are used they should preferably be given in water-dispersed form in doses of 3000 units per day because of possible defective absorption of some fats and fat-soluble vitamins. Occasionally, larger doses are required. The actual amounts may have to be determined by the method of trial and error, controlled with serial x-rays of the extremities and repeated determinations of plasma, calcium, inorganic phosphorus, and phosphatase. Prematurely born infants may require a somewhat larger dose.

This therapy should be continued throughout the year, rather than depend on chance solar irradiation during the summer months. When mothers cannot be depended upon to continue this medication or where conditions exist that make adequate medical supervision impossible or in the presence of prolonged infection, the large single dose of 600,000 units every 6 months apparently may be used with favorable results. Clinical and pathological studies show that there is little risk of hypervitaminosis with such therapy.

For the treatment of rickets in the otherwise normal child a similar dose will suffice. Vitamin D highly dispersed in milk or in water seems to be more effective than when administered as a concentrated fish oil. As little as 400 units of vitamin D in milk will in due time cure the majority of ricketic children. When administered as vitamin D in oil, 1000 units daily is usually required. It is important that the diet contain adequate amounts of calcium and phosphorus, preferably in a 2 : 1 ration, as well as a mixture of good proteins.

Where rickets persists in spite of adequate vitamin D dosage, an explanation must be sought in a careful study of the organism itself. A number of such refractory cases have been described, and many of these have been subjected to exhaustive metabolic study. Defects of absorption (coeliac disease, cystic fibrosis of the pancreas, sprue, idiopathic steatorrhea, intestinal shunts, intestinal anomalies, ulcerative colitis) may explain the refractory state.

Where bile fails to enter the intestinal tract, as in acquired common duct obstruction, congenital absence of bile ducts, or atresia of these structures or biliary fistulae, absorption of fat-soluble vitamins, including vitamin D is impaired and rickets may fail to respond to the usual doses of vitamin D. Similarly, in cases of liver damage, as in cirrhosis, additional vitamin D may be needed both to prevent as well as to cure rickets. For the child with defective intestinal absorption the vitamin is preferably given in the form of a water dispersion.

In some unknown manner infections may reduce the Ca $\times$ P product in the blood plasma, giving rise to ricketic changes in the bones that are demonstrable histologically but not clinically or radiologically. Subsidence of the infection results in a correction of the plasma calcium and inorganic phosphorus concentration and healing of the ricketic lesion in the bones. Increased dosage of vitamin D or its administration in highly dispersed form in a watery dispersion or parenteral administration of the vitamin may solve the difficulty in some of these cases. In other cases functional disease of the kidney or diseases of the parathyroids may explain the persistence of the ricketic state and its progress in spite of therapy. In some instances much larger doses of vitamin D will suffice, whereas in others supplementation of vitamin D with other substances is required. In one such case, Albright, Butler, and Bloomberg found it necessary to increase the daily dose of vitamin D to 1,500,000 units in order to initiate healing and to give 150,000 units daily in order to maintain the normal state. However, before one concludes that a patient has refractory rickets, one must be certain that he is not dealing with some endocrine imbalance (hyperparathyroidism) or some other abnormality such as a disturbance of acid-base equilibrium, renal insufficiency, hypercalcemic rickets, liver damage, the De Toni-Fanconi syndrome, the hyperplastic form of chondrodystrophy, or rickets due to a disturbance of cysteine metabolism or due to biliary obstruction.

Refractoriness due to chronic acidosis should be treated with alkalies in addition to large doses of vitamin D. Some cases of chronic acidosis are due to a defect in the ammonia-producing mechanism in the renal tubules. This is corrected by the administration of large amounts of base such as sodium, potassium, calcium, or magnesium, an alkaline ash-yielding diet, along with adequate doses of vitamin D, or simple sodium bicarbonate or citrate. A form of rickets associated with chronic renal disease and hyperchloremia has been described. This responds to a mixture of sodium citrate and citric acid, in addition to massive doses of vitamin D. In the De Toni-Fanconi syndrome there is evidence of renal tubular dysfunction. There is normal excretion of ammonia, but the blood shows a low bicarbonate, evidence of compensated acidosis, marked and persistent hypophosphatemia, occasional hypocalcemia, and, in the later stages, a decrease in the blood sodium, potassium, and chlorides. Treatment is ineffective.

Although the practice is widespread of discontinuing prophylactic use of the vitamin after the age of 2, when a mixed diet is ingested, Park's studies have demonstrated histological evidence of rickets in children even up to 14 years.[11] This would indicate the need for the continuance of supplementary vitamin D up to that age, in doses about half that for infants. Normal adults may rely on sunshine and incidental ingestion of the vitamin, but women during pregnancy and lactation require about 1000 units daily to avoid the deleterious effects of vitamin D deficiency.

Single massive doses of vitamin D sometimes may be used. This method

[11] R. H. Follis, Jr., D. Jackson, M. M. Eliot, and E. A. Park, *Am. J. Diseases Children* **66**, 1 (1943).

is advised when the mother cannot be trusted to give oral medication regularly, or when rapid healing of rickets is indicated, as in thoracic rickets, or in rickets complicated by pneumonia or whooping cough, when the persistence of the ricketic state is itself a menace to the life of the child. It is especially useful in tetany. For the single massive dose therapy 600,000 units may be given orally or by intramuscular injection. Post-mortem studies have failed to reveal any detectable harm from such therapy.

Although the primary indication for the use of vitamin D is the prevention and treatment of rickets and infantile tetany, there is some evidence that the use of this vitamin may also help in the normal development of the teeth.

In recent years vitamin D has been used extensively, usually in massive doses, in the treatment of diseases having no obvious relationship to rickets, tetany, or dental caries. Favorable results have been reported in intestinal, bone, and lymph-node tuberculosis,[12] in arthritis,[13] in acne vulgaris,[14] in hay fever,[15] in asthma and urticaria,[16] in psoriasis,[17] in the prevention of anterior poliomyelitis;[18] in the treatment of toxemia of pregnancy,[19] and in the amelioration of the bleeding tendency in obstructive jaundice.[20] More recently, Pascher has summarized the evidence in favor of vitamin D in the treatment of lupus vulgaris.[21] Sobel and his coworkers have studied the role of vitamin D in experimental lead poisoning.[22] It should be emphasized that some of these therapeutic reports have by no means been substantiated, and that most of the instances of vitamin D poisoning have arisen in the course of such treatment.

Table XIII summarizes the forms in which vitamin D may be given, and the daily doses required for prevention and treatment of rickets.

[12] B. L. Wyatt, R. A. Hicks, and H. E. Thompson, *Ann. Internal Med.* **10**, 534 (1936).

[13] B. L. Wyatt, R. A. Hicks, and H. E. Thompson, *Ann. Internal Med.* **10**, (1936); I. Dreyer and C. I. Reed, *Arch. Phys. Therapy* **16**, 537 (1935); E. G. Vritak and R. S. Lang, *J. Am. Med. Assoc.* **106**, 1162 (1936).

[14] C. A. Simpson, F. A. Ellis, and H. Kirby-Smith, *Arch. Dermatol. and Syphilol.* **41**, 835 (1940); M. B. Sulzberger, Year Book of Dermatology and Syphilology, p. 14. Year Book Publishers, Chicago, 1949; F. C. Combes, *Med. Times*, Chicago **77**, 473 (1949).

[15] B. Z. Rappaport and C. I. Reed, *J. Am. Med. Assoc.* **101**, 105 (1933).

[16] B. Z. Rappaport, C. I. Reed, M. L. Hathaway, and H. C. Struck, *J. Allergy* **5**, 541 (1934).

[17] L. Olivetti and E. Ratto, *Giorn ital. dermatol. e sifilol.* **90**, 187 (1949); H. Schmitz, *Praxis* **36**, 307 (1947); J. Krafka, Jr., *J. Lab. Clin. Med.* **21**, 1147 (1936); E. T. Cedar and L. Zon, *Publ. Health Repts.* (*U. S.*) **52**, 1580 (1937).

[18] J. A. Toomey, *Am. J. Diseases Children* **53**, 1202 (1937).

[19] G. W. Theobold, *Lancet* **I**, 1397 (1937).

[20] L. B. Johnston, *J. Med.* **18**, 235 (1937).

[21] F. Pascher, M. G. Silverberg, I. E. Marks, and J. Markel, *J. Invest. Dermatol.* **13**, 89 (1949).

[22] A. E. Sobel, H. Yuska, D. D. Peters, and B. Kramer, *J. Biol. Chem.* **132**, 239 (1940).

TABLE XIII
Vitamin D Dosage

Form of vitamin D	Vitamin concentration, U.S.P. units	Daily dose prophylaxis against rickets			Daily dose for treatment of rickets	Normal adult dosage	Dosage during pregnancy or lactation	Method of manufacture	Advantages or disadvantages; comments
		Full-term infant	Premature	Childhood					
Mother's milk	Variable	Does not always protect against rickets.	It is best to ignore the amount of vitamin D in the milk.	Supplementary vitamin is usually indicated.	It is best to ignore the vitamin D in the milk when treating rickets or tetany.				
Irradiated vitamin D milk	135 to 200 per reconstituted quart	Estimate amount of vitamin D taken in milk and administer enough of a concentrate to bring the total to 1200 units.				1 or 2 glasses will probably meet ordinary adult requirements.	1 quart daily will probably meet requirements.	Milk—fresh, evaporated or dry—in thin layers is exposed to artificial light.	The vitamin is taken in in a natural food. Enough of the milk must be taken if a sufficient dose is to be received. Adequate calcium and phosphorus should be ingested with the vitamin D.
Metabolized vitamin D milk	400 per quart							Irradiated yeast fed to cows.	
Fortified vitamin D milk	400 per quart							To milk is added nonsaponifiable fish liver oils or viosterol itself.	

Preparation					daily		Manufacture	Remarks
						known, but suggested dosage is 5 drops. Additional amounts required for: a. pregnant and lactating women b. persons confined indoors c. persons on calcium-poor diet (no milk) d. the aged e. persons with fractures or after bone operations		use in prematures. Taste objectionable. Aspiration may lead to lipoid pneumonia.
Viosterol in oil	222 per drop	6 drops	From 10 drops to 1 teaspoon, depending on monthly survey of evidences of normal development:	4 drops	Dosage depends on degree of disease and rapidity with which a cure is needed. From 10 drops to 1 teaspoon of the concentrates. Afterprogress of the disease has been stopped, taper off the dose. High doses required in: a. prematures b. thoracic rickets c. refractory rickets Treat infantile tetany with the same dosage of vitamin D but administer calcium salts during the first week of treatment.		Ergosterol (irradiated or bombarded by low-velocity electrons, and dissolved in oil).	Tasteless; small amounts needed. No vitamin A.
Viosterol in propylene glycol	222 per drop	6 drops		4 drops			Manufactured as above but dissolved in propylene glycol.	Can be mixed directly with milk.
Halibut liver oil enriched with viosterol	222 per drop	6 drops	a. serum calcium over 9 mg.% c. phosphorus over 5 mg.% d. absence of clinical signs of rickets	4 drops			To halibut liver oil, rich in vitamin A, is added viosterol enough to give the high concentration of vitamin D.	Advantages of viosterol in oil but also has vitamin A.
Percomorph oil	222 per drop	6 drops		6 drops			A mixture of natural oils, the final product being as rich in vitamin D as irradiated ergosterol, and also rich in vitamin A.	A natural oil having advantages of viosterol plus high concentration of vitamin A.
Vitamin D dispersed in water	222 per drop	—	—		Same as other concentrates. Preferable in cases of defective fat absorption: coeliac disease, fibrocystic disease of the pancreas, obstructive jaundice, etc.		A dispersion of vitamin D and A, usually from fish oils, with added vitamin C and B complex; dispersing agent Tween 80.	Miscible with milk; tasteless. More readily absorbed. Gives higher vitamin A levels in blood and greater storage in the liver.
Eggs	Variable	3 egg yolks daily	—	3 egg yolks daily	Same	No studies available	Vitamin D content varies with amount of vitamin D in hen's diet and amount of irradiation.	Is part of well-balanced diet.

1. Hypervitaminosis D

The pathologic effects of overdosage with vitamin D have been studied chiefly in individuals who have received massive doses of calciferol in the treatment of arthritis. In children there have been additional cases reported as a side effect of vitamin D treatment for tuberculosis or after receiving imperfectly irradiated ergosterol preparations containing large amounts of toxic intermediates (vigantol). The basic pathologic effect is the precipitation of calcium in various tissues. As a result of metastatic calcification in the kidneys, kidney insufficiency may develop. Finally, withdrawal of large amounts of calcium into these abnormal foci may result in demineralization of bone.

The gross and histologic findings have been frequently reported and are similar in both children and adults, although fatalities seem to occur more frequently in the young. There is diffuse calcinosis affecting the joints, synovial membranes, kidneys, myocardium, pulmonary alveoli, parathyroid glands, pancreas, skin, lymph glands, large and medium-sized arteries, the conjunctivae and cornea, and the acid-secreting portion of the stomach. The abnormal calcification can be seen grossly as a whitish, chalky material. The bones in the early stages may show accelerated calcification of the provisional zone of calcification with thickening of the periosteum. In more advanced cases, however, there is interference with cartilage growth, and several authors[23] have demonstrated diffuse demineralization of the bones. Shelling and Asher[24] pointed out that osteoporosis produced by hypervitaminosis differs from that produced by parathormone in that the resorbed areas are not replaced by fibrous tissue. Freeman et al.[25] have reported an instance in a child in which doses of ertron resulted in a negative calcium balance. The most serious involvement is that of the kidneys, and most of the fatal cases terminated in uremia. The best evidence seems to indicate that the initial kidney damage is due to deposition of calcium in the basement membranes of the cells of the distal tubules.[26] There results an inflammatory reaction, and later complete obstruction. As a result of the obstruction, several nephrons at first dilate and then atrophy. As a result of the inflammatory reaction, the lesion may spread rapidly through the entire kidney. The kidney damage in turn is responsible for such pathology as hypertension, hypertensive retinopathy, and chemical evidence of renal insufficiency.

[23] D. H. Shelling, The Parathyroids in Health and Disease. C. V. Mosby Co., St. Louis, 1935.

[24] D. H. Shelling, and D. Remsen, *Bull. Johns Hopkins Hosp.* **57**, 158 (1935).

[25] S. Freeman, P. S. Rhoads, and L. B. Yeager, *J. Am. Med. Assoc.* **130**, 197 (1946).

[26] R. H. Freyberg and J. M. Bauer, *Univ. Hosp. Bull. (Michigan)* **11**, 61 (1945); T. S. Danowski, A. W. Winkler, and J. P. Peters, *Ann. Internal Med.* **23**, 22 (1945).

The dosages administered before evidence of intoxication appeared varied tremendously. As little as 400 units daily seemed to have produced fatal pathology in one instance. The shortest length of time over which the vitamin had been given before demonstrable calcification was produced was 14 days. The problem as to whether the toxic effects are due to the vitamin D itself or to contaminating sterols cannot be answered. However, it has been shown that pure, crystalline vitamin D, or any factor which can cause an increase in the serum ionic calcium can produce toxic symptoms. Albright and Reifenstein[27] ascribed all the manifestations of hypervitaminosis D to an exaggeration of the normal action of the vitamin: (a) to an increase in the absorption of calcium from the gastrointestinal tract, and (b) to an increase in the urinary excretion of phosphorus.

Clinical symptoms in non-fatal cases are anorexia, nausea, vomiting, diarrhea, polyuria, weakness, lassitude, headache, hyperesthesia, the appearance of areas of brown pigmentation over the skin, and evidence of renal insufficiency.

There is no agreement as to the mechanism by which the abnormal calcification takes place. Some believe that the first step is the appearance of cellular damage followed by calcium deposition. On the basis of experimental data with rats it is believed that abnormal deposition of calcium is the first step. The exact factors which are related to the precipitation of calcium are not known. Abnormal calcification may occur in the presence of a normal total serum clacium.

Conversely a high serum calcium may be present for a long time without the occurrence of precipitation. It has been found that in rats, following administration of large doses of calciferol, there was abnormal calcification while the total serum calcium concentration was on the decline rather than while the level was rising. The explanation seems to be that as the serum calcium declined there was a rapid release of the part of the total calcium held by the parathyroids and that this fraction was too great to be held in solution. It would appear, therefore, that a fluctuating serum calcium is more apt to produce abnormal calcification than a high constant level. Calcification is also aided by any factor which produces some degree of alkalosis, as in continued vomiting. Reed et al.[28] have pointed out that patients with gastrointestinal complaints are more susceptible to the toxic effect of vitamin D. Other factors of importance are the dose of vitamin D ingested, the vehicle, the degree of exposure to sunlight, the amount of dietary calcium ingested, the susceptibility of the individual, the pathologic state for which

[27] F. Albright and E. C. Reifenstein, Parathyroid Gland and Metabolic Bone Disease, p. 95. Williams & Wilkins Co., Baltimore, 1948.

[28] C. I. Reed, I. E. Steck. H. C. Struck, and H. Deutsch, *Ann. Internal Med.* **10**, 951 (1937).

the vitamin is administered, the status of the endocrine system, and the age of the patient.

The story of vitamin D, its identification as a separate calcifying vitamin, its isolation in pure form, and its application in eradicating what was a serious and crippling disease, represents a brilliant chapter in sterol chemistry, in nutritional physiology, and in clinical medicine. However, little is known as to its action. In some mysterious manner it facilitates the absorption of calcium from the intestinal tract and deposits it as a phosphate or carbonate in osteoid and cartilage matrix. It controls in part the clearance of inorganic phosphorus by the kidney, and still more remarkably it molds the deformed tissue of the ricketic animal into a normal configuration and pattern characteristic of the involved tissue. Little is known concerning the mechanism of absorption of the vitamin itself, its manner of transport, or its storage in the tissues. Much has been revealed, much still remains to be discovered. Newer methods are needed for these studies.

Chapter 7

ESSENTIAL FATTY ACIDS

I. Nomenclature and Formulas

ROBERT S. HARRIS

Accepted names: Essential fatty acids
Obsolete name: Vitamin F
Empirical formulas: Linoleic acid: $C_{18}H_{32}O_2$
                   Linolenic acid: $C_{18}H_{30}O_2$
                   Arachidonic acid: $C_{20}H_{32}O_2$
Chemical names: Linoleic acid: $\Delta9,12$-octadecadienoic acid
                   Linolenic acid: $\Delta9,12,15$-octadecatrienoic acid
                   Arachidonic acid: $\Delta5,8,11,14$-eicosatetraenoic acid
Structural formulas:

$$CH_3(CH_2)_4CH=CHCH_2CH=CH(CH_2)_7COOH$$
Linoleic acid

$$CH_3CH_2CH=CHCH_2CH=CHCH_2CH=CH(CH_2)_7COOH$$
Linolenic acid

$$CH_3(CH_2)_4CH=CHCH_2CH=CHCH_2CH=CHCH_2CH=CH(CH_2)_3COOH$$
Arachidonic acid

II. Chemistry

RALPH T. HOLMAN

Rigid exclusion of fat from an otherwise adequate diet of a variety of animals results in the delayed appearance of a deficiency syndrome first described in 1929 by Burr and Burr.[1a] This deficiency has been shown to be caused by the lack of certain fatty acids which have come to be called the essential fatty acids. Incorporation of these acids in the diet either prevents or cures the deficiency symptoms. Although the fat deficiency phenomenon parallels vitamin deficiency phenomena, the term *vitamin* has not been generally applied to the essential fatty acids, probably because they are required in larger quantity than are most vitamins.

Fatty acid deficiency and the essential fatty acids have been the subject

[1a] G. O. Burr and M. M. Burr, *J. Biol. Chem.* **82,** 345 (1929).

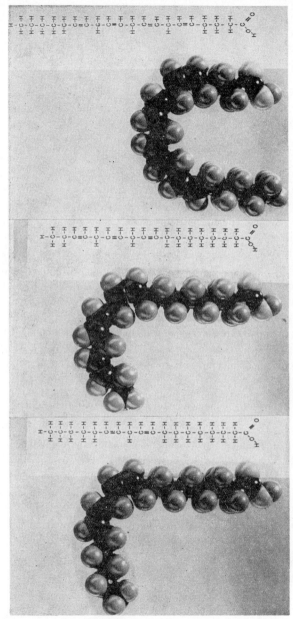

FIG. 1. Molecular models and conventional formulas for linoleic, linolenic, and arachidonic acids.

of several previous reviews to which the reader is referred.[1b-4] In the present treatment, the discussion of the essential fatty acids and the deficiency phenomenon caused by their absence from the diet of animals will be general, reference being made only to selected papers from which the reader can obtain more detailed reference.

The essential fatty acids are a group of naturally occurring polyunsaturated fatty acids, some of whose structures are well established. They possess the common structure of methylene-interrupted polyunsaturation. The group is generally regarded as consisting of three members, linoleic acid (9,12-octadecadienoic acid), linolenic acid (9,12,15-octadecatrienoic acid), and arachidonic acid (probably 5,8,11,14-eicosatetraenoic acid). However, the higher polyunsaturated acids, clupanodonic acid and docosahexaenoic acid, are closely related to the essential fatty acids and should be included with them in the more general sense of the classification. Molecular models and conventional structural formulas for the first three acids are shown in Fig. 1. Linoleic and linolenic acids are of vegetable origin and are probably the dietary precursors of the animal polyunsaturated acids. Arachidonic acid is found only in animal lipids and is probably a functional essential fatty acid. As will be mentioned later, linoleic and linolenic acids are not entirely equivalent in action, and linoleic acid is the only vegetable acid which meets all the requirements of the animal for essential fatty acid. Thus, it is apparent that the term essential fatty acids, as ordinarily used, is generic, including many members not equivalent in metabolic action. As more information is gained regarding the roles of the various acids, best usage will require their individual names.

A. ISOLATION

Linoleic acid is a major constituent of a variety of vegetable oils. Excellent sources of the acid for preparative purposes are corn oil, cottonseed oil, and safflower seed oil, in which little or no conjugated or more highly unsaturated acids are found. The problem in isolation is the separation of linoleic acid from saturated and unsaturated acids of various chain lengths. The various acids present in such mixtures have such slight differences in chemical and physical properties that separation is a difficult procedure, and the product gained is rarely pure.

The classical procedure for linoleic acid preparation is the bromination-

[1b] G. O. Burr, *Federation Proc.* **1**, 224 (1942).

[2] A. E. Hansen and G. O. Burr, *J. Am. Med. Assoc.* **132**, 855 (1946).

[3] R. T. Holman, *Proc. 3rd. Conf. on Research, Am. Meat Inst. Univ. Chicago* p. 1 (1951); *Fette u. Seifen* **53**, 332 (1951).

[4] R. T. Holman, *Symposium on Biol. Significance of Lipids*, Robert Gould Research Foundation, 1950.

debromination method of Rollet.[5] Advantage is taken of the differences in petroleum ether solubility of tetrabromostearic acid formed from linoleic acid and the solubilities of the saturated acids and the dibromostearic acid formed from oleic acid. This method has been carefully worked out and standardized by McCutcheon.[6] Best practice requires constant protection of the unsaturated material from oxygen. Thus during saponification, debromination, washing, and transferring, the material should be kept under a blanket of nitrogen. The resulting methyl ester after final distillation through an efficient fractionation column should have an iodine number of 172 to 173, less than 0.1 % conjugated acids, and consist of only C_{18} acid. Preparations of linoleate or more highly unsaturated acids should always be kept in evacuated or nitrogen-filled ampules at low temperature to prevent oxidation of these very easily oxidizable esters or acids.

Rollet[7] and McCutcheon[8] have developed similar bromination-debromination procedures for preparation of linolenic acid from the acids of linseed oil. Arachidonic acid is prepared by bromination-debromination of the acids from beef adrenal phospholipids[9] or from fresh hog liver fatty acids. With these preparations the danger of oxidation is even greater and extreme care must be taken to prevent entry of oxygen. The quality of the preparation is roughly indicated by its color—the lighter the color, the better the preparation. Spectral absorption should be low in the ultraviolet, and iodine number should be close to theoretical. Hydrogen number is a better characteristic constant for the highly unsaturated acids than is iodine number.

Low-temperature crystallization methods developed by Brown and his coworkers[10-12] provide a means of preparing these acids without danger of isomerization by chemical treatment. The low-temperature crystallization methods yield natural isomers, but numerous recrystallizations are required to approach purity.

Chromatographic procedures yield very pure natural products, but as yet the method has not been used on a large scale. Swift et al. and Riemenschneider et al. have prepared linoleate[13] and linolenate [14] in a high degree of

[5] A. Rollet, *Hoppe-Seyler's Z. physiol. Chem.* **62**, 410 (1909).

[6] J. W. McCutcheon *Org. Syntheses* **22**, 75 (1942).

[7] A. Rollet, *Hoppe-Seyler's Z. physiol. Chem.* **62**, 422 (1909).

[8] J. W. McCutcheon, *Org. Syntheses* **22**, 82 (1942).

[9] W. C. Ault and J. B. Brown, *J. Biol. Chem.* **107**, 615 (1934).

[10] J. B. Brown and J. Frankel, *J. Am. Chem. Soc.* **60**, 54 (1938).

[11] G. Y. Shinowara and J. B. Brown, *J. Am. Chem. Soc.* **60**, 2734 (1938).

[12] D. T. Mowry, W. R. Brode, and J. B. Brown, *J. Biol. Chem.* **142**, 671 (1942).

[13] C. E. Swift, W. G. Rose, and G. S. Jamieson, *Oil & Soap* **20**, 249 (1943).

[14] R. W. Riemenschneider, S. F. Herb, and P. L. Nichols, *J. Am. Oil Chemists' Soc.* **26**, 371 (1949).

purity for use as analytical standards, and White and Brown[15] and Herb
et al.[16] have isolated arachidonate by chromatography for the same purpose.
Of the methods available, chromatography yields the purest product, but
can handle only small amounts. Bromination-debromination is most convenient for preparing large quantities, but the product contains isomers of
the desired unsaturated acid.

B. SYNTHESIS

Only linoleic acid of the polyunsaturated acids has yielded to a total
synthesis. Noller and Girvin[17] and Baudart[18] have succeeded in the synthesis of an unnatural isomer of 9,12-octadecadienoic acid by condensation
methods. More recently Walborsky et al.[19] synthesized natural cis,cis-
linoleic acid through acetylenic compounds:

$$C_5H_{11}C{\equiv}CCH_2Br \; + \; BrMgC{\equiv}C(CH_2)_7CH \begin{array}{c} OCH_2 \\ | \\ | \\ OCH_2 \end{array} \quad \xrightarrow{Cu_2Br_2}$$

$$C_5H_{11}C{\equiv}C{-}CH_2C{\equiv}C(CH_2)_7CH \begin{array}{c} OCH_2 \\ | \\ | \\ OCH_2 \end{array}$$

$$\downarrow \text{hydrolysis}$$

$$C_5H_{11}C{\equiv}C{-}CH_2{-}C{\equiv}C(CH_2)_7CHO$$

$$\xleftarrow{AgNO_3}$$

$$C_5H_{11}C{\equiv}C{-}CH_2{-}C{\equiv}C(CH_2)_7COOH \quad \xleftarrow{H_2}$$

cis,cis-9,12-octadecadienoic acid

This latter synthesis will be useful in the preparation of radioactively
labeled linoleic acid for use in pertinent metabolic studies.

C. COMMERCIAL PREPARATIONS

The investigator should be critical of the source of commercially available
linoleic, linolenic, or arachidonic acids. Products available commercially
under the name of linoleic acid are far from pure and in all likelihood are
merely corn oil or cottonseed oil fatty acids. One such preparation labeled
C.P. linoleic acid was analyzed in the author's laboratory and found to

[15] M. F. White and J. B. Brown, J. Am. Chem. Soc. 70, 4269 (1948).
[16] S. F. Herb, R. W. Riemenschneider, and J. Donaldson, J. Am. Oil Chemists' Soc.
28, 55 (1951).
[17] C. R. Noller and M. D. Girvin, J. Am. Chem. Soc. 59, 606 (1937).
[18] P. Baudart, Bull. soc. chim. [5] 11, 336 (1944).
[19] H. M. Walborsky, R. H. Davis, and R. Howton, J. Am. Chem. Soc. 73, 2590 (1951).

contain less than 50 % linoleic acid. It was packaged in an ordinary screw-cap bottle and thus had access to oxygen of the air. The essential fatty acids and their compounds are readily attacked by oxygen, and any preparation which is not stored in an ampule or sealed under nitrogen or under vacuum should not be accepted as pure. To the writer's knowledge, the only source of authentic bromination-debromination linoleic and linolenic acids and their esters is the Hormel Foundation of Austin, Minnesota. Arachidonate concentrate containing a maximum of 70 % arachidonic acid was once available from the Nutritional Biochemicals Corporation.

D. CHEMICAL PROPERTIES

The polyunsaturated acids belonging to the essential fatty acid group are similar in their properties. Chemically their reactivity is restricted to reactions of double bonds and of carboxyl groups, and segregation of these acids on the basis of chemical reaction is difficult and only partial. For practical purposes, there is negligible difference between the carboxyl reactivities of the various members of the group, and all separative procedures based upon chemical reactivity utilize the differences in the number of double bonds of the various members of the group. Thus, the preparation of linoleate is based upon the insolubility of tetrabromostearic acid in petroleum ether, and the preparation of linolenic acid is based upon the insolubility of hexabromostearic acid and the solubility of tetrabromostearic acid in ethyl ether. The more highly unsaturated acids form polybromides which are all virtually insoluble in ether, and thus separation of the higher members of the series is impossible by this method. For example, arachidonic acid prepared by bromination-debromination always contains a considerable amount of pentaenoic acid.

All the essential fatty acids add halogens, and this reaction is the basis of the commonest method for determination of total unsaturation. Various halogenating reagents have been employed for the addition reaction, but the results are expressed as grams of iodine absorbed per 100 g. of fat, and the value is called the iodine value.

Thiocyanogen also adds to double bonds, but not to all double bonds, presumably because of steric hindrance. Thus oleic acid adds one mole of thiocyanogen, linoleic acid adds one, and linolenic acid adds two. The thiocyanogen value, combined with the iodine value, can be used to calculate the linoleic acid content of fats.

The unsaturated linkages in the essential fatty acids are readily hydrogenated, and in hydrogenated vegetable oils the essential fatty acid content is reduced. Partial hydrogenation disproportionately reduces the essential fatty acid content of fats, for the polyunsaturated acids are preferentially hydrogenated. Although hydrogenation of essential fatty acids is the basis of preparation of shortenings from liquid vegetable oils, the resultant products contain essential fatty acids in quantities in the same order as that found in other edible fats.[20]

The essential fatty acids, which contain only *cis* double bonds, can be catalytically converted by selenium isomerization to *trans* forms. The isomerization has been accomplished on both linoleic[21] and linolenic[22] acids. The isomers thus formed have no biological value, although they are metabolized by the animal.[23]

Treatment of the essential acids with alkali at high temperatures causes the double bonds to shift, yielding conjugated isomers. Because such conjugated polyenes possess strong ultraviolet absorption, this reaction has been made the basis of a spectrophotometric method for the analysis of the essential acids. The conjugated acids themselves have no biological potency.

The saponification and esterification reactions are the only important carboxyl reactions of the essential fatty acids. However, the differences in saponification or esterification rates of the different long-chain acids are so small as to be of no practical importance. For discussion of these reactions, the reader is referred to Markley.[24]

E. OXIDATION

The polyene acids are highly susceptible to oxidative rancidity. After a variable induction period, the oxygen absorption increases autocatalytically. The maximum rates of oxidation of the various polyunsaturated acids increase with each additional double bond in the molecule, so that with arachidonic acid autoxidation is very rapid. In Fig. 2 the rates of oxidation of the esters of essential fatty acids are compared with ethyl oleate. The rates of oxidation are roughly $1:40:100:200$ for oleate, linoleate, linolenate, and arachidonate, respectively.[25]

The autoxidation of the essential fatty acids is accompanied by radical changes in the ultraviolet absorption spectrum.[26] The major changes are development of a strong absorption in the conjugated diene region (2340 A.) and a smaller increase around 2700 A. The former has been shown to be due to the conjugated diene hydroperoxide which is the primary product of oxidation, and the latter is probably due to unsaturated ketonic sec-

[20] H. J. Deuel, Jr., S. M. Greenberg, L. Anisfeld, and D. Melnick, *J. Nutrition* **45**, 535 (1951).

[21] J. P. Kass and G. O. Burr, *J. Am. Chem. Soc.* **61**, 1062 (1939).

[22] J. P. Kass, J. Nichols, and G. O. Burr, *J. Am. Chem. Soc.* **63**, 1060(1941).

[23] R. T. Holman, *Proc. Soc. Exptl. Biol. Med.* **76**, 100 (1951).

[24] K. S. Markley, Fatty Acids. Interscience Publishers, New York, 1947.

[25] R. T. Holman and O. Elmer, *J. Am. Oil Chemists' Soc.* **24**, 127 (1947).

[26] R. T. Holman and G. O. Burr, *J. Am. Chem. Soc.* **68**, 562 (1946).

ondary products. The general mechanism of oxidation is given on the following page.

For a more detailed discussion of autoxidation of the essential fatty acids, the reader is referred to a recent review.[27]

Oxidative rancidity of edible oils is due largely to the oxidation of the essential acids contained in them. The products of oxidation of these acids, at least in large quantities, are probably harmful, for rancid fats are toxic.

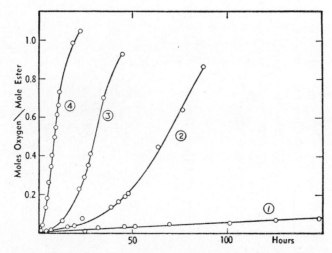

FIG. 2. Rates of oxidation of ethyl oleate (1), ethyl linoleate (2), ethyl linolenate (3), and methyl arachidonate.[25] (4)

F. PHYSICAL PROPERTIES

The essential fatty acids are colorless oils at room temperature. Their light absorption in the ultraviolet region is negligible but increases with decrease in wavelength.[28] These acids do exhibit strong maxima in the vacuum ultraviolet, or Schumann region.[29]

The acids themselves boil under high vacuum with some decomposition, but their esters can conveniently be distilled at pressures of 2 to 4 mm. Hg. They have negligible solubility in water, but are highly soluble in organic solvents such as ether, ethanol, acetone, and chloroform. They form colloidal soap solutions above pH 9. By virtue of their high unsaturation, these compounds have high refractive indexes, and the refractive index

[27] S. Bergström, and R. T. Holman, Advances in Enzymol. 8, 425 (1948).

[28] I. I. Rusoff, R. T. Holman, and G. O. Burr, Oil & Soap 22, 290 (1945).

[29] I. I. Rusoff, J. R. Platt, H. B. Klevens, and G. O. Burr, J. Am. Chem. Soc. 67, 673 (1945).

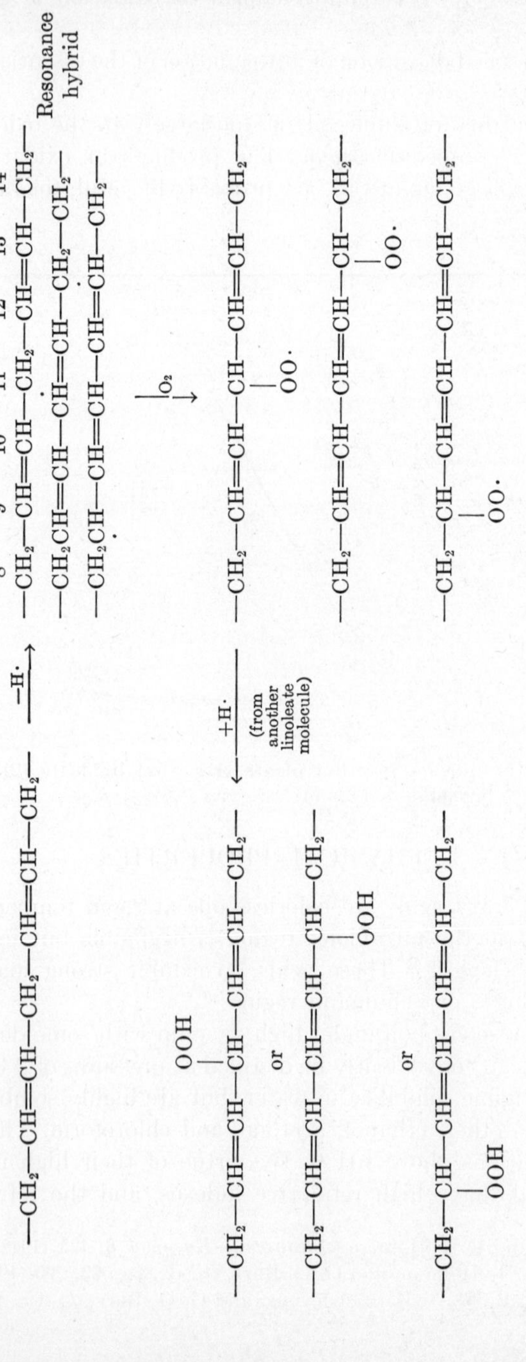

Resonance hybrid

$$8 \quad 9 \quad 10 \quad 11 \quad 12 \quad 13 \quad 14$$

$$-CH_2-CH=CH-CH_2-CH=CH-CH_2- \xrightarrow{-H\cdot}$$

$$-CH_2-CH=CH-CH_2-CH=CH-CH_2-$$

$$\dot{-}CH_2CH=CH-CH=CH-CH_2-CH_2-$$

$$-CH_2CH-CH=CH-CH=CH-CH_2-\cdot$$

$$\xrightarrow{O_2}$$

$$-CH_2-CH=CH-CH-CH=CH-CH_2- \quad | \quad OO\cdot$$

$$-CH_2-CH=CH-CH=CH-CH-CH_2- \quad | \quad OO\cdot$$

$$-CH_2-CH-CH=CH-CH=CH-CH_2- \quad | \quad OO\cdot$$

$$\xrightarrow[\text{(from another linoleate molecule)}]{+H\cdot}$$

$$-CH_2-CH=CH-CH-CH=CH-CH_2- \quad | \quad OOH$$

or

$$-CH_2-CH=CH-CH=CH-CH-CH_2- \quad | \quad OOH$$

or

$$-CH_2-CH-CH=CH-CH=CH-CH_2- \quad | \quad OOH$$

$$-CH_2-CH=CH-CH_2-CH=CH-CH_2-$$

of mixed acids or oils can be used as a measure of the unsaturation. A few important physical and chemical properties are summarized in Table I.

TABLE I

PHYSICAL AND CHEMICAL PROPERTIES OF THE ESSENTIAL FATTY ACIDS

	Linoleic	Linolenic	Arachidonic
Refractive index, 50°	1.4588	1.4678	—
Specific gravity, 20°/4° C.	0.903	0.914	—
Melting point	−5°	−11°	−50°
Boiling point	149.5/1 mm.	—	160–165/1 mm.
	182.4/4 mm.	184/4 mm.	
Molecular weight	280.4	278.4	304.5
Iodine value	181.0	273.5	333.5

III. Biochemical Systems

RALPH T. HOLMAN

The biological role of the essential fatty acids has not yet been elucidated, and only a few pieces of isolated information bear on the matter. The polyunsaturated acids present in animal tissues are found in greater concentration in the phospholipids than in the depot fats,[1, 2] and the concentration of these acids in the total fatty acids of the so-called vital tissues is greater than in the remainder of the carcass or in skeletal muscle. Changes in phospholipid unsaturated fatty acids are greater than corresponding changes in neutral fat fatty acids caused by fat deficiency or supplementation. It appears that these substances are associated with tissue structural elements rather than depot lipids, for alkaline hydrolysis of the tissues gives greater yield of these acids than does exhaustive extraction with solvents.

A study of the effects of fat deficiency upon enzyme systems should reveal some information about the metabolic role of the essential fatty acids. Thus far the effects upon a few enzyme systems have been reported. Hess and Violler[3] found that lipase activity in blood of rats decreases to about half of normal on a fat-deficient diet, but that cholinesterase activity remained unchanged. Kunkel and Williams[4] found that fat deficiency caused an increase in liver cytochrome oxidase activity and an increase in endogenous respiration, whereas succinoxidase activity remained normal. They

[1] I. G. Rieckehoff, R. T. Holman, and G. O. Burr, *Arch. Biochem.* **20,** 331 (1949).
[2] R. Reiser, *J. Nutrition* **42,** 325 (1950).
[3] W. Hess and G. Viollier, *Helv. Chim. Acta* **31,** 381 (1948).
[4] H. O. Kunkel and J. N. Williams, *J. Biol. Chem.* **189,** 755 (1951).

reported that choline oxidase activity rose slightly in the deficient state. With the exception of choline oxidase, all enzyme systems reverted toward normal activities upon the administration of linoleate to the deficient animals. Thus it appears that essential fatty acid is involved in at least some enzyme systems. The lipid in concentrated cytochrome oxidase preparations has been found to contain polyunsaturated fatty acids, and the lipoprotein of blood is subject to autoxidation, as are the polyunsaturated acids, indicating that these acids occur in important lipoprotein structures.

The essential fatty acids are themselves the substrates for a highly specific enzyme in the plant kingdom. The occurrence of this enzyme, lipoxidase, in animal tissues is not conclusively established. For more detailed information concerning this enzyme and its action, the reader is referred to several reviews.[5-7] Lipoxidase attacks compounds in which there is multiple methylene-interrupted unsaturation of all *cis* configuration. The commonest and simplest substrate is linoleate, containing the structure

$$
\begin{array}{c}
-\mathrm{CH} \\
\parallel \\
\mathrm{CH-CH_2-CH} \\
\parallel \\
\mathrm{CH-}
\end{array}
$$

This enzyme is of considerable importance in plant seeds where linoleic and linolenic acids are storage materials, but it is doubtful that the lipoxidase is of much metabolic importance in animal tissue if it exists there, for the potential substrate is largely bound in structural lipid.

IV. Specificity of Action

RALPH T. HOLMAN

There has been considerable uncertainty over the comparative curative values of the various fatty acids and over their minimum daily requirements. Through the mass of collected information it is clear that the polyunsaturated fatty acids are divided into two classes: those that cure skin symptoms and restore growth, and those that restore growth but do not cure skin symptoms.

Linoleic and arachidonic acids both restore growth and cure skin symptoms. Turpeinen[1] reported that arachidonic acid was three times as effective

[5] S. Bergström and R. T. Holman, *Advances in Enzymol.* **8**, 425 (1948).

[6] R. T. Holman and S. Bergström, *in* The Enzymes, Vol. 2, Part 1, Chapter 60. Academic Press, New York, 1951.

[7] W. Franke, *Fette u. Seifen* **52**, 11 (1949).

[1] O. Turpeinen, *J. Nutrition* **15**, 531 (1938).

as linoleic acid, using the method of minimum dose for maximum response. Hume *et al.*[2] found arachidonic acid doubly as effective as linoleic acid when fed at low levels. Tests by Burr *et al.*[3] indicate a slightly greater response

TABLE II

BIOLOGICAL ACTIVITY OF UNSATURATED ACIDS AND THEIR DERIVATIVES

Compound	Growth effect	Skin effect	Water intake	References
cis,cis-9,12-Octadecadienoic acid	+	+	Normal	3
trans,trans-9,12-Octadecadienoic acid	0	0		5, 6
Conjugated linoleic acid	−	−		5-7
10,13-Nonadecadienoic acid	0	0		8
11,14-Eicosadienoic acid	0	0		8
9,10-Octadecadienoic acid	0	0		8
9,11-Octadecadienoic acid	0	0		8
Oleic acid	0	0		9, 10
Elaidic acid	0	0		11
12-Octadecenoic acid	0	0		1
Linoleyl alcohol	+	+		1
Erucic acid	0	0		1
Ricinoleic acid	0	0		1
Linolenic acid	+	0	High	9
Hexahydroxystearic acid	+	0		12
Elaidolinolenic acid	+	0		6, 7
Eleostearic acid	0	0		9
Dioxidostearic	0	0		12
Trihydroxystearic	0	0		12
Tetrahydroxystearic	0	0		12
Chaulmoogric acid	0	0		1, 12
Clupanodonic acid	Toxic			13
Arachidonic acid	+	+	Normal	1, 3
Docosahexaenoic acid	+	0		12
Cod liver oil esters	+	0	High	

[2] E. M. Hume, L. C. A. Nunn, I. Smedley-Maclean, and H. H. Smith. *Biochem. J.* **34**, 379, 384 (1940).

[3] G. O. Burr, J. B. Brown, J. P. Kass, and W. O. Lundberg. *Proc. Soc. Exptl. Biol. Med.* **44**, 242 (1940).

[4] S. M. Greenberg, C. E. Calbert, H. J. Deuel, Jr., and J. B. Brown, *J. Nutrition* **45**, 521 (1951).

[5] G. O. Burr, Chemistry and Medicine, p. 101. University of Minnesota Press, 1940.

[6] R. T. Holman, *Proc. Soc. Exptl. Biol. Med.* **76**, 100 (1951).

[7] R. T. Holman, *Proc. 3rd Conf. on Research, Am. Meat Inst. Univ. Chicago* p. 1 (1951); *Fette u. Seifen* **53**, 332 (1951).

[8] P. Karrer and H. Koenig, *Helv. Chim. Acta* **26**, 619 (1943).

[9] G. O. Burr, M. M. Burr, and E. S. Miller, *J. Biol. Chem.* **97**, 1 (1932).

[10] H. M. Evans and S. Lepkovsky, *J. Biol. Chem.* **96**, 143 (1932).

[11] R. G. Sinclair, *J. Nutrition* **19**, 131 (1940).

[12] E. M. Hume, L. C. A. Nunn, I. Smedley-Maclean, and H. H. Smith, *Biochem. J.* **32**, 2162 (1938).

[13] U. Tange, *Sci. Papers Inst. Phys. Chem. Research* (*Tokyo*) **20**, 13 (1933).

from arachidonic acid than from linoleic acid. Very recent tests in which natural methyl arachidonate, prepared by physical means, was compared with bromination-debromination linoleic acid, seem to indicate that the arachidonate was six times as effective as the linoleic acid in promoting growth (see Greenberg *et al.*[4]). The proper comparison between comparable natural linoleate and arachidonate esters has not yet been made.

Linolenic acid and docosahexaenoic acid restore growth but do not improve the animal's skin condition, indicating that these acids are not able to meet all the metabolic requirements for polyunsaturated fatty acid. Many unsaturated fatty acids and compounds related to them have been tested for potency. The results of such tests are gathered in Table II. From the table it is apparent that only linoleic and arachidonic acids are fully effective in restoring fat-deficient rats to normal, and that linolenic and docosahexaenoic acids allow growth without meeting the requirement for normal skin condition. This points to the dual character of the essential fatty acid deficiency.

V. Biogenesis and Metabolism

RALPH T. HOLMAN

The formation of linoleic and linolenic acids in the plant is generally considered to be a conversion from carbohydrate. The mechanism has not been worked out beyond the observation that in a ripening seed the fat content increases whereas the carbohydrate decreases. The reverse is true during germination,[1] a time when linoleic and linolenic acids are oxidized preferentially, lipoxidase activity is initially high, and catalase activity is temporarily high.

The synthesis of the essential fatty acids in the animal body appears to be a slow and inadequate process. Although many reports indicate that essential fatty acid is not synthesized by the animal,[2, 3] more recent reports indicate that synthesis can take place to a limited degree.[4, 5] The polyunsaturated fatty acids are dietary essentials because the animal cannot synthesize them in sufficient quantity for its needs. The animal, however, is able to make interconversions in the polyunsaturated fatty acids. Smed-

[1] R. T. Holman, *Arch. Biochem.* **17**, 459 (1948).

[2] K. Bernhard, H. Steinhauser, and F. Bullet, *Helv. Chim. Acta* **25**, 83 (1942).

[3] R. Schonheimer, The Dynamic State of Body Constituents, p. 18. Harvard University Press, 1949.

[4] G. Medes and D. C. Keller, *Arch. Biochem.* **15**, 19 (1947).

[5] V. H. Barki, R. A. Collins, E. B. Hart, and C. A. Elvehjem, *Proc. Soc. Exptl. Biol. Med.* **71**, 694 (1949).

ley-Maclean[6] has shown by means of polybromide analysis that the poly-unsaturated acids decrease in rats in a deficiency state and that curing the deficiency with linoleate restores the polyunsaturated content of the animal. By means of the spectrophotometric method of analysis, this has been verified in greater detail, showing that, when supplements of different oils[7] or pure fatty acids[8] are made, changes take place in the polyunsaturated fatty acids in the animal, depending on the substance fed. From these studies it appears that the dominant interconversions in some tissues are the synthesis of arachidonate from linoleate and hexaenoate from linolenate. Increases of pentaenoate were observed in blood and kidney as the result of linolenate supplementation in fat-deficient rats.[8] Hearts of fat-deficient

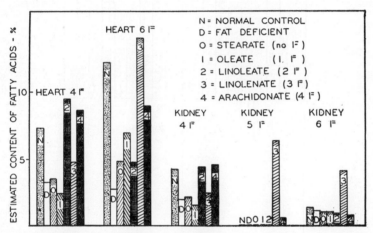

Fig. 3. Changes in the polyunsaturated fatty acids of the heart and kidney as the result of single fatty acid supplementation.[8-10]

rats accumulate a high proportion of trienoic acid which is not normally present.[7] The administration of arachidonate to fat-deficient rats results in its slow deposition.[9] During a period of 7 weeks daily supplementation with 30 mg. of methyl arachidonate, the total arachidonate content of the animals increased equivalent to only 10 % of that fed. The recovery in poly-unsaturated acid content of the animal parallels the slow recovery from the deficiency disease and emphasizes the low rate of turnover of these acids in the tissue. The typical metabolic changes in polyunsaturated acids are il-

[6] I. Smedley-Maclean, The Metabolism of Fat. Methuen & Co., London, 1943. .

[7] I. G. Rieckehoff, R. T. Holman, and G. O. Burr, Arch. Biochem. 20, 331 (1949).

[8] C. Widmer and R. T. Holman, Arch. Biochem. 25, 1 (1950).

[9] R. T. Holman and T. S. Taylor, Arch. Biochem. 29, 295 (1950).

[10] R. T. Holman, Proc. 3rd Conf. on Research, Am. Meat. Inst. Univ. Chicago p. 1 (1951); Fette u. Seifen 53, 332 (1951).

lustrated in Fig. 3, for the fatty acids of heart and kidney, in which these changes are most pronounced.

The metabolic conversions have been studied using some unnatural isomers of the essential fatty acids.[11] The responses to the natural and

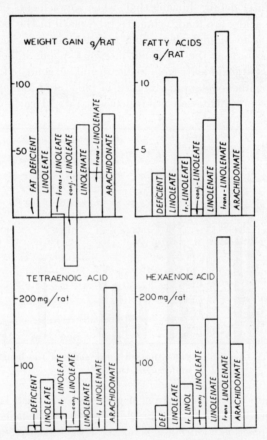

FIG. 4. Weight response, total fatty acid synthesis, tetraenoic acid synthesis, and hexaenoic acid synthesis as the result of supplementation of fat-deficient rats with isomeric essential fatty acids.[10, 11]

unnatural isomers are summarized in Fig. 4. Only the natural (*cis*) isomers promote normal growth, but elaidolinolenic acid (*trans,trans,trans*-linolenic) promotes a suboptimal weight gain. Total fatty acid synthesis is stimulated by the natural essential fatty acids and by *trans*-linolenic acid. Tetraenoic acid deposition is stimulated only by the natural essential acids, and hexaenoic acid deposition by the natural isomers plus *trans*-linolenate.

[11] R. T. Holman, *Proc. Soc. Exptl. Biol. Med.* **76,** 100 (1951).

Linolelaidate (*trans*,*trans*-9,12-octadecadienoic) is totally ineffective as an essential acid, and conjugated linoleic acid is deleterious.

Similar interconversions have been observed to take place in the chicken as evidenced by the analyses of eggs of a laying hen.[12] There appears to be a difference between the hen and the rat in the conversions possible. Reiser reported conversion of dienoic acid to pentaenoic and tetraenoic acids and the conversion of trienoic acid to all acids having from two to six double bonds. However, a word of caution should be spoken concerning the extensive interpretation of spectrophotometric data of the type used for these studies when as yet no analytical standards exist for the determinations of five and six double bonds. It is questionable whether calculations of saturated, oleic, linoleic, and linolenic acid contents are valid when the estimations of four, five, and six double-bonded acids are only relative and proper corrections for their concentrations cannot be made (see p. 287).

Two studies have been made of the metabolic conversions of conjugated unsaturated fatty acids. It was observed by Miller and Burr[13] that the eleo-stearic acid (9,11,13-octadecatrienoic acid) of tung oil was converted to conjugated dieneoic acid in the rat. Reiser[14] has confirmed this finding and studied the metabolism of conjugated dienoic acid in the laying hen. However, the established conversion of conjugated trienoic acid to conjugated dienoic acid in the animal should not be confused with similar conversions in the non-conjugated essential fatty acids. The two groups of acids differ markedly in physical and chemical properties and in biological activity, and in their metabolism and in mechanism of *in vitro* oxidations they bear no relation one to the other.

A. DIETARY FACTORS AFFECTING METABOLISM

The first recognized relationship of essential fatty acids to other dietary essentials was that pyridoxine deficiency produces deficiency symptoms in rats very similar to those of fat deficiency.[15-17] A double deficiency of fat and pyridoxine results in rapid development of more severe symptoms, and supplementation with either linoleate or pyridoxine reduces the severity of the symptoms (see Fig. 5). Medes *et al.*[4] studied the relationship of these two dietary essentials, and the results showed that relief from the double

[12] R. Reiser, *J. Nutrition* **44,** 159 (1951).

[13] E. S. Miller and G. O. Burr, *Proc. Soc. Exptl. Biol. Med.* **36,** 726 (1937).

[14] R. Reiser, *Arch. Biochem. and Biophys.* **32,** 113 (1951).

[15] L. R. Richardson, A. G. Hogan, and K. F. Itschner, *Univ. Missouri Research Bull.* **333.**

[16] F. W. Quackenbush, H. Steenbock, F. A. Kummerow, and B. R. Platz, *J. Nutrition* **24,** 225 (1942).

[17] R. Jürgens, H. Pfaltz, and M. Reinert. *Helv. Physiol. et Pharmacol. Acta* **3,** 41 (1945).

deficiency by supplementation with either pyridoxine or linoleate caused an increase in body fat and an increase in polyunsaturated acids. These results indicated that a fat-deficient rat could synthesize unsaturated acids if given pyridoxine.

Kummerow et al.[18] made a similar study with linolenate and pyridoxine and observed that doubly deficient rats given linolenate showed lower gains and worsened symptoms than did unsupplemented controls. When pyridoxine was present in the diet, more polyunsaturated acid was present in the tissues.

Experiments in the author's laboratory indicate that total arachidonate and hexaenoate in rats remains low when weanling animals are kept on a at-deficient diet or a diet deficient in fat and pyridoxine. Preliminary

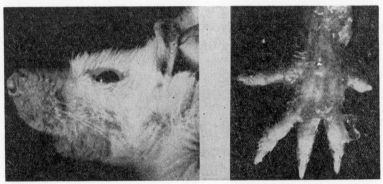

Fig. 5. Severe acrodynia in the rat. (Jürgens et al.[17])

experiments showed that supplementation with either pyridoxine or linoleate caused increases in arachidonate and hexaenoate and that, when linoleate plus pyridoxine is administered to the animals, greater increases in arachidonate and hexaenoate are observed.[10] The same was true for linolenate.

A more extensive study of the pyridoxine–essential fatty acid relationship has recently been completed.[19] Rats which had been on a doubly deficient diet one month after weaning age were given supplements of pyridoxine, linoleate, pyridoxine plus linoleate, linolenate, or pyridoxine plus linolenate for an 8-week period. Deficiency symptoms disappeared with linoleate feeding but disappeared more rapidly with linoleate plus pyridoxine. Animals fed linolenate developed even worse symptoms, a finding parallel to Kummerow's observations on weights. Linolenate plus pyridoxine caused

[18] F. A. Kummerow, E. Otto, G. Jacobson and P. Randolph, *Trans. 4th Conf. on Biol. Antioxidants, New York* (1949).

[19] P. W. Witten and R. T. Holman *Arch. Biochem. and Biophys.* **41,** 266 (1952).

no change in symptoms. Total fatty acids in the rats were highest in the animals given linolenate plus pyridoxine, and these animals also contained the greatest amounts of hexaenoic acid. The animals receiving linoleate plus pyridoxine synthesized the largest amounts of arachidonic acid. These results again point to the dual nature of the polyunsaturated acids: *Linoleate is converted by the animal principally to arachidonic acid and symptoms of deficiency disappear, whereas linolenate is converted principally to hexaenoate and symptoms are not alleviated but growth and fat synthesis are stimulated.* Pyridoxine is involved in the conversion process, possibly as a coenzyme in some enzyme system.

Hove and Harris[20] demonstrated a relationship between tocopherol and linoleate. Tocopherol increased the effectiveness of suboptimal doses of linoleate in preventing or curing essential fatty acid deficiency. The effect was not limited to antioxidant action of the tocopherol within the gastrointestinal tract, for the effect was observed when the linoleate and tocopherol were fed separately on alternate days. However, tocopherol fed alone aggravates fat-deficiency symptoms.

Anisfeld *et al.*[21] were unable to show any relationship between linoleate and tocopherol requirements in fat-deficient rats, using growth response as a criterion. The metabolic relationship between tocopherol and essential fatty acids is not clear, but suggestions have been made that tocopherol has a sparing effect on the unsaturated acids by virtue of its antioxidant properties.

The Conferences on Biological Antioxidants[22] produced much discussion of possible *in vivo* antioxidant action. Tocopherol is a well-known effective antioxidant *in vitro*, and suggestion has been made that it may act as an antioxidant in living organisms. Little information has been brought to bear on the problem. The keeping time of rat fats is extended by inclusion of tocopherol in the diet.[23] Tocopherol has been shown to stimulate the utilization of linolenate and oleate synthesis in rats,[18] and other antioxidants have been shown to have a similar action. Dam and coworkers[24] observed that tocopherol-deficient rats deposit an oxidized polymerized fatty material when fed highly unsaturated fats. This deposition of oxidized fat contains peroxides and is presumably the result of abnormal oxidation of the unsaturated acids. The effect is prevented by administration of cystine

[20] E. L. Hove and P. L. Harris. *J. Nutrition* **31,** 699 (1946).

[21] L. Anisfeld, S. M. Greenberg, and H. J. Deuel, Jr., *J. Nutrition* **45,** 599 (1951).

[22] *1st–5th Conferences on Biol. Antioxidants* Josiah Macy, Jr. Foundation, New York (1946–1950).

[23] W. O. Lundberg, R. H. Barnes, M. Clausen, N. Larson, and G. O. Burr, *J. Biol. Chem.* **168,** 379 (1947).

[24] H. Dam and H. Granados, *Acta Physiol. Scand.* **10,** 162 (1945).

or nordihydroguaiaretic acid,[25] substances that have antioxidant action. Conversely, feeding oxidized fat to animals has toxic effects.

These various observations suggest a possible antioxidant action for tocopherol in sparing metabolic unsaturated acids. Hickman[22] has suggested that perhaps a balance of pro-oxidants and antioxidants is maintained in tissue to insure the proper metabolism of such substances as essential fatty acids, that a "pro-oxidant condition" would promote oxidation and that an "antioxidant condition" would protect the acids against oxidation. In recent experiments testing this hypothesis some unexpected results were obtained.[26] The conversions of linoleic and linolenic acids to more unsaturated acids by fat-deficient rats were used as measures of utilization of these substances, when they were administered either alone or in combination with benzoyl peroxide (pro-oxidant) or tocopherol. Best growth response and greatest synthesis of body fat was obtained with supplements of benzoyl peroxide plus linoleate, and least with benzoyl peroxide alone. The toxic effect of benzoyl peroxide was thus reversed when fed with linoleate. The synthesis of arachidonate from linoleate or linolenate was unaffected by either benzoyl peroxide or tocopherol. Benzoyl peroxide increased the formation of hexaenoate from linoleate but not from linolenate. Thus it will be seen that the matter of relationship between tocopherol and essential fatty acids is at present rather confused.

The riboflavin requirement for normal growth of rats has been found to be increased when cottonseed oil is incorporated in the diet at a moderately high level.[27] Although the effect of the oil on intestinal flora may be a cause of the diminished growth, an alternate explanation may be that riboflavin is involved in the metabolism of unsaturated acids. Riboflavin is a constituent of the enzyme which causes the reduction of cytochrome c,[28] and cytochrome c is an essential component of the enzyme system which oxidizes saturated fatty acids.[29] Thus, an increased metabolism of fat may require an increased amount of riboflavin.

VI. Estimation

RALPH T. HOLMAN

A. SPECTROPHOTOMETRIC ANALYSIS

Observations by Dann and Moore[1] that prolonged saponification of oils increases their ultraviolet light absorption has led to a spectrophotometric

[25] H. Granados, E. Aaes-Jorgensen, and H. Dam, *Brit. J. Nutrition* **3**, 322 (1949).
[26] P. W. Witten and R. T. Holman, *Arch. Biochem. and Biophys.* **37**, 90 (1952).
[27] R. Reiser and P. B. Pearson, *J. Nutrition* **38**, 247 (1949).
[28] A. L. Lehninger and E. P. Kennedy, *J. Biol. Chem.* **173**, 753 (1948).
[29] E. Haas, B. L. Horecker, and T. R. Hogness, *J. Biol. Chem.* **136**, 747 (1940).
[1] W. J. Dann and T. Moore, *Biochem. J.* **27**, 1166 (1933).

method of analysis for the essential fatty acids. Mitchell *et al.*[2] reduced the phenomenon to a quantitative method using 7.3 % KOH in ethylene glycol as reagent and a treatment of 30 minutes at 180°. This has been modified and improved by Brice and Swain.[3] They used 11 % KOH in glycerol to reduce the variable blank absorption, and they have introduced background corrections in the calculations to improve the accuracy of the method. Protection of the sample during isomerization by an atmosphere of nitrogen has also been recommended. The method, even in its present highly developed form, is still subject to some limitations. The 11 % KOH reagent is optimum for linoleic and linolenic acids, but gives only a low degree of the specific conjugated isomers of the more highly unsaturated acids.[4]

The isomerization treatment of a hexaenoic acid results in production of a variety of hexaene isomers in which six, five, four, three, or two of the double bonds are conjugated. Thus the spectrum of such an isomerized sample shows principal maxima at 3750 A., 3475 A., 3000 A., 2700 A., and 2340 A. Treatment of a pentaenoic acid will give rise to similar maxima showing pentaene, tetraene, triene, and diene conjugation. Arachidonic acid will give rise to three types of conjugation, linolenic acid two, and linoleic acid only one. Thus it is apparent that, if linoleic acid is to be determined in the presence of the more highly unsaturated acids, appropriate correction must be made for each of the others.

The ratios of the various kinds of conjugated isomers derived from a single polyunsaturated acid can be varied by alkali concentration and time of treatment. For example, the conjugated tetraene yield from arachidonate treated with 23 % KOH for 8 minutes is twice that from arachidonate treated with 11 % KOH for 30 minutes.[4] Thus, use of 11 % KOH reagent for "determination" of linoleic and linolenic acids in animal fats can lead to error, because the tetraene, pentaene, and hexene acid content of the sample is ordinarily overlooked and no correction is made for it. The polyunsaturated acids of all types are thus unknowingly reported as linoleic and linolenic acids. The confusion is compounded by the present lack of empirical analytical standards for the five and six double-bond values. Thus any analysis which pretends to give the contents of various polyunsaturated, oleic, and saturated acids of animal fats by use of the 11 % KOH alkaline isomerization method and iodine value should be regarded only as an approximation.

By use of 23 % KOH reagent the sensitivity of the method for the four, five, and six double-bond acids is doubled. The author has used this reagent in estimating the relative contents of these acids in animal fatty acids. To

[2] J. H. Mitchell, Jr., H. R. Kraybill, and F. P. Zscheile, *Ind. Eng. Chem. Anal. Ed* **15**, 1 (1943).

[3] B. A. Brice and M. L. Swain, *J. Opt. Soc. Amer.* **35**, 532 (1945).

[4] R. T. Holman and G. O. Burr, *Arch. Biochem.* **19**, 474 (1948).

express the results in a relative manner, standard values based on certain assumptions[5] have been employed, but it should be understood that the results, as expressed, are tentative relative approximations. No attempt has been made to extend the calculations to include linoleic and linolenic acids.

Objection has been raised that the spectral methods are not specific for the essential fatty acids but will detect unnatural isomers as well. This apparently is the case, judging from the results of a study of metabolism of unnatural isomers of the essential fatty acids in which spectrophotometrically detectable polyunsaturates were found in animals suffering from fat-deficiency symptoms.[6] Even so, this is not a serious criticism of the method, for it is used largely on natural substances where unnatural isomers are not often encountered.

The spectrophotometric method is the best current method for determination of linoleic and linolenic acids in natural vegetable oils. The method as employed by Brice and Swain,[3] requiring 100-mg. samples, is excellent for use on vegetable oils where linolenic acid is the most unsaturated acid present. Some micro modifications of the method have been developed for smaller samples,[7, 8] but these are of more limited application. When pure hexaene and pentaene acids have been isolated and their responses measured under various conditions, a modified method will be available for the quantitative measurement of more highly unsaturated members of the group.[8a] However, it seems doubtful that a spectrophotometric method of precision for the simultaneous determination of all members of the polyunsaturated group will be forthcoming.

B. CHEMICAL METHODS

1. THIOCYANOGEN VALUE

The estimation of the content of oleic, linoleic, and linolenic acids in a fat can be made if the thiocyanogen value, iodine value, and saturated fatty acid content are known. Theoretically, thiocyanogen adds to the double bond of oleic acid, one of the two double bonds of linoleic acid, and two of the three in linolenic acid. The halogen in the iodine value reagent adds to all double bonds. Correction for the total saturated acid content of the fat then allows the setting up of a set of simultaneous equations for the calculation of the contents of the three unsaturated fatty acids. Although

[5] C. Widmer, Master's Thesis, Agricultural and Mechanical College of Texas, 1949.

[6] R. T. Holman, *Proc. Soc. Exptl. Biol. Med.* **76,** 100 (1951).

[7] L. C. Berk, N. Kretchmer, R. T. Holman, and G. O. Burr. *Anal. Chem.* **22,** 718 (1950).

[8] P. W. O'Connell and B. F. Daubert, *Arch. Biochem.* **25,** 444 (1950).

[8a] Recently S. F. Herb and R. W. Riemenschneider have made a detailed study of the effect of alkali on the conjugation of polyunsaturated fatty acids, and have established some constants for pentaene and tetraene acids. *J. Am. Oil Chemists Soc.* **29,** 456 (1952).

the method has been made official by the American Oil Chemists' Society,[8b] it is not popular because the preparation of thiocyanogen reagent is tedious, and the method is not applicable to oils containing acids of higher unsaturation. The method is empirical in nature, for pure acids do not give the theoretical thiocyanogen uptake. The method has been largely superseded by spectrophotometric analysis for routine work.

2. POLYBROMIDE METHODS

An empirical method has been worked out for the determination of linoleic acid in mixed fatty acids by bromination in cold petroleum ether.[9] The weight of the insoluble tetrabromides formed from linoleic acid can be related to the linoleic acid content of the sample. The yield of tetrabromides is affected by sample size and by the presence of other acids. However, if the empirical conditions are strictly followed, the analysis can be made quite accurate for determination of linoleic acid in samples containing no linolenic or more unsaturated acids.

The hexabromide number of fatty acids can be used to determine the linolenic acid content, if linolenic acid is the most unsaturated acid present.[10] The bromination is done in cold ethyl ether, and the weight of insoluble hexabromides precipitated is a measure of the amount of linolenic acid in the sample. The yield is affected by size of sample and the presence of other acids. Application of a similar bromination technique to methyl esters allows the detection and measurement of arachidonate, subject to the same errors mentioned above.[11] The advantage claimed for these polybromide methods is that only the natural isomers of polyunsaturated acids and thus only the physiologically active forms are measured. These methods employ a sample of the order of 1 g.

C. ENZYMATIC METHOD

Soybean lipoxidase has been shown to be specific in attacking only linoleic, linolenic, and arachidonic acids.[12, 13] The reaction can be carried out under conditions in which the conjugated end product is proportional to the amount of linoleic acid in the sample. The method is applicable to the measurement of 10 to 100 γ of linoleic acid. The method has been used to detect and measure linoleic acid in chromatographic eluates.[14] The presence of oleic and saturated acids partially inhibits the enzyme, thus limiting its

[8b] Official and Tentative Methods, American Oil Chemists' Society Cd 2–38 (1946).

[9] M. F. White and J. B. Brown, J. Am. Oil Chemists' Soc. **26**, 385 (1949).

[10] M. F. White and J. B. Brown, J. Am. Oil Chemists' Soc. **26**, 133 (1949).

[11] M. F. White and J. B. Brown, J. Am. Oil Chemists' Soc. **26**, 85 (1949).

[12] S. Bergström and R. T. Holman, Advances in Enzymol. **8**, 425 (1948).

[13] R. T. Holman and S. Bergström, The Enzymes, Vol. 2, Part 1, Chapter 60. Academic Press, New York, 1951.

[14] R. T. Holman and W. T. Williams, J. Am. Chem. Soc. **73**, 5285 (1951).

use to samples in which linoleic acid is the major component. Empirical conditions might be found to extend its usefulness as a micromethod. Because of its specificity, the enzymatic method should be useful in measurement of total essential fatty acids on a microscale.

D. ANIMAL ASSAY

Recently a method has been developed for the assay of essential fatty acids by measurement of the growth response induced by supplementing fat-deficient rats with the test fat.[15] Male rats maintained on a fat-deficient diet until growth ceased resumed growth when they were given supplements containing linoleate, and this growth has been shown to be proportional

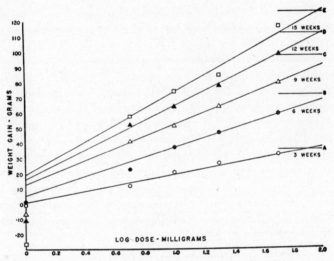

Fig. 6. Relationship between weight gain and logarithm of dose of linoleate in male fat-deficient rats.[15]

to the logarithm of the linoleate dose. This proportionality is shown in Fig. 6. This assay has been used to measure the essential fatty acid content of butter and margarine.[16]

The advantage of this assay is that it measures physiological response, non-active isomeric forms which would be measured by other analyses not affecting the assay. It suffers the disadvantages of the inaccuracy of biological assay methods, the large sample required, and the long time consumed for the assay.

[15] S. M. Greenberg, C. E. Calbert, E. E. Savage, and H. J. Deuel, Jr., *J. Nutrition* **41**, 473 (1950).

[16] H. J. Deuel, Jr., S. M. Greenberg, L. Anisfeld, and D. Melnick, *J. Nutrition* **45**, 535 (1951).

Thus far no microbiological assay methods have been developed for essential fatty acids, although it would seem possible to find an organism which requires essential fatty acids. The demonstration of essential fatty acid deficiency in insects points to their possible use as assay animals.[17]

VII. Occurrence in Foods

RALPH T. HOLMAN

The essential fatty acids are abundant in nature. Most common vegetable oils contain linoleic acid or linolenic acid, and lard and other animal lipids contain linoleic, arachidonic, and more highly unsaturated acids. Although linoleic and linolenic acids occur as major constituents in numerous vegetable oils, arachidonate is found only as a minor constituent in

TABLE III

ESSENTIAL FATTY ACID CONTENTS OF SOME COMMON FATS AND OILS

Fat or oil	Linoleic acid	Linolenic acid	Arachidonic acid
Corn oil	34–42%	—	—
Cottonseed oil	40–48%	—	—
Soybean oil	50–60%	2–8%	—
Olive oil	0.5–9.0%	—	—
Lard	6.0%	—	0.4%
Butterfat	1–4%	—	Trace
Beef tallow	1–3%	—	—

common animal fats. Its concentration in certain tissue lipids, however, may be as high as a few per cent.[1, 2] The presence of linolenic acid in animal fats is probable, but unequivocal evidence for its presence is not available except in a few cases. Many of the reports of linoleic acid and linolenic acid in animal fats are based upon analyses not specific for linoleic acid, such as iodine plus thiocyanogen values, or upon spectrophotometric analyses in which the higher polyunsaturated acids were overlooked (see p. 287). However, the occasional very high values reported for linoleate and linolenate, even when such methods of analysis are used, speak loudly for the occurrence of these acids in animal lipids.

As an illustration of the amounts of the essential fatty acids available in common fats and oils, a few examples are given in Table III. Similar

[17] G. Fraenkel and M. Blewett, *J. Exptl. Biol.* **22,** 172 (1946).

[1] C. Widmer and R. T. Holman, *Arch. Biochem.* **25,** 1 (1950).

[2] R. T. Holman and T. S. Taylor, *Arch. Biochem.* **29,** 295 (1950).

data can be found in standard references on the composition of fats and oils, and for more information the reader is referred to them.[3-5]

The highly unsaturated fatty acids are abundant in fish oils such as cod and shark liver oils, but their value as essential fatty acids is doubtful. The structures of some acids isolated from these sources differ from the essential fatty acids in that they have ethylene-interrupted rather than methylene-interrupted polyunsaturated systems. The literature contains a few hints that fish oil acids are toxic to the animal.

The widespread occurrence of linoleate in vegetable oils and arachidonate in animal tissues makes the possibility of spontaneous fat deficiency unlikely n man or in animals if a natural selection of food is allowed.

VIII. Effects of Deficiency

A. IN ANIMALS AND INSECTS

RALPH T. HOLMAN

1. RAT

The discovery of a fat-deficiency syndrome arose through the attempts of Evans and Burr to produce a synthetic diet free of vitamin E.[1] The syndrome was first recognized and described as fat deficiency by Burr and Burr,[2] and since then the deficiency has often been called the Burr and Burr syndrome. Simultaneously McAmis et al. reported a reduced growth on fat-free diets[3] but did not recognize the essential nature of the fatty acids responsible. These workers were able to produce the deficiency because of their departure from past practice in substituting sucrose for starch as carbohydrate energy source. (Starch contains an appreciable amount of unsaturated fat as a component of the granule.) Using sucrose as energy source and exhaustively extracted casein as protein component, they were able to reduce the fat content of the ration enough to demonstrate fat deficiency. Rats maintained on fat-deficient rations reach an early growth plateau, their skin becomes scaly and their coat rough, usually within a

[3] G. S. Jamieson, Vegetable Fats and Oils. Reinhold Publishing Co., New York, 1943.

[4] A. E. Bailey, Industrial Oil and Fat Products. Interscience Publishers, New York, 1945.

[5] T. P. Hilditch, The Chemical Constitution of Natural Fats, 2nd. ed. John Wiley and Sons, New York, 1947.

[1] H. M. Evans and G. O. Burr, Proc. Soc. Exptl. Biol. Med. 24, 740 (1927).

[2] G. O. Burr and M. M. Burr, J. Biol. Chem. 82, 325 (1929).

[3] A. J. McAmis, W. E. Anderson, and L. B. Mendel, J. Biol. Chem. 82, 247 (1929).

period of 3 to 4 months. Necrosis of the tail often develops in late stages of the deficiency, and hematuria is sometimes observed. These outward manifestations of derangement are not exhibited regularly, but histological changes are invariably found in kidneys of fat-deficient rats.

Subsequent studies by Burr and his coworkers indicated that the water consumption[4] and basal metabolic rate[5] of the fat-deficient rat are higher than those of the normal animal. The ability of animals to reproduce is impaired by fat deprivation.[4] In the female rat, conception is followed by resorption of all or some of the fetuses,[4, 6, 7] the gestation period is pro-

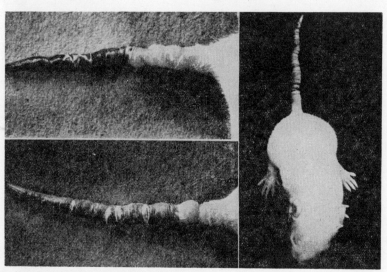

FIG. 7. Schachtelhalmschwanz—exaggerated caudal symptoms of fat deficiency in the young rat. (From Guggenheim and Jürgens.[9])

longed, and only a variable and low number of live young are produced. These, however, do not live long after birth, and even at the age of a few days show damage of the tail (Fig. 7). The male rat on a fat-free diet becomes sterile and will not mate.[4, 8] The ability to reproduce returns when the animals are given diets containing adequate essential fatty acid.

When weanling rats are placed upon a fat-free diet, fat-deficiency symptoms begin to appear within 3 months, and the animals can be maintained in the fat-deficient condition well over a year with moderate mortality.

[4] G. O. Burr and M. M. Burr, J. Biol. Chem. 86, 587 (1930).
[5] G. O. Burr and A. J. Beber, Proc. Soc. Exptl. Biol. Med. 31, 911 (1934).
[6] E. C. Maeder, Anat. Record 70, 73 (1937).
[7] H. M. Evans, S. Lepkovsky, and E. A. Murphy, J. Biol. Chem. 106, 431 (1934).
[8] H. M. Evans, S. Lepkovsky, and E. A. Murphy, J. Biol. Chem. 106, 445 (1934).

If the dams are maintained on a fat-free diet from the time of conception, the young which are born show symptoms within a few days and do not live beyond a month.[9] The accentuated caudal degeneration observed

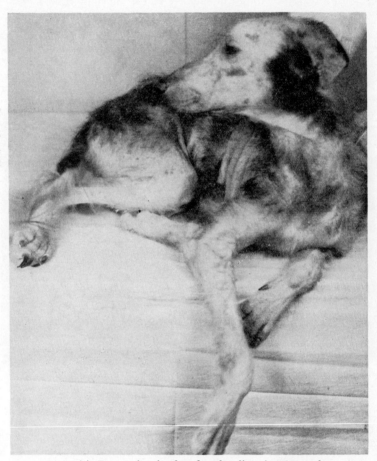

FIG. 8 (a) Dog maintained on low fat diet. Age 9 months.

under these conditions (Schachtelhalmschwanz) appears within a few days and may lead to the complete necrosis of the tail (see Fig. 7).

Older animals placed on fat-free diet do not spontaneously develop classical fat-deficiency symptoms. Only by superimposing a strain can adult animals be brought to show fat-deficiency symptoms. Barki et al.[10] severely

[9] M. Guggenheim and R. Jürgens, *Helv. Physiol. et Pharmacol. Acta* **2,** 417 (1944).
[10] V. H. Barki, H. Nath, E. B. Hart, and C. A. Elvehjem, *Proc. Soc. Exptl. Biol. Med.* **66,** 474 (1947).

depleted adult rats by restricting food intake until the animals were half their starting weight. When the animals were then fed fat-free diet *ad libitum*, classical symptoms of fat deficiency appeared. These symptoms could be prevented or cured by ethyl linoleate. The symptoms disappeared

FIG. 8. (*b*) Dog maintained on low fat diet for 7 months, then given diet containing 5% of total calories as fat for 3 months. At 7 months this animal showed similar symptoms to those illustrated in (a). (From Hansen and Wiese.[11])

spontaneously after prolonged periods of *ad libitum* feeding of fat-free diet, indicating the possibility of synthesis of some essential fatty acid.

2. DOG

The fat-deficiency syndrome has been observed in a variety of animals. Hansen and Wiese[11-14] have made extensive studies in fat deficiency of dogs.

11 A. E. Hansen and H. F. Wiese, *Texas Repts. Biol. Med.* **9,** 491 (1951).
12 H. F. Wiese and A. E. Hansen, *Texas Repts. Biol. Med.* **9,** 516 (1951).
13 H. F. Wiese and A. E. Hansen, *Texas Repts. Biol. Med.* **9,** 545 (1951).
14 A. E. Hansen, S. G. Holmes, and H. F. Wiese, *Texas Repts. Biol. Med.* **9,** 555 (1951).

Young puppies develop dermal symptoms after 4 to 5 months on a low fat diet. The flaky desquamation of the skin and loss of hair is usually followed by secondary infections. Alopecia and emaciation accompanied by a greasy skin condition develop at later stages of deficiency. Dogs first develop an excitable temperament and later become tremulous. This syndrome in dogs can be prevented or cured by inclusion of unsaturated fats such as lard, bacon fat, butterfat, or Crisco at a level of 16 % of the calories. One per cent of calories as linoleate or arachidonate caused definite improvement, but did not provide a complete cure within 6 months. Dogs have been main-

FIG. 9. Four-week-old chicks on fat-free and 2% cottonseed oil diets. (From Reiser.[16])

tained on fat-deficient diet for as long as 6 years. Figures 8a and 8b show a fat-deficient dog compared with his normal control.

3. CHICKEN

Early experiments by Russell and his coworkers,[15] in which natural diets were solvent-extracted to reduce the fat content, indicated that fat was not needed in quantity for the growth of the chicken. The more recent work of Reiser, in which synthetic fat-free diets were used, indicates that total exclusion of fat from the diet of chicks causes slow weight gain and high mortality.[16] Chicks which received supplements of lard or cottonseed oil

[15] W. C. Russell, M. W. Taylor, and L. J. Polskin, *J. Nutrition* **19,** 555 (1940).
[16] R. Reiser, *J. Nutrition* **42,** 319 (1950).

grew as rapidly as chicks on a mash diet and showed a much lower mortality. In chicks, fat deficiency is sometimes associated with subcutaneous edema, and in a few cases general edema in the body cavity was observed. The deficient birds were unthrifty and had poor feathering (Fig. 9). Removal of yolk sacs from the newly hatched chicks did not seem to affect the development of the deficiency.

4. MOUSE

Mice kept on a fat-deficient diet develop the same general symptoms as do rats.[17] The first symptom to appear is a dandruff-like dermatitis on the scruff of the neck, which spreads over the animal. The dermatitis is followed by necrosis of the extremities, and hematuria is observed in a few cases. Decker et al.[18] have shown that adult mice can be brought to a state of chronic essential fatty acid deficiency without showing any external symptoms, and that in these animals acute symptoms may be brought out by stresses such as injuries, pregnancy, and x-irradiation. Although most studies in the field of essential fatty acid nutrition and metabolism have been carried out upon rats, it would seem that the mouse could effectively replace the rat as an experimental animal because mice develop deficiency symptoms more quickly, consume less food, and require less space.

5. LARGE ANIMALS

No conclusive work has been done on the essential fatty acid requirement of large animals because of the tremendous cost of such experimentation. Cows require a minimum of 4 % extractable fat in the diet for milk production,[19, 20] and calves on a low fat diet do not thrive.[21] However, no evidence has been brought out to relate these observations to essential fatty acid requirements. Hogs on a low fat diet have a drastically reduced linoleic acid content, but no deficiency symptoms have been observed.[22-25]

All the vertebrates in which fat-deficiency symptoms have been produced experimentally have straight alimentary canals. In the author's laboratory, attempts to develop fat deficiency in guinea pigs failed, although many animals were maintained on a fat-free diet for periods of time longer than

[17] E. A. White, J. R. Foy, and L. R. Cerecedo, Proc. Soc. Exptl. Biol. Med. 54, 301 (1943).

[18] A. B. Decker, D. L. Fillerup, and J. F. Mead, J. Nutrition 41, 507 (1950).

[19] G. Gibson and C. F. Huffman, Michigan Agr. Expt. Sta. Quart. Bull. 244, (1939).

[20] L. A. Maynard, K. E. Gardner, and A. Z. Hodson, Cornell Univ. Agr. Expt. Sta. Bull. 722 (1939).

[21] T. W. Gullickson, F. C. Fountaine, and J. B. Fitch, J. Dairy Sci. 25, 117 (1942).

[22] N. R. Ellis and O. G. Hankins, J. Biol. Chem. 66, 101 (1925).

[23] N. R. Ellis and H. S. Isbell, J. Biol. Chem. 69, 219 (1926).

[24] N. R. Ellis and H. S. Isbell, J. Biol. Chem. 69, 239 (1926).

[25] N. R. Ellis and J. H. Zeller, J. Biol. Chem. 89, 185 (1930).

are required to develop fat deficiency in rats. It seems possible that for animals having a cecum, intestinal bacteria may play a role in the synthesis of essential fatty acids as well as of many of the water-soluble vitamins.

6. INSECTS

Fat-deficiency phenomena are not limited to vertebrates, for Fraenkel and Blewett[26] were able to develop fat-deficient moths of four species. Feeding fat-free diets during the larval stage prevents proper wing development in the adult (see Fig. 10). Linoleic and linolenic acids prevent this condition, but docosahexaenoic acid does not. However, the latter does benefit growth. Results with these lower animals again point to the differences between the members of the polyunsaturated fatty acid group. Emer-

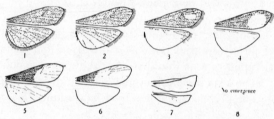

FIG. 10. Response of *Ephestia keuhniella* wing development to various levels of linoleic acid in the larval diet. 1. Normal wing, 8. Fat-free diet. (From Fraenkel and Blewett.[26])

gence from the pupal stage and scale development of the adult wing parallels the linoleic acid content of the diet. It appears that these moths or other insects might be useful and inexpensive animals for essential fatty acid assay.

As yet studies of the requirements of microorganisms for essential fatty acids have not been made, nor have mutants requiring these acids been isolated. It seems likely, however, that mutants requiring the acids could be produced and isolated for use in the assay of these essential fatty acids.

7. HISTOPATHOLOGY

In addition to the gross abnormalities of fat-deficient animals mentioned in the previous section, a few observations have been made on the histopathology accompanying fat deficiency. Histological examinations of the kidneys of deficient rats[27, 28] indicate that the renal tubules are calcified

[26] G. Fraenkel and M. Blewett, *J. Exptl. Biol.* **22,** 172 (1946).
[27] V. G. Borland and C. M. Jackson, *Arch. Pathol.* **11,** 687 (1931).
[28] R. H. Follis, The Pathology of Nutritional Disease. Charles C Thomas, Springfield, Ill., 1948.

and necrotic areas of the renal medulla appear in some cases. The cells of the tubular epithelium are filled with lipoid and the tubular lumena contain fat droplets and albuminous material. In cured animals the gross appearance of the kidneys was normal and histologically no difference could be demonstrated between cured and normal animals. The implication that choline deficiency may have been a contributing factor[28] to the histopathology thus does not seem to be justified.

Histological studies of the reproductive system of the female rat[6] indicate underdevelopment of the uterine mucosa and failure of corpora lutea to develop during pregnancy. Embryos are resorbed or remain in utero beyond the normal gestation period.

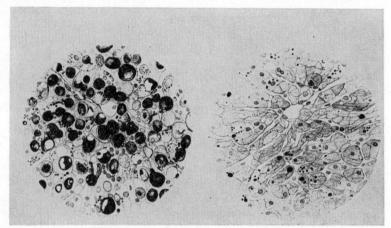

Fig. 11. Liver sections from fat-deficient and linoleate-fed young rats. Sudan stain. Dark areas indicate fat deposition. (From Guggenheim and Jürgens.[9])

In the male fat-deficient rat the testis is macroscopically atrophied.[8] The tubular epithelium degenerates, sperm are absent, and giant cells are present. Seminal vesicles are small and flaccid, and the prostate is atropic. The epididymis shows no significant deviation from the normal, but the penis and associated glands are atrophied. If male rats in this condition are given gonadotropin, the accessory sex organs tend to revert to normal, indicating that the fat-deficient animal can probably still synthesize testosterone.[29] However, the testes remain degenerate, indicating that they have lost the ability to respond to gonadotropin. Essential fatty acids are thus required to maintain testicular structure and function.

Histological examination of the livers of young fat-deficient rats showed

[29] P. E. Barrios, Master's Thesis, Agricultural and Mechanical College of Texas, 1949

a fatty infiltration of the liver (Fig. 11) which is prevented by fat in the diet.[9] In this respect, essential fatty acids are lipotropic.

The best histological studies on the skin lesions of fat deficiency have been made on the dog.[14] The abnormalities include loss of hair and desquamation, and compactness of the stratum corneum. The epidermis thickens and there is edema in the dermis. Hair follicles become hyperkeratinized, the hair shafts become plugged, and the sebaceous glands enlarge. Illustrations of the epidermis of dogs on low fat and normal diets are shown in Fig. 12.

The pathological conditions recognized as essential fatty acid deficiency are generally produced by maintaining animals on a low-fat or fat-free diet. Such diets are used because it is difficult to prepare a diet free of essential

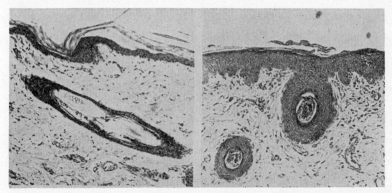

FIG. 12. Epidermis of dogs (a) on control diet and (b) on low-fat diet. 120×. (From Hansen et al.[14])

fatty acids without removing all fat. These diets supplemented with essential fatty acids in adequate amounts still do not allow optimum growth, reproduction, and lactation, but the pathological states developed on such a dietary regime are still poorly characterized. The studies of pathology of fat-deficient animals have not differentiated between the two types of fat deficiency, but the pathological changes described are prevented or cured by linoleate, thus making it reasonably certain that the conditions described are due to essential fatty acid deficiency.

B. IN HUMAN BEINGS

ARILD E. HANSEN and HILDA F. WIESE

Specific information regarding the essentiality of linoleic acid and arachidonic acid in relation to human nutrition is completely lacking. Hence, in a discussion of the human requirement for these fatty acids, it is necessary to interpret some of the observations and experimental findings which have been made with human subjects on various fat regimens in the light of fundamental facts established from experimental work with animals. Consideration will be given to observations from studies on the use of low fat diets in human subjects and to indirect evidences of possible special need for fat as gained from other clinical studies. Inasmuch as correlations have been found between dietary fat and the composition of the tissue lipids as well as the gross and histologic alterations in dogs maintained on diets with and without fat,[30-33] these data will serve as a chief source of material for evaluating fat requirements for man. Reference also will be made to the measurement of diene, triene, and tetraene fatty acids in blood serum as a possible means for ascertaining the human requirement for these fatty acids.

1. Low Fat Diets in Human Beings

Reports concerning the effect of comparatively low fat diets in human subjects are meager and of a rather general nature. An attempt was made as early as 1919 by von Gröer[34] to determine the need of infants for dietary fat. Detailed observations were made on two infants by this worker, and although gain in weight was not entirely satisfactory, no striking abnormalities developed within a period of 9 months. The low fat diet was discontinued in one infant because of anorexia and in the second infant because of infection. Holt and coworkers[35] used a low fat diet in the study of three infants. Although these studies were of short duration, one of the infants repeatedly developed a skin eruption when fat was lacking in the diet. In 1937, von Chwalibogowski[36] observed two infants on a low fat regimen for periods of 13 to 15 months. No typical findings were evident, and this led the author to conclude that fat in the diet was not essential for infants. Four human subjects have been studied in our clinic and laboratories for periods of 2 to 23 months. The first was one of twins who, when on a low fat diet, was found to have a definitely lower iodine number of the serum fatty acids than the twin infant who was maintained on a normal diet. Another infant on the low fat diet developed a rather intractable impetigo but showed no other clinical abnormalities. The third case concerned a rather extensive study which was made on a child with chylous ascites. Beginning

[30] A. E. Hansen and H. F. Wiese, *Texas Repts. Biol. Med.* **9**, 491 (1951).

[31] H. F. Wiese and A. E. Hansen, *Texas Repts. Biol. Med.* **9**, 516 (1951).

[32] H. F. Wiese and A. E. Hansen, *Texas Repts. Biol. Med.* **9**, 545 (1951).

[33] A. E. Hansen, S. G. Holmes, and H. F. Wiese, *Texas Repts. Biol. Med.* **9**, 555 (1951).

[34] F. von Gröer, *Biochem. Z.* **97**, 311 (1919).

[35] L. E. Holt, Jr. H. C. Tidwell, C. M. Kirk, D. M. Cross, and S. Neale, *J. Pediat.* **6**, 427 (1935).

[36] A. von Chwalibogowski, *Acta paediat.* **22**, 110 (1938).

at the age of 3 weeks, this infant was fed on a diet composed mostly of skim milk and added carbohydrate, with supplements of minerals and vitamins so that the food intake was complete in so far as other dietary essentials were known. Development of this child was satisfactory, and his appetite remained good. Owing to marked abdominal enlargement, at various intervals it was necessary to remove the chylous fluid from the peritoneal cavity, thereby causing marked fluctuations in his weight curve. During the mid-summer season when the child was about 7 months of age, he developed marked prickly heat. The eruption later took on the appearance of a chronic dermatitis which persisted for a period of about 3 months, long after other infants in the same ward who also had suffered from prickly heat were free from eruption. Later the infant developed impetigo along with several other infants in the same ward. Again the eruption persisted and was much more resistant to treatment than in the other infants. On several occasions small eczematous patches developed, but these responded readily to local treatment. There was no family history of eczema, asthma, or hay fever. The vitamin A and β-carotene values in the blood were similar to those of control subjects. The iodine number of the total fatty acids of the serum was much lower than that of normal infants of a similar age. There was no change in the serum fatty acids or their iodine number following a cream meal. Observations were terminated when the child died during an operation in which an attempt was made to establish a continuity between the venous circulation and the peritoneal cavity by means of reflecting the internal saphenous vein superiorly. As reported by Brown and coworkers,[37] the fourth patient was an adult male subject who was maintained on low fat diet for a period of 6 months. His total intake was not more than 1 g. of fat daily. A study of the respiratory quotient during the low fat period showed an increase similar to that observed in rats. The iodine number of the total fatty acids of the serum was definitely less while on the low fat diet. The linoleic and arachidonic acid content of the serum determined as tetra- and polybromides at the end of the low fat period were 3.2 and 1.9 % of the total fatty acids, respectively. Six months after the normal diet was resumed, these values were 5.7 and 3.2 %, respectively.

Summary. Although experimental observations are scanty and of relatively short duration, the effects of a low fat diet in human subjects appear to be the following: Highly unsaturated fatty acids are not synthesized; respiratory quotients follow the pattern of those of experimental animals on low fat diets; possibly there is increased susceptibility to infection (skin and respiratory); there may be a tendency to develop a mild dermatitis; growth and development are not greatly affected; and the appetite in most instances remains fairly satisfactory.

[37] W. R. Brown, A. E. Hansen, G. O. Burr, and I. McQuarrie, *J. Nutrition* **16,** 511 (1938).

2. INDIRECT EVIDENCES OF NEED FOR ESSENTIAL FATTY ACIDS

a. Observations on Patients with Eczema

Inasmuch as one of the outstanding features of the low fat diet in experimental animals results in a development of skin abnormalities, the relationships which have been found between dietary fat and eczematous conditions of the skin may be more than incidental. Study[38, 39] of the iodine number of the serum fatty acids of patients with eczema disclosed definitely lower values than for those of control groups of patients. For example: four out of five infants under 2 years of age suffering eczematous eruptions, three out of four children from 2 to 15 years, and over half of the subjects over 15 years had iodine values of the serum fatty acids definitely below the normal range. In the study by Hansen et al.,[40] there were 171 patients with eczema and 101 in the control group. This observation has been confirmed by a number of investigators.[41-44] The tetra- and polybromide numbers of the total fatty acids from pooled samples of serum from patients with eczema were found to be lower than in serum samples from control subjects.[45] Finnerud et al.[43] found no consistent differences in the polybromide numbers of the fatty acids between control subjects and eczematous patients, and there was no correlation between the polybromide number and the clinical condition of the patient.

A number of workers[39, 40, 43, 44, 46-48] have reported that the addition of fat rich in unsaturated fatty acid to the diet of patients with chronic eczema favorably influences the condition of the skin. In studies in our own clinics, before a change was made in therapeutic regimen the patients usually were observed from periods of 3 weeks to 3 months. As a rule, fresh lard or vegetable oil was added beginning with 1 teaspoonful two or three times a day, and gradually increased so that by 2 weeks the patient was receiving the equivalent of 1 tablespoonful two or three times a day. In most instances no particular difficulty was encountered in consuming the extra fat; however, in some instances the patients preferred to use fresh lard as a

[38] A. E. Hansen, Proc. Soc. Exptl. Biol. Med. 30, 1198 (1933).

[39] A. E. Hansen, Am. J. Diseases Children 53, 933 (1937).

[40] A. E. Hansen, E. M. Knott, H. F. Wiese, E. Shaperman, and I. McQuarrie, Am. J. Diseases Children 73, 1 (1947).

[41] H. K. Faber and D. B. Roberts, J. Pediat. 6, 490 (1935).

[42] L. Schornstein, Z. Kinderheilk. 59, 52 (1937).

[43] C. W. Finnerud, R. L. Kesler, and H. F. Wiese, Arch. Dermatol. and Syphilol. 44, 849 (1941).

[44] A. V. Stoesser, J. Allergy 18, 29 (1947).

[45] W. R. Brown and A. E. Hansen, Proc. Soc. Exptl. Biol. Med. 36, 113 (1937).

[46] A. E. Hansen, Proc. Soc. Exptl. Biol. Med. 31, 160 (1933).

[47] T. Cornbleet and E. R. Pace, Arch. Dermatol. and Syphilol. 31, 224 (1935).

[48] E. Azerad and C. Grupper, Bull. mém. soc. méd. hôp. Paris 64, 21 (1948); Bull. soc. franç. dermatol. syphilig. 55, 24, 230 (1948); Semaine hôp. Paris 25, 684 (1949).

spread on crackers or bread or mixed with cinnamon, jelly, or jam. When favorable results occurred, usually the first evidence of improvement was observed 2 to 4 weeks after the addition of fat to the diet. From the clinical viewpoint it was felt that if improvement was to occur it would be evident within 2 or 3 months. It must be emphasized that, although the attempt was made to change only one factor, it was necessary to continue the same local medication and dietary regimen as used previously and to prevent injury from scratching. One continued to be on the alert for possible allergens as playing a role. In order to control the clinical observations as closely as possible, graphic records were used, as illustrated in a previous report.[40]

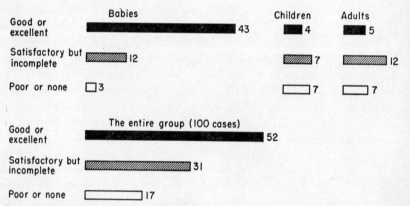

Fig. 13. Summary of results of Grupper and Azerad in a study of 100 patients with eczema. (A. Burgos.[48a])

Azerad and Grupper[48] of Paris summarized their experience with the addition of fat to the diet of 100 patients, as indicated in Fig. 13. These results have been confirmed in a second series of 100 patients (personal conversation, 1950). One of the most striking clinical results obtained by Azerad and Grupper is illustrated in Fig. 14 through the courtesy of these workers. The clinical results, in general, are similar to those reported earlier by Hansen et al.[40] It must be pointed out that not all workers[49-51] report the addition of fat to the diet to be so helpful in altering the course of patients with eczema.

[48a] A. Burgos, Contribution au traitment de l'eczema par les acides gras non saturés. R. Toulon, Paris, 1949.

[49] S. J. Taub and S. J. Zakon, J. Am. Med. Assoc. 105, 1675 (1935).

[50] J. E. Ginsberg, C. Bernstein, and L. V. Iob, Arch. Dermatol. and Syphilol. 36, 1033 (1947).

[51] N. N. Epstein and D. Glick, Arch. Dermatol. and Syphilol. 35, 427 (1937).

It may be of some significance that the incidence of eczema[52] and skin eruptions[53] is less in infants maintained on breast milk than on cow's milk mixtures. Admittedly many factors may be concerned with this difference; however, it may be pointed out that the content of linoleic acid is much greater in breast milk than in cow's milk.[54]

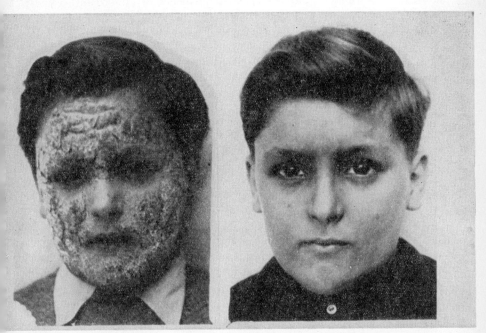

FIG. 14. Photographs of a patient included in the study of Grupper and Azerad. (A. Burgos.[48a])

b. *Low Fat Intake Because of Necessity or Because of Derangement in Fat Absorption*

It is recognized that a prolonged low fat diet leads to a craving for fat. This is due probably to the satiety value of fat *per se* rather than to a need for specific acids. It has been observed, however, that when people are deprived of fat for long periods of time, an increase in the incidence of skin abnormalities seems to appear. Freudenberg of Basel, Switzerland, in a personal conversation, stated that he had observed this phenomena in Central Europe in both World Wars I and II. It may well be that some of

[52] C. G. Grulee and H. N. Sanford, *J. Pediat.* **9**, 223 (1936).
[53] E. C. Robinson, *Am. J. Diseases Children* **59**, 1002 (1940).
[54] T. P. Hilditch and M. L. Meara, *Biochem. J.* **38**, 29 (1944); **38**, 437 (1944).

this reflects a need for certain fatty acids. Luzzatti and Hansen,[55] in studying the serum lipids of patients suffering from the celiac syndrome, found the iodine number of the serum fatty acids to be abnormally low. This finding is in keeping with a relatively low intake of unsaturated fatty acids. In addition, in reviewing the literature Luzzatti and Hansen found that a number of authors[56-58] reported a high incidence of abnormalities of the skin in patients with poor fat absorption. This type of disorder is almost always associated with malnutrition and recurrent respiratory infections, two symptoms which were consistently observed in fat-deficient dogs.[30] To accentuate the situation, patients with inability to absorb fat adequately usually are placed on a low fat diet, by their own choice or upon the recommendation of the physician. If there is a need for specific unsaturated fatty acids one might expect latent abnormalities to become manifest.

c. Summary

Study of the serum lipids in patients with eczema suggest that abnormally low iodine values are common. The feeding of dietary fats rich in the unsaturated fatty acids to patients suffering from eczema frequently appears to improve the condition of the skin. Prolonged maintenance on a diet low in fat because of faulty absorption regularly results in a low iodine value of the serum fatty acids. Children suffering from faulty fat absorption quite commonly develop chronic dermatitis, frequently suffer from respiratory tract infections, and often become severely malnourished. The role of specific fats in producing such conditions has not been ascertained.

3. Data from Animal Studies with Possible Applications

The work of Burr and Burr[59, 60] regarding the essential nature of linoleic and arachidonic acid for the rat is the basis of nutritional interest in these fatty acids. Observations from studies with the rat as the experimental animal which possibly may be applicable to the human subject are the effect of fat deficiency on the condition of the skin and the loss in weight of the animals. In an attempt to establish a means for ascertaining the human need for special fatty acids, Hansen and Wiese[61] undertook detailed studies with the dog in regard to the interrelationships of dietary fat, composition of serum, and tissue lipids, and the gross and microscopic alterations of the tissues. Reference to some of their findings are presented.

[55] L. Luzzatti and A. E. Hansen, *J. Pediat.* **24**, 417 (1944).
[56] T. I. Bennett, D. Hunter, and J. M. Vaughan, *Quart. J. Med.* [N.S.] **1**, 603 (1932).
[57] C. Konstam and H. Gordon, *Proc. Roy. Soc. Med.* **29**, 629 (1936).
[58] I. D. Riley and M. B. Leeds, *Lancet* **I**, 262 (1939).
[59] G. O. Burr and M. M. Burr, *J. Biol. Chem.* **82**, 345 (1929); **86**, 587 (1930).
[60] G. O. Burr, M. M. Burr, and E. S. Miller, *J. Biol. Chem.* **97**, 1 (1932).
[61] A. E. Hansen and H. F. Wiese, *Proc. Soc. Exptl. Biol. Med.* **52**, 205 (1943).

a. Gross Changes

Maintenance of young dogs on diets practically devoid of fat (less than 1 % of the total calories consumed) resulted in marked changes in the appearance of the animals.[30] The distinctive abnormalities were dryness of the skin and hair with desquamation, increased susceptibility to infection and later tremulousness, drainage from the auditory canals, swelling and redness of the paws, and emaciation. Animals placed on a low fat diet at weaning began to show skin changes within a period of about 3 months. Improvement varied both with the amount and type of fat fed. When fat was fed to equal 5 % of the total calories, there was little improvement in the appearance of the skin; at the 10 % level some improvement resulted; but even at a 15 % level healing was rather prolonged. Lard or bacon drippings as the source of dietary fat were more effective in bringing about restitution of the abnormalities than butter fat, both in relation to time and degree. When the deficient animals were given fat at the 30 % caloric level, improvement was rapid (few weeks) and definite, being more rapid with lard and bacon drippings than with butter fat. One animal was on the low fat diet for as long as 6 years, and it is rather remarkable that, although the skin and hair abnormality had been present for this length of time, when sufficient fat again was added to the diet the skin and hair resumed a healthy appearance. In only a few instances in the studies with dogs was it possible to use linoleic or arachidonic acid as the source of fat. When fed at a 1 % caloric level, however, there was definite improvement in the skin and renewed growth of hair. Nevertheless, it was found that this level was not sufficient to effect complete and permanent cures within a 6-month period. In control animals given the same diet from the time of weaning except for the isocaloric substitution of sucrose with lard, bacon drippings, or butter fat in amounts equal to approximately 30 % of the total calories, no abnormalities developed. Illustrations of the gross appearance of dogs suffering fat deficiency are presented in the discussion by Holman in another portion of this volume.

b. Tissue Lipids

Rather extensive studies[31] of the tissue lipids have demonstrated that the degree of unsaturation of the fatty acids of the blood serum, skin, subcutaneous fat, liver, kidney, and heart is definitely decreased in the animals on the low fat regimen. In general, the differences in the iodine number of the fatty acids between healthy control animals and fat-deficient animals are much greater in the serum than in the skin or other tissues. The iodine number of the serum fatty acids which are particularly involved have been those present as cholesterol ester. Direct correlations have been observed between the appearance of the skin and hair of the animals and the iodine number of the serum fatty acids as well as the kind and amount of dietary fat.

c. Spectral Analysis for Unsaturated Fatty Acids

The total fatty acids of the serum, skin, liver, and heart consistently showed high percentages of diene fatty acid[32] when adequate levels of fat

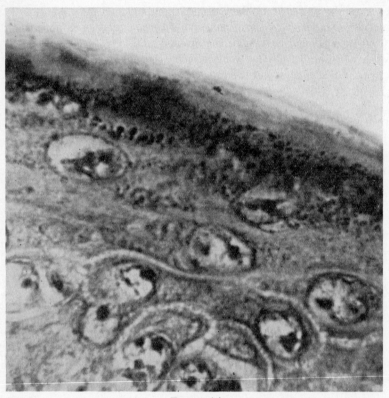

FIG. 15 (a)

containing linoleic acid were fed, and all animals receiving these diets presented a normal appearance of the skin and hair. The total fatty acids of the serum showed more tetraene fatty acid when diets containing linoleic or arachidonic acids were fed than when the diet was extremely low in fat. Dogs maintained on a low fat diet and exhibiting fat-deficiency symptoms showed definitely lesser amounts of diene and tetraene acids in the liver, kidney, skin, and heart than animals with healthy skin. At 2350 A., $E_{1\,cm}^{1\%}$ values of the serum ranged from 125 to 150, and at 3000 A. from 11 to 20, whereas the serum from healthy dogs receiving 15 % or more of their caloric intake as fat (lard or bacon drippings) varied from 250 to 315 for the former and from 40 to 90 for the latter. In animals receiving amounts of fat inadequate to effect a completely normal skin, the serum diene and tetraene values were intermediate between the normal and fat-deficient groups. The correlations observed between the dietary history, the serum lipids, and the

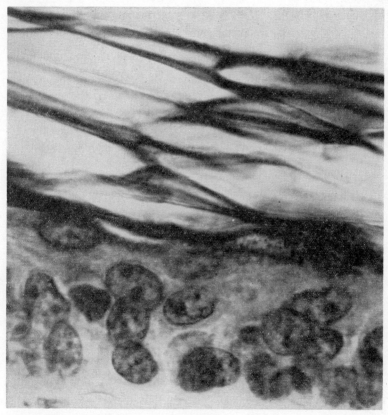

FIG. 15 (b)

FIG. 15. Photomicrograph (magnification 1425×) section through the skin of a dog (a) on a low fat diet and (b) after 6 months on a diet with 29% calories as fresh lard substituted isocalorically for sucrose. (From Hansen and Wiese.[33])

gross changes in the animals seem to be very significant and have been valuable in interpreting the results of spectral analysis of serum fatty acids in human subjects.

d. Histologic Features

Definite alterations occur in the histologic structures of the skin of dogs which have been deprived of dietary fat.[33] Changes are discernible in the stratum corneum, epidermis, and dermis (see Figs. 15a and 15b; see also

Figs. 12a and 12b, p. 300). Control animals having fat in the diet and grossly exhibiting healthy skin and hair present an epidermis 2 to 3 cell layers in thickness, a stratum corneum which is thin, wavy, and lacelike, the cell outlines and nuclei being well delineated, a dermis with well-defined collagen fibers, normal hair follicles, thin endothelial cells with large lumina to the small vessels, and slight cellular infiltration. In the fat-deficient dog presenting distinct abnormalities of the skin with marked desquamation and loss of hair, the stratum corneum is smudgy and indistinct and often there is parakeratosis, the epidermis is greatly thickened with palisade formation at the basilar layer with intracellular bridges evident, and the dermis shows evidence of irregular collagen bundles, extensive edema, presence of cellular material, swollen endothelial cells with small lumina of the vessels, increase in the cells of the hair follicles, plugging of the hair shafts, degeneration of the hair, and enlarged sebaceous glands. Later the sebaceous glands become shrunken. When fat is added to the diet there is good correlation between the amount and kind of dietary fat and a reversal in the microscopic appearance of the skin. Changes similar to these have been found in many human subjects, but heretofore no attempt has been made to relate such changes to the dietary history.

e. Summary

On the basis of data obtained from studies with laboratory animals including the dietary history, serum lipid values, especially for the diene and tetraene fatty acids, and gross and histologic observations regarding the skin have given leads for study of the human requirements for essential fatty acids.

4. Spectroscopic Study of Serum Lipids in Human Subjects

In so far as is known, no sustained effort has been made to determine for human subjects the highly unsaturated fatty acid levels of serum. Wiese,[62] in work done at our laboratories under a contract sponsored by the Bureau of Human Nutrition and Home Economics, U. S. Department of Agriculture, adapted the spectrographic technique to a semimicro basis which makes it possible to study the values for diene, triene, and tetraene fatty acids on samples of serum on a clinical basis. Under the same contract, and with this method of analysis, the serum levels of these fatty acids were determined for 75 human subjects.[63] The individuals studied were either healthy adult subjects or hospitalized children who were considered to be in a good nutritional state clinically, or children markedly underweight and appearing malnourished. The $E_{1\,cm}^{1\%}$. values at 2350 A. (diene fatty acids)

[62] H. F. Wiese and A. E. Hansen, *J. Biol. Chem.* **202,** 417 (1953).
[63] A. E. Hansen and H. F. Wiese, *Federation Proc.* **11,** 446 (1952).

were between 250 and 325 in thirty-three subjects, and both children and adults in this group were considered to be in a good state of nutrition. The $E_{1\,cm}^{1\%}$. values at 3000 A. (tetraene fatty acids) ranged from 30 to 76. In contrast, in a group of eighteen infants and children who were markedly underweight and malnourished in appearance, the $E_{1\,cm}^{1\%}$. values at 2350 A. varied from 90 to 170 and at 3000 A. from 15 to 42. These subjects were suffering from cystic fibrosis of the pancreas or celiac disease, or had been on notoriously inadequate diets. In the remaining one-third of the subjects studied, intermediate values both for serum diene and tetraene fatty acids were observed. In general, the clinical appearance suggested quite a good state of nutrition in all these children. The disorders among these included celiac disease, eczema, cystic fibrosis of the pancreas, healed osteomyelitis, tuberculosis meningitis, laryngeal obstruction, mental retardation, lymphatic leukemia, and rheumatic heart disease. The relative proportion of triene fatty acids was extremely low in all three groups of subjects studied.

a. Summary

Spectrographic analysis of the serum fatty acids of human subjects indicates that the content of diene and tetraene fatty acids varies with the nutritional status of the individual. The proportion of two, three, and four double-bond fatty acids of the total fatty acids in a group of thirty-three well-nourished adults and children averaged 27.8, 1.3, and 12.7 %, respectively. In a group of eighteen subjects in poor nutritional state, these values, were 10.5, 2.5, and 7.5 %, respectively.

5. SUMMARY OF EFFECTS OF DEFICIENCY

Human beings appear not to synthesize fatty acids with two and four double bonds (linoleic and arachidonic acid) sufficient to maintain high blood serum levels. There is a possibility that poor nutritional status and susceptibility to dermatitis, skin infections, and respiratory infections may be related to an inadequacy of dietary fat containing essential fatty acids. No data whatsoever are available to indicate the magnitude of the human requirement for linoleic and arachidonic acids.

IX. Pharmacology

ARILD E. HANSEN and GEORGE A. EMERSON

A. CHEMICAL ASPECTS

Progress in basic chemical knowledge has aided in clearer interpretation of biological phenomena in relation to essential fatty acids. The linoleic acid of beef tallow has been identified as cis,cis-9,12-linoleic acid, and the linolenic acid from the same source as cis,cis,cis-9,12,15-linolenic acid, which implies that these should function as essential fatty acids.[1] Canadian lard[2] has been found to contain, on the average, 8.7 % of linoleic, 0.6 % of linolenic, and 0.4 % of arachidonic acid. Arachidonic acid has been identified[3,4] in pig back fat. The liquid fatty acids of shark liver oil,[5] which are 60 % of the total, contain 15 % linoleic and 2.6 % linolenic acid. It is realized[6] that the fatty acid composition of oils such as linseed oil cannot be predicted from the iodine value alone. Cardiolipin has been recognized[7] as a complex phosphatidic acid containing a large amount of linoleic acid.

Relative reactivities toward hydrogenation have been noted[8] for several mono-, di- and triethenoic acids, and a saturase has been found[9] in pumpkin seedlings. Oxidation of the essential fatty acids has been intensively studied, both with soybean lipoxidase,[10-12] which is specific for the essential fatty acids, and with heme compounds.[13-15] Both hemin and hemoglobin are destroyed during catalyzed autoxidation of linoleic and linolenic acids, with liberation of inorganic iron, under physiologic conditions.[16] Crude linoleic acid in the diet causes a progressive secondary anemia in rats.[17] Oxygenated linoleic acid is very susceptible to further oxidation.[18] Copper, in trace amounts, greatly accelerates autoxidation of linoleic acid,[19] and it has been suggested that peroxides formed in the brain may be destroyed by linolenic and linoleic acids in a reaction catalyzed by copper,[20] since the catalase con-

[1] H. B. Knight, E. F. Jordan, Jr., and D. Swern, *J. Biol. Chem.* **164,** 477 (1946).

[2] H. J. Lips and G. A. Grant, *Can. J. Research* **F25,** 63 (1947).

[3] F. B. Shorland and P. B. D. de la Mare, *Biochem. J.* **39,** 246 (1945).

[4] P. B. D. de la Mare and F. B. Shorland, *New Zealand J. Sci. Technol.* **B27,** 465 (1946).

[5] I. M. Gajjar, *J. Sci. Ind. Research (India)* **5,** 18 (1946).

[6] E. P. Painter and L. L. Nesbitt, *Oil & Soap* **20,** 208 (1943).

[7] M. C. Pangborn, *J. Biol. Chem.* **168,** 351 (1947).

[8] A. E. Bailey and G. S. Fisher, *Oil & Soap* **23,** 14 (1946).

[9] A. Zeller and F. Maschek, *Biochem. Z.* **312,** 354 (1942).

[10] R. T. Holman and G. O. Burr, *Arch. Biochem.* **7,** 47 (1945).

[11] S. Bergström, *Arkiv Kemi, Mineral. Geol.* **21A,** No. **15,** 1 (1946).

[12] R. T. Holman, *Arch. Biochem.* **10,** 519 (1946).

[13] F. Haurowitz, *Compt. rend. ann. et arch. soc. turq. sci. phys. et nat.* **8,** 10 (1941–1942).

[14] F. Haurowitz and P. Schwerin, *Enzymologia* **9,** 193 (1941).

[15] F. P. Simon, M. K. Horwitt, and R. W. Gerard, *J. Biol. Chem.* **154,** 421 (1944).

[16] F. Haurowitz, P. Schwerin, and M. M. Yenson, *J. Biol. Chem.* **140,** 353 (1941).

[17] P. György, R. Tomarelli, R. P. Ostergard, and J. B. Brown, *J. Exptl. Med.* **76,** 413 (1942).

[18] H. von Euler, L. Ahlström, and B. Ek, *Arkiv Kemi, Mineral. Geol.* **24A,** No. **17,** 1 (1947).

[19] F. G. Smith and E. Stotz, *N. Y. State Agr. Expt. Sta. Tech. Bull.* **276,** 1 (1946).

[20] I. Huszak, *Orvosok Lapja* **2,** 1245 (1946).

tent of the brain is so low. The essential fatty acids are capable of destroying the chemical carcinogens 3,4-benzopyrene[21] and 20-methylcholanthrene by a coupled oxidation, but 1,2,5,6-dibenzanthracene is destroyed much more slowly.[22] Linoleic and arachidonic acids[17] also destroy N,N-dimethylamino-azobenzene. Linseed oil and lard have no effect on actions of carcinogens incorporated in these lipids.[23]

The RQ of isolated rat liver is increased to 1.23 by linolenic acid, and to 0.95 by a mixture of oleic and linoleic acids, although both the latter acids decrease it when added singly.[24]

B. BIOLOGICAL ASPECTS

Considerable progress has been made in the study of the normal role of the essential fatty acids in microorganisms, plants, and animals. Linoleic acid is a growth stimulant for some species of *Lactobacillus*,[25, 26] but not for others.[26-28] Linoleic, linolenic, and arachidonic acids are essential to growth of an unidentified *Micrococcus*,[29] and enhance growth of others,[30] whereas the saturated acids are ineffective. Linoleic acid is essential for sustained growth *in vitro* of *Trichomonas vaginalis*.[31]

A possible relation of linolenic acid content to longevity and germination of pine seeds is suggested[32] through parallel species variation.

The biological importance of variation in linoleic acid content of plants used as food by insects is noted[33] in regard to the sugar beet webworm, *Loxostege sticticalis* L. Sterile females of this species are also abnormal in that they contain no linoleic acid; of their host plants, lamb's quarters contain 20.5 % and sugar beets or sage less than 1 % of linoleic acid, in terms of total fatty acids, suggesting the significance of diet in sterility in this species. *Ephestia* spp., *Tenebrio molitor*, and various beetles and moths have been

[21] G. C. Mueller and H. P. Rusch, *Cancer Research* **5**, 480 (1945).

[22] G. C. Mueller, J. A. Miller, and H. P. Rusch, *Cancer Research* **5**, 401 (1945).

[23] H. A. Davenport, J. L. Savage, M. J. Dirstine, and F. B. Queen, *Cancer Research* **1**, 821 (1941).

[24] E. Annau, A. Eperjessy, and Z. L. Zanthureczky, *Hoppe-Seyler's Z. physiol. Chem.* **279**, 66 (1943).

[25] W. L. Williams, H. P. Broquist, and E. E. Snell, *J. Biol. Chem.* **170**, 619 (1947).

[26] B. M. Guirard, E. E. Snell, and R. J. Williams, *Arch. Biochem.* **9**, 361 (1946).

[27] E. Kodicek and A. N. Worden, *Biochem. J.* **39**, 78 (1945).

[28] V. R. Williams and E. A. Fieger, *J. Biol. Chem.* **166**, 335 (1946).

[29] R. J. Dubos, *Proc. Soc. Exptl. Biol. Med.* **63**, 56 (1946).

[30] R. J. Dubos, *J. Exptl. Med.* **85**, 9 (1947).

[31] H. Sprince and A. B. Kupferberg, *J. Bacteriol.* **53**, 441 (1947).

[32] N. T. Mirov, *Nature* **154**, 218 (1944).

[33] J. H. Pepper and E. Hastings, *Montana Agr. Expt. Sta. Bull.* **413**, 1 (1943).

studied in regard to their requirements for essential fatty acids;[34-36] it is possible in *Ephestia* to differentiate effects of linoleic and arachidonic acids.

Several studies have dealt with the requirements of mammals for essential fatty acids under various conditions. Rats are most commonly used, since the deficiency causes well-defined signs and symptoms. In dogs, fat deficiency is characterized by skin changes and decreased resistance to infection.[37] Although nutritive value of dietary fats depends on their content of linoleic, linolenic, and arachidonic acids, the relative proportions are also important, and forced exercise can elicit deficiency symptoms in rats fed a diet containing horse fat, even though this fat supports growth better than does linseed oil.[38] In rapidly growing pigs, less linoleic acid is incorporated into back fat than during slower growth.[39] In rats, there is no sex difference in the composition of stored fat, but males are more susceptible to essential fatty acid deficiency.[40] Deficiency in essential fatty acids does not affect fat absorption in rats.[41] Effects of diet on distribution and composition of fat in the rat have been intensively studied.[42, 43] Synthetic margarine, containing no unsaturated fatty acids or phosphatides, is well absorbed but produces diarrhea, renal damage, and yellow atrophy of the liver.[44] Rats maintained for long periods on a high carbohydrate diet with deficiency in essential fatty acids show a markedly increased absorptive capacity for glucose, whereas mature rats fed a high fat diet for relatively short periods show a decreased absorption of glucose.[45] Caffeine is reputed[46] to increase the unsaturated fatty acid content of the liver when it is given orally, but not subcutaneously. If a fat-free diet is given to rats during pregnancy, *cis*,*cis*-9,12-linoleic acid may be found in the mother but not in the young.[47] Offspring of rats fed a fat-poor diet develop Schachtelhalmschwanz, a rush-like jointed tail.[48] If deuterium-tagged fatty acids are fed to pregnant rats, they are found also in the fetuses.[49] It is possible to produce an essential

[34] G. Fraenkel and M. Blewett, *Nature* **155,** 392 (1945).

[35] G. Fraenkel and M. Blewett, *Biochem. J.* **40,** xii (1946).

[36] G. Fraenkel and M. Blewett, *Biochem. J.* **41,** 475 (1947).

[37] A. E. Hansen and H. F. Wiese, *Proc. Soc. Exptl. Biol. Med.* **52,** 205 (1943).

[38] A. von Beznak, M. von Beznak, and I. Hajdu, *Ernährung* **8,** 209 (1943).

[39] F. B. Shorland and P. B. D. de la Mare, *J. Agr. Sci.* **35,** 33 (1945).

[40] H. G. Loeb and G. O. Burr, *J. Nutrition* **33,** 541 (1947).

[41] R. H. Barnes, E. S. Miller, and G. O. Burr, *J. Biol. Chem.* **140,** 773 (1941).

[42] I. Smedley-MacLean and E. M. Hume, *Biochem. J.* **35,** 990 (1941).

[43] I. Rieckehoff, R. Holman, and G. O. Burr, *Federation Proc.* **6,** 418 (1947).

[44] F. H. Rein, *Food Inds.* **19,** 1353, 1466 (1947).

[45] R. G. Sinclair and R. J. Fassina, *J. Biol. Chem.* **141,** 509 (1941).

[46] H. Hindemith, *Arch. exptl. Pathol. Pharmakol.* **199,** 167 (1942).

[47] K. Bernhard and H. Bodur, *Helv. Chim. Acta* **29,** 1782 (1946).

[48] K. Bernhard and H. Bodur, *Helv. Physiol. et Pharmacol. Acta* **4,** C41 (1946).

[49] W. H. Goldwater and D. Stetten, Jr., *J. Biol. Chem.* **169,** 723 (1947).

fatty acid deficiency in mice,[50] preventable or curable by lard, as in rats. A deficiency may also be produced in the *mature* as well as the young rat, and ethyl linoleate rapidly relieves the symptoms; recovery also follows a sufficiently prolonged maintenance on a fat-free diet, suggesting that synthesis of essential fatty acids can occur under these circumstances.[51] On the other hand, no synthesis of linoleic or linolenic acids is detected in rats given D_2O, as reflected by incorporation of deuterium into the fatty acid molecule, although deuterium is found in palmitic, stearic, and even oleic acids of rats so treated.[52, 53] As mentioned above, plants[33] and some insects[34] can synthesize linoleic acid. Among the unsaturated fatty acids of hair of human adults, the essential fatty acids may have a bactericidal role akin to the fungicidal action postulated for the odd-number C_{7-13} acids present, in conferring resistance to ringworm in the adult.[54]

C. VITAMIN INTERRELATIONSHIPS

Supplementation of the diet of rats fed carotene with the unsaturated fatty acids of butter results in accumulation of twice as much vitamin A in the liver as when saturated fatty acids are given.[55] Other work[56] indicates that the utilization of carotene from oils depends on the vitamin E rather than linoleic acid content. Gossypol has been shown to increase the effects of suboptimal supplements of vitamin A and lard or methyl linoleate in diets deficient in both vitamin A and the essential fatty acids, acting as an antoxidant.[57] An antagonism between carotene and linoleic or linolenic esters in rats deficient in vitamin A is said to be prevented by α-tocopherol, probably by the same mechanism.[58] Among the vitamin B complex, the essential fatty acids antagonize the lipotropic effect of inositol in rats but have no effect on the action of choline.[59] In rat dermatitis, ethyl linoleate has a curative action whereas pyridoxine at best only alleviates, but pyridoxine will potentiate subcurative doses of ethyl linoleate.[60] The anti-

[50] E. A. White, J. R. Foy, and L. R. Cerecedo, *Proc. Soc. Exptl. Biol. Med.* **54**, 301 (1943).

[51] V. H. Barki, H. Nath, E. B. Hart, and C. A. Elvehjem, *Proc. Soc. Exptl. Biol. Med.* **66**, 474 (1947).

[52] K. Bernhard, H. Steinhauser, and F. Bullet, *Helv. Chim. Acta* **25**, 1913 (1942).

[53] F. Bullet and K. Bernhard, *Helv. Physiol. et Pharmacol. Acta* **1**, C39 (1943).

[54] A. W. Weitkamp, A. M. Smiljanic, and S. Rothman, *J. Am. Chem. Soc.* **69**, 1936 (1947).

[55] E. F. Brown and W. R. Bloor, *J. Nutrition* **29**, 349 (1945).

[56] S. D. Rao, *Nature* **156**, 234, 449 (1945).

[57] E. L. Hove, *J. Biol. Chem.* **156**, 633 (1944).

[58] W. C. Sherman, *Proc. Soc. Exptl. Biol. Med.* **47**, 199 (1941).

[59] J. M. R. Beveridge and C. C. Lucas, *J. Biol. Chem.* **157**, 311 (1945).

[60] F. W. Quackenbush, H. Steenbock, F. A. Kummerow, and B. R. Platz, *J. Nutrition* **24**, 225 (1942).

acrodynic potency of various seed oils is related to the linoleic acid content, except when the linolenic acid content is high, in which case less effect than expected is obtained.[61] Earlier studies[62, 63] indicated that ethyl linoleate has no sparing action on pyridoxine, or that both are necessary for complete cure. In rats on a diet deficient in both pyridoxine and essential fatty acids, pyridoxine or linoleic acid supplements are equally effective in permitting growth,[64] and the content of highly unsaturated fatty acids increases in rats regardless of which supplement is given. When chicks deficient in vitamin E are fed different fractions of hog liver fatty acids, the most highly unsaturated fraction is the most toxic,[65] and unsaturated fatty acids increase symptoms of vitamin E deficiency in chicks.[66] Vitamin E-deficient rats given unsaturated fatty acids show a diffuse brown pigmentation of stored fat, together with a lack of the normal pigment of the incisors which is due to iron.[67] The pigmentation of lipids is taken to indicate[68] a metabolic interrelation of vitamin E and the essential fatty acids. Vitamin E increases symptoms of essential fatty acid deficiency but potentiates strongly with the effects of unsaturated fatty acids in counteracting this deficiency.[69]

D. ACTION ON PHYSIOLOGIC PROCESSES

The essential fatty acids are necessary for normal reproduction and lactation in the rat.[70, 71] The comparative potencies of the actions of methyl arachidonate and methyl linoleate on growth are different from relative curative effects on other disturbances in essential fatty acid deficiency in rats.[72, 73] Very small amounts of methyl linoleate greatly increase fat storage in the rat.[74]

If linseed meal is added to an otherwise adequate diet, chicks show in-

[61] D. S. Anthony, F. W. Quackenbush, A. J. Ihde, and H. Steenbock, *J. Nutrition* **26,** 303 (1943).

[62] G. A. Emerson, *Proc. Soc. Exptl. Biol. Med.* **47,** 445 (1941).

[63] P. Gross, *J. Invest. Dermatol.* **3,** 505 (1940).

[64] G. Medes and D. C. Keller, *Arch. Biochem.* **15,** 19 (1947).

[65] H. Dam, *J. Nutrition* **28,** 297 (1944).

[66] H. Dam, *J. Nutrition* **27,** 193 (1944).

[67] L. J. Filer, R. E. Rumery, and K. E. Mason, *Anat. Record* **97,** 387 (1947).

[68] H. Granados, K. E. Mason and H. Dam, *Acta Pathol. Microbiol. Scand.* **24,** 86 (1947).

[69] E. L. Hove and P. L. Harris, *J. Nutrition* **31,** 699 (1946).

[70] F. W. Quackenbush, F. A. Kummerow, and H. Steenbock, *J. Nutrition* **24,** 213 (1942).

[71] J. K. Loosli, J. F. Lingenfelter, J. W. Thomas, and L. A. Maynard, *J. Nutrition* **28,** 81 (1944).

[72] E. M. Hume, L. C. A. Nunn, I. Smedley-Maclean, and H. H. Smith, *Biochem. J.* **34,** 879 (1940).

[73] F. E. Visscher and R. C. Corley, *J. Biol. Chem.* **147,** 291 (1943).

[74] I. Smedley-Maclean and L. C. A. Nunn, *Biochem. J.* **34,** 884 (1940).

hibition of growth; this can be prevented by prior soaking of the meal in water, and drying before mixing with the diet.[75, 76] Since formation of HCN was previously shown[77] to be the most toxic factor in use of the meal, it is not likely that the essential fatty acids are involved. Linoleic acid decreases the synthesis of acetylcholine.[78] Linoleic and linolenic acid deficiency is accompanied by a reduction in time of excitation of peripheral motor nerves and a prolongation of muscular excitation;[79] these aberrances are corrected by treatment with linoleic and linolenic acids. The incidence of ulcers of the gizzard in chicks fed a diet containing cinchophen decreases if methyl arachidonate or the methyl esters of highly unsaturated fatty acids from the phosphatides of beef adrenals are fed.[80]

E. CHEMOTHERAPY

Antibiotics from yeasts and *Torula utilis* are a mixture of unsaturated fatty acids;[81] that from the mycelia of *Penicillium crustosum* is linoleic acid;[82] and the antibiotic lipid from *Tetrahymena geleii* is a mixture of unsaturated C_{22-24} acids.[83] It is probable that other, unidentified antibiotics may ultimately be found to be essential fatty acids. Linoleic and linolenic acids inhibit oxygen uptake by *Mycobacterium tuberculosis hominis*.[84] These acids also inhibit germination of spores of *Clostridium botulinum* at a concentration of 1 mg. % but have no effect on vegetative cells; addition of 1 % starch to the medium antagonizes this inhibition.[85] These acids also inactivate the neurotropic strain of yellow fever virus, while the virus retains its antigenicity in mice.[86] Fever appears to cause a flooding of unsaturated fatty acids into the blood, and the temporarily beneficial effect of fever in eczema may be related to this.[87]

[75] H. I. MacGregor and J. McGinnis, *Poultry Sci.* **27,** 141 (1948).

[76] F. H. Kratzer and D. E. Williams, *Poultry Sci.* **27,** 236 (1948).

[77] R. Vuillaume and J. Gillet, *Compt. rend. soc. biol.* **136,** 614 (1942).

[78] C. Torda and H. G. Wolff, *Proc. Soc. Exptl. Biol. Med.* **59,** 246 (1945).

[79] R. Lecoq, P. Chauchard, and H. Mazoué, *Bull. soc. chim. biol.* **29,** 717 (1947).

[80] H. Dam, *Acta Physiol. Scand.* **12,** 189 (1946).

[81] E. Uroma and E. A. Virtanen, *Ann. Med. Exptl. et Biol. Fenniae (Helsinki)* **25,** 36 (1947).

[82] R. F. Riley and D. K. Miller, *Arch. Biochem.* **18,** 13 (1948).

[83] C. M. McKee, J. D. Dutcher, V. Groupé, and M. Moore, *Proc. Soc. Exptl. Biol. Med.* **65,** 326 (1947).

[84] S. Bergström, H. Theorell, and H. Davide, *Nature* **157,** 306 (1946).

[85] J. W. Foster and E. S. Wynne, *J. Bacteriol.* **55,** 495 (1948).

[86] G. M. Findlay, *Trans. Roy. Soc. Trop. Med. Hyg.* **36,** 247 (1943).

[87] A. V. Stoesser, *J. Allergy* **18,** 29 (1947).

X. Requirements

RALPH T. HOLMAN

A. OF ANIMALS

The daily linoleic acid requirement for maximum growth of rats has been variously set at 20 to 100 mg.[1-5] The prophylactic dose of linoleic acid seems to be of the order of 20 mg. per day. Using highly purified diet, Mac-Kenzie et al.[6] found that 23 mg. of methyl linoleate per day was sufficient to allow normal growth and reproduction. Greenberg et al.[7] found that the daily dietary requirement for the male rat was in the range of 50 to 100 mg. of linoleic acid, whereas the female requires between 10 and 20 mg. They also found that linolenic acid, if sparked by some linoleic acid, had growth-promoting activity equal to that of linoleic acid. However, Deuel et al.[8] found that 10 % cottonseed oil in the diet of rats receiving an optimum level of linoleate gave added growth, indicating the possibility of a beneficial effect of oil itself or of some constituent of the oil.

The linoleic acid requirement varies with the composition of the diet. Rations including corn starch or rice starch fail to produce fat deficiency[9] because of unsaturated fatty acids bound in the starch granules. Diets containing saturated fats as the sole source of energy accentuate fat deficiency.[10] When Sinclair fed trielaidin as dietary fat, the deficiency symptoms could not be cured by a daily dose of 20 mg. of corn oil.[11] These scattered observations suggest that either the requirement for linoleic acid is increased when non-essential fat is metabolized, or that some synthesis of essential fatty acids is possible from sucrose.

Several early studies seemed to indicate that tissue linoleic acid parallels

[1] G. O. Burr and M. M. Burr, J. Biol. Chem. **86,** 587 (1930).

[2] O. Turpeinen, J. Nutrition **15,** 531 (1938).

[3] G. O. Burr, J. B. Brown, J. P. Kass, and W. O. Lundberg, Proc. Soc. Exptl. Biol. Med. **44,** 242 (1940).

[4] E. M. Hume, L. C. A. Nunn, I. Smedley-Maclean, and H. H. Smith, Biochem. J. **32,** 2162 (1938).

[5] E. M. Hume, L. C. A. Nunn, I. Smedley-Maclean, and H. H. Smith, Biochem. J. **34,** 879 (1940).

[6] C. G. MacKenzie, J. B. MacKenzie, and E. V. McCollum, Biochem. J. **33,** 935 (1939).

[7] S. M. Greenberg, C. E. Calbert, E. E. Savage, and H. J. Deuel, Jr. J. Nutrition **41,** 473 (1950).

[8] H. J. Deuel, S. M. Greenberg, C. E. Calbert, E. E. Savage, and T. Fukui, J. Nutrition **40,** 351 (1950).

[9] H. M. Evans and S. Lepkovsky, J. Biol. Chem. **96,** 143 (1932).

[10] H. M. Evans and S. Lepkovsky, J. Biol. Chem. **96,** 157 (1932).

[11] R. G. Sinclair. J. Nutrition **19,** 131 (1940).

the dietary intake of this acid.[12-14] Bernhard *et al.*[15] and Schoenheimer[16] found that tissue linoleic and linolenic acids incorporated deuterium from the body water enriched with heavy water at a much lower rate than did the other fatty acids, suggesting that the animal does not synthesize essential acids. On the other hand, studies using spectrophotometric techniques for the measurement of the unsaturated acids seem to indicate synthesis of small amounts of essential fatty acids by animals on a fat-deficient diet. Medes and Keller[17] found that rats synthesized polyunsaturated fatty acids when diets deficient in B_6 and fat were supplemented with vitamin B_6 . In their studies on fat deficiency in adult rats, Barki *et al.* found spontaneous cures and demonstrated that the essential fatty acid content of the animals rose when they recovered spontaneously.[18] The discrepancies between the deuterium experiments and these latter observations were probably due to the relatively short-term nature of the deuterium experiments and the apparent slow rate of turnover of the polyunsaturated fatty acids. It appears that the essential fatty acids can be synthesized by the animal, but not in sufficient quantity to provide for the needs of the growing animal.

B. HUMAN BEINGS

There is no specific information regarding the essentiality of linoleic acid, or similar unsaturated fatty acids, in human nutrition. The evidence indicates that these fatty acids may be essential, that the requirement is relatively small, and that ordinary diets easily supply this requirement. The Food and Nutrition Board of the National Research Council recommends that an adequate diet should contain essential fatty acids to the extent of 1 % of the total calories.

[12] N. R. Ellis and O. G. Hankins, *J. Biol. Chem.* **66,** 101 (1925).

[13] A. Banks, T. P. Hilditch, and E. C. Jones, *Biochem. J.* **27,** 1375 (1933).

[14] H. E. Longenecker, *J. Biol. Chem.* **128,** 645 (1939).

[15] K. Bernhard, H. Steinhauser, and F. Bullet, *Helv. Chim. Acta* **25,** 83 (1942).

[16] R. Schoenheimer, The Dynamic State of Body Constituents, p. 18. Harvard University Press, Cambridge, Mass., 1949.

[17] G. Medes and D. C. Keller, *Arch. Biochem.* **15,** 19 (1947).

[18] V. H. Barki, R. A. Collins, E. B. Hart, and C. A. Elvehjem, *Proc. Soc. Exptl. Biol. Med.* **71,** 694 (1949).

I. Nomenclature and Formula

ROBERT S. HARRIS

Accepted name: Inositol
Obsolete names: *meso*-Inositol
             Dambose
             Meat sugar
             i-Inositol
             Inosite
             Nucite
             Phaseomannite
Empirical formula: $C_6H_{12}O_6$
Chemical name: Hexahydroxycyclohexane
Structures of natural inositols:

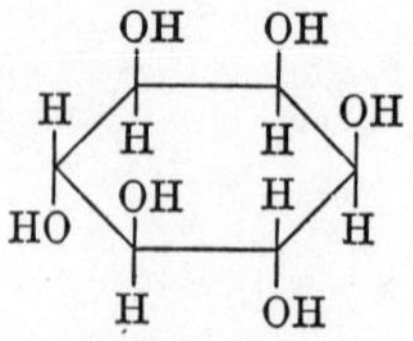

myo-Inositol   D-Inositol

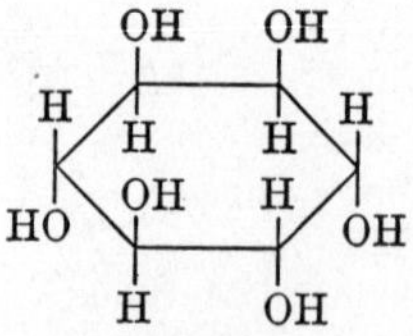

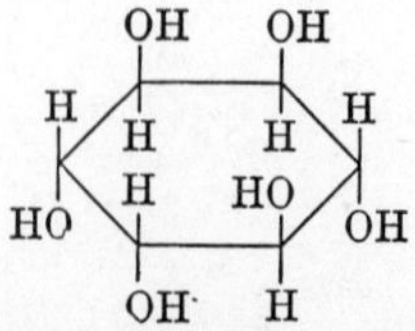

L-Inositol   Scyllitol

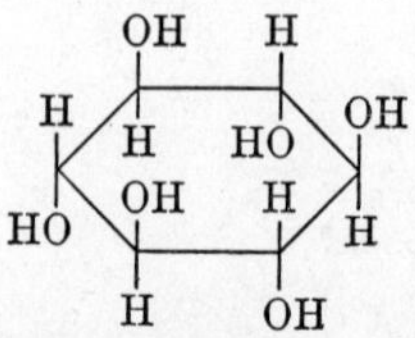

A. DISCUSSION OF TERMINOLOGY[1]

HENRY A. LARDY

There are nine possible stereoisomeric forms of hexahydroxycyclohexane, commonly called inositols or cyclohexitols.[1a] Several of these isomers occur naturally, and a few others have been synthesized. Of the nine isomers, seven are optically inactive or *meso* forms, and two are asymmetric enantiomorphs which have been designated *d* and *l*. The isomer which is most widely distributed in nature, and which is of importance for the nutrition of animals and certain microorganisms, has been called *meso*-inositol or *i*-inositol (referring to the fact that it is optically inactive). It has been renamed *myo*-inositol.[2] The prefixes *i* or *meso* are not at all suitable for distinguishing this isomer from the other six optically inactive isomers, since they too are *meso* forms. Furthermore, derivatives of *myo*-inositol may become optically active by asymmetric substitution, and to use *i* or *meso* in the name of such derivatives is chemically incorrect and confusing. For these reasons it seemed desirable, when proposing a systematic nomenclature for the inositols and their derivatives,[2] to rename this isomer. Since Scherer[3] had originally isolated this compound from muscle and had in fact called it "muscle sugar," the name *myo*-inositol[4] (Greek, μῦσ, μυός, muscle) was proposed[2] and soon adopted in the chemical literature.[5]

In Table I the structures of the nine stereoisomeric inositols are shown, together with their trivial names and a designated[2] sequence for numbering the carbon atoms. In the formulas the hydroxyl groups are indicated by vertical lines. Four of the isomers—*myo*-, D-, and L-inositols, and scyllitol—occur naturally, either in the free form or as a wide variety of derivatives.[6, 7] Three of the remaining isomers—*epi*, *allo*, and *muco*—have been synthesized, the first by Posternak[8] and the latter two by Dangschat.[9, 9a]

---

[1] (*Editors' note.*) At the present time the nomenclature of the inositols is confusing. This section was written by Dr. Lardy in an attempt to eliminate this confusion. The systemic nomenclature suggested by Dr. Lardy has not yet been approved and adopted by the American Association of Biological Chemists, or some similar scientific body. For this reason the Editors have not insisted that all contributors to this chapter use the proposed nomenclature. Instead, each author has been permitted to use the nomenclature he prefers.

[1a] L. Maquenne, Les Sucres et leurs Principaux Dérivés, p. 190, Carre et Naud, Paris, 1900.

[2] H. G. Fletcher, Jr., L. Anderson, and H. A. Lardy, *J. Org. Chem.* **16**, 1238 (1951).

[3] J. Scherer, *Ann. Chem. Justus Liebigs* **73**, 322 (1850).

[4] Compare the analogous myoglobin, myoblast, myocyst, myosin.

[5] B. Magasanik, *J. Am. Chem. Soc.* **73**, 5919 (1951).

[6] H. G. Fletcher, Jr., *Advances in Carbohydrate Chem.* **3**, 45 (1948).

[7] W. W. Pigman and R. M. Goepp, Jr., Carbohydrate Chemistry. Academic Press, New York, 1948.

[8] T. Posternak, *Helv. Chim. Acta* **19**, 1333 (1936).

[9] G. Dangschat, *Naturwissenschaften* **31**, 146 (1942).

The systematic naming of derivatives of the inositols is complicated by the fact that optically inactive parent inositols can yield optically active derivatives by asymmetric substitution. Furthermore, monoketo-inositols may be related to two different parent inositols. It can be readily appreciated how this situation gave rise to inconsistencies of nomenclature as more derivatives of known types were prepared and as new types of derivatives were discovered.

TABLE I

THE NUMBERING OF THE NINE STEREOISOMERIC INOSITOLS

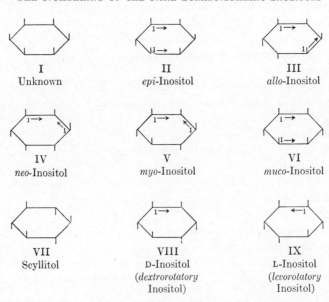

I Unknown	II *epi*-Inositol	III *allo*-Inositol
IV *neo*-Inositol	V *myo*-Inositol	VI *muco*-Inositol
VII Scyllitol	VIII D-Inositol (*dextrorotatory* Inositol)	IX L-Inositol (*levorotatory* Inositol)

To eliminate the confusion, a systematic nomenclature for this important class of compounds and its derivatives was developed.[2] The system is based on the numbering sequence shown in Table I and on three rules.

The numbering sequence provides identical numbers for stereochemically equivalent carbon atoms. For D- or L-inositols the numbering begins with the carbon atom marked 1 and must proceed in the designated direction. Isomer IV and *epi*-, *allo*-, *myo*-, and *muco*-inositols may be numbered either clockwise or counterclockwise, depending on which results in the lower numbers of substituents. In isomer I (all *cis*) and in scyllitol (all *trans*) all carbon atoms are equivalent, and derivatives of these isomers

[9a] Since this was written, an inositol corresponding to IV has been synthesized by S. J. Angyal and N. K. Matheson (*Abstr. 123rd Meeting, Am. Chem. Soc.*, p. 120, 1953) and named *neo*-inositol.

would be named to give the lowest possible number to the carbon atoms bearing groups other than unsubstituted hydroxyl.

The explicit rules for naming inositol derivatives are presented below with amplifications in which emphasis is given to naming derivatives of the vitamin *myo*-inositol.

RULE 1. *In accordance with established practice in the carbohydrate field the trivial names of the parent inositols will be used.*

This rule is self-explanatory from Table I and from what has been said above concerning reasons for using the prefix *myo* rather than *i* or *meso* to designate the nutritionally important isomer.

RULE 2. *The structures of the optically active cyclitols and of all optically active derivatives of the other cyclitols are designated as belonging to the D or L series, based upon the configuration of the highest numbered carbon atom.*

Some method is obviously needed to distinguish the name of a compound from that of its enantiomorph. In the field of carbohydrate chemistry it has been the general practice to designate the configuration of a sugar molecule according to the configuration of its highest numbered asymmetric carbon atom. The configuration of this carbon atom is established by relating it to the configurations of the recognized standard compounds, D- and L-glyceraldehyde. This practice may be extended to the inositols by projecting the highest numbered carbon atom (i.e., number 6) onto a plane with carbon atoms 1 and 5 projecting below the plane (away from the viewer) and the H and OH above the plane (toward the viewer).

D series   L series

This rule would be applied to naming two enantiomorphic monophosphoric esters of *myo*-inositol, X and XI, in the following manner.

X   XI

By comparison with Table I it is apparent that both are *myo*-inositol-1-phosphates. Their configurations are determined by projecting carbon atom 6 onto a plane, as described above. Hudson's[10] projection formulas

---

[10] C. S. Hudson, *Advances in Carbohydrate Chem.* **3**, 1 (1948).

of the two structures in question are:

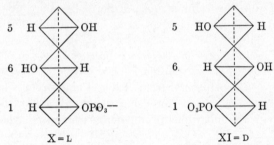

$$X = L$$ $$XI = D$$

Thus X would be named L-*myo*-inositol-1-phosphate, and XI would be D-*myo*-inositol-1-phosphate.

RULE 3. *When an inositol derivative contains less than six asymmetric carbon atoms, the compound will be given the trivial name of one of the parent inositols to which it is related, the choice being that parent inositol which has the maximum number of cis-hydroxyl groups.* Where this offers more than one possibility, as in the diketoinositols, the following also apply. *Secondarily, the parent inositol chosen is that which has the lowest possible number for its substituents cis to the hydroxyl on carbon 1, or, finally, that which would confer the lowest possible numbering on substituents other than hydroxyl.*

This rule may be illustrated by its application to the ketoinositols (named inososes by Posternak[8]) obtainable by oxidation of *myo*-inositol.

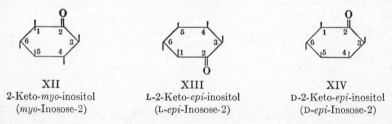

XII	XIII	XIV
2-Keto-*myo*-inositol	L-2-Keto-*epi*-inositol	D-2-Keto-*epi*-inositol
(*myo*-Inosose-2)	(L-*epi*-Inosose-2)	(D-*epi*-Inosose-2)

The bacterium *Acetobacter suboxydans* oxidizes *myo*-inositol[11, 12] to a mono-ketoinositol which was shown by Posternak[13] to have the structure XII. This compound (XII) has three hydroxyl groups projecting upward and only two projecting downward. Hence, according to rule 3 it receives the trivial name of *myo*-inositol which has an hydroxyl group projecting upward in position 2. The name of choice for XII is therefore 2-keto-*myo*-inositol or *myo*-inosose-2. It had previously been named *scyllo-meso*-inosose by

[11] A. J. Kluyver and A. G. J. Boezaardt, *Rec. trav. chim.* **58**, 956 (1939).
[12] H. E. Carter, C. Belinsky, R. K. Clark, Jr., E. H. Flynn, B. Lytle, G. E. McCasland, and M. Robbins, *J. Biol. Chem.* **174**, 415 (1948).

Posternak,[13] since it could be selectively reduced to either scyllitol or *meso*-inositol (*myo*-inositol).

Nitric acid oxidation of *myo*-inositol produces a monoketoinositol which is a racemic mixture of XIII and XIV. Posternak[14] resolved this mixture and demonstrated that the levorotatory isomer had structure XIV. Although this compound was obtained from *myo*-inositol, according to rule 3 it must be assigned the trivial name of the inositol in which the hydroxyl on carbons 1, 2, 3, 4, and 5 are *cis*, i.e., *epi*-inositol. By rule 2, structure XIV is placed in the D configurational series, and the exact name is therefore D-2-keto-*epi*-inositol or D-*epi*-inosose-2. The enantiomorphic XIII is L-2-keto-*epi*-inositol or L-*epi*-inosose-2.

The diketoinositol shown in formula XV is related to both *myo*- and *muco*-inositols (but not to either D- or L-inositol, because these have fewer *cis*-hydroxyl groups—see rule 3). Since the substituents *cis* to the hydroxyl on carbon 1 in *myo*-inositol have a numbering sequence (1, 2, 3, 5) lower than that in *muco*-inositol (1, 2, 4, 5), the compound is correctly named 1,3-diketo-*myo*-inositol.

XV → XVI-*a*
1,3-Diketo-*myo*-inositol
not XVI-*b*
1,5-Diketo-*muco*-inositol

Aminodesoxyinositols. Several derivatives of inositol in which amino groups replace hydroxyl groups have been prepared synthetically,[15-18] and at least one, streptamine, is known to occur naturally. Carter and his co-workers[16] have coined the term *inosamine* as a generic designation for this class of substance, and other authors[17, 18] have continued the usage. The two monoaminodesoxyinositols derivable from 2-keto-*myo*-inositol (XII) have been synthesized[16, 18] and their configurations established[18, 19, 20] as XVII and XVIII. Each of these *meso* structures may readily be named

[13] T. Posternak, *Helv. Chim. Acta* **25**, 746 (1942).

[14] T. Posternak, *Helv. Chim. Acta* **29**, 1991 (1946).

[15] J. Grosheintz and H. O. L. Fischer, *J. Am. Chem. Soc.* **70**, 1479 (1948).

[16] H. E. Carter, R. K. Clark, Jr., B. Lytle, and G. E. McCasland, *J. Biol. Chem.* **175**, 683 (1948).

[17] E. May and E. Mosettig, *J. Org. Chem.* **14**, 1137 (1949).

[18] L. Anderson and H. A. Lardy, *J. Am. Chem. Soc.* **72**, 3141 (1950).

[19] T. Posternak, *Helv. Chim. Acta* **33**, 1597 (1950).

[20] G. E. McCasland, *J. Am. Chem. Soc.* **73**, 2295 (1951).

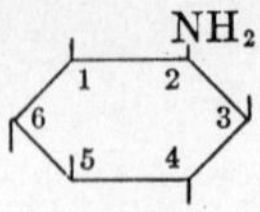

NH₂

XVII
2-Amino-2-desoxy-*myo*-inositol
(*myo*-Inosamine-2)

XVIII
Aminodesoxyscyllitol
(*scyllo*-Inosamine)

through reference to the corresponding inositol, the *myo*-inositol relative, XVII, being called 2-amino-2-desoxy-*myo*-inositol (or *myo*-inosamine-2), while XVIII is simply aminodesoxyscyllitol (or *scyllo*-inosamine). The reduction of nitrogenous derivatives of DL-2-keto-*epi*-inositol (XIII, XIV) gives two enantiomorphic pairs of inosamines: DL-2-amino-2-desoxy-*epi*-inositol (DL-*epi*-inosamine-2, XIX–XX) and DL-4-amino-4-desoxy-*myo*-inositol (DL-*myo*-inosamine-4, XXI–XXII). One of these compounds was made by Carter and his coworkers.[16] The other has been synthesized by Rieke *et al.*[21] The methods of synthesis (cf. Anderson and Lardy[18]) and properties of the compounds indicate that the compound prepared by Carter *et al.*[16] (and designated EA) is DL-*epi*-inosamine-2 (XIX–XX), and that prepared by Rieke *et al.*[21] is DL-*myo*-inosamine-4 (XXI–XXII).

The antibiotic, streptomycin, contains a diamino didesoxyinositol, which has been given the trivial name, streptamine. Previous evidence indicated that streptamine has the configuration shown in XXIII.[22] Wintersteiner

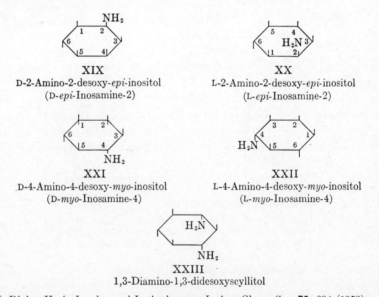

XIX
D-2-Amino-2-desoxy-*epi*-inositol
(D-*epi*-Inosamine-2)

XX
L-2-Amino-2-desoxy-*epi*-inositol
(L-*epi*-Inosamine-2)

XXI
D-4-Amino-4-desoxy-*myo*-inositol
(D-*myo*-Inosamine-4)

XXII
L-4-Amino-4-desoxy-*myo*-inositol
(L-*myo*-Inosamine-4)

XXIII
1,3-Diamino-1,3-didesoxyscyllitol

[21] H. Rieke, H. A. Lardy, and L. Anderson, *J. Am. Chem. Soc.* **75,** 694 (1953).
[22] M. L. Wolfrom, S. M. Olin, and W. J. Polglase, *J. Am. Chem. Soc.* **72,** 1724 (1950).

et al.[23] prepared a monoamino monodesoxyinositol by nitrous acid deamination of a derivative of streptamine in which one amino group was blocked. Such deamination generally occurs with Walden inversion.[19] Synthetic DL-*myo*-inosamine-4 (XXI–XXII) is identical with the compound produced from streptamine by Wintersteiner, thus confirming the all *trans* structure (XXIII) for streptamine.[21]

II. Chemistry

ERWIN CHARGAFF

The inositols[1] are a family of isomeric hexahydroxy derivatives of cyclohexane. They are the ultimate representatives of the series of hydroxycyclohexanes that can be subsumed under the general term cyclitol.[2] The designation cyclohexitol to describe the inositols is also sometimes encountered in the literature, in contrast to the cyclopentitols or desoxyinositols (quercitols), the cyclotetritols, etc. The hexahydroxycyclohexanes can exist in two optically active and seven inactive configurations, in addition to the racemic *dl* compound. Only a few of those, however, have so far been found to occur in nature, and two of the isomers do not appear to have been prepared as yet.

A. NOMENCLATURE

In a cyclic compound of the molecular formula $(CHOH)_6$ it is sufficient to indicate the positions of the hydroxyl groups; the corresponding steric positions of the hydrogen atoms are thereby defined and need not be specified. In the following discussion all numbers and graphic representations will, therefore, refer only to the hydroxyl groups.

The difficulties facing attempts at arriving at a numbering system that, with a single convention, will permit an unequivocal description of all inositol isomers and their derivatives are almost insuperable. Maquenne[3] adopted the practice, at that time followed in carbohydrate chemistry, of denoting the numbers of the carbon atoms carrying hydroxyl groups situated above and below the plane of the ring respectively by way of a fraction. *meso*-Inositol thus would be $\frac{1235}{46}$ or $\frac{1246}{35}$ or $\frac{1356}{24}$ or $\frac{1345}{26}$, if the

---

[23] O. Wintersteiner and A. Klingsberg, *J. Am. Chem. Soc.* **73**, 2917 (1951).

[1] P. Fleury and P. Balatre, Les Inositols—Chimie et Biochimie. Masson, Paris, 1947.

[2] For a recent review on the chemistry of cyclitols, see H. G. Fletcher, Jr., *Advances in Carbohydrate Chem.* **3**, 45 (1948).

[3] L. Maquenne, Les Sucres et leurs Principaux Dérivés, Carré et Naud, Paris, 1900.

numbering proceeds in a clockwise direction. The multitude of possibilities points to the unsatisfactoriness of this system, especially if inositol derivatives are to be described.

Magasanik and Chargaff[4] proposed a system, which they applied to the cyclohexitols and their keto and desoxy derivatives, in which the carbon atoms are numbered clockwise, positions 1 and 6 chosen with their hydroxyls in *trans* position. The structure is arranged in such a manner as to have as many hydroxyl groups as possible *cis* to the one in position 1. Where this scheme allows two possibilities, that arrangement is chosen in which the carbon atoms with hydroxyls *cis* to the one in position 1 have the lowest positional numbers. The planar projection of *meso*-inositol would, consequently, be numbered in the following manner.

The inositol isomers are designated cyclohexanehexol, their desoxy derivatives cyclohexanepentol, their monocarbonyl derivatives cyclohexanepentolone, the corresponding diketones cyclohexanetetroldione, etc. In the case of the inositols it is sufficient to indicate the position of the *cis* hydroxyls. *meso*-Inositol is designated as cyclohexane-(1,2,3,5)*cis*-hexol. Similarly, its 2-keto derivative is described as cyclohexane-(1,3,5)*cis*-pentol-2-one. The corresponding 2-desoxyinositol is cyclohexane-(1,3,5)-*cis*-4,6-pentol. In this case the numbers of all hydroxyl groups must be given.

This system has the advantage that structures can be derived from designations without reference to any visual aid. It leads, however, to rather clumsy names, when sterically different polyfunctional derivatives are to be described. Moreover, it requires enantiomorphs to be numbered differently in equivalent positions.

A scheme which avoids the last-mentioned disadvantage has been proposed by Fletcher *et al.*[5] (see the preceding section by Henry A. Lardy, p. 323).

B. PLANAR PROJECTIONS

The planar projections of the cyclohexitols, including those not yet encountered or prepared, are shown in Table I. The structure of *meso*-inositol (V) is based on the work of Dangschat and Fischer[6] and Posternak[7]. The

[4] B. Magasanik and E. Chargaff, *J. Biol. Chem.* **174,** 173 (1948).
[5] H. G. Fletcher, Jr., L. Anderson, and H. A. Lardy, *J. Org. Chem.* **16,** 1238 (1951).
[6] G. Dangschat, *Naturwissenschaften* **30,** 146 (1942).
[7] T. Posternak, *Helv. Chim. Acta* **25,** 746 (1942).

structures of II,[8] VII,[7] and IX[9] were elucidated by Posternak, those of III and VI by Dangschat and Fischer.[10, 11] Table I also indicates the numbering devices and trivial names suggested by Fletcher et al.[5]

C. SPATIAL CONSTELLATIONS

Most textbooks and even review articles represent meso-inositol and its isomers in the form of planar structures. This is, however, far from acceptable, since it could lead to the assumption that the various hydroxyls situated in what would be considered as the same plane are chemically equivalent. Actually, it has been shown by Magasanik and Chargaff[4, 12-14] that the several hydroxyl groups in cis position are treated differently in a biological system, according to their position in space. These findings on the selective oxidation of the inositol isomers by resting cells of Acetobacter suboxydans, to yield mono- or dicarbonyl derivatives, were later extended to cell-free enzyme preparations.[15, 16]

It is, of course, evident that the structural formulas I–IX in Table I, representing the series of inositol isomers, do not describe the actual positions in space of the various atoms, but merely represent planar projections based on the conventions introduced into stereochemistry by Emil Fischer.[17] If the biological function and fate of meso-inositol and its isomers are to be understood, the element of rigidity, i.e., the lack of free rotation around carbon-to-carbon bonds, prevailing in these derivatives of cyclohexane, cannot be ignored.

The well-known Sachse-Mohr concept postulates the existence of puckered rings in cyclohexane; two strain-free forms are possible, the chair configuration and the boat configuration. Recent work based on electron diffraction studies[18] and spectroscopic[19] and thermodynamic[20] properties has led to the conclusion that at room temperature cyclohexane exists predominantly in the chair form. Similar considerations have been brought to bear upon the structures of the mono- and dimethyl derivatives of cyclo-

[8] T. Posternak, Helv. Chim. Acta 29, 1991 (1946).

[9] T. Posternak, Helv. Chim. Acta 19, 1007 (1936).

[10] G. Dangschat and H. O. L. Fischer, Naturwissenschaften 27, 756 (1939).

[11] H. O. L. Fischer, Harvey Lectures 40, 156 (1945).

[12] E. Chargaff and B. Magasanik, J. Biol. Chem. 165, 379 (1946).

[13] B. Magasanik and E. Chargaff, J. Biol. Chem. 175, 929 (1948).

[14] B. Magasanik and E. Chargaff, J. Biol. Chem. 175, 939 (1948).

[15] R. E. Franzl and E. Chargaff, Federation Proc. 9, 173 (1950).

[16] R. E. Franzl and E. Chargaff, Nature 168, 955 (1951).

[17] K. Freudenberg, Stereochemie, p. 662, Deuticke, Leipzig and Vienna, 1933.

[18] O. Hassel, Tidsskr. Kjemi, Bergvesen Met. 3, 32 (1943); Quart. Revs. (London) 7, 221 (1953).

[19] R. S. Rasmussen, J. Chem. Phys. 11, 249 (1943).

[20] C. W. Beckett, K. S. Pitzer, and R. Spitzer, J. Am. Chem. Soc. 69, 2488 (1947).

hexane[20, 21] and upon the various hexachlorocyclohexanes.[22] If the conceptions applied to cyclohexane and its derivatives are extended to the cyclohexitols, it will be seen that six of the substituents (hydroxyl or hydrogen) surround the ring of carbon atoms in an equatorial belt; the six others are perpendicular to the plane formed by the carbon ring: three above (north polar), three below (south polar). Each carbon atom will

TABLE II

SPATIAL CONFIGURATIONS OF CYCLOHEXITOLS[a]

| Planar projection | Compound | | Position of hydroxyls on carbon atoms | | |
	Trivial name	Designation	Equatorial	North polar	South polar
I		Cyclohexane-(1,2,3,4,5,6)-cis-hexol	1, 3, 5	2, 4, 6	—
II	epi-Inositol	Cyclohexane-(1,2,3,4,5)-cis-hexol	1, 3, 5, 6	2, 4	—
III	allo-Inositol	Cyclohexane-(1,2,3,4)-cis-hexol	1, 3, 6	2, 4	5
IV		Cyclohexane-(1,2,3)-cis-hexol	1, 3, 4, 5	2	5
V	meso-Inositol	Cyclohexane-(1,2,3,5)-cis-hexol	1, 3, 4, 5, 6	2	—
VI	muco-Inositol	Cyclohexane-(1,2,4,5)-cis-hexol	1, 5, 6	2, 4	3
VII	Scyllitol	Cyclohexane-(1,3,5)-cis-hexol	1, 2, 3, 4, 5, 6	—	—
VIII	d-Inositol	Cyclohexane-(1,2,5)-cis-hexol	1, 4, 5, 6	2	3
IX	l-Inositol	Cyclohexane-(1,2,4)-cis-hexol	2, 3, 4, 5	1	6

[a] Based on the chair configuration and on the numbering system of Magasanik and Chargaff.[4]

therefore carry one polar and one equatorial substituent. A twist of the six carbon atoms through a single plane to the opposite chair form renders the equatorial substituents polar and *vice versa*.[21] Two geometrically tautomeric forms will, consequently, exist for each inositol isomer. By analogy to the methyl-substituted cyclohexanes,[20] it may, however, be assumed that the tautomer possessing the smaller number of polar hydroxyls will predominate.

The constellations of the hydroxyl groups in the chair forms of the iso-

[21] F. D. Rossini and K. S. Pitzer, *Science* **105**, 647 (1947).
[22] O. Bastiansen, Ø. Ellefsen, and O. Hassel, *Research (London)* **2**, 248 (1949).

meric cyclohexitols are listed in Table II, with the use of the designations and the numbering system proposed by Magasanik and Chargaff.[4] The scheme of Fletcher *et al.*[5] cannot be followed for this purpose, since, as may be seen in Table I, it employs two alternative routes of numbering for five of the nine cyclohexitols. A system for the graphic presentation of the constellations of the cyclitols has been proposed recently by Magasanik *et al.*[23] In this notation, which is employed for the depiction of the inositol constellations in Table III, north polar hydroxyls are indicated by full

TABLE III

CONSTELLATIONS OF CYCLOHEXITOLS[a]

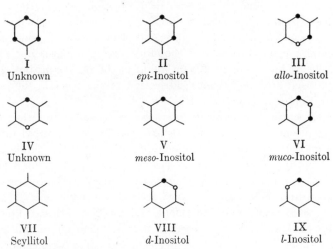

I	II	III
Unknown	*epi*-Inositol	*allo*-Inositol
IV	V	VI
Unknown	*meso*-Inositol	*muco*-Inositol
VII	VIII	IX
Scyllitol	*d*-Inositol	*l*-Inositol

[a] Based on the chair configuration. Graphic notation[23]: north polar hydroxyls, full circles; south polar hydroxyls, open circles; equatorial hydroxyls, lines.

circles, south polar hydroxyls by open circles, equatorial hydroxyls by radial lines; the hydrogen atoms are not shown.

The biological significance of the spatial configurations of the cyclohexitols has been demonstrated by the selectivity, dependent upon the stereochemistry of the different substrates, with which specific hydroxyl groups are oxidized by *Acetobacter suboxydans* to mono- or dicarbonyl derivatives. These studies have led to the following rules defining the steric requirements for oxidation:[4, 13, 14, 23] (1) Only polar hydroxyl groups are oxidized. (2) The carbon in *meta* position to the one carrying the polar hydroxyl group (in counterclockwise direction, if north polar; clockwise, if south polar) must carry an equatorial hydroxyl group.

[23] B. Magasanik, R. E. Franzl, and E. Chargaff, *J. Am. Chem. Soc.* **74**, 2618 (1952).

D. DISTRIBUTION

1. meso-INOSITOL

meso-Inositol, discovered by J. Scherer[24] in 1850, appears to be an almost ubiquitous and possibly essential cellular component. A survey of its occurrence in plant and animal tissues has been given by Fleury and Balatre.[1] The extent to which it is present in all microorganisms cannot yet be stated. It is doubtless an important constituent of the lipids and other fractions of acid-fast bacteria from which it has been isolated in quantity.[25, 26]

When meso-inositol is stated to occur in almost all types of cell, this must not be taken to mean that it can always be isolated from them without more or less extensive degradative action. There are obviously many types of derivatives in which inositol is able, and often has been shown, to exist, such as ethers, esters, lipids, and therefore also in lipoproteins, phosphoproteins, etc. It has frequently been found in the free form; but this may often have been due to enzymatic liberation taking place in the course of the preparation or the assay.

Among the naturally occurring derivatives of meso-inositol, the following may be mentioned. Bornesitol, a dextrorotatory monomethyl ether;[27, 28] sequoitol, an optically inactive monomethyl ether;[29, 30] and dambonitol, an inactive dimethyl ether.[31-33] One of the most widely distributed forms of meso-inositol is phytin, the hexaphosphoric acid ester. The various phosphates of inositol have been reviewed recently by Courtois.[34] The occurrence of meso-inositol as a component of an entire series of lipids is of great interest. It was first discovered, in this combination, in lipid preparations from tubercle bacilli and related acid-fast microorganisms,[25, 26] and later it was shown to occur in soybean phosphatides[35, 36] and in brain phosphatides.[37] The structure of the soybean inositide, for which the name

[24] J. Scherer, Ann. Chem. Justus Liebigs **73**, 322 (1850).

[25] R. J. Anderson, J. Am. Chem. Soc. **52**, 1607 (1930).

[26] E. Chargaff and R. J. Anderson, Hoppe-Seyler's Z. physiol. Chem. **191**, 172 (1930).

[27] A. Girard, Compt. rend. **73**, 426 (1871).

[28] E. R. Flint and B. Tollens, Ann. Chem. Justus Liebigs **272**, 288 (1893).

[29] E. C. Sherrard and E. F. Kurth, J. Am. Chem. Soc. **51**, 3139 (1929).

[30] N. V. Riggs, J. Chem. Soc. **1949**, 3199.

[31] A. Girard, Compt. rend. **67**, 820 (1868).

[32] C. O. Weber, Ber. deut. chem. Ges. **36**, 3108 (1903).

[33] A. W. K. De Jong, Rec. trav. chim. **27**, 257 (1908).

[34] J. E. Courtois, Bull. soc. chim. biol. **33**, 1075 (1951).

[35] E. Klenk and R. Sakai, Hoppe-Seyler's Z. physiol. Chem. **258**, 33 (1939).

[36] D. W. Woolley, J. Biol. Chem. **147**, 581 (1943).

[37] J. Folch and D. W. Woolley, J. Biol. Chem. **142**, 963 (1942).

lipositol has been suggested,[36] appears to be complex. The best characterized inositol-containing lipid doubtless is the diphosphoinositide isolated from brain by Folch,[38] which contains *meso*-inositol in the form of a diphosphate. The structure of this diphosphoric acid ester is not yet known except for the relative position of the two acid residues, which is *meta*. There exist probably many other forms in which inositol occurs in tissues; one could think of polyinositol phosphates and even of inositol polyphosphates. Indications of the existence of highly polymerized substances containing inositol have been reported.[39, 40] No more than brief reference can be made here to streptamine, a component of streptomycin, which is a *meta*-diaminocyclotetritol.[41]

2. SCYLLITOL

This cyclohexitol (structure VII) has been found in the organs of several fish varieties (dogfish, sharks, etc.),[42-44] in acorns,[45] and in the leaves of the coconut palm[46] and of dogwood.[47] Its occurrence in human urine has been reported recently.[48] A C-methyl derivative[49] of scyllitol, mytilitol, has been isolated from the mussel *Mytilus edulis*.[50-52]

3. *d*- AND *l*-INOSITOL

The optically active cyclohexitols occur in nature in the form of monomethyl ethers. The dextrorotatory pinitol, which gives rise to *d*-inositol (structure VIII), was first found in *Pinus lambertiana*,[53] but it occurs also in a variety of other plants or plant products (Madagascar rubber, redwood, loco weed).[1, 2] The following structure has recently been assigned to

[38] J. Folch, *J. Biol. Chem.* **177,** 505 (1949).
[39] D. W. Woolley, *J. Biol. Chem.* **139,** 29 (1941).
[40] J. Folch and F. N. Le Baron, *Federation Proc.* **10,** 183 (1951).
[41] R. U. Lemieux and M. L. Wolfrom, *Advances in Carbohydrate Chem.* **3,** 337 (1948).
[42] G. Staedeler and F. T. Frerichs, *J. prakt. Chem.* **73,** 48 (1858).
[43] D. Ackermann and M. Mohr, *Z. Biol.* **98,** 37 (1937).
[44] M. Mohr, *Z. Biol.* **98,** 276 (1937).
[45] C. Vincent and Delachanal, *Compt. rend.* **104,** 1855 (1887).
[46] H. Müller, *J. Chem. Soc.* **91,** 1767 (1907); **101,** 2383 (1912).
[47] C. E. Sando, K. S. Markley, and M. B. Matlack, *J. Biol. Chem.* **114,** 39 (1936).
[48] P. F. Fleury, J. E. Courtois, and A. L. Jouannet, *Abstr. 12th Intern. Congr. Pure and Applied Chem. New York* p. 82 (1951).
[49] T. Posternak, *Helv. Chim. Acta* **27,** 457 (1944).
[50] B. C. P. Jansen, *Hoppe-Seyler's Z. physiol. Chem.* **85,** 231 (1913).
[51] D. Ackermann, *Ber. deut. chem. Ges.* **54,** 1938 (1921).
[52] R. J. Daniel and W. Doran, *Biochem. J.* **20,** 676 (1926).
[53] M. Berthelot, *Compt. rend.* **41,** 392 (1855); *Ann. chim. phys.* **46,** 66 (1856).

pinitol.[54] According to the nomenclature of Fletcher *et al.*[5] it would conse-

quently be designated as 5-methyl-D-inositol.

The levorotatory quebrachitol is a monomethyl ether of *l*-inositol (structure IX). It was discovered by Tanret[55] in the bark of the quebracho tree. In addition to several other plants,[1, 2] it occurs in the latex of *Hevea brasiliensis*,[56] which appears to be the best source. The natural occurrence of racemic inositol also has been reported.[57]

4. OTHER CYCLOHEXITOLS

None of the other isomers of *meso*-inositol appears as yet to have been found in nature. It is, however, perhaps suggestive that the γ isomer of hexachlorocyclohexane ("gammexane"), widely used as an insecticide, has been shown to have the configuration of *muco*-inositol (structure VI).[58] In this connection, a brief mention of the structures of the other hexachlorocyclohexanes may be of interest: the α isomer corresponds to *d*,*l*-inositol (structures VIII and IX), the β isomer to scyllitol (structure VII), the δ isomer to *meso*-inositol (structure V), and the ε isomer to the unknown cyclohexitol IV.[22]

E. PROPERTIES

The cyclohexitols are white crystalline, non-reducing substances, soluble in water, the most sparingly soluble being scyllitol (VII). They are usually recrystallized from aqueous ethanol. For additional characterization the hexaacetates are often employed; and the distillation in vacuum of similar hexa derivatives has been suggested as a procedure for final purification.[11]

Some of the characteristics of the various isomers are as follows: *epi*-inositol (II), m.p. 285° (with decomposition); hexaacetate, m.p. 188°; *allo*-inositol (III), m.p. 270–275°; *meso*-inositol (V), m.p. 225–227°; hexaacetate, m.p. 216–217°; *muco*-inositol (VI), m.p. 285–290° (with decomposition); scyllitol (VII), m.p. 352° (with decomposition); hexaacetate, m.p.

[54] A. B. Anderson, D. L. MacDonald, and H. O. L. Fischer, *J. Am. Chem. Soc.* **74**, 1479 (1952).

[55] C. Tanret, *Compt. rend.* **109**, 908 (1889).

[56] A. W. K. De Jong, *Rev. trav. chim.* **25**, 48 (1906).

[57] C. Tanret, *Compt. rend.* **145**, 1196 (1907).

[58] G. W. van Vloten, C. A. Kruissink, B. Strijk, and J. M. Bijvoet, *Nature* **162**, 771 (1948).

296–297°; d-inositol (VIII), m.p. 249–250°; $[\alpha]_D^{25} = +65.0°$ (in water); l-inositol (IX), m.p. 249–250°; $[\alpha]_D^{22} = -63.8°$ (in water).

The behavior of cyclohexitols toward oxidizing agents is not yet completely understood. Vigorous action of nitric acid, as it is employed in the Scherer test for the qualitative demonstration of inositol, leads to aromatization and a whole series of six- and five-membered polycarbonyl compounds, such as tetrahydroxyquinone and rhodizonic, croconic, and leuconic acids. Under milder conditions $meso$-inositol (V) is converted by nitric acid to DL-2-keto-epi-inositol (numbering as in Table I).[59]

$meso$-Inositol (V) behaves in an anomalous fashion toward oxidation by periodic acid.[60] Instead of the expected uptake of 6 equivalents of oxidizing agent, only 4 equivalents are consumed in a first rapid phase, which is followed by a second, much slower one. The reaction mechanism is not yet understood completely. It is the opinion of this writer, however, that the spatial constellation of the hydroxyl group in a given inositol isomer, as discussed in Section II.C and in Tables II and III, will probably be found to influence the course of its oxidation by periodate. In this connection it is noteworthy that the product of the oxidation of $meso$-inositol by $Acetobacter\ suboxydans$,[7, 61] which carries a carbonyl group in position 2 instead of the polar hydroxyl,[4] is cleaved in a normal manner by periodic acid,[62] and that, on the other hand, the tetraacetyl derivative of $meso$-inositol containing a cis-glycol structure, which comprises a polar and an adjacent equatorial hydroxyl, is not attacked by periodate.[6]

A number of mono- and dicarbonyl derivatives of the different cyclohexitols may be obtained through the action of $Acetobacter\ suboxydans$. (Compare also Section II. C.) The inosose produced from $meso$-inositol[61] has the following structure.[7]

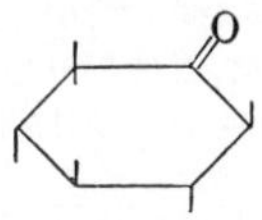

epi-Inositol (II) yields a levoratory keto derivative with the following structure.[4, 8, 12]

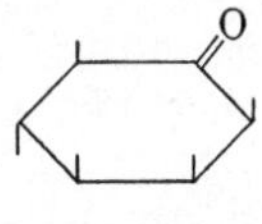

[59] T. Posternak, $Helv.\ Chim.\ Acta$ **19**, 1333 (1936).
[60] P. Fleury, G. Poirot, and J. Fievet, $Compt.\ rend.$ **220**, 664 (1945).
[61] A. J. Kluyver and A. G. J. Boezaardt, $Rec.\ trav.\ chim.$ **58**, 956 (1939).
[62] D. B. Sprinson and E. Chargaff, $J.\ Biol.\ Chem.$ **164**, 433 (1946).

Mono- and dicarbonyl derivatives also have been prepared from the optically active isomers.[4, 12, 13]

Conversions of one inositol isomer into another have frequently been effected with the use of the keto derivatives as intermediaries. In this manner, *meso*-inositol (V) has been converted to *epi*-inositol (II)[59] and to scyllitol (VII),[63] and *meso*-inositol has been produced from *d*-inositol (VIII).[13] The preparation of *allo*-inositol (III) and *muco*-inositol (VI) from the naturally occurring tetritol conduritol[10] should also be mentioned. Another type of conversion is carried out through the drastic action of halogen acids at elevated temperature.[64] Thus, *meso*-inositol (V) is converted to *dl*-inositol (VIII + IX).[65, 66] Corresponding reactions have also been described with quebrachitol and *l*-inositol (IX) as the starting products.[67]

The synthesis of *meso*-inositol by the catalytic hydrogenation of hexahydroxybenzene[68] appears to have been repeated recently,[69] although other workers[70, 71] experienced difficulty in confirming it.

Addendum: Among other literature reports, the following may be mentioned: a new total synthesis of *meso*-inositol (V);[72] the demonstration

OCH₃

of the structure of quebrachitol, a monomethyl ether of *l*-inositol (IX);[73] and a discussion of the nomenclature of the cyclitols and of some of their isopropylidene derivatives.[74]

[63] T. Posternak, *Helv. Chim. Acta* **24**, 1045 (1941).
[64] H. Müller, *J. Chem. Soc.* **91**, 1780 (1907); **101**, 2383 (1912).
[65] T. Posternak, *Helv. Chim. Acta* **31**, 2242 (1948).
[66] H. G. Fletcher, Jr., and G. R. Findlay, *J. Am. Chem. Soc.* **70**, 4050 (1948).
[67] A. Contardi and B. Ciocca, *Gazz. chim. ital.* **79**, 694 (1949).
[68] H. Wieland and R. S. Wishart, *Ber. deut. chem. Ges.* **47**, 2082 (1914).
[69] R. Kuhn, G. Quadbeck, and E. Röhm, *Ann. Chem. Justus Liebigs* **565**, 1 (1949).
[70] M. R. Stetten and D. Stetten, Jr., *J. Biol. Chem.* **164**, 85 (1946).
[71] R. C. Anderson and E. S. Wallis, *J. Am. Chem. Soc.* **70**, 2931 (1948).
[72] T. Posternak, *Helv. Chim. Acta* **33**, 1597 (1950).
[73] T. Posternak, *Helv. Chim. Acta* **35**, 50 (1952).
[74] S. J. Angyal and C. G. Macdonald, *J. Chem. Soc.* **1952**, 686.

III. Industrial Preparation

E. R. WEIDLEIN, JR.

In the absence of a practical chemical synthesis for inositol, the compound has been obtained industrially by isolation of the natural vitamin from plant sources.

A. PRESENCE IN PLANTS

Inositol is found widely distributed in many different types of plants. It is most frequently encountered in combination with phosphoric acid, although free inositol and monomethyl and dimethyl ethers of inositol have also been isolated from some plant species. Phospholipids which contain inositol, rather than glycerol, as the polyalcohol are an important class of phosphoric acid derivatives in plants as well as in animals. However, the most common form for the occurrence of inositol in plants is as a hexaphosphoric acid ester called phytic acid, a compound which is capable of forming salts with potassium, calcium, magnesium, iron, manganese, and other metals of importance in plant nutrition.

Phytic acid and its salts appear to be heavily concentrated in seeds and cereal grains, in which phytate may account for as much as 86 % of the total phosphorus present.[1] In some instances the phytate has also been shown to exist in combination as a protein complex.[2] Little is known of the functions of phytates in plant metabolism, but they have been presumed to act as stores of phosphoric acid which may be utilized by the plant during sprouting. This opinion is supported by the fact that the concentration of free inositol has been found to increase in several different types of seeds during germination.[3] It also has been recognized that phytates may function as carriers for trace metals needed to insure normal plant growth.[4]

Approximately 80 % of the phosphorus in corn exists as phytate, corn having been reported to have a content of phytic acid phosphorus which varies from 0.199 to 0.270 %, compared with a variation in total phosphorus of 0.248 to 0.330 % on the same basis.[1] Among the other plants in which phytic acid has been found are wheat, rye, oats, peas, beans, barley, rice, cottonseed, flaxseed, soybeans, and peanuts.

In extracting the phytate from plant materials, investigators have most

[1] H. Mollgaard, K. Lorenzen, I. G. Hansen, and P. E. Christensen, *Biochem. J. (London)* **40,** 589 (1946).

[2] T. D. Fontaine, W. A. Pons, Jr., and G. W. Irving, Jr., *J. Biol. Chem.* **164,** 487 (1946).

[3] V. H. Cheldelin and R. L. Lane, *Proc. Soc. Exptl. Biol. Med.* **54,** 53 (1943).

[4] E. R. Weidlein, Jr., *Mellon Inst. Bibliographic Ser. Bull.* **6** (1951).

often used dilute hydrochloric or sulfuric acids to treat the whole seed or individual fractions of the seed, but other reagents have also been used. From these extracts, various phytate salts have been precipitated and free inositol obtained by hydrolysis of the phytate salt.

B. CORN STEEPWATER AS A SOURCE OF INOSITOL

Because of the relatively high concentration of contained phytate and. the large volume of raw material available, corn steepwater has proved to be a highly satisfactory source of inositol. At least two commercial producers of inositol are known to have developed processes utilizing corn steepwater as a basis for the isolation of the natural vitamin.

Steepwater is obtained during the process for the industrial wet-milling of corn. Shelled corn entering the wet-milling plant is first soaked in a warm, dilute, aqueous sulfur dioxide solution. This operation softens the kernel and facilitates the subsequent separation of hull and fiber, germ, gluten, and starch. The presence of sulfur dioxide in the steepwater inhibits the action of microorganisms on the grain, and the liquid medium completes the cleansing of the kernels before milling. Most important, the effect of the steeping process is to remove the water-soluble and acid-soluble substances present in corn, phytates being included in this category. Soluble protein, sugars, gums, and similar organic compounds, as well as inorganic substances, are present in the steepwater along with phytate.

In the form of phytic acid and its salts, inositol ordinarily constitutes approximately 2 % of the steepwater total solids. Precipitation of the phytate in steepwater, hydrolysis of the phytate, and isolation of inositol from the hydrolyzate are the steps involved in current industrial processes for the preparation of inositol.

C. PRECIPITATION OF PHYTATE FROM CORN STEEPWATER

The phytate in steepwater is effectively separated by the addition of a slurry of slaked lime which reacts with the soluble phytate present in the steepwater to precipitate an insoluble phytate salt. Steepwater itself contains calcium, magnesium, iron, sodium, and potassium; consequently free phytic acid as such undoubtedly is not present in steepwater. Rather, it appears probable that the phytate is present as soluble partial salts of calcium, magnesium, iron, sodium, and potassium. Thus, the phytate product precipitated from corn steepwater by the addition of lime is not a pure calcium salt of phytic acid but is a mixed salt which contains other metal ions present in steepwater, as well as some protein.

In the precipitation step,[5] lime is usually added until the steepwater is brought to a pH of 5 to 7. The resultant heavy slurry is then filtered, and

[5] F. A. Hoglan and E. Bartow, *Ind. Eng. Chem.* **31,** 749 (1939).

the filter cake is washed thoroughly with water to remove retained steep-water. The crude product, essentially a mixed calcium-magnesium salt of phytic acid which contains the impurities mentioned, has often been referred to in the literature as "phytin" or as "calcium phytate." This product may be dried by conventional procedures or may be used directly for hydrolysis to inositol.

Various procedures also may be employed to improve the quality of crude phytate obtained from steepwater. Use of so-called "light steepwater" for precipitation of the phytate, purification of the crude phytate by treatment with alkali, and other modifications may help to reduce the nitrogen content of the crude phytate and give a better raw material for hydrolysis to inositol.[6, 7]

D. HYDROLYSIS OF PHYTATE TO INOSITOL

Inositol has been obtained from steepwater phytate by hydrolysis under a variety of conditions.[8-10] Temperature, pressure, pH, and time of hydrolysis are variables which have been considered. Temperatures employed have ranged from approximately 100° to 200°, pressures from atmospheric to mild autoclaving conditions, and the medium for hydrolysis from a 25 % calcium hydroxide slurry to a 60 % sulfuric acid solution. The time required for completion of hydrolysis has usually been several hours.

According to Bartow and Walker[8] inositol can be obtained conveniently by heating phytate under pressure with either water or acid. The quality of the phytate used and the nature of the impurities present during hydrolysis appear to have as much influence on the yield of inositol as does any other factor, including the nature of the conditions chosen for hydrolysis. The calculated yield of inositol based on pure dry calcium phytate is 20.27 %, but the yields of inositol reported to be obtained from steepwater phytate have generally been in the range of 7 to 12 %.

E. ISOLATION OF INOSITOL FROM HYDROLYZATE

Hydrolysis of phytate produces 6 moles of inorganic phosphate for each mole of inositol. The inorganic phosphate produced by hydrolysis of phytate may be removed by filtration if the hydrolyzate is first adjusted to a pH that is slightly alkaline.

The phosphate filter cake is washed with hot water to remove dissolved and adsorbed inositol, and the wash filtrate is combined with the original filtrate. The combined filtrate, a crude aqueous solution of inositol, may be

[6] F. A. Hoglan and E. Bartow, *J. Am. Chem. Soc.* **62**, 2397 (1940).

[7] Corn Products Refining Co., Brit. Pat. 601,273 (May 3, 1948).

[8] E. Bartow and W. W. Walker, *Ind. Eng. Chem.* **30**, 300 (1938).

[9] E. Bartow and W. W. Walker, U. S. Pat. 2,112,553 (March 29, 1938).

[10] E. Elkin and C. M. Meadows, U. S. Pat. 2,414,365 (January 14, 1947).

decolorized with bone black or activated carbon, filtered to remove carbon, and concentrated by vacuum-pan evaporation.

Crystallization of inositol from the mother liquor is generally accomplished by gradual cooling to as low a temperature as practical with continuous, moderate agitation. Crystals are separated from the mother liquor by centrifugation and are then further washed and dried. Several crops of crystals may be recovered by concentration of the mother liquor and a repetition of the crystallization process.

The inositol obtained in this manner is an anhydrous, colorless, crystalline material having a melting point of approximately 225°, which is characteristic of the pure *myo* isomer.

IV. Biochemical Systems

HENRY A. LARDY

The widespread occurrence and relatively great abundance of *myo*-inositol make this compound unique among the vitamins in that it may act both catalytically, like the other vitamins, and as an energy-yielding foodstuff or metabolite. These two aspects of the biochemical systems in which *myo*-inositol participates will therefore be discussed separately.

A. BIOCATALYTIC FUNCTIONS OF *MYO*-INOSITOL

myo-Inositol is an essential nutrient for several strains of yeast,[1-3] for fungi,[4, 5] for a mutant of *Neurospora crassa*,[6] and for mice,[7, 8] rats,[9] cotton rats,[10, 11] hamsters,[12] and chicks[13] under certain deitary regimens. In spite

[1] E. V. Eastcott, *J. Physiol. Chem.* **32,** 1094 (1928).

[2] R. J. Williams, R. E. Eakin, and E. E. Snell, *J. Am. Chem. Soc.* **62,** 1204 (1940).

[3] L. Atkin, A. S. Schultz, W. L. Williams, and C. N. Frey, *Ind. Eng. Chem. Anal. Ed.* **15,** 141 (1943).

[4] F. Kögl and N. Fries, *Hoppe-Seyler's Z. physiol. Chem.* **249,** 93 (1937).

[5] W. J. Robbins, J. E. Mackinnon, and R. Ma, *Bull. Torrey Botan. Club* **69,** 509 (1942).

[6] G. W. Beadle, *J. Biol. Chem.* **156,** 683 (1944).

[7] D. W. Woolley, *J. Biol. Chem.* **136,** 113 (1940).

[8] D. W. Woolley, *J. Biol. Chem.* **139,** 20 (1941).

[9] T. J. Cunha, S. Kirkwood, P. H. Phillips, and G. Bohstedt, *Proc. Soc. Exptl. Biol. Med.* **54,** 236 (1943).

[10] J. M. McIntire, B. S. Schweigert, and C. A. Elvehjem, *J. Nutrition* **27,** 1 (1944).

[11] B. S. Schweigert, *Vitamins and Hormones* **6,** 55 (1948).

[12] J. M. Cooperman, H. A. Waisman, and C. A. Elvehjem, *Proc. Soc. Exptl. Biol. Med.* **52,** 250 (1943).

[13] D. M. Hegsted, G. M. Briggs Jr., R. C. Mills, C. A. Elvehjem, and E. B. Hart, *Proc. Soc. Exptl. Biol. Med.* **47,** 376 (1941).

of the great variety of organisms which require inositol, virtually nothing is known of the function of the vitamin in terms of enzymes or coenzymes. Since animals probably can synthesize *myo*-inositol (see Section VI), it has been assumed that the dietary requirement of this compound reflects a requirement of the intestinal flora. Woolley[14] found that feeding pantothenic acid benefited mice deficient in inositol. White rats do not require *myo*-inositol when fed purified diets,[15, 16] but Cunha *et al.*[9] found that rats on diets containing soybean meal showed poor growth and hair loss. These symptoms lessened after feeding of inositol. The fact that biotin or the sulfur-containing amino acids can prevent the deficiency symptoms[17] lends support to the hypothesis that the beneficial effect of inositol is indirect and is probably exerted through intestinal microorganisms.

1. STUDIES WITH INHIBITORY ANALOGS

The possibility that the insecticide, hexachlorocyclohexane, exerts its physiological action by antagonizing a normal function of *myo*-inositol was first suggested by Slade.[18] Evidence tending to support this possibility has been obtained with several inositol-requiring microorganisms.[19-21] For example, Kirkwood and Phillips[19] found the γ isomer of hexachlorocyclohexane to inhibit growth of an inositol-requiring strain of *Saccharomyces cerevisiae*. The inhibitory effect was competitively, but incompletely, reversed by *myo*-inositol. The δ, α, and β isomers, in decreasing order, were not as strongly inhibitory as the γ isomer, and their effects were not influenced by increasing concentrations of *myo*-inositol. The relatively low inhibition index,[22] indicating a close similarity of structure between the inhibitor and metabolite, was taken by Kirkwood and Phillips[19] to indicate that the γ isomer of hexachlorocyclohexane had the same configuration as *myo*-inositol. Bijvoet[23] and coworkers[24] as well as Blekkingh[25] conclude from physical measurements that the γ isomer does not have the configuration of *myo*-inositol but appears to have that of *muco*-inositol. Dissimilarity of configuration between the γ isomer and *myo*-inositol introduces complica-

[14] D. W. Woolley, *J. Exptl. Med.* **75**, 277 (1942).
[15] T. H. Jukes, *Proc. Soc. Exptl. Biol. Med.* **45**, 625 (1940).
[16] L. R. Richardson, A. G. Hogan, B. Long, and K. I. Itschner, *Proc. Soc. Exptl. Biol. Med.* **46**, 530 (1941).
[17] R. R. Spitzer and P. H. Phillips, *Proc. Soc. Exptl. Biol. Med.* **63**, 10 (1946).
[18] R. E. Slade, *Chemistry & Industry* **64**, 314 (1945).
[19] S. Kirkwood and P. H. Phillips, *J. Biol. Chem.* **163**, 251 (1946).
[20] H. W. Buston, S. E. Jacobs, and A. Goldstein, *Nature* **158**, 22 (1946).
[21] R. C. Fuller, R. W. Barratt, and E. L. Tatum, *J. Biol. Chem.* **186**, 823 (1940).
[22] H. McIlwain, *Brit. J. Exptl. Pathol.* **23**, 95 (1942).
[23] J. M. Bijvoet, *Rec. trav. chim.* **67**, 777 (1948).
[24] G. W. Von Vloten, C. A. Kruissink, B. Strijk, and J. M. Bijvoet, *Nature* **162**, 771 (1948).
[25] J. J. A. Blekkingh, *Rec. trav. chim.* **68**, 345 (1949).

tions of interpretation but should not lessen interest in the biological competition between these two compounds.

Several workers have been unable to demonstrate a competitive relationship between *myo*-inositol and γ-hexachlorocyclohexane.[26-28] However, the negative results have, for the most part, been obtained with strains of microorganisms which do not require preformed *myo*-inositol. From the results of Kirkwood and Phillips,[19] Schopfer *et al.*[26] and Fuller *et al.*[21] it appears that the competitive relationship is demonstrable only in organisms which are nutritionally dependent upon *myo*-inositol and that there is a second, non-specific, inhibitory effect of hexachlorocyclohexanes which is not influenced by *myo*-inositol.

myo-Inositol has also been reported by Chargaff and coworkers[29] to counteract the arrest of nuclear division and the tumor formation induced in onion root tips by either colchicine or γ-hexachlorocyclohexane. D-Inositol and sorbitol were ineffective. The effect of *myo*-inositol has been confirmed,[30, 31] although a number of sugars were found to have similar activity.[30] Other workers[32, 33] were unable to confirm the competitive relationship between *myo*-inositol and colchicine in onion root cells. However, a more detailed study of this effect in fibroblast cultures from areolar tissue of the adult rat has again shown *myo*-inositol to exert a distinct inhibition of the effect of colchicine on mitosis.[33a] Other compounds which were found not to influence the effect of colchicine were D-inositol, *myo*-inosose-2, DL-*epi*-inosose-2,[34] sorbitol, ribose, sucrose, and glucose.

In higher animals the toxic effects of γ-hexachlorocyclohexane appear not to be counteracted by *myo*-inositol.[35-38] The convulsive effects of γ-hexachlorocyclohexane appear to be prevented by previous administration of the β or δ isomers.[37] Another interesting finding is that the δ isomer

[26] W. H. Schopfer, T. Posternak, and M. L. Boss, *Schweiz. Z. allgem. Pathol. u. Bakteriol.* **10**, 443 (1947).

[27] C. Fromageot and M. Confino, *Biochim. et Biophys. Acta* **2**, 142 (1948).

[28] P. Chaix, *Bull. soc. chim. biol.* **30**, 835 (1948).

[29] E. Chargaff, R. N. Stewart, and B. Magasanik, *Science* **108**, 556 (1948).

[30] F. D'Amato, *Carylogia* **1**, 223 (1949) [*C. A.* **43**, 9170 (1949)].

[31] F. D'Amato, *Carylogia* **1**, 358 (1949) [*C. A.* **44**, 4089 (1950)].

[32] G. Deysson and M. Deysson, *Bull. soc. chim. biol.* **32**, 276 (1950) [*C. A.* **44**, 10052 (1950)].

[33] S. Carpentier and C. Fromageot, *Biochim. et Biophys. Acta* **5**, 290 (1950).

[33a] M. R. Murray, H. H. de Lam, and E. Chargaff, *Exptl. Cell Research* **2**, 165 (1951).

[34] For clarification of the nomenclature of these inositol derivatives, see Section I of this chapter.

[35] E. A. Doisy, Jr., and B. C. Bocklage, *Proc. Soc. Exptl. Biol. Med.* **71**, 490 (1949).

[36] E. A. Doisy, Jr., and B. C. Bocklage, *Proc. Soc. Exptl. Biol. Med.* **74**, 613 (1950).

[37] B. P. McNamara and S. Krop, *J. Pharmacol. Exptl. Therap.* **92**, 140 (1948).

[38] B. P. McNamara and S. Krop, *J. Pharmacol. Exptl. Therap.* **92**, 147 (1948).

(which probably has the configuration of *myo*-inositol[39]) stimulates the respiration of rat brain homogenates.[40] The hexamethyl ether of *myo*-inositol produces convulsions in rabbits similar to those produced by γ-hexachlorocyclohexane; however, the ether is only 1/100 as active as the chlorine-containing analog.[41]

Several workers[29, 36] consider it likely that the biological antagonism between hexachloroxycyclohexane and *myo*-inositol is actually exerted between the former and a bound or complex form of the latter. Since the hexachlorocyclohexanes are much more soluble in fat solvents than in aqueous systems, it is possible that they exert their effect on systems reacting with phospholipids containing *myo*-inositol.

Some years ago Williams and coworkers[42] found relatively high concentrations (0.4 %) of inositol in a partially purified preparation of α-amylase from pancreas. This led Lane and Williams[43] to test the effect of γ-hexachlorocyclohexane on the catalytic activity of the enzyme. Their report that the chlorine-containing analog inhibited the enzyme and that *myo*-inositol competitively reversed the inhibition could not be confirmed by two groups[44, 45] who used the more purified and crystalline enzyme.

2. BOUND FORMS OF *myo*-INOSITOL

Although there are appreciable quantities of free *myo*-inositol in many biological materials, by far the greater part of this substance exists in various complex forms. The more common materials with which it combines include phosphate, proteins, fatty acids, glycerol, and galactose. Although these complex compounds may be considered "structural material" of the cell, they may be expected to have specific biocatalytic functions as well.

a. Inositol-Containing Phospholipids

The phosphatides of the tubercle bacillus,[46, 47] the soybean,[48, 49] cotton seed,[50] and brain[51, 52] and liver[53] tissue contain inositol. Inositol mono-

[39] O. Bastiansen, Ø. Ellefson, and O. Hassel, *Research* **2**, 248 (1949).

[40] B. P. McNamara and S. Krop, *Science* **109**, 330 (1949).

[41] N. P. Buu-Hoï, E. Philippot, M. J. Dallemagne, and M. A. Gerebtzoff, *Compt. rend. soc. biol.* **144**, 1568 (1950).

[42] R. J. Williams, F. Schlenk, and M. A. Eppright, *J. Am. Chem. Soc.* **66**, 896 (1944).

[43] R. L. Lane and R. J. Williams, *Arch. Biochem.* **19**, 329 (1948).

[44] E. H. Fischer and P. Bernfeld, *Helv. Chim. Acta* **32**, 1146 (1949).

[45] S. Schwimmer and A. K. Balls, *J. Biol. Chem.* **179**, 1063 (1949).

[46] R. J. Anderson, *J. Am. Chem. Soc.* **52**, 1607 (1930) [*C. A.* **24**, 2490 (1930)]

[47] J. Cason and R. J. Anderson, *J. Biol. Chem.* **126**, 527 (1938).

[48] E. Klenk and R. Sakai, *Hoppe-Seyler's Z. physiol. Chem.* **258**, 33 (1939).

[49] D. W. Woolley, *J. Biol. Chem.* **147**, 581 (1943).

[50] H. S. Olcott, *Science* **100**, 226 (1944).

phosphate has been isolated as an hydrolysis product of the phosphatides from the tubercle bacillus[47] and from soybean.[48] However, inositol diphosphate was obtained by Folch[52] from brain phosphatide. Periodate oxidation demonstrated that the phosphate groups were in *meta* position to one another. The brain phosphatide contains, in addition to inositol diphosphate, an equimolar proportion of fatty acid (of rather high equivalent weight) and glycerol. Soybean "lipositol"[49] was found to contain *myo*-inositol, galactose, oleic acid, a mixture of three saturated fatty acids—cerebronic, palmitic, and stearic—phosphoric acid, L(+)-tartaric acid, and smaller quantities of ethanolamine. Folch[53a] has obtained from a purified soybean phosphatide: inositol 2 (moles), carbohydrate (as galactose) 2, phosphoric acid 2, glycerol 2, fatty acids 3, and amine 1.

Claude[54] has found that inositol is present in relatively high concentration in the mitochondria and submicroscopic particles (microsomes) of the liver cell. Approximately 40 to 45 % of the dry weight of the microsomes is lipid material, and 2 % of this is inositol. Claude calculates that, if all the inositol were bound as "lipositol," this component would comprise more than one-fourth of the total lipid and almost one-half of the phospholipid.

b. Phytic Acid

In plant materials, and especially in the seeds of the grasses, a major part of the inositol is present as the hexaphosphoric ester.[55-57] This compound is called *phytic acid,* and its mixed calcium and magnesium salt is called *phytin.* The phytic acid of corn is the source of commercial inositol (Section III). Several possible formulas have been proposed for phytin or phytic acid, including those in which adjacent phosphoric groups may combine to form pyrophosphate linkages or in which hydroxyphosphoric acid groups may be present.

Although a specific biological function for this compound has not been established, it is known to act as a reservoir of phosphate which becomes available to the young plant at germination. Complexes between phytic acid and animal or plant proteins have been obtained by a number of workers. However, it appears likely that these are merely non-specific combinations, for the phytic acid may be separated by dialysis.[58]

[51] J. Folch and D. W. Woolley, *J. Biol. Chem.* **142,** 963 (1942).
[52] J. Folch, *J. Biol. Chem.* **177,** 505 (1949).
[53] L. B. Macpherson and C. C. Lucas, *Federation Proc.* **6,** 273 (1947).
[53a] J. Folch, *Federation Proc.* **6,** 252 (1947).
[54] A. Claude, *J. Exptl. Med.* **84,** 61 (1946).
[55] S. Posternak, *Compt. rend.* **137,** 202 337, 439 (1903).
[56] C. Neuberg, *Biochem. Z.* **9,** 557 (1908).
[57] R. J. Anderson, *J. Biol. Chem.* **44,** 429 (1920).
[58] J. Bourdillon, *J. Biol. Chem.* **189,** 65 (1951).

Phytin occurs also in animal tissues, for example, in the nucleated erythrocytes of the chicken and turtle.[59]

3. LIPOTROPIC EFFECT OF INOSITOL

There are a number of dietary variables which can lead to deposition of unusually large amounts of lipid in the liver. Certain nutrients favor this deposition, whereas others (lipotropic agents[60]) favor mobilization of the lipids and a return to the normal fat content of the liver. Choline[60] and other biological methyl donors are particularly well known as dietary lipotropic agents, but inositol is also effective under certain conditions in both experimental animals[61-63] and human subjects.[64, 65] The effect of inositol is apparent even with diets containing an adequate supply of methyl group donors.[62, 66] Although relatively little is known concerning the mode of action of lipotropic agents, at least two of them—choline and inositol—are essential constituents of phospholipids, and it seems likely that their effectiveness in reducing liver fat may be a reflection of that fact. Since all other vitamins eventually become structural units of protoplasm too, it seems arbitrary to separate the lipotropic activities of choline and inositol from their respective "vitamin" activities.[66]

B. METABOLISM OF INOSITOL

1. IN BACTERIA

Although the pathways of inositol metabolism in bacteria are better understood than those in animal tissues, knowledge in this field is still in a relatively primitive state.

The oxidation of *myo*-inositol[67] to yield *myo*-inosose-2[68] can serve as the major source of energy for the growth of *Acetobacter suboxydans*. The oxidation system is not specific for *myo*-inositol; other polyhydric cyclohexanes having polar hydroxyl groups are also attacked.[69] Polar hydroxyl groups

[59] J. Rapoport, *J. Biol Chem.* **135,** 403 (1940).

[60] C. H. Best, M. E. Huntsman, and J. H. Ridout, *Nature* **135,** 821 (1935).

[61] G. Gavin and E. W. McHenry, *J. Biol. Chem.* **139,** 485 (1941).

[62] C. H. Best, C. C. Lucas, J. M. Patterson, and J. H. Ridout, *Biochem. J.* (*London*) **40,** 368 (1946).

[63] R. W. Engel, *J. Nutrition* **24,** 175 (1942).

[64] J. C. Abels, C. W. Kupel, G. T. Pack, and C. P. Rhoads, *Proc. Soc. Exptl. Biol. Med.* **54,** 157 (1943).

[65] I. M. Ariel, J. C. Abels, H. T. Murphy, G. T. Pack, and C. P. Rhoads, *Ann. Internal Med.* **20,** 570, 580 (1944).

[66] C. H. Best, C. C. Lucas, J. Patterson, and J. Ridout, *Biochem. J.* (*London*) **48,** 452 (1951).

[67] A. J. Kluyver and A. G. J. Boezaardt, *Rec. trav. chim.* **58,** 956 (1939).

[68] T. Posternak, *Helv. Chim. Acta* **25,** 746 (1942).

[69] B. Magasanik and E. Chargaff, *J. Biol. Chem.* **174,** 173 (1948).

are those oriented at approximately right angles to the thick plane of carbon atoms in the "chair" conformation of the cyclohexane ring. Equatorial
hydroxyl groups, i.e., those extending the thick plane formed by the carbon
atoms, are not oxidized by this organism. Franzl and Chargaff[70, 71] have
obtained cell-free enzyme preparations from *A. suboxydans* which oxidize
myo-inositol and other inositols in the same manner as do the whole cells.
The enzyme is present in particulate material which is sedimented by
20,000g for 2 hours but which remains in the supernatant fluid after
centrifugation at 2000g for 30 minutes. A heat-stable cofactor, obtained
from whole cells, accelerates the oxidation of *myo*-inositol by the enzyme
but is not required for the oxidation of glucose. This factor may be replaced
in part by Ca^{++} or Mg^{++}. The cell-free preparations did not oxidize sorbitol,
which would seem to indicate that separate enzymes are involved in the
oxidation of polyhydric alcohols and cyclitols, respectively, by this
organism.

Aerobacter aerogenes may be grown under aerobic conditions with *myo*-
inositol as the sole source of carbon. Magasanik[72] has obtained considerable information about the pathway of inositol degradation by this
organism. Cells grown on *myo*-inositol under aerobic conditions fermented
myo-inositol to yield 0.68 mole of CO_2, 0.72 mole of ethanol, and 1.54
equivalents of an unknown acid. Experiments with inhibitors led to the
conclusion that glucose was not an intermediate. 2-Keto-*myo*-inositol and
L-1,2-diketo-*myo*-inositol were fermented by these cells two to three times
more rapidly than *myo*-inositol. L-1-Keto-*myo*-inositol was also fermented,
but no more rapidly than *myo*-inositol. The following metabolic pathway
was proposed by Magasanik.

It is to be expected that more work of this nature with bacterial preparations will help elucidate the pathway by which animals metabolize *myo*-inositol. It is already apparent that, if the pathway in animal tissues is similar to that shown above, the formation of pyruvate or lactate would be an adequate explanation of the antiketogenic effect of inositol and of the conversion of stably bound deuterium in inositol to stably bound deuterium in urinary glucose (see below).

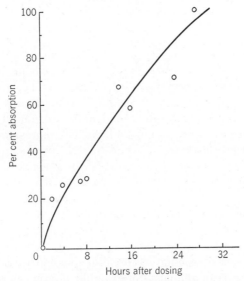

FIG. 1. Rate of inositol absorption in fasted rats.[73]

2. IN ANIMALS

a. *Absorption*

myo-Inositol is absorbed from the digestive tract of animals but at a relatively slow rate compared with glucose. Figure 1 (from Wiebelhaus *et al.*[73]) shows the rate of absorption of approximately 280-mg. doses of *myo*-inositol administered by stomach tube to rats of approximately 200-g. body weight. The rate of absorption was measured by quantitative determinations[3] of the inositol remaining in the gastrointestinal tract. A comparison of the assay values for the hydrolyzed and unhydrolyzed samples indicated that no conversion of administered inositol to a bound form had occurred in the intestine. However, about one-half of the 8 to 12 mg. of inositol present in the tract of fasted animals (or of the experimental ani-

[70] R. E. Franzl and E. Chargaff, *Federation Proc.* **9**, 173 (1950).
[71] R. E. Franzl and E. Chargaff, *Nature* **168**, 955 (1951).
[72] B. Magasanik, *J. Am. Chem. Soc.* **73**, 5919 (1951).
[73] V. D. Wiebelhaus, J. J. Betheil, and H. A. Lardy, *Arch. Biochem.* **13**, 379 (1947).

mals after absorption of the test dose was complete) was in a form not available to the strain of yeast used in these assays.

The urinary excretion of inositol varied from 3 to 5 mg. per rat for a 24-hour period and was not significantly greater for the rats which had received from 260 to 335 mg. of inositol *per os* than for the fasted control rats. The limit of accuracy of the inositol assay permits the conclusion that urinary excretion accounted for less than 1 % of the administered inositol.

The absorption of inositol monophosphate was also studied.[73] From 150 to 200 mg. of the monophosphate isolated from soybean lipositol was administered to 200-g. rats. The rate of absorption appeared to be more rapid than for inositol, especially during the first 2 hours. Approximately 80 % of the dose was absorbed in from 1 to 2 hours, and complete absorption occurred in rats killed at 12 and 24 hours. In all animals killed later than 2 hours after administering inositol monophosphate, almost all the inositol in the intestinal contents was found to be in a form available to the assay organism. Since the original isolated inositol monophosphate gave a growth response equivalent to only 8 to 15 % of its contained inositol, it appeared that the phosphoric ester was rapidly hydrolyzed in the intestine. The initial rapid disappearance of inositol might indicate an extremely rapid absorption of the inositol monophosphate *per se*, with subsequent slow absorption of the free inositol which was presumably liberated by intestinal phosphatases.

Other bound forms of *myo*-inositol are also apparently readily hydrolyzed in the intestinal tract of animals. For example, phytin can supply both the inositol[74] and inorganic phosphate requirements of rodents. Soybean cephalin and even synthetic inositol hexaacetate can replace dietary inositol for the mouse, indicating that they are cleaved to free inositol.[74]

Intraperitoneally administered *myo*-inositol appears to be absorbed, since it is as effective in depressing ketone body excretion in fasted rats as is the orally administered compound.[73]

b. *Catabolism*

Inositols are isomeric with the common 6-carbon sugars, and perhaps for this reason the possible conversion of *myo*-inositol to carbohydrate or carbohydrate breakdown products in animal tissues has been studied by many investigators. Although earlier results were inconclusive, it is now certain that inositol is metabolized, at least in part, like carbohydrate. Stetten and Stetten[75] fed deuterium-labeled *myo*-inositol to a phlorhizin-ized rat and found that at least 7 % of the dose fed appeared in urinary

[74] D. W. Woolley, *J. Biol. Chem.* **140,** 461 (1941).

[75] M. R. Stetten and D. W. Stetten, Jr., *J. Biol. Chem.* **164,** 85 (1946).

glucose. The slow rate of absorption of myo-inositol apparently precludes the formation of any significant amount of liver glycogen when this compound is fed to fasted rats.[73] However, myo-inositol given either orally or intraperitoneally does depress urinary ketone body excretion. This provides additional evidence that myo-inositol is metabolized to carbohydrate or to intermediates which are common to carbohydrate metabolic pathways. Virtually nothing is known about the pathways by which the inositol molecule is cleaved and converted to the carbohydrate-like products in animal tissues.

V. Specificity of Action

ARTHUR H. LIVERMORE

There are nine theoretically possible isomers of inositol, differing only in the steric arrangements of their hydroxyl groups. Determining the specific steric configuration which is essential for vitamin activity in a particular organism becomes, then, simply a matter of testing all the available isomers of inositol on the organism in question. Only seven of the nine possible isomers are known, but of those tested only one, myo-inositol, has vitamin activity for all the inositol-requiring organisms which have been found up to the present time. There are some organisms for which myo-inositol is the only isomer which serves as a vitamin, and other organisms for which other isomers have slight vitamin activity.

The vitamin activity of myo-inositol for yeast was first demonstrated in 1928 by Eastcott,[1] and for mice in 1940 by Woolley.[2] Following this, Woolley determined the comparative vitamin activities of various inositols and inositol derivatives for mice and yeast. The results of this investigation are summarized in Table IV.[3] Alopecia in mice was cured not only by myo-inositol but also by phytin, the hexaphosphate of myo-inositol, and by mytilitol, which has since been shown to be C-methylscyllitol.[4] Other inositol isomers were completely inactive for mice. The yeast *Saccharomyces cerevisiae*, on the other hand, utilized the mono- and tetraphosphate esters to a small extent only and did not utilize phytin at all. Mytilitol was much less effective as a growth stimulant than was myo-inositol. As in mice, the other isomers of inositol which were tested had no vitamin activity.

[1] E. V. Eastcott, *J. Phys. Chem.* **32**, 1094 (1928).
[2] D. W. Woolley, *Science* **92**, 384 (1940).
[3] D. W. Woolley, *J. Biol. Chem.* **140**, 461 (1941).
[4] T. Posternak, *Bull. soc. chim. biol.* **33**, 1041 (1951).

More recent work with other organisms has demonstrated that L-inositol has some vitamin activity for *Eremothecium ashbyii* and for the inositol-less mutant of *Neurospora crassa*, but that D-inositol is completely inactive for these organisms.[5] Two other isomers, *epi*-inositol and scyllitol, were also tested and found to have some vitamin activity for the former but not for the latter organism. For *Eremothecium ashbyii myo*-inositol monophosphate has from 50 to 100 % of the activity of the free form;[5] for *Neurospora crassa*, the ester has little or no activity.[5-7] For another organism, *Rhizopus Cohnii*[8, 9] *myo*-inositol was the most active isomer, but mytilitol, isomytili-

TABLE IV

ACTIVITY OF COMPOUNDS RELATED TO INOSITOL FOR MICE AND FOR YEAST[a]

Compound	Curative effect on mice	Growth effect on yeast as compared to *myo*-inositol, %
myo-Inositol	+	100
Phytin	+	1
Sodium phytate	—	1
L-Inositol	—	1
D-Inositol	—	1
Quercitol	—	1
Quebrachitol (monomethyl ether of L-inositol)	—	1
Pinitol (monomethyl ether of D-inositol)	—	1
Mytilitol (monomethyl ether of *myo*-inositol)	+	10
Quinic acid (tetrahydroxyhexahydrobenzoic acid)		1
Soybean cephelin	+	1
myo-Inositol hexaacetate	+	1
myo-Inositol monophosphate		5
myo-Inositol tetraphosphate		2
Inosose		1

[a] Hansen No. 1 strain of Toronto yeast (*Saccharomyces cerevisiae*).

tol, hydroxyisomytilitol, and *epi*-inositol also had some activity. *myo*-Inositol monophosphate was also quite well utilized by this organism.

The reversal of the inhibitory action of malonate on *Clostridium saccharobutyricum* by *myo*-inositol has been shown to be quite specific.[10] The D and L isomers did not reverse the inhibition.

It has been suggested[9] that, for certain microorganisms at least, three

[5] P. Chaix, *Bull. soc. chim. biol.* **30**, 835 (1948).

[6] B. M. Iselin, *J. Am. Chem. Soc.* **71**, 3822 (1949).

[7] W. H. Schopfer, T. Posternak, and M. L. Boss, *Intern. Z. Vitaminforsch.* **20**, 121 (1948) [*C. A.* **43**, 1457 (1949)].

[8] W. H. Schopfer, *Helv. Chim. Acta* **27**, 468 (1944).

[9] W. H. Schopfer, *Bull. soc. chim. biol.* **33**, 1113 (1951).

[10] A. J. Rosenberg, *Compt. rend. soc. biol.* **142**, 443 (1948).

adjacent *cis*-hydroxyl groups, as in *myo*-inositol, are essential for activity. The activity for some organisms of scyllitol and mytilitol (C-methylscyllitol), which have no *cis*-hydroxyl groups, and L-inositol, which has two pairs of *cis*-hydroxyl groups, one on each side of the ring, indicates that the three adjacent *cis*-hydroxyls are not always essential.

A different kind of specificity is suggested by the work of Magasanik and Chargaff[11] on the oxidation of inositol isomers by *Acetobacter suboxydans*. This organism, which can oxidize inositol to a cyclic ketone, shows a

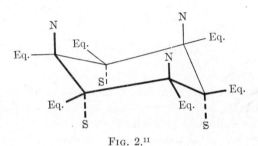

FIG. 2.[11]

TABLE V

OXIDATION OF INOSITOL BY *Acetobacter suboxydans*

Inositol isomer	Number of oxygen atoms used per mole of inositol	Position of OH groups in this isomer			Positions of OH group(s) oxidized
		Equatorial	North	South	
myo-Inositol	1	1, 3, 4, 5, 6	2	—	2
L-Inositol	2	2, 3, 4, 5	1	6	1, 6
D-Inositol	2	1, 4, 5, 6	2	3	2, 3
Scyllitol	0	1, 2, 3, 4, 5, 6	—	—	—
epi-Inositol	1	1, 3, 5, 6	2,4	—	2
D-Quercitol	2	1, 5, 6	2	3	(Not determined)

very interesting enzyme specificity for inositol isomers. In the isomers which were oxidized by this organism, either one or two hydroxyl groups in the molecule were oxidized depending upon the inositol isomer tested. To explain this specificity Magasanik and Chargaff[11] made two assumptions: first, that the inositols exist chiefly in the "chair" form, as cyclohexane does; and, second, that the most stable configuration of an inositol molecule has the maximum possible number of hydroxyl groups in the equatorial plane (positions marked "Eq." in Fig. 2) and the minimum number of hydroxyl groups in the pole regions (positions marked "N" and "S" in Fig. 2). The results of these experiments are summarized in Table V.[11]

[11] B. Magasanik and E. Chargaff, *J. Biol. Chem.* **174**, 173 (1948).

It will be noted that in every case it was the "pole" hydroxyl groups which were oxidized by *Acetobacter suboxydans*. Another organism, *Aerobacter aerogenes*, has also been found to oxidize the polar hydroxyl group of *myo*-inositol.[12] It has not yet been determined whether the relationship between the polar and the equatorial groups is also a factor in the vitamin activity of inositol for various organisms.

VI. Biogenesis

ARTHUR H. LIVERMORE

That plant tissues can synthesize inositol is evident; that animal tissues can do so has not yet been established. Increases in the inositol content of animal tissues may represent synthesis by intestinal flora rather than synthesis by the animal body itself. Increases in the inositol content of plant tissues, on the other hand, can be accounted for only by synthesis in the plant tissues. The mechanism of this synthesis has not yet been demonstrated, but present evidence implicates the sugars, and particularly glucose, as the precursors of inositol. Fischer[1] has suggested that

. . . it could be deduced from chemical evidence . . . that inositol is most likely an intermediate between carbohydrates and aromatic substances; moreover it very likely serves as a reserve carbohydrate, storing away glucose in a form which could be easily mobilized. Finally, there is the speculative possibility that inositol could act as an intermediate enabling the easy transformation of one hexose into another.

Fischer also presented chemical evidence to support his suggestion that inositol may be synthesized from glucose in biological tissues.

A. INOSITOL SYNTHESIS BY MICROORGANISMS

The presence of inositol in the phosphatides of the tubercle bacillus was first reported in 1930.[2] The ability of two strains of this bacillus to synthesize inositol[3] indicates that the tubercle bacillus need not be dependent upon the host for a supply of this vitamin. The synthesis of inositol by other bacteria, grown in vitamin-free media, has also been demonstrated.[4, 5] The amounts synthesized were indicated by the observation[4] that various

[12] B. Magasanik, *J. Am. Chem. Soc.* **73**, 5919 (1951).
[1] H. O. L. Fischer, *Harvey Lectures* **40**, 156 (1945).
[2] R. J. Anderson and E. G. Roberts, *J. Biol. Chem.* **89**, 599, 611 (1930).
[3] H. Pope and D. T. Smith, *Am. Rev. Tuberc.* **54**, 559 (1946) [*C. A.* **42**, 3017 (1948)].
[4] R. C. Thompson, *Univ. Texas Publ.* **4237**, 87 (1942).
[5] L. W. Jones and J. E. Greaves, *Soil Sci.* **55**, 393 (1943) [*C. A.* **37**, 6300 (1943)].

types of bacteria grown in an inositol-free medium for 24 hours contained from 870 γ (*Clostridium butylicum*) to 1700 γ (*Pseudomonas fluorescens*) of inositol per gram of dry cells.

The ability of various yeasts to synthesize inositol can be modified by various procedures. It has been shown,[6] for example, that *Saccharomyces cerevisiae* can be converted from a heterotrophic to an autotrophic habit by successive changes in the medium. If inhibitors are included in the medium[7] or if the cells are damaged by ultraviolet light,[8] the ability of the yeast to synthesize inositol is also changed. *Torulopsis utilis* has been shown[9] to synthesize less inositol in an iron-deficient medium than in one containing an adequate amount (0.1 to 3 p.p.m.) of iron.

The suggestion[10] that *Aerobacter aerogenes* catabolizes *myo*-inositol to CO_2, acetate, and pyruvate through the intermediate formation of 2-keto- and 1,2-diketo-*myo*-inositol, leads one to speculate on the possibility that these metabolic products might in turn be precursors of inositol in this organism. There is as yet no experimental evidence for this speculation.

B. INOSITOL SYNTHESIS BY HIGHER PLANTS

A number of studies of the changes in the inositol content of seeds, leaves, and fruits have been made. Although the total inositol content of plants increases during growth, the concentration in the plant tissues may decrease. For example, it was shown[11] that there was a higher concentration of inositol in the growing tips of cucurbit and tomato plants than in the mature leaves. In addition it was found[12] that the inositol concentration in the fruits of these plants remained relatively constant or decreased slightly during development.

The possibility that inositol is synthesized from glucose and glucose derivatives in plants was strengthened somewhat by the observation[13] that the leaves of the rubber plant, *Lactuca virosa L.*, yielded an aqueous extract which, when incubated with glucose for 3 days, gave rise to a substance which appeared to be inositol. It has also been reported[14] that apricot leaves produced inositol when incubated with glucose and glucose phosphates.

[6] L. H. Leonian and V. G. Lilly, *Science* **95**, 658 (1942).
[7] M. A. Eppright and R. J. Williams, *J. Gen. Physiol.* **30**, 61 (1946).
[8] A. M. Webb and J. R. Loofbourow, *Biochem. J. (London)* **41**, 114 (1947).
[9] J. C. Lewis, *Arch. Biochem.* **4**, 217 (1944).
[10] B. Magasanik, *J. Am. Chem. Soc.* **73**, 5919 (1951).
[11] C. L. Withner, *Am. J. Botany* **36**, 355 (1949).
[12] C. L. Withner, *Am. J. Botany* **36**, 517 (1949).
[13] O. Fernandez, G. Izquierdo, and E. Martinez, *Farm. nueva (Madrid)* **9**, 563 (1944) [*C. A.* **40**, 4115 (1946)].
[14] O. Fernandez, M. de Mingo, and E. Martinez, *Farm. nueva (Madrid)* **10**, 541 (1945) [*C. A.* **43**, 4229 (1949)].

When fresh tea leaves were stored in the dark for 20 hours, the glucose and sucrose contents decreased and the inositol content increased.[15] Infiltration of the leaves with glucose, fructose, sucrose, and mannose as well as other glucosides also increased the inositol content of the leaves, the glucosides being more effective than the free glucose.[16, 17] Glucose-1-phosphate likewise resulted in a more rapid synthesis of inositol than did free glucose.[16] All this work suggests, but in no way proves, that inositol is synthesized from sugars in these plants.

The observation[18] that the phloroglucinol content of tea leaves increased during the infiltration of the leaves with sugar solutions was interpreted to mean that *myo*-inositol is a precursor of this aromatic compound in the tea leaves. This is in agreement with Fischer's suggestion[1] that inositol is an intermediate between the sugars and aromatic substances. Apparently, in the tea leaves the reverse reaction—conversion of phloroglucinol to inositol—does not take place, for infiltration of the leaves with phloroglucinol did not increase their inositol content.[15]

The possible interconversion of inositol and ascorbic acid has been suggested,[19] following the observations that these are the only two vitamins present in significant amounts in citrus fruits. No experimental evidence for such a conversion has yet been presented.

C. INOSITOL SYNTHESIS BY ANIMALS

Rosenberger,[20] in 1908, found that he could isolate inositol from rabbits which had been allowed to stand for several days after being killed, although he was unable to find inositol in freshly killed rabbits. He also stated that he found an increase in the inositol content of beef muscle on standing and postulated the presence in muscle of an "inositogenic substance." Winter[21] likewise reported an increase in the inositol content of dog heart muscle on standing. Since both investigators used an alkaline hydrolysis to liberate inositol, some doubt is cast on these observations, for it is now known that inositol is somewhat alkali-labile.

Woolley[22] found that young mice which were fed on an inositol-deficient

[15] A. L. Kursanov, N. N. Kryukova, and E. Vyskrebentseva, *Biokhimiya* **13,** 530 (1948) [*C. A.* **43,** 3070 (1949)].

[16] A. L. Kursanov, M. Vorob'eva, and E. Vyskrebentseva, *Doklady Akad. Nauk. S.S.S.R.* **68,** 737 (1949) [*C. A.* **44,** 1568 (1950)].

[17] A. L. Kursanov, *Izvest. Akad. Nauk. S.S.S.R., Ser. Biol.* **2,** 44 (1951) [*C. A.* **45,** 7644 (1951)].

[18] A. L. Kursanov, E. Vyskrebentseva, and M. Vorob'eva, *Doklady Akad. Nauk. S.S.S.R.* **68,** 893 (1949) [*C. A.* **44,** 1172 (1950)].

[19] W. A. Krehl and G. R. Cowgill, *Food Research* **15,** 179 (1950).

[20] F. Rosenberger, *Z. Physiol. Chem.* **56,** 373 (1908).

[21] L. B. Winter, *Biochem. J. (London)* **28,** 6 (1934).

[22] D. W. Woolley, *J. Exptl. Med.* **75,** 277 (1942).

diet for 4 weeks after weaning showed an increase in the inositol content of their tissues from a total of 3.4 mg. at weaning to 8.6 mg. after 4 weeks on the experimental diet. However, when the experimental diet was deficient in pantothenic acid as well as in inositol, there was no increase in the total inositol content of the animals. Woolley compared the intestinal flora of the mice which recovered spontaneously from the inositol deficiency symptoms (alopecia) with the flora from mice which retained the symptoms and found that in the first case the flora had the ability to synthesize inositol but in the latter case they did not. It would appear, therefore, that in the mouse at least the intestinal flora can synthesize all the inositol required by the animal, provided that sufficient pantothenic acid is provided for normal growth of the intestinal organisms.

It was observed[23] that the inositol content of hen's eggs increased from 73 to 456 γ per gram of tissue during 23 days of incubation. This increase

TABLE VI

CHANGE IN INOSITOL CONTENT OF EGGS

Day of incubation	Inositol content, γ/g.	
	Free	Total
0	46	220
20	190	240

is apparently not due to synthesis of inositol by the egg tissues but rather to the liberation of inositol from a bound form. This liberation of bound inositol was demonstrated by Woolley,[24] who determined both the free and bound inositol in the incubated eggs. The results of this experiment are shown in Table VI.

Although there has not yet been a clear-cut demonstration of the synthesis of inositol by animal tissues, an interconversion of inositol and glucose has been reported.[25] myo-Inositol labeled with deuterium was fed to phlorizinized rats, and the deuterium content of the urinary glucose was determined. The high deuterium content of the glucose indicated its formation from inositol, but since the location of the deuterium in the glucose was not determined the significance of the observation has been questioned.[26, 27]

[23] E. E. Snell and E. Quarles, *J. Nutrition* **22**, 483 (1941).
[24] D. W. Woolley, *Proc. Soc. Exptl. Biol. Med.* **49**, 540 (1942).
[25] M. R. Stetten and D. Stetten, Jr., *J. Biol. Chem.* **164**, 85 (1946).
[26] T. Posternak, *Bull. soc. chim. biol.* **33**, 1041 (1951).
[27] W. H. Schopfer, *Bull. soc. chim. biol.* **33**, 1113 (1951).

It is tempting to assume that inositol is synthesized from glucose in plant tissues and that the reverse reaction can take place in the animal. The fact remains, however, that up to the present no unequivocal experiments to demonstrate either conversion have been reported.

VII. Estimation of Inositol

Although qualitative color tests for inositol (e.g., the Scherer test) have been developed, none of them can be used for a quantitative determination of the vitamin. Neither is there a specific chemical reaction of any sort by which inositol can be determined unequivocally in biological material. This lack of specificity is due in part to the fact that there are a number of biologically inactive isomers of inositol and in part to the similarity of inositol to the sugars in structure and chemical reactivity. Any chemical determination of inositol requires, therefore, a preliminary separation and purification of the vitamin to remove sugars. Such procedures inevitably result in losses of material and are less desirable for a quantitative determination of the vitamin than are the microbiological procedures which require no separation of the vitamin from the tissues. The recently developed paper chromatographic method, however, is a promising improvement in the chemical determination of inositol.

A. BY ISOLATION

ARTHUR H. LIVERMORE

The earliest methods for determination of inositol were developed before it was recognized to be a vitamin. Scherer[1] in 1850 discovered inositol in animal tissues and determined its presence after precipitating it with basic lead acetate, a reagent used also by many subsequent investigators. Scherer found[2] that, by treating the inositol first with nitric acid and then with ammonia and calcium chloride and finally evaporating the solution, he obtained a red-colored product. It has been shown that this colored compound is a salt either of rhodizonic acid or of tetrahydroxyquinone.[3, 4] This test is quite specific for the inositol structure and has been used as a qualitative test for inositol by many investigators (see, for example, Hutt

[1] J. Scherer, *Ann. Chem. Justus Liebigs* **73**, 322 (1850).

[2] J. Scherer, *Ann. Chem. Justus Liebigs* **81**, 375 (1852); *Beilsteins Handbuch der Organischen Chemie* **VI**, 1196 (1923).

[3] F. A. Hoglan and E. Bartow, *J. Am. Chem. Soc.* **62**, 2397 (1940).

[4] P. W. Preisler and L. Berger, *J. Am. Chem. Soc.* **64**, 67 (1942).

et al.[5]). The Scherer test has recently been discussed in some detail by Fleury.[6]

The introduction of the use of 70 % acetone for the extraction of inositol[7] improved the isolation procedure. Estimation by isolation and weighing remains, however, a very crude method for inositol determination.

B. BY CHEMICAL METHODS

ARTHUR H. LIVERMORE

The introduction of chemical methods for the estimation of inositol was some improvement over the earlier procedures. However, considerable purification of the inositol to remove interfering substances was still required.

1. REACTION WITH POTASSIUM IODOMERCURATE[8, 9]

Potassium iodomercurate in alkaline solution is reduced to free mercury by inositol and also by sugars. The mercury can then be dissolved in a measured excess of a standard iodine solution and the unreacted iodine determined by titration with thiosulfate.

2. REACTION WITH PERIODATE

The most satisfactory chemical method for determining inositol is to oxidize it with periodate.[6, 10-12] In the method of Platt and Glock,[10] the inositol must first be extracted from tissues with boiling water and impurities removed by precipitating some with 70 % acetone and extracting others with ether. Glucose can be destroyed by fermentation with yeast, and then lactic acid and other interfering substances can be removed by adsorption on carbonaceous zeolite and M.P.D. resin.

The inositol solution obtained in this fashion is treated with HIO_4 at 6° to 8° for 48 hours, at which time the theoretical amount of HIO_4 required by equation 1 is used up. The formic acid produced is then titrated with

$$C_6H_6(OH)_6 + 6HIO_4 \rightarrow 6HIO_3 + 6HCOOH \tag{1}$$

0.01 N NaOH. Platt and Glock found that, when the theoretical amount of HIO_4 had reacted, 90 % of the theoretical amount of formic acid was present in the solution.

[5] H. H. Hutt, T. Malkin, A. G. Poole, and P. R. Watt, *Nature* **165,** 314 (1950).

[6] P. Fleury, *Bull. soc. chim. biol.* **33,** 1061 (1951).

[7] G. Momose, *Biochem. J.* (*London*) **10,** 120 (1916).

[8] P. Fleury and J. Marque, *J. pharm. chim.* [8] **10,** 241 (1929).

[9] L. Young, *Biochem. J.* (*London*) **28,** 1435 (1934).

[10] B. S. Platt and G. E. Glock, *Biochem. J.* (*London*) **37,** 709 (1943).

[11] P. György, Vitamin Methods, p. 252, Academic Press, New York, 1950.

[12] P. Fleury and M. Joly, *J. pharm. chim.* [8] **26,** 341, 397 (1937).

In order to differentiate between inositol and glycerol which might be present in the solution, a titration is carried out 90 minutes after the start of the periodate oxidation. At that time 100 % of the glycerol but only 2 % of the inositol has been oxidized by the periodate.

In an earlier application[12] of the periodate oxidation method, the inositol-periodate mixture was treated after 24 hours with 0.1 N As$_2$O$_3$ and 20 % KI, and 10 minutes later the excess As$_2$O$_3$ was titrated with standard iodine solution.

More recently[13] the CO$_2$ which was produced during the periodate oxidation was determined in a Warburg apparatus. At 30°, between 1.1 and 1.3 moles of CO$_2$ were produced in 4 hours from 1 mole of inositol. Interfering sugars were destroyed by heating the mixture with MgO at 100°. Lactic acid was removed by alcohol and ether extractions.

It would appear that at the low temperatures used by Platt and Glock[10] there is little formation of CO$_2$ (in 48 hours), whereas at the higher temperature used by Fleury and Recoules[13] some CO$_2$ is produced. The source of the CO$_2$ has been determined by Fleury, who has shown[6] that oxidation of inositol by periodate at 30° takes place in two steps. The first is a rapid one in which 2 moles of formic acid and 2 moles of glycolic acid are formed, within a few minutes, from each mole of inositol. This is followed by a slow phase in which the glycolic acid is oxidized by the periodate according to equation 2. This reaction is still incomplete after several days.

$$2CH_2OHCOOH + 4O \rightarrow 2HCOOH + 2CO_2 + 2H_2O \qquad (2)$$

The possibility of estimating inositol by determining the amount of glycolic acid formed during periodate oxidation led Fleury and his co-workers to develop a semimicro method for determining this compound.[6, 14] In this method the violet color obtained by heating glycolic acid with chromotropic acid and H$_2$SO$_4$ is measured.

3. OTHER CHEMICAL METHODS

The Hagedorn-Jensen method for determining sugars has been used for inositol estimation.[15] Also, inositol in the form of its hexaphosphate ester (phytin) has been estimated[16] by determining the amount of organic phosphate in a partially purified tissue extract.

[13] P. Fleury and A. Recoules, *Compt. rend.* **227**, 691 (1948).

[14] P. Fleury, J. E. Courtois, and R. Perles, *Mikrochemie ver. Mikrochim. Acta* **36/37**, 863 (1951) [*C. A.* **45**, 5073 (1951)].

[15] W. R. Todd, J. Vreeland, J. Myers, and E. S. West, *J. Biol. Chem.* **127**, 269 (1939).

[16] J. E. Courtois and C. Perez, *Bull. soc. chim. biol.* **30**, 195 (1948).

C. BY PAPER CHROMATOGRAPHY

ARTHUR H. LIVERMORE

A qualitative determination of inositol can be made readily with filter paper chromatograms.[17-19] Although inositol is not readily oxidized in solution by ammoniacal silver nitrate, this reagent can be used to detect inositol on the filter paper chromatogram. The reduction of the silver by the inositol spot proceeds more readily if a little NaOH is added to the silver reagent.[17]

Quantitatively the inositol can be extracted from the filter paper, oxidized with periodate, and the resultant formic acid titrated.[18] No data have been given from which the accuracy and precision of this method can be determined.

D. BY MOUSE ASSAY

ARTHUR H. LIVERMORE

Woolley[20] demonstrated that inositol-deficient mice developed alopecia and that administration of inositol to the deficient animals cured this disorder. He used this method[21-23] to determine the inositol activity of various analogs of the vitamin. The mouse assay has not been developed into a strictly quantitative method for determining inositol. Moreover, it has now been supplanted by the more convenient and rapid microbiological assays.

E. BY MICROBIOLOGICAL ASSAY

E. E. SNELL

Inositol, the first component of "bios" to be identified, was first shown to promote growth of yeast by Eastcott.[24] Many, but not all, yeasts require this compound, together with one or more other vitamins,[25] and the response of suitable strains of yeast to it remains the basis for the most convenient procedures for its estimation.

Of the several naturally occurring compounds related to inositol, only the

[17] S. M. Partridge and R. G. Westall, *Biochem. J.* (*London*) **42**, 238 (1948).

[18] L. Hough, *Nature* **165**, 400 (1950).

[19] E. L. Hirst and J. K. N. Jones, *J. Chem. Soc.* **1949**, 1659.

[20] C. L. Withner, *Am. J. Botany* **36**, 355 (1949).

[21] D. W. Woolley, *J. Biol. Chem.* **140**, 461 (1941).

[22] D. W. Woolley, *J. Biol. Chem.* **139**, 29 (1941).

[23] D. W. Woolley, *J. Biol. Chem.* **140**, 453 (1941).

[24] E. V. Eastcott, *J. Phys. Chem.* **32**, 1094 (1928).

[25] P. R. Burkholder, I. McVeigh, and D. Moyer, *J. Bacteriol.* **48**, 385 (1944).

free vitamin, *meso*-inositol, has growth-promoting activity for yeast.[21, 26] Bound forms, such as phytic acid and those occurring in lipids, are inactive. For estimation of total inositol, therefore, hydrolysis of the sample is essential. Treatment of the finely divided sample with 18 % HCl under reflux for 6 hours, followed by evaporation of excess HCl and neutralization of the dissolved residue, is the method of choice.[26]

Of the several suggested yeast growth procedures, an unpublished modification of the procedure of Atkin *et al.*[26a] for determination of vitamin B$_6$ is simple and highly satisfactory. Inositol is omitted from the basal medium, and an excess of pyridoxine is added. Increased growth of the test organism, *Saccharomyces carlsbergensis* 4228, in response to increased amounts of inositol is obtained in the concentration range of 0 to 1 γ of inositol per milliliter. Incubation is for 18 to 24 hours, with shaking, at 30°. Other details of the assay resemble those for vitamin B$_6$ assay with the same organism,[26a] and have also been given in detail elsewhere.[26b] Good results are also obtainable by the method of Woolley,[26] which employs a strain of *Saccharomyces cerevisae* as the test organism; the basal medium, however, is much more troublesome to prepare, and the method does not appear to possess compensating advantages.

A fundamentally different assay procedure for inositol is possible by use of an inositol-less mutant of *Neurospora crassa.*[26b, 27, 28] The amount of mycelium formed in response to added inositol is determined by direct weighing after 3 days of incubation. Although the procedure appears accurate, it is more tedious than yeast assay and requires considerably longer time.

None of the lactic acid bacteria or artificially induced mutants of bacteria require inositol; indeed, it is not certain whether or not bacterial cells contain any of this substance. Assay procedures that utilize such organisms consequently are not available.

[26] D. W. Woolley, *in* Biological Symposia, XII. Estimation of the Vitamins, p. 279, Jaques Cattell Press, Lancaster, Pa., 1947.

[26a] L. Atkin, A. S. Schultz, W. L. Williams, and C. N. Frey, *Ind. Eng. Chem. Anal. Ed.* **15,** 141 (1943).

[26b] E. E. Snell, *in* Vitamin Methods, Vol. I, p. 327, Academic Press, New York, 1950.

[27] G. W. Beadle, *J. Biol. Chem.* **146,** 109 (1942).

[28] E. L. Tatum, M. G. Ritchie, E. V. Cowdry, and L. F. Wicks *J. Biol. Chem.* **163,** 675 (1946).

VIII. Occurrence

ARTHUR H. LIVERMORE

The naturally occurring inositol isomers are found in many plants and in some animal tissues.[1,2] The two optically active isomers have been found chiefly in various trees. D-Inositol occurs as the monomethyl ether, pinitol, and L-inositol as the monomethyl ether, quebrachitol. The other naturally occurring isomer of inositol is scyllitol. Scyllitol has been found both in plant products and in elasmobranch fishes. It has also recently been found, together with *myo*-inositol, in urine and in blood.[3] In addition to these compounds, other related substances have also been found in plant products. Among these are the desoxyinositols, C-methylinositols, inososes (pentahydroxycyclohexanones), and also the tri- and tetrahydroxy hexane carboxylic acids (quinic acid and shikimic acid).[1,2]

A. IN FOODS

Since *myo*-inositol is the only inositol isomer having significant vitamin activity, only this isomer has been determined extensively in food products. Most of the determinations of the inositol content of foods have been made by microbiological methods. Since the microorganisms which are used for these determinations use *myo*-inositol specifically, the results of these determinations undoubtedly give the *myo*-inositol content of the food products. The same cannot be said of chemical methods since these procedures (e.g., periodate oxidation) will not distinguish between the various isomers, and it is possible that scyllitol and D- or L-inositol might in some cases be determined as well as *myo*-inositol.

Some of the results of analyses of various food products for inositol have been collected in Table VII. This is by no means an exhaustive list of the food products studied. The original literature cited should be consulted for other foods.

B. NATURAL ANTIVITAMINS OF INOSITOL

The structure of the streptamine moiety of streptomycin is very similar to the structure of inositol. Streptamine is a diaminotetrahydroxycyclo-

[1] H. G. Fletcher, Jr., *Advances in Carbohydrate Chem.* **3**, 45 (1948).

[2] W. W. Pigman and R. M. Goepp, Jr., Chemistry of the Carbohydrates, p. 266, Academic Press, New York, 1948.

[3] P. Fleury, *Bull. soc. chim. biol.* **33**, 1061 (1951).

[4] V. H. Cheldelin and R. J. Williams, *Univ. Texas Publ.* **4237**, 105, (1942).

TABLE VII

The Inositol Content of Various Biological Materials

Vegetable Products

	Inositol content, γ/g. of fresh tissue	Reference
Cereals		
Wheat germ	6,900	4
Whole wheat	1,700	4
	1,900[a]	5
Bread, whole wheat	644	6
	1,030	4
Flour, white	830	4
Flour, whole wheat	1,105	6
Oats	3,160[a]	5
	1,000	7
Barley	3,920[a]	5
Corn	500	7
Fruits		
Oranges	2,100	4
Orange juice	1,040–1,700 (per ml.)	8
Grapefruit	1,500	4
Grapefruit juice	880–1,120 (per ml.)	8
Cantaloupe	1,200	4
Tomatoes	460	4
Apples	240	4
Vegetables		
Peas, English, green	1,620	4
Cabbage	950	4
Potatoes, sweet	660	4
Potatoes, white	290	4
Lettuce	550	4
Carrots	480	4
Spinach	270	4
Miscellaneous		
Peanuts, roasted	1,800	4
Molasses	1,500	4
	3,200[b]	9
Tea leaves, dry	10,000	8
Yeast, *Torulopsis utilis*	2,700	10
Yeast, brewer's	500	7

Animal Products

Meats		
Beef, muscle	115	4
	2,640	7
Beef, heart	2,600	4
	16,000	7
Beef, brain	2,000	4
	6,000	7
Beef, liver	3,400	7
	510	4
Pork, loin	360–450	4
Veal, chop	320–350	4

TABLE VII—*Continued*

Animal Products

	Inositol content, γ/g. of fresh tissue	Reference
Fowl and Fish		
Chicken, breast	480	4
Oyster	440	4
Halibut	170	4
Salmon	170	4
Egg	220	7
Milk Products		
Whole milk, cow	500	7
	180 (per ml.)	4
Whole milk, human	330 (per ml.)	4
Cheese	250	4

[a] Determined as phytin phosphorus. These inositol weights were calculated from Courtois and Perez values for phytin phosphorus, assuming a formula $Ca_5Mg(C_6H_{12}O_{24}P_6 \cdot 3H_2O)_2$ for phytin.

[b] This included 1340 γ of free inositol and 1860 γ of bound (phytin) inositol.

hexane which is an analog of either the scyllitol structure (1)[11] or the *myo*-inositol structure (II).[12] It has been observed[13] that lipositol from brain

I   II

inhibited the action of streptomycin on *Staphlococcus aureus*, and a confirmation of this observation has been reported.[14] However, it has been found[15] that lipositol has no antistreptomycin effect on *Escherichia coli*.

Another relationship between inositol and streptomycin has been reported.[16] The yeast *Torula utilis* was adapted to grow on a medium containing inositol in place of glucose. In contrast to the parent strain, this yeast which had been adapted to inositol was sensitive to streptomycin.

[5] P. György, Vitamin Methods, p. 252, Academic Press, New York, 1950.

[6] R. R. Sealock and A. H. Livermore, *J. Nutrition* **25**, 265 (1943).

[7] D. W. Woolley, *Biol. Symposia* **12**, 279 (1947).

[8] W. A. Krehl and G. W. Cowgill, *Food Research* **15**, 179 (1950).

[9] W. W. Binkley, M. G. Blair, and M. L. Wolfrom, *J. Am. Chem. Soc.* **67**, 1789 (1945).

[10] J. J. Stubbs, W. M. Noble, and J. C. Lewis, *Food Ind.* **16**, 9, 68, 125 (1944).

[11] M. L. Wolfrom, S. M. Olin, and W. J. Polglase, *J. Am. Chem. Soc.* **72**, 1724 (1950).

[12] T. Posternak, *Bull. soc. chim. biol.* **33**, 1041 (1951).

[13] I. Rhymer, G. I. Wallace, L. W. Byers, and H. E. Carter, *J. Biol. Chem.* **169**, 457 (1947).

[14] L. Söderhjelm and B. Zetterberg, *Upsala Läkareförén. Förh.* **5/6**, 235 (1948). As quoted by W. H. Schopfer, *Bull. soc. chim. biol.* **33**, 1113 (1951).

[15] T. F. Paine, Jr. and F. Lipmann, *J. Bacteriol.* **58**, 547 (1949).

[16] Y. H. Loo, H. E. Carter, N. Helm, and B. Anderlik, *Arch. Biochem.* **26**, 144 (1950).

No other natural antivitamins of inositol have been found. *myo*-Inositol has been reported[17] to reverse the inhibitory effect of malonate on *Clostridium saccharobutyricum*, whereas the D- and L-inositols do not. However, borate also reversed the malonate inhibition, so a specific inhibition of inositol by malonate was probably not involved.

IX. Effects of Deficiency

A. IN MICROORGANISMS

E. E. SNELL

The physiological activity of inositol was first discovered by Eastcott,[1] who showed that the substance was required for growth of a strain of yeast. Since these initial observations, many yeasts have been shown to be stimulated by it; for 15 of 163 strains investigated by Burkholder *et al.*[2] inositol was *essential* for growth. Several fungi are known that require the vitamin, e.g., *Nematospora gossypii*,[3, 4] *Lophodermium pinastri*,[3] and others. Mutants of *Neurospora crassa* that require it have also been produced.[5] In all such organisms, growth increases with the inositol concentration over a definite range of concentrations below the optimum; microbiological assay methods for inositol depend upon this fact.[6] Although the vitamin is required for growth of these microorganisms, nothing is known of the essential metabolic role played by it; no distinctive metabolic aberrations due to its lack have been reported. Presumably, in these organisms as in higher plants and animals, inositol may be required for the formation of essential lipid components of the cell;[7, 8] this, however, is mere speculation. It is a striking fact that no bacteria have so far been reported to require inositol, and it is not certain whether inositol is present at all in some bacteria, e.g., *Escherichia coli*.[9] Other bacteria, e.g., the tubercle bacillus, are known to contain it.[10] Indeed, the occurrence of inositol in the phosphatide

[17] A. J. Rosenberg, *Compt. rend. soc. biol.* **142**, 443 (1948).
[1] E. V. Eastcott, *J. Phys. Chem.* **32**, 1094 (1928).
[2] P. R. Burkholder, I. McVeigh, and D. Moyer, *J. Bacteriol.* **48**, 385 (1944).
[3] H. W. Buston and B. N. Pramanik, *Biochem. J.* (*London*) **25**, 1656 (1931).
[4] F. Kögl and N. Fries, *Hoppe-Seyler's Z. physiol. Chem.* **249**, 93 (1937).
[5] G. W. Beadle and E. L. Tatum, *Am. J. Botany* **32**, 678 (1945).
[6] E. E. Snell *in* P. György, Vitamin Methods, Vol. I, p. 327, Academic Press, New York, 1950.
[7] I. Rhymer, G. I. Wallace, L. W. Byers, and H. E. Carter, *J. Biol. Chem.* **169**, 457 (1947).
[8] D. W. Woolley, *J. Biol. Chem.* **147**, 581 (1943).
[9] D. W. Woolley, *J. Exptl. Med.* **75**, 277 (1942).
[10] R. J. Anderson, *J. Am. Chem. Soc.* **52**, 1607 (1930).

fraction of the latter organism[10] was the first evidence that inositol was associated with lipid material in any organism. In some yeasts and fungi that require inositol as a nutrient, the toxic action of γ-hexachlorocyclohexane is directed against inositol and can be overcome by it; the phenomenon, however, does not throw additional light on the metabolic role played by inositol. The insecticide also has a pronounced toxic action that is not overcome by inositol; it appears both in inositol-requiring and in inositol-synthesizing microorganisms.[11]

B. IN ANIMALS

T. J. CUNHA

Woolley[12-14] showed that an inositol deficiency in the mouse resulted in retarded growth and alopecia. Of considerable interest was the pattern of the hair loss obtained. No hair loss occurred from the tail or head or from the legs below the knees. The areas of loss of hair on most other parts of the body were bilaterally symmetrical, and in most of these areas the alopecia was nearly complete. Martin[15] observed only slight alopecia in mice fed an inositol-deficient diet. Woolley[16, 17] also observed that only about 50 % of the animals showed signs of an inositol deficiency and that spontaneous cures of the deficiency occurred frequently. He also found that, in the absence of pantothenic acid, alopecia developed even though the ration contained enough inositol. With large amounts of pantothenic acid and a lack of inositol, however, some animals still developed signs of inositol deficiency and died unless inositol was administered. Woolley[17] also showed that inositol is synthesized under certain conditions by the intestinal flora of mice. Frequently, the amount of inositol synthesized was equivalent to the minimum dose effective in the prevention of the alopecia. Thus, it appears that inositol deficiency symptoms in mice are most likely affected by intestinal synthesis.

Pavcek and Baum[18] reported that inositol cured "spectacled eye" in rats fed a purified diet. Subsequently, Nielsen and Elvehjem[19] were able to cure a similar spectacled eye condition in the rat with biotin. The fact that both groups of investigators were able to cure the spectacled eye condition with two different vitamins might well indicate that therapy

[11] R. C. Fuller, R. W. Barratt, and E. L. Tatum, *J. Biol. Chem.* **186**, 823 (1950).

[12] D. W. Woolley, *Science* **92**, 384 (1940).

[13] D. W. Woolley, *J. Biol. Chem.* **136**, 113 (1940).

[14] D. W. Woolley, *J. Biol. Chem.* **139**, 29 (1941).

[15] G. J. Martin, *Science* **93**, 422 (1940).

[16] D. W. Woolley, *Proc. Soc. Exptl. Biol. Med.* **46**, 565 (1941).

[17] D. W. Woolley, *J. Exptl. Med.* **75**, 277 (1942).

[18] P. L. Pavcek and H. M. Baum, *Science* **93**, 502 (1941).

[19] E. Nielsen and C. A. Elvehjem, *Proc. Soc. Exptl. Biol. Med.* **48**, 349 (1941).

with one vitamin in one case may have stimulated the intestinal synthesis of the other. This would mean that the spectacled eye condition could be due to a biotin deficiency, but in the work of Pavcek and Baum[18] the inositol may have acted indirectly in stimulating the intestinal synthesis of biotin. This postulation is strengthened by the finding of Lindley and Cunha[20] that inositol alleviated to a large extent the deficiency symptoms prevented by biotin with the pig fed a purified diet. Cunha et al.[21] reported an alopecia in rats reared on a natural diet composed chiefly of corn and soybean meal which could be prevented and cured by inositol. The hair loss started in the dorsal part of the head and proceeded bilaterally along the sides to the tail region and then downward to the hind legs. With inositol therapy the hair returned inversely, proceeding from the caudal portions forward. Of interest is the finding that the hair loss did not occur until pyridoxine and a folic acid preparation were added to the control ration. The addition of these two factors caused a decrease in growth and the development of the alopecia. This may have been due to some imbalance, some interrelationship of the vitamins, some change in intestinal synthesis, or to other unknown causes. Spitzer and Phillips,[22] using a sucrose-soybean oil meal ration, produced an alopecia in the rat similar to that observed by Cunha et al.[21] The hair loss was prevented by supplementation with inositol or biotin or with both. However, the hair loss did not occur if the ration contained added cystine or methionine. They also stated that, whereas low levels (1 to 4 γ) of biotin have been shown to prevent the loss of hair, higher levels (12 γ) of this vitamin may actually accentuate the condition. The hair loss resulting from feeding the high level of biotin was prevented by supplementation with adequate inositol. No explanatation is available for their results, but, undoubtedly, the ultimate answer will be of considerable interest. Nielsen and Black[23] also found that inositol prevents the development of a symmetrical alopecia in the rat fed a purified ration plus sulfasuxidine. The sulfonomide in some way brought out a need for inositol. It must be pointed out that in many experiments rats are fed purified diets apparently free of inositol and they do not develop spectacled eye or alopecia. An example is the report of Ershoff,[24] who found that inositol and PABA, in combination or separately, had no effect on growth of rats fed a purified diet. Thus, it appears that under special conditions the type of diet influences the need for inositol by the rat. Under ordinary conditions it is of no benefit, but occasionally the diet is such that a need

[20] D. C. Lindley, and T. J. Cunha, *J. Nutrition* **32,** 47 (1946).
[21] T. J. Cunha, S. Kirkwood, P. H. Phillips, and G. Bohstedt, *Proc. Soc. Exptl. Biol. Med.* **54,** 236 (1943).
[22] R. R. Spitzer and P. H. Phillips, *Proc. Soc. Exptl. Biol. Med.* **63,** 10 (1946).
[23] E. Nielsen and A. Black, *Proc. Soc. Exptl. Biol. Med.* **55,** 14 (1944).
[24] B. H. Ershoff, *Proc. Soc. Exptl. Biol. Med.* **56,** 190 (1944).

for inositol can be shown. Whether the inositol is effective *per se* or whether it acts indirectly by stimulating the synthesis of biotin or other factors is not yet clear.

Sure[25] reported that inositol and *p*-aminobenzoic acid improved the rate of survival of newborn rats. Later, Sure[26] found that *p*-aminobenzoic acid was primarily responsible for this action. Climenko and McChesney[27] reported that, on a purified diet, either with or without *p*-aminobenzoic acid, the addition of inositol reduced the mortality rate of the young rats and increased the milk yield of lactating rats. The inclusion of *p*-aminobenzoic acid alone, however, appeared to have an adverse effect upon lactation. The reverse of this finding was reported by Sure.[26] Ershoff and McWilliams[28] reported reduced fertility when inositol was fed in a purified ration containing both *p*-aminobenzoic acid and sulfaguanidine. However, the reduced fertility did not occur if either sulfaguanidine or inositol was omitted from the diet. Ershoff[24] later found that massive doses of inositol or *p*-aminobenzoic acid exerted no deleterious effects on growth or reproduction and that lactation may occur on diets containing 1 % *p*-aminobenzoic acid or inositol. The divergent findings of these various investigators cannot be definitely explained. It is possible that the differences are due to the different diets used and their subsequent effect on the type of intestinal flora present in the rats.

Lindley and Cunha[20] found that inositol was of no benefit when added to the ration of the pig fed a purified diet. They concluded that either the pig synthesizes enough inositol or it does not need the vitamin added to the ration. In that trial, however, it was found that, if a biotin deficiency was produced by using sulfathalidine in the ration, inositol alleviated to a large extent the deficiency symptoms prevented entirely by biotin. A possible explanation is that inositol acted indirectly by stimulating intestinal synthesis of biotin. Data by Ross *et al.*[29] and Cunha *et al.*[30] have shown that inositol was beneficial in lactation when added to a corn-soybean ration for brood sows and rats. However, these studies need more confirmation with other types of natural rations.

Hegsted *et al.*[31] reported that inositol supplementation slightly increased the growth rate of chicks fed a partially purified diet. Dam[32] found that

[25] B. Sure, *Science* **94**, 167 (1941).

[26] B. Sure, *J. Nutrition* **26**, 275 (1943).

[27] D. R. Climenko and E. W. McChesney, *Proc. Soc. Exptl. Biol. Med.* **51**, 157 (1942).

[28] B. H. Ershoff and H. B. McWilliams, *Proc. Soc. Exptl. Biol. Med.* **54**, 227 (1943).

[29] O. B. Ross, P. H. Phillips, and G. Bohstedt, *J. Animal Sci.* **1**, 353 (1942).

[30] T. J. Cunha, O. B. Ross, P. H. Phillips, and G. Bohstedt, *J. Animal Sci.* **3**, 415 (1944).

[31] D. M. Hegsted, G. M. Briggs, R. C. Mills, C. A. Elvehjem, and E. B. Hart, *Proc. Soc. Exptl. Biol. Med.* **47**, 376 (1941).

[32] H. Dam, *J. Nutrition* **27**, 193 (1944).

encephalomalacia and exudative diathesis, two symptoms frequently encountered in chicks fed vitamin E-deficient diets, were prevented by adding inositol to the diet.

Hogan and Hamilton[33] found that the rate of growth of guinea pigs fed a partially purified diet was increased by inositol supplementation.

Cooperman et al.[34] reported an increased rate of growth of hamsters when inositol was added to a purified diet. Hamilton and Hogan,[35] however, found that inositol supplementation did not increase the growth rate of hamsters; but the vitamin did counteract reproductive difficulties in hamsters in which the young were born dead or as shapeless bloody masses and where the mothers frequently failed to survive parturition.

McIntire[36] found that the addition of inositol to a purified diet almost doubled the rate of growth of cotton rats. This increase in growth rate is the greatest observed with any species fed a purified diet which was not supplemented with a sulfonamide.

There appears to be general agreement among investigators that inositol is a lipotropic factor. Gavin and McHenry[37] found that the addition of biotin to a purified diet caused a fatty liver in rats that could be prevented by the further addition of inositol. The lipotropic action of inositol in rats has been confirmed by Engel,[38] Forbes,[39] Handler,[40] and McFarland and McHenry.[41] Gavin et al.[42] found that, when thiamine was the only B-complex vitamin supplement added to a purified diet, the liver fat of the rat could be maintained at a normal level by supplying one lipotropic agent, choline. However, when other B vitamins were added to the ration, the fatty livers responded to both inositol and choline. All the observations of McFarland and McHenry[41] indicate that a fatty liver, of the type produced by in vivo fat synthesis, is made resistant to choline and responsive to inositol by increasing the intake of B vitamins, both in kind and in quantity. Handler[40] has suggested that a large increase in food intake, with a surge in fatty acid synthesis, may be the factor causing choline resistance and inositol responsiveness. However, McFarland and McHenry[41] reported on paired feeding tests which showed that food consumption is a contri-

[33] A. G. Hogan and J. W. Hamilton, J. Nutrition 23, 533 (1942).

[34] J. M. Cooperman, H. A. Waisman, and C. A. Elvehjem, Proc. Soc. Exptl. Biol. Med. 52, 250 (1943).

[35] J. W. Hamilton and A. G. Hogan, J. Nutrition 27, 213 (1944).

[36] J. M. McIntire, B. S. Schweigert, and C. A. Elvehjem, J. Nutrition 27, 1 (1944).

[37] G. Gavin and E. W. McHenry, J. Biol. Chem. 139, 485 (1941).

[38] R. W. Engel, J. Nutrition 24, 175 (1942).

[39] J. C. Forbes, Proc. Soc. Exptl. Biol. Med. 54, 89 (1943).

[40] P. Handler, J. Biol. Chem. 162, 77 (1946).

[41] M. L. McFarland and E. W. McHenry, J. Biol. Chem. 176, 1 (1948).

[42] G. Gavin, J. M. Patterson, and E. W. McHenry, J. Biol. Chem. 148, 275 (1943).

buting factor, but there is also a specific effect from the B vitamin supplements.

C. PATHOLOGY IN HUMAN BEINGS

A. T. MILHORAT

Evidence of a specific need for inositol by human beings has not been presented, nor have symptoms of deficiency of inositol in humans been described. However, the wide distribution of inositol in the body[43-46] and the data accumulated in investigations in animals make it reasonable to predict that increased knowledge probably will demonstrate an important role of inositol in the human organism. The observations of Best and others[47] on the lipotropic action of inositol and choline were made in animals maintained on diets deficient in this substance. These observations form the basis for the use of inositol in the management of fatty infiltration and cirrhosis of the liver in patients, but when one considers that these abnormalities may be due to a variety of causes, of which inositol deficiency probably is of great rarity and perhaps even non-existent, the paucity of evidence on the therapeutic usefulness of inositol in liver disease is not surprising.

Ariel et al.[48] found a high incidence of fatty infiltration of the liver in patients with gastrointestinal cancer. In 28 fasted patients Abels et al.[49] observed an average concentration of 16.4 g. of fat in 100 g. of wet liver tissue. The administration of 280 mg. of inositol to 10 patients and of 1200 mg. to 8 patients 10 hours before the operation appeared to reduce the amounts of fat in the liver, since the average concentration in the first group was 8.2 g. per 100 g. of wet liver tissue, and in the second group 6.9 g., representing, in the authors' opinion, reductions of 50 and 58 %, respectively. Lipocaic and choline similarly reduced the concentration of fat in the liver. It was concluded, on the basis of comparative experiments, that the effect of lipocaic could not be explained entirely by the choline content of the lipocaic but may be due to the inositol content.[49, 50] Echaurren and Jor-

---

[43] F. Rosenberger, *Hoppe-Seyler's Z. physiol. Chem.* **64,** 341 (1910).

[44] L. B. Winter, *J. Physiol.* **103,** 27 P (1944).

[45] J. Needham, *Biochem. J. (London)* **18,** 891 (1924).

[46] J. Folch and D. W. Woolley, *J. Biol. Chem.* **142,** 963 (1942).

[47] C. H. Best, C. C. Lucas, J. H. Ridout, and J. M. Patterson, *J. Biol. Chem.* **186,** 317 (1950).

[48] I. M. Ariel, J. C. Abels, H. T. Murphy, G. T. Pack, and C. P. Rhoads, *Ann. Internal Med.* **20,** 570 (1944).

[49] J. C. Abels, C. W. Kupel, G. T. Pack, and C. P. Rhoads, *Proc. Soc. Exptl. Biol. Med.* **54,** 157 (1943).

[50] J. C. Abels, I. M. Ariel, H. T. Murphy, G. T. Pack, and C. P. Rhoads, *Ann. Internal Med.* **20,** 580 (1944).

quera[51] treated 10 patients with cirrhosis of the liver with a regimen of a high protein diet plus 600 mg. of inositol daily, and in 7 noted gain in body weight, disappearance of gastrointestinal symptoms, increase in diuresis, and definite subjective improvement. However, Patek and Post[52] had previously demonstrated the beneficial effects of diets of high nutritive value in 54 patients with cirrhosis of the liver. The diets employed by Patek were of high protein content and were supplemented with yeast, liver extract, and thiamine chloride. Goldstein and Rosahn[53] and Broun[54] considered inositol to be of value in the treatment of cirrhosis of the liver, but definitive clinical experiments in which the diet was controlled are lacking, and the data at hand make it difficult to ascribe any observed effects to the administered inositol and not to general composition of the diet. In this connection, it should be noted that Sellers et al.[55] could find no evidence that inositol favorably influences the course of cirrhosis experimentally produced in rats by the administration of carbon tetrachloride. In contrast, the addition of either choline or dl-methionine to the diet induced considerable improvement in the cirrhotic livers. Felch and Dotti[56] administered 3 g. of inositol daily to 30 diabetic patients with hypercholesteremia and concluded that inositol is an effective agent in lowering serum cholesterol and lipid P, but neither Shay,[57] who gave 1.2 g. of inositol daily to patients with diabetes, nor Gephart,[58] who gave 3 g. daily to a patient with xanthomatous biliary cirrhosis, observed any significant change in the concentration of cholesterol in the blood. Similar negative results were obtained by Lupten et al.,[59] who likewise found no change in the insulin requirements of the patients. Gross and Kesten[60] noted significant reductions in the concentration of serum cholesterol of 55 out of a series of 64 patients with psoriasis whose blood levels of cholesterol were above normal, when preparations obtained from soybeans were administered. The daily dose of these preparations contained 0.6 g. inositol, but the presence of other factors such as choline permit no interpretation regarding the effect of the inositol or indeed of any single component of the preparations.

[51] A. P. Echaurren and R. Jorquera, Rev. Medica de Chile 71, 755 (1943) [abstr. in J. Am. Med. Assoc. 124, 66 (1944)].

[52] A. J. Patek, Jr., and J. Post, J. Clin. Invest. 20, 481 (1941).

[53] M. R. Goldstein and P. D. Rosahn, Connecticut State Med J. 9, 351 (1945).

[54] G. O. Broun, Postgrad. Med. 4, 203 (1948).

[55] E. A. Sellers, C. C. Lucas and C. H. Best, Brit. Med. J. 1948, I, 1061.

[56] W. C. Felch and L. B. Dotti, Proc. Soc. Exptl. Biol. Med. 72, 376 (1949); Bull. N. Y. Acad. Med. 26, 261 (1950).

[57] H. Shay, Am. J. Digest. Diseases 10, 48 (1943).

[58] M. C. Gephart, Ann. Internal Med. 26, 746 (1947).

[59] A. M. Lupton, T. W. Battafarano, F. E. Murphy, and C. L. Brown, Ann. West Med. Surg. 3, 342 (1949).

[60] P. Gross and B. Kesten, N. Y. State J. Med. 50, 2683 (1940).

However, observations indicating that factors other than the absolute level of cholesterol in the blood may contribute to the production of atherosclerosis leave open the possibility that inositol could function as a therapeutic or prophylactic agent in man, not necessarily by its effect on the concentration of cholesterol but in some other manner not yet defined, for example, by regulating the cholesterol:phospholipid ratio in the blood. Thus, Ladd et al.[61] found that atherosclerosis experimentally produced in rabbits by the feeding of cholesterol was accompanied by considerable increase in the concentration of cholesterol and only a slight increase in the phospholipid level in the blood. These investigators observed that the intravenous administration of Tween 80 to animals fed cholesterol increased the blood phospholipids to levels that were as high or higher than the corresponding cholesterol levels, and decreased both the incidence and the severity of the atherosclerosis. Several other workers also have emphasized the importance of the relative levels of phospholipids and cholesterol.[62-65] Duff and Payne[66] in their formulation of the pathogenesis of experimental cholesterol atherosclerosis in the rabbit have stated the opinion that instability of cholesterol in the blood rather than hypercholesterolemia per se is the general condition responsible for the deposition of cholesterol in the arterial walls. Duff and Payne considered the interrelations of the lipids to be more important for their stability than is their relation to the serum protein. In their experiments on normal and alloxan-diabetic rabbits that were fed cholesterol, they found, as had Ladd, Kellner and Correll, that the elevation of phospholipids was the important factor for the stability of serum cholesterol, with a minor effect being exerted by the neutral fats. Observations along similar lines by Ahrens and Kunkel[67] indicate that the clarity of sera of high lipid content is related closely to proportional elevation of the phospholipids; conversely, "milkiness" is present in such sera when the relative concentrations of phospholipids are low. Ahrens and Kunkel considered the concentration of serum phospholipids available for complex formation with serum proteins to be an important factor in determining the size of the lipid particles in the serum. More recently, Pollak[68] has emphasized the role of albumin in the protection of the blood vessels by its ability to stabilize cholesterol. Leinwand and Moore[69] noted that the administration of a total of 3 g. of inositol daily

[61] A. T. Ladd, A. Kellner, and J. W. Correll, *Federation Proc.* **8,** 360 (1949).
[62] J. P. Peters and E. B. Man, *J. Clin. Invest.* **22,** 707 (1943).
[63] T. Leary, *Arch. Pathol.* **47,** 1 (1949).
[64] M. M. Gertler and S. M. Garn, *Science* **112,** 14 (1950).
[65] A. Steiner, *Geriatrics* **6,** 209 (1951).
[66] G. L. Duff and T. P. B. Payne, *J. Exptl. Med.* **92,** 299 (1950).
[67] E. H. Ahrens and H. G. Kunkel, *J. Exptl. Med.* **90,** 409 (1949).
[68] O. J. Pollak, *Geriatrics* **6,** 183 (1951).
[39] I. Leinwand and D. H. Moore, *Am. Heart J.* **38,** 467 (1949).

to patients with disorders of lipid metabolism decreased the total lipids and increased the lipid phosphorus and cholesterol levels of the blood during the earlier periods of treatment, but subsequently lowered both the lipid phosphorus and the cholesterol concentrations as the treatment was continued. They concluded that inositol may have potential value in the management of atherosclerosis in man.

Inositol has been employed in the management of several other conditions in man. For example, on the basis of observations of Woolley[70] on the relationship of inositol to the growth of hair in the mouse, Vorhaus et al.[71] administered inositol to subjects with alopecia but observed no beneficial effect. Milhorat and Bartels[72] in their observations on creatinuria in patients with muscular dystrophy noted that the simultaneous administration of inositol and α-tocopherol lowered the creatine output, although the use of either compound alone was without effect. This effect was seen only in patients in the early or moderately advanced stage of the facioscapulohumeral form of the disease and not in either the advanced stages of this form or in the pseudohypertrophic type. Moreover, certain other sugars such as galactose and mannose had similar effects, and the mechanism of action of these substances is obscure. Beckmann[73] has confirmed these observations on inositol and believes that their application may be of value in the management of muscular dystrophy. On the other hand, John[74] noted no effect of inositol and vitamin E on creatinuria in this condition.

In summary, it may be stated that, although on the basis of theoretical considerations inositol would appear to be of therapeutic promise in certain pathologic states in humans, the usefulness of inositol in the management of any pathologic condition in man still remains to be established

Inosituria. The occurrence of inosituria appears to have been noted first by Cloetta,[75] who in 1856 isolated inositol from the urine of a patient with chronic nephritis. The observations that actually stimulated interest in this subject, however, were those of Vohl,[76] who, 2 years later, isolated from 18 to 20 g. of inositol per day from the urine of a patient with diabetes insipidus. Inosituria as an inconstant occurrence in diabetes insipidus was soon confirmed by a number of investigators, (e.g., Strauss[77] and v.d

[70] D. W. Woolley, *J. Biol. Chem.* **139**, 29 (1941).

[71] M. G. Vorhaus, M. L. Gompertz, and A. Feder, *Am. J. Digest. Diseases* **10**, 4 (1943).

[72] A. T. Milhorat and W. E. Bartels, *Federation Proc.* **6**, 414 (1947).

[73] R. Beckmann, *Deut. Z. Nervenheilk.* **167**, 16 (1951).

[74] S. John, *Z. klin Med.* **148**, 245 (1951).

[75] A. Cloetta, *Ann. Chem. Justus Liebigs* **99**, 289 (1856).

[76] H. Vohl, *Arch. physiol. Heilk.* **17**, 410 (1858).

[77] Strauss, Dissertation, University of Tübingen, 1864.

Heyden[78]) and a number of hypotheses were proposed to account for the urinary excretion of the inositol. Considering the type and limited amount of data available at the time, these hypotheses are easily understandable. For example, in one study, inositol was found in the urine of patients with diabetes insipidus who likewise had lesions of the fourth ventricle of the brain, whereas inositol was absent from the urine of two other patients with diabetes insipidus in whom no lesion of the fourth ventricle was present.[79] The fact that inosituria is not limited to cases of diabetes insipidus was indicated not only by the original observation of Cloetta,[75] which seems to have been neglected by the workers of that time, but also by the discovery that the urine of adults and children with a wide variety of diseases may contain inositol. An account of these early observations was published by Külz.[80] Reichardt[81] and Külz[82] made the important observation that, following the ingestion of large amounts of water, inosituria could occur simultaneously with the polyuria. Külz found inosituria in normal students who had consumed large volumes of wine or beer, and, although these beverages contain inositol (Perrin[83] and Meillère[84]) the diuresis, and not the inositol intake, was considered to be the cause of the inositol excretion. Evidence for this opinion was produced when Külz administered from 6 to 10½ l. of water to six normal adults, who previously had excreted no inositol. From the large quantities of urine obtained in each case, Külz was able to isolate from 0.4 to 0.9 g. of inositol. Later he[85] showed that urinary excretion of inositol could be elicited by the parenteral administration of saline in rabbits. Meillère and Fleury[86] attempted to extend the earlier work of Gallois[87] and Meillère and Camus[88] and to establish a correlation between glycosuria and inosituria. Gallois had found inositol in the urine of one out of every six patients with glycosuria, and Meillère and Camus had previously produced both glycosuria and inosituria by means of puncture of the floor of the fourth ventricle. Meillère and Fleury confirmed the

[78] v. d. Heyden, Dissertation, University of Leiden, 1875.

[79] Schultzer, *Klin. Wochschr.* **35** (1875).

[80] E. Külz, *in* C. Gerhardt, Handbuch der Kinderkrankheiten, Vol. 3, p. 285, Tübingen, 1878.

[81] E. Reichardt, *in* C. Gerhardt, Lehrbuch der Kinderkrankheiten, p. 540, Tübingen, 1874.

[82] E. Külz, *Sitzber. Ges. Beförder. ges. Naturwiss. Marburg* **7** (1875); *Centr. med. Wiss.* **550** (1876); *Z. anal. Chem.* **16**, 135 (1877); *Beiträge Pathol. u. Therap. d. Diabetes melitus u. insipidus* **1, 2,** Marburg (1877).

[83] G. Perrin, *Ann. chim. anal.* **14**, 182 (1909).

[84] G. Meillère, *J. pharm. chim.* [6] **30**, 247 (1909); *Chem. Zentr.* **2**, 1776 (1909).

[85] E. Külz, *J. pharm. chim.* **29**, 187 (1879).

[86] G. Meillère and P. Fleury, *Compt. rend. soc. biol.* **2**, 343 (1909).

[87] Gallois, *Z. anal. Chem.* **4**, 264 (1865).

[88] G. Meillère and L. Camus, *Compt. rend. soc. biol.* **2**, 159 (1906).

observation of Gallois and were further able to demonstrate the existence of inosituria in phlorhizin diabetes and in experimentally produced diabetes after removal of the pancreas. They concluded that inosituria is intimately linked with glycosuria,[89] whatever the cause of the latter might be, and that it accompanied polyuria only when this is associated with glycosuria. The situation appeared to be resolved by the observations of Starkenstein[90] and Needham.[45] Starkenstein showed that inositol has no significant relation to diabetes mellitus except that, when the volume of urine is large, inosituria may occur. The urine of diabetic patients, when of small volume, contains no inositol. Needham induced polyuria and inosituria in rats by feeding them a salt diet over a period of 110 days. Although the diet contained no inositol and the inosituria was of considerable magnitude and duration, no diminution in the inositol content of the tissues could be demonstrated. These experiments are important, since they not only prove that urinary excretion of inositol may be induced by measures that produce polyuria but they demonstrate also that the animal body is able to synthesize inositol. How profound an inosituria may accompany polyuria is indicated by the early observation of Vohl[76] and the later isolation by Hopkins[91] of about 15 g. of inositol daily from the urine of a patient with diabetes insipidus. Using a modification of the *Saccharomyces cerevisiae* G. M. method of Williams *et al.*,[92] Johnson *et al.*[93] studied the excretion of inositol in the sweat and urine of four adult male subjects under constant environmental and dietary conditions. The average excretion of inositol in the sweat during an 8-hour period of exposure to "hot moist" conditions was 0.118 mg. per hour. Under the same conditions, the average urinary loss was 0.494 mg. per hour. The corresponding average losses under "comfortable" conditions were 0.027 mg. in sweat and 0.626 mg. in the urine. Thus, with a greater loss of inositol in the sweat under the hot moist conditions, there appeared to be a compensatory decrease in the excretion of inositol in the urine.

[89] G. Meillère and P. Fleury, *Répert. pharm.* [3]**21,** 498 (1909) [from the *Tribune méd.* Sept. 4, 1909; *C. A.* **4,** 934 (1910)].

[90] E. Starkenstein, *Z. exptl. Pathol.* **5,** 378 (1908).

[91] F. G. Hopkins, (1923), quoted by J. Needham, ref. 45.

[92] R. J. Williams, A. K. Stout, H. K. Mitchell, and J. R. McMahan, *Univ. Texas Publ.* **4137,** 27 (1941).

[93] B. C. Johnson, H. H. Mitchell, and T. S. Hamilton, *J. Biol. Chem.* **161,** 357 (1945).

X. Pharmacology

A. T. MILHORAT

A. HEART

A physiologic role of inositol in cardiac function is suggested by the demonstration of the cyclitol in the heart muscle of rabbit, dog, sheep, pig, and ox.[1-3] The ventricle of the ox heart was found by Winter[4] to contain from 85.7 to 134.8 mg. of inositol per 100 g. of tissue, and the auricle contained from 77.1 to 92.2 mg. Less inositol was found in the bundle of His than in tissue from another part of the same ventricle. The inositol content of the Purkinje fibers was 53 mg. per 100 g. of tissue. Winter[2] found the survival changes in the heart muscle of the dog to be accompanied by an increase in the inositol content and, therefore, postulated the existence of a combined from of inositol, in addition to the free substance. Moreover, since a combined form of inositol could not be detected in the hearts of herbivorous animals such as the sheep and ox or in the heart of the carnivorous pig, it appeared unlikely that the combined form in the heart of the carnivorous dog was a substance such as phytin and had been derived from plant sources in the food. His evidence for the presence of a combined form of inositol in heart muscle is reminiscent of the experiments of Rosenberger,[5] who reported on the presence of both free and combined inositol in the white mouse. Rosenberger's determinations were made on the entire carcass after removal of the stomach and intestines (see also reference 6). Whether the function of inositol in heart muscle is similar to that in striated muscle, as postulated by Portmann, cannot be stated in a definitive way at the present time. Portmann[7] found that the fin muscles of fish, and especially of the shark, contain large amounts of inositol. Since the liver of these fish contains no glycogen or other reserve carbohydrate, Portmann believed that the inositol probably is a reserve carbohydrate that is formed from glucose and is stored in the fins to serve as an available source of glucose for the blood by the reopening of the inositol ring. Suggestive support of this hypothesis is furnished by the success of Grosheintz and Fischer[8] in the cyclization of glucose to inositol by purely chemical

[1] J. Needham, *Biochem. J.* **17**, 422 (1923).

[2] L. B. Winter, *Biochem. J.* **28**, 6 (1934).

[3] L. B. Winter, *Biochem. J.* **34**, 249 (1940).

[4] L. B. Winter, *J. Physiol. (London)* **103**, 27P (1944).

[5] F. Rosenberger, *Z. physiol. Chem.* **64**, 341 (1910).

[6] A. Taylor, M. A. Pollack, and R. J. Williams, *Univ. Texas Publ.* **4237**, 41 (1942);
V. H. Cheldelin and R. J. Williams, *Univ. Texas Publ.* **4237**, 105 (1942).

[7] A. Portmann, quoted by H. O. L. Fischer, *Harvey Lectures* **40**, 156 (1944–1945).

[8] J. M. Grosheintz and H. O. L. Fischer, *Harvey Lectures* **40**, 156 (1944–1945).

means, and by the demonstration by others that inositol in the organism can be converted into glucose. Although Mayer[9] had found no increase in the amounts of liver glycogen of three rabbits given 10 g. of inositol, nor had he observed an increase in urinary glucose of diabetic patients given as much as 50 g., Greenwald and Weiss[10] later found a small but unmistakable increase in the urinary glucose: nitrogen ratio when inositol was administered to dogs with phlorhizin diabetes. Perhaps pertinent to this problem are the observations of Needham,[11] who found that the injection of glucose into the fertilized unincubated egg causes a very large rise in the inositol content of the egg during its subsequent development. More recently, Stetten and Stetten[12] demonstrated a transformation of meso-inositol into glucose in the phlorhinized rat, when they found significant concentration of deuterium in the urinary glucose after administration of deuterio-inositol. The differences in the results and interpretations of the earlier workers, using less definitive methods, are easily understood when one considers that the data of Stetten and Stetten indicate a transformation to glucose of only 7 % of the administered meso-inositol. Moreover, in this experiment the inositol was administered by intraperitoneal injection, whereas the earlier investigators used the oral route by which absorption is incomplete.

The original observations of Sachs[13] that inositol affects cardiac function was confirmed by subsequent workers. Sachs perfused the frog's heart with Ringer's solution and noted increased amplitude and rate of contraction when inositol in low concentrations was added to the perfusion fluid. However, when an isotonic solution of inositol was substituted for the Ringer's solution containing inositol, the heart immediately was stopped in systole. Hewitt and de Souza[14] employed approximately the same concentrations of inositol in their perfusion studies on the frog's heart. The heart responded rapidly to inositol by an increase in the force of its beat and just as rapidly returned to its original state when the inositol was replaced by Ringer's solution alone. In six of the twenty-five experiments inositol had no apparent effect on the heart, and in two its perfusion led to diminution in force of beat. The rate of the heart, as a rule, was not altered by inositol. The action of inositol was considered to be on the heart muscle, since the effects were noted also in the atropinized heart. A concentration of 6 %, such as was employed by Sachs, was found to be strongly toxic and soon stopped the heart in systole. Brissemoret and

[9] P. Mayer, Biochem. Z. **2,** 393 (1907).

[10] I. Greenwald and M. L. Weiss, J. Biol. Chem. **31,** 1 (1917).

[11] J. Needham, Biochem. J. **18,** 1371 (1924).

[12] R. Stetten and D. Stetten, Jr., J. Biol. Chem. **164,** 85 (1946).

[13] F. Sachs, Pflügers Arch. ges. Physiol. **115,** 550 (1906).

[14] J. A. Hewitt and D. de Souza, J. Physiol. (London) **54,** CXIX (1921).

Chevalier[15] perfused the rabbit's heart with inositol in concentrations of 0.05 and 0.1 %. The lower concentration of inositol produced definite acceleration and more forceful activity, but use of the larger amounts of inositol was followed by gradual slowing of the heart and stoppage in systole. Meyer[16] observed that, in the perfused rabbit's heart, inositol concentrations of 0.01 and 0.02 % produced a decrease in amplitude and arrythmias. However, since the concentrations of inositol employed in these experiments are higher than those that occur normally in the blood, no definitive conclusions can be drawn relative to the physiologic role of inositol in cardiac activity. Sonne and Sobotka,[17] in their application of the nephelometric micro bioassay with *Saccharomyces carlsbergensis* to the determination of inositol, observed levels of from 0.37 to 0.76 mg. per 100 ml. in the blood plasma of fasting patients and normal persons. Pooled samples from miscellaneous patients showed values that ranged from 0.54 to 1.87 mg. per 100 ml. Moderate increases in the plasma inositol levels followed the ingestion of 1.5 g. of inositol daily. Waldstein and Steigmann[17a] gave amounts up to 1 g. of inositol by intravenous injection to patients and concluded that relatively large amounts are well tolerated and appear to be without untoward effects.

B. GASTROINTESTINAL TRACT

The effect of inositol on the activity of the stomach and small intestine was studied in dogs by radiographic means by Martin *et al.*,[18] who found considerable increase in the peristalsis of these organs. No spastic state was produced except a pylorospasm which the authors attributed in part to the constipating diet and in part to a possible contracting effect of the administered inositol on the pyloric sphincter. Other observations are of a more precursory nature but, in general, suggest a stimulating action of inositol on the gastrointestinal tract. For example, Anderson[19] and Bly *et al.*[20] noted diarrhea in dogs after administration of inositol, whereas Vorhaus *et al.*[21] and Shay[22] administered from 1 to 2 g. of inositol daily to patients without production of gastrointestinal symptoms. As indicated in the discussion on the factors influencing its requirements, inositol prob-

[15] A. Brissemoret and J. Chevalier, *Compt. rend.* **147**, 217 (1908).

[16] A. E. Meyer, *Proc. Soc. Exptl. Med.* **62**, 111 (1946).

[17] S. Sonne and H. Sobotka, *Arch. Biochem.* **14**, 93 (1947).

[17a] S. S. Waldstein and F. Steigmann, *Am. J. Digest. Diseases* **19**, 323 (1952).

[18] G. J. Martin, M. R. Thompson, and J. de Carvajal-Forero, *Am. J. Digest. Diseases* **8**, 290 (1941).

[19] R. J. Anderson, *J. Biol. Chem.* **25**, 391 (1916).

[20] C. G. Bly, F. W. Heggeness, and E. S. Nasset, *J. Nutrition* **26**, 161 (1943).

[21] M. G. Vorhaus, M. L. Gompertz, and A. Feder, *Am. J. Digest. Diseases* **10**, 45 (1943).

[22] H. Shay, *Am. J. Digest. Diseases* **10**, 48 (1943).

ably is relatively poorly absorbed, and it is probable that the effect on motility of the gastrointestinal tract is due to an irritating action. In this connection, the observations of Clark and Geissman[23] that inositol does not potentiate the action of epinephrine on an isolated smooth muscle preparation are of interest. Torda and Wolff[24] found that inositol increases the sensitivity of striated muscle of the frog to acetylcholine, but data on the smooth muscle of the gastrointestinal tract are not available.

C. THYROID

The presence of inositol in the thyroid gland was demonstrated by Tambach[25] and Meyer.[16] However, few data on the effect of inositol on thyroid function are available. Abelin[26] produced toxic symptoms in rats by the administration of 100 mg. of thyroglobin daily for 1.5 months, with reduction in body weight and in muscle creatine and increase in rate of respiration. The daily parenteral administration of 50 to 100 mg. of pantothenic acid prevented the occurrence of toxic symptoms. Inositol and pyridoxine had similar effects. Handler and Follis[27] observed that a decreased level of thyroid activity induced by thyroidectomy or by thiouracil or p-aminobenzoic acid feeding prevented or retarded the development of hepatic necrosis or fibrosis associated with choline and cystine deficiencies in the rat and that thyroid administration hastened the death of cystine-deficient rats. Inositol, as well as sulfasuxidine and taurine, prevented the development of hepatic cirrhosis in animals on a diet deficient in choline. This effect of inositol, however, was not due to lipotropic action or antithyroid activity, since inositol did not reduce the fat content of the fatty livers, nor did it produce morphological changes in the thyroid.

D. NEUROMUSCULAR SYSTEM

Inositol is a constituent of striated muscle[17, 21, 24, 28] and of the spinal cord and brain.[29] Investigations on the pharmacologic action of inositol on the brain apparently have not been done, but Lecoq et al.[30] in their studies on the effect of a number of compounds on nerve chronaxia in rats observed that inositol caused an increase in nerve chronaxia. Moreover, inositol had no effect on the increase in chronaxia after repeated adminis-

[23] W. G. Clark and T. A. Geissman, *J. Pharmacol. Exptl. Therap.* **95**, 363 (1949).

[24] C. Torda and H. G. Wolff, *Am. J. Physiol.* **145**, 608 (1945–1946).

[25] R. Tambach, *Pharm. Zentralhalle* **37**, 167 (1896).

[26] I. Abelin, *Experientia* **1**, 231 (1945).

[27] P. Handler and R. H. Follis, Jr., *J. Nutrition* **35**, 669 (1948).

[28] J. Scherer, *Ann. Chem. Justus Liebigs* **73**, 322 (1850).

[29] J. Folch and D. W. Woolley, *J. Biol. Chem.* **142**, 963 (1942).

[30] R. Lecoq, P. Chauchard, and H. Mazoué, *Bull. soc. chim. biol.* **30**, 296 (1948); *Compt. rend.* **227**, 307 (1948); *Compt. rend. soc. biol.* **142**, 428 (1948).

tration of epinephrine, and it abolished the reduction in chronaxia produced by adrenochrome.[31] Inositol does not potentiate the action of epinephrine on a smooth muscle preparation, however, nor does it affect the autoxidation of epinephrine.[23] Torda and Wolff[24] found that inositol increases the sensitivity of the rectus abdominis muscle of the frog to acetylcholine.

E. MISCELLANEOUS

Inositol was found by Williams and Watson[32] to activate slightly if at all, transamination by the rat kidney.

Doisy and Bocklage[33] in their studies on hexachlorocyclohexane noted that the toxicity of the α, β, γ, and δ isomers was not affected by inositol.

The thromboplastin inhibitory action of inositol phosphatide observed by Overman and Wright[34] is believed by Kay and Balla[35] to be due to the adsorption of the inositol phosphatide by the surface of the thromboplastin, thereby preventing the typical reaction which normally occurs when thromboplastin alone is employed. Inositol phosphatide was found by Kay and Delancey[36] to be without influence on the mortality rate of rats suffering experimental burns.

XI. Requirements

A. OF ANIMALS

T. J. CUNHA

No definite requirements have been worked out for the inositol needs of animals. Many investigators have been able to obtain good growth of rats, mice, chicks, pigs, and hamsters when these animals were fed purified diets without inositol. On the other hand, other groups of workers, under different conditions, have shown inositol to benefit the diet of rats, mice, chicks, pigs, hamsters, guinea pigs, and cotton rats. It is apparent that under certain conditions a need for inositol can be shown. The reason for the need under those conditions is not exactly known. Since inositol has been shown to be synthesized by rats[1] and mice,[2] it is logical to assume that

[31] P. Chauchard, H. Mazoué, and R. Lecoq, Compt. rend. soc. biol. **142**, 1346 (1948).
[32] H. L. Williams and E. M. Watson, Rev. can. biol. **6**, 43 (1947) [C. A. **41**, 4182 (1947)].
[33] E. A. Doisy, Jr., and B. C. Bocklage, Proc. Soc. Exptl. Biol. Med. **74**, 613 (1950).
[34] R. S. Overman and I. S. Wright, J. Biol. Chem. **174**, 759 (1948).
[35] J. H. Kay and G. A. Balla, Proc. Soc. Exptl. Biol. Med. **73**, 465 (1950).
[36] J. H. Kay and H. Delancey, Surg. Forum Proc. **1951**, 514.
[1] J. Needham, Biochem. J. **18**, 891 (1924).
[2] D. W. Woolley, J. Exptl. Med. **75**, 277 (1942).

under many conditions intestinal synthesis of inositol is altered, and so are the inositol requirements of the animal. There are also interrelationships of nutrients, and thus the diet fed and its content of various nutrients may influence inositol needs. It is also possible that there are substances, anti-metabolites for example, in natural feeds which may have an effect on the inositol needs of the animal. There undoubtedly are other possible explanations. Regardless of which may be the right one, there is still no definite postulate which can be regarded as established. Considerably more work is needed to clear up the problem of the factors influencing inositol requirements of animals.

Many investigators have used levels of 0.05 to 0.3 % of inositol in their experimental rations. However, none of these levels are regarded as definite requirements.

Several investigators have studied the utilization of phytate P.[3-5] Mollgaard and his associates have indicated the importance in the pig of the intestinal pH and of the presence of phytase in the food. Woolley[6] investigated the ability of several substances to replace *meso*-inositol in the nutrition of the mouse. Inositol hexaacetate, phytin, and soybean cephalin were effective in curing alopecia in this series. In contrast, the strain of yeast used was incapable of utilizing esters of inositol. Wiebelhaus *et al.*[7] found the quantity of inositol absorbed from the intestinal tract of fasting rats to be approximately a linear function of time and observed that the absorption of inositol monophosphate was more rapid than the absorption of inositol.

B. OF MAN

A. T. MILHORAT

Williams[8] estimated that an average mixed diet of 2500 cal. contains about 1 g. of inositol. Since evidences of inositol deficiency are not observed on good mixed diets, the requirements of man cannot, under ordinary circumstances, exceed this amount. Williams concludes that 1 g. daily is a "safe" level of intake but emphasizes that definite data are lacking. Anderson and Bosworth[9] found that of 0.5 g. of inositol per kilo of body weight, given by mouth, only 9 % was found in the urine, and none in the feces. The inositol in the diet is predominantly from vegetable sources. How

[3] H. M. Bruce and R. K. Callow, *Biochem. J.* **28**, 517 (1934).

[4] M. Gedroyc and S. Otolski, *Arch. Chem. i Farm.* **68**, 106 (1936).

[5] H. Mollgaard, K. Lorenzen, I. G. Hansen, and P. E. Christensen, *Biochem. J.* **40**, 589 (1946).

[6] D. W. Woolley, *J. Biol. Chem.* **140**, 461 (1941).

[7] V. D. Wiebelhaus, J. J. Betheil, and H. A. Lardy, *Arch. Biochem.* **13**, 379 (1947).

[8] R. J. Williams, *J. Am. Med. Assoc.* **119**, 1 (1942).

[9] R. J. Anderson and A. W. Bosworth, *J. Biol. Chem.* **25**, 399 (1916).

efficiently man can utilize the inositol of phytic acid is not known, but on the basis of investigations in various species of animals it is probable that appreciable amounts of phytic acid may be hydrolyzed in the human intestinal tract. The enzymic cleavage of phytic acid in the intestinal tract would be determined, at least in some measure, by the type of grain ingested, for certain grains such as wheat,[10] rye, and barley contain phytase, whereas oats and maize do not.[5] Cruickshank and his associates,[11] in their observations on four adult subjects, consuming a diet rich in oatmeal, noted that the phytate P of oatmeal was almost completely digested when the calcium intake was normal. Additional calcium decreased the digestibility of phytate P if the supplementary calcium was taken together with the oatmeal and not if it was taken separately. Sonne and Sobotka[12] noted moderate increases in the concentration of the blood from average levels of 0.37 to 0.76 mg. per 100 ml. when 1.5 g. of inositol was administered orally. Definite data on utilization and on possible synthesis of inositol in the human organism as well as on the effect of other constituents of the diet on the requirements for inositol are not available. For the present, these questions can be answered only by inference based on data obtained in animals.

Anderson[13] found inositol to be absorbed very slowly from the intestines of the dog and was able to recover in the feces as much as 77 % of the administered amount. He noted that the urine contained only minimal amounts. It would appear that the differences between his findings in the dog and in man[9] might be explained by the fact that in the dog inositol produced diarrhea, but his findings in the dog were corroborated by Dubin.[14] However, it should be noted that Bly et al.[15] found inositol to act as a cathartic. Greenwald and Weiss,[16] who administered inositol to dogs with phlorhizin diabetes, found increases in urinary glucose that suggested most of the administered inositol had been utilized.

C. INFLUENCE OF OTHER CONSTITUENTS OF DIET

A. T. MILHORAT

Considerable evidence has accumulated indicating that the composition of the diet influences the requirements for inositol. Thus, Best et al.[17]

[10] R. J. Anderson, J. Biol. Chem. 20, 475 (1915).
[11] E. W. H. Cruickshank, J. Duckworth, H. W. Kosterlitz, and G. M. Warnock, J. Physiol. (London) 104, 41 (1945).
[12] S. Sonne and H. Sobotka, Arch. Biochem. 14, 93 (1947).
[13] R. J. Anderson, J. Biol. Chem. 25, 391 (1916).
[14] H. Dubin, J. Biol. Chem. 28, 429 (1916–1917).
[15] C. G. Bly, F. W. Heggeness, and E. S. Nasset, J. Nutrition 26, 161 (1943).
[16] I. Greenwald and M. L. Weiss, J. Biol. Chem. 31, 1 (1917).
[17] C. H. Best, C. C. Lucas, J. H. Ridout, and J. M. Patterson, J. Biol. Chem. 186, 317 (1950).

have pointed out the necessity not only of dose-response curves but also of standardized dietary conditions for estimating requirements. These investigators observed that the lipotropic effect exerted by inositol when it is administered with fat-free diets is absent when the diet contains fat. Beveridge et al.[18] in their studies with other lipotropic agents noted the influence of protein on the effect of these agents. In another study, Beveridge and Lucas[19] stated the opinion that the antagonistic effect of corn oil on the lipotropic action of inositol might be due to the glycerides of the essential fatty acids. Pertinent to this problem are the investigations of Dam and Glavind[20] and Dam,[21] who showed that the effect of cod liver oil in increasing the exudative diathesis of vitamin E-deficient chicks may be counteracted by inositol. Handler[22] obtained suggestive evidence of a synergistic activity of inositol and tocopherol in his studies on the inhibition of the lipotropic action of inositol by unsaturated fatty acids.

The role of B vitamins in increasing the lipotropic action of choline has been demonstrated by Gavin et al.[23] and McFarland and McHenry.[24] The observation of Sure[25] that, in the albino rat, inositol has an injurious influence on lactation which is counteracted by p-aminobenzoic acid is at variance with that of Climenko and McChesney,[26] who in the same species found that the addition of inositol to a diet containing B vitamins resulted in normal lactation. p-Aminobenzoic acid in these experiments had no significant influence on the effect of the inositol. Martin and Ansbacher[27] and Martin[28] had previously studied the effects of adding inositol and p-aminobenzoic acid to a diet containing thiamine, riboflavin, pyridoxine, choline, nicotinic acid, and calcium pantothenate and reported that the addition of one produced a deficiency syndrome of the other. However, Ershoff[29] was unable to confirm these observations. Pantothenic acid was found by Woolley[30] to influence alopecia in mice. Concomitant administration of magnesium was found by Muset[31] to increase the effect of inositol

[18] J. M. R. Beveridge, C. C. Lucas, and M. K. O'Grady, J. Biol. Chem. **154,** 9 (1944); ibid. **160,** 505 (1945).

[19] J. M. R. Beveridge and C. C. Lucas, J. Biol. Chem. **157,** 311 (1945).

[20] H. Dam and J. Glavind, Science **96,** 235 (1942).

[21] H. Dam, J. Nutrition **27,** 193 (1944); ibid. **28,** 289 (1944).

[22] P. Handler, J. Biol. Chem. **162,** 77 (1946).

[23] G. Gavin, J. M. Patterson, and E. W. McHenry, J. Biol. Chem. **148,** 275 (1943).

[24] M. L. MacFarland and E. W. McHenry, J. Biol. Chem. **176,** 429 (1948).

[25] B. Sure, J. Nutrition **26,** 275 (1943).

[26] D. R. Climenko and E. W. McChesney, Proc. Soc. Exptl. Biol. Med. **51,** 157 (1942).

[27] G. J. Martin and S. Ansbacher, Proc. Soc. Exptl. Biol. Med. **48,** 118 (1941).

[28] G. J. Martin, Am. J. Physiol. **136,** 124 (1942).

[29] B. H. Ershoff, Proc. Soc. Exptl. Biol. Med. **56,** 190 (1944).

[30] D. W. Woolley, J. Biol. Chem. **140,** 461 (1941); J. Nutrition **21,** Suppl., 17 (1941).

[31] P. Puig Muset, Acta Med. Hispanica **36,** (1947).

in decreasing the cholesterol content of guinea pigs given fats *per os*. More recently, Waldstein and Steigmann[32] noted that inositol had no effect on either the degradation or excretion of choline when these substances were administered orally or by intravenous injection. Observations somewhat along the same lines were made by Diognardi and Magnoni,[33] who observed that 300 mg. of inositol daily did not alter the amounts of trigonellin excreted in the urine by a normal subject.

D. SYNTHESIS IN THE BODY

A. T. MILHORAT

The demonstration of Needham[1] that rats could be maintained on inositol-free diets for periods as long as 8 months without diminution in the inositol content of the body gave evidence that inositol can be synthesized in the organism. Even more convincing were his studies in which inosituria was experimentally induced for a period of 110 days; although there was a continuous and vigorous excretion of inositol, and the diet contained no inositol, there was no change in the amount of inositol contained in the tissues of the rat. Previously Vohl[34] had isolated more inositol from the urine of a person with diabetes insipidus than could have been contained in the diet.

Woolley[2] showed that the mouse can synthesize inositol when pantothenic acid is present in the diet, but it is unable to carry out the synthesis when pantothenic acid is absent. He observed, further, that the intestinal tract of animals which showed spontaneous cure of alopecia contained microorganisms which could synthesize more inositol than could the organisms from the intestines of mice that did not recover spontaneously. Mitchell and Isbell[35] also have presented evidence of synthesis of inositol in the intestinal tract of rats. Johansson and Sarles[36] have reviewed the general problem of intraintestinal synthesis of the B vitamins. Fenton *et al.*[37] studied the cecal flora of mice and found that the presence or absence of inositol in the diet appeared to have no influence on the number of organisms present. Seeler and Silber[38] were able to maintain dogs in apparent good health for a period of as long as 4.5 years on a diet containing no significant amounts of inositol. These findings might suggest a synthesis of inositol in the body, but of course they do not offer definitive evidence.

[32] S. S. Waldstein and F. Steigmann, *Am. J. Digest. Diseases* **19**, 323 (1952).

[33] N. Diognardi and A. Magnoni, *Acta Vitaminol.* **5**, 264 (1951) [*C. A.* **46**, 5707 (1952)].

[34] H. Vohl, *Arch. physiol. Heilk.* **17**, 410 (1858).

[35] H. K. Mitchell and E. R. Isbell, *Univ. Texas Publ.* **4237**, 125 (1942).

[36] H. R. Johansson and W. R. Sarles, *Bacteriol. Revs.* **13**, 25 (1949).

[37] P. F. Fenton, G. R. Cowgill, M. A. Stone, and D. H. Justice, *J. Nutrition* **42**, 257 (1950).

[38] A. O. Seeler and R. H. Silber, *Am. J. Med. Sci.* **209**, 692 (1945).

Starkenstein[39] had early postulated that inositol may be destroyed in the intestines by bacteria, but data to support such a view are not available. The addition of sulfasuxidine to the diet was found by Nielsen and Black[40] and Handler[22] to increase the need for inositol, presumably as a result of inhibition of intraintestinal synthesis.

[39] E. Starkenstein, *Z. exptl. Path.* **5,** 378 (1908).
[40] E. Nielsen and A. Black, *Proc. Soc. Exptl. Biol. Med.* **55,** 14 (1944).

CHAPTER 9

VITAMIN K GROUP

I. Nomenclature and Formulas

ROBERT S. HARRIS

Accepted name: Vitamin K

Obsolete names: Antihemorrhagic vitamin
Phylloquinones
Koagulations vitamin
Coagulation vitamin
Prothrombin factor

Empirical formulas: Vitamin K_1: $C_{31}H_{46}O_2$
Vitamin K_2: $C_{41}H_{56}O_2$
Phthiocol: $C_{11}H_8O_3$
Menadione: $C_{11}H_8O_2$

Chemical names: Vitamin K_1: 2-methyl-3-phytyl-1,4-naphthoquinone
Vitamin K_2: 2-methyl-3-difarnesyl-1,4-naphthoqui-
none
Phthiocol: 2-methyl-3-hydroxy-1,4-naphthoquinone
Menadione: 2-methyl-1,4-naphthoquinone

Structure:

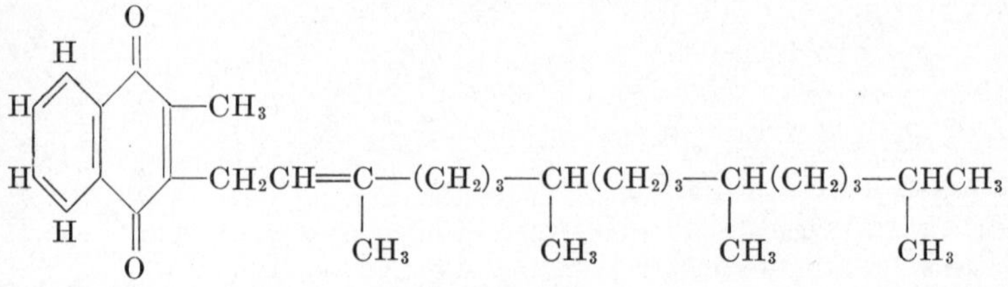

Vitamin K_1

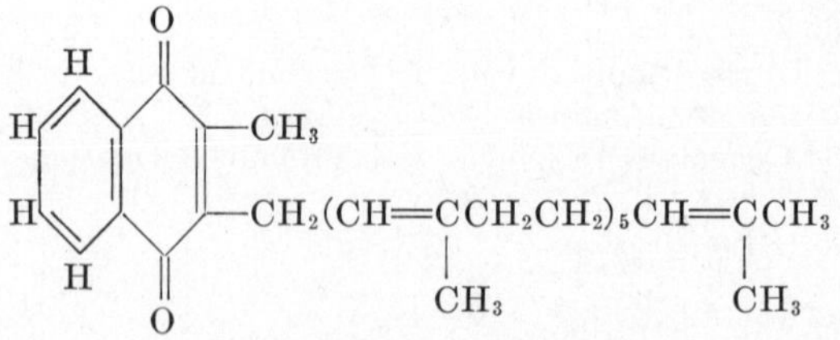

Vitamin K_2

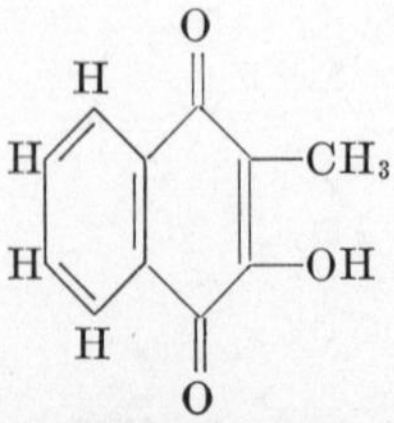

Phthiocol 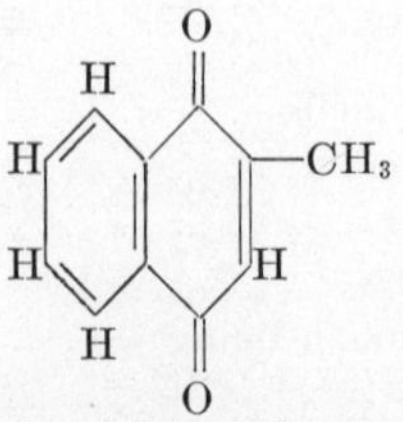　　　　　　　　　　　　Menadione

II. Chemistry

H. J. ALMQUIST

There had appeared, prior to 1935, several reports of modifications of the diet[1-7] which had led to hemorrhagic symptoms or changes in the blood-clotting power of the chicken. Although these reports may now be interpreted in terms of vitamin K, they did not contain sufficient information which would clearly link the condition with a lack of a new vitamin-like factor, as distinguished from possible deficiency effects of known dietary requisites, or toxic substances, impaired absorption, etc.

In 1935, papers by Dam[8, 9] and by Almquist and Stokstad[10, 11] furnished the first strong chemical evidence of a new vitamin which was shown to be in the fat-soluble, non-saponifiable, non-sterol fraction. It was also shown that the vitamin was formed in certain feedstuffs otherwise relatively free of it if these were subjected to the action of microorganisms. Schønheyder[12, 13] made studies of blood composition in this deficiency disease and found a specific lowering of the prothrombin fraction, but no other abnormalities. This evidence, collectively, was sufficient to permit recognition of a new vitamin, distinct from the known fat-soluble vitamins.

A. ISOLATION

Green leafy material was found to be a relatively rich source of the vitamin. The good heat stability of the vitamin[10] made possible the use of commercially dehydrated alfalfa meal as a starting source for isolation studies.

Extraction of the vitamin was carried out by means of a solvent such as ethyl ether, petroleum ether, or hexane. It was soon found that the vitamin was too labile during alkaline saponification to permit use of this step for the removal of green pigments and fats.[14, 15] Chlorophyll and similar

[1] H. Dam, *Biochem. Z.* **215**, 475 (1929).

[2] H. Dam, *Nature* **133**, 909 (1934).

[3] H. Dam and F. Schønheyder, *Biochem. J.* **28**, 1355 (1934).

[4] W. F. Holst and E. R. Halbrook, *Science* **77**, 354 (1933).

[5] A. A. Horvath, *Am. J. Physiol.* **94**, 65 (1930).

[6] W. D. McFarlane, W. R. Graham, Jr., and G. E. Hall, *J. Nutrition* **4**, 331 (1931).

[7] W. D. McFarlane, W. R. Graham, Jr., and F. Richardson, *Biochem. J.* **25**, 358 (1931).

[8] H. Dam, *Nature* **135**, 652 (1935).

[9] H. Dam, *Biochem. J.* **29**, 1273 (1935).

[10] H. J. Almquist and E. L. R. Stokstad, *Nature* **136**, 31 (1935).

[11] H. J. Almquist and E. L. R. Stokstad, *J. Biol. Chem.* **111**, 105 (1935).

[12] F. Schønheyder, *Nature* **135**, 653 (1935).

[13] F. Schønheyder, *Biochem. J.* **30**, 890 (1936).

[14] H. J. Almquist, *J. Biol. Chem.* **114**, 241 (1936).

coloring matter could be removed by adsorption on carefully added amounts of activated magnesium oxide or carbon. There followed a series of steps which consisted typically in chilling the preparations in various solvents to crystallize out impurities. By such means, for example, there was obtained a reddish oil which protected chicks against the hemorrhagic disease when fed at 2 mg. per kilogram of diet.[14] The vitamin was further purified in a molecular still, a fourfold concentration being effected.[16] The hemorrhagic disease in chicks was then prevented by 0.5 mg. of the preparation per kilogram of diet.

Dam and Schønheyder[17] concentrated the vitamin by adsorption on calcium carbonate or sucrose. Dam et al.[18] announced isolation of the vitamin in a highly purified form. Important details in the isolation steps were disclosed later by Karrer et al.[19]

McKee et al.[20] used primarily chromatographic adsorption on Decalso and Permutit on a large scale in their isolation of the vitamin from a petroleum ether extract of alfalfa meal and from putrified fish meal. Details of the procedures were published, ultimately, by Binkley et al.[21] Many other adsorbents were found to be inefficient or destructive for the retention of the vitamin. Repeated adsorptions yielded practically pure vitamin K_1.

Tishler and Sampson[22] have isolated from Bacillus brevis a vitamin K which proved to be identical with the vitamin K_2 previously obtained by McKee et al.[20] This isolation was accomplished by reducing the vitamin by hydrosulfite, then extracting it from a petroleum ether layer by dilute potassium hydroxide containing hydrosulfite, recovering the vitamin in petroleum ether on dilution of the alkaline layer with water, and crystallizing the product from chloroform and methanol.

B. CHEMICAL AND PHYSICAL PROPERTIES

Dam et al.[18] reported their yellowish oil preparation to have constant composition and biological activity after repeated chromatographic adsorption. It contained carbon 82.2 %, hydrogen 10.7 %, and 2 atoms of

[15] H. J. Almquist, J. Biol. Chem. 117, 517 (1937).

[16] H. J. Almquist, J. Biol. Chem. 115, 589 (1936).

[17] H. Dam and F. Schønheyder, Biochem. J. 30, 897 (1936).

[18] H. Dam, A. Geiger, J. Glavind, P. Karrer, W. Karrer, E. E. Rothschild, and H. Salomon, Helv. Chim. Acta 22, 310 (1939).

[19] P. Karrer, A. Geiger, R. Legler, A. Ruegger, and H. Salomon, Helv. Chim. Acta 22, 1464 (1939).

[20] R. W. McKee, S. B. Binkley, D. W. MacCorquodale, S. A. Thayer, and E. A. Doisy, J. Am. Chem. Soc. 61, 1295 (1939).

[21] S. B. Binkley, D. W. MacCorquodale, S. A. Thayer, and E. A. Doisy, J. Biol. Chem. 130, 219 (1939).

[22] M. Tishler and W. L. Sampson, Proc. Soc. Exptl. Biol. Med. 68, 136 (1948).

oxygen per molecule. Karrer and Geiger[23] reported a provisional formula of C_{30-32}, $H_{46, 48, or 50}$, O_2, and a molecular weight of 445 to 450. Doisy and coworkers had obtained two final products, one from alfalfa and one from putrified fish meal.[20, 24] The first was a yellow oil and was called K_1; the melting point was given as 53.5 to 54.5[25] and 52.5 to 53.5.[22] The vitamin from alfalfa contained carbon 82.76 and 82.54 %, and hydrogen 10.65 and 10.66 %. Its molecular weight was determined as 443 to 464, and its probable formula as $C_{32}H_{48-50}O_2$. Almquist and Klose[26] investigated the alkaline degradation product of vitamin K_1. This derivative is weakly acid, which facilitates its purification. Analyses and molecular weight determination indicated a provisional formula of $C_{31}H_{50}O_4$. This showed that no appreciable fragment of the vitamin had been split off and that 2 oxygen atoms and probably several hydrogen atoms had been added. At least one of the oxygen atoms was phenolic. The empirical formula of vitamin K_1 is now known to be $C_{31}H_{46}O_2$, and its molecular weight 450.37. Figure 1 shows the structural formulas of the various forms of vitamin K.

The vitamin was found to be unstable to light.[15, 24] Phenyl isocyanate, cyanic acid, and dinitrobenzoyl chloride, which are reagents for an alcoholic hydroxyl group, did not form an isolatable derivative or affect the activity of the vitamin. Bromine was readily absorbed. Oxidation destroyed activity. A positive nitration test was obtained for an aromatic structure.[27] A diacetate was formed upon reductive acetylation from which the vitamin could be regenerated.[21, 23]

Almquist[15] reported that the vitamin absorbed strongly in the ultraviolet range with considerable destruction. Dam et al.[18] reported ultraviolet absorption maxima at 248, 261, 270, and 328 mμ. The extinction coefficient, $E_{1 cm.}^{1\%}$, for the 248 line was 280. McKee et al.[20] found the extinction coefficient at 248 to be 385 and suggested that their product was purer than the one described by Dam et al. However, the biological activity of preparations from these laboratories was found to be equivalent in simultaneous assays by another laboratory.[29]

Ewing et al.[30] investigated very carefully the ultraviolet absorption spec-

[23] P. Karrer and A. Geiger, *Helv. Chim. Acta* **22,** 945 (1939).
[24] D. W. MacCorquodale, S. B. Binkely, R. W. McKee, S. A. Thayer, and E. A. Doisy, *Proc. Soc. Exptl. Biol. Med.* **40,** 482 (1939).
[25] R. W. McKee, S. B. Binkley, S. A. Thayer, D. W. MacCorquodale, and E. A. Doisy, *J. Biol. Chem.* **131,** 327 (1939).
[26] H. J. Almquist and A. A. Klose, *J. Biol. Chem.* **130,** 791 (1939).
[27] A. A. Klose, H. J. Almquist, and E. Mecchi, *J. Biol. Chem.* **125,** 681 (1938).
[28] S. B. Binkley, D. W. MacCorquodale, L. C. Cheney, S. A. Thayer, R. W. McKee, and E. A. Doisy, *J. Am. Chem. Soc.* **61,** 1612 (1939).
[29] H. J. Almquist and A. A. Klose, *J. Biol. Chem.* **130,** 787 (1939).
[30] D. T. Ewing, J. M. Vandenbelt, and O. Kamm, *J. Biol. Chem.* **131,** 345 (1939).

tra of vitamins K_1 and K_2 prepared by Doisy and coworkers. Each vitamin showed maxima at 243, 249, 260, and 270 mμ and a broad absorption in the region of 310 and 340. The $E_{1\,cm}^{1\%}$ at 249 mμ was 540 for K_1 and 305 for K_2. These extinction coefficients were higher than those reported previously.[18, 20] The purified vitamin K_1 in hexane solution exposed to daylight decreased in absorption so fast that in 15 minutes the extinction coefficient at 249 was about 420 and at 1 hour about 350. The other maxima also

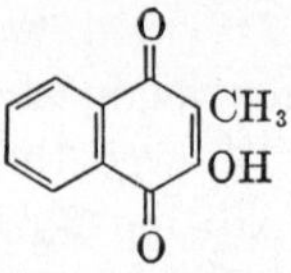

2-Methyl-3-hydroxy-
1,4-naphthoquinone
Phthiocol

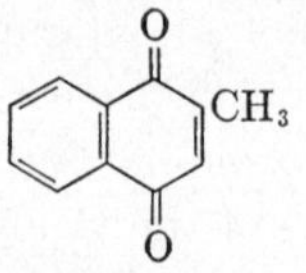

2-Methyl-1,4-naphthoquinone
Menadione

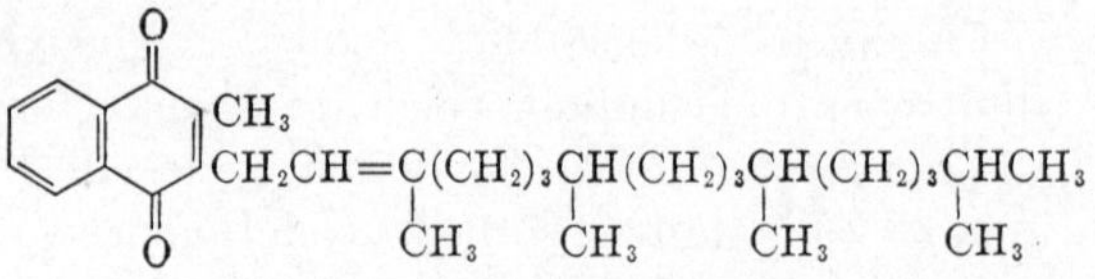

2-Methyl-3-phytyl-1,4-naphthoquinone
Vitamin K_1

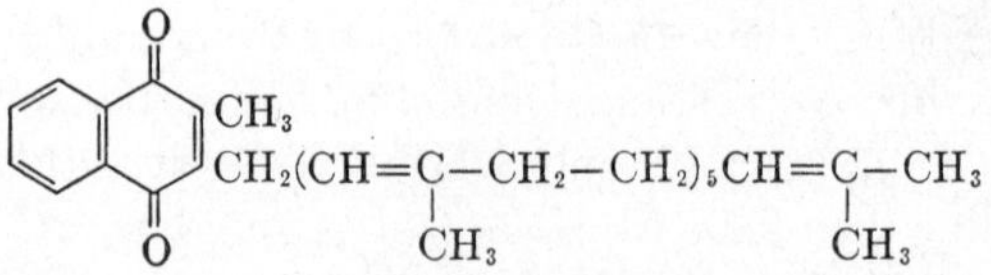

2-Methyl-3-difarnesyl-1,4-naphthoquinone
Vitamin K_2

Fig. 1. Forms of vitamin K.

dropped similarly. Ewing *et al.*[31] have further studied the absorption spectrum of vitamin K_1, again finding evidence of rapid drops in absorption as the vitamin in hexane solution was exposed to ultraviolet light. A new value for the extinction coefficient at 249 mμ was given at 435 ± 5. The literature was thoroughly discussed. More recently, the extinction coefficient for K_2 at 249 mμ has been given as 520, which is considerably higher than the earlier values.[22] It seems evident, therefore, that unless determined almost instantly after the vitamin was exposed to light the absorption at 249 mμ would have decreased by an indeterminate amount and could hardly be used as a criterion of purity.

[31] D. T. Ewing, F. S. Tomkins, and O. Kamm, *J. Biol. Chem.* **147**, 233 (1943).

At very low pressures, 10^{-4} to 10^{-5} mm. of mercury, vitamin K_1 could be distilled at 120 to 140° with little or no loss.[16, 21] Vitamin K_2 was distilled with some loss at 2×10^{-4} mm. and 200°.

C. CONSTITUTION

The characteristic yellow color of these purified vitamins, the loss of color upon hydrogenation, and its reappearance upon exposure to oxygen in air suggested that the vitamins might be quinones.[21, 25] Among a number of bacteria tested *Mycobacterium tuberculosis* had been found to possess

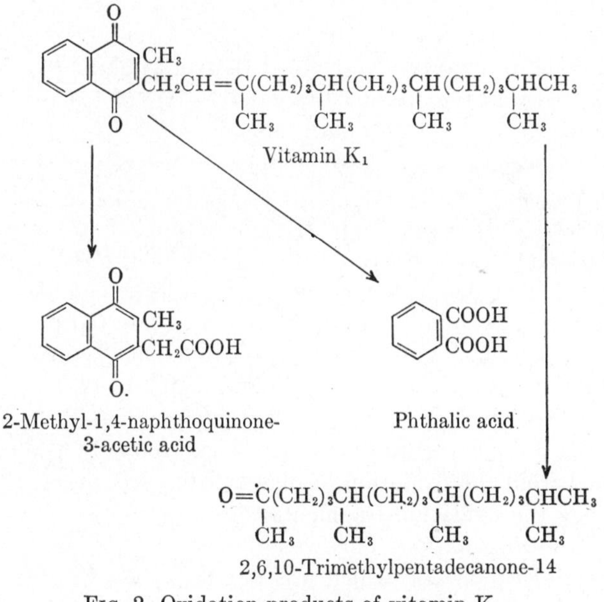

Vitamin K_1

2-Methyl-1,4-naphthoquinone-3-acetic acid

Phthalic acid

2,6,10-Trimethylpentadecanone-14

FIG. 2. Oxidation products of vitamin K_1.

appreciable vitamin K activity.[32] The principal pigment in the lipids of this organism had been isolated and synthesized by Anderson and coworkers several years before.[33] The pigment, phthiocol, was 2-methyl-3-hydroxy-1,4-naphthoquinone (Fig. 2). Certain features of the absorption curve and other properties of this compound compared closely with those reported for vitamin K_1. Synthetic phthiocol tested with vitamin K-deficient chicks was found to be distinctly active in restoring normal blood-clotting time and thus became the first completely identified form of vitamin K.[34] The next step was to test the functional importance of the methyl and hydroxyl

[32] H. J. Almquist, C. F. Pentler, and E. Mecchi, *Proc. Soc. Exptl. Biol. Med.* **38**, 336 (1938).

[33] R. J. Anderson and M. S. Newman, *J. Biol. Chem.* **101**, 773 (1933).

[34] H. J. Almquist and A. A. Klose, *J. Am. Chem. Soc.* **61**, 1611 (1939).

groups. Chick assays of the 2-methyl, the 2-hydroxy, and the 2-methyl-3-hydroxynaphthoquinone showed that the 2-methyl compound (see Fig. 1) was more active and the 2-hydroxy compound less active than phthiocol. This indicated that the methyl group was functionally important whereas the hydroxyl group seemed to reduce activity.[35] Phthiocol was readily brought into water solution which was effective by intramuscular or intravenous injection. It is probably the first synthetic form of the vitamin to be employed in human cases.   •

Confirming reports of vitamin K activity of these and certain other synthetic and natural substituted naphthoquinones immediately appeared.[36-39] It had also been noted that the absorption spectrum of 2,3-dimethyl-1,4-naphthoquinone most closely resembled that of vitamins K_1 and K_2, and it was suggested that the vitamins were derivatives of 1,4-naphthoquinone with side chains at the 2 and 3 positions.

Since it had become plainly evident that the active nucleus of the naturally occurring vitamin was represented by 2-methyl-1,4-naphthoquinone with substituents at position 3, the remaining problem in the cases of vitamins K_1 and K_2 was to determine the nature of the substituents. MacCorquodale et al.[40] have published the details of their studies on the structure of vitamin K_1. Oxidation with chromic acid resulted in the formation of a mixture from which two acids were isolated. One of these was phthalic acid, and the other was ultimately identified with 2-methyl-1,4-napthoquinone-3-acetic acid by comparison of melting point and other properties with those of products synthesized for this purpose. A comparable acid was obtained from the oxidation of diacetyl dihydro vitamin K_1 (Fig. 2).

Also among the oxidation fragments was a ketone which could be separated by steam distillation. This was found to be identical with 2,6,10-trimethylpentadecanone-14, which was previously known to be formed in the oxidation of phytol (Fig. 2). Phytol, if present as a side chain on the vitamin, was evidently located so that its double bond was between the second and third carbon atoms from the quinone ring, since this was the point of scission upon oxidation. The formula of vitamin K_1 was given as 2-methyl-3-phytyl-1,4-naphthoquinone (Fig. 2).

[35] H. J. Almquist and A. A. Klose, J. Am. Chem. Soc. **61**, 1923 (1939).

[36] S. Ansbacher and E. Fernholz, J. Am. Chem. Soc. **61**, 1924 (1939).

[37] L. F. Fieser, D. M. Bowen, W. P. Campbell, M. Fieser, E. M. Fry, R. N. Jones, B. Riegel, C. W. Schweitzer, and P. G. Smith, J. Am. Chem. Soc. **61**, 1925 (1939).

[38] L. F. Fieser, D. M. Bowen, W. P. Campbell, E. M. Fry, and M. D. Gates, Jr., J. Am. Chem. Soc. **61**, 1926 (1939).

[39] S. A. Thayer, L. C. Cheney, S. B. Binkley, D. W. MacCorquodale, and E. A. Doisy, J. Am. Chem. Soc. **61**, 1932 (1939).

[40] D. W. MacCorquodale, L. C. Cheney, S. B. Binkley, W. F. Holcomb, R. W. McKee, S. A. Thayer, and E. A. Doisy, J. Biol. Chem. **131**, 357 (1939).

McKee *et al.*[25] stated that vitamin K_2 was a 2,3-substituted naphthoquinone with six double bonds in the side groups. It would take up 9 molecules of hydrogen, 3 for the naphthoquinone portion. Iodine absorption indicated 6 molecules of halogen taken up by non-aromatic unsaturated bonds. Upon oxidation vitamin K_2 yielded the same quinone acid (or aldehyde) and phthalic acid that had been obtained from K_1 (Binkley *et al.*[41]). The vitamin K_2 was, evidently, similar to K_1, but with a much longer side chain at position 3. Fragments of the side chain were isolated and identified as acetone and levulinaldehyde in a mole ratio of 1:5 per mole of K_2. This aldehyde is also obtainable from the oxidation of farnesol. A structural formula was proposed having two farnesyl groups linked together to form a long side chain at position 3 (Fig. 1). The empirical formula was given as $C_{41}H_{56}O_2$.

D. SYNTHESIS

Synthesis of vitamin K_1 was accomplished by simple procedures. It was evident that a phytyl side chain would account for the difference in molecular weight between the methylnaphthoquinone and vitamin K_1. 2-Methyl-3-phytyl-1,4-naphthoquinone was synthesized by Almquist and Klose[42] by coupling methylnaphthoquinone with phytyl bromide in petroleum ether and glacial acetic acid in contact with zinc dust. The product was refined in a molecular still. It exhibited color, oily form, color reaction, carbon and hydrogen analysis, and biological potency very similar to those of vitamin K_1.

Doisy and coworkers[43] submitted a report of synthesis of the same compound by condensing phytyl bromide with the monosodium salt of 2-methyl-1,4-naphthohydroquinone in benzene, and by direct coupling of phytol and methylnaphthoquinone with zinc chloride. Details of these methods were given later.[40] Fieser[44] carried out the synthesis of this compound by condensation of phytol with methylnaphthoquinone in dioxane with oxalic acid as catalyst. These preliminary reports appeared in the same issue of the same journal. Synthesis of vitamin K_2 has not yet been accomplished.

The ultraviolet absorption of synthetic vitamin K_1 was identified with that of the natural vitamin[31] (Fig. 3).

[41] S. B. Binkley, R. W. McKee, S. A. Thayer, and E. A. Doisy, *J. Biol. Chem.* **133**, 721 (1940).
[42] H. J. Almquist and A. A. Klose, *J. Am. Chem. Soc.* **61**, 2557 (1939); *J. Biol. Chem.* **132**, 469 (1940).
[43] S. B. Binkley, L. C. Cheney, W. F. Holcomb, R. W. McKee, S. A. Thayer, D. W. MacCorquodale, and E. Doisy, *J. Am. Chem. Soc.* **61**, 2558 (1939).
[44] L. F. Fieser, *J. Am. Chem. Soc.* **61**, 2559 (1939).

E. SPECIFICITY

In contrast to the history of most other vitamins, synthesis of vitamin K_1 did not prove to be the ultimate goal in the search for antihemorrhagic vitamins. Immediately after the report on phthiocol,[34] a number of communications appeared on tests of other naphthoquinones, mostly based upon rapid curative assays which may be done in a few hours. Ansbacher and Fernholz[36] confirmed the activity of phthiocol and indicated an even

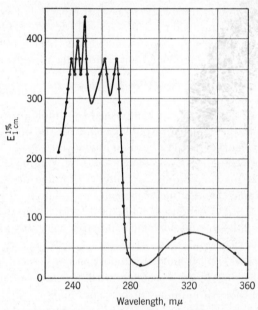

Fig. 3. Ultraviolet absorption spectrum of synthetic vitamin K_1. (From Ewing et al.[31])

higher potency for 2-methyl-1,4-naphthoquinone than reported by Almquist and Klose[35] or Thayer et al.[39] Ultimately, this compound was reported to have a greater activity than vitamin K_1, by two to three times.[29, 45-52]

Methylnaphthohydroquinone was equally as active as its oxidized

[45] H. J. Almquist and A. A. Klose, Proc. Soc. Exptl. Biol. Med. **45**, 55 (1940).

[46] S. Ansbacher, J. Biol. Chem. **133**, iii (1940).

[47] F. P. Dann, Proc. Soc. Exptl. Biol. Med. **42**, 663 (1939).

[48] A. D. Emmett, R. A. Brown, and O. Kamm, J. Biol. Chem. **132**, 467 (1940).

[49] E. Fernholz and S. Ansbacher, Science **90**, 215 (1939).

[50] S. A. Thayer, R. W. McKee, S. B. Binkley, and E. A. Doisy, Proc. Soc. Exptl. Biol. Med. **44**, 585 (1940).

[51] H. Dam, J. Glavind, and P. Karrer, Helv. Chim. Acta **33**, 224 (1940).

[52] L. F. Fieser, M. Tishler, and W. L. Sampson, J. Biol. Chem. **137**, 659 (1941).

form.[43, 45] The diesters of this compound were also found to be active. The bisulfite addition product of methylnaphthoquinone is water soluble and highly active.[53] A number of other compounds easily convertible to methylnaphthoquinone in metabolism probably owe their activity to such conversion. Among these are 1-hydroxy-2-methyl-, 1-hydroxy-3-methyl-, and 1-amino-2-methylnaphthalene, 3-methyl-1-tetralone, and 2-methyl-1-tetralone.[54] The water-soluble compounds, 4-amino-2-methyl-1-naphthol hydrochloride and 4-amino-3-methyl-1-naphthol hydrochloride were found to be approximately as potent as vitamin K_1.[55] Using the Craven's ethyl cyanoacetate color reaction for quinones as a quantitative method, Richert[56] demonstrated the biological conversion of 4-amino-2-methyl-1-naphthol, 2-methyl-1,4-naphthohydroquinone diphosphate, and 2-methyl tetralone to methylnaphthoquinone. The excretion of the latter in the urine of the rabbit and chicken increased significantly when any of the first three were fed.

Several naturally occurring 3-hydroxynaphthoquinones having a larger side chain in place of the methyl group of phthiocol were reported to show some activity,[37] but this could not be confirmed.[35, 57] Among these were lapachol, hydrolapachol, and lomatiol. 1-Methyl-2-hydroxy-, 2-methyl-3-hydroxy-, and 1-methyl-4-hydroxynaphthalenes were not appreciably active.[54] A discussion of the relation of structure to activity has been published by Fieser et al.[52]

In view of the results with the above-mentioned compounds it was surprising that the 2-methyl-1,4-naphthohydroquinone diphosphoric acid ester was found to be more active on a molecular basis than the parent methylnaphthoquinone.[45, 52, 58] The corresponding disulfate, however, was markedly less potent.[52, 55] These differences may be related to differences in speed of absorption or of regeneration of the methylnaphthoquinone. The interest in these and other water-soluble forms of vitamin K hinges on their greater convenience for injection and their independence on bile or bile salts for absorption from the alimentary tract.

Comparative five-day assays of vitamins K_1 and K_2 have indicated that the relative potencies are in the ratio of 1.25:1.[45] This is the approximate ratio of the amount of the active methylnaphthoquinone nucleus contained in each. Assays by shorter procedures have indicated a potency ratio of

[53] B. R. Baker, T. H. Davies, L. McElroy, and G. H. Carlson, J. Am. Chem. Soc. 64, 1096 (1942).

[54] M. Tishler, L. F. Fieser, and W. L. Sampson, J. Am. Chem. Soc. 62, 1881 (1940).

[55] D. Richert, S. A. Thayer, R. W. McKee, S. B. Binkley, and E. A. Doisy, Proc. Soc. Exptl. Biol. Med. 44, 601 (1940).

[56] D. A. Richert, J. Biol. Chem. 154, 1 (1944).

[57] L. F. Fieser, W. P. Campbell, and E. M. Fry, J. Am. Chem. Soc. 61, 2206 (1939).

[58] R. H. K. Foster, J. Lee, and U. V. Solmssen, J. Am. Chem. Soc. 62, 453 (1940).

approximately 1.5,[59] which may mean that K_1 is more rapidly absorbed or metabolized than K_2 during a short period of time. It is obvious, however, that the long side chains on these vitamins are not specifically required for activity.

An additional form of vitamin K has been reported in extracts of alfalfa.[60] This form did not give the typical strong color reaction in sodium ethylate which has been reported[18] for vitamin K_1 yet it showed considerable potency.[60] The product was nearly colorless. Vitamin K_1 has been converted into a 2,3-oxido derivative, a nearly colorless oil, which gives no color reaction with sodium ethylate and resembles in these respects the second form of vitamin K reported to be in alfalfa.[61] This second form may be one which was reported as existing in the form of relatively colorless crystals at low temperature after isolation from alfalfa.[62]

Antihemorrhagic activity in the anthraquinone series was investigated briefly by Almquist and Klose,[42] who found no activity in anthraquinone and 1,2-dihydroxyanthraquinone, and by Thayer et al.[39] who found none in phenanthraquinone, anthraquinone sulfonic acid, and dihydroanthraquinone diacetate. Martin and Lischer[63] extended these studies and detected very slight activity in 1,2,4-trihydroxyanthraquinone and certain other polyhydroxyanthraquinones having three hydroxyls on one ring. These workers suggested that such polyhydroxy compounds might be more labile to ring rupture and subsequent formation of 2,3-substituted napthoquinones.

A few distinct examples of activity are known where conversion to methylnaphthoquinone does not seem possible. 2,5-Dimethylbenzoquinone and perhaps certain other substituted benzoquinones have very low but measurable activity.[63-65] A degradation product of vitamin E, α-tocopherylquinone, appears to have slight antihemorrhagic activity.[66] It is a benzoquinone with three methyl groups and a long side chain derived from phytol. This compound is also reported to be antagonistic to vitamin K.[66a] Both of these reports may be correct if the α-tocopherylquinone displaces vitamin K from an enzyme system forming another enzyme of very low but

[59] S. A. Thayer, R. W. McKee, S. B. Binkley, D. W. MacCorquodale, and E. A. Doisy, Proc. Soc. Exptl. Biol. Med. 41, 194 (1939).
[60] S. Ansbacher, E. Fernholz, and H. B. MacPhillamy, Proc. Soc. Exptl. Biol. Med. 42, 655 (1939).
[61] L. F. Fieser, M. Tishler, and W. L. Sampson, J. Am. Chem. Soc. 62, 1628 (1940).
[62] H. J. Almquist, Nature 140, 25 (1937).
[63] G. J. Martin and C. F. Lischer, J. Biol. Chem. 137, 169 (1941).
[64] S. Ansbacher and E. Fernholz, J. Biol. Chem. 131, 399 (1939).
[65] H. J. Almquist, Physiol. Revs. 21, 194 (1941).
[66] R. Kuhn, K. Wallenfels, F. Weggand, T. Moll, and L. Hepding, Naturwissenschaften 27, 518 (1939).
[66a] D. W. Woolley, J. Biol. Chem. 159, 59 (1945).

positive antihemorrhagic efficiency (somewhat after the mechanism proposed by Quick and Collentine[67]). 3-Methyl-4-hydroxycoumarin also appears to have activity.[68] This compound may be regarded as analogous to phthiocol in which the 4-carbonyl has been replaced by an oxygen atom.

Several reports have appeared of antihemorrhagic activity of phthalic acid and its diesters.[69] However, Dam[70] was unable to detect any activity in potassium acid phthalate or diethylphthalate. Blumberg and Arnold[71] carried out further investigations on this question but were unable to detect any activity in diethyl-, dipropyl-, diisopropyl-, or dibutylphthalate, even at high levels per chick. The diethyl ester also showed no antagonistic action to methylnaphthoquinone.

III. Industrial Preparation

ROBERT S. HARRIS

There is no important demand by the food industries for vitamins K as concentrated from natural sources or as synthesized, because the amounts present in the food supply and the amounts synthesized in the intestinal tracts of most species, including man, are adequate for normal individuals.

The clinical demand for vitamins K is now met by synthetic processes. Concentrates prepared[1] from natural sources are sometimes preferred because they contain vitamin K_1. Synthetic vitamin K_1 is also available,[2, 3] but it is not widely used because of high cost of production. Synthetic 2-methyl-1,4-naphthoquinone[4-10] is now preferred in the clinic because it is highly effective and least expensive to produce.

[67] A. J. Quick and G. E. Collentine, *Am. J. Physiol.* **164**, 716 (1951); *J. Lab. Clin. Med.* **36**, 976 (1950).

[68] P. Meunier and C. Mentzer, *Bull. soc. chim. biol.* **25**, 80 (1943).

[69] M. M. Shemiakin and L. A. Schukina, *Nature* **154**, 513 (1944).

[70] H. Dam, *Nature* **152**, 355 (1943).

[71] H. Blumberg and A. Arnold, *Proc. Soc. Exptl. Biol. Med.* **57**, 255 (1944).

[1] S. Ansbacher, E. Fernholz, and M. L. Moore, U. S. Pat. 2,233,279 (1941).

[2] H. J. Almquist and A. A. Klose, *J. Am. Chem. Soc.* **61**, 2557 (1939).

[3] L. F. Fieser, *J. Am. Chem. Soc.* **61**, 2559 (1939).

[4] L. F. Fieser, W. P. Campbell, E. M. Frey, and M. D. Gates, Jr., *J. Am. Chem. Soc.* **61**, 2559, 3216 (1939).

[5] S. B. Binkley, R. W. McKee, S. A. Thayer, and E. A. Doisy, *J. Biol. Chem.* **133**, 721 (1940).

[6] R. T. Arnold and R. Larson, *J. Org. Chem.* **5**, 250 (1940).

[7] P. P. T. Sah, W. Brüll, and H. Holzen, *Ber.* **73**, 762 (1940).

[8] P. P. T. Sah, *Rec. trav. chim.* **59**, 461 (1940).

[9] P. P. T. Sah and W. Brüll, *Ber.* **73**, 1430 (1940).

[10] E. A. Poulsson, *J. Soc. Chem. Ind.* (*London*) **60**, 123 (1941).

Because vitamins K_1 and K_2 and also 2-methylnaphthoquinone are fat-soluble, it is necessary that bile acids be present for their proper absorption from the intestinal tract. Water-soluble forms of vitamin K can be absorbed as such and are more effective in cases where the flow of bile is impaired; furthermore they are useful for intravenous injection. Several water-soluble forms have been introduced commercially: 2-methyl-1,4-naphthohydroquinone-3-sodium sulfonate,[11] 4-amino-2-methyl-1-naphthol hydrochloride,[12-14] and sodium 2-methyl-1,4-naphthoquinone dphosiphate.[15-17]

IV. Biochemical Systems

H. J. ALMQUIST

Very little is known concerning the mechanism by which vitamin K-active substances promote the formation of prothrombin. Vitamin K is not found to any significant extent in blood. Large quantities of the prothrombin fraction of normal chicken blood fed to small vitamin K-deficient chicks failed to effect a cure.[1] Dried beef blood fed at 10 % of the diet to deficient chicks also showed no activity.[2] The vitamin in contact with prothrombin-deficient chick blood *in vitro* does not accelerate clotting.[1, 3] Even the more water-soluble forms such as the methylnaphthoquinone, phthiocol, and the diphosphoric acid ester have no direct effect on deficient chick blood.[2] When vitamin K_1 emulsion is given intravenously to deficient chicks, the prothrombin does not rise immediately but requires at least 5 hours to reach a normal level.[1] It is unlikely that the vitamin occurs in blood except in transport. Therefore, the vitamin does not seem to act as a prosthetic group in combination with any blood elements.

That the principal site of prothrombin formation is the liver is indicated

[11] M. B. Moore, *J. Am. Chem. Soc.* **61**, 2049 (1941).

[12] E. A. Doisy, D. W. MacCorquodale, S. A. Thayer, S. B. Burkley, and R. W. McKee, *Science* **90**, 407 (1939).

[13] D. Richert, S. A. Thayer, R. W. McKee, S. B. Binkley, and E. A. Doisy, *Proc. Soc. Exptl. Biol. Med.* **44**, 601 (1940).

[14] H. J. Almquist and A. A. Klose, *Proc. Soc. Exptl. Biol. Med.* **45**, 55 (1940).

[15] L. F. Fieser and E. M. Frey, *J. Am. Chem. Soc.* **62**, 228 (1940).

[16] R. H. K. Foster, J. Lee, and U. V. Solmssen, *J. Am. Chem. Soc.* **62**, 453 (1940).

[17] S. Ansbacher, E. Fernholz, and M. A. Dolliver, *Proc. Soc. Exptl. Biol. Med.* **43**, 652 (1940).

[1] H. Dam, J. Glavind, L. Lewis, and E. Tage-Hansen, *Skand. Arch. Physiol.* **79**, 121 (1938).

[2] H. J. Almquist, *Physiol. Revs.* **21**, 194 (1941).

[3] H. Dam, F. Schønheyder, and E. Tage-Hansen, *Biochem. J.* **30**, 1075 (1936).

by much evidence. Andrus *et al.*[4] and Warren and Rhoads[5] found that removal of the liver from dogs was followed by a blood prothrombin drop which could not be prevented by administration of vitamin K and bile salts. Warner[6] reported that removal of two-thirds of the liver from rats caused a decrease in blood prothrombin. Liver damage from such toxic agents as chloroform also impairs prothrombin formation.[7, 8] Traumatic injury to the liver can cause a marked loss of blood prothrombin.[9] Prothrombin loss from these causes is not readily alleviated by vitamin K. For other examples of liver damage and prothrombin deficiency, the reader is referred to a review by Ferguson.[10]

In marked contrast to the chick and other species, the dog is reported to utilize methylnaphthoquinone less efficiently than K_1.[11] Quick and Collentine[11] have proposed that vitamin K_1 is a prosthetic group on an enzyme in liver which takes part in the formation of prothrombin. This subject is discussed more fully in Section VIII of this chapter.

The suggestion has been advanced that vitamin K-active quinones act through their oxidation-reduction powers.[12] The redox potential values found were 328 for vitamin K_1, 458 for 2-methyl-1,4-naphthoquinone, and 256 for phthiocol, which are in same general order as the potencies of these compounds. Trenner and Bacher[13] have also reported some standard oxidation-reduction potentials which are of the same order for the compounds mentioned above. Within the same range are found some naphthoquinones which possess practically no vitamin K activity, so it is evident that potency is not a simple matter of redox activity, yet this is not excluded as a factor in potency.

Nothing has yet been reported to link vitamin K and its homologs in moderate doses to any body component other than prothrombin. Deficiency of the vitamin has no effect on growth until animals become ill because of hemorrhages.[14] Lesions or erosions of the chick gizzard lining were observed[14, 15] but did not prove to be a characteristic symptom of vitamin

[4] W. D. Andrus, J. W. Lord, Jr., and R. A. Moore, *Surgery* **6**, 899 (1939).
[5] R. Warren and J. E. Rhoads, *Am. J. Med. Sci.* **198**, 193 (1939).
[6] E. D. Warner, *J. Exptl. Med.* **68**, 831 (1938).
[7] K. M. Brinkhous and E. D. Warner, *Proc. Soc. Exptl. Biol. Med.* **44**, 609 (1940).
[8] J. L. Bollman, H. R. Butt, and A. M. Snell, *J. Am. Med. Assoc.* **115**, 1087 (1940).
[9] J. W. Lord, *Surgery* **6**, 896 (1939).
[10] J. H. Ferguson, *Ann. Rev. Physiol.* **8**, 231 (1946).
[11] A. J. Quick and G. E. Collentine, *Am. J. Physiol.* **164**, 716 (1951); *J. Lab. Clin. Med.* **36**, 976 (1950).
[12] E. L. McCawley and C. Gurchot, *Univ. Calif. (Berkeley) Publs. Pharmacol.* **1**, 325 (1940).
[13] N. R. Trenner and F. A. Bacher, *J. Biol. Chem.* **137**, 745 (1941).
[14] H. J. Almquist and E. L. R. Stokstad, *J. Biol. Chem.* **111**, 105 (1935).
[15] H. Dam and F. Schønheyder, *Biochem. J.* **28**, 1355 (1934).

K deficiency. Although crude sources of the vitamin would protect against gizzard erosion, more purified fractions did not, nor did any of the known vitamins. The existence of a separate unidentified anti-gizzard erosion factor was shown.[16] Further evidence on the non-identity of these factors was found when it was observed that pure bile acids, especially cholic acid, in the diet would protect the gizzard lining irrespective of large or no intake of vitamin K or prolonged clotting time.[17, 18] Arachidonic acid has been reported as the gizzard erosion preventive agent in fats.[19]

Hypoprothrombinemia induced in chicks by vitamin K deficiency or by adding dicoumarol to a practical diet does not furnish any histological evidence of liver damage.[20]

V. Estimation

H. J. ALMQUIST

A. BIOLOGICAL ESTIMATION

The biological assay for vitamin K must be viewed in a somewhat different light from that of certain other vitamins. General dietary deficiency in humans is practically unknown, and only in a few pathological or emergency conditions and in pregnancy is administration of the vitamin indicated. Synthesis of the vitamin by microorganisms in the intestinal tract is usually sufficient to supply the needs of most animals, except fowls. Ample supplies of cheap synthetic forms and substitutes render dependence on natural sources of minor importance.

The assay methods therefore, are still primarily for research and may differ greatly, depending upon the nature of the investigation. If intended for the study of comparative potencies of vitamin K-active substances, a relatively simple and convenient assay with the chick may suffice. On the other hand, a study of the metabolism of vitamin K or of some substance similar or synergistic or antagonistic to vitamin K may require a more specific measurement of blood components and excretion products. For general purposes it would seem advisable to employ an assay method which is as simple as possible and which alters the blood from its natural composition to the least extent compatible with a degree of accuracy. No assay

[16] H. J. Almquist and E. L. R. Stokstad, *Nature* **137**, 581 (1936).
[17] H. J. Almquist, *Science* **87**, 538 (1938).
[18] H. J. Almquist and E. Mecchi, *J. Biol. Chem.* **126**, 407 (1938); *Proc. Soc. Exptl. Biol. Med* **46**, 168 (1941).
[19] H. Dam, *Acta Physiol. Scand.* **12**, 189 (1946).
[20] V. M. Emmel and H. Dam, *Proc. Soc. Exptl. Biol. Med.* **56**, 11 (1944).

method as yet devised is free from some theoretical objections; nevertheless, there are several good procedures which may yield results as consistent and reproducible as can generally be expected from a bioassay with animals.

The early development of knowledge on vitamin K was accompanied by the usual mistakes and errors in bioassays which have not been uncommon with other vitamins. More specifically, the sources of error included the following.

1. The test animals were so few that individual variability was a large factor in the accuracy of the data.

2. The assay time was too short (in some cases only a few hours), thereby placing more emphasis upon speed of absorption than upon intrinsic potency in an equilibrated animal.

3. The dose level was too high or too low, placing the response outside the most sensitive range.

4. The vitamin was lost or destroyed during assay, as by volatility or oxidation when dispersed over the large surface of a ground diet, or the sharply increased sensitivity to light in purified preparations of the vitamin.[1]

5. The test animals were exposed to the dust of green plants containing vitamin K or other antihemorrhagic materials (cases are known in which alfalfa dust and the manufacture of 2-methyl-1,4-naphthoquinone nearby were sufficient to vitiate an assay).

6. Owing to bacterial contamination and synthesis of the vitamin, some ingredient of the diet may unexpectedly contain vitamin K. Also, coprophagy may be a significant source of the vitamin.

1. ANIMALS

The young chick is the most readily depleted animal and has been used almost exclusively. The chick presents a further advantage in that the platelets do not furnish thromboplastin which might affect the clotting power of the blood sample.[2]

Chicks from good stock fed practical breeder rations are most desirable. Although a carryover of the vitamin from the parent hen to the chick may be demonstrated,[3, 3a] this does not seriously interfere with depletion of the chick. Rapid chick growth is most desirable since it leads to earlier depletion of the chick in respect to vitamin K.

Attempts to use the rat for the study of vitamin K have not been suc-

---

[1] D. W. MacCorquodale, S. B. Binkley, R. W. McKee, S. A. Thayer, and E. A. Doisy, *Proc. Soc. Exptl. Biol. Med.* **40,** 482 (1939).

[2] H. Dam, *Acta Physiol. Scand.* **12,** 189 (1946).

[3] H. J. Almquist and E. L. R. Stokstad, *J. Nutrition* **12,** 329 (1936).

[3a] W. W. Cravens, S. B. Randle, C. A. Elvehjem, and J. G. Halpin, *Poultry Sci.* **20,** 313 (1941).

cessful quantitatively except when the bile is diverted away from the gut by ligation of the bile duct, thus interfering with absorption.[4, 5] Bile-fistula dogs have been used in studies of vitamin K and blood prothrombin level.[6] Dogs in which the bile was diverted to the kidneys also became vitamin K deficient and were used for estimating the requirement of this species.[7] Individually standardized rabbits were employed in the investigations of the hemorrhagic sweet-clover disease which also produces prothrombin variations in the blood.[8]

2. Diet

The formulation of a successful diet involves the problem of avoiding ingredients which may contain vitamin K, at the same time providing all other nutrients for substantially normal maintenance and growth of the animal during the period of the assay. For the chick assay, the basal test ration[9] given in Table I, or minor variations of it, has been widely used.

The ration is principally ground polished rice, chosen because this type of cereal is free of vitamin K or any extraneous material that may contain the vitamin. As a protein supplement to the polished rice, the most satisfactory single product is sardine fish meal that has been extracted continuously with ethyl ether for 24 hours or more to remove small amounts of vitamin K. The fish meal also provides most of the mineral supplements in the form of bone and trace elements. Instead of the 17.5 parts of fish meal a mixture of 12.0 parts of ether-extracted casein, 2.5 parts of ether-extracted gelatin, and 3.0 parts of bone ash may be used.

Dried brewer's yeast is a convenient source of the water-soluble vitamins required by the chicks. The yeast should be extracted with ethyl ether to remove possible traces of vitamin K. The full amount specified is needed to supplement the ration adequately in the well-known and less well-known vitamins and dietary factors of the water-soluble class required by chicks.

Cod liver oil U.S.P. is recommended as a source of vitamins A and D. Other types of animal feeding oils have been found to contain significant amounts of vitamin K and should not be used in vitamin K assay. Purified β-carotene and synthetic vitamins A and D may also be used in an oil such as refined cottonseed oil with an antioxidant, such as hydroquinone.

[4] J. E. Flynn and E. D. Warner, *Proc. Soc. Exptl. Biol. Med.* **43,** 190 (1940).

[5] J. D. Greaves and C. L. A. Schmidt, *Proc. Soc. Exptl. Biol. Med.* **37,** 43 (1937).

[6] H. P. Smith, E. D. Warner, K. M. Brinkhous, and W. H. Seegers, *J. Exptl. Med.* **67,** 911 (1938).

[7] A. J. Quick and G. E. Collentine, *Am. J. Physiol.* **164,** 716 (1951); *J. Lab. Clin. Med.* **36,** 976 (1950).

[8] R. S. Overman, M. A. Stahmann, W. R. Sullivan, C. F. Huebner, H. A. Campbell, and K. P. Link, *J. Biol. Chem.* **142,** 941 (1942).

[9] H. J. Almquist and A. A. Klose, *Biochem. J.* **33,** 1055 (1939).

The ration is probably deficient in vitamin E. However, the storage of this vitamin in chicks from hens fed practical diets is sufficient to carry the chicks over the short period required for a vitamin K assay. Addition of vitamin E to the ration is not advisable, since some of the oxidation products of vitamin E that may be formed possess antihemorrhagic activity.

A diet has been proposed in which the grain portion is heated for 1 week at 120°.[10] Chicks grow very poorly on such a diet, and it is doubtful if it possesses any real advantage over the one described above. Multiple deficiencies should be avoided in biological assays. Another proposed diet[11] is extremely deficient in calcium for the chick, and it is difficult to understand how chicks could survive and grow on the diet as described.

TABLE I

BASAL RATION FOR CHICK VITAMIN K ASSAY

Ingredient	Per cent
Sardine meal, ether extracted	17.5
Dried brewer's yeast, ether extracted	7.5
Ground polished rice	72.5
Cod liver oil	1.0
Calcium carbonate	0.5
Salt, common (contains 0.5% Mn in form of the sulfate or carbonate)	1.0

3. ADMINISTRATION OF SUPPLEMENTS

Considerable influence on potency by the carrier of the vitamin supplement has been reported. Dann[12] found 2-methyl-1,4-naphthoquinone to be three times as potent when given orally in oil as compared to water, whereas Ansbacher et al.[13] reported the quinone to be twice as potent in water as in oil. Almquist and Klose[14] obtained the same potency for the quinone in water and ethyl laurate solutions. Vitamin K_1 manifested different potencies in reference to 2-methyl-1,4-naphthoquinone, depending upon the volume of oil carrier in a very short (6-hour) assay.[15] Whatever solvent is chosen, it should be the same and in the same volume per dose for the assayed substances as for the standard employed, so far as possible.

Methods for parenteral administration have also been used. Phthiocol

[10] S. Ansbacher, Proc. Soc. Exptl. Biol. Med. **44,** 248 (1940).
[11] A. J. Quick and M. Stefanini, J. Biol. Chem. **175,** 945 (1948).
[12] F. P. Dann, Proc. Soc. Exptl. Biol. Med. **42,** 663 (1939).
[13] S. Ansbacher, E. Fernholz, and M. A. Dolliver, J. Am. Chem. Soc. **62,** 155 (1940); Proc. Soc. Exptl. Biol. Med. **43,** 652 (1940).
[14] H. J. Almquist and A. A. Klose, Proc. Soc. Exptl. Biol. Med. **45,** 55 (1940).
[15] S. A. Thayer, R. W. McKee, S. B. Binkley, and E. A. Doisy, Proc. Soc. Exptl. Biol. Med. **44,** 585 (1940).

showed the same potency whether given orally, intramuscularly, or intravenously.[16] 2-Methyl-1,4-naphthoquinone appeared somewhat less potent by the intravenous route.[7, 17] An emulsion of vitamin K_1 was effective by intramuscular but not by subcutaneous administration.[18]

For most purposes the oral dosing for 4 to 5 days should lead to a satisfactory assay.[14, 19] If a quantitative assay is desired, a definite level of intake should be maintained in the test animal for a sufficient period of time so that potency-modifying factors such as solubility, absorption, and rate of metabolism have been able to approach a balance or plateau of influence on activity. A period of 3 to 4 days is required for the depleted chick to become adjusted to intake levels of the vitamin in an assay range. If the work of setting up an assay has been carried out properly, the extra 3 or 4 days is only a small addition to the task and may lend greater precision. From the emergency standpoint there is perhaps some advantage in a very short assay which will evaluate a compound as much from its speed of action as its intrinsic potency. For example, the effective dose of vitamin K_1 is greater for a 6-hour assay than for 18 hours.[20, 21] These are matters to be adjusted to the particular problem and the purpose of the antihemorrhagic substances.

Dam and Søndergaard have recently shown that in promoting prothrombin restoration in depleted chicks vitamin K_1 is more rapidly effective than menadione or the sodium salt of the corresponding hydroquinone diphosphoric acid ester.[21a]

4. MEASUREMENT OF SUPPLEMENT EFFECT

The earliest quantitative measurement of supplement effect was the simple clotting time of whole blood. If a sufficiently large number of chicks is included in each group, the average blood-clotting time for the group has a fairly close relation to the activity of the supplement, like that of the prothrombin time as illustrated in Fig. 4.[22] Some objections to simple whole blood-clotting time may be mentioned.

1. Blood-clotting time may remain nearly normal when the blood pro-

[16] H. J. Almquist and A. A. Klose, *J. Am. Chem. Soc.* **61,** 1923 (1939).
[17] D. Richert, S. A. Thayer, R. W. McKee, S. B. Binkley, and E. A. Doisy, *Proc. Soc. Exptl. Biol. Med.* **44,** 601 (1940).
[18] H. Dam, J. Glavind, L. Lewis, and E. Tage-Hansen, *Skand. Arch. Physiol.* **79,** 121 (1938).
[19] H. J. Almquist and A. A. Klose, *J. Biol. Chem.* **130,** 787 (1939).
[20] E. Fernholz, S. Ansbacher, and H. B. MacPhillamy, *J. Am. Chem. Soc.* **62,** 430 (1940).
[21] L. F. Fieser, M. Tishler, and W. L. Sampson, *J. Biol. Chem.* **137,** 659 (1941).
[21a] H. Dam and E. Søndergaard, *Experientia* **9,** 26 (1953).
[22] H. J. Almquist, E. Mecchi, and A. A. Klose, *Biochem. J.* **32,** 1897 (1938).

thrombin level is less than half the normal, and it is probably less sensitive to moderate reductions in prothrombin.[23]

2. Blood-clotting time may be influenced by tissue juice or extract. It is nearly impossible to avoid contamination with tissue juice completely by any method of withdrawing blood samples that is not almost hopelessly laborious when applied to a large number of chicks.

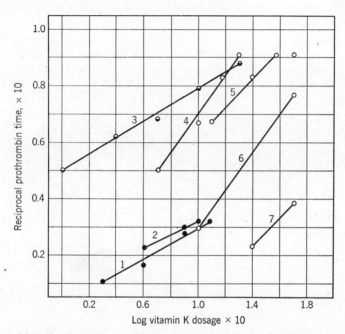

FIG. 4. The relation of the reciprocal prothrombin time to the logarithm of the vitamin K intake. Numbers have been multiplied by 10 for convenience in plotting. Curves 1 and 2 from data by Almquist and Klose.[9] Curve 3 adapted from data by Stamler *et al.*[23] Curves 4, 5, 6, and 7 from data by Quick and Stefanini.[11]

3. Blood-clotting time may actually decrease in certain chicks after severe loss of blood. For this reason it is not advisable to test all chicks for blood-clotting time before administering supplements.

4. Blood-clotting time is measured in periods from 2 to 30 minutes or longer. It is often impossible to obtain any distinct values from certain chicks with prolonged clotting time.

To avoid the above objections, Almquist and Klose[9] employed for vitamin K assay the "prothrombin-time" method of Quick,[11, 24] which depends

[23] R. T. Tidrick, F. T. Joyce, and H. P. Smith, *Proc. Soc. Exptl. Biol. Med.* **42**, 853 (1939).

[24] A. J. Quick, *Am. J. Physiol.* **118**, 260 (1937).

more specifically on the blood prothrombin level and, in turn, the effect of vitamin K supplements on the prothrombin level. The improved method, while requiring more preliminary preparation, has several advantages over simple blood-clotting time, namely:

1. A larger sample of blood is used and is, therefore, more likely to be an accurate sample from the chick.

2. Measurements are made in seconds rather than minutes, and the gathering of the final data is expedited. Determinations can be made in duplicate.

3. Conveniently measurable values can be obtained from every chick.

4. The variability of the results within a test group is much lower than that of the simple blood-clotting times[23, 25] (Table II).

TABLE II

MEANS, STANDARD ERRORS, AND COEFFICIENTS OF VARIABILITY OF SIMPLE BLOOD-CLOTTING TIMES, AND WHOLE BLOOD-PROTHROMBIN TIMES

Reference standard of vitamin K per kilogram of diet, mg.	No. of chicks	Blood-clotting time		Whole blood-prothrombin time	
		Mean and standard error, min.	Coefficient of variability	Mean and standard error, sec.	Coefficient of variability
3	15	10.07 ± 2.31	61.1	51.2 ± 1.9	17.1
6	15	3.42 ± 0.55	60.2	37.3 ± 1.0	9.6
12	15	1.97 ± 0.37	72.1	30.5 ± 0.5	6.1

Blood samples may be taken simply by cutting off the head of the chick.[9] Samples have also been taken from a carotid artery,[26] or from a jugular vein,[27, 28] or from a wing vein.[11, 29] Prothrombin has been determined by an elaborate two-stage method,[27, 30] or by a method in which the ratio of the strength of a clotting agent (thromboplastin) required to clot the plasma in a specified time to the strength required to clot normal plasma[26] is determined. The reader should consult the original papers for details of these methods.

5. COMPUTATION OF RESULTS

It was found that over the sensitive assay range a plot of the reciprocal mean prothrombin time against the logarithm of the vitamin K dosage

[25] H. J. Almquist, *Physiol. Revs.* **21**, 194 (1941).

[26] H. Dam and J. Glavind, *Biochem. J.* **32**, 485 (1938).

[27] F. W. Stamler, R. T. Tidrick, and E. D. Warner, *J. Nutrition* **26**, 95 (1943).

[28] E. D. Warner, *J. Exptl. Med.* **68**, 831 (1938).

[29] H. J. Almquist and E. L. R. Stokstad, *J. Nutrition* **14**, 235 (1937).

[10] H. P. Smith, E. D. Warner, and K. M. Brinkhous, *J. Exptl. Med.* **66**, 801 (1937).

yields practically a straight line.[9] This relation, although possibly only empirical, proves to be applicable to data from different laboratories, using different procedures for estimating prothrombin and different methods of administering supplements (Fig. 4).

Stamler et al.,[27] employing this relation to compare calculated prothrombin levels with observed levels, have stated that the agreement is not "very exact." Very exact results are rarely obtained in biological assays; nevertheless the data plotted by the direct method of Almquist and Klose[9] appear to be quite consistent (Fig. 4, curve 3). Quick and Stefanini[11] have objected to the use of an extract of chicken muscle instead of chicken brain as a clotting agent for prothrombin determination. Whether or not this criticism is important, the assay method operates well with either preparation (Fig. 4, curves 1 and 2). Of course the linear relation no longer holds after an optimal prothrombin level or time has been reached.

In any assay it is desirable to establish some such line by means of at least two groups fed different levels of a standard preparation, such as 2-methyl-1,4-naphthoquinone. It is then possible to interpolate and express the potency of an assayed supplement in terms of the reference standard.[31] Reproducibility of results by this method has been adequately demonstrated.

Another method is to measure whole blood-clotting time to the nearest minute and then to compare the percentages of the chicks in which the clotting time is reduced to 10 minutes or less;[32] or the quantity of material which will cure 50 % of the group by the above criteria may be estimated from several dose levels.[33] This is called the CD_{50} and is compared with the CD_{50} of some standard substance which was employed in the same assay. Improved methods have been suggested from time to time. The reader is referred to papers by Almquist,[31] Quick and Stefanini,[11] Stamler et al.,[27] and Dam et al.[34]

6. STANDARDS OF POTENCY

It has been suggested[35] that the highly potent compound, 2-methyl-1,4-naphthoquinone, can be employed as a standard of activity and that 1 unit be defined as the antihemorrhagic activity of 1 γ of this compound. The name menadione has been adopted as a non-proprietary term for this

[31] H. J. Almquist, Biol. Symposia 12, 508 (1947).

[32] S. Ansbacher, J. Nutrition 17, 303 (1939).

[33] S. A. Thayer, D. W. MacCorquodale, R. W. McKee, and E. A. Doisy, J. Bi-? Chem. 123, cxx (1938).

[34] H. Dam, I. Kruse, and E. Søndergaard, cited by H. Dam, Ann. Rev. Biochem. 20, 265 (1951).

[35] S. A. Thayer, S. B. Binkley, D. W. MacCorquodale, E. A. Doisy, A. D. Emmett, R. A. Brown, and O. D. Bird, J. Am. Chem. Soc. 61, 2563 (1939).

substance by the American Medical Association.[36] Although one-half as potent as the methylnaphthoquinone, 2-methyl-1,4-naphthohydroquinone diacetate might serve as a better standard.[37] Both of these compounds are cheaply and easily prepared in a high state of purity, which can be tested conveniently by means of melting point. The melting point of methylnaphthoquinone should be 105 to 106°, that of the diacetate 112 to 113°. The diacetate has the advantage of greater stability when mixed in the diet; this, however, is of little or no importance for oral administration. For convenience the methylnaphthoquinone 1-γ unit will be used for expressing comparative activities, with the caution that this unit may not represent any fixed proportion of activity to weight units of vitamins K_1 or K_2 (Table III).

TABLE III

ACTIVITIES OF CERTAIN ANTIHEMORRHAGIC COMPOUNDS BASED ON CHICK 5-DAY ASSAYS AND EXPRESSED IN 2-METHYL-1,4-NAPHTHOQUINONE UNITS PER MILLIGRAM

Compound	Units per milligram
2-Methyl-1,4-naphthoquinone (menadione)	1000
2-Methyl-1,4-naphthohydroquinone diacetate	450
2-Methyl-4-amino-1-naphthol hydrochloride	500
2-Methyl-1,4-naphthohydroquinone diphosphoric acid ester (tetrasodium salt, hexahydrate)	500
2,3-Dimethyl-1,4-naphthoquinone	25
2-Methyl-3-phytyl-1,4-naphthoquinone (vitamin K_1)	500
2-Methyl-3-difarnesyl-1,4-naphthoquinone (vitamin K_2)	400
2-Methyl-3-phytyl-1,4-naphthohydroquinone diacetate	170

During the phases of isolation, purification, and synthesis the different laboratories employed different assay methods and different standards or units of potency which served their temporary purposes. These methods and standards or units have been reviewed by Ansbacher.[38]

7. COMPARISON OF ASSAYS BY DIFFERENT METHODS

Several of the present methods when carefully adhered to will yield equivalent results. Repeated assays of 2-methyl-1,4-naphthohydroquinone diacetate have all indicated that the potency of this compound is close to one-half that of the methylnaphthoquinone.[31] An average of relative values obtained in other assays, as reviewed by Dam,[2] leads to the same conclusion.

[36] Council on Pharmacy and Chemistry, J. Am. Med. Assoc. **116**, 1054 (1941).
[37] D. T. Ewing, J. M. Vandenbelt, and O. Kamm, J. Biol. Chem. **131**, 345 (1939).
[38] S. Ansbacher, J. Nutrition **21**, 1 (1941).

Almquist and Klose,[14] assaying the compound 2-methyl-1,4-naphtho-hydroquinone diphosphoric acid ester in comparison to 2-methyl-1,4-naph-thoquinone by 4-day oral feeding to depleted chicks and comparison of average prothrombin time 24 hours from the last dose, found the phosphoric ester to be 1.5 times as potent as the quinone on a molar basis (one-half as potent on a weight basis.) Assay of the identical preparations was made by Lee et al.[39] by subcutaneous administration, measurement of whole blood-clotting time 18 hours from dosage, and expression of results as the single dose required to bring the blood-clotting time of 50 % of the chicks to 10 minutes or less. The phosphoric ester was found to be 50 % more potent than the quinone on a molar basis in close agreement with the above results.

The potency of vitamin K_1 was found to be approximately one-third that of methylnaphthoquinone (Almquist[31]). This ratio was also found in an 18-hour curative assay by Fieser et al.[21] Emmett et al.,[40] by the method of Thayer et al.,[33] obtained 450 methylnaphthoquinone units per milligram. Assays by the Dam-Glavind technique, as reported by Dam,[2] indicate an average potency approximately 39 % of that of the methylnaphthoquinone on a weight basis.

Quick and Stefanini[11] have provided further data on the relative potencies of these compounds in a 12-day preventive assay with chicks. These data, plotted by the method of Almquist and Klose,[9] are represented by curves 4, 5, 6, and 7 in Fig. 4. Curve 4, obtained with methylnaphthoquinone dosages, has a slope of 1.35. Curve 5, obtained with vitamin K_1, has a slope of 1.00. These curves converge at lower dose levels. The difference between the curves at any prothrombin value or reciprocal prothrombin time is the logarithm of the potency ratio of the two compounds. This ratio is not constant. Curve 6 represents results from methylnaphthoquinone dosage applied to chicks also receiving dicoumarol in their diets (p. 405). As would be expected, the curve is displaced toward higher dose levels of vitamin K; the slope of this curve turns out to be 1.35, however, the same as in the absence of dicoumarol (curve 4). Curve 7 represents data from similarly dicoumarol-poisoned chicks which received vitamin K_1. This curve is also displaced toward higher vitamin K levels, but it has the same slope as the vitamin K_1 curve (5) in the absence of dicoumarol. Such agreement could hardly be accidental. The remarkable consistency of these data is brought out clearly by the graphical method of expression.

The fact becomes evident that there is no constant ratio of activity for methylnaphthoquinone and vitamin K_1. This ratio varies over a range

[39] J. Lee, U. V. Solmssen, A. Steyermark, and R. H. K. Foster, Proc. Soc. Exptl. Biol. Med. 45, 407 (1940).

[40] A. D. Emmett, R. A. Brown, and O. Kamm, J. Biol. Chem. 132, 467 (1940).

from 1, or less, to as high as 2, approximately. At the lower levels, on a molar basis, vitamin K_1 is clearly the more efficient form of the vitamin. It is probable that these compounds are so dissimilar that they cannot be evaluated in terms of each other except at stated dose levels. Therefore, they cannot be used interchangeably for assay standards.

These experimental observations are in agreement with relations that may be derived on the basis of certain assumptions.[41] If the relation of vitamin K to prothrombin formation is expressed as follows:

$$K + A \overset{C}{\rightleftarrows} KA \overset{E}{\rightarrow} P \tag{1}$$

where K = any form of vitamin K.
  A = proenzyme.
  KA = enzyme which forms prothrombin.
  C = constant.
  E = efficiency of formation of prothrombin by KA.
  P = prothrombin = $KA \times E$.

Then

$$-\frac{dK}{dt} = \frac{K \times A \times C}{KA} = \frac{K \times A \times C \times E}{P} \tag{2}$$

which may be written

$$\frac{d \log K}{dt} = \frac{P}{A \times C \times E}$$

or integrated and simplified to eq. 3 as a practical expression of the relation of these factors, over a given time interval.

$$\log K = \frac{P}{A \times C \times E} \tag{3}$$

It is recognized that within the assay range P is for practical purposes equal to a constant times the reciprocal of the prothrombin-clotting time, T.

$$P = \frac{C'}{T} \tag{4}$$

Hence

$$\log_{10} K = \frac{C'}{A \times C \times E \times T \times 2.3} = \frac{S}{T} \tag{5}$$

It appears that A, which is similar to the "apoenzyme" recently proposed by Quick and Collentine,[7] is relatively constant in respect to the above

[41] H. J. Almquist, *Arch. Biochem. and Biophys.* **35,** 464 (1952).

variables. At any value of P which is maintained by two different forms of vitamin K,

$$\frac{\log K_a}{\log K_b} = \frac{C_b \times E_b}{C_a \times E_a} = \text{Constant} \tag{6}$$

As previously mentioned, in the data on the prothrombin times and levels in chicks maintained by two forms of vitamin K, namely 2-methyl-1,4-naphthoquinone (menadione) and vitamin K_1,[11] the prothrombin values tend to converge at very low vitamin K dosage and diverge by a constant ratio toward higher dosages until, of course, the physiological limit of P is approached (Fig. 4). This is in agreement with eq. 6. A further implication of this equation is that the potency ratio K_a/K_b with respect to maintenance of different P levels is not a constant. This conclusion derived from the stated assumptions agrees with the experimental facts. The agreement does not, of course, prove that the assumptions are correct; however, it would appear that they are concordant with the facts.

A further analysis of the dicoumarol data brings out some indications of interest. The feeding of a constant amount of dicoumarol does not change the slope of the regression lines of prothrombin on log vitamin K. This means that the terms in eq. 3, such as A, C, and E, the net effect of which is that of a constant, are unaffected by the dicoumarol. From this observation one may conclude that the effect of the dicoumarol is only upon the vitamin K. Furthermore, the effect cannot be merely that of a quantitative inactivation of vitamin K but must be applied uniformly to the entire quota of K present. The effect is, evidently, that of a competitive displacement, or some form of reversible inhibition, or reduction of activity, which is applied prior to the reaction system as expressed in eq. 1. In dog blood the effects of both avitaminosis K and of dicoumarol are due to a decrease of prothrombin.[42] For another discussion of these relations the reader should consult ref. 43.

The relative potency of vitamin K_1 with respect to K_2 was found to be 1.25 (Almquist and Klose[14]), 1.5 (Thayer et al.[44]), 1.4 (Dam[2]), and between 1 and 1.5 (Tishler and Sampson[45]).

B. CHEMICAL AND PHYSICAL ESTIMATION

The absorption spectra of vitamins K_1 and K_2 have been studied in detail by several investigators. A most careful measurement of the ultraviolet

[42] A. J. Quick, C. V. Hussey, and G. E. Collentine, *Proc. Soc. Exptl. Biol. Med.* **79**, 131 (1952).

[43] G. E. Collentine and A. J. Quick, *Am. J. Med. Sci.* **222**, 7 (1951).

[44] S. A. Thayer, R. W. McKee, S. B. Binkley, D. W. MacCorquodale, and E. A. Doisy, *Proc. Soc. Exptl. Biol. Med.* **41**, 194 (1939).

[45] M. Tishler and W. L. Sampson, *Proc. Soc. Exptl. Biol. Med.* **68**, 136 (1948).

absorption has been reported[46] (Fig. 3). As already mentioned, the absorption of these vitamins deteriorates rapidly on exposure to ultraviolet light. Vitamin K can also be determined polarographically.[47, 48] These physical methods have been used only for relatively pure concentrates. Oxidation-reduction methods have also been described,[49, 50] but they seem to be subject to much interference from other non-vitamin K substances.

Numerous color reactions would be expected from a compound of the naphthoquinone structure. Vitamin K_1 gives a strong transient blue color reaction with sodium ethylate, which fades to a more permanent red-brown stage. This color reaction may apparently be expected only from vitamins K_1 and K_2, which have a double bond between the β- and γ-carbon atoms in the side chain, or from similar naphthoquinone derivatives.[51, 52] The more stable red-brown end stage of the reaction has a roughly quantitative relation to the activities of concentrates.[53] It was stated that the end-stage color was due to phthiocol.[51] However, the principal pigment produced in this reaction possessed an analysis and molecular weight indicating that it was a derivative of vitamin K_1.[54] A colorimetric assay based upon the reaction of 2,3-substituted 1,4-naphthoquinones with sodium diethyl dithiocarbamate has been reported.[55]

Colorimetric methods for 2-methyl-1,4-naphthoquinone have excited interest because of the wide use of this compound in vitamin K-active pharmaceutical preparations. There have been used such color developers as dichlorophenolindophenol,[56] dinitrophenylhydrazine,[57, 58] and ethyl cyanoacetate.[59] A specific color test for 4-amino-2-methyl-1-naphthol was described.[60] The reaction with aniline has been used for determination of methyl naphthoquinone in blood and tissues.[61]

[46] D. T. Ewing, F. S. Tomkins, and O. Kamm, *J. Biol. Chem.* **147**, 233 (1943).

[47] E. B. Hershberg, J. K. Wolfe, and L. F. Fieser, *J. Am. Chem. Soc.* **62**, 3516 (1940).

[48] H. Onrust and B. Wöstman, *Rec. trav. chim.* **69**, 1208 (1950).

[49] G. V. Scudi and R. P. Buhs, *J. Biol. Chem.* **141**, 451 (1941); *J. Biol. Chem.* **143**, 665 (1942).

[50] N. R. Trenner and F. A. Bacher, *J. Biol. Chem.* **137**, 745 (1941).

[51] L. F. Fieser, W. P. Campbell, and E. M. Fry, *J. Am. Chem. Soc.* **61**, 2206 (1939).

[52] P. Karrer, *Helv. Chim. Acta* **22**, 1146 (1939).

[53] H. J. Almquist and A. A. Klose, *J. Am. Chem. Soc.* **61**, 1610 (1939).

[54] H. J. Almquist and A. A. Klose, *J. Biol. Chem.* **130**, 791 (1939).

[55] F. Irreverre and M. X. Sullivan, *Science* **94**, 497 (1941).

[56] W. Bosecke and W. Laves, *Biochem. Z.* **314**, 285 (1943).

[57] A. Novelli, *Science* **93**, 358 (1941).

[58] E. E. van Koetsveld, *Rec. trav. chim.* **69**, 1217 (1950).

[59] D. A. Richert, *J. Biol. Chem.* **154**, 1 (1944).

[60] A. R. Menotti, *Ind. Eng. Chem. Anal. Ed.* **14**, 601 (1942).

[61] E. E. Martinson and G. I. Meerovich, *Biokhimiya* **10**, 258 (1945).

VI. Occurrence in Nature

H. J. ALMQUIST

A. IN PLANTS

Green leafy tissue is a rich natural source of the vitamin. One or two per cent of commercially dehydrated alfalfa meal in the diet of the chick meets normal requirements.[1, 2] The tops of carrots are a good source, but the roots contain little or no vitamin.[3] The vitamin is more abundant in peas sprouted in the light than in those sprouted in the dark, and the inner leaves of the cabbage have about one-fourth the activity of the outer leaves.[4] Other sources of the vitamin are spinach, kale, cauliflower, nettle, and chestnut leaves.[4] The vitamin is present to some extent in tomato, hempseed, seaweed,[4] and soybean oil.[5] Berries of the European mountain ash are reported to be a good source.[6]

Dam, Glavind, and Gabrielsen[7] have reviewed and extended earlier work on the distribution of vitamin K in plants. Parts of plants which do not normally form chlorophyll contain little vitamin K. Although conifers are able to form chlorophyll in the dark, the amounts of chlorophyll and vitamin K formed in the dark or light remain approximately proportional. However, the yellow spotted leaf areas of certain plants contained as much vitamin K as did the green areas.

Leaves of various plants with markedly different natural green color did not show a proportional amount of vitamin K activity by assay with chicks. Neither was there any close relation to the amounts of carotene or xanthophyll. Maize plants that were grown on an iron-deficient medium showed marked deficiency of chlorophyll, xanthophyll, and carotene and a reduction in vitamin K as compared to normal control plants. Natural loss of chlorophyll, as in the fall yellowing of leaves, does not bring about a corresponding change in vitamin K. Dam, Hjorth, and Kruse[8] have also shown that the vitamin K in the press juice of spinach leaves does not decrease on standing overnight and nearly all the vitamin is present in the chloroplasts. It seems evident, therefore, that any relation between the concentrations of the chloroplast pigments and vitamin K in leaves is only incidental to the general synthesis of all these substances in the leaves. It

[1] H. J. Almquist and E. L. R. Stokstad, *J. Biol. Chem.* **111**, 105 (1935).

[2] A. J. Quick, *Am. J. Physiol.* **118**, 260 (1937).

[3] H. J. Almquist, *Nature* **140**, 25 (1937).

[4] H. Dam and J. Glavind, *Biochem. J.* **32**, 485 (1938).

[5] H. J. Almquist and E. L. R. Stokstad, *J. Nutrition* **14**, 235 (1937).

[6] G. Y. Shinowara, J. C. DeLor, and J. W. Means, *J. Lab. Clin. Med.* **27**, 897 (1942).

[7] H. Dam, J. Glavind, and E. K. Gabrielson, *Acta Physiol. Scand.* **13**, 9 (1947).

[8] H. Dam, E. Hjorth, and I. Kruse, *Physiologia Plantarum* **1**, 379 (1948).

should be recalled that vitamin K_1 and chlorophyll are both compounds of phytol and may be dependent on the supply of this substance.

Vivino et al.[9] have made the interesting observation that honey contains distinct antihemorrhagic activity equivalent to approximately 0.25 γ of 2-methyl-1,4-naphthoquinone per gram as determined by the chick assay procedure and interpretation method of Almquist.[10]

B. IN MICROORGANISMS

Early observations on the development of antihemorrhagic activity in foodstuffs during bacterial spoilage[1] and in the droppings of vitamin K-deficient chicks,[11] led to a further study of vitamin K production by micro-

TABLE IV

VITAMIN K ACTIVITIES OF PREPARATIONS OF CERTAIN MICROORGANISMS, EXPRESSED IN 2-METHYL-1,4-NAPHTHOQUINONE UNITS PER GRAM[a]

Microorganism	Units per gram
Bacillus cereus	115
Bacillus mycoides	155
Bacillus subtilis	190
Bacterium aerogenes	20
Bacterium flexneri	30
Bacterium proteus	75
Bacterium typhosum	15
Erythrobacillus prodigiosus	20
Escherichia coli	15
Mycobacterium tuberculosis	55
Sarcina lutea	100
Staphylococcus aureus	60

[a] Adapted from Almquist.[13] For data on several other microorganisms, see this reference.

organisms.[12, 13] Various pure strains of bacteria were grown on vitamin K-free media, killed by heat, dried, and assayed with the chick. Comparative data on those which showed vitamin K activity are given in Table IV. When receiving very little vitamin K in the diet, the cow is, nevertheless, well supplied with the vitamin which is synthesized by microorganisms in the rumen.[14] In general, species of the mold, yeast, and fungus types were inactive.

[9] E. E. Vivino, M. H. Haydak, L. S. Palmer, and M. C. Tanquary, Proc. Soc. Exptl. Biol. Med. 53, 9 (1943).

[10] H. J. Almquist, Biol. Symposia 12, 508 (1947).

[11] H. J. Almquist and E. L. R. Stokstad, J. Nutrition 12, 329 (1936).

[12] H. J. Almquist, C. F. Pentler, and E. Mecchi, Proc. Soc. Exptl. Biol. Med. 38, 336 (1938).

[13] H. J. Almquist, Physiol. Revs. 21, 194 (1941).

[14] L. W. McElroy and H. Goss, J. Nutrition 20, 527 (1940).

Bacterial action on wet fish meal has been employed in the preparation of vitamin K concentrates.[1, 15] The vitamin K_2 isolated from putrified fish meal[16] has also been obtained from a culture of *Bacillus brevis*.[17] Experimental animals for vitamin K studies must be prevented from obtaining the vitamin from food in which bacterial action may have synthesized the vitamin, and from coprophagy.

The remarkably high vitamin K content of certain microorganisms raised the question of the role of antihemorrhagic quinones in their metabolism. Woolley and McCarter[18] found a microorganism, Johne's bacillus, which responded with increased growth when vitamin K, phthiocol, or methylnaphthoquinone was added to the synthetic medium. Using another strain of this bacillus Glavind and Dam[19] were unable to demonstrate any growth effect from methylnaphthoquinone or phthiocol. Iland[20] investigated the requirement of *Mycobacterium tuberculosis* for vitamin K and found evidence of a growth-depressing action. Kimler[21] found bacteriostatic action against this organism to be exhibited by methylnaphthohydroquinone diphosphate, 2-methyl-4-amino-1-naphthol and the bisulfite addition compound. The critical concentrations were 100, 1, and 2 γ per milliliter, respectively. The antihemorrhagic naphthoquinones can act as non-specific antibiotics in some cases, as shown by Armstrong *et al.*[22] It is obvious from the above facts that microbiological methods for estimating vitamin K are not very feasible. For references to other recent reports on miscellaneous effects of vitamin K on caries, tumors, and microorganisms, the reader is referred to a review by Dam.[23]

Inhibition of bacterial action in the digestive tract by ingestion of sulfonamides causes a decrease in the synthesis of vitamin K and also of prothrombin if the vitamin K intake is inadequate to meet the needs of the animal. Black *et al.*[24] found that sulfaguanidine or sulfasuxidine added to a synthetic vitamin K-free diet of rats caused a relatively rapid onset of

[15] R. W. McKee, S. B. Binkley, D. W. MacCorquodale, S. A. Thayer, and E. A. Doisy, *J. Am. Chem. Soc.* **61**, 1295 (1939).

[16] S. B. Binkley, D. W. MacCorquodale, S. A. Thayer, and E. A. Doisy, *J. Biol. Chem.* **130**, 219 (1939).

[17] M. Tishler and W. L. Sampson, *Proc. Soc. Exptl. Biol. Med.* **68**, 136 (1948).

[18] D. W. Woolley and J. R. McCarter, *Proc. Soc. Exptl. Biol. Med.* **45**, 357 (1940).

[19] J. Glavind and H. Dam, *Physiol. Plantarum* **1**, 1 (1948).

[20] C. N. Iland, *Nature* **161**, 1010 (1948).

[21] A. Kimler, *J. Bacteriol.* **60**, 469 (1950).

[22] W. D. Armstrong, W. W. Spink, and J. Kahnke, *Proc. Soc. Exptl. Biol. Med.* **53**, 230 (1943).

[23] H. Dam, *Ann. Rev. Biochem.* **20**, 265 (1951).

[24] S. Black, R. S. Overman, C. A. Elvehjem, and K. P. Link, *J. Biol. Chem.* **145**, 137 (1942).

prothrombin deficiency. This could be prevented by adding vitamin K to the diet. Confirming observations have been reported.[25, 26]

C. NATURAL ANTAGONISTS

A hemorrhagic agent isolated from spoiled sweet clover hay has been shown to be a dicoumarin by Link and coworkers.[27] The compound isolated is 3,3'-methylenebis(4-hydroxycoumarin). When given to various species of animals this compound induces a decrease in prothrombin which is most profound when associated with low vitamin K intake and can be reversed by vitamin K administration.[27, 28] The dicoumarin is easily degraded to salicylic acid by chemical means, and this fact suggested that the acid might be produced by the metabolism of the dicoumarin. Administration of salicylic acid to rats, either in the vitamin K-low diet or intravenously, caused a hypoprothrombinemia similar to that produced by the dicoumarin or by vitamin K deficiency. The effect was reversed by vitamin K. Neither the dicoumarin nor salicylic acid had any effect on the clotting power of blood *in vitro* (Link *et al.*[29]). This subject is more fully discussed in Section VII B of this chapter (p. 432).

Woolley[30] observed that α-tocopherolquinone administered to pregnant mice caused hemorrhagic symptoms in the reproductive system and resorption. The action of the α-tocopherolquinone was not prevented by large doses of vitamin E but was reversed by small doses of vitamin K. The structural similarity of α-tocopherolquinone and vitamin K_1 was pointed out as an explanation of the antivitamin activity.

Excessive intake of vitamin A is known to cause a variety of toxic effects among which is a hemorrhagic tendency and prolonged coagulation time of blood. The clotting defect as produced in rats may be remedied by a generous intake of vitamin K.[31] The condition has been produced by alcohol and ester forms of vitamin A prepared from natural sources, but it has not yet been reported as caused by synthetic vitamin A. It remains to be seen if vitamin A itself or some associated substance is the cause of these hemorrhagic tendencies. In chicks, even large doses of vitamin A had no effect on the prothrombin time although the chicks received only a minimal level of vitamin K. The effects in rats, therefore, may have been due to interference in the synthesis of vitamin K by intestinal microorganisms.[28]

[25] A. D. Welch and L. D. Wright, *J. Nutrition* **25**, 555 (1943).
[26] H. G. Day, K. G. Wakim, M. M. Krider, and E. E. O'Banion, *J. Nutrition* **26**, 585 (1943).
[27] H. A. Campbell and K. P. Link, *J. Biol. Chem.* **138**, 21 (1941).
[28] A. J. Quick and M. Stefanini, *J. Biol. Chem.* **175**, 945 (1948).
[29] K. P. Link, R. S. Overman, W. R. Sullivan, C. F. Huebner, and L. D. Scheel, *J. Biol. Chem.* **147**, 463 (1943).
[30] D. W. Woolley, *J. Biol. Chem.* **159**, 59 (1945).
[31] R. F. Light, R. P. Alscher, and C. N. Frey, *Science* **100**, 225 (1944).

VII. Effects of Deficiency

A. IN ANIMALS

H. J. ALMQUIST

The pathology of vitamin K deficiency is unique among the vitamins because the only primary effect yet known on any tissue is that upon the prothrombin level of the blood. The prothrombin content of blood is greatly decreased, and the clotting time is markedly prolonged. Thus the occurrence of subcutaneous and intramuscular hemorrhages is frequently observed.

B. IN HUMAN BEINGS

CHARLES A. OWEN, JR.

A deficiency of vitamin K is characterized by a bleeding tendency secondary to an alteration of the coagulability of the blood. The deficiency may result from ingestion of insufficient vitamin K, lack of bacterial synthesis of the vitamin within the intestinal tract, inadequate intestinal absorption, or hepatic inability to utilize the available vitamin K.

1. HEMORRHAGE RESULTING FROM A DEFICIENCY OF VITAMIN K

Serious abnormalities of the blood coagulation mechanism may be present without any evidence of bleeding. However, it is frequently stated that when the plasma prothrombin falls to about 20 % of normal[1] the danger of bleeding exists; this is based on repeated observations that bleeding only infrequently occurs in vitamin K deficiency when the prothrombin is above this level.

Prior to the discovery of vitamin K and recognition of its deficiency in obstructive jaundice, bleeding was most commonly seen after surgical correction of a biliary obstruction.[2] This is now rare because of the generous use of vitamin K in biliary surgery. At the present time hemorrhage from injudicious use of dicoumarol—an "antagonist" of vitamin K—is probably commonest.[3]

The bleeding caused by vitamin K deficiency may be first recognized by slow oozing from the mucous membranes of the nasopharynx, by the appearance of ecchymoses associated with mild trauma, or in surgical cases by hematomas and persistent bleeding at the site of operation. Massive hemorrhage may occur beneath the skin and within muscles, particularly of the extremities. Hemorrhagic disease of the newborn is often first sus-

---

[1] Values as high as 35 to 40% [K. M. Brinkhous, H. P. Smith, and E. D. Warner, *Am. J. Med. Sci.* **196**, 50 (1938)] and as low as 5% [F. Koller and P. Frick, *Helv. Chim. Acta* **32**, Part 1, 717 (1949)] have been suggested.

[2] E. W. Boland, *Proc. Staff Meetings Mayo Clinic.* **13**, 70 (1938).

[3] I. F. Duff and W. H. Shull, *J. Am. Med. Assoc.* **139**, 762 (1949).

pected on the basis of melena or hematemesis; although bleeding may occur almost anywhere, areas of predilection are: umbilicus, skin, nose and mouth, intestine, and cerebrum.[4, 5] Ecchymoses and hematomas are usually related to trauma in those receiving too intensive dicoumarol therapy.

For an extensive study of the gross and microscopic pathology of experimental vitamin K bleeding the work of Ferraro and Roizin[6] is referred to. They concluded that three factors are important in the causation of bleeding: the degree of hypoprothrombinemia, the age of the animal (the younger, the more severe the hemorrhage), and trauma.

TABLE V

DIFFERENTIAL DIAGNOSIS OF THE BLEEDING CAUSED BY VITAMIN K DEFICIENCY

	Vitamin K deficiency	Scurvy	Hemophilia	Thrombocytopenia
Clot time	Long	N[a]	Long	N
Plasma prothrombin	Low	N[b]	N	N
Bleeding time	N	Long	N	Long
Capillary fragility	N	Incr.	N	Incr.
Response to vitamin K	+	0	0	0
Response to vitamin C	0	+	0	0
Response to "antihemophilic globulin"	0	0	+	0
Response to transfusion of whole blood	+		+	+

[a] N = normal; Incr. = increased; + = positive response; 0 = no response
[b] Unless there is a coexisting deficiency of vitamin K.

Although the gross appearance is not in itself diagnostic, the bleeding tendency in vitamin K deficiency differs to some extent from that of scurvy, hemophilia, or thrombocytopenia (Table V). In scurvy there are swollen, spongy, bleeding gums and subperiosteal and intramuscular hemorrhagic extravasations. The hemophiliac tends to bleed in and about joints, with resultant hemarthroses and ankyloses.[7] The petechial bleeding of thrombocytopenia and scurvy may be confusing, but the platelets are severely depressed only in the former.

[4] L. Salomonsen, *Acta paediat.* **27**, *Suppl.* 1, 1 (1939).
[5] R. B. Scott, *Practitioner* **165**, 182 (1950); B. P. Clark, *J. Med. Assoc. State Alabama* **20**, 130 (1950); G. Fanconi, Die Störungen der Blutgerinnung beim Kinde mit besonderer Berücksichtigung des K-Vitamins und der Neugeborenenpathologie. G. Thieme, Leipzig, 1941.
[6] A. Ferraro and L. Roizin, *Am. J. Pathol.* **22**, 1109 (1946).
[7] R. K. Ghormley and R. S. Clegg, *J. Bone Joint Surg.* **30A**, 589 (1948).

2. INDUCTION OF VITAMIN K DEFICIENCY

a. Dietary Lack of Vitamin K

It was first noted that on certain inadequate diets superficial and internal bleeding developed in chicks.[8] The ability of dietary means alone to induce a deficiency of vitamin K is almost exclusively an avian characteristic;[9] but in the rat,[10] rabbit,[11] mouse,[12] and perhaps man[13] moderate hypoprothrombinemia may occasionally develop. The newborn of man,[14, 15] sheep, goat,[16] and guinea pig[17] are critically lacking in vitamin K, as shown by the fact that small doses of this vitamin will correct the blood-clotting abnormality. The infant undergoes a potentially serious blood-clotting change during its first week of life; this can be corrected or prevented by administration of vitamin K either to the baby or, shortly before the baby's birth, to the mother. The cause of the vitamin K deficiency is not clear, but apparently negligible amounts of the naphthoquinone have been stored by the infant at the time of birth. Salomonsen[4] suggested that there is probably some storage during the summer months, since the incidence of actual bleeding is less during the summer and fall than at other seasons. Waddell and Lawson[18] are in agreement, adding that the peak month for hypoprothrombinemia is March, at which time there is the greatest incidence of deaths from birth injuries. On the basis of a very limited observation Thordarson[19] was unable to find a seasonal trend in the prothrombin levels of infants.

Just as the cause of the hypoprothrombinemia, or rather the neonatal lack of stored vitamin K, is unexplained, there is little agreement on the spontaneous recovery which most infants undergo by about the seventh

[8] H. Dam, Biochem. Z. **215**, 475 (1929); **220**, 158 (1930); W. D. McFarlane, W. R. Graham, Jr., and G. E. Hall, J. Nutrition **4**, 331 (1931); W. D. McFarlane, W. R. Graham, Jr., and F. Richardson, Biochem. J. **25**, Part 1, 358 (1931); W. F. Holst and E. R. Halbrook, Science [N. S.] **77**, 354 (1933). An analysis of the distribution of hemorrhages in the chick has been made by S. Ansbacher, J. Nutrition **17**, 303 (1939).

[9] H. Dam, F. Schønheyder, and L. Lewis, Biochem. J. **31**, Part 1, 22 (1937).

[10] H. Dam and J. Glavind, Z. Vitaminforsch. **9**, 71 (1939).

[11] H. Dam and J. Glavind, Acta Med. Scand. **96**, 108 (1938).

[12] R. Murphy, Science [N. S.] **89**, 203 (1939).

[13] R. Kark and E. L. Lozner, Lancet **II**, 1162 (1939); C. M. Thompson and D. J. Hilferty, Med. Clin. N. Amer. **33**, 1685, (1949).

[14] K. M. Brinkhous, H. P. Smith, and E. D. Warner, Am. J. Med. Sci. **193**, 475 (1937).

[15] W. W. Waddell, Jr., D. Guerry, III, W. E. Bray, and O. R. Kelley, Proc. Soc. Exptl. Biol. Med. **40**, 432 (1939).

[16] A van Vyve, Acta Brevia Neerl. Physiol. Pharmacol. Microbiol. **11**, 101 (1941).

[17] F. Widenbauer and U. Krebs, Monatsschr. Kinderheilk. **91**, 223 (1942).

[18] W. W. Waddell, Jr., and G. McL. Lawson, J. Am. Med. Assoc. **115**, 1416 (1940).

[19] O. Thordarson, Klin. Wochschr. **20**, 645 (1941).

day of life. Adler[20] attributes the entire process to a transient hepatic defect, whereas Quick and Grossman[21] believe that vitamin K becomes available to the infant only after sufficient bacteria have developed in the bowel to produce vitamin K. Sells and associates[22] found insufficient vitamin K in human colostrum to maintain the baby's blood coagulability; however, minimally adequate vitamin K was present in cow's milk. This might explain the older observation[23] that the prelacteal feedings of cow's milk prevent hemorrhagic disease of the newborn. Sells' group[22] further found that coagulability of the blood remained impaired as long as food (other than aqueous glucose solution) was withheld from the infants.

When vitamin K was found to prevent newborn hypoprothrombinemia, it was anticipated that this hemorrhagic disease could be eliminated by the simple expedient of routine prophylactic administration of vitamin K to the baby or mother. Early, carefully controlled studies[18, 24] indicated that this was overoptimistic but that some benefit was to be obtained. Recently several reports[25] have questioned whether the routine use of vitamin K is of any benefit. Since few clotting studies were carried out, judgment should be reserved. The problem merits further careful study.

b. Inhibition of Synthesis of Vitamin K by Intestinal Bacteria

The most important source of vitamin K for the mammal is its own intestinal bacteria,[26, 27] in particular, *Escherichia coli*.[28] In the absence of dietary vitamin K this source alone is usually sufficient to maintain a normally coagulable blood. It is felt that the bacterial (farnesyl) vitamin[28a]

[20] B. Adler, *Monatschr. Geburtschülfe u. Gynäkol.* **118,** 225 (1944).

[21] A. J. Quick and A. M. Grossman, *Am. J. Med. Sci.* **199,** 1 (1940).

[22] R. L. Sells, S. A. Walker, and C. A. Owen, *Proc. Soc. Exptl. Biol. Med.* **47,** 441 (1941).

[23] H. N. Sanford, H. J. Morrison, and L. Wyat, *Am. J. Diseases Children* **43,** 569 (1932).

[24] L. M. Hellman, L. B. Shettles, and N. J. Eastman, *Am. J. Obstet. Gynecol.* **40,** 844 (1940).

[25] E. L. Potter, *Am. J. Obstet. Gynecol.* **50,** 235 (1945); H. N. Sanford, M. Kostalik, and B. Blackmore, *Am. J. Diseases Children* **78,** 686 (1949); J. D. Hay, F. P. Hudson, and T. S. Rodgers, *Lancet* I, 423 (1951).

[26] H. J. Almquist, *Physiol. Revs.* **21,** 194 (1941).

[27] H. J. Almquist, C. F. Pentler, and E. Mecchi, *Proc. Soc. Exptl. Biol. Med.* **38,** 336 (1938); H. J. Almquist and E. L. R. Stokstad, *J. Biol. Chem.* **111,** 105 (1935); H. R. Butt and A. E. Osterberg, *J. Nutrition* **15,** *Suppl.,* 11 (1938).

[28] S. Orla-Jensen, A. D. Orla-Jensen, H. Dam, and J. Glavind, *Zentr. Bakt. Parasitenk.* Abt. 2, **104,** 202 (1941–1942); H. Dam and J. Glavind, *Biochem. J.* **32,** Part 1, 1018 (1938).

[28a] It is generally stated that the intestinal bacteria produce the farnesyl vitamin [H. Dam, *Med. Welt.* **20,** 958 (1951)]; however, Taveira reported the recovery of the phytyl vitamin from *Escherichia coli* [M. Taveira, *Ann. pharm. franç.* **9,** 344 (1951)].

is less effective than the leafy plant (phytyl) one.[29] Presumably, then, the intestinally synthesized vitamin exceeds that obtained from food, for, though less potent, it can maintain an efficient clotting system, whereas the reverse does not seem to be true. Fowls have a short, large intestine which is believed to be inadequate for absorption of the bacterially produced vitamin K.[30] Also, the mammalian lower colon is probably incapable of absorbing the fat-soluble vitamins K even in the presence of bile, for retention enemas of vitamin K have proved ineffective,[31] and Greaves[32] was able to produce a vitamin K deficiency in rats by means of bile fistulas into the colon. However, the cecum may be an important site of bacterial synthesis of the vitamin.[33] More careful attention to prevention of coprophagy —the feces contain large amounts of vitamin K even when the diet is vitamin K-free[11, 30, 32]—may account for the greater than average success that certain investigators[30, 34] have had in inducing a dietary vitamin K deficiency in mammals.

Reduction of intestinal synthesis of vitamin K is most simply accomplished by bacteriostatic or bactericidal agents such as the sulfonamides[35] and possibly by certain antibiotic agents.[36] p-Aminobenzoic acid, whether given orally or parenterally, concentrates in the bowel and prevents sulfonamide depression of the intestinal flora,[37] thus it is not possible to assume a non-intestinal effect of a parenterally administered drug.

[29] H. J. Almquist and A. A. Klose, *Proc. Soc. Exptl. Biol. Med.* **45**, 55 (1940).

[30] H. J. Almquist and E. L. R. Stokstad, *J. Nutrition* **12**, 329 (1936).

[31] H. P. Smith, S. E. Ziffren, C. A. Owen, G. R. Hoffman, and J. E. Flynn, *J. Iowa State Med. Soc.* **29**, 377 (1939).

[32] J. D. Greaves, *Am. J. Physiol.* **125**, 429 (1939).

[33] H. G. Day, K. G. Wakim, M. M. Krider, and E. E. O'Banion, *J. Nutrition* **26**, 585 (1943).

[34] H. Dam, *Advances in Enzymol.* **2**, 285 (1942).

[35] The sulfonamides depress *E. coli* [H. J. White, *Bull. Johns Hopkins Hosp.* **71**, 213 (1942)] and inhibit intestinal synthesis of vitamin K in the same order of effectiveness [W. H. Sebrell, *Harvey Lectures* **39**, 288 (1943–1944) (from most to least effective)]: sulfapyrazine, sulfadiazine [A. Kornberg, F. S. Daft, and W. H. Sebrell, *Publ. Health Repts.* (*U. S.*) **59**, Part 1, 832 (1944)], sulfathiazole [B. M. Braganca and M. V. Radhakrishna Rao, *Indian J. Med. Research* **35**, 15 (1947)], sulfasuxidine [A. D. Welch and L. D. Wright, *J. Nutrition* **25**, 555 (1943)], and sulfaguanidine [S. Black, R. S. Overman, C. A. Elvehjem, and K. P. Link, *J. Biol. Chem.* **145**, 137 (1942)].

[36] Z. A. Lewitus and A. Aschireli, *Harefuah* **35**, 13 (1948); W. K. Rieben, *Helv. Med. Acta* **13**, 295 (1946); C. M. Thompson and D. J. Hilferty, *Med. Clin. N. Amer.* **33**, 1685 (1949). The coagulation changes resulting from prolonged treatment with antibiotic substances are to be distinguished from their clot-accelerating activities during the first hour or two after administration [L. F. Moldavsky, W. B. Hasselbrock, C. Cateno, and D. Goodwin, *Science* [N. S.] **102**, 38 (1945); D. I. Macht, *ibid.* **105**, 313 (1947); Editorial, *J. Am. Med. Assoc.* **141**, 924 (1949)].

[37] A. Kornberg, F. S. Daft, and W. H. Sebrell, *J. Biol. Chem.* **155**, 193 (1944).

Since small doses of vitamin K correct the hypoprothrombinemia accompanying intestinal "sterilization," the possibility of prothrombin changes secondary to hepatic damage would seem to be excluded. However, Braganca and Radhakrishna Rao[35] reported that infiltration with fat developed in the livers of rats after 2 weeks of a diet containing sulfathiazole; this hepatic change was prevented by addition of vitamin K to the sulfonamide-treated diet. The data of Mushett and Seeler[38] suggest that in sulfonamide hypoprothrombinemia vitamin K_1 is 100 to 250 times as effective as menadione; by analogy with vitamin K suppression of dicoumarol action, an hepatic site of action might be considered, for in simple vitamin K deficiency states menadione is the more potent.

Rats develop hypoprothrombinemia when subjected to a diet high in triglycerides containing dihydroxystearic acid.[38a] The clotting change is accompanied by disappearance of vitamin K from the intestinal contents and is corrected by the administration of the vitamin (0.1 mg. per day). Since the intestinal bacteria are qualitatively and quantitatively normal during the period of vitamin K deficiency, it seems that the vitamin-synthesizing systems of the bacteria are blocked.[38b]

c. Reduced Absorption of Vitamin K

(1) *Absence of Bile.* Quick *et al.*[39] first reported blood-clotting changes in human obstructive jaundice comparable to those already demonstrated in vitamin K-deficient chicks. Hawkins and Brinkhous[40] found the same clotting condition in experimental biliary fistulas in dogs. The lack of bile in the intestine was common to both states and was soon recognized to be etiologically important in vitamin K deficiency.[41] Fantl and coworkers[41a] have recently questioned this concept.

In rapid succession Warner *et al.*,[42] Butt *et al.*,[43] and Dam and Glavind[44] reported the successful correction of the clotting changes and of the bleed-

[38] C. W. Mushett and A. O. Seeler, *J. Pharmacol. Exptl. Therap.* **91**, 84 (1947).

[38a] E. E. Lockhart, H. Sherman, and R. S. Harris, *Science* [N. S.] **96**, 542 (1942).

[38b] G. Nightingale, E. E. Lockhart, and R. S. Harris, *Arch. Biochem.* **12**, 381 (1947).

[39] A. J. Quick, M. Stanley-Brown, and F. W. Bancroft, *Am. J. Med. Sci.* **190**, 501 (1935).

[40] W. B. Hawkins and K. M. Brinkhous, *J. Exptl. Med.* **63**, 795 (1936).

[41] H. P. Smith, E. D. Warner, K. M. Brinkhous, and W. H. Seegers, *J. Exptl. Med.* **67**, 911 (1938).

[41a] P. Fantl, J. F. Nelson, and G. J. Lincoln, *Australian J. Exptl. Biol. Med. Sci.* **29**, 433 (1951).

[42] E. D. Warner, K. M. Brinkhous, and H. P. Smith, *Proc. Soc. Exptl. Biol. Med.* **37**, 628 (1938).

[43] H. R. Butt, A. M. Snell, and A. E. Osterberg, *Proc. Staff Meetings Mayo Clinic* **13**, 74 (1938).

[44] H. Dam and J. Glavind, *Lancet* **I**, 720 (1938).

ing in patients with obstructive jaundice when crude vitamin K concentrates were administered orally, along with bile. Bile alone was slowly effective, but the vitamin alone was without any effect. Thus it became established that, like the other fat-soluble vitamins, vitamin K requires bile for its transport through the intestinal wall. Desoxycholic acid, which unites with vitamin K to form vitamin K-choleic acid,[45] is claimed to be the principal component of bile for absorption of the vitamin.[46] Butt and Snell[47] demonstrated that human acholic stools are rich in vitamin K, so that for coagulation all that seems to be lacking in obstructive jaundice is the bile. It is therefore puzzling why bile alone, although free of vitamin K,[48] is not more efficacious when one considers the small amount of vitamin K necessary to correct the deficiency (1 mg. or less).[49]

As might be expected, water-soluble analogs of vitamin K may be given orally, without supplementary bile, to animals or man lacking intestinal bile.[50] However, the water-soluble preparations are usually given parenterally because of the prompter action and insured dosage.[51]

(2) *Intestinal Disease.* Altered blood coagulation is at times found in a variety of intestinal diseases and conditions: intestinal obstruction, gastrocolic fistula, external enterostomy, chronic ulcerative colitis, regional ileitis, intestinal polyposis,[47, 52] and tuberculous enteritis.[53] Apparently vitamin K is mechanically prevented from being absorbed in these conditions. The vitamin deficiency which occurs in sprue, both tropical[54] and non-tropical,[47] and in prolonged diarrhea (such as in pellagra)[55] likewise represents an inability to absorb the vitamin K which is abundantly present; this state may be duplicated experimentally by a high concentration of mineral oil in the diet.[56] Activated carbon, by firmly adsorbing vitamin K, also pre-

[45] H. J. Almquist and A. A. Klose, *J. Am. Chem. Soc.* **61,** 745 (1939).

[46] E. T. Cohn and C. L. A. Schmidt, *Proc. Soc. Exptl. Biol. Med.* **41,** 443 (1939).

[47] H. R. Butt and A. M. Snell, Vitamin K. W. B. Saunders Company, Philadelphia, (1941).

[48] H. J. Almquist, *Science* [N. S.] **87,** 538 (1938).

[49] E. Fernholz and S. Ansbacher, *Science* [N. S.] **90,** 215 (1939).

[50] E. D. Warner and J. E. Flynn, *Proc. Soc. Exptl. Biol. Med.* **44,** 607 (1940); H. P. Smith and C. A. Owen, *J. Biol. Chem.* **134,** 783 (1940).

[51] H. P. Smith, S. E. Ziffren, C. A. Owen, and G. R. Hoffman, *J. Am. Med. Assoc.* **113,** 380 (1939); H. R. Butt, A. M. Snell, and A. E. Osterberg, *Proc. Staff Meetings Mayo Clinic* **14,** 497 (1939).

[52] R. L. Clark, Jr., C. F. Dixon, H. R. Butt, and A. M. Snell, *Proc. Staff Meetings Mayo Clinic* **14,** 407 (1939); T. T. Mackie, *N. Y. State J. Med.* **40,** Part 2, 987 (1940).

[53] E. Tanner and F. Suter, *Schweiz. med. Wochschr.* **74,** 552 (1944).

[54] R. S. Diaz y Rivera, *Puerto Rico J. Public Health Trop. Med.* **17,** 124 (1941).

[55] E. D. Warner, T. D. Spies, and C. A. Owen, *Southern Med. J.* **34,** 161 (1941).

[56] M. C. Elliott, B. Isaacs, and A. C. Ivy, *Proc. Soc. Exptl. Biol. Med.* **43,** 240 (1940); W. A. Barnes, *ibid.* **49,** 15 (1942).

vents its absorption.[26] Whether the hypoprothrombinemia and bleeding reported to occur in animals receiving large doses of vitamin A[57] is secondary to reduced vitamin K synthesis or absorption, or to an alteration of hepatic function, is not clear; addition of a vitamin K analog to the diet of the hypervitaminotic A animal prevents the clotting changes without, however, any alteration in the vitamin A concentration in the liver.[58] The status of quinine[59] and certain rare earths[60] is likewise uncertain; hypoprothrombinemia, which is corrected by vitamin K, has been observed following their administration. Quick[61] has questioned the quinine effect on clotting.

(3) *Diversion of Intestinal Lymph.* In the rat a profound incoagulability of the blood may be produced by withdrawal of intestinal or thoracic duct lymph;[62] correction with parenteral vitamin K is prompt.[63] The pathway for vitamin K absorption would thus seem to be via the intestinal lymphatics, through the thoracic duct, to the vascular tree. The possibility of a vitamin K deficiency in prolonged loss of lymph resulting from thoracic duct avulsion might be considered; actually, hematuria often does accompany lymphatic chyluria.

d. Hepatic Utilization of Vitamin K

(1) *Liver Damage.* It has long been known that severe liver damage[64] or hepatectomy[65] leads to a prolongation of the clotting time of whole blood. With the development of methods for estimating plasma prothrombin it was discovered that a lack of prothrombin in the blood was a prominent part of these clotting changes.[66] Furthermore, administration of vitamin K to man or animals with liver damage has proved ineffectual in correcting

[57] R. F. Light, R. P. Alscher, and C. N. Frey, *Science* **100**, 225 (1944).

[58] S. E. Walker, E. Eylenburg, and T. Moore, *Biochem. J.* **41**, 575 (1947).

[59] L. A. Pirk and R. Engelberg, *J. Am. Med. Assoc.* **128**, 1093 (1945).

[60] E. Vincke and E. Schmidt, *Hoppe-Seyler's Z. physiol. Chem.* **273**, 39 (1942).

[61] A. J. Quick, *J. Lab. Clin. Med.* **31**, 79 (1946).

[62] C. A. Owen, Jr., Studies on the Conversion of Prothrombin to Thrombin; Effect of Conversion Variations on Prothrombin Tests. Thesis, Graduate School, University of Minnesota, 1950.

[63] J. D. Mann, F. D. Mann, and J. L. Bollman, *Am. J. Physiol.* **158**, 311 (1949).

[64] M. Doyon, *Compt. rend. soc. biol.* **58**, 30 (1905); M. Doyon, A. Morel, and N. Kareff, *ibid.* **58**, 493 (1905).

[65] M. Doyon and N. Kareff, *Compt. rend. soc. biol.* **56**, 612 (1904); P. Nolf, *Arch. intern. physiol.* **3**, 1 (1905–1906).

[66] H. P. Smith, E. D. Warner, and K. M. Brinkhous, *J. Exptl. Med.* **66**, 801 (1937); E. D. Warner, *ibid.* **68**, 831 (1938); W. D. Andrus, J. W. Lord, Jr., and R. A. Moore, *Surgery* **6**, 899 (1939); K. M. Brinkhous and E. D. Warner, *Proc. Soc. Exptl. Biol. Med.* **44**, 609 (1940); J. L. Bollman, H. R. Butt, and A. M. Snell, *J. Am. Med. Assoc.* **115**, 1087 (1940); B. Uvnäs, *Acta Physiol. Scand.* **3**, 97 (1941); D. J. Ingle, J. E. Nezamis, and M. C. Prestrud, *Am. J. Physiol.* **161**, 199 (1950).

the lack of prothrombin or the lengthening of clot time;[67] however, large doses of vitamin K before exposure of animals to chloroform are reported to be hepatoprotective.[68] A practical application is the evaluation of hypoprothrombinemia of uncertain origin; if parenteral vitamin K analogs are not corrective, hepatic function is presumed to be subnormal (vitamin K tolerance test).[69] Clotting studies suggest that mild hepatic insufficiency results from fever,[70] anesthesia,[71] or simple manipulation of the liver.[72]

(2) *Anticoagulant Drugs.* In contradistinction to such substances as chloroform, carbon tetrachloride, and phosphorus, which depress a variety of hepatic activities, including the synthesis of prothrombin and fibrinogen, a class of chemicals has been developed within the past decade, primarily by Link's group,[73] which has found wide clinical use: the anticoagulant coumarins, which include dicoumarol,[74] hydrocoumarol,[75] tromexan,[76] phenylindanedione,[77] and anticoagulant "63."[78] These chemicals are adminis-

[67] S. J. Wilson, *Proc. Soc. Exptl. Biol. Med.* **41,** 559 (1939); F. J. Pohle and J. K. Stewart, *J. Clin. Invest.* **19,** 365 (1940); R. Kark and A. W. Souter, *Lancet* I, 1149 (1940).

[68] M. A. Pessagno Espora, *Día méd.* **22,** 1264 (1950).

[69] P. N. Unger, S. Shapiro, and S. Schwalb, *J. Clin. Invest.* **27,** 39 (1948); P. N. Unger, M. Weiner, and S. Shapiro, *Am. J. Clin. Path.* **18,** 835 (1948).

[70] R. K. Richards, *Science* **97,** 313 (1943).

[71] S. C. Cullen, S. E. Ziffren, R. B. Gibson, and H. P. Smith, *J. Am. Med. Assoc.* **115,** 991 (1940).

[72] J. W. Lord, Jr., *Surgery* **6,** 896 (1939).

[73] K. P. Link, *Harvey Lectures* **39,** 162 (1943–1944).

[74] 3,3'-Methylenebis(4-hydroxycoumarin); dicumarin, dicoumarin, dikumarin, dicumarol, "A. P.," bishydroxycoumarin (Formula 10); R. S. Overman, M. A. Stahmann, W. R. Sullivan, C. F. Huebner, H. A. Campbell, and K. P. Link, *J. Biol. Chem.* **142,** 941 (1942); H. R. Butt, E. V. Allen, and J. L. Bollman, *Proc. Staff Meetings Mayo Clinic* **16,** 388 (1941); Council on Pharmacy and Chemistry, *J. Am. Med. Assoc.* **137,** 1533 (1948); 145, **644,** (1951); H. Dyckerhoff, *Biochem. Z.* **316,** 397 (1944).

[75] 3,3'-Methylenebis(3,4-hydro, 4-hydroxycoumarol) (Formula 11); F. Ericksen, E. Jacobsen, and C. M. Plum, *Acta Pharmacol. Toxicol.* **1,** 379 (1945).

[76] 3,3'-Carboxymethylenebis(4-hydroxycoumarin) ethyl ester or 4,4'-dioxydicoumaryl ethyl acetate; pelentan, "B.O.E.A.," ethyl biscoumacetate (Formula 12); K. N. von Kaulla and R. Pulver, *Schweiz. med. Wochschr.* **78,** 806 (1948); R. Della Santa, *ibid.* **79,** 195 (1949); C. Solomon, H. J. McNeile, and R. Lange, *J. Lab. Clin. Med.* **36,** 19 (1950); G. E. Burke and I. S. Wright, *Conf. on Blood Clotting and Allied Problems, New York* **3,** 57 (1950).

[77] Phenyl-2-indanedione-1,3; "P.I.D."; "danilone"; "hedulin" (Formula 13); P. Meunier, C. Mentzer, and D. Molho, *Compt. rend. acad. sci. U.R.S.S.* **224,** 1666 (1947); J. P. Soulier and J. Guéguen, *Rev. hématol.* **3,** 180 (1948); N. W. Barker, J. E. Estes, Jr., and F. D. Mann, *Proc. Staff Meetings Mayo Clinic* **26,** 162 (1951); L. B. Jaques, E. Lepp, and E. Gordon, *Conf. on Blood Clotting and Allied Problems, New York* **3,** 11 (1950).

[78] 2-Methyl-2-methoxy-4-phenyl-5-oxodihydropyrano(3,2-C) (1)-benzopyran; coumopyran; M. Ikawa, M. A. Stahmann, and K. P. Link, *J. Am. Chem. Soc.* **66,** 902

tered clinically in order to reduce the ability of the blood to clot and thus lessen the chances for the development or progression of thromboses. Since the complications of hemorrhage may be as serious as those of thrombosis, the margin of safety is rather narrow. The therapeutic goal is an amount of anticoagulant which will depress prothrombin and associated clotting factors but not quite prolong the whole blood-clotting time. Clinical results have been very encouraging and seem to bear out the empirical method of evaluating therapy.[79]

Even before the specific toxic agent (dicoumarol) of spoiled sweet clover was known, Roderick[80] recognized that the incoagulability of the blood of cattle that had eaten the moldy clover was associated with a prothrombin deficiency. The hypoprothrombinemia requires at least 12 to 24 hours to develop after ingestion of the anticoagulant, probably because an interval of time is required for circulating prothrombin to be catabolized after the production of new prothrombin has been halted.[81, 82] This conclusion seems warranted from studies of prothrombin disappearance rates; Carter et al.[83] found no evidence of prothrombin stores.

Vitamin K concentrates (from alfalfa) or the pure analogs have been found to counteract the prothrombin-depressing activity of dicoumarol.[84, 85] The problem remains unsettled as to whether dicoumarol injures the liver, an action reversed by vitamin K or whether there is a competitive inhibition of vitamin K activity by dicoumarol. Glavind and Jansen[86] found that in vitamin K-depleted chicks the reaction to dicoumarol was counteracted by an amount of vitamin K which followed no fixed ratio; they concluded that dicoumarol injures the liver. In a comparable experiment Collentine

(1944); W. D. Battle, R. T. Capps, O. S. Orth, and O. O. Meyer, *J. Lab. Clin. Med.* **35**, 8 (1950); R. Rotter and O. O. Meyer, *ibid.* **36**, 981 (1950); H. H. Hanson, N. W. Barker, and F. D. Mann, *Circulation* **4**, 844 (1951).

[79] E. V. Allen, N. W. Barker, and J. M. Waugh, *J. Am. Med. Assoc.* **120**, 1009 (1942); H. R. Butt, E. V. Allen, and J. L. Bollman, *Proc. Staff Meetings Mayo Clinic* **16**, 388 (1941); N. W. Barker, H. R. Butt, E. V. Allen, and J. L. Bollman, *J. Am. Med. Assoc.* **118**, 1003 (1942); N. W. Barker, H. E. Cromer, Jr., M. Hurn, and J. M. Waugh, *Surgery* **17**, 207 (1945).

[80] L. M. Roderick, *Am. J. Physiol.* **96**, 413 (1931).

[81] K. P. Link, R. S. Overman, W. R. Sullivan, C. F. Huebner, and L. D. Scheel, *J. Biol. Chem.* **147**, 463 (1943).

[82] M. Stefanini and A. V. Pisciotta, *Science* [N. S.] **111**, 364 (1950).

[83] J. R. Carter, G. H. Chambers, and E. D. Warner, *Proc. Soc. Exptl. Biol. Med.* **72**, 52 (1949).

[84] R. S. Overman, J. B. Field, C. A. Baumann, and K. P. Link, *J. Nutrition* **23**, 589 (1942).

[85] J. Lehmann, *Science* [N. S.] **96**, 345 (1942); S. Shapiro, M. H. Redish, and H. A. Campbell, *Proc. Soc. Exptl. Biol. Med.* **52**, 12 (1943); H. E. Cromer, Jr., and N. W. Barker, *Proc. Staff Meetings Mayo Clinic* **19**, 217 (1944).

[86] J. Glavind and K. F. Jansen, *Acta Physiol. Scand.* **8**, 173 (1944).

[87] G. E. Collentine and A. J. Quick, *Am. J. Med. Sci.* **222**, 7 (1951).

and Quick[87] depleted dogs of vitamin K stores by cholecystnephrostomy; small doses of vitamin K_1 (or analogs) and of dicoumarol counteracted each other. Because of the minuteness of the doses, Collentine and Quick feel that the only explanation is a mutual competition for prothrombinogenic enzyme systems. Almquist[87a] has presented an interesting theoretical analysis of the action of dicoumarol.

Certain observations suggest a primary hepatotoxicity from dicoumarolization. Overdoses of dicoumarol produce fatty livers in rabbits[88] and central necrosis of the liver in rats.[89] Bollman and Preston[90] reported that in the presence of an already damaged liver the effect of dicoumarol was accentuated. Similarly, Roller and Mudrak[91] demonstrated that, if the liver had been damaged, smaller doses of dicoumarol gave the same effect as large doses when hepatic function was normal. Irish and Jaques[92] noted that dicoumarol, like known hepatotoxins, stimulated fibrinogen production if given in small doses, and in larger doses depressed the fibrinogen of the blood.

The concept of a competition between vitamin K and dicoumarol has been explored extensively by Meunier and Mentzer;[93] these investigators have stressed the similarity between compounds with hemorrhagic and antihemorrhagic activity. Menadione (Fig. 5) (1) is a potent vitamin K analog; addition of an hydroxyl in the 3 position, phthiocol (2), reduces the activity; replacement of the methyl by an ethyl radical (3) further weakens the antihemorrhagic power; combining two phthiocols through their methyl groups yields an antivitamin K[94] (4), as does doubling menadione[95] (5). Replacing the 2-methyl group in menadione by methoxy (6) also reverses the compound's action,[96] and if one substitutes for the methyl in phthiocol's 2 position 3-cyclohexylpropyl (7), or 2-methyloctyl (8), or 3-(decahydro-2-naphthyl)propyl (9) radicals, a similar reversal occurs.[97] Some of the more potent hemorrhagic agents tend to resemble (4) and (5), that is, "double molecules." Although most clinical anticoagulants are

[87a] H. J. Almquist, *Arch. Biochem. and Biophys.* **35,** 463 (1952).

[88] K. F. Jansen, *Nord. med.* **20,** 1993 (1943).

[89] C. L. Rose, P. N. Harris, and K. K. Chen, *Proc. Soc. Exptl. Biol. Med.* **50,** 228 (1942).

[90] J. L. Bollman and F. W. Preston, *J. Am. Med. Assoc.* **120,** 1021 (1942).

[91] D. Roller and O. Mudrak, *Z. ges. exptl. Med.* **114,** 75 (1944).

[92] U. D. Irish and L. B. Jaques, *Am. J. Physiol.* **143,** 101 (1945).

[93] Reviewed in several articles in the International Colloquy "Les Vitamins," *Bull. soc. chim. biol.* (1948).

[94] P. Meunier, C. Mentzer, N. P. Buu-Hoï, and P. Cagniant, *Bull. soc. chim. biol.* **25,** 384 (1943).

[95] C. Mentzer, *Bull. soc. chim. biol.* **30,** 872 (1948).

[96] D. Molho, J. Moraux, and P. Meunier, *Bull. soc. chim. biol.* **30,** 637 (1948).

[97] C. C. Smith, R. Fradkin, and M. D. Lackey, *Proc. Soc. Exptl. Biol. Med.* **61,** 398 (1946).

symmetrical "double molecules"—dicoumarol (10), hydrocoumarol (11), and tromexan (12) (Fig. 6)—they need not be, for the asymmetric phenylindanedione (13) and others (14 and 15)[98] are also active. Dithiocoumarol (16)

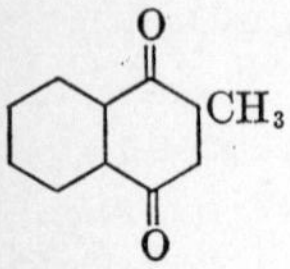
(1)

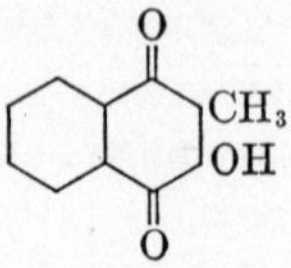
(2)

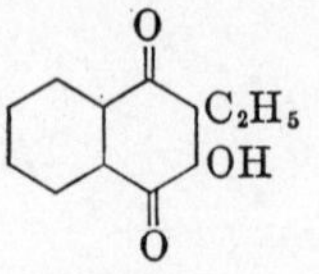
(3)

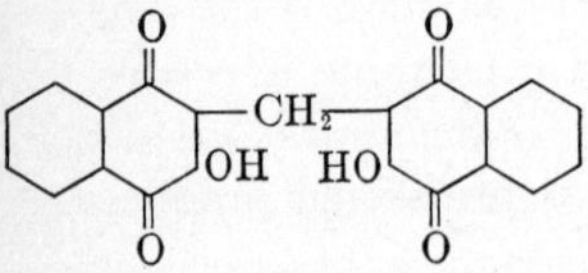
(4)

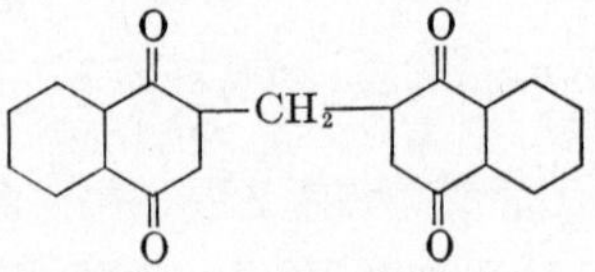
(5)

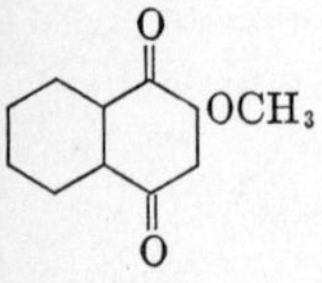
(6)

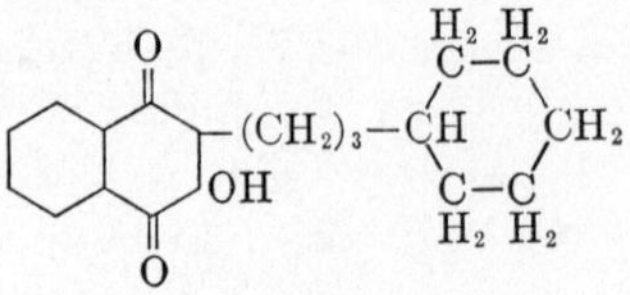
(7)

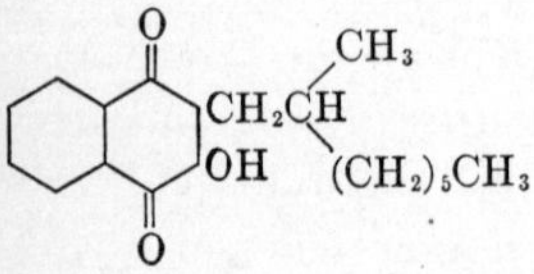
(8)

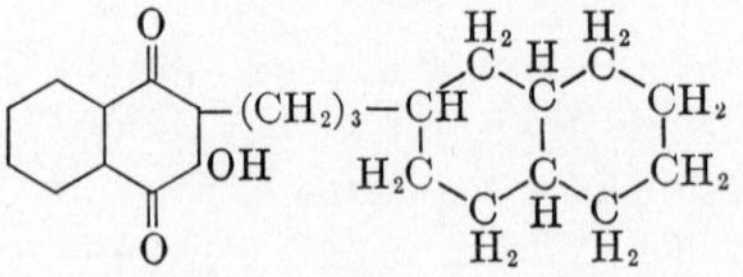
(9)

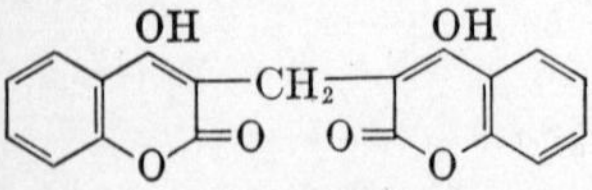
(10)

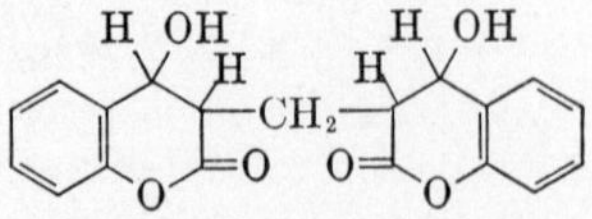
(11)

FIG. 5.

is weakly hemorrhagic.[95] R in compound (17) determines the activity: if R is CH_3, the compound is vitamin K-like; if R is an halide or a phenyl derivative, it is an antivitamin K compound.[99]

[98] P. Meunier, C. Mentzer, and A. Vinet, *Helv. Chim. Acta* **29**, Part 1, 1291 (1946).
[99] P. Meunier, C. Mentzer, and D. Molho, *Compt. rend. acad. sci.* (*U.R.S.S.*) **224**, 1666 (1947).

Woolley[100] remarks that the dicoumarol-vitamin K antagonism differs in several respects from the characteristic analog competitions: vitamin K counteracts dicoumarol over only a limited dosage range; within this range the inhibition index is not constant; and most unusual is an index of less than 1.0 (for example, in the rat 10 mg. of dicoumarol is inhibited by 25 mg. of vitamin K; that is, an index of 0.4).

Regardless of the exact nature of the antagonism between vitamin K and dicoumarol, the recent evidence of Jaques' group[101] suggests that the hepatic cell is involved. Dicoumarol labeled with carbon[14] in the methylene bridge was administered intravenously to mice and rabbits; significant radio-

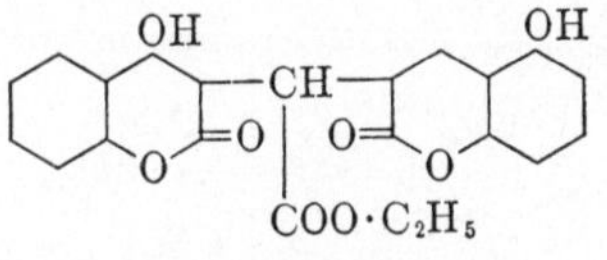

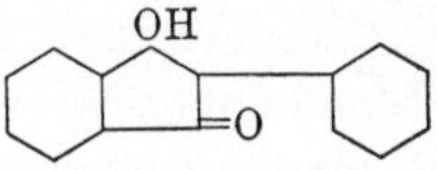

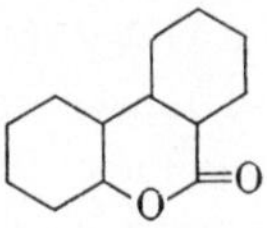

FIG. 6.

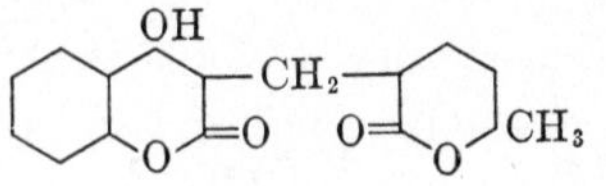

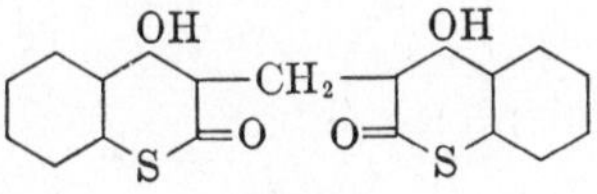

activity was found only in the liver, gallbladder, feces, and urine (only degradation products in the urine). Intravenous administration of vitamin K expedited disappearance of radioactivity from the mouse liver. Measuring plasma dicoumarol directly, Shapiro et al.[102] were unable to demonstrate more rapid disappearance of dicoumarol from the blood when vitamin K was administered. Dicoumarol or its active products are apparently excreted by the kidneys, for nephrectomy or experimental nephritis prolongs the anticoagulant activity.[90] The suggestion[103] has been made that the action of

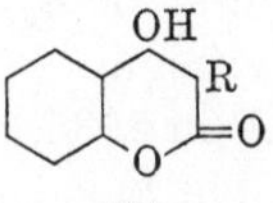

100 D. W. Woolley, Physiol. Revs. 27, 308 (1947); Advances in Enzymol. 6, 129 (1946).
101 C. C. Lee, L. W. Trevoy, J. W. T. Spinks, and L. B. Jaques, Proc. Soc. Exptl. Biol. Med. 74, 151 (1950); J. W. T. Spinks and L. B. Jaques, Nature 166, 184 (1950).
102 S. Shapiro, M. Weiner, and G. Simson, New Engl. J. Med. 243, 775 (1950).
103 P. Gley and J. Delor, Bull. soc. chim. biol. 30, 891 (1948); J. Badin, C. Mentzer, J. Moraux, and P. Meunier, Compt. rend. soc. biol. 144, 871 (1950).

phenylindanedione is relatively brief because this substance reduces glomerular capillary resistance and is excreted rapidly; to counteract this phenomenon, vitamin P has been used to increase the capillary resistance, apparently successfully.

Link's group[104] has synthesized dicoumarol from and degraded it to salicylic acid. Since salicylates have a limited anticoagulant action, it has been suggested that dicoumarol may act through its degradation products.[81, 105, 106] The relative inefficiency of salicylates (1/500 the activity of dicoumarol) makes this unlikely; however, one might speculate with Jaques and Lepp[107] that intestinal bacteria convert a small portion of ingested salicylate into dicoumarol. Arguing along similar lines, Shemiakin and coworkers[108] believe that phthalates are biologic degradation products of vitamin K and are responsible for the naphthoquinone's coagulant activity.

For the effect of other drugs on blood clotting the excellent review of Seegers[108a] is referred to.

3. Blood Coagulation Changes with Vitamin K Deficiency

Hemorrhage associated with obstructive jaundice has been known and reported for centuries; vascular changes, deficiency of various clotting components, and the presence of clot-inhibiting agents have all been suggested. Of the older concepts only the suggestion that antithrombin is excessive in vitamin K deficiency persists. Dyckerhoff and Marx[109] claim that the increased thrombin-destroying function of plasma is corrected by administration of the vitamin.

Quick et al.,[39] in 1935, announced that prothrombin was lacking in the poorly coagulable blood of a patient with obstructive jaundice. In the hemorrhagic chick disease of dietary origin Schønheyder[110] suspected a deficiency of plasma prothrombin; Dam et al.[111] clearly demonstrated that adding prothrombin from normal plasma corrected this deficiency; further, they were unable to recover prothrombin, by acetone or isoelectric precipitation, from the plasma of bleeding chicks. Quick[112] convincingly confirmed the prothrombin lack in the chick bleeding state. In the bleeding of dogs

[104] M. A. Stahmann, C. F. Huebner, and K. P. Link, *J. Biol. Chem.* **138**, 513 (1941).

[105] S. Shapiro, *J. Am. Med. Assoc.* **125**, 546 (1944).

[106] O. O. Meyer and B. Howard, *Proc. Soc. Exptl. Biol. Med.* **53**, 234 (1943); S. Rapoport, M. Wing, and G. M. Guest, *ibid.* **53**, 40 (1943).

[107] L. B. Jaques and E. Lepp, *Proc. Soc. Exptl. Biol. Med.* **66**, 178 (1947).

[108] M. M. Shemiakin, L. A. Schukina, and J. B. Shevezov, *Nature* **151**, 585 (1943); M. M. Shemiakin and L. A. Schukina, *ibid.* **154**, 513 (1944).

[108a] W. H. Seegers, *Pharmacol. Revs.* **3**, 278 (1951).

[109] H. Dyckerhoff and R. Marx, *Biochem. Z.* **311**, 1 (1942).

[110] F. Schønheyder, *Biochem. J.* **30**, Part 1, 890 (1936).

[111] H. Dam, F. Schønheyder, and E. Tage-Hansen, *Biochem. J.* **30**, Part 1, 1075 (1936).

[112] A. J. Quick, *Am. J. Physiol.* **118**, 260 (1937).

with biliary fistulas, Hawkins and Brinkhous[40] detected severe hypoprothrombinemia. In these various hemorrhagic states, all attributable to a deficiency of vitamin K, and studied by a variety of methods, the common denominator has been found to be a lack of the plasmatic precursor of thrombin. When this clotting change was found to be readily corrected by vitamin K it was felt[113]—and is still generally believed—that the lack of prothrombin is the only immediate result of vitamin K deficiency, and hence the sole cause of bleeding in this deficiency state.

Such a simple, attractive concept—pure hypoprothrombinemia—overlooks some disturbing facts. The newborn infant has a prothrombin value only one-fourth to one-third that of adults.[14] The prothrombin titer rises slowly, reaching normal adult levels near the end of the first year of life. Despite this rather pronounced hypoprothrombinemia, the newborn's clot time is normal or even shortened, and the "prothrombin time" of Quick is usually normal; bleeding rarely occurs under these circumstances.[4, 15, 21, 114, 115] During the first week of life drastic changes occur; generally between the second and fifth days the "prothrombin time" is prolonged and clot times may be lengthened; if these changes are extreme, hemorrhage may ensue—clinically described as "hemorrhagic disease of the newborn." Actual bleeding is uncommon, and spontaneous return to normal takes place by the end of the first week of life, if digestive disturbances have not intervened.[116] It is well known that vitamin K and its analogs can prevent or quickly correct these clotting and bleeding changes. Yet, throughout this brief neonatal period the true prothrombin level of the blood is low and fluctuates little.

Here, then, is one instance of hemorrhagic diathesis developing without a significant alteration in the plasma prothrombin concentration, and whatever the abnormality may be, vitamin K is corrective.

Mann and Hurn[117] have described a new blood coagulation factor whose activity appears to be related to the function of thromboplastin in the first stage of clotting, hence "cothromboplastin." When this factor is deficient, prothrombin, regardless of how much is present, can convert to thrombin only with difficulty; as a result of a deficiency of cothromboplastin the "prothrombin time" of Quick is prolonged. It has been found that cothrom-

[113] Reviewed by K. M. Brinkhous, *Medicine* **19,** 329 (1940).

[114] W. W. Waddell, Jr., and D. Guerry, III, *J. Am. Med. Assoc.* **112,** 2259 (1939).

[115] C. A. Owen, G. R. Hoffman, S. E. Ziffren, and H. P. Smith, *Proc. Soc. Exptl. Biol. Med.* **41,** 181 (1939); H. Dam, E. Tage-Hansen, and P. Plum, *Lancet* **II,** 1157 (1939); E. Oehler, *Monatsschr. Kinderheilk.* **90,** 394 (1942).

[116] F. Widenbauer and U. Krebs, *Monatsschr. Kinderheilk.* **90,** 173 (1942); S. Rapoport and K. Dodd, *Am. J. Diseases Children* **71,** 611 (1946).

[117] F. D. Mann, *Am. J. Clin. Pathol.* **19,** 861 (1949); F. D. Mann and M. M. Hurn, *ibid.* **20,** 225 (1950).

boplastin diminishes in the vitamin K deficiency of obstructive jaundice and returns to normal under the influence of vitamin K therapy.[118] Certain characteristics of cothromboplastin are its presence in normal plasma or serum and even in aged plasma [thus clearly differentiating it from both prothrombin and Ac-globulin (factor V or labile factor)].

During the interval when the "prothrombin time" of the newborn is prolonged, a prothrombin conversion factor was found lacking by Randall and Randall;[119] this factor is present in normal plasma, aged plasma, and serum.

Among the clotting changes resulting from dicoumarol therapy is a diminution of stable prothrombin conversion factor;[120] this precedes the drop in prothrombin. The stable factor—so named to distinguish it from the labile factor of Quick—is present in normal plasma, prothrombin-poor serum, and aged plasma. Cothromboplastin, in these and other respects, appears to be identical with the stable factor. Both resemble, at least superficially, the factor of Randall and Randall.

Dam and coworkers[121] have given their support to the opinion that there are non-prothrombic clotting changes in both simple vitamin K deficiency and dicoumarolization; however, they suggest that a "delta" factor is lacking in the former, but a different ("kappa") factor is reduced in the latter (delta present in dicoumarol plasma and kappa in vitamin K-deficient plasma). That a difference exists between dicoumarol plasma and plasma of simple vitamin K deficiency has been both confirmed[121a] and denied.[121b]

It becomes increasingly clear that the "hypoprothrombinemia" of the newborn infant, of obstructive jaundice, and of dicoumarol therapy involves, in addition to lowered prothrombin, one or more non-prothrombic factors.[122] Since vitamin K overcomes the coagulation defect in all three conditions, one is inclined to recall the statement of Boyd and Warner:[123]

[118] F. D. Mann, E. S. Shonyo, and F. C. Mann, *Am. J. Physiol.* **164**, 111 (1951).

[119] A. Randall, IV, and J. P. Randall, *Proc. Soc. Exptl. Biol. Med.* **70**, 215 (1949).

[120] C. A. Owen, Jr., and J. L. Bollman, *Proc. Soc. Exptl. Biol. Med.* **67**, 367 (1948); C. A. Owen, Jr., T. B. Magath, and J. L. Bollman, *Am. J. Physiol.* **166**, 1 (1951).

[121] H. Dam, *Nature* **161**, 1010 (1948); H. Dam and E. Søndergaard, *Biochim. et Biophys. Acta* **2**, 409 (1948); Ø. Sørbye, I. Kruse, and H. Dam, *Acta Chem. Scand.* **4**, 549, 831 (1950); Anonymous, *Nutrition Revs.* **9**, 36 (1951).

[121a] M. Verstraete and R. Verwilghen, *Acta clin. belg.* **6**, 269 (1951).

[121b] A. J. Quick, C. V. Hussey, and G. E. Collentine, *Proc. Soc. Exptl. Biol. Med.* **79**, 131 (1952).

[122] See also: F. Koller, A. Loeliger, and F. Duckert, *Acta Haematol.* **6**, 1 (1951); R. F. Jacox and R. F. Bays, *Blood* **5**, 313 (1950); R. L. MacMillan. *Science* [N. S.] **108**, 416 (1948); P. A. Owren, *Rev. hématol.* **6**, 135 (1951); C. A. Mawson, *J. Lab. Clin. Med.* **34**, Part 1, 458 (1949); H. E. Schultze, *Arch. exptl. Pathol. Pharmakol.* **207**, 173 (1949); G. Y. Shinowara and W. B. Smith, *Am. J. Clin. Pathol.* **20**, 341 (1950); L. A. Sternberger, *Blood* **4**, 1131 (1949).

[123] E. J. Boyd and E. D. Warner, *J. Lab. Clin. Med.* **33**, 1431 (1948).

"It is possible that vitamin K affects factors which govern prothrombin conversion as well as those which control its concentration."

VIII. Pharmacology

CHARLES A. OWEN, JR.

A. VITAMIN K PREPARATIONS

Phytyl menadione (thylloquinone, vitamin K_1, 2-methyl-3-phytyl-1,4-naphthoquinone) has been synthesized and is commercially available, although expensive. Concentrates of natural vitamin K and synthetic menadione (U.S.P.) (menaphthone B.P., 2-methyl-1,4-naphthoquinone) are relatively inexpensive. All these substances are fat-soluble, and when given orally in the absence of intestinal bile they require the administration of bile salts.

For the simple deficiencies of vitamin K the water-soluble analogs are generally preferred, such as the following: menadione sodium bisulfite; 4-amino-2-methyl naphthol HCl; or 2-methyl-1,4-naphthohydroquinone diphosphate tetra sodium (a menadiol derivative). In the uncomplicated vitamin K deficiencies menadione has been found to be the strongest corrective analog with approximately two to four times the activity of phytyl menadione.[1, 2] Despite an occasional objection,[3] the weight of evidence is that vitamin K_1 is more effective than menadione in counteracting the effects of the anticoagulant dicoumarins.

B. DOSAGES

For the vitamin K deficiency of obstructive jaundice, biliary fistula, or hemorrhagic disease of the newborn, daily doses of 1 to 5 mg. of any of the vitamin K analogs are usually adequate. One milligram is stated to be sufficient to prevent the clotting changes produced by 1 g. of sodium acetyl-salicylate.[4] Ten to twenty milligrams has been recommended for administration to the mother during the last few hours of labor to prevent hemorrhagic disease of the infant. These doses are so much greater than minimal effective ones that the slight differences of potency of the various vitamin

[1] H. J. Almquist and A. A. Klose, *Proc. Soc. Exptl. Biol. Med.* **45,** 55 (1940).

[2] S. A. Thayer, R. W. McKee, S. B. Binkley, and E. A. Doisy, *Proc. Soc. Exptl. Biol. Med.* **44,** 585 (1940); S. A. Thayer, R. W. McKee, S. B. Binkley, D. W. MacCorquodale, and E. A. Doisy, *ibid,* **41,** 194 (1939); H. J. Almquist and A. A. Klose, *J. Biol. Chem.* **130,** 787 (1939).

[3] S. Shapiro, M. Weiner, and G. Simson, *New Engl. J. Med.* **243,** 775 (1950).

[4] S. Shapiro, *J. Am. Med. Assoc.* **125,** 546 (1944).

analogs become inconsequential. Little has been done to investigate the possibility of using smaller quantities of vitamin K, but from a practical point of view there would seem to be little advantage.

Richards and Shapiro[5] stress that larger doses of vitamin K are needed for the treatment of overdicoumarolization, in the presence of hepatic damage, or simply in the performance of an evaluation of hepatic function. Cromer and Barker, among others,[6] found that 60 mg. of anhydrous menadione bisulfite (equivalent to 72 mg. of the hydrated ester) was sufficient to correct the prolonged "prothrombin time" of most patients who had responded to dicoumarol with unusual vigor. However, an occasional dicoumarolized patient is unresponsive to the water-soluble analogs even in doses of 600 mg. given intravenously. In such cases the administration of phytyl menadione (up to 1 g. orally or intravenously) has been remarkably successful.[7] The more stable oxide of phytyl menadione may prove to be practical.

C. MODE OF ADMINISTRATION

The water-soluble naphthoquinones may be given orally, subcutaneously, intramuscularly, intraperitoneally, or intravenously with substantially the same results; regardless of the route a lag of 1 to 2 hours occurs before any clotting response is perceptible.[8] Inunctions of water-soluble vitamin K derivatives have proved effective,[9] but they may be irritating.[10] The fat-soluble K-quinones are generally given orally, accompanied by bile salts in the case of obstructive jaundice or biliary fistula but not in antidicoumarol therapy where bile is available to the bowel. Davidson and MacDonald[7] have described the suspension of fat-soluble preparations for intravenous use: up to 450 mg. of vitamin K_1 was dissolved in 15 to 20 ml. of absolute

[5] R. K. Richards and S. Shapiro, *J. Pharmacol. Exptl. Therap.* **84**, 93 (1945).

[6] J. Lehmann, *Science* [N. S.] **96**, 345 (1942); S. Shapiro, M. H. Redish, and H. A. Campbell, *Proc. Soc. Exptl. Biol. Med.* **52**, 12 (1943); H. E. Cromer, Jr., and N. W. Barker, *Proc. Staff Meetings Mayo Clinic* **19**, 217 (1944).

[7] C. S. Davidson and H. MacDonald, *New Engl. J. Med.* **229**, 353 (1943); S. P. Lucia and P. M. Aggeler, *Proc. Soc. Exptl. Biol. Med.* **56**, 36 (1944); D. F. James, I. L. Bennett, Jr., P. Scheinberg, and J. J. Butler, *Arch. Internal Med.* **83**, 632 (1949); R. Miller, W. P. Harvey, and C. A. Finch, *New Engl. J. Med.* **242**, 211 (1950); E. T. Phelps and S. N. Jones, *Bull. Georgetown Univ. Med. Center* **4**, 41 (1950); D. M. Watkin, T. B. Van Itallie, W. B. Logan, R. P. Geyer, C. S. Davidson, and F. J. Stare, *J. Lab. Clin. Med.* **37**, 269 (1950); A. S. Douglas and A. Brown, *Brit. Med. J.* **I**, 412 (1952); A. Rehbein, A. Jaretzki, III, and D. V. Habif, *Ann. Surg.* **135**, 454 (1952); R. Stragnell, *Am. Heart J.* **44**, 124 (1952); F. Koller, A. Loeliger, and P. Flückiger, *Helv. Med. Acta* **19**, 411 (1952).

[8] H. C. Willumsen, H. E. Stadler, and C. A. Owen, *Proc. Soc. Exptl. Biol. Med.* **47**, 116 (1941).

[9] H. K. Russell and R. C. Page, *Am. J. Med. Sci.* **202**, 355 (1941).

[10] R. C. Page and Z. Bercovitz, *Am. J. Med. Sci.* **203**, 566 (1942).

alcohol, which was then slowly mixed with 1 to 1.5 l. of 5 to 10% sterile glucose solution (the alcohol may lead to transient euphoria). Phelps and Jones[7] employed a similar technique but increased the dose of phytyl menadione or its oxide to 1 g. Blood transfusions were reported by Kinsey[11] to be more effective in the treatment of the bleeding of hepatic failure if the blood donor was pretreated with vitamin K; confirmation is lacking.[12]

D. ACTION OF VITAMIN K

As has already been suggested, prothrombin production is believed to be intimately related to the liver, for a constant level of prothrombin in the blood is found only if hepatic function is approximately normal. Assays of prothrombin in portal lymph demonstrated a concentration near that of the blood, whereas lymph from other sources had lesser concentrations.[13] These facts suggest either that the plasma prothrombin is synthesized in the liver or that the finishing touches of proteins made elsewhere are accomplished by the liver. Furthermore, the action of vitamin K is demonstrable only if hepatic function is adequate. The work of Jaques' group[14] indicates that vitamin K displaces dicoumarol from the liver and so apparently acts on that organ. There is other evidence that may link vitamin K with the liver: Nassi and Ragazzini[15] found that relatively large doses of vitamin K (60 to 500 mg.) depressed hepatic glycogen. Dogs on normal diets when given cinchophen did not show clotting changes, according to Hueper,[16] but did show changes when they were given a vitamin K-free diet. Honorato's group[17] has reported that on either a choline-free or vitamin K-free diet rats developed fatty livers; administration of choline or vitamin K in either case reduced the hepatic defect. Field and Dam[18] were unable to detect any change in hepatic lipids of vitamin K-deficient chicks, however, and the results of the common clinical tests of hepatic function are normal in uncomplicated vitamin K deficiency states.[19]

Whether vitamin K acts as a coenzyme for a prothrombin-synthesizing enzyme in the liver or whether a part or all of the vitamin is incorporated in the prothrombin molecule is not known. The latter might be suspected,

[11] R. E. Kinsey, *Arch. Internal Med.* **73,** 131 (1944).
[12] H. R. Butt, T. B. Magath, and T. H. Seldon, *Arch. Internal Med.* **81,** 131 (1948).
[13] K. M. Brinkhous and S. A. Walker, *Am. J. Physiol.* **132,** 666 (1941).
[14] C. C. Lee, L. W. Trevoy, J. W. T. Spinks, and L. B. Jaques, *Proc. Soc. Exptl. Biol. Med.* **74,** 151 (1950); J. W. T. Spinks and L. B. Jaques, *Nature* **166,** 184 (1950).
[15] L. Nassi and F. Ragazzini, *Boll. soc. ital. biol. sper.* **24,** 703 (1948).
[16] W. C. Hueper, *Arch. Pathol.* **41,** 592 (1946).
[17] C. R. Honorato and H. Molina, *Rev. soc. argentina biol.* **18,** 431 (1942); G. S. Topelberg and C. R. Honorato, *ibid.* **19,** 409 (1943).
[18] J. B. Field and H. Dam, *Proc. Soc. Exptl. Biol. Med.* **60,** 146 (1945).
[19] M. A. Pessagno Espora, *Día méd.* **22,** 1264 (1950).

since Lyons[20] found evidence for a quinone structure in thrombin. The consensus, however, is that vitamin K does not actually constitute a part of the prothrombin molecule. Dam and associates[21] were unable to find any vitamin K activity in refined prothrombin preparations. Quick[22] has calculated that the amount of vitamin K which will raise the plasma pro-thrombin is significantly less than 1 mole for each mole of prothrombin (assuming a prothrombin molecular weight of 140,000[23] and concentration of 20 mg. per 100 ml. in the plasma).[24] Such calculations have no meaning for non-prothrombic factors whose homeostatic level also seems to depend on vitamin K, for molecular data and plasma concentrations are unknown. The preparation of menadione with $C^{14}H_3$ in the 2 position, or C^{14} in either of the rings, has been described;[25] preliminary biologic studies with such preparations have been reported.[26]

What enzymes or types of enzyme are involved in the vitamin K reaction is by no means clear. A variety of isolated experiments has been performed in which naphthoquinones with vitamin K activity have had a stimulating or inhibitory effect; in most cases the evidence is not clear whether the phenomena are actually vitamin K-specific or are a general property of naphthoquinones. Enzyme systems reported to be inhibited by 1,4-naph-thoquinones include heart muscle succinoxidase,[27] choline acetylase,[28] and lactic acid-producing bacterial enzymes.[29] The configuration of menadione and phytyl menadione is theoretically and actually adequate for Stecker degradation of α-amino acids.[30]

McCawley and Gurchot[31] reported that the redox potential of vitamin K is characteristic of those substances inhibiting catheptic proteolysis. They

[20] R. N. Lyons, *Nature* **155**, 633 (1945).

[21] H. Dam, J. Glavind, L. Lewis, and E. Tage-Hansen, *Skand. Arch. Physiol.* **79**, *Suppl.* 121 (1938).

[22] A. J. Quick, The Physiology and Pathology of Hemostasis. Lea and Febiger Philadelphia, 1951.

[23] W. H. Seegers and A. G. Ware, *Federation Proc.* **7**, 186 (1948).

[24] W. H. Seegers, E. C. Loomis, and J. M. Vandenbelt, *Proc. Soc. Exptl. Biol. Med* **56**, 70 (1944).

[25] P. P. T. Sah, *Z. Vitaminforsch.* **3**, 40 (1949–1950); C. J. Collins, *J. Am. Chem. Soc* **73**, 1038 (1951); A. Murray and A. R. Ronzio, *ibid.* **74**, 2408 (1952); R. V. Phillips L. W. Trevoy, L. B. Jaques, and J. W. T. Spinks, *Can. J. Chem.* **30**, 844 (1952).

[26] P. F. Solvonuk, L. B. Jaques, J. E. Leddy, L. W. Trevoy, and J. W. T. Spinks *Proc. Soc. Exptl. Biol. Med.* **79**, 597 (1952).

[27] E. G. Ball, C. B. Anfinsen, and O. Cooper, *J. Biol. Chem.* **168**, 257 (1947).

[28] C. Torda and H. G. Wolff, *Proc. Soc. Exptl. Biol. Med.* **57**, 236 (1944); C. Torda and H. G. Wolff, *Science* [N. S.] **103**, 645 (1946).

[29] W. D. Armstrong, W. W. Spink, and J. Kahnke, *Proc. Soc. Exptl. Biol. Med.* **53** 230 (1943); P. Atkins and J. L. Ward, *Brit. J. Exptl. Pathol.* **26**, 120 (1945).

[30] A. Schønberg, R. Moubasher, and A. Said, *Nature* **164**, 140 (1949).

[31] E. L. McCawley and C. Gurchot, *Univ. California Publs. Pharmacol.* **1**, 325 (1940)

feel that certain naphthoquinones act as plant respiratory pigments. This is of interest, since the plant leaves in which vitamin K is found are capable of synthesizing the vitamin to any extent only if exposed to sunlight.[32, 33] Wright[34] intimates that vitamin K may be an essential metabolite of all forms of life.

Bacteria are known to produce vitamin K, and the possibility that the vitamin is a growth factor has been entertained. According to Guérillot-Vinet[35] phthiocol and menadione in concentrations of 10^{-6} to 10^{-9} are growth factors for *Mycobacterium paratuberculosis* and *Aspergillus niger*, but at the concentration at which vitamin K is produced by bacteria (8 to 152 γ per gram of dry weight) it is definitely bacteriostatic. The inhibition *in vitro* of many bacteria by vitamin K analogs has been reported: *Streptococcus*, pneumococcus, *Salmonella typhosa* and *paratyphi*, *Brucella*, *Staphylococcus*,[36] anthrax,[37] mycobacteria,[38] corynebacteria;[39] the mode of action on the various bacteria may vary with the analog employed.[39] Iland[40] doubts that the vitamins K are true growth factors but suspects they may play some metabolic role in the bacteria. The quinone growth-stimulating properties may be unrelated to antihemorrhagic activity, since the 4-aminonaphthol analog has only an inhibitory action.[38] Bacterial inhibition by dicoumarol is not reversed by vitamin K, but is reversed by vitamin P.[41] However, the strong bacteriostatic action of salicylic acid is opposed by vitamin K (weakly), and, in the case of the inhibition of *Fusaria* by 2-chloromenadione, menadione is strongly competitive.[35] Inhibition of streptococcal growth by the pigment iodinin[42] and of the growth of yeasts by 2,3-dichloro-1,4-naphthoquinone[43] is counteracted by menadione.

Other inhibitory actions of menadione have been demonstrated, again without information as to the specificity of the inhibition. Menadione and derivatives shorten the life of *Daphnia magna*;[44] inhibit the growth of roots of *Allium cepa*, the onion roots becoming yellow and flaccid within a week;[45]

[32] H. J. Almquist and E. L. R. Stokstad, *J. Nutrition* **12**, 329 (1936).

[33] H. Dam and J. Glavind, *Biochem. J.* **32**, 485 (1938); J. Erkama and N. Pettersson, *Acta Chem. Scand.* **4**, 922 (1950).

[34] L. D. Wright, *J. Am. Dietet. Assoc.* **23**, 289 (1947).

[35] M. Guérillot-Vinet, *Bull. soc. chim. biol.* **30**, 863 (1948).

[36] F. Mulé, *Il Policlinico (Rome) sez. prat.* **53**, 653 (1946).

[37] L. Donatelli and R. Davoli, *Boll. soc. ital. biol. sper.* **22**, 134 (1946).

[38] A. Kimler, *J. Bacteriol.* **60**, 469 (1950).

[39] L. Nassi, *Boll. soc. ital. liol. sper.* **22**, 141 (1946).

[40] C. N. Iland, *Nature* **161**, 1010 (1948).

[41] J. Naghski, M. J. Copley, and J. F. Couch, *Science* [N. S.] **105**, 125 (1947).

[42] H. McIlwain, *Biochem. J.* **37**, 265 (1943).

[43] D. W. Woolley, *Proc. Soc. Exptl. Biol. Med.* **60**, 225 (1945).

[44] V. Schecter, *Proc. Soc. Exptl. Biol. Med.* **74**, 747 (1950).

[45] M. Levine and S. A. Rice, *Proc. Soc. Exptl. Biol. Med.* **74**, 310 (1950).

gel the cytoplasm of *Arbacia punctulata* eggs, stimulating parthenogenesis;[46] and inhibit respiration of these sea urchin eggs.[47] Respiration of *Plasmodium knowlesi* and of yeast cells is also depressed.[27]

In mammals a variety of actions, which seem unrelated to its blood coagulating function, has been attributed to vitamin K. For example: Chamorro[48] administered 10 to 20 mg. of vitamin K daily to prepubertal rabbits over a 2-week period; mammary, uterine, and vaginal changes were of the estrogenic type. Somewhat similar estrogenic effects have been observed in the guinea pig and rat.[49] Vitamin K administered in conjunction with follicular hormone is reported to elevate the prothrombin level of normal tomcats.[50] In one case of breast malignancy vitamin K seemed to oppose the action of stilbestrol.[51] Another reported correlation between vitamin K and hormones is the apparently successful treatment of Rh-sensit zed pregnant women with the vitamin plus progesterone.[52] Woolley[53] was able to induce toxic changes in pregnant rats and mice with α-tocopherolquinone; these were apparently a manifestation of the quinone, for vitamin K but not α-tocopherol prevented the toxicity. Chauchard *et al.*[54] noted peripheral nerve chronaxial alterations in the vitamin K-deficient rat; changes were also induced by either menadione or dicoumarol treatment, but not if both were given together. Muscle strip sensitivity to acetylcholine and potassium is increased by vitamin K according to Torda and Wolff.[55] Vitamin K is said to lower glutathione in the blood of man or the dog,[56] elevate the blood sugar of children,[57] reduce the cholesterolemia of parkinsonian encephalitis,[58] elevate the depressed concentration of platelets produced by salicylate therapy,[59] alter the serologic reaction and erythrocyte sedimentation rates of syphilitic patients,[60] raise plasma euglobulin

[46] A. Halaban, *Biol. Bull.* **97,** 240 (1949).

[47] C. B. Anfinsen, *J. Cellular Comp. Physiol.* **29,** 323 (1947).

[48] A. Chamorro, *Compt. rend. soc. biol.* **140,** 498 (1946).

[49] F. Vicari and M. Gaglio, *Boll. soc. ital. biol. sper.* **23,** 1142 (1947); T. Paladino, *ibid.* **24,** 303 (1948); V. Truglio and G. Arcidiacono, *ibid.* **24,** 1059 (1948).

[50] E. Szirmai, *Gynaecologia* **133,** 163 (1952).

[51] G. G. Binnie, *Brit. J. Radiol.* [N. S.] **24,** 691 (1951).

[52] P. B. Hoffman and D. E. Edwards, *Am. J. Obstet. Gynecol.* **59,** 207 (1950); L. J. Paquette and J. T. Schmitz, *Wisconsin Med. J.* **51,** 473 (1952).

[53] D. W. Woolley, *J. Biol. Chem.* **159,** 59 (1945).

[54] P. Chauchard, H. Mazoué, and R. Lecoq, *Compt. rend. soc. biol.* **140,** 474 (1946); R. Lecoq, P. Chauchard, and H. Mazoué, *ibid.* **140,** 743 (1946).

[55] C. Torda and H. G. Wolff, *Exptl. Med. Surg.* **4,** 50 (1946).

[56] E. Azerad, Seeman, and Obadia, *Semaine hôp. Paris* **27,** 110 (1951).

[57] L. Nassi, *Boll. soc. ital. biol. sper.* **24,** 706 (1948).

[58] G. Fattovich, *Acta Vitaminol.* **1,** 26 (1946); Abstr. *Intern. Z. Vitaminforsch.* **20** 328 (1948).

[59] M. Pellegrini and M. Ghirlanda, *Il Progr. med.* **5,** 434 (1948); Abstr. *Intern. Z Vitaminforsch.* **21,** 381 (1949–1950).

[60] G. Buccellato, *Boll. soc. ital. biol. sper.* **24,** 126, 127 (1948).

and albumin values[61] (not confirmed by Piacentini[62]), accentuate the tuberculin reaction,[63] raise the serum bilirubin level in cases of hepatitis,[64] and rectify increased fragility.[65] Maltaner and Thompson[66] quote Schønheyder's dissertation as reporting elevated phosphorus and lowered calcium in the blood of vitamin K-deficient chicks; their data do not substantiate the claim. The anemia of vitamin K deficiency is apparently not a primary effect, as suggested by Thayer and associates,[67] but secondary to hemorrhage.[68] According to Büsing and Zuzak,[69] reduction of complement accompanies the hypoprothrombinemia of vitamin K deficiency in chicks and rises when the vitamin is administered; yet Felix and associates[70] found no clear depression of complement with dicoumarol treatment. The effect of menadione derivatives on serum agglutinins is disputed.[71] Hypoprothrombinemia associated with pernicious anemia has been found responsive to liver extracts but not to vitamin K.[72]

Clinical syndromes and diseases reported to be improved or cured by vitamin K, other than hypoprothrombinemic bleeding states, include: angioneurotic edema,[73] arterial hypertension[74] (Taveira[75]), bacillary dysentery,[76] brucellar meningitis,[77] chilblain,[78] cirrhosis of the liver,[79] dental caries[80] (questioned by Granados and associates[81]), hemophilia[61] (contrary

[61] R. Breda, *Atti soc. lombarda sci. med. e biol.* **1**, 85 (1946); Abstr. *Intern. Z. Vitaminforsch.* **20**, 328 (1947–1948).

[62] C. Piacentini, *Boll. soc. ital. biol. sper.* **24**, 530 (1948).

[63] C. Rossi and L. Brighenti, *Boll. soc. ital. biol. sper.* **23**, 327 (1947).

[64] G. Gottsegen, Z. Horn, and M. C. Háry, *Acta Med. Scand.* **140**, 127 (1951).

[65] G. Leonardi, *Acta Vitaminol.* **1**, 54 (1947).

[66] F. Maltaner and W. R. Thompson, *Arch. Biochem.* **2**, 49 (1943).

[67] S. A. Thayer, R. W. McKee, D. W. MacCorquodale, and E. A. Doisy, *Proc. Soc. Exptl. Biol. Med.* **37**, 417 (1937).

[68] H. J. Almquist, E. Mecchi, and A. A. Klose, *Biochem. J.* **32**, 1897 (1938).

[69] K. H. Büsing and H. Zuzak, *Z. Immunitätsforsch.* **102**, 401 (1943).

[70] K. Felix, I. Pendl, and L. Roka, *Hoppe-Seyler's Z. physiol. Chem.* **284**, 198 (1949).

[71] J. K. Narat, *J. Am. Med. Assoc.* **116**, 1310 (1941); M. R. H. Stoppelman, *Acta Med. Scand.* **111**, 408 (1942); A. Gammelgaard, E. H. Larsen, and P. V. Marcussen, *ibid.* **116**, 8 (1943); G. Trönnberg, *Nord. Med.* **21**, 13 (1944).

[72] E. D. Warner and C. A. Owen, *Am. J. Med. Sci.* **203**, 187 (1942).

[73] P. Kallós, *Gastroenterologia* **71**, 171 (1946).

[74] E. Bellini, *Minerva med.* **39**, Part 1, 56 (1948); M. Lippi, *Acta Vitaminol.* **1**, 113 (1947); J. Nasello and P. B. Camponovo, *Prensa méd. argent.* **37**, 2864 (1950).

[75] M. Taveira, *Ann. pharm. franç.* **9**, 344 (1951).

[76] M. F. Krause, *Hospital O (Rio de Janeiro)* **39**, 361 (1951).

[77] R. Virgili and V. Del Vecchio, *Boll. soc. ital. biol. sper.* **24**, 748 (1948).

[78] A. A. Cordero, *Prensa méd. argent.* **38**, 1158 (1951).

[79] M. Küley, *Schweiz. med. Wochschr.* **79**, 365 (1949).

[80] D. Y. Burrill, J. C. Calandra, E. B. Tilden, and L. S. Fosdick, *J. Dental Researc* **24**, 273 (1945); L. S. Fosdick, *ibid.* **27**, 235 (1948).

[81] H. Granados, A. Snog-Kjaer, J. Glavind, and H. Dam, *Proc. Soc. Exptl. Biol. Med.* **72**, 669 (1949).

to almost universal opinion), hepatitis,[82] menometrorrhagia,[83] "scours" in calves,[84] serofibrinous pleurisy,[85] thrombocytopenia,[61, 86] (denied by Zucker[87]), tinea kerion,[88] and whooping cough.[89] The hypoprothrombinemia of tuberculosis may be related to gastroenteric or hepatic involvement and thus may be amenable to vitamin K therapy.[90]

E. TOXICITY

Before the advent of dicoumarol, vitamin K was given in doses of only a few milligrams a day. Now, doses of several hundred milligrams are given liberally to overcome dicoumarol's anticoagulant activity; for the most part no toxic effects have been observed. Phelps and Jones[7] did note nausea in patients receiving 150 mg. of a menadiol derivative intravenously; with 600 mg. doses more severe reactions at times occurred. Intravenous injections of 1 g. of phytyl menadione led to no reactions, but the oxide of this compound in the same dose was followed by a febrile response in one patient. From studies on animals it seems likely that man can tolerate amounts of vitamin K and its analogs much larger than those now being tentatively employed.

Table VI outlines the toxicity of various menadione preparations given in single doses by various routes; the amount administered in milligrams per kilogram of body weight of the animal is recorded as that causing death in half the animals tested. The immediate cause of death may be circulatory[91] or respiratory failure.[92, 93]

Molitor and Robinson[94] demonstrated that lethal doses of menadione and phthiocol were 500 and 350 mg. per kilogram of body weight, respectively

[82] P. Gøtzsche, *Ugeskrift Laeger* **112,** 1753 (1950); H.-O. Mossberg, *Brit. Med. J.* I 1382 (1952).

[83] T. Baranowski, H. Beck, and S. Liebhardt, *Am. Rev. Soviet Med.* **3,** 173 (1945) R. Gubner and H. E. Ungerleider, *Southern Med. J.* **37,** 556 (1944).

[84] G. W. Anderson, W. M. DuPré, and J. P. LaMaster, *Am. J. Vet. Research* **13,** (1952).

[85] M. A. Josserand, *Lyon méd.* **176,** 168 (1946); P. Pichat and H. Boucher, *ibid.* **176,** 169 (1946).

[86] F. Groër, T. Baranowski, and J. Rosenbusch, *Am. Rev. Soviet Med.* **3,** 173 (1945)

[87] M. B. Zucker, *Proc. Soc. Exptl. Biol. Med.* **62,** 245 (1946).

[88] L. Nékám, Jr., and P. Polgár, *Acta Dermato-Venereol.* **31,** 344 (1951); H. Grimme and S. Rust, *Z. Haut- u. Geschlechtskrank.* **12,** 102 (1952).

[89] J. C. Oyhenart, *Día méd.* **23,** 527 (1951); J. Nemirovsky, *Prensa méd. argent.* **38,** 1955 (1951); W. B. Pereira da Silva, *Rev. brasil. med.* **8,** 673 (1951).

[90] R. F. Sheely, *J. Am. Med. Assoc.* **117,** 1603 (1941); E. Tanner and F. Suter, *Schweiz. med. Wochschr.* **74,** 552 (1944).

[91] S. Ansbacher, W. C. Corwin, and B. G. H. Thomas, *J. Pharmacol. Exptl. Therap.* **75,** 111 (1942).

[92] R. H. K. Foster, *Proc. Soc. Exptl. Biol. Med.* **45,** 412 (1940).

[93] M. B. Shimkin, *J. Pharmacol.* **71,** 210 (1941).

[94] H. Molitor and H. J. Robinson, *Proc. Soc. Exptl. Biol. Med.* **43,** 125 (1940).

when given to rats daily for 30 days. The growth rate of rats was found by Hatton and associates[95] to be diminished if 0.3 % of the diet was menadione; when the concentration was raised to 0.8 %, depression of growth was severe and was accompanied by anemia and splenomegaly. Sublethal doses of menadione derivatives (but not of phytyl menadione) have induced anemia in dogs,[96] rats,[94] and rabbits,[92] but occasionally polycythemia has been

TABLE VI

LD₅₀ OF MENADIONE DERIVATIVES ADMINISTERED IN SINGLE DOSES TO ANIMALS

Animal	Route of administration								
	Intravenous			Intramuscular or subcutaneous			Oral		
	Dose[a]	Compound[e]	Reference	Dose[a]	Compound[e]	Reference	Dose[a]	Compound[e]	Reference
Mouse	250	3	5	138	2[b]	91	200	1	94
	450	5	92	250	2	93	500	2[c]	94
	275	4	98	300	4	98	620	2[b]	91
				100	5[d]	91	800	2	93
				80	5	93	300	5	91
							400	5	93
							400	4	98
Chick							840	2	91
Dog	100+	3	5						
	100	4	98						
Rabbit	15–20	2	98	15–20	2	98	250	2	91
	120	3	5						
	100	4	98						

[a] Dose in mg. per kg. body weight.

[b] No toxicity with 6 g. phytyl menadione per kg. body weight when administered subcutaneously or with 25 g. per kg. given orally.

[c] No toxicity with 25 g. phytyl menadione per kg. body weight when administered orally.

[d] Esters of menadiol were progressively less toxic, in order: diacetate, dipropionate, di-n-valerate, di-n-butyrate, di-isovalerate; this last one was not lethal in doses of 18 g. per kg. when administered orally.

[e] Compounds administered: 1, phthiocol; 2, menadione; 3, menadione bisulfite; 4, menadiol disuccinate; 5, menadiol.

observed in the same animals,[91] apparently the result of chronically decreased oxygen consumption.[97] Excess menadione has been found to cause methemoglobinemia;[98] Cannavá[99] has duplicated the hemoglobin change

[95] E. H. Hatton, A. Dodds, H. C. Hodge, and L. S. Fosdick, *J. Dental Research* **24**, 283 (1945).

[96] F. Koller, *Schweiz. med. Wochschr.* **69**, 1159 (1939).

[97] A. Cannavá and L. Untersteiner Occhialini, *Boll. soc. ital. biol. sper.* **23**, 1041 (1947).

[98] K. Fromherz, *Z. Vitaminforsch.* **11**, 65 (1941).

[99] A. Cannavá, *Boll. soc. ital. biol. sper.* **24**, 593 (1948).

in vitro. Other toxic manifestations in animals are prophyrinuria, albuminuria,[93] and hemorrhagic extravasations into the liver and kidneys.[96]

It may be noted that the naturally occurring phytyl menadione is nontoxic in amounts that would be lethal if comparable quantities of the artificial vitamins had been given. Similarly, when the solubilizing ester chains are lengthened, toxicity decreases (Table VI). As the toxicity decreases with increasing molecular size, so does the antihemorrhagic activity; the two functions seem not to be directly related, however, for the former diminishes at a much greater rate than the latter. An even more striking example of disparity between activity and toxicity is the effect of methylation of naphthoquinone: toxicity diminishes 75%, prothrombinogenic activity increases 2000-fold.[91]

Potentially, one of the more serious toxic manifestations of vitamin K would be overcorrection of the prothrombin deficiency, that is, "hyperprothrombinemia." This has actually been reported[100, 101] and also denied.[102, 103] Curiously, the excess prothrombin is detected by one method alone: "prothrombin times" on diluted (1:8) plasma. It should be noted that with this method the fibrinogen concentration of the tested plasma is suboptimal and the test may reflect fibrinogen changes[104] as readily as it does other clotting factors; elevation of plasma fibrinogen has been noted with large doses of vitamin K.[105]

IX. Requirements

A. OF ANIMALS

H. J. ALMQUIST

1. CHICK

Factors influencing the incidence of dietary hemorrhagic disease in chicks were discussed by Almquist and Stokstad.[1] It was found that the vitamin was synthesized in the droppings of chicks and in the lower intestinal tract where appreciable absorption did not take place. The vitamin K intake of

100 R. S. Overman, J. B. Field, C. A. Baumann, and K. P. Link, *J. Nutrition* **23,** 589 (1942).

101 J. B. Field and K. P. Link, *J. Biol. Chem.* **156,** 739 (1944); P. N. Unger and S. Shapiro, *Blood* **3,** 137 (1948).

102 A. J. Quick, *J. Lab. Clin. Med.* **31,** 79 (1946).

103 C. E. Brambel and F. F. Loker, *Proc. Soc. Exptl. Biol. Med.* **53,** 218 (1943).

104 H. F. Deutsch and H. W. Gerarde, *J. Biol. Chem.* **166,** 381 (1946).

105 G. A. Nitsche, Jr., H. W. Gerarde, and H. F. Deutsch, *J. Lab. Clin. Med.* **32,** Part 1, 410 (1947).

1 H. J. Almquist and E. L. R. Stokstad, *J. Nutrition* **12,** 329 (1936).

the parent hen was important in the survival of the chick on a K-deficient diet and in controlling the blood-clotting time of the day-old chick.[2] These observations showed a transfer of the vitamin from the hen diet to the chick. Alfalfa meal in the hen diet at a level of 2.5 % was sufficient for protection of the chick. The vitamin was found in egg yolk but not in egg white. Certain indications[3] that the prothrombin content of chick blood rises for the first 3 or 4 days of life despite very low vitamin K intake may have been due to assimilation of vitamin K remaining in the unabsorbed yolk which normally is present in the chick for some time after hatching. Cravens et al.[4] have also found that the blood-clotting time and prothrombin content of day-old chicks is dependent upon the vitamin K content of the ration fed the parent hen. One to two per cent of dried alfalfa or grasses was required in the hen diet to maintain a normal prothrombin content in the day-old chick. In these studies[1, 4] higher intake by the hen of vitamin K in the form of dried greens had little or no further effect on the chick.

Tidrick et al.[5] injected 2-methyl-1,4-naphthohydroquinone disulfate into hatching eggs and obtained chicks with superior reserve stores of vitamin K, as indicated by retention of prothrombin levels in the chicks when fed a vitamin K-deficient diet.

On constant submarginal levels of vitamin K in the diet chicks tend to show a progressive increase of blood clotting time up to approximately two weeks of age and then a decrease.[2, 3, 6] At this age the hemoglobin level of chicks, even on a normal diet, passes through a minimum phase and begins to increase again. The riboflavin requirement is probably at a maximum. After 2 weeks the gain in weight per unit weight of food consumed decreases, and the food intake of vitamins in reference to the weight of the bird begins to increase. The age of 2 weeks appears to be a sensitive, if not critical, physiological stage of the chick. It is evident, therefore, that the vitamin K intake required to maintain any particular clotting time would vary with the age of the chick over the first 2 to 3 weeks of life. However, the vitamin K requirement does not seem to be related to the body weight of the chick.[3]

If the vitamin K-deficient chick is given a sufficiently large dose of the vitamin the clotting time or prothrombin time can be restored in 4 to 6 hours.[7-10]

[2] H. J. Almquist, E. Mecchi, and A. A. Klose, *Biochem. J.* **32**, 1897 (1938).

[3] F. W. Stamler, R. T. Tidrick, and E. D. Warner, *J. Nutrition* **26**, 95 (1943).

[4] W. W. Cravens, S. B. Randle, C. A. Elvehjem, and J. G. Halpin, *Poultry Sci.* **20**, 313 (1941).

[5] R. T. Tidrick, F. W. Stamler, F. T. Joyce, and E. D. Warner, *Proc. Soc. Exptl. Biol. and Med.* **47**, 438 (1941).

[6] H. J. Almquist and E. L. R. Stokstad, *J. Nutrition* **14**, 235 (1937).

[7] H. Dam, J. Glavind, L. Lewis, and E. Tage-Hansen, *Skand. Arch. Physiol.* **79**. 121 (1938).

Much of the data on which comparisons of time of action and kind of vitamin K may be based were expressed in terms of the number or percentage of depleted chicks in which the blood-clotting time was reduced to 10 minutes or less in 18 hours after dosage. A clotting time of 10 minutes probably represents a blood prothrombin level of only 20 to 30 % of normal.[10] Nevertheless, the data obtained in these assays have comparative value. The amount of vitamin K_1 for a curative effect by these standards was found to be approximately 1 γ per chick by several groups of investigators.[9, 11, 12] The corresponding dose of methylnaphthoquinone was 0.3 γ[11] to 0.64 γ.[13] With the same criterion of effect the curative dose in a 6-hour assay was 1.5 γ of vitamin K_1 and 0.5 γ of methylnaphthoquinone.[11]

Later assays based upon the prothrombin-clotting time have shown that 5 γ of methylnaphthoquinone was sufficient to bring the blood prothrombin content of a chick from 10 % of normal to normal in 4 hours.[8] In another example, a 16 γ dose of methylnaphthoquinone was required for complete recovery of prothrombin in 6 hours, whereas 8 γ gave about 50 % recovery.[10] In 18 hours the prothrombin was restored to normal by a dose of 6 to 8 γ of methylnaphthoquinone while, at the same time, the whole blood-clotting time was reduced to 2 minutes by as little as 1 γ.[10]

In longer assays, 5 days or more, approximately 2 γ of methylnaphthoquinone daily per chick is required for a normal range of prothrombin.[3, 8, 14, 15] Vitamin K_1 at a daily level of 2 γ is insufficient,[14] and the full requirement may be as high as 3.8 γ[8] in the young chick.

Qualitative requirement for the vitamin has been shown to exist with several other kinds of birds.[16]

2. RAT

Greaves and Schmidt[17] found that the low prothrombin in bile fistula rats could be corrected by administration of a vitamin K concentrate. It was difficult to deplete rats of vitamin K by dietary means, but eventually this

[8] A. J. Quick and M. Stefanini, *J. Biol. Chem.* **175,** 945 (1948).

[9] E. Fernholz, S. Ansbacher, and H. B. MacPhillamy, *J. Am. Chem. Soc.* **62,** 430 (1940).

[10] R. T. Tidrick, F. T. Joyce, and H. P. Smith, *Proc. Soc. Exptl. Biol. Med.* **42,** 853 (1939).

[11] L. F. Fieser, M. Tishler, and W. L. Sampson, *J. Biol. Chem.* **137,** 659 (1941).

[12] A. D. Emmett, R. A. Brown, and O. Kamm, *J. Biol. Chem.* **132,** 467 (1940).

[13] J. Lee, U. V. Solmssen, A. Steyermark, and R. H. K. Foster, *Proc. Soc. Exptl. Biol. Med.* **45,** 407 (1940).

[14] H. J. Almquist and A. A. Klose, *J. Biol. Chem.* **130,** 787 (1939).

[15] H. J. Almquist and A. A. Klose, *Proc. Soc. Exptl. Biol. Med.* **45,** 55 (1940).

[16] H. J. Almquist, *Physiol. Revs.* **21,** 194 (1941).

[17] J. D. Greaves and C. L. A. Schmidt, *Proc. Soc. Exptl. Biol. Med.* **37,** 43 (1937).

was done by Greaves[18] and by Dam and Glavind[19] and the curative effect of vitamin K demonstrated. Some individual rats remained highly resistant to depletion attempts. Flynn and Warner[20] found that depleted bile fistula rats required approximately 1000 γ of phthiocol or 2 γ of methylnaphthoquinone daily for moderate recovery of prothrombin level in 2 days. The disulfuric acid ester of methylnaphthohydroquinone, which is much less potent than the parent compound, was required at 8 γ per day to cure depleted rats.[21]

3. Dog

Dogs rendered vitamin K-deficient by cholecystnephrostomy were found by Collentine and Quick[22] to respond to 9 γ of phytyl menadione per kilogram of body weight when administered intravenously. With this dose the "prothrombin time" returned to normal in 4 hours and persisted at that level for 24 hours. From this rapid response it seems likely that much smaller doses would have appreciable effects. It should be stated that changes in "prothrombin time" and in the actual prothrombin concentration bear no fixed relationship to each other, so that no direct comparison can be made of minimal dosages determined by the various methods.

B. OF HUMAN BEINGS
CHARLES A. OWEN, JR.

Few studies have been conducted on human beings to ascertain the minimal quantities of vitamin K derivatives necessary to correct the clotting changes of the vitamin's deficiency. Even in animals few reports have been published, primarily because a severe deficiency of vitamin K which will be uniform for a period sufficient to enable one to analyze various dosages is difficult to obtain. Another problem which faces the investigator is the one of vitamin K stores. Although only small amounts of vitamin K can be recovered from the various organs of normal animals,[23, 24] it is apparent that these stores are significant when the minuteness of daily needs is realized. Direct evidence that these stores are important may be deduced from the observation that a prolonged vitamin K-free diet scarcely alters the blood coagulability of rats; if ligation of the common duct is now

[18] J. D. Greaves, *Am. J. Physiol.* **125,** 429 (1939).

[19] H. Dam and J. Glavind, *Z. Vitaminforsch.* **9,** 71 (1939).

[20] J. E. Flynn and E. D. Warner, *Proc. Soc. Exptl. Biol. Med.* **43,** 190 (1940).

[21] E. D. Warner and J. E. Flynn, *Proc. Soc. Exptl. Biol. Med.* **44,** 607 (1940).

[22] G. E. Collentine and A. J. Quick, *Am. J. Med. Sci.* **222,** 7 (1951).

[23] H. J. Almquist and E. L. R. Stokstad, *J. Nutrition* **12,** 329 (1936).

[24] H. Dam, J. Glavind, L. Lewis, and E. Tage-Hansen, *Skand. Arch. Physiol.* **79,** Suppl. 121 (1938).

performed, the plasma prothrombin falls much more rapidly than that of
rats similarly operated on, which, however, had a normal diet.[25-27]

In the newborn infant it has been suggested[28] that a single intramuscular
dose of 10 γ of 4-amino-2-methyl naphthol HCl given at birth will prevent
almost completely a prolongation of the "prothrombin time" during the
first week of life; daily doses of 1 γ were equally effective. Once the "physiologic hypoprothrombinemia" had developed, 1 γ was sufficient to reduce
the "prothrombin time" to normal. Hardwicke,[29] using a diphosphoric acid
ester of menadiol, reported comparable results when the vitamin was given
orally. Adler's[30] results also tend to be confirmatory.

Taylor and coworkers[31] have found that the hypoprothrombinemia of
sprue is rectified by administration of cortisone; they suggest that improved
intestinal absorption of fats and fat-soluble vitamins is the explanation.
An attempt was personally made to find the least daily dose of vitamin
K which would elevate the plasma prothrombin in such patients. Repeated determinations of the plasma prothrombin of an untreated patient
with non-tropical sprue yielded values ranging from 2 to 4 % of normal, yet
with no signs of bleeding. 4-Amino-2-methyl naphthol HCl given intramuscularly on consecutive days induced no response in doses of 1 and 2 γ;
the prothrombin level rose to 11 % with 5 γ, to 21 % with 10 γ, and to 34 %
with 20 γ. Although no further vitamin K was given, it seems likely that
much less than 1 mg. would have raised this patient's prothrombin to
normal.

[25] J. D. Greaves, *Am. J. Physiol.* **125,** 429 (1939).
[26] C. A. Owen, Jr., Studies on the Conversion of Prothrombin to Thrombin; Effect
    of Conversion Variations on Prothrombin Tests. Thesis, Graduate School, Uni-
    versity of Minnesota, 1950.
[27] J. E. Flynn and E. D. Warner, *Proc. Soc. Exptl. Biol. Med.* **43,** 190 (1940).
[28] R. L. Sells, S. A. Walker, and C. A. Owen, *Proc. Soc. Exptl. Biol. Med.* **47,** 441
    (1941).
[29] S. H. Hardwicke, *J. Pediat.* **24,** 259 (1944).
[30] B. Adler, *Monatschr. Geburtschülfe u. Gynäkol.* **118,** 225 (1944).
[31] A. B. Taylor, M. W. Comfort, E. E. Wollaeger, and M. H. Power, *J. Clin. Invest.*
    30, 678 (1951).

CHAPTER 10

NIACIN

I. Nomenclature and Formulas

ROBERT S. HARRIS

Accepted names: Niacin, niacinamide (United States)
     Nicotinic acid, nicotinic acid amide (British)
Obsolete names: Vitamin PP
     PP factor
     Pellagra preventive factor
     Pellagramine
     Niamid
Empirical formulas: Niacin: $C_6H_5O_2N$
      Niacinamide: $C_6H_6ON_2$
Chemical names: Niacin: pyridine-3-carboxylic acid
     Niacinamide: pyridine-3-carboxylic acid amide
Structural formulas:

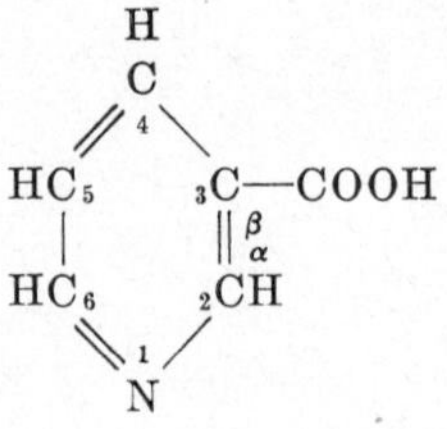

Niacin 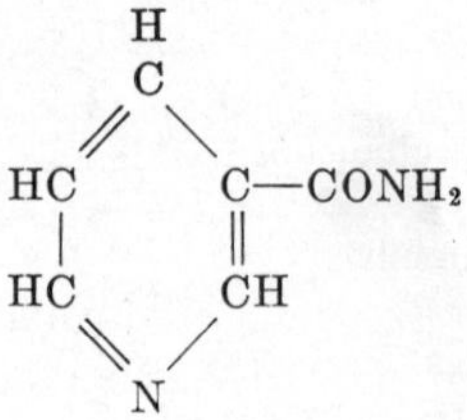   Niacinamide

II. Chemistry

J. M. HUNDLEY

A. ISOLATION

Nicotinic acid, so named because it was first discovered as an oxidation product of nicotine, was first isolated from natural materials by Funk in 1911.[1] Funk thought, at first, that the substance which he obtained from yeast and rice polishings was the pigeon beriberi factor. Almost simultaneously Suzuki and associates,[2] who also were searching for the antiberiberi vitamin, isolated nicotinic acid from rice. Considerably later Vickery[3] iso-

[1] C. Funk, *J. Physiol.* **43**, 395 (1911) [*C. A.* **6**, 1923 (1912)]; *J. Physiol.* **46**, 173 (1913); *Brit. Med. J.* **I**, 814 (1913).

[2] U. Suzuki, T. Shimamura, and S. Odake, *Biochem. Z.* **43**, 89 (1912); U. Suzuki and S. Matsunaga, *J. Agr. Tokyo Imp. Univ.* **5**, 59 (1912).

[3] H. B. Vickery, *J. Biol. Chem.* **68**, 585 (1926).

lated nicotinic acid from yeast. However, none of these investigators realized the true biological significance of the substance they had isolated.

The first demonstration of a biochemical function for this substance came from the work of Warburg and Christian[4, 5] who isolated nicotinamide from coenzyme II (TPN) and demonstrated its function as part of a hydrogen-transporting coenzyme.[6, 7] Almost at the same time von Euler *et al.*[8] isolated a substance from coenzyme I which was identified as nicotinamide (see p. 482). Coenzyme I (DPN, cozymase) had long been known as a substance necessary for the alcoholic fermentation of carbohydrates by yeast. Kuhn and Vetter[9] further established the potential importance of nicotinamide in metabolism by isolating it from heart muscle.

The true nutritional and biological significance of nicotinic acid became evident in 1937 following the reports of Elvehjem *et al.*[10] that it would cure blacktongue in dogs and that nicotinamide could be isolated from liver concentrates which were active in curing canine blacktongue.[11] The activity of nicotinic acid in curing blacktongue was quickly confirmed by Street and Cowgill.[11a] Late in 1937 Spies *et al.*,[12] Fouts *et al.*,[13] and Smith *et al.*,[14] almost simultaneously announced that nicotinic acid would cure pellagra, a fact confirmed by innumerable reports since that time. The rather universal biological significance of nicotinic acid was further confirmed by the reports of Knight,[15] Mueller,[16] Koser *et al.*,[17] Fildes,[18] and Landy[19] in 1937 and 1938, showing that this substance was an essential growth factor for a variety of bacteria.

[4] O. Warburg and W. Christian, *Biochem. Z.* **274,** 112 (1934).
[5] O. Warburg and W. Christian, *Biochem. Z.* **275,** 112, 464 (1935).
[6] O. Warburg, W. Christian, and W. Griese, *Biochem. Z.* **282,** 157, (1935).
[7] O. Warburg and W. Christian, *Biochem. Z.* **287,** 291 (1936)
[8] H. von Euler, H. Albers, and F. Schlenk, *Hoppe-Seyler's Z. physiol. Chem.* **237,** 180 I (1935); **240,** 113 (1936).
[9] R. Kuhn and H. Vetter, *Ber.* **68,** 2374 (1935).
[10] C. A. Elvehjem, R. J. Madden, F. M. Strong, and D. W. Woolley, *J. Am. Chem. Soc.* **59,** 1767 (1937); *J. Biol. Chem.* **123,** 137 (1938).
[11] C. J. Koehn, Jr., and C. A. Elvehjem, *J. Nutrition* **11,** 67 (1936).
[11a] H. R. Street and G. R. Cowgill, *Proc. Soc. Exptl. Biol. Med.* **37,** 547 (1937).
[12] T. D. Spies, C. Cooper, and M. A. Blankenhorn, Paper presented before the Central Society for Clinical Research, Chicago, Ill., November 5, 1937; *J. Am. Med. Assoc.* **110,** 622 (1938).
[13] P. J. Fouts, O. M. Helmer, S. Lepkovsky, and T. H. Jukes, *Proc. Soc. Exptl. Biol. Med.* **37,** 405 (1937).
[14] D. T. Smith, J. M. Ruffin, and S. G. Smith, *J. Am. Med. Assoc.* **109,** 2054 (1937).
[15] B. C. J. G. Knight, *Biochem. J.* **31,** 731 (1937).
[16] J. H. Mueller, *J. Biol. Chem.* **120,** 219 (1937).
[17] S. A. Koser, A. Dorfman, and F. Saunders, *Proc. Soc. Exptl. Biol. Med.* **38,** 311 (1938).
[18] P. Fildes, *Brit. J. Exptl. Pathol.* **19,** 239 (1938).
[19] M. Landy, *Proc. Soc. Exptl. Biol. Med.* **38,** 504 (1938).

1. Isolation of Nicotinic Acid

Nicotinic acid is easily isolated from most natural materials, the exact technique to be adopted depending on the nature of the material. In yeast, nicotinic acid may be extracted directly without preliminary hydrolysis.[3] With most materials, acid or alkaline hydrolysis is necessary to liberate the free acid. Removal of fat with suitable solvents is a desirable preliminary to hydrolysis, especially when dealing with animal tissue. Nicotinic acid may be extracted directly from the acidified hydrolyzed material using organic solvents (see p. 460). The free acid may be separated from this extract as such, or in the form of an ester, or as the copper salt. The free acid can be obtained from the copper salt using hydrogen sulfide. Nicotinic acid can be purified by recrystallization from water or alcohol or by sublimation.

Nyc et al.[20] isolated nicotinic acid from Neurospora mycelium in the following fashion. The mycelium was extracted with acetone. The acetone extract was dried, redissolved in water, filtered, and treated with $Ba(OH)_2$ and heat. After neutralization with H_2SO_4 filtration and further adjustment of the pH to 4.2 with HCl, the nicotinic acid was adsorbed on charcoal (Norit A). The active material was eluted with hot 4% aniline in water, the aniline removed with ether, and the watery eluate taken to dryness. The dry residue was dissolved in hot absolute alcohol, the solution filtered, again taken to dryness, and dissolved in water. Nicotinic acid was crystallized from the concentrated aqueous solution and was recrystallized from a 1:4 mixture of acetic acid and benzene. In a later publication[21] this procedure was modified. A paper strip chromatogram developed with n-butanol saturated with 0.2 N ammonium hydroxide was used to separate nicotinic acid (labeled with C^{14}) from unwanted materials. Nicotinic acid could be eluted from the appropriate part of the paper strip and crystallized with added "carrier" nicotinic acid. The very small amount of nicotinic acid (300 to 900 γ) which was present in the extracts studied by these workers made special techniques necessary. Yanofsky and Bonner[22] also have described procedures for isolating small quantities of nicotinic acid using paper strip chromatograms.

2. Isolation of Nicotinamide

This substance can be isolated usually by water extraction, followed by partial hydrolysis with 0.1 N sulfuric acid to liberate free nicotinamide

[20] J. F. Nyc, H. K. Mitchell, E. Leifer, and W. H. Langham, J. Biol. Chem. **179**, 78 (1949).

[21] E. Leifer, W. H. Langham, J. F. Nyc, and H. K. Mitchell, J. Biol. Chem. **184**, 58 (1950).

[22] C. Yanofsky and D. M. Bonner, J. Biol. Chem. **190**, 211 (1951).

This solution can then be extracted with n-butanol or chloroform,[23, 24] in which nicotinamide is soluble. The chloroform solution may be subjected to fractional distillation, nicotinamide distilling at 150 to 160° at 5×10^{-4} mm. Hg.[9] The distillate may be recrystallized from organic solvents such as chloroform, benzene, or ethylene glycol.

Warburg and Christian[7] have described the procedure they used to obtain nicotinamide from red blood cells. Coenzyme I (DPN) and coenzyme II (TPN) were first isolated in a purified state (see p. 482 for method). The coenzyme (DPN) could then be hydrolyzed with dilute sulfuric acid, liberating free nicotinamide. Adenine could be precipitated as the silver salt. The mother liquor and washings from this step were cleared of silver with hydrogen sulfide and the nicotinamide extracted with amyl alcohol. After filtration and concentration, nicotinamide was precipitated from the amyl alcohol solution with picrolonic acid. The picrolonic acid salt could be recrystallized from hot water. Treatment with hydrochloric acid yielded the free nicotinamide hydrochloride,[5] which was in turn recrystallized from hot ethanol.

The procedure used by the Wisconsin workers in isolating nicotinamide from liver was somewhat involved but essentially as follows.[10, 11, 25, 26] Liver paste was suspended and extracted with a 40% ethanol, 50% diethyl ether, and 10% water mixture. The concentrate from this step was extracted with acetone. Several successive concentrations and extractions with amyl alcohol, 95% ethanol, acetone, and finally water were used. The nicotinamide was adsorbed from the water extract using charcoal (Norit A) and eluted with a mixture of 4 parts methanol and 1 part pyridine. Methanol and pyridine were removed by evaporation. The dry residue was extracted with acetone and the extract evaporated to dryness. This dry residue was placed in a molecular still and held at 160 to 165° and 1×10^{-4} mm. pressure for 3 hours. The distillate was dissolved in alcohol and treated with alcoholic mercuric chloride to yield a precipitate which was dissolved in dilute HCl and decomposed with H_2S. Crystalline nicotinamide appeared in the concentrated filtrate.

Bovarnick[27] has described a procedure by which she isolated pure nicotinamide from heated asparagine-glutamic acid mixtures. Presumably, a paper strip chromatogram technique similar to that described for nicotinic acid could be used in the isolation of small quantities of nicotinamide, although this has not yet been reported. It is known, however, that nico-

[23] H. von Euler, F. Schlenk, L. Melzer, and B. Högberg, *Hoppe-Seyler's Z. physiol. Chem.* **258,** 212 (1939).

[24] P. Karrer and H. Keller, *Helv. Chim. Acta* **22,** 1292 (1939).

[25] C. A. Elvehjem and C. J. Koehn, Jr., *J. Biol. Chem.* **108,** 709 (1935).

[26] C. J. Koehn, Jr., and C. A. Elvehjem, *J. Biol. Chem.* **118,** 693 (1937).

[27] M. R. Bovarnick, *J. Biol. Chem.* **153,** 1 (1944).

tinic acid and nicotinamide, as well as related metabolites, can be separated on paper strips with appropriate solvent systems.[28-32]

3. SEPARATION OF NICOTINIC ACID AND NICOTINAMIDE

This can be effected by extraction of a water solution with ether, chloroform, or benzene. The amide dissolves in the organic solvent while the acid remains in the watery phase. Nitranilic acid may also be used for this purpose, since it forms an alcohol-soluble compound with the acid but an alcohol-insoluble compound with the amide.[33] Certain amines such as piperidine, n-butylamine, morpholine, or diethylamine will react with a suspension of nicotinic acid, but not with nicotinamide, in a non-aqueous solvent such as benzene to give a soluble amine salt. The unreacted nicotinamide can be filtered and recovered almost 100 % pure.[34]

The acid and the amide may be separated using paper strip chromatography as mentioned previously. This technique also separates free nicotinamide from that which is bound in coenzymes.[28, 29] Free nicotinamide may also be separated from coenzyme-bound nicotinamide by acetone extraction which dissolves free nicotinamide but not the coenzymes.[23, 35, 36] This separation must be carried out promptly when extracting mammalian tissues, since many of them contain very active nucleotidases which break down the coenzymes unless inhibited by acetone or some other agent (see p. 507).

4. ISOLATION OF N¹-METHYLNICOTINAMIDE

This substance was isolated in pure form from urine by Huff and Perlzweig,[37] using a rather simple procedure. The urine was acidified with acetic acid, clarified with charcoal, partially evaporated, the residue extracted with 95 % ethanol, this extract again evaporated, and the residue extracted with 80 % ethanol. After evaporation of this extract, the residue was taken up in water and adjusted to pH 4 with acetic acid and sodium

[28] B. C. Johnson and Pei-Hsing Lin, Federation Proc. 10, 203 (1951).
[29] E. Leifer, L. J. Roth, D. S. Hogness, and M. H. Corson, J. Biol. Chem. 190, 595 (1951).
[30] C. F. Huebner, Nature 167, 119 (1951).
[31] E. Kodicek and K. K. Reddi, Nature 168, 475 (1951).
[32] E. G. Wollish, M. Schmall, and E. G. Shafer, Anal. Chem. 23, 768 (1951).
[33] E. Müller, Hoppe-Seyler's Z. physiol. Chem. 268, 245 (1941).
[34] J. R. Berg, U. S. Pat. 2,496,114 (January 31, 1950).
[35] H. von Euler and G. Günther, Hoppe-Seyler's Z. physiol. Chem. 243, 1 (1936).
[36] H. von Euler, H. Heiwinkel, and F. Schlenk, Hoppe-Seyler's Z. physiol. Chem. 247, IV (1937).
[37] J. W. Huff and W. A. Perlzweig, J. Biol. Chem. 150, 395 (1943).

acetate. The N^1-methylnicotinamide was adsorbed on a Decalso (Permutit) column. After the column had been washed to remove impurities, the N^1-methylnicotinamide was eluted, using 25 % potassium chloride solution. The eluate was alternately evaporated and extracted with ethanol until almost entirely free of potassium chloride. The characteristic picrate of N^1-methylnicotinamide was then formed, recrystallized, and decomposed with hydrochloric acid to yield the free N^1-methylnicotinamide which could be crystallized from absolute ethanol. Other investigators have used methods differing but slightly from that described above.[38, 39] Beher[40] has referred briefly to a method for isolating semimicro amounts of N^1-methylnicotinamide in which the compound is adsorbed on a cation exchange resin and eluted with dilute hydrochloric acid which in turn is removed with an anion exchange resin. The procedure was stated to give better yields and was less time consuming than older methods.

5. ISOLATION OF 6-PYRIDONE OF N^1-METHYLNICOTINAMIDE

Knox and Grossman[41] isolated this substance from urine. The urine was decolorized with basic lead acetate and the compound adsorbed on Lloyds' reagent. After washing with 0.01 N hydrochloric acid, the compound was eluted from the Lloyd's reagent with absolute ethanol. After evaporation, the residue was dissolved in water and the compound extracted into isobutanol. This extract was dried with calcium sulfate, evaporated, and the residue extracted with acetone. Crystals were obtained from the concentrated acetone extract. Recrystallization could be accomplished from either acetone or water.

6. ISOLATION OF OTHER NICOTINIC ACID METABOLITES

The isolation of dinicotinylornithine from chicken droppings has been described by Dann and Huff.[42] Ackerman[43] was apparently the first to isolate nicotinuric acid. He administered nicotinic acid and isolated both nicotinuric acid and trigonelline from urine. The nutritional significance of nicotinic acid was not known at that time. Linneweh and Reinwein[44] also isolated this substance from human urine.

[38] M. Hochberg, D. Melnick, and B. L. Oser, *J. Biol. Chem.* **158**, 265 (1945).

[39] J. M. Hundley and H. W. Bond, *J. Biol. Chem.* **173**, 513 (1948).

[40] W. T. Beher, *Abstr. 118th Meeting, Am. Chem. Soc., Chicago*, p. 73C (September 3–8, 1950).

[41] W. E. Knox and W. I. Grossman, *J. Biol. Chem.* **166**, 391 (1946); **168**, 363 (1947).

[42] W. J. Dann and J. W. Huff, *J. Biol. Chem.* **168**, 121 (1947).

[43] D. Ackerman, *Z. Biol.* **59**, 17 (1912).

[44] W. Linneweh and H. Reinwein, *Hoppe-Seyler's Z. physiol. Chem.* **207**, 48 (1932); **209**, 110 (1932).

7. ISOLATION OF COENZYMES I AND II

a. Coenzyme I (Diphosphopyridine nucleotide, DPN, cozymase)

This substance has not yet been isolated in an absolute chemically pure form.[44a] It can, however, be prepared in 95 % or better purity. Ohlmeyer[45] obtained a product of exceptional purity, as judged by extinction coefficients at 340 mμ and other criteria, by isolating reduced DPN from a purified oxidized DPN preparation (see p. 483). The early investigations of von Euler and his group and Warburg and associates in isolating this coenzyme have been cited elsewhere (p. 480 and 482). The methods applied by these workers to purify DPN and to separate DPN from TPN and other impurities have been outlined in Section IV. It should be noted that none of the procedures described to date for isolating "pure" DPN (or TPN) has yielded crystalline products.

Improved and less cumbersome procedures have been devised in more recent years which permit the isolation of DPN in a purity quite satisfactory for most biochemical work. Williamson and Green[46] and Sumner *et al.*[47] have devised methods which have found considerable use. These and other methods have been reviewed by LePage.[48] Still more recently Kornberg and Pricer[49] have described a modification of Williamson and Green's method which yields DPN in about 95 % purity. This method is attaining increasingly wide acceptance and use. The coenzyme is extracted from starch-free baker's yeast with hot water. This extract is treated with basic lead acetate, and DPN precipitated with silver nitrate. The precipitate is decomposed with H_2S and the DPN again precipitated with acetone. The product at this stage has a purity of 76 to 83 %. Further purification is achieved by adsorption on Dowex-1 resin, elution with 0.1 N formic acid, and reprecipitation with acetone. Other investigators have also employed ion exchange chromatography to purify DPN.[50]

b. Coenzyme II (Triphosphopyridine nucleotide, TPN)

TPN has been isolated in a form almost as pure as DPN, but it has not been completely purified. Warburg *et al.*[6, 7] were the first to describe a method for isolating purified TPN. The details of their procedure are de-

[44a] K. Wallenfels and W. Christian [*Angew. Chem.* **64**, 419 (1952)] have recently announced the crystallization of DPN as a quinine salt. This product crystallized as fine, almost featherlike needles arranged in sheaves and gave a melting point between 162 and 170° with decomposition.

[45] P. Ohlmeyer, *Biochem. Z.* **297**, 66 (1938).

[46] S. Williamson and D. E. Green, *J. Biol. Chem.* **135**, 347 (1940).

[47] J. B. Sumner, P. S. Krishnan, and E. B. Sisler, *Arch. Biochem.* **12**, 19 (1947).

[48] G. A. LePage, *Biochem. Preparations* **1**, 28 (1949).

[49] A. Kornberg and W. E. Pricer, Jr., *Biochem. Preparations* **2**, (1952).

[50] J. B. Neilands and Å. Åkeson, *J. Biol. Chem.* **188**, 307 (1951).

TABLE I. PROPERTIES OF NICOTINIC ACID AND RELATED COMPOUNDS

Compound	Molecular weight	Crystal form	Melting point, °C.	Melting point of picrate, °C.	Ultraviolet absorption maximum	Other properties	Solubility	Reference
Nicotinic acid $C_5H_4N \cdot CO_2H$	123.11	Needles from EtOH (see text)	235	225–227	2615 A.	Sublimes $K_a = 1.4 \times 10^{-5}$ at 25°	Sol. in hot H_2O Sol. in hot EtOH Slightly sol. in ether	See text; 3, 53
Nicotinic acid hydrochloride $C_5H_4N \cdot HCl \cdot CO_2H$	159.57	Prisms from H_2O	274–275 272 (3)				Sol. in EtOH Sol. in H_2O Insol. in ether and benzene	54
Nicotinamide $C_5H_4N \cdot CONH_2$	122.12	Needles from benzene	133 129–131 (53)	193	2615 A.	Sublimes 150–160° at 5 $\times 10^{-4}$ mm. Hg	Very sol. in H_2O Very sol. in EtOH Very slightly sol. in ether	See text
Nicotinuric acid $C_5H_4N \cdot CONHCH_2CO_2H$	180.15	Crystallized from dilute HCl	240–242	160–162			Very sol. in H_2O Very sol. in EtOH	43, 55, 56
N¹-Methylnicotinamide $C_5H_4NCH_3Cl \cdot CONH_2$	172.5	Rosettes or prismatic bars from abs. alc.	230.5 (39) 233–234 (37) 240 (57)	189.5	2645 A.	Crystals decompose at 233° (39)	Sol. in H_2O Sol. in EtOH Slightly sol. in hot abs. alc.	37, 39, 57; for infrared spectrum see 58
6-Pyridone of N¹-methylnicotinamide $C_5H_3ONCH_3 \cdot CONH_2$	152.15	White crystals from acetone	212–214		2600 A. and 2900 A.	Ultraviolet absorption at 2600 much more intense than nicotinic acid or nicotinamide	Sol. in H_2O Sol. in EtOH Insol. in less polar solvents	41
Dinicotinyl Ornithine Potassium Salt $C_{17}H_{17}O_4N_3K$	380.4	White non-hygroscopic solid from abs. EtOH	262–263				Sol. in H_2O, EtOH Sl. sol. in abs. EtOH Insol. in ether, acetone, chloroform	42
3-Acetyl pyridine hydrochloride $C_5H_4NHCl \cdot COCH_3$	157.5	White crystalline powder	176–177.5			Free base boils at 90–92° (5 mm.) and melts at 13–14°	Sol. in H_2O Sol. in EtOH	59
Quinolinic acid $C_5H_3N \cdot (CO_2H)_2$	167.12	Colorless monoclinic crystals from H_2O	232–237 when heated quickly			Slow heating sublimation begins at 166, gas evolution at 188–190°	Sol. in hot H_2O Slightly sol. in EtOH Very sol. in ether Insol. in benzene	60

scribed in Section IV. LePage and Muller[51] have described a procedure for obtaining TPN from hog liver. More recently, Kornberg and Horecker[52] have developed a method, part of which is a modification of the method of Warburg and Christian, which can produce TPN of 92 % purity. TPN is extracted from freshly killed sheep liver with hot water. Proteins and nucleic acids are removed by precipitation with trichloroacetic acid. TPN is precipitated from the filtrate with mercuric acetate, the salt decomposed with H_2S, and TPN precipitated with acetone. This product, which has a purity of 8 to 13 %, is further purified by ion exchange chromatography using a Dowex-1 formate column, and reprecipitation with acetone.

B. CHEMICAL AND PHYSICAL PROPERTIES

1. NICOTINIC ACID

Nicotinic acid is an odorless, white crystalline compound which melts at 234 to 237° and sublimes without decomposition above this temperature. It has a molecular weight of 123.11, and the composition $C_6H_5O_2N$. It has a tart taste. Table I summarizes many of the properties of nicotinic acid and related compounds.

a. Solubility

One gram is soluble in 60 ml. of water or in 80 ml. of ethanol at 25°. It is almost insoluble in ether but is freely soluble in boiling water, in boiling ethanol, and in aqueous solutions of alkali hydroxides and carbonates.[53] The solubility of nicotinic acid, its hydrochloride, and its sodium salt in some common solvents is shown in Table II.

b. Stability

Nicotinic acid is non-hygroscopic and very stable in the dry state. Solutions may be autoclaved at 120° for 20 minutes without destruction. It is stable on heating with 1 or 2 N mineral acid and alkali.

[51] G. A. LePage and G. C. Mueller, *J. Biol. Chem.* **180**, 775 (1949).

[52] A. Kornberg and B. L. Horecker, *Biochem. Preparations* **2** (1952).

[53] Vitamins Reviews, Niacin and Niacinamide. Merck & Co., Rahway, N. J., 1947.

[54] N. A. Lange, Handbook of Chemistry, 6th ed. Handbook Publishers, Sandusky, Ohio, 1946.

[55] Y. Sendju, *J. Biochem. (Japan)* **6**, 161 (1926).

[56] C. A. Elvehjem and L. J. Teply, *Chem. Revs.* **33**, 185 (1943).

[57] P. Karrer, G. Schwarzenbach, F. Benz, and U. Solmssen, *Helv. Chim. Acta* **19**, 826 (1936).

[58] O. H. Gaebler and W. T. Beher, *J. Biol. Chem.* **188**, 343 (1951).

[59] F. M. Strong and S. M. McElvain, *J. Am. Chem. Soc.* **55**, 816 (1933).

[60] L. M. Henderson, *J. Biol. Chem.* **178**, 1005 (1949).

c. *Crystal Structure*

Commercial nicotinic acid crystallized from water or ethanol occurs as needle-like crystals or as a crystalline powder.[53] Keenan[61] and Wright and King[62] have made extensive studies of the crystal structure of nicotinic acid. When carefully crystallized from water, 95% ethanol, or 1:1 mixtures of water and 95% ethanol, the crystals appeared either as small rods or as flat, colorless monoclinic plates with {010} as the predominant form and a characteristic edge angle of 114°. All crystals were found to be twinned either about the c axis or across the 100 plane to a greater or lesser degree and exhibited a fibrous structure. Examination under the polarizing

TABLE II

SOLUBILITY[a] OF NICOTINIC ACID, SODIUM NICOTINATE (HEMIHYDRATE), AND NICOTINIC ACID HYDROCHLORIDE AT VARIOUS TEMPERATURES (FROM Y. M. SLOBODIN AND M. M. GOLDMAN[60a])

	Nicotinic acid			Na nicotinate	Nicotinic acid·HCl
Temperature, °C.	H_2O	96% EtOH	Saturated NaCl solution	H_2O	H_2O
0	0.86	0.57	0.8	9.5	1.73
15	1.3	0.92	1.03	23.11	8.5
38	2.47	2.1	1.61	31.16 (30°)	14.23
61	4.06	4.2	2.45	39.11	17.01
78	6.0	7.06	3.54	43.2	19.5
100	9.76	—	5.9	49.78	21.48

[a] Solubility as grams per 100 ml.

microscope gave the results shown in Table III. The density of nicotinic acid crystals was 1.473 ± 0.002 (g. cm.$^{-3}$) as determined by a flotation method.[62] Debye-Scherrer x-ray, oscillation, and Weissenberg photographs were also taken and the results recorded.[62]

d. *Absorption Spectrum*

Solutions of nicotinic acid exhibit a characteristic absorption spectrum. The absorption spectrum in aqueous solution has been studied by Hünecke,[63] who reported a maximum at 385 A. Hughes et al.[64] have made an extensive

[60a] Y. M. Slobodin and M. M. Goldman, *Zhur. Priklad. Khim.* **21,** 859 (1948) [*C. A.* **43,** 6207 (1949)].

[61] G. L. Keenan, *J. Assoc. Offic. Agr. Chemists* **26,** 514 (1943).

[62] W. B. Wright and G. S. D. King, *Acta Cryst.* **3,** 31 (1950).

[63] H. Hünecke, *Ber.* **60,** 1451 (1927).

[64] E. B. Hughes, H. H. G. Jellinek, and B. A. Ambrose, *J. Phys. & Colloid Chem.* **53,** 414 (1949).

study of the ultraviolet absorption spectrum of nicotinic acid at pH values from 1.28 to 13.0 (Fig. 1). The concentration of nicotinic acid used in deriving the curves shown in Fig. 1 was 0.0004 M, and the ionic strength was the same at each pH. It will be noted that the molecular extinction coefficient varied with pH, although the absorption maximum was at the same wavelength, 2615 A., in each instance. There was a straight-line relationship between extinction coefficients and concentration of nicotinic acid (Beer's law, Fig. 2). The validity of Beer's law was also confirmed using nicotinic acid solutions at pH 1.28 and pH 13.

TABLE III

OPTICAL PROPERTIES OF NICOTINIC ACID FOR SODIUM LIGHT (FROM W. B. WRIGHT AND G. S. D. KING[62])

	Wright and King	Keenan
n_1	1.424 ± 0.002	1.428 ± 0.003
n_2	1.717 ± 0.005	Indeterminate
n_3	>1.75 (~1.79)	>1.734
Extinction	Both straight and inclined; the maximum extinction angle observed was 13½°	Parallel, although the substance showed many rod-like fragments which did not extinguish sharply
Acute bisectrix	X_1 in a direction 13½° from the c axis in the obtuse angle β	—
Optic plane	Optic plane and X_3 normal to [010]	—
Optic axial angle	$2V_1 = 46°$	—
Optic sign	Negative	—
Maximum birefringence	>0.32	—
Monoclinic angle	$\beta = 114°$	—

e. Dissociation Constants

From the data depicted in Fig. 1, Hughes et al.[64] were able to calculate dissociation constants for nicotinic acid. The spectra fell into two groups, each having two isobestic points indicating two equilibria. The first two isobestic points were at wavelengths of 2495 A. and 2695 A. and were associated with pH values from 1.28 to 4.08. They belong to the dissociation equilibrium of nicotinic acid when acting as a base.

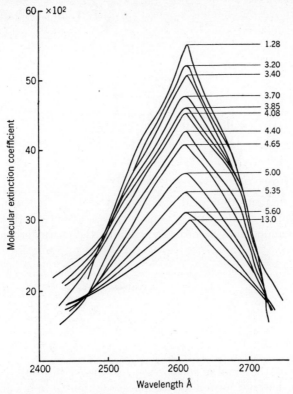

Fig. 1. Absorption spectra of nicotinic acid at different pH values. (From Hughes et al.[64])

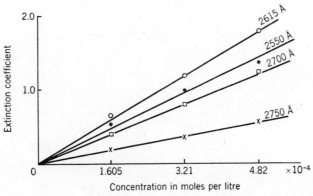

Fig. 2. Demonstration of Beer's law in buffer at 4.25. (From Hughes et al.[64])

The second group of isobestic points at 2465 A. and 2710 A. covering a range of pH values from 4.4 to 13.0 is associated with the acid equilibrium of nicotinic acid.

$$+ H_2O \rightleftharpoons \qquad + H_3O^+$$

The acid and base dissociation constants as calculated by two methods are shown in Table IV. Ostwald[65] reported the acid dissociation constant of nicotinic acid as $K_a = 1.4 \times 10^{-5}$ (25°).

f. Chemical Properties

The fact that nicotinic acid is an amino acid is often overlooked. Although not an α-amino acid, it is nevertheless at once both a carboxylic acid and an amine and, accordingly, exhibits the characteristic properties

TABLE IV

THERMODYNAMIC DISSOCIATION CONSTANTS FOR NICOTINIC ACID AT AN AVERAGE
TEMPERATURE OF 22° ± 2°

	pK_a	K_a	pK_b	K_b	Isoelectric point
Method 1	4.95	1.12×10^{-5}	10.45	3.55×10^{-11}	4.25
Method 2	4.91	1.23×10^{-5}	10.45	3.55×10^{-11}	4.23

associated with the simultaneous presence of these two groups in a molecule (although it does not form a zwitterion in solution[64]). It is soluble in both acids and bases, forming quaternary salts with the former and carboxylic acid salts with the latter. It possesses an isoelectric point (pH 4.23–4.25). Its high melting point is characteristic of amino acids. Its strength as an acid exceeds its strength as a base. A 1% aqueous solution has a pH of about 3.[53]

(1) Properties associated with its basic character

Nicotinic acid, like other compounds containing a basic amino group, forms quaternary ammonium compounds. Thus, hydrogen chloride converts it to nicotinic acid hydrochloride, a white crystalline solid readily soluble in water (see Tables I and II) but insoluble in benzene and ether. It has a melting point at 272° (with decomposition).[3]

$$+ HCl \rightarrow$$

[65] W. Ostwald, Z. physik. Chem. 3, 369 (1889).

Similar reactions occur with other acids. Nicotinic acid nitrate[3] melts at 184 to 185°. The picrate of nicotinic acid separates from absolute alcohol in modular aggregates of short rhombic prisms which melt at 221 to 222° to a red oil which begins to decompose at 250°.[3] This compound contains 65.5 % picric acid.[3]

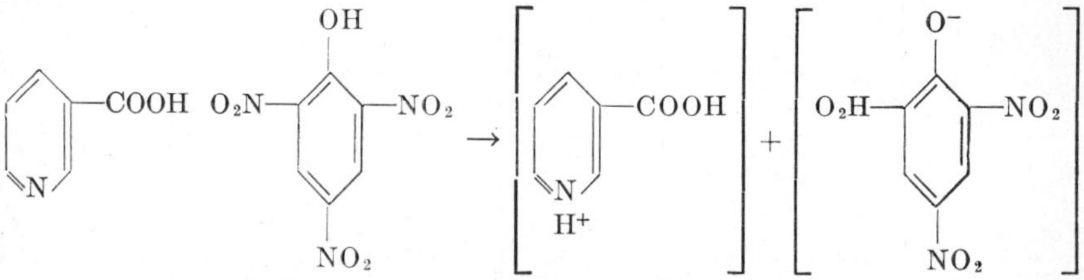

Nicotinic acid (and nicotinamide) react with methyl iodide and similar alkyl iodides to yield compounds which are readily soluble in water (see p. 492).

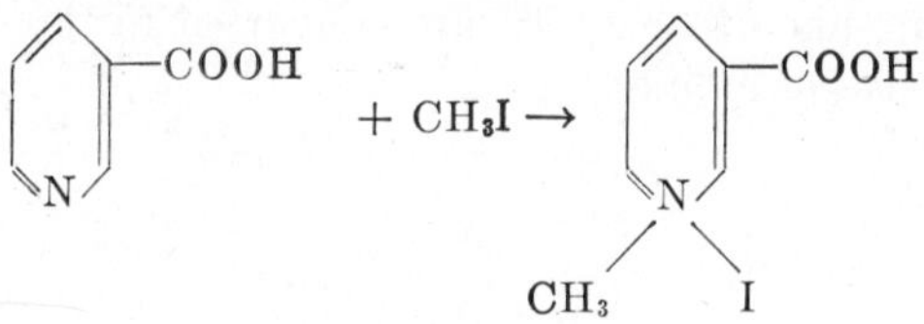

(2) *Properties associated with its acidic character*

Salt formation occurs when nicotinic acid is treated with alkali or an alkaline earth hydroxide. The ammonium, sodium, potassium, calcium, magnesium, etc., salts are readily formed as white crystalline solids by titration of the acid with the hydroxides, viz.:

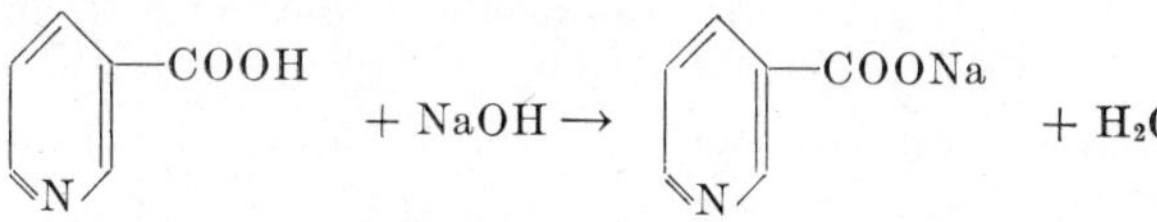

Heavy metal salts convert nicotinic acid to the metallic nicotinates. This property has proved useful in recovering nicotinic acid from reaction mixtures[66] and from dilute nicotinic acid solutions, since salts such as copper nicotinate are quite insoluble at certain pH values. Nicotinic acid (and nicotinamide) reacts with $HgCl_2$ to form insoluble chloromercurates which crystallize in characteristic forms. Gautier[67] has proposed the use of this reaction as a means of microchemically characterizing nicotinic acid and nicotinamide. Nicotinic acid will react with mercuric acetate as shown in the following equation.

[66] F. C. Huber, U. S. Pat. 2,487,874 (November 15, 1949).
[67] J. A. Gautier, *Ann. chim. anal.* **26**, 89 (1944).

$$2 \left[\underset{N}{\bigcirc}\text{—COOH} \right] + \text{Cu(C}_2\text{H}_3\text{O}_2)_2 \rightarrow \left(\underset{N}{\bigcirc}\text{—COO} \right)_2 \text{Cu} + \text{HC}_2\text{H}_3\text{O}_2$$

Esters of nicotinic acid are obtained by heating the acid in the appropriate alcohol in the presence of a catalyst, usually sulfuric acid.[68] Esters are also obtained when nicotinyl chloride is treated with an excess of the alcohol.

$$\underset{N}{\bigcirc}\overset{O}{\overset{\|}{\text{C}}}\text{—Cl} + \text{ROH} \rightarrow \underset{N}{\bigcirc}\overset{O}{\overset{\|}{\text{C}}}\text{—OR} + \text{HCl}$$

The esters of nicotinic acid possess characteristic aromatic odors. The physical properties of a number of these esters are given in Table V.

Nicotinic esters, like other esters, are converted to the amides by treatment with an excess of amines.

$$\underset{N}{\bigcirc}\overset{O}{\overset{\|}{\text{C}}}\text{—OC}_2\text{H}_5 + \text{NH}_3 \rightarrow \underset{N}{\bigcirc}\overset{O}{\overset{\|}{\text{C}}}\text{—NH}_2 + \text{C}_2\text{H}_5\text{OH}$$

2. NICOTINAMIDE

This compound is a white crystalline powder, odorless or nearly so, with a bitter taste. It crystallizes as needles from benzene and melts at 129 to 131°. It has a molecular weight of 122.12, and the composition $C_6H_6N_2O$.[53, 69] A solution in water is neutral to litmus (1 % solution in water = pH 6).

a. *Solubility.* One gram is soluble in 1 ml. of water, in 1.5 ml. of 95 % ethanol, and in 10 ml. of glycerol. It is soluble in acetone, amyl alcohol, ethylene glycol, chloroform, and butanol. It is slightly soluble in ether and benzene. Nicotinamide has a strong solvent effect on riboflavin.[70]

b. *Stability.* In the dry state nicotinamide is quite stable if kept below 50°. In aqueous solutions it may be autoclaved at 120° for 20 minutes without appreciable destruction.[53] It distills at 150 to 160° and 5×10^{-4} mm. Hg.[9] It is converted to nicotinic acid by acid and by alkali.

[68] C. O. Badgett, R. C. Provost, Jr., C. N. Ogg, and C. F. Woodward, *J. Am. Chem. Soc.* **67**, 1135 (1945).

[69] U. S. Pharmacopeia, 14th Revision, p. 379, 1950.

[70] D. V. Frost, *J. Am. Chem. Soc.* **69**, 1064 (1947).

(c) *Crystal Structure.* The detailed crystal structure of nicotinamide has been investigated by Keenan,[61] by McCrone and Cook,[71] and by Wright and King.[62] Keenan reported that nicotinamide crystallized in colorless small rods which exhibited both parallel and oblique extinction. He gives the following values for the refractive indices: α equal to 1.485 ± 0.002 and γ greater than 1.734. McCrone and Cook encountered considerable difficulty in preparing crystals suitable for microscopic examination but

TABLE V

SOME ESTERS OF NICOTINIC ACID (ADAPTED FROM BADGETT *et al.*[68])

R	Boiling point		Density	n_D^{25}	Solubility in H_2O, g./100 ml. soln., 25°	Melting point of picrate, °C.
	°C.	Mm.				
Methyl	m.p. 38°	—	—	—	—	—
Ethyl	88	3.5	1.1047	1.5008	5.60	147.5–148.0
n-Propyl	72–73	0.2	1.0711	1.4964	0.950	129.5–130.0
n-Butyl	75–76	0.15	1.0471	1.4933	0.261	113.5–114.0
n-Amyl	93	0.22	1.0217	1.4847	0.081	98.5–99.0
Isoamyl	259	Atm.	—	—	—	—
n-Hexyl	103–104	0.2	1.0133	1.4897	0.046	87.5–88.5
n-Heptyl	116	0.19	0.9939	1.4846	0.040	92.5–93.5
n-Octyl	116–117	0.2	0.9871	1.4856	0.019	89.5–90.0
n-Nonyl	133.5	0.28	0.9852	1.4853	0.020	99.5–100.0
n-Decyl	140–141	0.25	0.9714	1.4847	0.017	94.0–94.5
n-Undecyl	159–160	0.5	0.9606	1.4829	0.017	103.5–103.8
n-Dodecyl	f.p. 22.7	—	0.9356	1.4750	0.015	99.5–100.5
n-Tetradecyl	m.p. 40.2–40.8	—	—	—	0.012	102.4–103.0
n-Hexadecyl	m.p. 46.7–47.0	—	—	—	0.013	103.0–103.5
n-Octadecyl	m.p. 55.3–55.8	—	—	—	0.014	107.7–107.9

finally obtained crystals from ethylene glycol on a microscopic slide, as shown in Fig. 3. In addition they found any one of four polymorphic forms when nicotinamide was crystallized from a melt, two of which are shown in Fig. 3. Nicotinamide I recrystallized from common solvents appeared as long, prismatic monoclinic rods showing well-developed prisms and domes. McCrone and Cook present the various measurements of the crystal morphology and crystal optics of nicotinamide I. The density was 1.401 ± 0.002 (g. cm.$^{-3}$) as determined by a buoyancy method using carbon tetrachloride and petroleum ether.

[71] W. C. McCrone, Jr., and J. W. Cook, *The Frontier* **10**, 12–23 (1947).

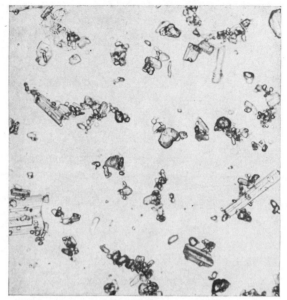

(a) Crystals of a commercial product of nicotinamide.

(b) Characteristic sublimate of nicotinamide; crossed Nicols.
FIG. 3 (a-d). Various crystalline forms of nicotinamide. (From McCrone and Cook.[71])

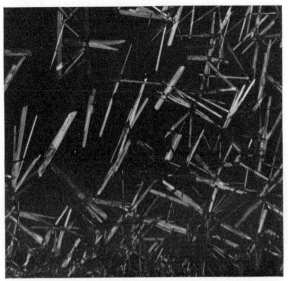

(c) Crystals of nicotinamide from ethylene glycol on a microscopic slide; crossed Nicols.

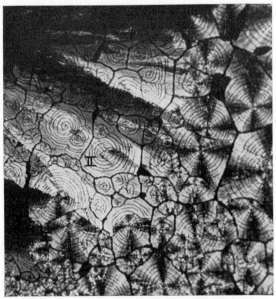

(d) Polymorphic transformation. Nicotinamide I growing into nicotinamide II; crossed Nicols.

Wright and King[62] obtained nicotinamide crystals which differed in some respects from those of McCrone and Cook. In their work nicotinamide crystallized from ethylene glycol as monoclinic crystals of prismatic habit, elongated parallel to the c axis and showing {110} as the predominant form. All crystals were twinned either about the c axis or across the 100 plane. When crystallized from water, acetone, benzene, glycerol, or from mixtures of ethylene glycol and water (50 % or more), they appeared as lath-shaped monoclinic crystals, elongated parallel to the c axis and exhibiting {010} as the predominant form with a characteristic edge angle of 99°. The optical properties of nicotinamide for sodium light, and the

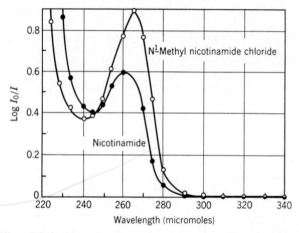

FIG. 4. Ultraviolet absorption spectrum of nicotinamide (●) and N[1]-methylnicotinamide (○). The concentration of both compounds was $2 \times 10^{-4} M$, in water, at pH 7.0. (From Cantoni.[71b])

findings from Debye-Scherrer x-ray, oscillation and Weissenberg photographs of nicotinamide crystals are presented in Wright and King's publication.

(d) *Absorption Spectrum.* The absorption spectrum of nicotinamide in water was determined by Warburg et al.,[6] who found a maximum absorption of 2600 A. with a molecular extinction coefficient of 4.5×10^3. Kuhn and Vetter[9] reported a similar absorption maximum but with a slightly higher extinction coefficient. Figure 4 shows the ultraviolet absorption spectrum of nicotinamide in comparison to N[1]-methylnicotinamide.

Jellinek and Wayne[72] have studied the ultraviolet absorption spectrum of 0.0003 M nicotinamide solutions at pH values of 5.72 to −1.06 with the results depicted in Fig. 5. They found an absorption maximum at

[71b] G. L. Cantoni, *J. Biol. Chem.* **189**, 203 (1951).
[72] H. H. G. Jellinek and M. G. Wayne, *J. Phys. & Colloid Chem.* **55**, 173 (1951).

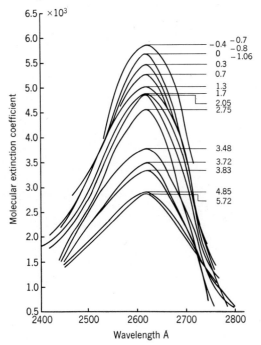

FIG. 5. Ultraviolet absorption spectra of nicotinamide at various pH values. (From Jellinek and Wayne.[72])

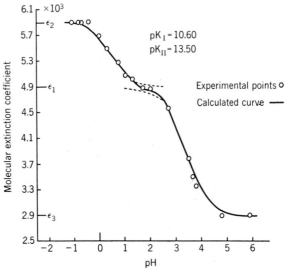

FIG. 6. Dissociation curve for nicotinamide at $\lambda = 2615$ A. (From Jellinek and Wayne.[72])

2615 A. (the same as for nicotinic acid), with the molecular extinctions of the maxima decreasing as the pH values increased. The molecular extinction coefficients for the peak values are plotted against the pH values in Fig. 6. (*e*) *Dissociation Constants.* Jellinek and Gordon[73] studied the hydrolysis of nicotinamide in hydrochloric acid solutions and found that it differed considerably from the hydrolysis of other amides such as benzamide in that the first-order rate constants for the hydrolysis did not pass through a maximum between 0.5 N and 8.6 N HCl. According to their results, two reactions occur. An equilibrium is set up rapidly: H^+ $RCONH_2$ + H^+ $\rightleftarrows$ $H^+RCONH_3^+$ followed by a slow hydrolysis: $H^+RCONH_3^+$ + H_3O^+ → H^+RCOOH + NH_4^+ + H^+. The hydrolysis showed a positive salt effect (NaCl). The effects of temperature and hydrochloric acid concentration on the rate of hydrolysis were determined.

The dissociation constant due to the amido group and the thermodynamic dissociation constant of the nitrogen in the ring were also evaluated spectroscopically by Jellinek and Wayne.[72] Their results indicated a constant of 2.24×10^{-11} for the nitrogen in the ring and 3.16×10^{-14} as the base constant for the amido group, the latter agreeing well with the studies of HCl hydrolysis.

(*f*) *Chemical Properties.* Many of the chemical properties of nicotinamide have been referred to previously. Nicotinamide undergoes the Hoffman degradation to 3-aminopyridine.[74] If nicotinamide is distilled with P_2O_5 at 25 mm. pressure or $SOCl_2$ at 100°, 3-cyanopyridine is formed.[75]

Nicotinamide and esters of nicotinic acid react with acids and alkyl halides to form quaternary salts as already depicted for nicotinic acid.[57, 76-78]

The carbon in the 6 position seems to be the most reactive ring carbon in nicotinamide.[79] Karrer *et al.*[80] have demonstrated that an amide group

[73] H. H. G. Jellinek and A. Gordon, *J. Phys. & Colloid Chem.* **53**, 996 (1949).

[74] A. Philips, *Ann.* **288**, 253 (1895).

[75] I. M. Heilbron and H. M. Bunbury, Dictionary of Organic Compounds, Vol. III. Oxford University Press, New York, 1946.

[76] W. König, *J. prakt. Chem.* **69**, 105 (1904); **70**, 19 (1904).

[77] W. Ciusa and G. Nebbia, *Gazz. chim. ital.* **79**, 521 (1949).

[78] M. F. Zienty, *J. Am. Pharm. Assoc.* **37**, 99 (1948).

[79] W. E. Knox and W. I. Grossman, *J. Am. Chem. Soc.* **70**, 2172 (1948).

[80] P. Karrer, F. Kahnt, R. Epstein, W. Jaffe, and T. Ishii, *Helv. Chim. Acta* **21**, 223 (1938).

in the β position of the pyridine ring specifically facilitates the reversible reduction of corresponding pyridinium salts.

3. OTHER COMPOUNDS RELATED TO NICOTINIC ACID

The properties of several compounds related to nicotinic acid are listed in Table I.

C. CONSTITUTION OF NICOTINIC ACID

The structure of nicotinic acid was determined shortly after it was first isolated from the oxidation products of nicotine.[81, 82] The presence of a pyridine ring can be established by boiling nicotinic acid with calcium hydroxide. Carbon dixoide is split off and free pyridine obtained. The carboxylic acid group can be identified by the formation of metallic salts and by the formation of derivatives such as esters and the acid chloride (see pp. 464–6). The existence of the basic ring nitrogen can be inferred by the formation of salts such as the hydrochloride and the hydrobromide and by the formation of quaternary ammonium compounds such as nicotinic acid methochloride and methoiodide.

The fact that the carboxylic acid group was in the 3 (β) position was proved by Skraup and Cobenzl[83, 84] by oxidation of 3-phenylpyridine the structure of which was proven. Benzo[f]quinoline was oxidized to 3-phenylpyridinecarboxylic acid, from which 3-phenylpyridine was formed by decarboxylation. This in turn oxidized to nicotinic acid.[85, 86] The 3 position of the carboxyl group was further established by the formation of nicotinic acid from synthetically prepared m-dipyridyl.[87]

Simpler proof of the constitution of nicotinic acid is cited by von Richter[85] from the behavior of 2,3-pyridinedicarboxylic acid (quinolinic acid) and 3,4-pyridinedicarboxylic acid (cinchomeronic acid). When the former is heated, nicotinic acid is formed by elimination of one carbon dioxide group. When the latter is heated, both nicotinic acid and isonicotinic acid (4-pyridinecarboxylic acid) are formed. Therefore nicotinic acid is 3-pyridinecarboxylic acid.

[81] C. Huber, *Ber.* **3**, 849 (1870); *Ann.* **141**, 271 (1867).

[82] H. Weidel, *Ann.* **165**, 331, 346 (1873).

[83] Z. H. Skraup, *Monatsh. Chem.* **1**, 800 (1880).

[84] Z. H. Skraup and A. Cobenzl, *Monatsh. Chem.* **4**, 436 (1883).

[85] V. von Richter, The Chemistry of the Carbon Compounds, Vol. IV, p. 214. Elsevier Publishing Co., New York, 1946.

[86] H. R. Rosenberg, Chemistry and Physiology of the Vitamins, p. 223. Interscience Publishers, New York, 1942.

[87] Z. H. Skraup and G. Vortmann, *Monatsh Chem.* **4**, 594 (1883).

D. SYNTHESIS

1. NICOTINIC ACID

a. From Nicotine

Nicotinic acid can be obtained from nicotine by treatment with fuming nitric acid,[82] with chromic acid,[81] or by permanganate[88] as indicated below. When nicotine is treated with bromine water, dibromoticonine is formed which decomposes in barium hydroxide solution, through the intermediate indicated in parentheses, to nicotinic acid, methylamine, and malonic acid.[89]

Nicotine   Dibromoticonine   Nicotinic acid

b. From β-Picoline and Other 3-Substituted Pyridines

Nicotinic acid can be synthesized from substituted pyridines such as β-picoline[90-92] and 3-ethylpyridine[93-95] by suitable oxidation methods. For example, β-picoline is refluxed for 2 to 3 hours with H_3PO_4 and HNO_3, the HNO_3 and H_2O distilled up to 200°, and the oxidation repeated with small portions of HNO_3. The final residue is diluted with water, treated with NaOH, giving nicotinic acid.[96] This oxidation may also be carried out with oxygen-containing gases in the presence of catalysts such as V_2O_5 or V_2O_5 containing small quantities of Fe_2O_3,[97]

β-Picoline can be prepared by heating glycerol with P_2O_5 and substances containing ammonia or, better, ammonium phosphate.[98] It may also be

88 R. Laiblin, Ber. **10**, 2136 (1877); Ann. **135**, (1879).

89 V. von Richter, The Chemistry of the Carbon Compounds, Vol. IV, p. 337. Elsevier Publishing Co., New York, 1946.

90 H. Weidel, Ber. **12**, 1992, 2004 (1879).

91 H. Ost, J. prakt. Chem. [2]**27**, 286 (1883).

92 E. Seyfferth, J. prakt. Chem. [2]**34**, 258 (1886).

93 H. Weidel and K. Hazura, Monatsh. Chem. **3**, 783 (1882).

94 A. Ladenburg, Ann. **301**, 152 (1898).

95 A. Wischnegradski, Ber. **12**, 1480 (1879).

96 F. E. Cislak and W. R. Wheeler, U. S. Pat. 2,396,457 (March 12, 1945).

97 F. E. Cislak and W. R. Wheeler, U. S. Pat. 2,437,938 (March 16, 1948).

98 P. Schwarz, Ber. **24**, 1676 (1891).

prepared by condensing β-oxocarboxylic acid esters and β-diketones with aldehydes and ammonia (Hantzsch's method).[99] β-Picoline is commonly recovered from coal tar.

c. From Quinoline

Quinoline can be oxidized to 2,3-pyridinedicarboxylic acid (quinolinic acid) with heat[100-103] or with acids.[91, 104, 105] For example, quinoline plus H_2SO_4, HNO_3, and HgO (as a catalyst) when heated to 300° gives an 88.4 % yield of nicotinic acid which can be recovered as the copper salt.[106] SeO_2 is also an effective catalyst in converting quinoline to nicotinic acid in high yield.[107, 108]

| Quinoline | Quinolinic acid | Nicotinic acid |

d. From Pyridine

Pyridine may be sulfonated with fuming sulfuric acid, yielding the 3-sulfonic acid. When the sodium salt of this compound is distilled with potassium cyanide, 3-cyanopyridine is formed.[109] This compound may then be hydrolyzed to nicotinic acid. An alternative procedure is to brominate pyridine in the 3 position and treat with cuprous cyanide to yield 3-cyanopyridine.[110]

[99] V. von Richter, The Chemistry of the Carbon Compounds, Vol. IV, p. 198. Elsevier Publishing Co., New York, 1946.

[100] S. Hoogewerff and W. A. van Dorp, Ann. **204,** 117 (1880); **207,** 219, 226 (1881); Rec. trav. chim. **1,** 122 (1882).

[101] R. Camps, Arch. Pharm. **240,** 353, 359 (1902).

[102] H. Weidel and J. Herzig, Monatsh. Chem. **1,** 16 (1880).

[103] F. B. Ahrens and R. Gorkow, Ber. **37,** 2063 (1904).

[104] S. Hoogewerff and W. A. van Dorp, Ber. **14,** 974 (1881).

[105] H. Weidel and J. Herzig, Monatsh. Chem. **6,** 982 (1885).

[106] M. S. Larrison, U. S. Pat. 2,475,969 (July 12, 1949).

[107] M. B. Mueller, U. S. Pat. 2,436,660 (February, 1948).

[108] F. Porter, M. Bumpers, and J. N. Crosby, U. S. Pat. 2,513,251 (July 27, 1950).

[109] O. Fischer, Ber. **15,** 63 (1882).

[110] S. M. McElvain and M. A. Goese, J. Am. Chem. Soc. **63,** 2283 (1941).

e. Other Methods

Trigonelline (the betaine of 3-pyridinecarboxylic acid) can be converted to nicotinic acid by heating at 200° for 1 to 3 hours with pyridine hydrochloride or hydrobromide. Nicotinic acid can be separated as the copper salt which can be decomposed with hydrogen sulfide in formic acid.[110a] Trigonelline may also be converted to nicotinic acid by heating with hydrochloric acid in a closed tube at 260°[111] or by heating in a mixture of potassium hydroxide and ammonia.[112]

f. Isotopic Nicotinic Acid

Murray *et al.*[113] have prepared carboxyl-labeled nicotinic acid in the following fashion with an over-all yield of 60 to 80%:

| 3-Bromo- | *n*-Butyl- | 3-Pyridyl- | Nicotinic |
| pyridine | lithium | lithium | acid |

Nicotinic acid may also be labeled with deuterium. Trenner *et al.*[114] have described a procedure whereby deuteronicotinic acid can be prepared by direct exchange of nicotinic acid with deuterosulfuric acid. The amount of tracer in the product can be determined using infrared spectroscopy.

2. NICOTINAMIDE

a. From Nicotinic Acid

Nicotinamide can be formed from nicotinic acid by treating with ammonia or molten urea at 230°,[115-118] preferably with a catalyst such as NH_4 molybdate.

b. From Esters of Nicotinic Acid

Esters of nicotinic acid such as the methyl and ethyl esters can be reacted with aqueous or alcoholic ammonia to yield nicotinamide.[101, 119-121]

[110a] J. Weijlard, J. P. Messerly, and M. Tischler, U. S. Pat. 2,381,794 (August 7, 1945).
[111] E. Jahns, *Ber.* **20**, 2840 (1887).
[112] J. W. Huff, *J. Biol. Chem.* **166**, 581 (1946).
[113] A. Murray, III, W. W. Foreman, and W. Langham, *Science* **106**, 277 (1947).
[114] N. R. Trenner, R. W. Walker, B. Arison, and C. Trumbauer, *Anal. Chem.* **23**, 487 (1951).
[115] S. Keimatsu, K. Kokata, and I. Satoda, *J. Pharm. Soc. Japan* **53**, 994 (1933).
[116] E. Cherbuliez and F. Landolt, *Helv. Chim. Acta* **29**, 1438 (1946).
[117] E. F. Pike and R. S. Shane, U. S. Pat. 2,412,749 (December 17, 1946).
[118] P. W. Garbo, U. S. Pat. 2,419,813 (April 29, 1947).
[119] C. Engler, *Ber.* **27**, 1787 (1894).
[120] F. Pollak, *Monatsh. Chem.* **16**, 53 (1895).
[121] F. B. LaForge, *J. Am. Chem. Soc.* **50**, 2377 (1928).

c. *From 3-Cyanopyridine*

Nicotinamide can be produced directly from the above compound by partial hydrolysis in an aqueous alkaline solution containing a sufficient quantity of alkali to produce a larger portion of nicotinamide than nicotinic acid but insufficient to complete the hydrolysis of the cyanopyridine.[122, 123] Nicotinamide can also be produced from this compound by treating with H_2O_2 and NaOH[124] or by heating the compound with water, NH_3, or an amine.[125]

3. SYNTHESIS OF RELATED COMPOUNDS OF BIOLOGICAL IMPORTANCE

a. *3-Acetylpyridine*

Ethylnicotinate undergoes normal Claisen-type condensations. With ethyl acetate in the presence of sodium ethoxide, ethylnicotinoacetate is formed in good yield.

The latter may be hydrolyzed to 3-acetylpyridine in excellent yield using hydrochloric acid.[59, 126]

b. *N¹-Methylnicotinamide*

Nicotinamide (and nicotinic acid) react readily with methyl iodide and similar alkyl iodides to yield the corresponding N^1-substituted derivatives.[57, 76] These may then be converted to the corresponding chloride (the form in which this compound is ordinarily used) by treatment with silver chloride.

[122] British Pat. 563,184 (August 2, 1944) [*C. A.* **40**, 2473 (1946)].
[123] B. F. Duesel and H. L. Friedman, U. S. Pat. 2,471,518 (May 31, 1949).
[124] J. F. Couch and C. F. Kreevson, U. S. Pat. 2,453,496 (November 9, 1948).
[125] H. R. Rosenberg, U. S. Pat. 2,446,957 (August 10, 1948).
[126] H. Gilman and H. S. Broadbent, *J. Am. Chem. Soc.* **70**, 2755 (1948).

c. 6-Pyridone of N¹-Methylnicotinamide

This compound has been prepared from coumalic acid by ring closure with methylamine.[127] It may also be prepared by an alkaline ferricyanide oxidation and subsequent treatment with $SOCl_2$ and ammonia, using either trigonelline or N¹-methylnicotinamide as starting material.[128]

d. Pyridine 3-Sulfonic Acid

This substance may be prepared by the direct sulfonation of pyridine with fuming sulfuric acid.[109, 129, 130] Mercury is an effective catalyst in the reaction.

E. SPECIFICITY

The biological effect of various modifications in the nicotinic acid molecule is discussed in Section V (p. 517).

III. Industrial Preparation

J. M. HUNDLEY

The current (1952) annual production of nicotinic acid is probably in excess of 2 million pounds. The latest available data[1] indicate that about $1\frac{1}{2}$ million pounds of nicotinic acid and nicotinamide were produced in the United States during 1950 (Table VI). This accounts, on a weight basis, for about 41 % of all vitamins produced. Since the period covered by this report, two new plants for the production of nicotinic acid have gone into operation.[2] One of these plants has an annual capacity of over 1 million pounds. This large production reflects a market demand stimulated not only by the widespread use of nicotinic acid and derivatives in vitamin preparations and other medicinal products but the large quantities used in the enrichment of bread and cereals.

The details of the manufacturing processes being used in the new plants, referred to above, have not been revealed. However, one will base its production on coal tar raw materials, presumably quinoline or β-picoline,

[127] H. von Pechman and W. Welsch, *Ber.* **17**, 2384 (1884).
[128] J. W. Huff, *J. Biol. Chem.* **171**, 639 (1947).
[129] A. J. P. van Gastel and J. P. Wibaut, *Rec. trav. chim.* **53**, 1031 (1934).
[130] G. Machek, *Monatsh. Chem.* **72**, 77 (1938).
[1] Synthetic Organic Chemicals. U. S. Production and Sales of Medicinals. U. S. Tariff Commission, Washington, D. C., 1950 (Preliminary Report published July, 1951).
[2] *Chem. Eng. News* **29**, 4686, 5136 (1951).

both of which can be obtained from coal tar distillation. Several of the chemical reactions which could be applied using these starting materials have already been described (see p. 474). The oxidation of bases from coal tar or petroleum[3] or from bone tar oil[4] which distill between 135 and 142° is a well-known procedure. The second plant will base its production on aldehyde collidine. This process is, in principle, the same as the quinoline process, i.e., the raw material is oxidized with manganese dioxide and sulfuric acid with or without a selenium catalyst, or with nitric acid, to yield the pyridinedicarboxylic acid which in turn is heated to remove one of the carboxyl groups (see p. 475). Details of a procedure which can be used to produce nicotinic acid from nicotine have been described by S. M. McElvain.[5]

TABLE VI

ANNUAL (1950) PRODUCTION OF NICOTINIC ACID AND OTHER VITAMINS IN THE UNITED STATES

	Pounds
Nicotinic acid and nicotinamide	1,447,600
Ascorbic acid and salts	1,227,500
Thiamine	237,400
Riboflavin	199,000
Pyridoxine	17,500
Calcium pantothenate	155,400
Choline	104,900
Vitamin A	95,300
Vitamin D_2 and D_3	2,600
Other (including vitamin K)	72,900

Many processes are available by which nicotinic acid could be produced. The choice of a commercial process depends not only on the efficiency of the chemical reactions but on the current availability and cost of the various starting materials and the market for secondary reaction products (e.g., isonicotinic acid derivatives). Chemical reactions which could be applied in the industrial preparation of nicotinic acid and of nicotinamide, as well as many of the pertinent patents and references have been listed in Section II.

[3] A. Pinner, *Ber.* **33,** 1227 (1900).
[4] H. Weidel, *Ber.* **12,** 1992, 2004 (1879).
[5] S. M. McElvain, *in* Organic Syntheses, Coll. Vol. I, 2nd ed., p. 385. John Wiley and Sons, New York, 1941.

IV. Biochemical Systems

J. M. HUNDLEY

A. INTRODUCTION

Like most other B vitamins, nicotinic acid (or a derivative) is required by all living cells. It is an essential part of certain coenzymes which catalyze chemical reactions essential to cellular life. So far as is known, nicotinic acid has no metabolic function other than that exerted through the coenzymes of which it is a part.

Actually, specific biochemical functions for nicotinic acid were discovered before it was known that this substance was a vitamin. In 1934 Warburg and Christian[1, 2] found that nicotinamide was part of the coenzyme II molecule. The following year nicotinamide was isolated from cozymase (coenzyme I) by von Euler and associates[3] and later by Warburg and Christian.[4] It was not until 1937, when Elvehjem et al.[5] discovered that nicotinic acid would cure blacktongue in dogs and the subsequent finding that it would cure pellagra in man, (see p. 453) that the full biological significance of this simple organic molecule was realized. Since these pioneer discoveries more than forty biochemical reactions have been identified which are dependent on these two coenzymes. More reactions will likely be discovered. Most of these reactions have been studied in great detail. Much exact information is available on the mechanism and kinetics of the reactions, on the effect of environmental influences, and on the interdependence of these with other biochemical reactions.

However, it is important to remember that most of the detailed information on coenzyme I and II catalyzed reactions has been obtained from *in vitro* studies using simplified enzyme systems. It is well known that these reactions are only steps in the very complex series of reactions which occur in the intact cell. There are undoubtedly many influences in the intact cell which modify the reactions observed in simplified systems. The *in vivo* consequences of blocking or impeding specific biochemical steps, the ability or inability to activate alternate reaction pathways, and effects due to the accumulation of substrate or abnormal metabolites are only examples of the complexities involved in evaluating the biochemical function of nicotinic acid in intact organisms. This field has hardly been explored.

[1] O. Warburg and W. Christian, *Biochem. Z.* **274**, 112 (1934).

[2] O. Warburg and W. Christian, *Biochem. Z.* **275**, 112, 464 (1935).

[3] H. von Euler, H. Albers, and F. Schlenk, *Hoppe-Seyler's Z. physiol. Chem.* **237**, 180 I (1935); **240**, 113 (1936).

[4] O. Warburg and W. Christian, *Biochem. Z.* **287**, 291 (1936).

[5] C. A. Elvehjem, R. J. Madden, F. M. Strong, and D. W. Woolley, *J. Am. Chem. Soc.* **59**, 1767 (1937); *J. Biol. Chem.* **123**, 137 (1938).

Nicotinamide containing coenzymes have significance not only in vertebrate biochemistry but in the vegetable kingdom as well. This became clear quite early not only from the studies on yeast fermentation[3] but especially due to the studies of the Lwoffs with factor V, an essential growth factor for *Hemophilus parainfluenza*.[6] They established the identity of factor V with the nicotinamide coenzymes and discovered that these substances functioned biochemically in these microorganisms much as had already been found in enzyme systems derived from mammalian sources (also see p. 550).

B. COENZYMES CONTAINING NICOTINIC ACID

Two, and only two, coenzymes are known to contain nicotinic acid.[6a] These have been described under various names in the literature.

1. *Coenzyme I*, codehydrogenase I, cozymase, Harden's coferment, coreductase, factor V, codehydrase I, and diphosphopyridine nucleotide.

2. *Coenzyme II*, codehydrogenase II, Warburg's coferment, codehydrase II, and triphosphopyridine nucleotide.

Since names which depict chemical structure are generally less confusing, the terminology of diphosphopyridine nucleotide (DPNH$_2$ for the reduced form) and triphosphopyridine nucleotide (TPN and TPNH$_2$) will be used in this chapter to refer to coenzymes I and II, respectively. It is recognized that this terminology is not quite correct chemically, since the term nucleotide itself implies phosphoric acid content. Nevertheless this terminology seems preferable by virtue of common usage and in view of the fact that these were the names originally suggested by Warburg and Christian.

C. ISOLATION AND IDENTIFICATION

1. TPN was the third coenzyme to be discovered and the first found to contain nicotinamide as part of its structure. In 1934 Warburg and Christian[1] isolated a nitrogen-containing base from their "Co-ferment" (TPN) which was quickly identified as nicotinamide.[2] These and later studies[4, 7] showed that their coenzyme contained 1 molecule each of adenine and nicotinamide, 3 molecules of phosphoric acid, and 2 molecules of pentose. However, there was some uncertainty that one of the sugar molecules

---

[6] A. Lwoff and M. Lwoff, *Proc. Roy. Soc. (London)* **B122,** 352, 360 (1937).

[6a] A probable exception to this has been recorded recently by T. P. Singer and E. B. Kearney [*Abstr. 2nd Intern. Congr. Biochem. Paris* p. 307 (1952)], who discovered a pyridine nucleotide, which was not identical with any known coenzyme, in *Proteus vulgaris*. This coenzyme was necessary for the oxidation of cysteinesulfinic acid to cysteic acid and for the dehydrogenation of β-sulfinylacetic acid. The structure of this pyridine nucleotide is not yet known.

[7] O. Warburg, W. Christian, and W. Griese, *Biochem. Z.* **282,** 157 (1935).

might be a hexose[4] and the manner of linkage of the various molecules
was not clarified.

Warburg and Christian encountered their "Co-ferment" as a factor
necessary for the action of Zwischenferment, an enzyme which oxidized
glucose 6-phosphate.[8] They isolated the coenzyme in a "pure" form from
hemolyzed horse erythrocytes by a rather involved procedure employing
acetone precipitation of the red cell stromata, fractionation with mercuric
acetate and barium hydroxide, precipitation from methanol-HCl with ethyl-
acetate, and further fractional precipitation with lead acetate and alcohol.
A fluorescent contamination which interfered with spectrophotometric
studies could be removed by bromine treatment.[4]

2. DPN was the first coenzyme to be discovered and the second found
to have nicotinamide as a part of its molecule. It was found by Harden
and Young[9] as a material which could be dialyzed from the complex zymase
system of yeast, the system which catalyzes the alcoholic fermentation of
carbohydrates. Actually, this soluble dialyzable component of the zymase
system contained, as later shown, two coenzymes, cozymase (DPN) and
phosphorylating coenzyme (adenosine phosphate).

By 1933 it was known, from the work of von Euler and Myrbäck,[10] that
cozymase was an adenine nucleotide. About a year after Warburg and
Christian identified nicotinamide as part of the TPN molecule, von Euler
et al.[3] isolated a base from cozymase which they believed to be nicotinamide.
Warburg and Christian[4] also isolated a pyridine base from cozymase and
published convincing evidence of its identity as nicotinamide. From the
work of both groups, it was evident that cozymase was closely related to
TPN, since it contained the same structural elements differing only in that
it contained one less phosphate group.

DPN was originally isolated from brewer's or baker's yeast, although
animal tissues were used in much of the early work. The first "pure"
preparations were obtained from yeast[3, 11] by a procedure which consisted
of hot water extraction, lead acetate precipitation of impurities, coenzyme
precipitation in consecutive steps as the phosphotungstate, Hg, Ag, and
Cu salts, followed by removal of contaminations by Ba and Pb treatment,
alcohol fractionation, and purification with aluminum oxide. In using animal tissue (erythrocytes) as a source material, Warburg and Christian[4]
were able to isolate not only DPN but TPN and adenosine phosphate as
well. They separated the three nucleotides, utilizing the fact that the
barium salt of adenosine phosphate is only slightly soluble in water. The
barium salt of TPN is only slightly soluble in dilute alcohol, whereas the

[8] O. Warburg and W. Christian, Biochem. Z. 242, 206 (1931).

[9] A. Harden and W. J. Young, J. Physiol. 32 Proc. 1904 (1905); Proc. Roy. Soc.
(London) B77, 405 (1906).

[10] K. Myrbäck, Ergeb. Enzymforsch. II, 139 (1933).

[11] H. von Euler and F. Schlenk, Svensk Kem. Tidskr. 48, 135 (1936).

barium salt of DPN is easily soluble in dilute alcohol. According to Le-Page,[12] when 3 volumes of alcohol are added to a water solution of DPN and TPN at pH 9 in the cold, DPN is soluble to the extent of 5 mg. per milliliter or greater while TPN is quantitatively precipitated. Ochoa[13] was able to isolate DPN from rabbit muscle in good yield and in "pure" form by modifying the procedure of Meyerhof and Ohlmeyer.[14]

In the light of more recent information, it is doubtful if any of these "pure" preparations of the early workers were actually pure in the chemical

TABLE VII

CONCENTRATION OF DPN AND TPN IN VARIOUS MATERIALS (ADAPTED FROM F. SCHLENK[15b])

(γ/g. of fresh weight)

	DPN	TPN
Brewer's yeast	1000–1500	<10
Baker's yeast	1000–1500	<10
Muscle (striated rabbit)	>600	
Liver (rat)	600–1200	30
Kidney (rat)	400–1000	40
Muscle (rat)	300–600	80
Muscle (human)	400	
Liver (cat)	430	
Thigh (cat)	250	
Oxyntic cells, stomach (cat)	2000	
Retina (cattle)	1700–4100^a	
Erythrocytes (human)	60–90	
Erythrocytes (horse)	100	>12
Erythrocytes (rat)	100	40
Lobster, Homarus vulgaris, tail	450	
Chilomonas paramecium	650	
Pollen (Salix, Populus)	700–1000	

^{a} Per gram of fat-free and dry tissue.

sense, although they may have been pure from the biochemical standpoint. A possible exception to this is the work of Ohlmeyer,[15] who isolated DPNH$_2$ from a purified DPN preparation. The high molecular extinction coeffi-

[12] G. A. LePage *in* Respiratory Enzymes. p. 87. Burgess Publishing Co., Minneapolis, 1949.

[13] S. Ochoa, *Biochem. Z.* **292,** 68 (1937).

[14] O. Meyerhof and P. Ohlmeyer, *Pflügers Arch. ges. Physiol.* **188,** 114 (1921).

[15] P. Ohlmeyer, *Biochem. Z.* **297,** 66 (1938).

[15a] K. Wallenfels and W. Christian [*Angew. Chem.* **64,** 419 (1952)] have recently announced the crystallization of DPN as a quinine salt. This product crystallized as fine, almost featherlike needles arranged in sheaves and gave a melting point between 162 and 170° with decomposition. Using pure DPN recovered from the crystallized salt, they obtained an extinction coefficient of 9.43 cm.^{2} per milligram.

[15b] F. Schlenk, *in* The Enzymes, Vol. 2, Part 1, p. 255. Academic Press, New York, 1951.

cient he observed, 6.3×10^3 (340 mμ), indicates a product of exceptional purity.[15a]

The more recent methods which have been developed to isolate DPN and TPN have been described in Section II (see p. 458).

D. OCCURRENCE OF DPN AND TPN

Pyridine nucleotides have been found in every living cell examined thus far. Table VII lists a number of substances and the concentrations of DPN and TPN found. Many of these figures must be regarded as approximations only because of analytical limitations. Many cells contain substances which rapidly destroy these coenzymes once their cellular structure is disrupted. Furthermore, it is known that TPN and DPN are interconvertible (see p. 493). Nevertheless it is clear that these coenzymes have a rather universal distribution, although their concentration varies widely in different substances. DPN and TPN tend to occur together, although the amount of TPN seems always to be less than DPN. In animal tissues, a fairly constant proportion (35 to 45 %) of the DPN is in the reduced state.[16]

Yeast, red blood cells, liver, and skeletal and cardiac muscle are good sources of DPN. Fresh yeast may contain as much as 0.5 g. per kilogram[17] and rabbit cardiac muscle 0.4 g. per kilogram.[18] Yeast contains very little TPN. Animal tissues, especially red blood cells, liver, and muscle are good sources of TPN, containing as much as 40 to 80 γ per gram.[19]

E. STRUCTURE AND PROPERTIES

1. DIPHOSPHOPYRIDINE NUCLEOTIDE (DPN)

a. Structure

The structural formula listed above is now firmly established for the oxidized form of DPN. This formula was established in the following way.

1. Acid hydrolysis splits the molecule to yield nicotinamide,[3, 4] adenine,[20] and 2 molecules of ribose-5-phosphate.[21, 22]

2. Hydrolysis by weak alkali at low temperature splits off nicotinamide and leaves adenosinediphosphate ribose moiety.[23]

3. Hydrolysis with weak alkali at high temperature yields adenosinediphosphate.[24]

4. Enzymatic hydrolysis under certain conditions yields nicotinamide riboside and adenosine.[25]

5. The fact that phosphate was linked to ribose in the 5 position was shown by von Euler et al.,[26] since the pentose phosphate from DPN gave no formaldehyde when reacted with periodic acid.

6. D-Ribose was already known to be the carbohydrate of adenosine.[27]

Von Euler et al.[28] partially hydrolyzed DPN with acid, treated with phosphatase, and isolated a pentose, the phenylosazone of which was identical with D-ribose. As pointed out by Schlenk,[22] these workers did not establish that the ribose came from the nicotinamide-linked portion of the molecule and furthermore the phenylosazones of D-ribose and D-arabinose are identical. He, however, reached the same conclusion by isolating the pentose from nicotinamide nucleoside (step 4) and forming the p-bromophenylhydrazone and studying its other properties. In addition, he confirmed the linkage of ribose and phosphate in the 5 position of ribose.

Thus the structural formula for DPN as proposed originally in 1936[29-31] seems well established. It should be noted, however, that the customary

---

[16] S. Ochoa and C. G. Ochoa, Nature 140, 1097 (1937).

[17] O. Meyerhof and P. Ohlmeyer, Biochem. Z. 290, 334 (1937).

[18] H. von Euler, Angew. Chem. 50, 831 (1937).

[19] H. von Euler, F. Schlenk, H. Heiwinkel, and B. Högberg, Hoppe-Seyler's Z. physiol. Chem. 256, 208 (1938).

[20] H. von Euler and K. Myrbäck, Hoppe-Seyler's Z. physiol. Chem. 177, 237 (1928); Naturwissenschaften 17, 291 (1929).

[21] F. Schlenk, Arkiv Kemi, Mineral. Geol. 12B, 20 (1936).

[22] F. Schlenk, J. Biol. Chem. 146, 619 (1942).

[23] F. Schlenk, H. von Euler, H. Heiwinkel, W. Gleim, and H. Nyström, Hoppe-Seyler's Z. physiol. Chem. 247, 23 (1937).

[24] R. Vestin, F. Schlenk, and H. von Euler, Ber. 70, 1369 (1937).

[25] F. Schlenk, Naturwissenschaften 28, 46 (1940); Arch. Biochem. 3, 93 (1943).

[26] H. von Euler, P. Karrer and B. Becker, Helv. Chim. Acta 19, 1060 (1936).

[27] P. A. Levene and L. W. Bass, Nucleic Acids. American Chemical Society Monograph No. 56, New York, 1931.

[28] H. von Euler, H. Karrer, and E. Usteri, Helv. Chim. Acta 25, 323 (1942).

[29] F. Schlenk and H. von Euler, Naturwissenschaften 24, 794 (1936).

[30] H. von Euler and F. Schlenk, Hoppe-Seyler's Z. physiol. Chem. 246, 64 (1937).

[31] K. Myrbäck, Tabulae Biol. 14, 110 (1937).

[32] L. J. Haynes and A. R. Todd, J. Chem. Soc. 1950, 303.

final proof of the structure of an organic compound by chemical synthesis has not yet been reported. Some progress in this direction has been made since some portions of the molecule can now be synthesized.[32] The lability of various portions of the DPN molecule, especially the nicotinamide-ribose bond, in the procedures ordinarily used in organic syntheses, makes this a most difficult problem.

b. Properties

DPN is a white amorphous powder which is colorless in water solution. It is moderately soluble in phenol and in methanol-HCl. Some of the

TABLE VIII

SOME PROPERTIES OF DPN AND TPN (FROM F. SCHLENK[32a])

	DPN	TPN
Empirical formula	$C_{21}H_{27}O_{14}N_7P_2$	$C_{21}H_{28}O_{17}N_7P_3$
Structural units	Nicotinamide, adenine, 2 moles of ribose, and 2 moles of phosphoric acid	Nicotinamide, adenine, 2 moles of ribose, and 3 moles of phosphoric acid
Base equivalent		
Oxidized state	1	3
Reduced state	2	4
Stability		
Oxidized state		
In 0.1 N HCl at 100°	50% destroyed after 8 min.	50% destroyed after 7.3 min.
In 0.1 N NaOH	50% destroyed after 17 min. (20°)	50% destroyed after 12 min. (23°)
Reduced state		
In 0.1 N HCl at 20°	Activity disappears immediately	Activity disappears immediately
In 0.1 N NaOH at 100°	Slight decrease in activity	
In 0.1 N NaOH at 20°	Stable	Stable
Absorption spectrum		
Oxidized state	$E_m = 16.5 \times 10^3$ at 260 mμ	$E_m = 16.5 \times 10^3$ at 260 mμ
Reduced state	$E_m = 14.5 \times 10^3$ at 260 mμ	$E_m = 14.5 \times 10^3$ at 260 mμ
Reduced state	$E_m = 4.5$ to 6.3×10^3 at 340 mμ	$E_m = 4.5$ to 6.3×10^3 at 340 mμ
Oxidation-reduction potential	$E_0 = -0.28$ to 0.31 v	

important properties are listed in Table VIII. It is stable to oxidants such as bromine, H_2O_2, and permanganate in acid solution unless catalysts such as iron are present.[4, 10, 31] Hypoiodide results in rapid destruction,[33] whereas hyposulfite reduces DPN to DPNH$_2$.[4] Alkaline ferricyanide converts DPN to a pyridone derivative. The latter can be condensed to yield a fluorescent product, which reaction has been used as the basis for assay methods.[34-36]

[32a] F. Schlenk, in The Enzymes, Vol. 2, Part 1, p. 263. Academic Press, New York 1951.

[33] P. Karrer, F. Schlenk, and H. von Euler, Arkiv Kemi, Mineral. Geol. 12B, 26 (1936)

[34] W. E. Knox and W. I. Grossman, J. Biol. Chem. 166, 391 (1946); 168, 363 (1947).

[35] F. Rosen, W. A. Perlzweig, and I. G. Leder, J. Biol. Chem. 179, 157 (1949).

[36] K. J. Carpenter and E. Kodicek, Biochem. J. 46, 421 (1950).

Treatment with bisulfite and cyanide give addition compounds[37] while strong acids give pyridinium salts.

DPN is sensitive to ultraviolet light, being destroyed thereby.[38-40] DPN shows no fluorescence in ultraviolet light, but $DPNH_2$ exhibits a whitish fluorescence. DPN is optically active, the specific rotation being $-20°$ at 643.9 mμ and $-70°$ at 546 mμ.[41]

DPN shows an absorption peak at 260 mμ in the ultraviolet. $DPNH_2$

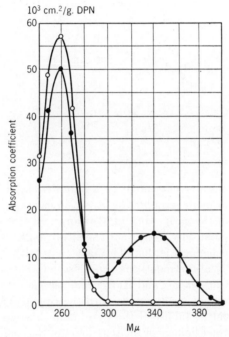

FIG. 7. Ultraviolet absorption spectrum of diphosphopyridine nucleotide (pH 9.7); oxidized (O) and reduced (●) forms. (Adapted from Warburg and Christian.[4])

also exhibits a peak at 260 mμ and, in addition, a peak at 340 mμ which is entirely absent in the oxidized form (Fig. 7). This band at 340 mμ has been the basis for innumerable assay methods and has major biochemical usefulness.

[37] O. Meyerhof, P. Ohlmeyer, and W. Möhle, *Biochem. Z.* **297**, 113 (1938).
[38] O. Warburg and W. Christian, *Biochem. Z.* **282**, 221 (1935).
[39] J. Runnström and L. Michaelis, *J. Gen. Physiol.* **18**, 717 (1935).
[40] H. von Euler and F. Schlenk, *Arkiv Kemi, Mineral. Geol.* **12B**, 19 (1936).
[41] K. Myrbäck, H. von Euler, and H. Hellström, *Hoppe-Seyler's Z. physiol. Chem.* **212**, 7 (1932).

2. Triphosphopyridine Nucleotide (TPN)

a. Structure

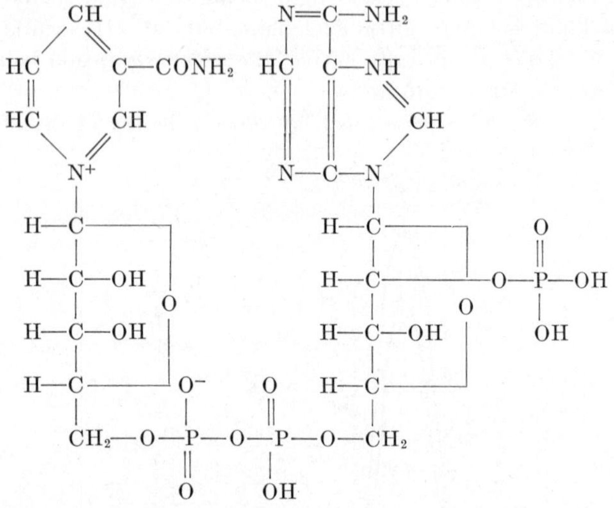

$$
\begin{array}{c}
\text{CH} \\
\text{HC} \quad \text{C—CONH}_2 \\
\text{HC} \quad \text{CH} \\
\text{N}^+ \\
\text{H—C} \\
\text{H—C—OH} \\
\text{H—C—OH} \\
\text{H—C} \quad \text{O}^- \\
\text{CH}_2\text{—O—P—O—P—O—CH}_2 \\
\text{O} \quad \text{OH}
\end{array}
\qquad
\begin{array}{c}
\text{N}{=}\text{C—NH}_2 \\
\text{HC} \quad \text{C—NH} \\
\text{CH} \\
\text{N—C—N} \\
\text{H—C} \quad \text{O} \\
\text{H—C} \quad \text{O—P—OH} \\
\text{H—C—OH} \quad \text{OH} \\
\text{H—C}
\end{array}
$$

As depicted in the above formula, TPN differs from DPN only by having an additional phosphate group. The close similarity of DPN and TPN became evident in the early work of Warburg and Christian[4] and of von Euler's group,[3, 29] not only from their chemical similarity but in the similarity of their biochemical action. The fact that DPN can be reversibly converted to TPN also strengthens this close relationship.[42-45]

Warburg and Christian[2, 4] and Karrer and associates[33, 46-51] investigated the mode of linkage of nicotinamide with the rest of the molecule. These investigations firmly established the pyridinium linkage as shown above.

However, the exact linkage of the remainder of the components remained uncertain, especially the position of the third phosphate. The rather cum-

[42] E. Adler, S. Elliot, and L. Elliot, *Enzymologia* **8,** 80 (1940).

[43] A. Kornberg, *J. Biol. Chem.* **182,** 805 (1950).

[44] H. von Euler and E. Adler, *Hoppe-Seyler's Z. physiol. Chem.* **252,** 41 (1938).

[45] R. Vestin, *Naturwissenschaften* **25,** 667 (1937).

[46] P. Karrer, F. Kahnt, R. Epstein, W. Jaffe, and T. Ishii, *Helv. Chim. Acta* **21,** 223 (1938).

[47] P. Karrer, T. Ishii, F. W. Kahnt, and I. von Bergen, *Helv. Chim. Acta* **21,** 1174 (1938).

[48] P. Karrer, B. H. Ringier, J. Büchi, H. Fritzsche, and U. Solmssen, *Helv. Chim. Acta* **20,** 55 (1937).

[49] P. Karrer, G. Schwarzenbach, and G. E. Utzinger, *Helv. Chim. Acta* **20,** 720 (1937).

[50] P. Karrer, G. Schwarzenbach, F. Benz, and U. Solmssen, *Helv. Chim. Acta* **19,** 811 (1936).

[51] P. Karrer and F. J. Stare, *Helv. Chim. Acta* **20,** 418 (1937).

bersome isolation procedure used by Warburg (p. 482) and the small yields inhibited research on this subject. However, as improved methods of preparing TPN were developed, the subject was again attacked so that the structure has now been clarified to some extent.

Two principal possibilities were considered. One that the three phosphates were linked in a chain[52] or, as later suggested by Schlenk et al.[53] that the third phosphate group was attached to the pentose of the adenosine portion of the molecule. This matter was not definitely settled until Kornberg and associates[54, 55] subjected TPN to the action of a nucleotide pyrophosphatase which split the coenzyme into two fragments, nicotinamide ribose phosphate and a diphosphoadenosine fragment which was not adenosinepyrophosphate. Kornberg and Pricer[56] were then able to hydrolyze specifically the phosphate esterified to carbon 5 of the diphosphoadenosine fragment leaving an adenosinemonophosphate. They then compared this monophosphate derivative to known samples of adenylic acid "a" and adenylic acid "b."[57, 58] Kornberg and Pricer could show that the monophosphate compound from TPN was not adenylic acid "b" and was indistinguishable from adenylic acid "a." This finding has been confirmed independently by Wang et al.[59] Adenylic acids "a" and "b" were thought at first to be adenosine-2-phosphate and adenosine-3-phosphate, respectively, but this is now uncertain.[60, 61] The 2 and 3 positions of ribose seem the only likely places where the third phosphate could be attached, since carbon 1 is in a glycosidic linkage with adenine, carbon 5 is esterified with the second phosphate, and carbon 4 is part of a furanose ring. However, the formula as shown above must be regarded as tentative until the structures of adenylic acid "a" and "b" are proved.

b. Properties

Many of the properties of TPN have already been listed (see Table VIII). In general its properties are similar to DPN. It has the same absorption spectrum. This might be expected, since the phosphates contribute little to absorption in the usual ultraviolet range. As with DPN, the absorption at 260 mμ is due principally to the adenylic acid moiety.[4, 7] Nicotinamide

[52] H. von Euler and F. Schlenk, Hoppe-Seyler's Z. physiol. Chem. **246,** 64 (1937).
[53] F. Schlenk, B. Högberg and S. Tingstam, Arkiv Kemi, Mineral. Geol. **13A,** No. 11 (1939).
[54] A. Kornberg, J. Biol. Chem. **174,** 1051 (1948).
[55] A. Kornberg and W. E. Pricer, Jr., J. Biol. Chem. **182,** 763 (1950).
[56] A. Kornberg and W. E. Pricer, Jr., J. Biol. Chem. **186,** 557 (1950).
[57] C. E. Carter, J. Am. Chem. Soc. **72,** 1466 (1950).
[58] W. E. Cohn, J. Am. Chem. Soc. **72,** 1471 (1950).
[59] T. P. Wang, L. Shuster, and N. O. Kaplan, J. Am. Chem. Soc. **74,** 3204 (1952).
[60] D. M. Brown and A. R. Todd, J. Chem. Soc. **1952,** 44.
[61] D. M. Brown, O. I. Magrath, and A. R. Todd, J. Chem. Soc. **1952,** 2708.

contributes slightly to absorption intensity at 260 mμ, and the slightly reduced absorption intensity of reduced DPN and TPN at 260 mμ is probably due to a disturbance in the conjugated double bonds of the pyridine ring. The absorption at 340 mμ of reduced DPN and TPN is a function of the addition of hydrogen to the pyridine ring. Since both DPN and TPN react to form the same type of reduced compounds, an identical spectrum at this wavelength would be expected.

There has been little uniformity in the reported values for the extinction coefficients of DPNH$_2$ and TPNH$_2$ at 340 mμ. The published values, recently reviewed by Drabkin,[62] have varied from 4.78 $\times$ 10^6 to 6.28 $\times$ 10^6 sq. cm. $\times$ mole^{-1}. More recent studies using DPN- or TPN-dependent reactions which go to completion with pure substrates have shown identical extinction coefficients for DPNH$_2$ and TPNH$_2$ at 340 mμ of 6.22 $\times$ 10^6 sq. cm. $\times$ mole^{-1}.[63]

TPN is destroyed by ultraviolet light, as is DPN. Electrophoresis determinations show two different dissociation constants, pK_1 = 1.8 and pK_2 = 6.1.[64] TPN is optically active, $[\alpha]_{589\,m\mu}$ = -24.6 and $[\alpha]_{546\,m\mu}$ = -29.4.[64]

F. MECHANISM OF ACTION

1. THE COENZYMES

DPN and TPN function in oxidation-reduction systems by virtue of their ability to accept hydrogen atoms (dehydrogenation) from certain substrates and transfer these hydrogen atoms to other hydrogen acceptors such as the flavin enzymes. In other words, DPN and TPN function by reversibly alternating between the oxidized (I) and the reduced state (II), as depicted below.

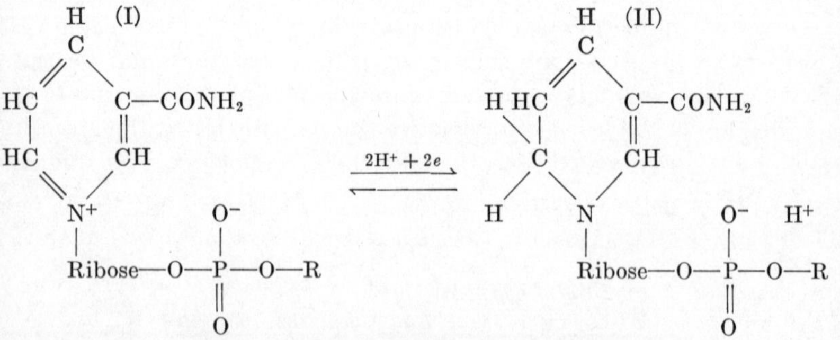

[62] D. L. Drabkin, *J. Biol. Chem.* **157**, 563 (1945).

[63] B. L. Horecker and A. Kornberg, *J. Biol. Chem.* **175**, 385 (1948).

[64] H. R. Rosenberg, Chemistry and Physiology of the Vitamins, p. 236. Interscience Publishers, New York, 1942.

In the oxidized state, the nicotinamide nucleus exists as a quaternary pyridinium ion which forms an inner salt with one of the ionizable acid groups in the pyrophosphate bridge. Upon reduction the pyridine nitrogen is converted to a weakly basic tertiary amine, hence changing the properties of the compound.

The hydrogen-transferring property of DPN had been postulated in 1934[65] on the basis of its function as coenzyme for a number of dehydrogenases. It remained, however, for Warburg and associates in their classic work[1, 2, 4] to clearly demonstrate this mechanism in their studies with TPN and later with DPN.

This reaction probably proceeds in more than one step with the intermediate formation of semiquinoid radicals. As shown by Warburg and associates,[4] when DPN or TPN are reduced by hydrosulfite, an intensely

$$
\begin{array}{c}
\text{H} \\
\text{C} \\
\diagup\diagup \quad \diagdown \\
\text{HC} \qquad \text{C—CONH}_2 \\
| \qquad\qquad \| \\
\text{HC} \qquad \text{CH} \quad + \text{Na}_2\text{S}_2\text{O}_4 + 2\text{H}_2\text{O} \rightarrow \\
\diagdown\diagdown \quad \diagup \\
\text{N} \\
| \quad \diagdown \\
\text{R} \quad \text{X}
\end{array}
\qquad
\begin{array}{c}
\text{H} \\
\text{C} \\
\diagup\diagup \quad \diagdown \\
\text{H HC} \qquad \text{C—CONH}_2 \\
\diagdown| \qquad\qquad \| \\
\text{C} \qquad \text{CH} \quad + 2\text{NaHSO}_3 + \text{HX} \\
\diagup \quad \diagdown \quad \diagup \\
\text{H} \qquad \text{N} \\
| \\
\text{R}
\end{array}
$$

yellow semiquinoid substance (monohydrocoenzyme) is observed as an intermediate in the reaction. This intermediate substance can be stabilized by carrying out the reaction in a strongly alkaline medium.[66-68]

2. The Apoenzymes

DPN and TPN function in biochemical reactions only when joined with, or activated by, specific proteins (apocodehydrogenases). Although the exact mechanism by which the protein apoenzyme unites with the coenzyme is very unsettled, it is clear that the coenzyme will not function catalytically without the influence of the apoenzyme. It has been postulated that the apoenzyme functions by facilitating formation of the semiquinoid intermediates referred to above.[69, 70]

Although the coenzymes are quite non-specific in that they function in

---

[65] H. von Euler, Chemie der Enzyme, Vol. II, Part 3. Bergman, Munich, 1934.

[66] P. Karrer and F. Benz, Helv. Chim. Acta **19**, 1028 (1936).

[67] E. von Euler, H. Hellström, and H. von Euler, Hoppe-Seyler's Z. physiol. Chem. **242**, 225 (1936).

[68] F. Schlenk and T. Schlenk, Arch. Biochem. **14**, 131 (1947).

[69] L. Michaelis and C. V. Smythe, Ann. Rev. Biochem. **7**, 1 (1938).

[70] L. Michaelis, Advances in Enzymol. **9**, 1 (1949).

a number of systems involving hydrogen transfer, the apoenzymes are generally specific, a different apoenzyme being required for each substrate system. The apoenzymes contribute more to specificity than the prosthetic group. In other words, these two coenzymes are capable of acting with a number of apoenzymes, alternating from one to another as needed, hence the term "mobile" coenzymes.[71] Some of the apoenzyme-coenzyme complexes are capable of catalyzing reactions other than that of their specific substrates, but the reaction rates are generally low. There are some exceptions to this, however, in which a given coenzyme-apoenzyme system can catalyze the oxidation of a number of substrates with efficiency.[72]

3. The Coenzyme-Enzyme Complex (Holoenzyme)

DPN and TPN are usually readily dissociable from their apoenzymes. Reduced DPN and TPN appear to have a lower affinity for their apoenzymes than the oxidized forms. This may be due to the fact that quaternary nitrogen of the pyridine ring is changed to a tertiary amine in the reduced coenzyme. The elimination of this strong basic group increases the acidic properties of the coenzyme and may increase its dissociability from the apoenzyme, hence leaving the coenzyme free to migrate to another enzyme system where it can donate its hydrogens to another substrate or hydrogen acceptor.

Some exceptions to the ready dissociability of coenzymes from their apoenzymes have been recorded. Cori et al.[73] have been able to crystallize phosphoglyceraldehyde dehydrogenase in combination with DPN. Others have reported a very firm attachment of coenzymes in the particulate matter of cells which catalyze reactions in the Krebs cycle.[74]

4. Point of Hydrogenation

The point of reversible attachment of hydrogen to the pyridine nucleus is not entirely certain. It is clear from the studies of Karrer and associates[33, 46-51] with N^1-substituted model compounds that hydrogen is attached to one of the carbons adjacent to the ring nitrogen. Available evidence, especially from the studies of Knox and Grossman,[34, 75] indicates the probable point as the 6 position.

[71] J. K. Parnas, Nature 151, 577 (1943).
[72] A. Meister, J. Biol. Chem. 184, 117 (1950).
[73] C. F. Cori, S. F. Velick, and G. T. Cori, Biochim. et Biophys. Acta 4, 160 (1950).
[74] F. M. Huennekens and D. E. Green, Arch. Biochem. 27, 418, 428 (1950).
[75] W. E. Knox and W. I. Grossman, J. Am. Chem. Soc. 70, 2172 (1948).

G. SPECIFICITY

1. DPN-TPN SPECIFICITY

Most DPN-TPN-linked enzyme systems exhibit a definite preference, if not a specific requirement, for either DPN or TPN. Well-known exceptions to this are liver glutamic dehydrogenase[76, 77] and glucose dehydrogenase[78], which react equally well with either TPN or DPN. Mehler et al.[77] studied the specificity of the DPN or TPN requirement for a number of enzyme systems. Malic and lactic dehydrogenases, for instance, reacted with either DPN or TPN, but the reaction rates were many times faster with DPN. On the other hand, isocitric dehydrogenase is strictly TPN-specific,[77, 79, 80] whereas triosephosphate dehydrogenase is strictly DPN-specific.[81]

Earlier reports which indicated a relatively non-specific DPN-TPN requirement for certain dehydrogenases may have been complicated by the fact that certain liver[77] and yeast[42] preparations can catalyze the conversion of DPN to TPN if ATP is present. It is also well known that some tissues contain phosphatases which convert TPN to DPN.[82, 83]

In addition Colowick and associates[84, 85] have obtained evidence of an enzyme in *Pseudomonas fluorescens* extracts which appears to catalyze the reaction $TPNH_2 + DPN \rightarrow TPN + DPNH_2$. An enzyme which carries out this reaction has been observed in animal tissue.[86]

2. SPECIFICITY OF THE MOLECULE

Only a few modifications or derivatives of the DPN-TPN molecules have been studied to determine the range within which these molecules can be modified and still retain enzymatic activity. Desamino DPN can be prepared by treating DPN with nitrous acid[87] or with an enzyme derived from takadiastase,[83] the free amino group of the adenine moiety

[76] H. von Euler, E. Adler, G. Günther, and N. B. Das, *Hoppe-Seyler's Z. physiol. Chem.* **254**, 61 (1938).
[77] A. H. Mehler, A. Kornberg, S. Grisolia, and S. Ochoa, *J. Biol. Chem.* **174**, 961 (1948).
[78] H. J. Strecker and S. Korkes, *J. Biol. Chem.* **196**, 769 (1952).
[79] S. Ochoa, *J. Biol. Chem.* **174**, 133 (1948).
[80] E. Adler, H. von Euler, G. Günther, and M. Plass, *Biochem. J.* **33**, 1028 (1939).
[81] G. T. Cori, M. W. Slein, and C. F. Cori, *J. Biol. Chem.* **159**, 565 (1945).
[82] H. von Euler, E. Adler, and T. S. Eriksen, *Hoppe-Seyler's Z. physiol. Chem.* **248**, 227 (1937).
[83] N. O. Kaplan, S. P. Colowick, and M. M. Ciotti, *J. Biol. Chem.* **194**, 579 (1952).
[84] S. P. Colowick, N. O. Kaplan, E. F. Neufeld, and M. M. Ciotti, *J. Biol. Chem.* **195**, 95 (1952).
[85] N. O. Kaplan, S. P. Colowick, and E. F. Neufeld, *J. Biol. Chem.* **195**, 107 (1952).
[86] J. Stern, quoted in *Federation Proc.* **11**, 238 (1952).
[87] F. Schlenk, H. Hellström, and H. von Euler, *Ber.* **71**, 1471 (1938).

being removed in the process. In the pig heart lactic dehydrogenase system, desamino $DPNH_2$ is actually more active than $DPNH_2$ for pyruvate reduction but is less active for lactate oxidation. In other dehydrogenase systems desamino DPN has activity sometimes equal to, but generally less than, the parent material.[88] Whether desamino DPN has any normal function, or even exists in tissues, is not known. Desamino TPN cannot be formed by the same procedures which yield desamino DPN apparently due to the influence of the third phosphate attached to the ribose adenine group.

3. Nicotinamide Mononucleotide

It has been shown that nicotinamide mononucleotide (nicotinamide-ribose-5-phosphate) accumulates in red blood cells incubated with nicotinamide and glucose.[89] Furthermore, certain tissues have been shown to contain a nucleotide pyrophosphatase which splits DPN to yield this compound.[55, 90] Although this substance cannot function enzymatically as DPN or TPN, it may have considerable significance as an intermediate in the biosynthesis of DPN and TPN (p. 506).

H. BIOCHEMICAL REACTIONS

DPN and TPN function in oxidation-reduction systems (although no oxygen is actually transferred). The redox potentials of the systems catalyzed by these coenzymes are generally quite similar to the redox potentials of the coenzymes themselves. Thus the reactions are generally reversible, depending on the concentration of the reactants and the products as well as changes in redox potential induced by other reactions in the cell.

Eakin[91] has classified the important reactions catalyzed by DPN and TPN into five categories. These are listed below, with some of the more important specific systems cited as examples. In addition, a miscellaneous category may be added to include reactions less clearly characterized or which are not included in this classification. Schlenk[92] has carefully described the most important of the enzyme reaction systems listed below.

1. Aldehyde $\rightleftharpoons$ Primary alcohol
   Acetaldehyde—ethanol (DPN)
2. Ketone $\rightleftharpoons$ Secondary alcohol
   Pyruvic acid—lactic acid (DPN)
   Pyruvic acid—malic acid (TPN)

[88] M. E. Pullman, S. P. Colowick, and N. O. Kaplan, *J. Biol. Chem.* **194,** 593 (1952).
[89] I. G. Leder and P. Handler, *J. Biol. Chem.* **189,** 889 (1951).
[90] A. Kornberg and O. Lindberg, *J. Biol. Chem.* **176,** 665 (1948).
[91] R. E. Eakin *in* The Biochemistry of the B Vitamins, American Chemical Society Monograph No. 110, p. 141. Reinhold Publishing Corp., New York, 1950.
[92] F. Schlenk *in* The Enzymes, Vol. II, Part 1, pp. 278–315. Academic Press, New York, 1951.

Oxalacetic acid—malic acid (DPN)
Oxalosuccinic acid—isocitric acid (DPN)
β-Hydroxybutyric acid—acetoacetic acid (DPN)
α-Ketoglutarate—isocitric acid (TPN)

3. Acyl phosphate $\rightleftharpoons$ Aldehyde-1-phosphate
   1,3-Diphosphoglyceric acid—3-phosphoglyceraldehyde (DPN)

4. Acid $\rightleftharpoons$ Aldehyde (hydrate)
   Gluconic acid—glucose (DPN) (TPN)
   6-Phosphogluconic acid—glucose-6-phosphate (TPN)
   Phosphoglyceric acid—phosphoglyceraldehyde (DPN)
   Phosphogluconic acid—ribulose phosphate (TPN)
   Acetic acid—acetaldehyde (DPN)

5. Imine $\rightleftharpoons$ Amine
   Iminoglutaric acid—L-glutamic acid (DPN–TPN)[92a]

6. Miscellaneous
   Reduction of nitrate to nitrite[93]
   The oxidation of liciferin to produce bioluminescence[94]
   Dehydration of formic acid[93, 95]

   $$HCOOH + DPN \rightarrow CO_2 + DPNH_2$$

   Conversion of choline to betaine (DPN)[96-98]
   Conversion of vitamin A_1 to rhodopsin (DPN)[99]
   Reduction of methemoglobin (DPN)[100]
   Destruction of testosterone by liver mince (DPN)[101]
   L-α-Glycerophosphate to dihydroxyacetone phosphate[102]
   Dismutation of pyruvate (in bacterial extracts)[103]

   Pyruvate + phosphate + DPN $\rightarrow$ Acetyl phosphate +
   CO_2 + DPNH; Pyruvate + DPNH $\rightarrow$ Lactate + DPN

I. SYSTEMS

The biochemical reactions listed previously do not occur independently but as a part of a series of reactions by which an organism carries out the

[92a] The glutamic acid dehydrogenase system of yeast and bacteria must be coupled with TPN, although the corresponding system in animal tissues is non-specific in its DPN-TPN preference.

[93] R. Adler and M. Srenwasaya, *Hoppe-Seyler's Z. physiol. Chem.* **249**, 24 (1937).

[94] F. H. Johnson and H. Eyring, *J. Am. Chem. Soc.* **66**, 848 (1944).

[95] J. C. Wirth and F. F. Nord, *Arch. Biochem.* **1**, 143 (1942).

[96] P. J. G. Mann and J. H. Quastel, *Biochem. J.* **31**, 869 (1937).

[97] J. R. Klein and P. Handler, *J. Biol. Chem.* **144**, 537 (1942).

[98] J. N. Williams, Jr., *J. Biol. Chem.* **195**, 37 (1952).

[99] R. Hubbard and G. Wald, *Science* **115**, 60 (1952).

[100] H. R. Gutman, B. J. Jandorf, and O. Bodansky, *J. Biol. Chem.* **169**, 145 (1947).

[101] M. L. Sweat and L. T. Samuels, *J. Biol. Chem.* **173**, 433 (1948).

[102] T. Baranowski, *J. Biol. Chem.* **180**, 535 (1949).

[103] S. Korkes, J. R. Stern, I. C. Gunsalus, and S. Ochoa, *Nature* **166**, 439 (1950).

complicated process of obtaining energy and building blocks from its nutrients or, during anabolic phases of metabolism, of synthesizing appropriate molecules for deposition or incorporation into other tissue substances. Only certain of these steps require the participation of DPN and TPN. Yet, these coenzymes are necessary for the catalysis of steps which are of such importance that, should these reactions be blocked, the cell cannot function and indeed the organism itself cannot survive.

1. Synthesis of High-Energy Phosphate Bonds

Phosphoric anhydride compounds such as adenosinetriphosphate occupy a key role in metabolism. They constitute a means whereby the cell can conserve and store energy in a readily transferable form. DPN and TPN are involved in the processes by which these high-energy phosphate bonds are synthesized. For example, if an aldehyde such as 1,3-diphosphoglyceraldehyde is dehydrogenated (i.e., oxidized) by DPN, one of the phosphate groups is converted into a reactive acyl phosphate which can be transferred to adenosinediphosphate (ADP), thus forming adenosinetriphosphate (ATP) as depicted below.[104-106]

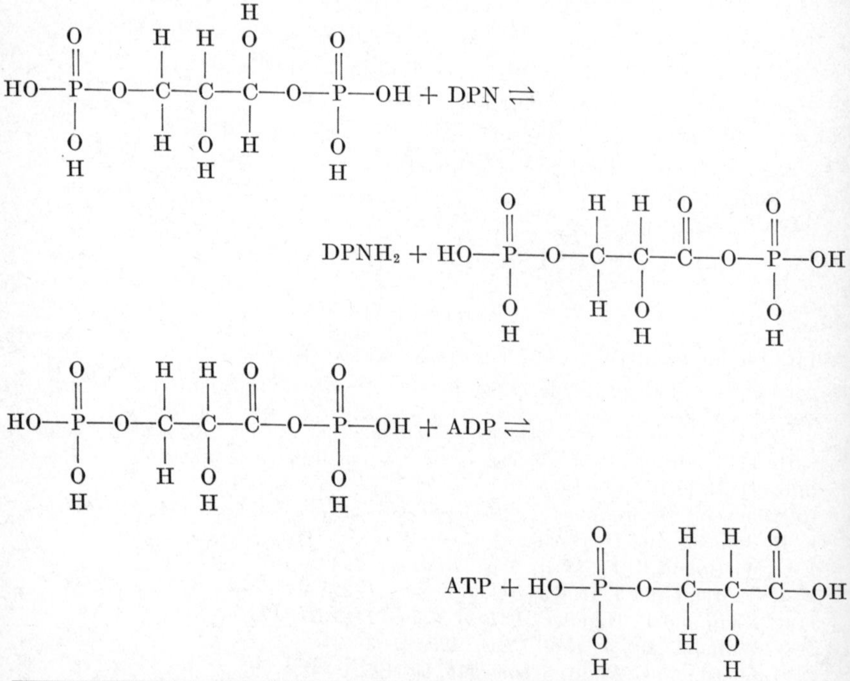

[104] O. Warburg and W. Christian, *Biochem. Z.* **301,** 221 (1939).
[105] O. Warburg and W. Christian, *Biochem. Z.* **303,** 40 (1939).
[106] E. Negelein and H. Bromel, *Biochem. Z.* **303,** 132 (1939).

Thus, during catabolic phases of cellular activity when organic substrates are being oxidized to provide energy, a part of the energy may be stored in the form of ATP. During anabolism, the process can be reversed, the net effect of which is to convert organic acids to aldehydes, liberating a reactive phosphate group which can be used to form glycosidic, ester, and perhaps other (peptide) bonds. This mechanism could be used, for instance, to supply the energy necessary to form the acetal bond by which glucose is polymerized into glycogen. Reactions such as these represent a general biological mechanism by which cells can convert the latent energy of organic substances into readily stored and utilized energy.

In addition to the type of reaction listed above, it is known that there are aerobic processes which convert inorganic phosphate into energy-rich pyrophosphates by reactions in which hydrogen atoms of $DPNH_2$ and $TPNH_2$ are transported to oxygen via the riboflavin and cytochrome enzymes.[107] Using a particulate (mitochondrial) fraction from rat liver, Friedkin and Lehninger[108] and Lehninger[109] have been able to demonstrate the synthesis of esterified phosphate during oxidations which are DPN linked. Adenosinediphosphate appeared to be the phosphate acceptor in their system. Lehninger[110] has recently published a careful analysis of the evidence pertaining to oxidative phosphorylation in DPN-linked systems. Although some of the evidence is conflicting, and many details are as yet unclear, it does seem probable that phosphorylation coupled to electron transport between $DPNH_2$ and oxygen constitutes a general biological mechanism for the esterification of high-energy phosphate. Green and associates,[111] using a different system derived from pig heart, have also obtained evidence indicating oxidative phosphorylation in DPN–TPN-linked systems.

DPN and TPN participate in phosphorylation reactions in yet another way. It has long been known that inorganic orthophosphate accumulates during the respiration of certain tissues. As inorganic phosphate accumulates, the balance between hexose phosphate and glycogen is disturbed, resulting in the breakdown of glycogen to glucose-1-phosphate. This supplies fuel for the glycolysis cycle, the energy from which can be utilized to resynthesize phosphoric acid anhydrides from inorganic phosphates. As the concentration of inorganic phosphate decreases and that of the organic phosphate increases, the equilibrium shifts toward the formation of glyco-

[107] F. Lipmann, Currents in Biochemical Research, pp. 137–148. Interscience Publishers, New York, 1946.

[108] M. Friedkin and A. L. Lehninger, J. Biol. Chem. **178,** 611 (1949).

[109] A. L. Lehninger, J. Biol. Chem. **178,** 625 (1949).

[110] A. L. Lehninger, in Phosphorus Metabolism, p. 344. The Johns Hopkins Press, Baltimore, 1951.

[111] D. E. Green and H. Beinert, in Phosphorus Metabolism, p. 330. The Johns Hopkins Press, Baltimore, 1951.

gen. This process is thought to constitute one of the important regulatory mechanisms in carbohydrate metabolism.

The source of the inorganic phosphate which accumulates has long been uncertain. It was widely held that most of it resulted from the hydrolytic cleavage of ATP. In certain systems, however, it could be clearly shown that ATP was not the source of the inorganic phosphate.[90, 112, 113] Kornberg[114, 115] recently established at least one source of this inorganic phosphate when he discovered an enzyme in yeast and in liver which catalyzed the reversible reaction:

Nicotinamide mononucleotide + ATP ⇌ DPN + inorganic pyrophosphate

This reaction plus the ubiquitous inorganic pyrophosphatase could yield orthophosphate. Schrecker and Kornberg[116] have demonstrated a similar phenomenon with flavin mononucleotide.

It should also be noted that this mechanism provides for a biosynthesis of DPN from nicotinamide mononucleotide (p. 506). The reverse of this reaction, i.e., the phosphorolysis of a dinucleotide by inorganic pyrophosphate, resembles the action of inorganic phosphate on the reversible splitting of polysaccharides referred to above (p. 497).

2. DPN AND TPN IN GLYCOLYSIS

Several pathways are known by which glucose can be utilized.[117] The classical series of reactions which seem to prevail in most organisms involves some eleven steps, with pyruvic acid as the end product.[118] Glucose is phosphorylated and converted through a series of steps to fructose-1,6-diphosphate. The latter compound is then split into two trioses, dihydroxyacetone phosphate and 3-phosphoglyceraldehyde. The latter compound forms an addition product with phosphate, 1,3-diphosphoglyceraldehyde, which is dehydrogenated by DPN and converted to 3-phosphoglyceric acid as depicted on p. 496. The latter compound is converted in three steps to pyruvic acid. The pyridine nucleotides are required for only one of these eleven steps as indicated above.

3. IN PYRUVATE METABOLISM

Pyruvic acid can be utilized in a number of ways.[119] When the supply of oxygen is limited, pyruvic acid can be converted to lactic acid.

[112] C. F. Cori, A Symposium on Respiratory Enzymes. Madison, 1942.

[113] R. J. Cross, J. V. Taggart, G. A. Covo, and D. E. Green, J. Biol. Chem. 177, 655 (1949).

[114] A. Kornberg, J. Biol. Chem. 182, 779 (1950).

[115] A. Kornberg and W. E. Pricer, Jr., J. Biol. Chem. 191, 535 (1951).

[116] A. W. Schrecker and A. Kornberg, J. Biol. Chem. 182, 795 (1950).

[117] E. S. G. Barron, Advances in Enzymol. 3, 149 (1943).

[118] O. Meyerhof, Biol. Symposia 5, 141 (1941).

[119] E. Stotz, Advances in Enzymol. 5, 129 (1945).

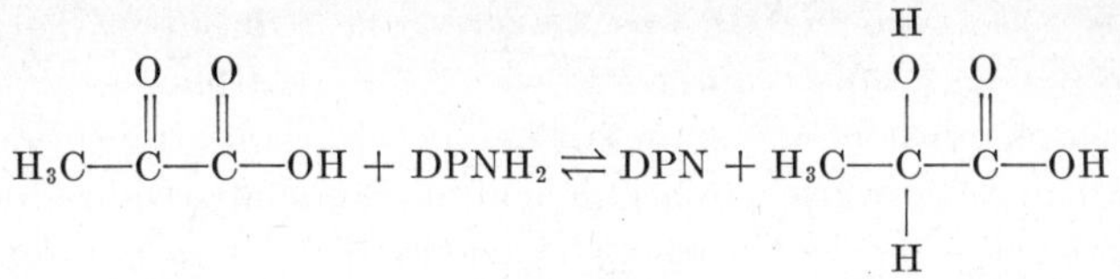

$$H_3C-\overset{\overset{\displaystyle O}{\|}}{C}-\overset{\overset{\displaystyle O}{\|}}{C}-OH + DPNH_2 \rightleftharpoons DPN + H_3C-\overset{\overset{\displaystyle H}{|}}{\underset{\underset{\displaystyle H}{|}}{C}}-\overset{\overset{\displaystyle O}{\|}}{C}-OH$$

It should be noted that this reaction could provide a mechanism to re-oxidize the DPN which was reduced in the conversion of phosphoglyceraldehyde to phosphoglyceric acid.

Also, under anaerobic conditions pyruvic acid may undergo β-carboxylation to yield oxalacetic acid,[120] which in turn can be converted by malic dehydrogenase, plus $DPNH_2$ as coenzyme, to malic acid as depicted below.

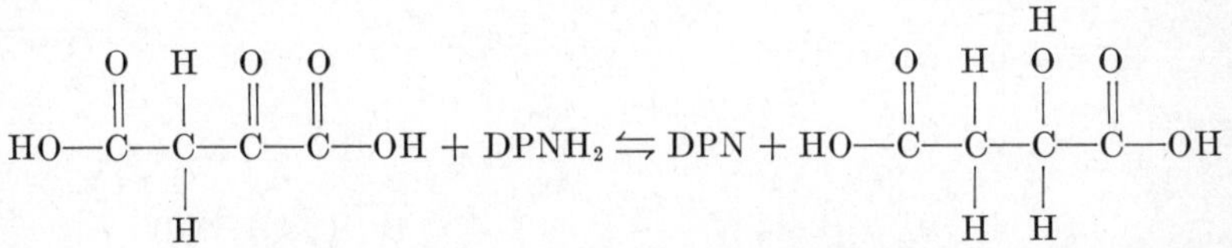

$$HO-\overset{\overset{\displaystyle O}{\|}}{C}-\overset{\overset{\displaystyle H}{|}}{\underset{\underset{\displaystyle H}{|}}{C}}-\overset{\overset{\displaystyle O}{\|}}{C}-\overset{\overset{\displaystyle O}{\|}}{C}-OH + DPNH_2 \rightleftharpoons DPN + HO-\overset{\overset{\displaystyle O}{\|}}{C}-\overset{\overset{\displaystyle H}{|}}{\underset{\underset{\displaystyle H}{|}}{C}}-\overset{\overset{\displaystyle H}{|}}{\underset{\underset{\displaystyle H}{|}}{C}}-\overset{\overset{\displaystyle O}{\|}}{C}-OH$$

Pyruvic acid may be converted by reductive fixation of carbon dioxide to malic acid[121] in the presence of "malic" enzyme, $TPNH_2$, and Mn^{++} as follows.

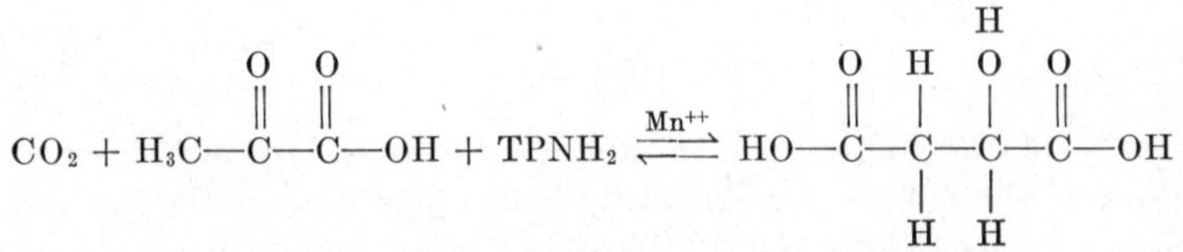

$$CO_2 + H_3C-\overset{\overset{\displaystyle O}{\|}}{C}-\overset{\overset{\displaystyle O}{\|}}{C}-OH + TPNH_2 \underset{}{\overset{Mn^{++}}{\rightleftharpoons}} HO-\overset{\overset{\displaystyle O}{\|}}{C}-\overset{\overset{\displaystyle H}{|}}{\underset{\underset{\displaystyle H}{|}}{C}}-\overset{\overset{\displaystyle H}{|}}{\underset{\underset{\displaystyle H}{|}}{C}}-\overset{\overset{\displaystyle O}{\|}}{C}-OH$$

It should be noted that this reaction provides a mechanism for carbon dioxide fixation (see p. 503).

A fourth type of anaerobic utilization of pyruvic acid (in yeast) involves decarboxylation to acetaldehyde which can be converted to ethanol.

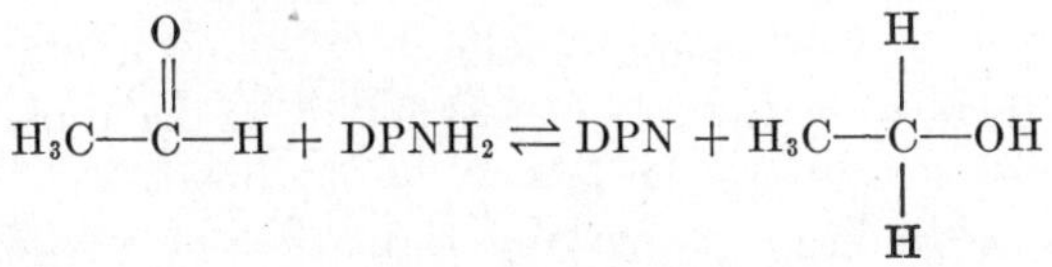

$$H_3C-\overset{\overset{\displaystyle O}{\|}}{C}-H + DPNH_2 \rightleftharpoons DPN + H_3C-\overset{\overset{\displaystyle H}{|}}{\underset{\underset{\displaystyle H}{|}}{C}}-OH$$

Pyruvic acid may be split to yield other 2-carbon compounds, i.e., acetic acid, or other 2-carbon acetyl fragments (activated acetate[122]) which are now known to be combined with coenzyme A (acetyl coenzyme A). Under aerobic conditions pyruvate may undergo oxidative decarboxylation to

---

[120] H. G. Wood and C. H. Werkman, *Biochem. J.* **32**, 1262 (1938).

[121] S. Ochoa, A. H. Mehler, and A. Kornberg, *J. Biol. Chem.* **174**, 979 (1948).

[122] F. Lipmann, *Advances in Enzymol.* **6**, 231 (1946).

yield acetyl coenzyme A. DPN is known to be reduced in the processes which lead to the formation of acetyl coenzyme A, although the exact biochemical mechanism is not known. The acetyl groups transferred by coenzyme A can be converted to acetic acid or commonly oxidized to carbon dioxide and water via the tricarboxylic acid cycle.[123, 124] In this complicated series of reactions DPN is required for the interconversion of malic and oxalacetic acids as described previously, and TPN is required for the conversion of isocitric to oxalosuccinic acid.

4. IN PENTOSE BIOSYNTHESIS

Because of the importance of ribose (and desoxyribose) in nucleotide metabolism, the biological origin of this substance has considerable interest. The exact mechanism of its synthesis has been obscure until recently. A series of reactions requiring TPN as a coenzyme has now been demonstrated which can account for the biosynthesis of pentose. The initial reaction:

Glucose-6-phosphate + TPN $\rightleftharpoons$ TPNH$_2$ + 6-phosphogluconic acid

was known from the early work of Warburg and associates.[7, 4] It was also known from studies by Lipmann[125] and by Warburg and Christian[126, 127] that yeast extracts were capable of further oxidizing 6-phosphogluconic acid in TPN-linked reactions. Dickens[128, 129] identified a pentose in similar reaction mixtures and postulated the formation of ribose-5-phosphate.

[123] H. A. Krebs, *Advances in Enzymol.* **3**, 247 (1943).
[124] H. A. Lardy and C. A. Elvehjem, *Ann. Rev. Biochem.* **14**, 1 (1945).
[125] F. Lipmann, *Nature* **138**, 588 (1936).
[126] O. Warburg and W. Christian, *Biochem. Z.* **287**, 440 1936).
[127] O. Warburg and W. Christian, *Biochem. Z.* **292**, 287 (1937).
[128] F. Dickens, *Biochem. J.* **32**, 1626, 1636 (1938).
[129] F. Dickens and G. E. Glock, *Nature* **166**, 33 (1950).

Cohen and Scott[130, 131] confirmed the formation of ribose-5-phosphate in these reactions.

Horecker and Smyrniotis[132] have purified the enzyme from yeast which catalyzes this reaction and have been able to characterize the reaction.

$$6\text{-Phosphogluconate} + \text{TPN} \rightleftharpoons \text{TPNH}_2 + \text{CO}_2 + \text{ribulose-5-phosphate}$$

$$\updownarrow$$

ribose-5-phosphate

The significance of these reactions may be considerably greater than just as a mechanism for ribose synthesis. They may consitute an important alternate pathway for the oxidation of glucose, and as a source of other biological compounds. All the steps in the further metabolism of these pentoses have not yet been elucidated. However, Horecker and Smyrniotis[133] have demonstrated the formation of a 7-carbon sugar, sedoheptulose, which is apparently formed by the condensation of ribulose phosphate and a 2-carbon fragment. In addition it should be noted that these reactions are reversible,[134] thus constituting a mechanism for the fixation of carbon dioxide, and may be of importance in photosynthesis.

5. In Lipid Metabolism

The dependence of fat metabolism on DPN–TPN-linked reactions has been studied less extensively than with carbohydrates. It is clear that DPN is required for the synthesis and degradation of glycerol. Dihydroxyacetone phosphate, derived from the splitting of fructose-1,6-diphosphate, can be reversibly converted to L-α-glycerophosphate by an enzyme which requires DPNH$_2$ as a hydrogen donor.[102, 135]

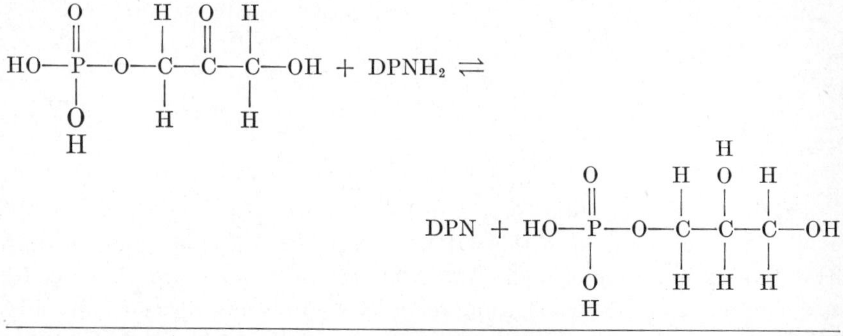

---

[130] S. S. Cohen and D. B. M. Scott, *Science* 111, 543 (1950).

[131] D. B. M. Scott and S. S. Cohen, *J. Biol. Chem.* 188, 509 (1951).

[132] B. L. Horecker and P. Z. Smyrniotis, *J. Biol. Chem.* 193, 371, 383 (1951).

[133] B. L. Horecker and P. Z. Smyrniotis, *Federation Proc.* 11, 232 (1952).

[134] B. L. Horecker and P. Z. Smyrniotis, *J. Biol. Chem.* 196, 135 (1952).

[135] E. Baer and H. O. L. Fisher, *J. Biol. Chem.* 128, 463 (1939).

It is also clear that the pyridine nucleotides are indirectly important in fatty oxidation, since the 2-carbon activated acetyl compounds which result from the β-oxidation of fatty acids are further oxidized via the tricarboxylic acid cycle. These substances enter the cycle principally by condensing with oxalacetic acid to form citric acid. Furthermore, these acetyl compounds seem to provide the common link between fat and carbohydrate metabolism. Since they can be formed from either carbohydrate or fat, they provide a means of synthesis of fat from carbohydrates or, vice versa, the oxidation of fat to provide energy.

Lehninger[136] has shown that DPN is required for fatty acid oxidation in crude rat liver homogenates. Green and associates[111] also have demonstrated fatty acid oxidation in enzyme systems which require DPN or TPN. The exact reactions and mechanisms involved in these complex systems and the specific role of the pyridine nucleotides (other than as a means of generating high-energy phosphate) is completely unknown.

The DPN requirement for fatty acid synthesis is even less clear. However, it is thought that fatty acid synthesis and degradation proceed through identical, albeit reverse, reaction pathways. On this basis, DPN–TPN would undoubtedly be required. Eakin[91] believes that the pyridine nucleotides are required for the numerous dehydrogenations which are probably involved and has proposed a scheme based on known reactions, some of which are DPN-linked, which could account for the synthesis of fatty acids.

DPN is important in the metabolism of the ketone bodies, since the interconversion of L-β-hydroxybutyric and acetoacetic acids is linked to this coenzyme.[137, 138]

$$H_3C-\overset{\overset{\displaystyle H}{|}}{\underset{\underset{\displaystyle H}{|}}{C}}-\overset{\overset{\displaystyle H}{|}}{\underset{\underset{\displaystyle H}{|}}{C}}-\overset{\overset{\displaystyle O}{\|}}{C}-OH + DPN \rightleftharpoons H_3C-\overset{\overset{\displaystyle O}{\|}}{C}-\overset{\overset{\displaystyle H}{|}}{\underset{\underset{\displaystyle H}{|}}{C}}-\overset{\overset{\displaystyle O}{\|}}{C}-OH + DPNH_2$$

6. In Nitrogen Metabolism

The pyridine nucleotides play a direct role in the metabolism of amino acids in only one system. Either DPN or TPN is required for the reversible oxidative deamination of L-glutamic acid. The α-amino group is converted to an α-imino group which spontaneously hydrolyzes to yield NH_3 and α-ketoglutaric acid. Since this reaction is reversible, it provides a link for the biological synthesis of an amino acid utilizing inorganic ammonia and a compound which can be derived from carbohydrate. Conversely it pro-

[136] A. L. Lehninger, *J. Biol. Chem.* **161,** 437 (1945).
[137] D. E. Green and J. Brosteaux, *Biochem. J.* **30,** 1489 (1936).
[138] D. E. Green, J. G. Dewan, and L. F. Leloir, *Biochem. J.* **31,** 934 (1937).

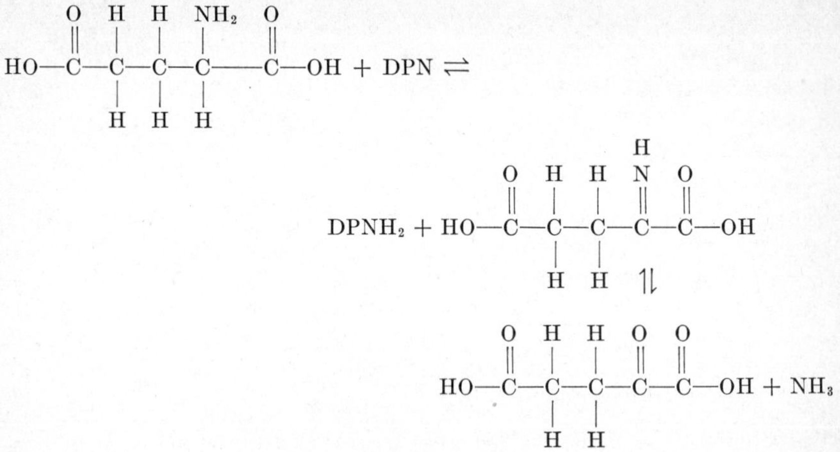

$$\text{HO—C—C—C—C——C—OH} + \text{DPN} \rightleftharpoons$$

(with structure bearing O, H, H, NH$_2$, O and H, H, H substituents)

$$\text{DPNH}_2 + \text{HO—C—C—C—C—C—OH}$$

(with structure bearing O, H, H, N, O and H, H substituents)

$$\text{HO—C—C—C—C—C—OH} + \text{NH}_3$$

(with structure bearing O, H, H, O, O and H, H substituents)

vides a means whereby the organism can derive energy from protein by converting the protein to glycogenic fragments.[76] This reaction probably has considerable biological significance, since glutamic acid is currently believed to constitute a central pool to receive or donate amino groups.

Indirectly, DPN and TPN are important in protein metabolism when the organism breaks down amino acids to provide energy. The deaminated derivatives of the glycogenic amino acids are further oxidized via conventional carbohydrate oxidative pathways as already described.

Meister[72] has recently shown that crystalline lactic dehydrogenase and DPNH$_2$ are capable of reducing a number of α, γ-diketo, and α-keto acids to products as yet unidentified (but not lactic acid). TPNH$_2$ can substitute for DPNH$_2$, but the reaction rate is much slower. This reaction may have biological significance in the utilization of the keto derivatives of amino acids as well as other metabolites.

7. In Photosynthesis

The biochemical mechanism of photosynthesis has been a subject of great interest but little information for many years. It is now known that animals as well as plants and bacteria can incorporate atmospheric carbon dioxide into organic compounds. Wood[139] has listed seventeen compounds in which carbon dioxide can be fixed, although only a few of these provide for primary fixation of carbon dioxide.

Two recent research findings have emphasized the fact that the pyridine nucleotides may have an important role in photosynthesis. Horecker and Symrniotis[134] have proved the reversibility of the following reaction:

Ribulose-5-phosphate + CO_2 + TPNH + H^+ $\rightleftharpoons$ 6-Phosphogluconate + TPN

[139] H. G. Wood, *Physiol. Revs.* **26**, 198 (1946).

Since 6-phosphogluconate can be converted to glucose-6-phosphate in a TPN-linked reaction (p. 500), it is evident that this could provide a mechanism for the incorporation of carbon dioxide directly into glucose.

An even more pertinent development was the demonstration by Ochoa et al.[121] of the following TPN-linked reaction catalyzed by "malic" enzyme:

$$CO_2 + pyruvate + TPNH_2 \overset{Mn^{++}}{\rightleftharpoons} \text{L-Malate} + TPN$$

When this reaction was coupled with a glucose-6-phosphate–TPN system to provide a steady supply of $TPNH_2$, a highly efficient means of fixing carbon dioxide resulted.[140] A similar reaction occurs in the formation of isocitric acid.[79]

$$CO_2 + \alpha\text{-ketoglutarate} + TPNH_2 \overset{Mn^{++}}{\rightleftharpoons} \text{D-Isocitrate} + TPN$$

Furthermore, evidence has been obtained that green grana from spinach chloroplasts can effect a reduction of DPN and TPN, presumably by utilizing the energy of light to transfer hydrogens from water to the coenzymes, thus supplying the reduced coenzymes needed for the above reactions.[141-143] Carbon dioxide fixation forming malate or isocitrate was shown to proceed in these green grana suspensions when illuminated, but not in the dark. Ochoa and Vishniac[140] also demonstrated that the $DPNH_2$ generated in the green grana could be utilized to catalyze other DPN linked reactions such as pyruvate $\rightleftharpoons$ lactate, oxalacetate $\rightleftharpoons$ malate, and α-ketoglutarate $\rightleftharpoons$ L-glutamate. It should also be noted that $DPNH_2$ and $TPNH_2$ produced by the action of light could be used to generate high phosphate bond energy, i.e., convert light energy to chemical energy (p. 496). Tolmach[144] and Arnon[145] have confirmed and extended much of the work reported above and have provided additional evidence for the view that photosynthesis in plants may operate basically through a reversal of a respiratory cycle which is powered by radiant energy rather than chemical energy.[146] The light-induced reduction of the pyridine nucleotides may be a key step in these processes.

J. BIOLOGICAL SYNTHESIS OF DPN AND TPN

It is now possible to account rather completely for the biological synthesis of these coenzymes. Reactions other than, or in addition to, the ones

[140] S. Ochoa and W. Vishniac, *Science* **115**, 297 (1952).
[141] W. Vishniac, *Federation Proc.* **10**, 265 (1951).
[142] W. Vishniac and S. Ochoa, *Nature* **167**, 768 (1951).
[143] W. Vishniac and S. Ochoa, *J. Biol. Chem.* **195**, 75 (1952).
[144] L. J. Tolmach, *Nature* **167**, 946 (1951).
[145] D. I. Arnon, *Nature* **167**, 1008 (1951).
[146] M. Calvin, J. A. Bassham, and A. A. Benson, *Federation Proc.* **9**, 524 (1950).

listed below may exist, but at least these reactions make possible one route of formation.

1. SYNTHESIS OF NICOTINIC ACID

The sources of nicotinic acid may be diet, the conversion of tryptophan to nicotinic acid (p. 523), or possibly intestinal microorganisms (p. 530).

2. AMIDATION OF NICOTINIC ACID

Ellinger[147] has shown that kidney and brain slices are capable of amidating nicotinic acid. Liver slices can also accomplish this conversion if a source of NH_3 such as glutamine is provided. Slices from several other tissues were unable to accomplish this conversion. It was assumed from early studies that erythrocytes (human) could also amidate nicotinic acid since, both *in vivo* and *in vitro*, nicotinic acid but not nicotinamide produced an increase within the erythrocytes of material which had activity for *Hemophilus parainfluenza*, for *Hemophilus influenza*, or for DPN-linked enzyme systems.[148-152] Furthermore, Liefer *et al.*[153] used carboxyl-C^{14}-labeled nicotinic acid and nicotinamide to show a rapid uptake and fixation of nicotinic acid within the erythrocyte (mice). Nicotinamide, on the other hand, was taken up by the erythrocytes but could be washed out readily, indicating that it had not been incorporated into fixed non-diffusible molecules.

More recently, Leder and Handler[89] have found just the contrary, i.e., that nicotinamide but not nicotinic acid resulted in an increased synthesis of coenzyme-active material in erythrocytes. A good explanation for these contradictory results is not apparent.

3. SYNTHESIS OF RIBOSE

A mechanism which can account for the synthesis of ribose from glucose has already been detailed (p. 500). Other mechanisms are possible.[154]

4. SYNTHESIS OF NICOTINAMIDE MONONUCLEOTIDE

This fragment of the molecule (nicotinamide-ribose-phosphate) can be synthesized by erythrocytes incubated with nicotinamide and glucose.[89] A

[147] P. Ellinger, *Biochem. J.* **42,** 175 (1948).
[148] H. I. Kohn and J. R. Klein, *J. Biol. Chem.* **130,** 1 (1939).
[149] H. I. Kohn and J. R. Klein, *J. Biol. Chem.* **135,** 685 (1940).
[150] C. L. Hoagland and S. M. Ward, *J. Biol. Chem.* **146,** 115 (1942).
[151] P. Handler and H. I. Kohn, *J. Biol. Chem.* **150,** 447 (1943).
[152] C. L. Hoagland, S. M. Ward, and R. E. Shank, *J. Biol. Chem.* **151,** 369 (1943).
[153] E. Leifer, J. R. Hogness, L. J. Roth, and W. H. Langham. *J. Am. Chem. Soc.* **70,** 2908 (1948).
[154] B. L. Horecker, *in* Phosphorus Metabolism, Chapter III. The Johns Hopkins Press, Baltimore, 1951.

mechanism which can account for the synthesis of this fragment has been described by Rowen and Kornberg.[155] A reversible reaction which is catalyzed by an enzyme preparation from hog liver and which requires orthophosphate was observed.

$$\text{Nicotinamide-riboside} + \text{orthophosphate}$$
$$\rightleftharpoons \text{Nicotinamide} + \text{ribose-1-phosphate} + \text{H}^+$$

The further reaction is tentative, but preliminary evidence indicates a direct phosphorylation of nicotinamide riboside by ATP:

$$\text{Nicotinamide-riboside} + \text{ATP} \rightleftharpoons \text{Nicotinamide-riboside-phosphate} + \text{ADP}$$

5. BIOSYNTHESIS OF DPN

The biosynthesis of DPN had been observed in erythrocytes as described earlier and in yeast fermentation systems.[156] Kornberg and associates[55, 114, 115] have observed the following reversible reaction in a purified enzyme system:

$$\text{Nicotinamide-ribose-phosphate} + \text{ATP} \rightleftharpoons \text{DPN} + \text{inorganic pyrophosphate}$$

This reaction has been confirmed, with P^{32} as a tracer.[115] From the kinetics of this reaction and the concentration of the enzyme in liver, Kornberg[114] estimates that the entire DPN content of liver could be synthesized in less than 5 minutes if the substrates were optimal. It can be seen that this reaction not only completes DPN synthesis but provides an origin for the adenine-ribose-phosphate portion of the molecule, i.e., from ATP. The mechanism of adenine biosynthesis is obscure, except that it is known to be synthesized by mammalian tissues.

6. BIOSYNTHESIS OF TPN

The biosynthesis of TPN from nicotinamide plus ribose and adenosinetriphosphate (ATP) in cell-free extracts has been reported.[157] This report has never been confirmed, and subsequent experience leaves considerable doubt as to its validity. It is known that TPN can be synthesized enzymatically from DPN[45, 158] when DPN is incubated with ATP and a yeast preparation. Mehler et al.[77] also observed the formation of TPN from DPN and ATP in crude liver fractions. The mechanism of this reaction has now been shown to be a direct phosphorylation of DPN by ATP which is catalyzed by an enzyme which can be purified from ale yeast.[43]

$$\text{DPN} + \text{ATP} \rightarrow \text{TPN} + \text{adenosinediphosphate (ADP)}$$

[155] A. Kornberg, in Phosphorus Metabolism, Chapter VI. The Johns Hopkins Press, Baltimore, 1951.
[156] A. Lennerstrand, Arkiv Kemi, Mineral. Geol. 14A, No. 16, 1 (1941).
[157] K. I. Altman and E. A. Evans, Jr., J. Biol. Chem. 169, 463 (1947).
[158] H. von Euler and R. Vestin, Arkiv Kemi, Mineral. Geol. 12B, No. 44 (1938).

TPN may be readily converted to DPN by phosphatases from a number of sources,[55, 159] by yeast,[44] and by "cyclophorase" preparations from rabbit kidney and rabbit liver.[160]

K. DESTRUCTION OF DPN AND TPN

Some of the ways in which these coenzymes can be degraded have already been described, since most of the reactions described under biosynthesis (p. 506) are reversible. Actually, it has long been known that many animal tissues, plants, and microorganisms can enzymatically split these coenzymes.[161] Ohlmeyer[162] and Heiwinkel[163] identified adenylic acid as a breakdown product of DPN. Das and von Euler[164, 165] found inorganic orthophosphate when DPN was destroyed in animal tissues. Handler and Klein[166] identified nicotinamide as a breakdown product when DPN was destroyed by brain, liver, kidney, and muscle preparations from several animal species. Mann and Quastel[167] also called attention to the potent destructive power of certain animal tissues, especially brain, and showed that this rapid breakdown could be inhibited with rather high concentrations of nicotinamide. McIlwain and associates[168, 169] have also studied the destruction of DPN in brain preparations. Govier and Jetter[170] have shown that α-tocopherol phosphate has an inhibitory effect on DPN breakdown by heart DPNase. From these and other studies it appears that the common DPNase of animal tissue splits DPN at the glycosidic linkage between nicotinic acid and ribose. Nason et al.[171] have concentrated a DPNase from Neurospora which acts in a fashion similar to animal DPNase. This enzyme is not inhibited by excess nicotinamide, however. Animal tissues also contain another type of DPNase which splits DPN at the pyrophosphate linkage.[90]

These DPN-destroying enzymes are particularly active when the cells

[159] D. R. Sanadi, J. J. Betheil, and B. J. Katchman, Abstr. Am. Chem. Soc. 118th Meeting, p. 52C, 1950.

[160] B. Katchman, J. J. Betheil, A. I. Schepartz, and D. R. Sanadi, Arch. Biochem. and Biophys. 34, 437 (1951).

[161] F. Schlenk, Advances in Enzymol. 5, 207 (1945).

[162] P. Ohlmeyer, Biochem. Z. 287, 212 (1936).

[163] H. Heiwinkel, Arkiv Kemi, Mineral. Geol. 13A, No. 19 (1939).

[164] N. B. Das and H. von Euler, Nature 141, 604 (1938).

[165] N. B. Das, Arkiv Kemi, Mineral. Geol. 13A, No. 7 (1939).

[166] P. Handler and J. R. Klein, J. Biol. Chem. 143, 49 (1942).

[167] P. J. G. Mann and J. H. Quastel, Biochem. J. 35, 502 (1941).

[168] H. McIlwain and D. E. Hughes, Biochem. J. 43, 60 (1948).

[169] H. McIlwain and R. Rodnight, Biochem. J. 44, 470 (1949); 45, 337 (1949).

[170] W. M. Govier and N. S. Jetter, Science 107, 146 (1948).

[171] A. Nason, Federation Proc. 10, 228 (1951); A. Nason, N. O. Kaplan, and S. P. Colowick, J. Biol. Chem. 188, 379 (1951).

are disrupted so that special precautions must be taken when making homogenates or extracts of tissue for DPN or TPN analysis.

The extent to which these "destroying" mechanisms may have physiological significance in the normal wear-and-tear breakdown of the pyridine nucleotides is unknown. It is of considerable interest, however, that Zatman[172] has recently used isotopic nicotinamide to demonstrate that spleen DPNase catalyzes an exchange between free nicotinamide and that bound into DPN. This provides a mechanism whereby the nicotinamide can be removed and replaced in DPN-TPN without destruction of the rest of the molecule.

L. INHIBITORS OF DPN AND TPN

Inhibitors in intact animals are considered elsewhere (p. 548).

Inhibitors such as cyanide and iodoacetate are known to inhibit some codehydrogenase enzyme systems *in vitro*. Of potentially greater biological significance is the fact that at least some DPN–TPN-linked systems can be inhibited by the components of the DPN molecule. The inhibitory effect of nicotinamide on DPN breakdown has already been mentioned (p. 507). Feigelson *et al.*[173] have shown that high levels of nicotinamide inhibit the respiration of rat liver homogenates, an effect reversible with DPN. From an analysis of the Michaelis constants they believe this to be due to a competition between nicotinamide and DPN for the apoenzyme. However, Adler *et al.*[174] believe that this phenomenon is more complicated than just enzyme displacement. They found that pyridine-3-sulfonic acid (a nicotinic acid inhibitor in bacteria) would inhibit glucose and lactic dehydrogenase systems, but so would salicylic acid, nicotinic acid, adenine, adenosine, and adenine dinucleotide. Inhibition could be reversed with DPN but not by adenine compounds. In addition, succinic dehydrase, which is not DPN-linked, was also inhibited by the compounds listed above. Williams[175] recently reported that adenine, adenosine, and adenosinetriphosphate would inhibit a malic dehydrogenase system in a manner competitive with DPN. Sulfathiazole and sulfapyridine have been reported to inhibit nicotinamide-stimulated respiration and growth in certain microorganisms.[176] However, Anderson and associates[176a] found no effect of these sulfa drugs on DPN-

[172] L. J. Zatman, *Federation Proc.* **11**, 315 (1952).

[173] P. Feigelson, J. N. Williams, and C. A. Elvehjem, *J. Biol. Chem.* **189**, 361 (1951).

[174] E. Adler, H. von Euler, and B. Skarzynski, *Arkiv Kemi, Mineral. Geol.* **16A**, No. **9**, 1, (1943); **17**, No. **2**, 1 (1943).

[175] J. N. Williams, Jr., *J. Biol. Chem.* **195**, 629 (1952).

[176] R. West and A. F. Coburn, *J. Exptl. Med.* **72**, 91 (1940).

[176a] E. G. Anderson, F. J. Pilgrim, and C. A. Elvehjem, *Proc. Soc. Exptl. Biol. Med.* **55**, 39 (1944).

linked enzyme systems or on the respiration of rat liver in the presence of fumarate or pyruvate.

M. ASSAY PROCEDURES FOR DPN AND TPN

Chemical methods have been described elsewhere (p. 537).

1. GENERAL PRINCIPLES

A number of enzymatic methods have been described which permit a quantitation of DPN or TPN. The most widely used are the spectrophotometric techniques which depend upon the fact that oxidized DPN-TPN exhibit no absorption at 340 mμ whereas the reduced enzymes absorb strongly and identically at this wavelength. Since the molecular extinction coefficients are known (p. 490) and since absorption is proportional to concentration, these coenzymes can be readily quantitated. The methods are fairly sensitive. There are few substances, either components or reaction products of the enzyme systems, which have interfering light absorption at 340 mμ. Determinations may be made quickly with small quantities of materials and are especially useful in following the progress of reactions. The methods may be adapted to measure either the appearance or disappearance of the reduced forms, depending on whether the particular enzyme system donates or accepts hydrogen. They may also be used to measure the concentration of the apoenzymes or the substrates when these are limiting factors in the reaction mixtures. Specificity for DPN or TPN can be attained when dealing with mixtures by using an apoenzyme and a substrate which specifically requires one or the other coenzyme. These systems also permit the measurement of reactions not amenable to direct spectrophotometric determination if they can be coupled to reactions dependent on these coenzymes.[177-179]

2. DPN

As an example, DPN may be determined as described by Kornberg,[114] using crystalline alcohol dehydrogenase and alcohol to reduce the DPN. The components of the test system are ethanol 0.3 ml., glycine (1.5%) 0.2 ml., sodium pyrophosphate buffer (0.03 M, pH 8.5) 1.5 ml., alcohol dehydrogenase 5 to 10 γ, and water or unknown q.s. 3.0 ml. Figure 8 shows the sensitivity and proportionality of the method with known amounts of DPN. The reaction was complete in 5 minutes. The specificity of the procedure could be verified by observing the complete disappearance of

[177] O. Warburg, *Ergeb. Enzymforsch.* **7**, 210 (1938).
[178] E. Schlenk, *in* Methoden der Fermentforschung. Academic Press, New York, 1945.
[179] T. R. Hogness and V. R. Potter, *Ann. Rev. Biochem.* **10**, 509 (1941).

absorption at 340 mμ when small amounts of pyruvate and lactic dehydrogenase were added.

DPN may also be determined as described by Cori *et al.*[180] utilizing a reaction originally proposed by Warburg and Christian[105] in which D-glyceraldehyde-3-phosphate is oxidized to D-glyceric acid phosphate by the appropriate crystalline dehydrogenase plus DPN as a hydrogen acceptor. Arsenate is required to make this reaction go to completion (arsenolysis). The DPNH$_2$ formed is measured spectrophotometrically at 340 mμ. This system is more complicated than the one described above since fructose-

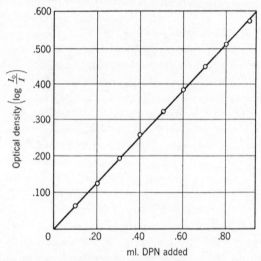

FIG. 8. Spectrophotometric assay for DPN; response to known amounts of DPN. (From Kornberg.[114])

1,6-diphosphate is used to produce D-glyceraldehyde-3-phosphate according to the following reaction:

Fructose-1,6-diphosphate + aldolase

$\updownarrow$

D-Glyceraldehyde-3-phosphate $\underset{\text{isomerase}}{\rightleftharpoons}$ Dihydroxyacetone phosphate

+ dehydrogenase

+ DPN

D-Glyceric acid 3-phosphate + DPNH$_2$

This system, however, has the advantage not only of providing for the quantitation of DPN, but of being a sensitive method for the determination

[180] G. T. Cori, M. W. Slein, and C. F. Cori, *J. Biol. Chem.* **173,** 605 (1948).

of fructose diphosphate and the triose phosphates either singly or together, depending on the order of addition of the three enzymes concerned. This may be considered an example of the way in which substances other than DPN may be quantitated by linking the reactions to DPN-dependent enzyme systems.

DPN may also be converted chemically to DPNH$_2$, using hydrosulfite reduction (p. 491), and measured by absorption at 340 mμ.[181] This procedure does not differentiate between DPN and TPN. Cyanide also will react with DPN (p. 487) to form a complex with an absorption maximum at 340 mμ This reaction may be used analytically for DPN, as shown by Colowick et al.[182]

DPNH$_2$ may be quantitated by oxidation with pyruvic acid and lactic dehydrogenase, the disappearance of absorption at 340 mμ being a measure of the amount of reduced coenzyme present.[183]

3. TPN

TPN can be determined spectrophotometrically in an isocitric dehydrogenase system which specifically requires TPN.[80] This system, as described by Ochoa,[79] is dependent on two reactions, the net result of which is:

$$\text{D-Isocitric acid} + \text{TPN} \xrightleftharpoons{\text{Mn}^{++}} \alpha\text{-Ketoglutaric acid} + CO_2 + \text{TPNH}_2$$

Oxalosuccinic acid is an intermediate in the reaction.

TPN may also be determined utilizing the glucose dehydrogenase reaction originally described by Warburg and Christian,[4, 7, 184, 185] which is also TPN-dependent.

$$\text{Glucose-6-phosphate} + \text{TPN} \rightleftharpoons 6\text{-Phosphogluconic acid} + \text{TPNH}_2$$

This reaction can be coupled to a system in which cytochrome c is the final hydrogen acceptor to form a very sensitive assay procedure.[186] It may also be linked to the system

$$\text{Glucose} + \text{ATP} \xrightleftharpoons{\text{hexokinase}} \text{Glucose-6-phosphate} + \text{ADP}$$

to supply glucose-6-phosphate for the TPN-dependent reaction listed above. If ATP is the limiting factor in the mixture, then the amount of TPN reduced in the combined reaction will have a proportionality to the amount of ATP present, permitting a quantitative ATP assay.[114]

[181] G. A. LePage, J. Biol. Chem. **168**, 623 (1947).

[182] S. P. Colowick, N. O. Kaplan, and M. M. Ciotti, J. Biol. Chem. **191**, 447 (1951).

[183] F. Kubowitz and P. Ott, Biochem. Z. **314**, 94 (1943).

[184] O. Warburg and W. Christian, Biochem. Z. **242**, 206 (1931).

[185] E. Negelein and W. Gerischer, Biochem. Z. **284**, 289 (1936).

[186] E. Haas, C. J. Harper, and T. R. Hogness, J. Biol. Chem. **142**, 835 (1942).

The conversion of 6-phosphogluconic acid to CO_2 and pentose phosphate is also TPN-dependent and can be used as an assay for either 6-phosphogluconate or TPN, as shown by Horecker and Smyrniotis.[132]

$$\text{6-Phosphogluconate} + \text{TPN} \rightleftharpoons \text{TPNH}_2 + CO_2 + \text{pentose phosphate}$$

These enzymatic methods have largely replaced the older manometric or methylene blue reduction procedures.[152, 187-191]

The spectrophotometric methods referred to above are possible only with purified or semipurified enzyme systems. Chemical and microbiological methods are available for use in crude tissue extracts (p. 537). However, Feigelson and associates[192] have developed a spectrophotometric method which measures both DPN and TPN and can be used in crude tissue extracts. The tissue is rapidly frozen, homogenized in 2% trichloroacetic acid with H_2O_2, to oxidize and stabilize the coenzymes, and centrifuged. The coenzymes in the supernatant are absorbed on charcoal (Nuchar C). After washing with trichloroacetic acid, the coenzymes are eluted with pyridine. The coenzyme concentration is determined by comparing the absorption at 340 mμ of oxidized and hydrosulfite-reduced samples, following the method of Gutcho and Stewart.[193] The concentration of DPN–TPN was calculated on the basis of dilution factors and the fact that 100 γ of reduced coenzymes per milliliter in a 1-cm. cell has an optical density of 0.840, according to Gutcho and Stewart[193] and Schlenk.[22] The correctness of the 0.840 factor just cited seems open to question. From recent data on the extinction coefficient of DPN–TPN (6.22×10^3) and with a 3-ml. cell and a 1-cm. light path, this factor should be about 0.939 if only DPN were present. By virtue of its somewhat higher molecular weight, TPN, if present, would reduce this factor slightly. Since the method of Feigelson *et al.* does not distinguish TPN, it would be difficult to determine how much the factor should be reduced, especially when working with a variety of animal tissues. In view of these considerations, it seems possible that the recent intensive studies of the Wisconsin group on DPN and TPN in animal tissue contain a small systematic error, which would, however, not affect the validity of the changes in tissue concentration which they observed under various conditions.

[187] K. Myrbäck, *Hoppe-Seyler's Z. physiol. Chem.* **177**, 158 (1928).

[188] H. von Euler, *Ergeb. Physiol.* **38**, 1 (1936).

[189] K. Myrbäck, *Ergeb. Enzymforsch.* **2**, 139 (1933).

[190] A. E. Axelrod and C. A. Elvehjem, *J. Biol. Chem.* **131**, 77 (1939).

[191] P. S. Krishnan, *Science* **105**, 295 (1947).

[192] P. Feigelson, J. N. Williams, Jr., and C. A. Elvehjem, *J. Biol. Chem.* **185**, 741 (1950).

[193] S. Gutcho and E. D. Stewart, *Anal. Chem.* **20**, 1185 (1948).

N. TISSUE DISTRIBUTION AND FATE

The tissue distribution and intermediary metabolism of administered nicotinic acid has been poorly understood. Some studies have been done measuring changes in tissue concentration and urinary excretion following administration of the vitamin. Although such studies are valuable, they are limited by their inability to distinguish the distribution and fate of administered vitamins in relation to pre-existing tissue stores.

1. EXCRETION

Roth and associates[194] have applied radioactive tracer techniques to this problem with very interesting results. They administered C^{14}-carboxyl-labeled nicotinic acid and nicotinamide intraperitoneally to mice and determined radioactivity in exhaled air, urine, feces, and tissues as a function of time.

A single dose of nicotinic acid, 0.7 mg., which is considerably in excess of the normal daily requirement, resulted in a large excretion of radioactivity in urine (about 60 % of administered dose) and in pulmonary carbon dioxide (about 3 % of administered dose) within the first 24 hours. The latter finding is of especial interest, since it proved, for the first time, that animal tissues are capable of decarboxylating nicotinic acid. The rather large urinary excretion would be expected, since the animals were, presumably, already well nourished with respect to nicotinic acid. Excretion was much less after 24 hours, and minimal after 48 hours. Nicotinic acid remaining in the animal at this point was assumed to be a part of the normal tissue enzyme stores. By comparing the amount of radioactivity excreted in urine and in pulmonary carbon dioxide after 48 hours, these investigators estimated that the mouse normally disposes of 15 to 20 % of the nicotinic acid liberated from the tissues as carbon dioxide. Since only the carboxyl group of the administered nicotinic acid was labeled, this does not necessarily mean that the pyridine ring was also oxidized to carbon dioxide. In later studies[195] these investigators showed that this phenomenon of pulmonary carbon dioxide excretion from labeled nicotinic acid and nicotinamide also existed in hamsters, rats, and dogs. Hamsters and rats excreted somewhat more in this fashion, and dogs much less than the mouse. Very little, if any, of the radioactivity appeared in the feces, a fact of significance in the problem of intestinal synthesis of nicotinic acid (p. 530).

[194] L. J. Roth, E. Leifer, J. R. Hogness, and W. H. Langham, *J. Biol. Chem.* **176**, 249 (1948).
[195] E. Leifer, L. J. Roth, D. S. Hogness, and M. H. Corson, *J. Biol. Chem.* **190**, 595 (1951).

2. Tissue Distribution and Turnover Rate

The uptake of radioactive nicotinic acid by various tissues and organs was determined and the concentration followed at intervals for 15 days. Uptake was highest in kidneys and lowest in erythrocytes. No radioactivity was found in plasma after 24 hours. The excretion half-time (i.e., turnover rate) was about 4 days in liver, kidney, and spleen, 5 days in cardiac muscle and erythrocytes, and 8 days in brain, sternum, and skeletal muscle. Since nicotinic acid exists in tissues almost entirely as coenzymes, it seems clear that coenzymes are broken down at an unexpectedly rapid rate. It is also of significance that the mouse handled nicotinic acid and nicotinamide identically in the above studies.

TABLE IX

Relative Per Cent Distribution of Radioactivity among Urinary Metabolites of C^{14}-Nicotinic Acid and C^{14}-Nicotinamide 12 to 24 Hours after Injection

Metabolites	C^{14} nicotinic acid				C^{14}-nicotinamide			
	Dog	Rat	Hamster	Mouse	Dog	Rat	Hamster	Mouse
N^1-Methylnicotinamide	94	56	23.6	13.6	94	73.5	35	20
Nicotinuric acid	1	10.5	2.8	24.8	0.5	0	0	0.5
Nicotinic acid	0.3	6.3	24.5	37.2	1	5.5	17	36.2
Unknown[a]	0	11.9	13.0	7.0	1	3.6	13	9
N^1-Methyl-6-pyridone-3-carboxylamide	2	11.9	10.6	11.6	2.5	12	10	20
Nicotinamide	2.4	3.5	25.5	6.1	1	5.6	25	14.3

[a] Unidentified but possibly 2-pyridone of N^1-methylnicotinamide.

The rather large excretion of carbon dioxide derived from nicotinic acid, as observed in the above experiments, also explains a fact noted by many investigators namely, that less nicotinic acid (including all known derivatives) may be excreted than is consumed or administered (in some species).

3. Urinary Metabolites

The urinary excretion pattern following administration of nicotinic acid and nicotinamide was generally similar, but it differed in some details. There was, also, considerable variation among species. Table IX summarizes the results of Leifer et al.[195] in four species. Paper chromatographic methods were used to separate the various metabolites. Trigonelline contained no C^{14}, indicating that it is not derived from nicotinic acid, in confirmation of many other workers.

Perlzweig and associates[196] have studied the urinary excretion pattern

[196] W. A. Perlzweig, F. Rosen, and P. B. Pearson, *J. Nutrition* **40**, 453 (1950).

of nicotinic acid in man and eight other mammalian species and have reviewed much of the earlier work on this subject. Table X has been adapted from their data to indicate the marked species variation. Apparently, man, dog, rat, and swine dispose of nicotinic acid largely as methylated products, whereas the herbivora, rabbits, guinea pigs, sheep, goats, and calves, dispose of nicotinic acid in some other fashion. Johnson et al.[197] also found that nicotinic acid was excreted principally in a methylated form in human subjects. Ellinger and associates[198] have studied this question extensively in man, dog, cat, rat, rabbit, and guinea pig. They obtained results essentially the same as Perlzweig et al.[196] with reference to the ability of

TABLE X
URINARY EXCRETION OF NICOTINIC ACID AND ITS DERIVATIVES

Species	Dose	NMN[a]	6-Pyridone[b]	N.A.[c]	Unaccounted for
		Per cent of administered or ingested nicotinic acid			
Man	Normal diet[d]	33	41	6	20
Man	500 mg. nicotinamide	38	43	1	18
Dog	10 mg./kg. nicotinamide	80	0	8	12
Rat	100–200 mg./kg. nicotinamide	50	3	15	32
Pig	75– 80 mg./kg. nicotinamide	7	10	9	74
Rabbit	90–100 mg./kg. nicotinamide	0.5[e]	3	43	53.5
Guinea pig	150–200 mg./kg. nicotinamide	0.5	5	8	86.5
Goat	70–100 mg./kg. nicotinamide	0.5	0.5	14	85.0
Sheep	30– 60 mg./kg. nicotinamide	0.5	0.3	30	69.0
Calf	30– 70 mg./kg. nicotinamide	0.6	0	35	64

[a] N^L-Methylnicotinamide.
[b] 6-Pyridone of N^L-methylnicotinamide.
[c] Includes nicotinic acid, nicotinamide, and nicotinuric acid, if present.
[e] The significance of these values below 1% is questionable owing to analytical limitations.
[d] Nicotinic acid content estimated at 17 mg.

various species to excrete methylated derivatives of nicotinic acid. The cat resembles other carnivorous and omnivorous species in that it does excrete N^1-methylnicotinamide. Chickens excrete a still different type of nicotinic acid derivative—dinicotinylornithine.[199] N^1-Methylnicotinamide is not a major urinary product in the horse,[200, 201] although it is in the cotton rat.[201]

The biochemical mechanisms by which the urinary derivatives of nico-

[197] B. C. Johnson, T. S. Hamilton, and H. H. Mitchell, *J. Biol. Chem.* **159**, 231 (1945).
[198] P. Ellinger and M. M. Abdel Kader, *Biochem. J.* **44**, 77, 627 (1949).
[199] W. J. Dann and J. W. Huff, *J. Biol. Chem.* **168**, 121 (1947).
[200] J. W. Huff, P. B. Pearson, and W. A. Perlzweig, *Arch. Biochem.* **9**, 99 (1946).
[201] B. S. Schweigert, P. B. Pearson, and M. C. Wilkening, *Arch. Biochem.* **12**, 139 (1947).

tinic acid are formed are almost completely unknown except for the amide
(p. 505) and N^1-methyl derivatives (*vide infra*).

O. N^1-METHYLATION OF NICOTINAMIDE

Nicotinamide can be methylated in certain tissues by an aerobic process
analogous to the methylation of guanidoacetic acid to creatine; i.e., the
reaction is dependent on oxygen and is inhibited by oxidation inhibitors.[202]
Perlzweig and associates[203] showed that rat liver slices, but not kidney or
muscle, can methylate nicotinamide and that methionine enhances the
reaction. This finding has been amply confirmed by others.[147] Cantoni[204]
has now obtained a soluble enzyme system (cell-free) from rat, pig, guinea
pig, and dog liver which catalyzes the methylation of nicotinamide in the
presence of methionine, Mg^{++}, and adenosinetriphosphate. Only L-methi-
onine could be used in the system. Betaine and dimethylthetin were inactive in replacing methionine unless homocysteine was present. The system
would not methylate nicotinic acid.

The methylation reaction is apparently irreversible under biological conditions, since N^1-methylnicotinamide cannot replace nicotinamide in the
diet. Likewise this methylated compound has no lipotrophic activity as it
would if it could give up its methyl group.[205] Keller *et al.*[206] used a tracer
technique to prove that N^1-methyl groups attached to nicotinamide do
not participate in transmethylation reactions.

The liver can, however, degrade N^1-methylnicotinamide to unknown compounds.[203] It is apparently a lack of this degradative reaction which accounts
for the paradoxical increase in urinary N^1-methylnicotinamide in animals
and in human subjects whose livers have been severely damaged by carbon
tetrachloride[207] or phosphorus.[208]

Beher *et al.*[209] have found that small doses of testosterone decrease the
urinary excretion of N^1-methylnicotinamide, apparently because of an increased storage of DPN and TPN in the tissues. Calvo *et al.*[210] found that
thyroidectomy or thiouracil administration decreased urinary N^1-methyl-
nicotinamide excretion. Excretion of this compound was also decreased by

[202] *Nutrition Revs.* **6,** 28 (1948).

[203] W. A. Perlzweig, M. L. C. Bernheim, and F. Bernheim, *J. Biol. Chem.* **150,** 401
(1943).

[204] G. L. Cantoni, *J. Biol. Chem.* **189,** 203 (1951).

[205] P. Handler and I. N. Dubin, *J. Nutrition* **31,** 141 (1946).

[206] E. B. Keller, J. L. Wood, and V. DuVigneaud, *Proc. Soc. Exptl. Biol. Med.* **67,**
182 (1948).

[207] W. A. Perlzweig, J. W. Huff, and F. Rosen, *Federation Proc.* **5,** 149 (1946).

[208] A. Bonsignore and L. Bevilacqua, *Bull. soc. ital. biol. sper.* **23,** 1219 (1947).

[209] W. T. Beher, E. M. Crigger, and O. H. Gaebler, *J. Nutrition* **47,** 353 (1952).

[210] J. M. Calvo, C. C. Boehme, and J. Goemine, *Bol. soc. biol. Santiago Chile* **6,** 88
(1949).

feeding thyroglobulin, but methionine or choline tended to bring the urinary levels back to normal. Vitamin B_{12} may also be involved in the methylation of nicotinamide, probably through its influence on the synthesis and transfer of labile methyl groups.[211]

V. Specificity of Action

J. M. HUNDLEY

A. MODIFICATIONS OF THE NICOTINIC ACID MOLECULE

Many substances related chemically to nicotinic acid have been tested for their ability to replace this vitamin in mammalian nutrition. Table XI represents a partial compilation of such compounds. The following conclusions may be drawn concerning the range within which the molecule may be modified and still retain biological activity.

1. The pyridine molecule must have a substituent group in the 3 position.

2. This substituent group must be a derivative of $-\overset{\overset{\displaystyle O}{\|}}{C}-R$. Molecules with other groups on the 3 position such as CH_3, NH_2 or CN have no, or much less, biological effectiveness, presumably because they must be converted to the $-\overset{\overset{\displaystyle O}{\|}}{C}-$ grouping.

3. The R group attached to the 3-carboxyl may be any one of a great number of compounds and types such as esters and N-substituted amides and still retain biological effectiveness.

4. Substitution of an acetyl $(\overset{\overset{\displaystyle O}{\|}}{C}-CH_3)$ for the 3-carboxyl group leads to a compound (3-acetylpyridine) which is a nicotinic acid antagonist under certain conditions[34] but can be converted to nicotinic acid under other conditions.[27]

---

[211] I. E. Liener and M. O. Schultze, *J. Nutrition* **46**, 223 (1952).

[1] P. J. Fouts, O. M. Helmer, S. Lepkovsky, and T. H. Jukes, *Proc. Soc. Exptl. Biol. Med.* **37**, 405 (1937).

[2] P. Ellinger, G. Fraenkel, and M. M. Abdel Kader, *Biochem. J.* **41**, 559 (1947).

[3] V. A. Najjar and L. E. Holt, Jr., *Proc. Soc. Exptl. Biol. Med.* **48**, 413 (1941).

[4] P. Ellinger and R. A. Coulson, *Biochem. J.* **38**, 265 (1944).

[5] W. A. Krehl, P. S. Sarma, L. J. Teply, and C. A. Elvehjem, *J. Nutrition* **31**, 85 (1946).

[6] D. W. Woolley, F. M. Strong, R. J. Madden, and C. A. Elvehjem, *J. Biol. Chem.* **124**, 715 (1938).

TABLE XI

Specificity of Compounds Related to Nicotinic Acid

Compounds	Man	Rat Urinary excretion	Rat Growth	Dog
Substitution on the Ring				
Nicotinic acid (3-carboxypyridine)	+ (1)[a, b]	+ (2–4)	+ (5)	+ (6)
Picolinic acid (2-carboxypyridine)				0 (6)
Isonicotinic acid (4-carboxypyridine)				0 (6)
Quinolinic acid (2,3-dicarboxypyridine)	+ (7, 8)	0 (3) + (2, 9, 10)	+ (10–12)	+ (13) 0 (6, 14)
Dinicotinic acid (3,5-dicarboxypyridine)	± (15) + (16)	0 (3)		
Isocinchomeronic acid (2,5-dicarboxypyridine)		+ (9)	± (12)	
Nipecotic acid (hydrogenated nicotinic acid)				0 (6, 17)
2,6-Dimethylnicotinic acid	+ (16) ± (15)			
2,6-Dimethyl-3,5-dicarboxypyridine	± (16)	0 (3)		
6-Methylnicotinic acid				0 (6)
3-Methylpyridine	± (16)	+ (2, 18)		± (6)
3-Aminopyridine	± (16)			+ (19) 0 (6)
3-Cyanopyridine		0 (2)	0 (11, 20)	0 (6)
N¹ Substitutions				
N^L-Methylnicotinamide		+ (2)	0 (5, 11, 21)	0 (6, 17) + (26)
Trigonelline (betaine of nicotinic acid)	0 (16, 22)	0 (2)	0 (5)	0 (6, 23)
Nicotinamide glucosidoiodide				+ (6)
Modifications of Carboxyl Group				
Nicotinamide	+ (22)	+ (2–4)	+ (5)	+ (6)
N-Methylnicotinamide				+ (6)
N-Ethylnicotinamide		+ (2)	+ (5)	+ (6)
N,N-Diethylnicotinamide	+ (22, 24)	+ (2–4)		+ (6, 25, 3)
N-Allylnicotinamide		+ (2)		
N-Phenylnicotinamide		+ (2)	0 (5)	
N,N-Diphenylnicotinamide		0 (2)		
4″-Methoxyphenylnicotinamide		+ (2)		
N-Benzyl		+ (2)		
N,N-Dibenzyl		0 (2)		
Nicotinuric acid				0 (26ᵃ 23) + (6, 3)
Ethyl nicotinate			+ (5)	+ (6)
3-Acetylpyridine		+ (27)	0 (20)	0 (6) + (28)
Pyridine-3-sulfonic acid			0 (20)	0 (6, 28)
Thionicotinamide				
N-(2-Thiazolyl)nicotinamide			+ (29)	
Substitutes for Pyridine Ring				
Pyrazinemonocarboxylic acid	+ (30, 24)	0 (3, 31)		0 (13)
Pyrazinemonocarboxylamide		0 (31)		
Pyrazine-2,3-dicarboxylic acid	+ (30)	0 (3)		0 (13)
Miscellaneous				
Ornithine		0 (9, 32)	+ (12)	
Pyridine				0 (6)
DPN (coenzyme I)				0 (33)

[a] + = active; 0 = no nicotinic acid activity; ± = questionable; urinary excretion = increased excretion of nicotinic acid metabolites, usually N^L-methylnicotinamide, after administration of the compound.

[b] Numbers in parentheses refer to appropriate references.

TABLE XII
COMPOUNDS RELATED TO OR DERIVED FROM TRYPTOPHAN.
ABILITY TO SUBSTITUTE FOR NICOTINIC ACID

| Compounds | Rat | |
	Urinary nicotinic acid excretion	Growth
DL-Tryptophan	+ (9, 43–45)[a, b]	+ (46)
Acetyl-L-tryptophan	+ (43)	
Indole-3-pyruvic acid	+ (43)	
Indole-3-proprionic acid	0 (43)	
Indole-3-butyric acid		0 (47)
Indole-3-acrylic acid		0 (47)
Indole-3-acetic acid	0 (43, 48)	0 (20, 47, 48)
	+ (49)	+ (49)
Indole		0 (12, 20)
Naphthylacetic acid	0 (49)	+ (49)
L-Kynurenine	0 (50)	0 (11, 51)
	+ (43)	+ (52)
N-Formylkynurenine		0 (11)
Acetylkynurenine		0 (11)
Kynurenic acid	0 (43, 50)	0 (11)
Xanthurenic acid	0 (43, 50)	
Anthranilic acid	0 (9)	0 (20)
		+ (12)
3-Hydroxyanthranilic acid	+ (53)	+ (10, 11, 52, 54)
3,4-Dihydroxyanthranilic acid	0 (55)	0 (55)
N-Formylanthranilic acid		0 (11)

[a] + = active in substituting for nicotinic acid; 0 = not active.
[b] Numbers in parentheses refer to appropriate references.

[7] R. W. Vilter and T. D. Spies, *Lancet* **II,** 423 (1939).

[8] H. P. Sarett, *J. Biol. Chem.* **193,** 627 (1951).

[9] L. V. Hankes and C. A. Elvehjem, *Proc. Soc. Exptl. Biol. Med.* **73,** 550 (1950).

[10] L. M. Henderson, *J. Biol. Chem.* **178,** 1005 (1949).

[11] W. A. Krehl, D. Bonner, and C. Yanofsky, *J. Nutrition* **41,** 159 (1950).

[12] L. V. Hankes, R. L. Lyman, and C. A. Elvehjem, *J. Biol. Chem.* **187,** 547 (1950).

[13] W. J. Dann, H. I. Kohn, and P. Handler, *J. Nutrition* **20,** 477 (1940).

[14] H. A. Waisman, O. Mickelsen, J. M. McKibbin, and C. A. Elvehjem, *J. Nutrition* **19,** 483 (1940).

[15] S. P. Vilter, W. B. Bean, and T. D. Spies, *Southern Med. J.* **31,** 901 (1938).

[16] T. D. Spies, H. M. Grant, and N. E. Huff, *Southern Med. J.* **31,** 901 (1938).

[17] L. J. Teply, W. A. Krehl, and C. A. Elvehjem, *Proc. Soc. Exptl. Biol. Med.* **58,** 169 (1945).

[18] H. N. De and P. Datta, Jr., *Current Sci. (India)* **19,** 279 (1950).

[19] Y. SubbaRow, W. J. Dann, and E. Meilman, *J. Am. Chem. Soc.* **60,** 1510 (1938).

[20] W. A. Krehl, L. M. Henderson, J. de la Huerga, and C. A. Elvehjem, *J. Biol. Chem.* **166,** 531 (1946).

[21] S. A. Singal, V. P. Sydenstricker, and J. M. Littlejohn, *J. Biol. Chem.* **176,** 1069 (1948).

[22] T. D. Spies, W. B. Bean, and R. E. Stone, *J. Am. Med. Assoc.* **111,** 584 (1938).

5. Almost any modification in the 2, 4, 5, or 6 position of nicotinic acid leads to inactive compounds. The exceptions to this are quinolinic acid,

[23] J. W. Huff and W. A. Perlzweig, *J. Biol. Chem.* **142**, 401 (1942).

[24] A. E. Axelrod, T. D. Spies, and C. A. Elvehjem, *J. Biol. Chem.* **138**, 667 (1941).

[25] D. T. Smith, G. Margolis, and L. H. Margolis, *J. Pharmacol. Exptl. Therap.* **68**, 458 (1940).

[26] V. A. Najjar, M. M. Hammond, M. A. English, M. B. Wooden, and C. C. Deal, *Bull. Johns Hopkins Hosp.* **74**, 406 (1944).

[26a] W. J. Dann and P. Handler, *Proc. Soc. Exptl. Biol. Med.* **48**, 355 (1941).

[27] W. T. Beher, W. M. Holliday, and O. H. Gaebler, *Abstr. 12th Intern. Congr. Pure and Appl. Chem., New York*, p. 84, 1951.

[28] O. H. Gaebler and W. T. Beher, *J. Biol. Chem.* **188**, 343 (1951).

[29] L. Cote and J. J. Oleson, *J. Bacteriol.* **61**, 463 (1951).

[30] C. E. Bills, F. G. McDonald, and T. D. Spies, *Southern Med. J.* **32**, 793 (1939).

[31] L. Cote, J. J. Oleson, and J. H. Williams, *Proc. Soc. Exptl. Biol. Med.* **80**, 434 (1952).

[32] P. Ellinger and M. M. Abdel Kader, *Nature* **160**, 675 (1947).

[33] F. S. Daft, H. F. Frazer, W. H. Sebrell, and M. Pittman, *Science* **88**, 128 (1938).

[34] D. W. Woolley, *J. Biol. Chem.* **157**, 455 (1945).

[35] B. C. J. G. Knight, *Biochem. J.* **31**, 731 (1937).

[36] J. H. Mueller, *J. Biol. Chem.* **120**, 219 (1937).

[37] S. A. Koser, A. Dorfman, and F. Saunders, *Proc. Soc. Exptl. Biol. Med.* **38**, 311 (1938).

[38] P. Fildes, *Brit. J. Exptl. Pathol.* **19**, 239 (1938).

[39] M. Landy, *Proc. Soc. Exptl. Biol. Med.* **38**, 504 (1938).

[40] C. A. Elvehjem and L. J. Teply, *Chem. Revs.* **33**, 185 (1943).

[41] B. C. J. G. Knight, *Vitamins and Hormones* **3**, 180–197 (1946).

[42] W. Shive *in* The Biochemistry of the B Vitamins, American Chemical Society Monograph No. 110, p. 606. Reinhold Publishing Corp., New York, 1950

[43] R. E. Kallio and C. P. Berg, *J. Biol. Chem.* **181**, 333 (1949).

[44] F. Rosen, J. W. Huff, and W. A. Perlzweig, *J. Biol. Chem.* **163**, 343 (1946)

[45] S. A. Singal, A. P. Briggs, V. P. Sydenstricker, and J. M. Littlejohn, *J. Biol. Chem.* **166**, 573 (1946).

[46] W. A. Krehl, L. J. Teply, P. S. Sarma, and C. A. Elvehjem, *Science* **101**, 489 (1945).

[47] L. M. Henderson, T. Deodhar, W. A. Krehl, and C. A. Elvehjem, *J. Biol. Chem.* **170**, 261 (1947).

[48] F. Rosen and W. A. Perlzweig, *Arch. Biochem.* **15**, 111 (1947).

[49] Y. Raoul and C. Marnay, *Bull. soc. chim. biol.* **31**, 839 (1949).

[50] F. Rosen, J. W. Huff, and W. A. Perlzweig, *J. Nutrition* **33**, 561 (1947).

[51] W. A. Krehl and D. Bonner, Unpublished data quoted in *Vitamins and Hormones* **7**, 140 (1949).

[52] O. Wiss, G. Viollier, and M. Müller, *Helv. Physiol. et Pharmacol. Acta* **7**, C64 (1949).

[53] P. W. Albert, B. T. Scheer, and H. J. Deuel, Jr., *J. Biol. Chem.* **175**, 479 (1948).

[54] H. K. Mitchell, J. F. Nyc, and R. D. Owen, *J. Biol. Chem.* **175**, 433 (1948).

[55] L. M. Henderson, H. N. Hill, R. E. Koski, and I. M. Weinstock, *Proc. Soc. Exptl. Biol. Med.* **78**, 441 (1951).

[56] H. P. Sarett and G. A. Goldsmith, *J. Biol. Chem.* **167**, 293 (1947).

[57] W. A. Perlzweig, F. Rosen, N. Levitas, and J. Robinson, *J. Biol. Chem.* **167**, 511 (1947).

which is known to be easily and preferentially decarboxylated in the 2 position, forming nicotinic acid, and compounds which have been tested principally by treating human pellagra, a difficult means of testing which is subject to considerable clinical interpretation. The reported activity of ornithine may be in a special category (p. 522). The reported activity of isocinchomeronic acid seems very questionable.

6. N^1-substituted derivatives of nicotinic acid or nicotinamide may be active or inactive, depending on the nature of the substituent group. The reported inactivity of DPN is puzzling, since this substance is known to be active in enzyme systems and for bacterial growth. This substance should be retested, using more sensitive systems than acute canine blacktongue.

7. Man, rat, and dog seem to have about the same ability to use various types of nicotinic acid derivatives.

The effectiveness of nicotinic acid derivatives in microorganisms has been reviewed, elsewhere.[29, 35-42]

B. TRYPTOPHAN AND DERIVATIVES

The amino acid and some of its derivatives can replace nicotinic acid, since many organisms possess the ability to convert tryptophan to nicotinic acid. This subject is considered in Section VI. The principal compounds of interest are listed in Table XII. Tryptophan can replace nicotinic acid in human nutrition,[56-59] in the dog,[60] and in many other species (p. 578), as well as in the rat.

VI. Biogenesis

J. M. HUNDLEY

A. DEMONSTRATION OF NICOTINIC ACID BIOSYNTHESIS

It has long been known that certain mammals can synthesize nicotinic acid. Several groups of investigators showed that rats thrive on diets which produced pellagra in humans, blacktongue in dogs, and deficiency states in pigs and monkeys.[1-5] Other investigators using various diets could dem-

[58] L. M. Henderson, G. B. Ramasarma, and B. C. Johnson, *J. Biol. Chem.* **181,** 731 (1949).

[59] W. I. M. Holman and D. J. de Lange, *Nature* **165,** 112 (1950).

[60] S. A. Singal, V. P. Sydenstricker, and J. M. Littlejohn, *J. Biol. Chem.* **176,** 1051 (1948).

[1] D. K. Miller and C. P. Rhoads, *J. Clin. Invest.* **14,** 153 (1935).

[2] T. W. Birch, H. Chick, and C. J. Martin, *Biochem. J.* **31,** 2065 (1937).

[3] T. W. Birch, *J. Nutrition* **17,** 281 (1939).

522   NIACIN

onstrate no nicotinic acid requirement for the rat.[6-8] Shourie and Swaminathan,[9] Dann and Kohn,[10] and Dann[11] showed that rats accumulated in their tissues and excreted more nicotinic acid than they ingested, unequivocal evidence of synthesis. Similar findings have been recorded for calves,[12-14] horses,[15, 16] sheep,[17, 18] and man.[19-21]

B. MECHANISM OF BIOSYNTHESIS

Although these data certainly established the fact that nicotinic acid could be synthesized *in vivo*, the mechanism of this synthesis was obscure for many years.

1. The Ornithine Scheme

Earlier workers suggested that nicotinic acid might be synthesized according to the scheme shown in Fig. 9. However, the evidence that this mechanism provides any substantial amount of nicotinic acid in mammals is very shaky. Neither proline, glutamic acid, nor ornithine will substitute for nicotinic acid in diets; indeed proline may, along with other amino acids, increase nicotinic acid requirements.[22, 23] However, Bovarnick[24, 25] has

[4] L. J. Harris, *Biochem. J.* **31**, 1414 (1937).
[5] L. J. Harris, *Biochem. J.* **32**, 1479 (1938).
[6] T. F. Macrae and C. E. Edgar, *Biochem. J.* **31**, 2225 (1937).
[7] C. A. Cook, M. F. Clarke, and A. E. Light, *Proc. Soc. Exptl. Biol. Med.* **37**, 514 (1937).
[8] W. J. Dann and Y. SubbaRow, *J. Nutrition* **16**, 183 (1938).
[9] K. L. Shourie and M. Swaminathan, *Indian J. Med. Research* **27**, 679 (1940).
[10] W. J. Dann and H. I. Kohn, *J. Biol. Chem.* **136**, 435 (1940).
[11] W. J. Dann, *J. Biol. Chem.* **141**, 803 (1941).
[12] B. C. Johnson, A. C. Wiese, H. H. Mitchell, and W. B. Nevens, *J. Biol. Chem.* **167**, 729 (1947).
[13] B. C. Johnson, *Euclides (Madrid)* **8**, 161 (1948).
[14] G. C. Esh and T. S. Sutton, *J. Dairy Sci.* **31**, 909 (1948).
[15] J. W. Huff, P. B. Pearson, and W. A. Perlzweig, *Arch. Biochem.* **9**, 99 (1946).
[16] B. S. Schweigert, P. B. Pearson, and M. C. Wilkening, *Arch. Biochem.* **12**, 139 (1947).
[17] A. H. Winegar, P. B. Pearson, and H. Schmidt, *Science* **91**, 508 (1940).
[18] P. B. Pearson, A. H. Winegar, and H. Schmidt, *J. Nutrition* **20**, 551 (1940).
[19] V. A. Najjar, L. E. Holt, Jr., G. A. Johns, G. C. Mediary, and G. Fleischmann, *Proc. Soc. Exptl. Biol. Med.* **61**, 371 (1946).
[20] P. Ellinger, R. A. Coulson, and R. Benesch, *Nature* **154**, 270 (1944).
[21] P. Ellinger, R. Benesch, and W. W. Kay, *Lancet* **I**, 432 (1945).
[22] A. C. Groschke, J. O. Anderson, and G. M. Briggs, *Proc. Soc. Exptl. Biol. Med.* **68**, 564 (1948).
[23] L. V. Hankes, L. M. Henderson, W. L. Brickson, and C. A. Elvehjem, *J. Biol. Chem.* **174**, 873 (1948).
[24] M. R. Bovarnick, *J. Biol. Chem.* **153**, 1 (1944).
[25] M. R. Bovarnick, *J. Biol. Chem.* **148**, 151 (1943); **151**, 467 (1943).

shown that a mixture of glutamic acid and asparagine (or glutamine) heated in the presence of manganese and iron gives rise to nicotinamide. Ellinger and Abdel Kader[26] have suggested that ornithine and glutamic acid may be involved in nicotinic acid synthesis on the basis of experiments using *Escherichia coli*. Guvacine will substitute for nicotinic acid in the nutrition of *Staphylococcus aureus* and *Proteus vulgaris*.[27] Nicotinic acid synthesis in rats may be increased by DL-δ-amino-*n*-valeric acid.[28] Hankes *et al*.[29] have

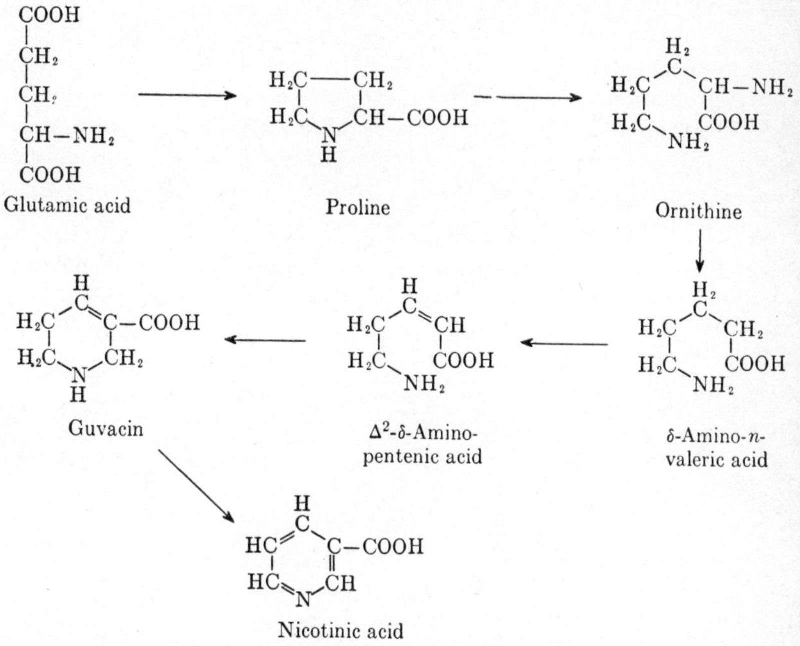

FIG. 9. The ornithine scheme for nicotinic acid biosynthesis. (Adapted from Williams.[27])

reported that anthranilic acid and ornithine together can apparently substitute for nicotinic acid under certain dietary circumstances.

2. Biosynthesis from Tryptophan

The mechanism of mammalian nicotinic acid biosynthesis which is now firmly established is conversion of the amino acid tryptophan to nicotinic acid. A series of brilliant investigations beginning in 1945 have unraveled

[26] P. Ellinger and M. M. Abdel Kader, *Biochem. J.* **44**, 285 (1949).

[27] R. J. Williams *in* The Biochemistry of the B Vitamins, American Chemical Society Monograph No. 110, p. 84. Reinhold Publishing Corp., New York, 1950.

[28] J. W. Huff and W. A. Perlzweig, *J. Biol. Chem.* **142**, 401 (1942).

[29] L. V. Hankes, R. L. Lyman, and C. A. Elvehjem, *J. Biol. Chem.* **187**, 547 (1950).

many of the details of this mechanism. The door to this fruitful chapter of biochemistry was opened by the report of Krehl et al.[30] that tryptophan could substitute for nicotinic acid in counteracting the unfavorable growth effects of corn in certain rat diets. Shortly thereafter it was shown that tryptophan markedly increased the urinary excretion of N^1-methylnicotinamide,[31-33] the first clear indication that tryptophan could substitute for nicotinic acid by virtue of the fact that it was transformed into nicotinic acid. Subsequent reports have fully confirmed the fact that tryptophan can substitute for nicotinic acid in the diet of rats, dogs, pigs, rabbits, chicks, ducks, monkeys, and cotton rats (p. 578). Impressive but indirect evidence that tryptophan is converted into nicotinic acid has been obtained in man,[34-39] rats,[16, 26, 36, 40-48] dogs,[49] mice,[50] rabbits,[51] horses and cotton rats,[16] pigs,[36, 52] calves, sheep, and guinea pigs.[36] Most of these studies have shown increased urinary excretion of nicotinic acid and its derivatives, or increased tissue levels following tryptophan administration.

[30] W. A. Krehl, L. J. Teply, P. S. Sarma, and C. A. Elvehjem, Science 101, 489 (1945).
[31] F. Rosen, J. W. Huff, and W. A. Perlzweig, J. Biol. Chem. 163, 343 (1946).
[32] S. A. Singal, A. P. Briggs, V. P. Sydenstricker, and J. M. Littlejohn, J. Biol. Chem. 166, 573 (1946).
[33] S. A. Singal, A. P. Briggs, V. P. Sydenstricker, and J. Littlejohn, Federation Proc. 5, 144 (1946).
[34] H. P. Sarett and G. A. Goldsmith, J. Biol. Chem. 167, 293 (1947).
[35] W. A. Perlzweig, F. Rosen, N. Levitas, and J. Robinson, J. Biol. Chem. 167, 511 (1947).
[36] L. M. Henderson, G. B. Ramasarma, and B. C. Johnson, J. Biol. Chem. 181, 731 (1949).
[37] W. I. M. Holman and D. J. de Lange, Nature 165, 112 (1950).
[38] H. P. Sarett and G. A. Goldsmith, J. Biol. Chem. 167, 293 (1947); 177, 461 (1949); 182, 679 (1950).
[39] S. E. Snyderman, K. C. Ketron, R. Carretero, and L. E. Holt, Jr., Proc. Soc. Exptl. Biol. Med. 70, 569 (1949).
[40] L. V. Hankes and C. A. Elvehjem, Proc. Soc. Exptl. Biol. Med. 73, 550 (1950).
[41] R. E. Kallio and C. P. Berg, J. Biol. Chem. 181, 333 (1949).
[42] J. M. Hundley, J. Nutrition 34, 253 (1947).
[43] J. M. Hundley and H. W. Bond, Arch. Biochem. 21, 313 (1949).
[44] P. B. Junqueira and B. S. Schweigert, J. Biol. Chem. 175, 535 (1948).
[45] Y. Raoul and C. Marnay, Bull. soc. chim. biol. 30, 450 (1948).
[46] C.-T. Ling, D. M. Hegsted, and F. J. Stare, J. Biol. Chem. 174, 803 (1948).
[47] J. N. Williams, Jr., P. Feigelson, and C. A. Elvehjem, J. Biol. Chem. 187, 597 (1950).
[48] J. N. Williams, Jr., P. Feigelson, C. A. Elvehjem, and S. S. Shahinian, J. Biol. Chem. 189, 659 (1951).
[49] S. A. Singal, V. P. Sydenstricker, and J. M. Littlejohn, J. Biol. Chem. 176, 1051 (1948).
[50] D. W. Woolley, J. Biol. Chem. 162, 179 (1946).
[51] J. G. Wooley, Proc. Soc. Exptl. Biol. Med. 65, 315 (1947).
[52] R. W. Luecke, W. N. McMillen, F. Thorp, Jr., and C. Tull, J. Nutrition 36, 417 (1948).

Subsequent investigations using isotope tracer techniques have clearly proved that, at least in the rat, tryptophan increases nicotinic acid synthesis by virtue of the fact that it is converted into nicotinic acid. Heidelberger and associates[53-56] showed that C^{14} from the 3 position in the indole nucleus of tryptophan became the carboxyl carbon of nicotinic acid. Likewise, Schayer and associates[57] found that N^{15} in the indole nucleus of tryptophan appeared as the ring nitrogen of urinary nicotinic acid derivatives.

These findings certainly established the conversion of tryptophan to nicotinic acid but did not elucidate the exact biochemical steps. Some additional information was gained from tracer experiments since Heidelberger et al.[53-56] and Shayer et al.[57] found that C^{14} in the β position of the side chain and Hundley and Bond[43] found that C^{13} from the carboxyl group of tryptophan did not appear in nicotinic acid. It was evident from these findings that the side chain of tryptophan was not used to form nicotinic acid.

a. Nicotinic Acid Biosynthesis in Neurospora

Much of our information on the exact mechanism by which tryptophan is converted to nicotinic acid came from a series of productive investigations using various strains of *Neurospora crassa*. Some of these strains, as has now been shown, synthesize nicotinic acid from tryptophan in a fashion quite similar to the mechanism in animals, whereas other strains have genetic blocks so that they cannot carry out certain of the biochemical steps. Beadle and associates[58] first noted that a mutant strain of *Neurospora* could use either nicotinic acid or tryptophan for growth and that kynurenine was involved in this interchangeable relationship. Bonner and Beadle[59] isolated a substance which they believed to be a precursor of nicotinic acid in this organism. Mitchell and Nyc[60] and Bonner[61] showed that this substance was 3-hydroxyanthranilic acid and that it could substitute for nicotinic acid. Later studies using tracer techniques have fully confirmed the fact that 3-hydroxyanthranilic acid can be converted to nicotinic acid by

[53] C. Heidelberger, M. E. Gullberg, A. F. Morgan, and S. Lepkovsky, *J. Biol. Chem.* **175**, 473 (1948).

[54] C. Heidelberger, M. E. Gullberg, A. F. Morgan, and S. Lepkovsky, *J. Biol. Chem.* **179**, 143 (1949).

[55] C. Heidelberger, E. P. Abraham, and S. Lepkovsky, *J. Biol. Chem.* **176**, 1461 (1948).

[56] C. Heidelberger, E. P. Abraham, and S. Lepkovsky, *J. Biol. Chem.* **179**, 151 (1949).

[57] R. W. Schayer, G. L. Foster, and D. Shemin, *Federation Proc.* **8**, 248 (1949).

[58] G. W. Beadle, H. K. Mitchell, and J. F. Nyc, *Proc. Natl. Acad. Sci. U. S.* **33**, 155 (1947).

[59] D. Bonner and G. W. Beadle, *Arch. Biochem.* **11**, 319 (1946).

[60] H. K. Mitchell and J. F. Nyc, *Proc. Natl. Acad. Sci. U. S.* **34**, 1 (1948).

[61] D. Bonner, *Proc. Natl. Acad. Sci. U. S.* **34**, 5 (1948).

Neurospora.[62, 63] It has also been shown by Yanofsky and Bonner[64] that kynurenine is converted into nicotinic acid. 3-Hydroxykynurenine probably is an intermediate between kynurenine and 3-hydroxyanthranilic acid.[60, 65] The exact steps between 3-hydroxyanthranilic acid and nicotinic acid are still uncertain. It has been suggested[66, 67] that the benzene ring of 3-hydroxyanthranilic acid is oxidatively cleaved in the 3–4 position to yield an intermediate similar to that shown in Fig. 10. This compound might then undergo ring closure with the amino nitrogen to give quinolinic acid which is in turn decarboxylated to nicotinic acid,[68] or this hypothetical intermediate might be decarboxylated prior to ring closure to yield nicotinic acid directly.[67] Leifer *et al.*[62] have suggested that a symmetrical diamino compound may be the intermediate between 3-hydroxyanthranilic acid and nicotinic acid, although the evidence supporting this theory has been questioned.[63] The details of the evidence for the various steps in the conversion of tryptophan to nicotinic acid in *Neurospora* have been carefully reviewed by Bonner and Yanofsky.[69]

b. Biosynthesis from Tryptophan in Mammals

The pathway by which tryptophan is converted to nicotinic acid in mammals is not as fully known as in *Neurospora*. Current information suggests that it may proceed substantially as shown in Fig. 10; however, the evidence is faulty, incomplete, and contradictory in some respects. Tryptophan is known to be converted into kynurenine and kynurenic acid in several animal species as first shown by Kotake[70] and later proved in isotope tracer experiments by Heidelberger *et al.*[53-56] However, kynurenic acid is inactive as a substitute for nicotinic acid in rats, and the reports on kynurenine are contradictory (see Table XII). Rosen *et al.*[71] and Krehl *et al.*[72] found kynurenine inactive when given in the diet or by injection, whereas Kallio and Berg[41] and Wiss *et al.*[73] reported that it would increase the urinary excretion

[62] E. Leifer, W. H. Langham, J. F. Nyc, and H. K. Mitchell, *J. Biol. Chem.* **184,** 589 (1950).

[63] C. Yanofsky and D. M. Bonner, *J. Biol. Chem.* **190,** 211 (1951).

[64] C. Yanofsky and D. M. Bonner, *Proc. Natl. Acad. Sci. U. S.* **36,** 167 (1950).

[65] F. A. Haskins and H. K. Mitchell, *Proc. Natl. Acad. Sci. U. S.* **35,** 500 (1949).

[66] L. M. Henderson, *J. Biol. Chem.* **178,** 1005 (1949).

[67] D. M. Bonner and C. Yanofsky, *Proc. Natl. Acad. Sci. U. S.* **35,** 576 (1949).

[68] L. M. Henderson, *J. Biol. Chem.* **181,** 677 (1949).

[69] D. M. Bonner and C. Yanofsky, *J. Nutrition* **44,** 603 (1951).

[70] Y. Kotake and J. Iwao, *Hoppe-Seyler's Z. physiol. Chem.* **195,** 139 (1931); Y. Kotake, *J. Japan. Biochem. Soc.* **21,** 155 (1949).

[71] F. Rosen, J. W. Huff, and W. A. Perlzweig, *J. Nutrition* **33,** 561 (1947).

[72] W. A. Krehl, D. Bonner, and C. Yanofsky, *J. Nutrition* **41,** 159 (1950).

[73] O. Wiss, G. Viollier, and M. Müller, *Helv. Physiol. et Pharmacol. Acta* **7,** C64 (1949).

of nicotinic acid metabolites and would promote growth. Knox and Mehler[74, 75] have shown that the liver of several animal species possesses an enzyme system which converts tryptophan to kynurenine through the intermediate n-formylkynurenine. However, the latter compound also was inactive in nicotinic acid-deficient rats.[72] Krehl[76] and Bonner and Yanofsky[69] have suggested that the well-known instability of kynurenine might account for these conflicting results.

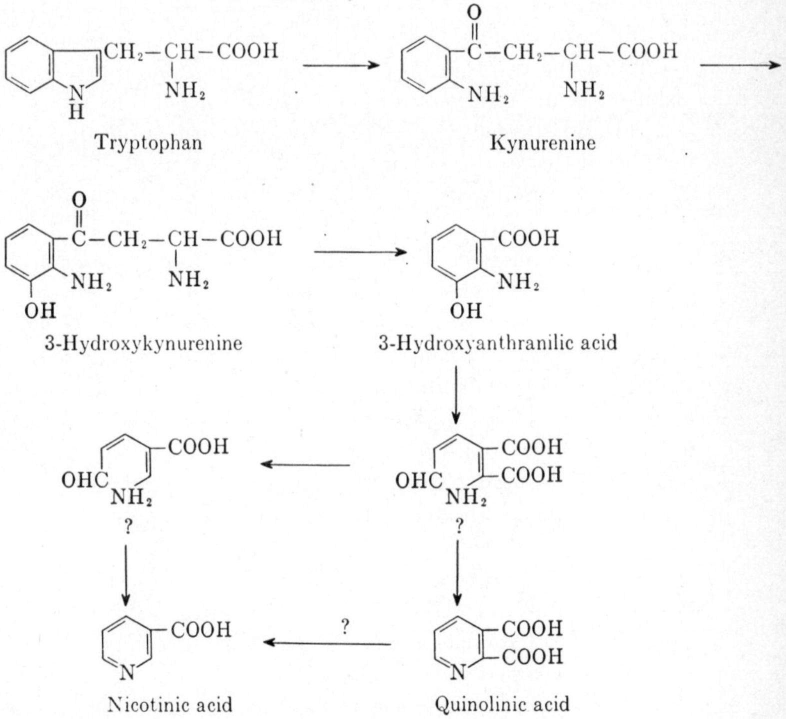

$$CH_2-CH-COOH \quad\longrightarrow\quad C-CH_2-CH-COOH \quad\longrightarrow$$
$$NH_2 \qquad\qquad NH_2 \quad NH_2$$

Tryptophan · Kynurenine

$$C-CH_2-CH-COOH \quad\longrightarrow\quad COOH$$
$$NH_2 \quad NH_2 \qquad\qquad NH_2$$
$$OH \qquad\qquad OH$$

3-Hydroxykynurenine · 3-Hydroxyanthranilic acid

$$OHC \quad COOH \quad\longleftarrow\quad OHC \quad COOH \quad COOH$$
$$NH_2 \qquad\qquad NH_2$$
? · ?

$$COOH \quad\longleftarrow\quad ? \quad COOH \quad COOH$$
$$N \qquad\qquad N$$

Nicotinic acid · Quinolinic acid

Fig. 10. Summary of known and probable steps in the conversion of tryptophan to nicotinic acid.

The situation with 3-hydroxyanthranilic acid is much clearer, since it does support growth in nicotinic acid-deficient rats[66, 72, 73, 77] and increases the urinary excretion of nicotinic acid metabolites.[78] Schweigert[79] reported that rat liver slices would convert 3-hydroxyanthranilic acid to a compound

[74] W. E. Knox and A. H. Mehler, *J. Biol. Chem.* **187,** 419 (1950).
[75] A. H. Mehler and W. E. Knox, *J. Biol. Chem.* **187,** 431 (1950).
[76] W. A. Krehl, Unpublished data quoted in *Vitamins and Hormones* **7,** 140 (1949).
[77] H. K. Mitchell, J. F. Nyc, and R. D. Owen, *J. Biol. Chem.* **175,** 433 (1948).
[78] P. W. Albert, B. T. Scheer, H. J. Deuel, Jr., *J. Biol. Chem.* **175,** 479 (1948).
[79] B. S. Schweigert, *J. Biol. Chem.* **178,** 707 (1949).

which had nicotinic acid activity after acid hydrolysis. Later studies using liver homogenates and other enzyme preparations[80, 81] showed that the actual compound formed in this system was quinolinic acid and that no free nicotinic acid was produced. Other investigators independently reported similar findings.[72, 82] Neither tryptophan nor kynurenine would give rise to quinolinic acid in these preparations, nor would quinolinic acid give rise to nicotinic acid. However, Makino *et al.*[83] reported that horse and cattle livers possess an enzyme system which will convert 3-hydroxyanthranilic acid to nicotinic acid, although it is difficult to be positive that the end product of the reaction may not have been quinolinic acid which either spontaneously or from heat and chemical treatment decarboxylated to nicotinic acid and so reacted in their chemical assay procedures. Hurt *et al.*[84] also reported that rat liver slices would convert tryptophan to nicotinic acid, although actually their procedure for determining nicotinic acid would not permit them to distinguish between nicotinic acid and quinolinic acid. Makino *et al.*[83] also reported that their enzyme preparation converted 3,4-dihydroxyanthranilic acid to nicotinic acid just as effectively as it did 3-hydroxyanthranilic acid, indicating that this substance may be an intermediate in the conversion. Their system also formed small amounts of nicotinic acid from tryptophan and from quinolinic acid. Henderson *et al.*[85] were unable to confirm these findings with 3,4-dihydroxyanthranilic acid using rat and hog liver preparations.

The intermediate between 3-hydroxyanthranilic acid and nicotinic acid is not entirely clear, although considerable evidence indicates that quinolinic acid is either an intermediate or a by-product of the reaction. Singal *et al.*[32] were the first to note that tryptophan administration in rats and in dogs[49] resulted in the urinary excretion of an unidentified substance which had nicotinic acid activity after acid, but not after alkaline, hydrolysis. This substance was identified by Henderson[66] as quinolinic acid. This compound can substitute for nicotinic acid in the rat (see Table XI), although it is far less effective than nicotinic acid, tryptophan, or 3-hydroxyanthranilic acid.[72] It seems clear that quinolinic acid can be used as a precursor of nicotinic acid by the rat. However, the relatively large amount required in comparison to the effective amounts of tryptophan, 3-hydroxyanthranilic acid, and nicotinic acid induces considerable doubt that it is a normal intermediate between 3-hydroxyanthranilic acid and nicotinic acid, although it

[80] B. S. Schweigert and M. M. Marquette, *J. Biol. Chem.* **181**, 199 (1949).

[81] A. H. Bokman and B. S. Schweigert, *J. Biol. Chem.* **186**, 153 (1950).

[82] L. M. Henderson and G. B. Ramasarma, *J. Biol. Chem.* **181**, 687 (1949).

[83] K. Makino, F. Itoh, and K. Nishi, *Nature* **167**, 115 (1951).

[84] W. W. Hurt, B. T. Scheer, and H. J. Deuel, Jr., *Arch. Biochem.* **21**, 87 (1949).

[85] L. M. Henderson, H. N. Hill, R. E. Koski, and I. M. Weinstock, *Proc. Soc. Exptl. Biol. Med.* **78**, 441 (1951).

may well be a side product which is normally excreted into the urine rather rapidly after it is formed.

The conversion of tryptophan to nicotinic acid is a rather inefficient process at best. Krehl *et al.*[72] list the relative activities of tryptophan, 3-hydroxyanthranilic acid, quinolinic acid, and nicotinic acid as 10, 10, 20 to 40, and 0.2 mg., respectively, in correcting nicotinic acid deficiency in the rat. On an equimolar basis 3-hydroxyanthranilic acid is somewhat less active than tryptophan, which might be explainable if the liver converted a considerable portion of the 3-hydroxyanthranilic acid to quinolinic acid which was then promptly excreted and thus lost to the nicotinic acid economy of the tissues.

Recent evidence by Schayer and Henderson[86] using doubly labeled tryptophan makes it very likely that the intermediate between 3-hydroxyanthranilic acid and quinolinic acid is a substance in which the benzene ring is split in the 3–4 position similar to that depicted in Fig. 10.

C. SITE OF BIOSYNTHESIS

There have been two principal schools of thought on this subject, one holding that the principal site of the tryptophan to nicotinic acid conversion is in the tissues and the other holding that the intestinal bacteria are the predominant factor in this conversion.

1. Synthesis in Tissues

In the rat it has been clearly demonstrated that the conversion of tryptophan to nicotinic acid can proceed with normal efficiency without the intervention of intestinal microbes. This conclusion could be inferred from studies previously cited showing (1) that enzyme systems exist in tissues which are capable of carrying out many of the steps in the conversion; (2) that tryptophan and some of the intermediates in the conversion are effectively changed into nicotinic acid when given parenterally; (3) that tryptophan given parenterally leads to an increase in the nicotinic acid-containing coenzymes of erythrocytes within 4 hours,[46] an effect too rapid to be explainable if tryptophan had to be excreted into the intestinal tract, converted to nicotinic acid, reabsorbed, and then picked up and incorporated into coenzymes by the erythrocytes; and (4) that a deficiency of pyridoxine interfered in the conversion of tryptophan to nicotinic acid or inhibited certain steps in this process in intact animals and in tissue preparations.[46, 71, 84, 87-94] Finally, it was shown by Henderson and Hankes[95] and

[86] R. W. Schayer and L. M. Henderson, *J. Biol. Chem.* **195,** 657 (1952).

[87] B. S. Schweigert and P. B. Pearson, *J. Biol. Chem.* **168,** 555 (1947).

[88] G. H. Bell, B. T. Scheer, and H. J. Deuel, Jr., *J. Nutrition* **35,** 239 (1948).

[89] P. B. Junqueira and B. S. Schweigert, *J. Biol. Chem.* **174,** 605 (1948).

by Hundley[96] that the conversion of tryptophan to nicotinic acid proceeded with normal efficiency in rats surgically deprived of their entire intestine.

2. SYNTHESIS BY INTESTINAL MICROORGANISMS

These findings, however, do not necessarily mean that under normal conditions the intestinal bacteria may not convert some tryptophan to nicotinic acid or, in addition perhaps, synthesize some nicotinic acid from other precursors which may be utilized by the host. The entire question of intestinal synthesis of vitamins in relation to the vitamin economy of the host is a complicated question which is very difficult to approach by direct, conclusive experimentation. Some aspects of this question have been reviewed in the section on requirements (p. 583).

There is little direct evidence indicating how much influence intestinal bacteria may have on the nicotinic acid requirement of the host by virtue of the participation of such bacteria in the conversion of tryptophan to nicotinic acid. There is little, if any, direct relationship between the nicotinic acid content of the cecum or of the feces and tryptophan in the diet.[23, 31, 32] Junqueira and Schweigert[44] found that sulfasuxidine, added to rat diets for the purpose of suppressing intestinal microbial activity, had no influence on the efficiency of conversion of tryptophan to nicotinic acid. However, if the diets were deficient in folic acid, then sulfasuxidine did reduce the amount of nicotinic acid formed from tryptophan. Furthermore, Ellinger and Abdel Kader[26, 97] found that oral tryptophan was two to five times as effective as parenteral tryptophan in increasing urinary N^1-methylnicotinamide whereas tryptophan given orally to rats receiving sulfasuxidine produced little or no increase in N^1-methylnicotinamide excretion. Other investigators have not found such a wide discrepancy between the relative effectiveness of oral and parenteral tryptophan. For instance, Rosen et al.[31] found oral tryptophan about two times as effective as parenteral tryptophan in increasing urinary nicotinic acid metabolites. Snyderman et al.[39] found oral and parenteral tryptophan equally effective in increasing urinary N^1-methylnicotinamide in infants. Sung and Tung[98]

[90] L. M. Henderson, I. M. Weinstock, and G. B. Ramasarma, *J. Biol. Chem.* **189**, 19 (1951).

[91] J. P. Kring, K. Ebisuzaki, J. N. Williams, Jr., and C. A. Elvehjem, *J. Biol. Chem.* **195**, 591 (1952).

[92] M. Mason and C. P. Berg, *J. Biol. Chem.* **195**, 515 (1952).

[93] A. E. Braunstein, E. V. Goryachenkova, and T. S. Paskhina, *Biokhimiya* **14**, 163 (1949).

[94] C. E. Dalgliesh, W. E. Knox, and A. Neuberger, *Nature* **168**, 20 (1951).

[95] L. M. Henderson and L. V. Hankes, *Proc. Soc. Exptl. Biol. Med.* **70**, 26 (1949).

[96] J. M. Hundley, *Proc. Soc. Exptl. Biol. Med.* **70**, 592 (1949).

[97] P. Ellinger and M. M. Abdel Kader, *Nature* **160**, 675 (1947).

[98] S. Sung and T. Tung, *J. Biol. Chem.* **186**, 637 (1950).

ound monomethyltryptophan (presumably amino-N-methyltryptophan) equally effective by mouth or parenterally in increasing the urinary excre-ion of nicotinamide and its derivatives in rats.

3. UTILIZATION OF L- AND D-TRYPTOPHAN AS PRECURSORS FOR NICOTINIC ACID

*. In Rat

There is a very limited amount of information on this subject. Both D-nd L-tryptophan can be used by the rat for nicotinic acid synthesis, al-hough D-tryptophan is somewhat less efficiently utilized.[41, 44, 72, 99] Acetyl->-tryptophan, however, was completely inactive, and acetyl-L-tryptophan was only about one-half as active as L-tryptophan.[41]

. In Poultry

In the chick, Grau and Almquist[100] found D-tryptophan to be completely nactive, although later studies by Wilkening and Schweigert[101] indicated hat the chick could use D-tryptophan 17 to 40 % as efficiently as L-tryp-ophan. Kratzer et al.[102] found D-tryptophan to be 30 % as active as L-tryp-ophan in turkey poults. These studies in poultry evaluated the utilization f D-tryptophan for growth. Its effect on nicotinic acid requirements was ot studied. Utilization of the isomers would not necessarily be the same 1 the conversion of tryptophan to nicotinic acid. Anderson et al.[103] studied his question in chicks under conditions where they could measure the icotinic acid-replacing value of the isomers of tryptophan. These workers ould find no evidence that D-tryptophan was utilized as a precursor of icotinic acid when the diet contained glucose as the principal carbohydrate. Iowever, when the ration contained starch, D-tryptophan was utilized to a mited extent. These facts, plus the finding that the utilization of D-tryp-ophan was reduced when the starch ration contained sulfasuxidine, indi-ate that intestinal microorganisms may play some role in the utilization f D-tryptophan.

. In Dogs

In dogs, Singal and associates[49] obtained evidence that only L-tryptophan as used as a precursor for nicotinic acid in spite of the fact that DL-tryp-

[9] W. A. Krehl, P. S. Sarma, L. J. Teply, and C. A. Elvehjem, J. Nutrition **31**, 85 (1946).

[0] C. R. Grau and H. J. Almquist, J. Nutrition **28**, 263 (1944).

[1] M. C. Wilkening and B. S. Schweigert, J. Biol. Chem. **171**, 209 (1947).

[2] F. H. Kratzer, D. E. Williams, and B. Marshall, J. Nutrition **43**, 223 (1951).

[3] J. O. Anderson, G. F. Combs, and G. M. Briggs, J. Nutrition **42**, 463 (1950).

tophan is used as efficiently as L-tryptophan for maintenance of nitrogen balance and for plasma protein synthesis.[104]

d. In Man

D-Tryptophan is apparently not utilized to any extent[105] for ordinary metabolic purposes in man. Sarett and Goldsmith[38] could find no evidence that D-tryptophan was used as a precursor of nicotinic acid in man.

4. TRYPTOPHAN-NICOTINIC ACID RELATIONSHIPS IN OTHER ORGANISMS

a. Eggs

It is well known that nicotinic acid is synthesized by the developing chick[106] and turkey[107] embryo. There is also an increase in the total amount of pyridine nucleotide as the embryo develops.[108] The precursors of this synthesized nicotinic acid are not known. However, Schweigert et al.[109] found that tryptophan introduced into the embryo resulted in a moderately increased synthesis of nicotinic acid. Kidder and associates[110] were unable to confirm this finding, although Denton and associates[111] were able to do so. Furthermore, Ackermann and Taylor[112] have found that both nicotinamide and tryptophan can prevent toxicity from 3-acetylpyridine in the developing embryo, although tryptophan was considerably less potent than nicotinamide. These findings seem to indicate a tryptophan–nicotinic acid relationship in this organism and have additional interest since this is a situation in which tryptophan can apparently be converted to nicotinic acid in the complete absence of any microorganisms.

b. Plants

The fact that plants can and do synthesize nicotinic acid during germination and growth from the simplest of inorganic elements is well known. There is some evidence that tryptophan may serve as a precursor of nicotinic acid under certain conditions. Nason[113] found that L- or DL-tryptophan and 3-hydroxyanthranilic acid increased nicotinic acid synthesis in the

[104] S. C. Madden, R. R. Woods, F. W. Shull, and G. H. Whipple, J. Exptl. Med. 79, 607 (1944).
[105] A. A. Albanese and J. E. Frankston, J. Biol. Chem. 155, 101 (1944).
[106] W. J. Dann and P. Handler, J. Biol. Chem. 140, 935 (1941).
[107] C. Furman, E. E. Snell, and W. W. Cravens, Poultry Sci. 26, 307 (1947).
[108] M. Levy and N. F. Young, J. Biol. Chem. 176, 185 (1948).
[109] B. S. Schweigert, H. L. German, and M. J. Garber, J. Biol. Chem. 174, 383 (1948).
[110] G. W. Kidder, V. C. Dewey, M. B. Andrews, and R. R. Kidder, J. Nutrition 37, 521 (1949).
[111] C. A. Denton, W. L. Kellogg, W. E. Rowland, and H. R. Bird, Arch. Biochem. and Biophys. 39, 1 (1952).
[112] W. W. Ackermann and A. Taylor, Proc. Soc. Exptl. Biol. Med. 67, 449 (1948).
[113] A. Nason, Science 109, 170 (1949); Am. J. Botany 8, 612 (1950).

incubating corn embryo. Gustafson[114] found that tryptophan increased, slightly, the nicotinic acid content of broccoli, cabbage, and tomato leaves. Banerjee and Banerjee[115] found that tryptophan increased nicotinic acid in germinating *Phaseolus mungo* seeds, although Terroine[116] could demonstrate no such relationship in *Phaseolus multiflorus* embryos.

c. Insects

Neither *Tribolium confusum* nor *Tenebrio molitor* can use tryptophan in place of nicotinic acid.[117] "Germ-free" *Drosophila* also require preformed nicotinic acid and cannot synthesize it from tryptophan.[118]

d. Microorganisms

Davis *et al.*[119] have reported that a tryptophan-nicotinic acid relationship exists in *Xanthomonas pruni* very similar to that in *Neurospora crassa.* Tryptophan can replace nicotinic acid for the growth of the fungus *Trichophyton equinum.*[120] Schopfer and Boss[121] found that 2-methyl-1,4-naphthoquinone inhibits growth and nicotinic acid synthesis in *Phycomyces blakesleeanus*, an effect reversible by tryptophan, kynurenine, anthranilic acid, indole, nicotinic acid, and nicotinamide. Whether this indicates a tryptophan-nicotinic acid conversion mechanism in this fungus is not yet clear. Kidder *et al.*[110] could demonstrate no tryptophan-nicotinic acid relationship in the animal microorganism *Tetrahymena.*

It is well known that many bacteria require nicotinic acid, and others require tryptophan, whereas some require both nicotinic acid and tryptophan for growth. Many bacteria can synthesize both nicotinic acid and tryptophan from simple inorganic molecules. However, little is known about the exact mechanism of nicotinic acid biogenesis in bacteria. A tryptophan-nicotinic acid interrelation in the same sense as it exists in *Neurospora* and in animals is not known to exist in bacteria.[122-124]

[114] F. G. Gustafson, *Science* **110**, 279 (1949).
[115] S. Banerjee and R. Banerjee, *Indian J. Med. Research* **38**, 153 (1950).
[116] T. Terroine, *Compt. rend.* **226**, 511 (1948).
[117] G. Frankel and H. R. Stern, *Arch. Biochem.* **30**, 438 (1951).
[118] J. Schultz and G. T. Rudkin, *Federation Proc.* **7**, 185 (1948).
[119] D. Davis, L. M. Henderson, and D. Powell, *J. Biol. Chem.* **189**, 543 (1951).
[120] L. K. Georg, *Proc. Soc. Exptl. Biol. Med.* **72**, 653 (1949).
[121] W. H. Schopfer and M. L. Boss, *Helv. Physiol. et Pharmacol. Acta* **7**, C20–2 (1949).
[122] B. E. Volcani and E. E. Snell, *Proc. Soc. Exptl. Biol. Med.* **67**, 511 (1948).
[123] P. Ellinger and M. M. Abdel Kader, *Nature* **163**, 799 (1949).
[124] P. Ellinger and M. M. Abdel Kader, *Biochem. J.* **44**, 506 (1949).

VII. Estimation

Biological, chemical, fluorometric, photometric, and microbiological tech niques have been employed for the estimation of nicotinic acid and relate substances.

A. BIOLOGICAL ASSAY

J. M. HUNDLEY

Animal assays offer little opportunity for the exact determination c nicotinic acid unless the substances to be tested are completely free fror protein and amino acids, especially tryptophan. Biological tests might offe possibilities in assessing the over-all pellagra-protective potency of foods a suitable way to quantitatively express and compare the results could b devised. Young nicotinic acid-deficient animals do show a growth respons proportional, within a narrow range, to the amount of nicotinic acid admir istered. This has been demonstrated with pure, or relatively pure, solution of nicotinic acid or nicotinamide in puppies,[1] weanling rats,[2-4] and chicks. Some idea of the nicotinic acid content of test solutions may be gained b attempting to cure blacktongue in adult dogs, but precise quantitative re sults are almost impossible. Test substances may also be evaluated b their ability to *prevent* blacktongue in dogs on suitable diets, but this tech nique also has many variables.

B. CHEMICAL METHODS

J. M. HUNDLEY

1. NICOTINIC ACID

The chemical determination of nicotinic acid is, in theory, quite simpl Utilizing the König reaction,[6] nicotinic acid is treated with cyanogen br mide and then with an aromatic amine to yield a colored compound whic can be quantitated photometrically. The underlying reaction proceeds i two steps: first, the intermediate production of a pyridinium derivativ by reaction of the nicotinic acid with cyanogen bromide, and, second, th production of a colored glutaconic dialdehyde derivative by reaction wit the aromatic amine.[6, 7]

[1] H. A. Waisman, O. Mickelsen, J. M. McKibbin, and C. A. Elvehjem, *J. Nutriti* **19**, 483 (1940).

[2] W. A. Krehl, P. S. Sarma, L. J. Teply, and C. A. Elvehjem, *J. Nutrition* **31**, (1946).

[3] J. M. Hundley, *J. Biol. Chem.* **181**, 1 (1949).

[4] L. J. Harris and E. Kodicek, *Brit. J. Nutrition* **4**, xiii (1950).

[5] M. E. Coates, S. K. Kon, and E. E. Shepheard, *Brit. J. Nutrition* **4**, 203 (1950).

[6] W. König, *J. prakt. Chem.* **69**, 105 (1904); **70**, 19 (1904).

[7] T. Zincke, *Ann.* **330**, 361 (1904).

However, the large number of modifications of this basic method which
ave appeared in the past twelve years attests to the fact that the proce-
ure is not so simple as it seems when applied to a variety of biological
materials. Difficulties are encountered in hydrolysis in obtaining complete
beration and maximum conversion of nicotinamide to nicotinic acid with-
ut formation of interfering chromogens and without conversion of tri-
onelline. The choice of reaction temperatures and proper pH, the choice
f the proper aromatic amine to yield the maximum stable color, and proper
lank corrections are important factors. Many of these difficulties have been
discussed and examined in detail in other publications.[8, 9] György and
Rubin[8] present detailed instructions for three methods: (1) a procedure
using metol, devised by Perlzweig et al.[10] and improved by Dann and
Handler,[11] which has been used extensively in examining animal tissues;
(2) the aniline procedure of Melnick,[12] which has been applied extensively
o cereals; and (3) a p-aminoacetophenone (or p-aminopropiophenone) pro-
edure developed by a British group.[13, 14] Dennis and Rees[15] have recently
proposed a method which uses procaine hydrochloride for color develop-
ent. The Association of Vitamin Chemists[16] has adopted two carefully
hecked chemical methods, one of which is essentially the method of Friede-
ann and Frazier.[9] A new method has recently been proposed for adoption
y the Association of Official Agricultural Chemists.[17, 18] The method uti-
zes sulfanilic acid or Tobias acid (2-naphthylamine-1-sulfonic acid) for
olor development and permits both a quantitative and a qualitative dif-
erentiation of nicotinic acid and nicotinamide.

DIFFERENTIAL ASSAY OF NICOTINIC ACID, NICOTINAMIDE, AND RELATED COMPOUNDS

These compounds may be differentially quantitated either by micro-
iological (p. 538) or by chemical methods. In addition to the method of
weeney and Hall, mentioned above,[17, 18] paper chromatography has proved
seful in separating and determining small quantities of these sub-
ances.[19-21]

8 P. György and S. H. Rubin in Vitamin Methods, Vol. I, pp. 223–239. Academic
  Press, New York, 1950.
9 T. E. Friedemann and E. I. Frazier, Arch. Biochem. 26, 361 (1950).
0 W. A. Perlzweig, E. D. Levy, and H. P. Sarett, J. Biol. Chem. 136, 729 (1940).
11 W. J. Dann and P. Handler, J. Biol. Chem. 140, 201 (1941).
2 D. Melnick, Cereal Chem. 19, 553 (1942).
3 E. M. James, F. W. Norris, and F. Wokes, Analyst 72, 327 (1947).
4 C. Klatzkin, F. W. Norris, and F. Wokes, Analyst 74, 447 (1949).
5 P. O. Dennis and H. G. Rees, Analyst 74, 481 (1949).
6 Association of Vitamin Chemists, Methods of Vitamin Assay, 2nd ed., pp. 184–203.
  Interscience Publishers, New York, 1951.
7 J. P. Sweeney, J. Assoc. Offic. Agr. Chemists 34, 380 (1951).
8 J. P. Sweeney and W. L. Hall, Anal. Chem. 23, 983 (1951).

Ciusa[22] described a procedure which depends on the König reaction be
fore and after the unknown solution is boiled with chlorobenzene. Since
chlorobenzene reacts with nicotinamide, but not with nicotinic acid, the
two forms of the vitamin can be determined by difference. Scudi[23] describec
a fluorometric procedure for the determination of nicotinamide which in
volves the conversion of nicotinamide to a fluorescent N^1-methyl derivative
Chaudhuri and Kodicek[24] have developed a somewhat related method which
measures only nicotinamide in biological materials. They used cyanogen
bromide and treatment with strong alkali to yield a fluorescent derivative
which could be quantitated in a photoelectric fluorometer. Kato and
Shimizu[25] had difficulty with this method, because of interference from
kynurenine, 3-hydroxykynurenine, and other substances. These interfer
ing substances could be removed by chromatographing on a carboxylic
type cation exchange resin and a strong-base-type anion exchange resin.

Ellinger and Abdel Kader[26] have developed chemical methods with which
they could differentially determine nicotinic acid, nicotinamide, nicotinuric
acid, N^1-methylnicotinamide, and trigonelline. The basis of the procedure
was hydrolysis of sample aliquots in various strengths of acid, alkali, and
alkali plus urea, with subsequent application of the König reaction. (N^1
methylnicotinamide was assayed fluorometrically.)

3. N^1-METHYLNICOTINAMIDE

Several methods have been devised to measure this substance in urine.[27-3]
Some of these measured trigonelline as well as N^1-methylnicotinamide. The
method in most general use at present is that devised by Huff et al.[32] This
method is sensitive, accurate, and rapid and has given excellent result:
in many hands. It depends on the reaction of N^1-methylnicotinamide and
acetone in the presence of alkali to yield a fluorescent derivative which car
be quantitated against an internal standard of synthetic N^1-methylnico

[19] C. F. Heubner, Nature 167, 119 (1951).
[20] E. Kodicek and K. K. Reddi, Nature 168, 475 (1951).
[21] E. G. Wollish, M. Schmall, and E. G. Schafer, Anal. Chem. 23, 768 (1951).
[22] W. Ciusa, Ann. chim. appl. 39, 93 (1949).
[23] J. V. Scudi, Science 103, 567 (1946).
[24] P. K. Chaudhuri and E. Kodicek, Biochem. J. 44, 343 (1949).
[25] M. Kato and H. Shimizu, Science 114, 12 (1951).
[26] P. Ellinger and M. M. Abdel Kader, Biochem. J. 44, 77, 627 (1949).
[27] J. W. Huff and W. A. Perlzweig, J. Biol. Chem. 150, 395 (1943).
[28] M. Hochberg, D. Melnick, and B. L. Oser, J. Biol. Chem. 158, 265 (1945).
[29] V. A. Najjar, Bull. Johns Hopkins Hosp. 74, 392 (1944).
[30] R. A. Coulson, P. Ellinger, and M. Holden, Biochem. J. 38, 150 (1944).
[31] H. P. Sarett, J. Biol. Chem. 150, 159 (1943).
[32] J. W. Huff, W. A. Perlzweig, and M. W. Tilden, Federation Proc. 4, 92 (1945)
    J. Biol. Chem. 167, 157 (1947).

;inamide using a fluorometer equipped with the same filters as for thio-
:hrome. As little as 0.3 γ of the compound per milliliter of diluted urine
:an be detected easily. This usually permits a sufficient dilution to eliminate
nterference from highly pigmented urines and other substances. Urines
;iving high blank values can be decolorized with charcoal and acetic acid.

4. 6-Pyridone of N¹-Methylnicotinamide

This compound[33] can be assayed directly by means of its intense ultraviolet absorption which has maxima at 260 and 290 mμ. As little as 1 γ
)er milliliter can be assayed in this way. Rosen et al.[34] found the spectro-
)hotometric technique somewhat inadequate in that the values were too
ligh largely because of inability to obtain a suitable blank. They devised
a fluorometric method which gave satisfactory results. This method, al-
hough somewhat laborious, is useful and does not detect N¹-methylnico-
inamide.

5. Trigonelline (N¹-Methyl Nicotinic Acid Betaine)

In spite of the close structural similarity of this substance to N¹-methyl-
iicotinamide, it is now well established that it is not a metabolic product
of nicotinic acid in mammals. Several methods have been devised to measure
t in urine.[26, 35, 35a]

6. DPN and TPN (Coenzymes I and II)

Enzymatic spectrophotometric methods have been described elsewhere
p. 509). Total pyridine nucleotides in red blood cells may be determined
)y means of a fluorometric procedure[36] based on the same principle as
luff, Perlzweig, and Tilden's fluorometric determination of N¹-methyl-
iicotinamide in urine.[32] The blood is made protein-free with trichloroacetic
icid. Acetone condensation is then carried out in the presence of alkali,
rielding a fluorescent derivative which can be quantitated fluorometrically.
The procedure yields results very similar to those obtained by *Hemophilus
parainfluenza* assay.

Essentially the same procedure can be applied to assay the contents of
oenzymes I and II in the tissues.[37] In this instance the tissue to be assayed
nust be immersed promptly in 2 % nicotinamide solution to inhibit break-

[33] W. E. Knox and W. I. Grossman, *J. Biol. Chem.* **168**, 121 (1947).

[34] F. Rosen, W. A. Perlzweig, and I. G. Leder, *J. Biol. Chem.* **179**, 157 (1949).

[35] S. W. Fox, E. W. McNeil, and H. Field, Jr., *J. Biol. Chem.* **147**, 645 (1943).

[35a] H. P. Sarett, W. A. Perlzweig, and E. D. Levy, *J. Biol. Chem.* **135**, 483 (1940).

[36] N. Levitas, J. Robinson, F. Rosen, J. W. Huff, and W. A. Perlzweig, *J. Biol. Chem.* **167**, 169 (1947).

[37] J. Robinson, N. Levitas, F. Rosen, and W. A. Perlzweig, *J. Biol. Chem.* **170**, 653 (1947).

down of the coenzymes. The reduced coenzymes are oxidized, after which the same procedure is used as for determining coenzymes in blood.

Kaplan *et al.*[38] have recently proposed a chemical method based on the facts that oxidized DPN and TPN are split by alkali and that treatment with strong alkali produces a bluish fluorescence which can be quantitated. When crude tissue extracts were used, the difference in fluorescence before and after the coenzymes were destroyed with an enzyme (DPNase from *Neurospora*) was a measure of the amount of DPN–TPN originally present. N^1-Methylnicotinamide interfered slightly in the test. The method has not yet received its baptism of fire by being tried in tissue studies by other investigators.

7. OTHER METHODS

Feinstein[39] has devised a rapid, simple test to determine whether flour has been enriched with nicotinic acid. A few drops of aniline are dropped into the center of a packed sample of the flour. A few drops of cyanogen bromide are dropped on top of the spot wet from the aniline. A canary yellow color appears promptly, and the depth of the color is roughly proportional to the amount of nicotinic acid in the flour.

C. MICROBIOLOGICAL METHODS

E. E. SNELL

Nicotinic acid and nicotinamide have been found essential for a great variety of bacteria and yeasts since the nutritive importance of these compounds for bacteria was first indicated by the work of Lwoff and Lwoff with influenza bacilli,[40] of Knight with staphylococci,[41] of Mueller with diphtheria organisms,[42] and of Snell and coworkers with lactic acid bacteria.[43]

A number of nicotinic acid derivatives occur naturally (e.g., nicotinamide, coenzymes I and II, N^1-methylnicotinamide, trigonelline, quinolinic acid, etc.), and selection of an assay organism for which the activity of these compounds parallels their activity for animals is important. Nicotinic acid and nicotinamide have widely different activities for staphylococci, corynebacteria, dysentery organisms, pasteurella, and several other bacteria, and hence these organisms are not entirely satisfactory for assay

[38] N. O. Kaplan, S. P. Colowick, and C. C. Barnes, *J. Biol. Chem.* **191**, 461 (1951).
[39] L. Feinstein, *Science* **101**, 675 (1945).
[40] A. Lwoff and M. Lwoff, *Proc. Roy. Soc. (London)* **B122**, 352 (1937).
[41] B. C. J. G. Knight, *Biochem. J.* **31**, 731, 966 (1937).
[42] J. H. Mueller, *J. Biol. Chem.* **120**, 219 (1937).
[43] E. E. Snell, F. M. Strong, and W. H. Peterson, *J. Am. Chem. Soc.* **60**, 2825 (1938); *J. Bacteriol.* **38**, 293 (1939).

purposes, quite apart from their pathogenic character.[44] Some nicotinic acid-requiring yeasts utilize trigonelline,[45] and special procedures to correct for this substance, which has no activity for animals, are necessary when they are used. A wide variety of lactic acid bacteria require nicotinic acid; furthermore, the most widespread of the active forms of the vitamin (nicotinic acid, nicotinamide, coenzymes I and II) are equally active on the molar basis. The method of Snell and Wright,[46] which uses *Lactobacillus arabinosus* as the assay organism, has been widely studied and has proved highly successful both in its original form and in any of several minor modifications.

The assay procedure of choice is the modification adopted after wide collaborative study by the U S. Pharmacopeia[47] and the American Association of Agricultural Chemists. The method has been treated in detail with respect to procedure, specificity, and reliability in several readily available treatises.[44, 47-49] Growth of *L. arabinosus* in the niacin-free basal medium used increases with the niacin concentration in the range from 0 to about 0.40 γ per 10 ml. of medium. Pure nicotinic acid and samples to supply the vitamin at several levels within this range are added to individual tubes containing 5 ml. of the double-strength basal medium. Each tube is then diluted to 10 ml., capped, autoclaved, cooled, and inoculated. Response of the test organism is usually determined by acid titration after 72 hours incubation at 30 to 37°; under favorable conditions, turbidimetric estimations of growth can be made as early as 24 hours. The niacin content of the sample is then determined by interpolation of the response obtained with known levels of the samples onto the standard curve obtained by plotting the responses to known levels of nicotinic acid. The procedure is usually considered accurate to within $\pm 10\%$, which compares very favorably with the best of the chemical procedures.

The extraction of nicotinic acid from natural materials preparatory to assay offers little difficulty because of the looseness with which the vitamin is bound, and because of the stability of nicotinic acid. Autoclaving of the finely divided sample at 15 lb. pressure for 15 minutes with 0.1 N sulfuric acid is the preferred procedure.[47, 48] Few interfering materials are known. In contrast to animals, the test organism is unable to utilize tryptophan or the intermediates between tryptophan and niacin for growth in the absence

[44] E. E. Snell, *Biol. Symposia* **12**, 183 (1947).

[45] W. L. Williams, *J. Biol. Chem.* **166**, 397 (1946).

[46] E. E. Snell and L. D. Wright, *J. Biol. Chem.* **139**, 675 (1941).

[47] U. S. Pharmacopeia, 14th revision, p. 737, 1950.

[48] E. E. Snell *in* Vitamin Methods, Vol. I, pp. 360–370. Academic Press, New York, 1950.

[49] Association of Vitamin Chemists, Methods of Vitamin Assay, 2nd ed., p. 245. Interscience Publishers, New York, 1951.

of niacin.[50] Although the assay values thus give the true niacin content of a foodstuff, they do not therefore necessarily reflect the effectiveness of a foodstuff in preventing pellagra or blacktongue. Indeed, the low values for niacin first found in eggs and milk by this procedure[46] and confirmed by improved chemical methods,[51] as contrasted with the known value of these foods in preventing pellagra, were among the first findings pointing to the importance of factors other than niacin in the etiology of pellagra.

For special purposes, assay methods with different specificities may be of value. A strain of *Leuconostoc mesenteroides* responds to nicotinic acid, but not to nicotinamide, and has been used for estimation of the former in the presence of the latter.[48, 52] Following appropriate hydrolysis, total niacin is obtained. By use of the yeast, *Torula cremoris*, together with a variety of hydrolytic procedures, one may estimate either (1) total niacin, (2) niacin plus trigonelline, or (3) niacin plus trigonelline plus N^1-methylnicotinamide.[45] Some organisms, e.g., *Pasteurella suiseptica*, utilize nicotinamide but not nicotinic acid;[53] assay of the former in the presence of the latter should thus be possible. None of these procedures has been widely used.

VIII. Standardization of Activity

J. M. HUNDLEY

Both nicotinic acid and nicotinamide are readily available from commercial sources in quite pure form. There is little need for reference standards for most purposes. The purity of commercial products can be checked readily by melting point and other tests; they are readily recrystallized if necessary. However, a U.S.P. reference standard of pure crystalline nicotinic acid is available for those who wish to use it.[1] Commercial nicotinic acid, U.S.P. grade,[2] must be at least 99.5 % $C_6H_5NO_2$. When dried at 105° for 1 hour it must lose no more than 1 % in weight. When ignited there must be no more than 0.1 % residue. It must have no more than 200 p.p.m. of chloride, 200 p.p.m. of sulfate, and 20 p.p.m. of heavy metals. Nicotinamide (U.S.P.)[2] must be at least 98.5 % $C_6H_6N_2O$ and must lose no more than 0.5 % of its weight after drying over H_2SO_4 for 4 hours. On ignition there must be no more than 0.1 % of residue, and it must contain no more than 30 p.p.m. of heavy metals.

[50] B. E. Volcani and E. E. Snell, *Proc. Soc. Exptl. Biol. Med.* **67,** 511 (1948).
[51] W. J. Dann and P. Handler, *J. Biol. Chem.* **140,** 201 (1941).
[52] B. C. Johnson, *J. Biol. Chem.* **159,** 227 (1945).
[53] S. Berkman and S. A. Koser, *J. Bacteriol* **41,** 38 (1941).
[1] U. S. Pharmacopeia Reference Standards, 46 Park Ave., New York 16, N. Y.
[2] U. S. Pharmacopeia, 14th revision, p. 379 (1950).

IX. Occurrence

J. M. HUNDLEY

There is a tremendous volume of literature which presents in detail the nicotinic acid content of practically every form of living matter or substances derived from living matter (Table XIII). Much of this information is of but limited value, from the standpoint of practical nutrition, since we know that there are many factors which influence the amount of nicotinic

TABLE XIII

OCCURRENCE OF NICOTINIC ACID IN ORGANISMS OF VARIOUS BIOLOGICAL PHYLA

(FROM WOODS et al.[1])

(γ/g. of moist tissue)

Frog (*Rana*)	11.7	Brewer's yeast	126.0
Horned toad	26.8	Rat (whole)	61.0
Snake (*Thamnophis*)	28.0	Lamb leg muscle	75.0
Red ant (*Dolichederus*)	20.5	Veal leg muscle	72.0
Cockroach (*Periplaneta americanus*)	33.0	Chicken leg muscle	38.0
Termites (*Zootermposis*)	32.0	Chick embryo	28.4
Drosophila virilis larvae NY	36.5	Salmon steak	64.0
Drosophila virilis larvae NO	37.5	Fish (*Crypinidae*)	23.9
Oyster (*Mytilus*)	11.7	Whole wheat (seed)	41.0
Earthworm (*Lumbricus terrestris*)	15.0	Lima beans (dry seed)	9.8
Protozoa (*Tetrahymena geleii*)	11.7	Cauliflower (flower)	5.7
Aerobacter aerogenes, aerobic	49.1	Carrots (root)	2.6
Serratia marcescens	40.1	Blackeye peas (dry seed)	13.0
Pseudomonas fluorescens	44.0	Apples (fruit)	0.8
Clostridium butylicum, anaerobic	73.0	Watermelon (fruit)	2.4
Mushroom (*Coprinus atranentarius*)	68.5	Lettuce (leaf)	2.5
Mold	12.2	Irish potato (tuber)	4.3

acid that can be derived from a given diet, factors which cannot be readily assessed quantitatively except by actual experiment. The amount of tryptophan in relation to the balance of other amino acids, the type and amount of carbohydrate, the amount of fat, the relative availability of the nicotinic acid in the food, and the possibility of intestinal microbial synthesis all influence the pellagra-preventive potency of a given diet. For this reason the data on the pellagra-preventive potency of foods, gathered by Goldberger and his associates by actual test on pellagrins and on blacktongue dogs, still are reliable for practical use.[1a-7] The potencies (good, fair, and

[1] A. M. Woods, J. Taylor, M. J. Hofer, G. A. Johnson, R. L. Lane, and J. R. McMahan, *Univ. Texas Publ.* **4237**, 84 (1942).

[1a] J. Goldberger and W. F. Tanner, *Public Health Repts.* (*U. S.*) **39**, 87 (1924).

[2] J. Goldberger, G. A. Wheeler, R. D. Lillie, and L. M. Rogers, *Public Health Repts.* (*U. S.*) **41**, 297 (1926).

little or none) found by these workers are listed in Table XIV. The nicotinic acid content of these foods is also listed. It is interesting that, with a few exceptions, the nicotinic acid values compare fairly well with the pellagra-preventive potency found by these workers in empirical testing.

TABLE XIV

PELLAGRA-PREVENTIVE POTENCY OF FOODSTUFFS (GOLDBERGER RATINGS)[a]

Good	Nicotinic acid content, mg./100 g.	Fair	Nicotinic acid content, mg./100 g.	Little or none	Nicotinic acid content, mg./100 g.
Beef (fresh)	4.2	Haddock (canned)	2.4	Pork, salt	0.9
Corned beef (canned)	3.4	Egg yolk (dried)	0.1	Butter	0.1
Chicken	8.0	Skim milk (fresh)	0.1	Casein (leached)	0.0
Pork liver	10.5	Skim milk (dried)	1.1	Cornmeal	1.0
Pork shoulder, lean	4.0	Evaporated milk	0.2	Cornstarch	0
Rabbit	8.8	Wheat, whole	4.3	Oats, rolled	1.0
Salmon (canned)	7.3	Kidney beans	2.5	Rye meal	1.6
Buttermilk	0.1	Soybeans	2.3	Cod liver oil	0
Kale	1.7	Cabbage, green	0.3	Cottonseed oil	0
Collards	2.0	Cowpeas	2.2	Lard	0
Green peas	2.7	Mustard greens (canned)	0.7	Green beans (canned)	0.3
Tomato juice (canned)	0.8	Green peas (dried)	3.1	Navy beans	2.2
Turnip greens (canned)	0.6	Spinach (canned)	0.3	Carrots	0.5
Wheat germ	4.6			Lettuce	0.2
Peanut meal	16.2			Green and mature onions	0.2
Yeast, baker's	28.2			Sweet potatoes	0.6
Yeast, brewer's (dried)	36.2			Irish potatoes	1.2
				Rutabaga	0.9
				Dried apples and prunes	1.7
				Gelatin	0
				Beets (canned)	0.1
				Whole whey	0.8
				American cheese	Trace

[a] Most of the nicotinic acid values are taken from "Composition of Foods," in U. S. Department of Agriculture Handbook No. 8.

A. OCCURRENCE IN FOOD

The nicotinic acid[7a] content of all common food items has been compiled by the Bureau of Human Nutrition and Home Economics of the

[3] J. Goldberger, G. A. Wheeler, R. D. Lillie, and L. M. Rogers, *Public Health Repts.* (*U. S.*) **43,** 1385 (1928).

[4] J. Goldberger and W. H. Sebrell, *Public Health Repts.* (*U. S.*) **45,** 3064 (1930).

[5] W. H. Sebrell, *Public Health Repts.* (*U. S.*) **49,** 754 (1934).

[6] W. H. Sebrell, G. A. Wheeler, and D. J. Hunt, *Public Health Repts.* (*U. S.*) **50,** 1333 (1935).

[7] W. H. Sebrell, R. H. Onstott, and D. J. Hunt, *Public Health Repts.* (*U. S.*) **53,** 72 (1938).

[7a] Nicotinic acid in this instance and in many other places in this section is used in its generic sense to mean total nicotinic acid, irrespective of whether the actual form present is the acid, the amide, or the bound forms of either.

U. S. Department of Agriculture.[8] The nicotinic acid content of various animal tissues has been determined and compiled by several groups.[9-14] Cereal products have been analyzed and the results compiled.[15-18] The nicotinic acid content of many fresh fruits and vegetables is listed by Russell et al.[19] Rich sources of nicotinic acid are yeasts and meats, especially organ meats such as liver, pancreas, heart, and kidneys. Wheat, barley, and rye are better sources than corn, oats, or rice. Peanuts are a much richer source than soy and other varieties of beans. Milk and related dairy products are low in nicotinic acid. Wheat germ and brewer's yeast are excellent sources.

B. FORMS OF OCCURRENCE

In living animal tissues almost all the nicotinic acid is found as the amide bound into nucleotides (DPN and TPN).[20] Meats as purchased for human consumption undoubtedly contain a considerable amount of free nicotinamide, since the pyridine nucleotides are rapidly inactivated and broken down after cellular death, particularly if the cells are disrupted (p. 507). Krehl and associates[21] studied the relative distribution of nicotinic acid and nicotinamide in a variety of cereals, vegetables, and other natural products. From 7 (yellow corn) to 70 % (white potatoes) of the total activity was found as nicotinamide, the remainder as nicotinic acid or as substances which yielded nicotinic acid on hydrolysis. Skim milk powder and rat tissues, on the other hand, contained 91 to 99 % in the amide form.[21, 22]

[8] B. K. Watt, A. L. Merrill, M. L. Orr, W. Wu, and R. K. Pecot, *U. S. Dept. Agr., Agr. Handbook* **8**, (1950).

[9] E. Bandier, *Biochem. J.* **33**, 1130 (1939).

[10] H. A. Waisman and C. A. Elvehjem, The Vitamin Content of Meat. Burgess Publishing Co., Minneapolis.

[11] Studies on the Vitamin Content of Tissues, Vols. I and II, *Univ. Texas Publs.* **4137** (1941); **4237** (1942).

[12] W. J. Dann and P. Handler, *J. Nutrition* **24**, 153 (1942).

[13] J. M. McIntire, H. A. Waisman, L. M. Henderson, and C. A. Elvehjem, *J. Nutrition* **22**, 535 (1941).

[14] B. de M. Braganca, *Ann. Biochem. and Exptl. Med. (India)* **4**, 41 (1944).

[15] L. J. Teply, F. M. Strong, and C. A. Elvehjem, *J. Nutrition* **23**, 417 (1942); **24**, 167 (1942).

[16] R. McVicar and G. H. Berryman, *J. Nutrition* **24**, 235 (1942).

[17] E. I. Frazier, *J. Am. Dietet. Assoc.* **26**, 264 (1950).

[18] E. B. Brown, J. M. Thomas, and F. F. Bina, *J. Biol. Chem.* **162**, 221 (1946).

[19] W. C. Russell, M. W. Taylor, and J. F. Beuk, *J. Nutrition* **25**, 275 (1943).

[20] J. Robinson, N. Levitas, F. Rosen, and W. A. Perlzweig, *J. Biol. Chem.* **170**, 653 (1947).

[21] W. A. Krehl, J. de la Huerga, C. A. Elvehjem, and E. B. Hart, *J. Biol. Chem.* **166**, 53 (1946).

[22] P. K. Chaudhuri and E. Kodicek, *Biochem. J.* **44**, 343 (1949).

The exact form in which nicotinic acid and its amide are bound in plant tissue is not known. Several groups of investigators[23-25] found evidence of an alkali-labile precursor of nicotinic acid in wheat bran. The substance was purified to some extent and found to have nicotinic acid activity for the dog.[26] The exact nature of this substance has never been determined, although the latter workers suggested that it might be a simple ester of nicotinic acid. Chaudhuri and Kodicek[27] obtained evidence of a precursor of nicotinic acid in wheat, barley, rice brans and corn.[28] This precursor is inactive for *L. arabinosus* and differs from Krehl and Strong's material in that it is not active in animals (rats) unless first hydrolyzed. This material has been purified to some extent, and the suggestion has been made that it may be nicotinic acid with a residual substance attached through the carboxyl group.[29]

These findings may offer an explanation for the work of Chitre and Desai.[30] These investigators developed an animal method for estimating the availability of nicotinic acid in foodstuffs. Using this method, which has some inaccuracies and limitations, they found that the availability of nicotinic acid was only 60 % in rice, 81 % in wheat, 76 % in gram, 70 % in tur, and 92 % in yeast. They also showed that *in vitro* digestion, using enzymes to simulate *in vivo* digestion, effected a release of nicotinic acid to a degree consistent with the *in vivo* availability experiments. Cheldelin and Williams[23] also noted the apparently incomplete release of nicotinic acid from cereals when enzyme digestion was compared to acid digestion.

C. SITES OF OCCURRENCE

The distribution of nicotinic acid, and its derivatives, is not uniform within a given food product. In most foods of vegetable origin nicotinic acid tends to be concentrated in the outer coverings. For example, wheat bran contained 330 γ per gram, and patent flour 12 γ per gram, whereas the whole wheat from which it was derived assayed 70 γ per gram;[24] polished rice contained 0.9 γ per gram, brown rice 6.9 γ per gram, and rice polishings 96.6 γ per gram.[15] Likewise, much of the nicotinic acid in corn is found in the bran and, like wheat, in the germ.[31] Apple peelings contain

[23] V. H. Cheldelin and R. R. Williams, *Ind. Eng. Chem. Anal. Ed.* **14**, 671 (1942).
[24] J. S. Andrews, H. M. Boyd, and W. A. Gortner, *Ind. Eng. Chem. Anal. Ed.* **14**, 663 (1942).
[25] W. A. Krehl and F. M. Strong, *J. Biol. Chem.* **156**, 1 (1944).
[26] W. A. Krehl, C. A. Elvehjem, and F. M. Strong, *J. Biol. Chem.* **156**, 13 (1944).
[27] D. K. Chaudhuri and E. Kodicek, *Biochem. J.* **47**, xxxiv (1950).
[28] E. Kodicek, *Biochem. J.* **48**, viii (1951).
[29] D. K. Chaudhuri and E. Kodicek, *Nature* **165**, 1022 (1950).
[30] R. G. Chitre and D. B. Desai, *Ind. J. Med. Research* **3**, 471, 479 (1949).
[31] P. R. Burkholder, I. McVeigh, and D. Moyer, *Yale J. Biol. Med.* **16**, 659 (1944).

more than twice the concentration of nicotinic acid as the rest of the apple; pear peelings have three times the concentration of peeled pears. Similar findings have been recorded for plums, sweet potatoes, tomatoes, and yams. White potatoes seem to be an exception in that peelings and the peeled potato have about the same nicotinic acid concentration.[15] In inactive bean seeds, the concentration of nicotinic acid was 40 γ per gram in the sprout, 28 γ per gram in the cotyledons, and 7 γ per gram in the cuticle. In the whole bean, 96 % of the nicotinic acid was in the cotyledon.[32]

Little information is available on the distribution of nicotinic acid within cells. E. R. Isbell and associates[33] studied the distribution of several vitamins between nuclei and the whole cell in beef heart and mouse mammary carcinoma cells. In beef heart the nuclei had a concentration of nicotinic acid nearly three times that of the entire cell. In mouse carcinoma the reverse was true in that the entire cell had considerably higher nicotinic acid concentration than the nuclei. On a weight basis, three-fourths of the total cellular nicotinic acid was in the cytoplasm of these cancer cells. In the hen's egg, the whites have seven times the concentration of the yolks (on a dry-weight basis).[8]

D. STABILITY IN FOOD

Nicotinic acid is one of the most stable of the vitamins against the ordinary conditions met in food processing, storage, and cooking. Some losses in cooking are encountered, particularly where there is an opportunity for leaching out. Nicotinic acid is quite stable in canning processes. In canned foods stored 2 years and at storage temperatures up to 100°F., the losses rarely exceed 15 %.[34-40] There is little or no loss with frozen storage or dry storage.[41-43] Usual methods of curing and cooking result in losses of 15 to

---

[32] T. Terroine and J. Desveaux-Chabrol, *Arch. sci. physiol.* **1**, 117 (1947).

[33] E. R. Isbell, H. K. Mitchell, A. Taylor, and R. J. Williams, Studies on the Vitamin Content of Tissues, Vol. II, *Univ. Texas Publ.* **4237**, 81 (1942).

[34] L. E. Clifcorn *Advances in Food Research*, **1**, 39–104 (1948).

[35] F. C. Lamb, A. Pressley, and T. Zuch, *Food Research* **12**, 273 (1947).

[36] N. B. Guerrant, O. B. Fardig, M. G. Vavich, and H. A. Ellenberger, *Ind. Eng. Chem.* **40**, 2258 (1948).

[37] S. Brenner, V. O. Wodicka, and S. G. Dunlop, *Food Technol.* **2**, 207 (1948).

[38] J. F. Feaster, M. D. Tompkins, and W. E. Pearce, *Food Research* **14**, 25 (1949).

[39] B. B. Sheft, R. M. Griswold, E. Tarlowsky, and E. G. Halliday, *Ind. Eng. Chem.* **41**, 144 (1949).

[40] R. Millares and C. R. Fellers, *Food Research* **14**, 131 (1949).

[41] P. F. Sharpe, J. B. Shields, and A. P. Stewart, Jr., *Proc. Inst. Food Technol.* p. 54 (1945).

[42] A. F. Morgan, L. E. Kidder, M. Hunner, B. K. Sharokh, and R. M. Chesbro, *Food Research* **14**, 439 (1949).

[43] B. B. Cook, A. F. Morgan, and M. B. Smith, *Food Research* **14**, 449 (1949).

20 %, although with some foods and cooking methods losses as high as 50 % have been recorded.[12, 44-48] The references cited are intended to be only representative and do not even begin to cover completely the voluminous literature on this subject.

E. INFLUENCE OF SOIL, ENVIRONMENT, AND HEREDITY

Soil and its nutrients can play some role in the nicotinic acid content of plants. McCoy and coworkers[49] found that a reduction in the major ions in their nutrient solution reduced the nicotinic acid content of oats. Hunt and associates[50] reported that liming the soil, or adding nitrates, increased the nicotinic acid content of wheat. Liming decreased the nicotinic acid content of oats in a dry year. Gough and Lantz[51] studied eight varieties of beans grown in three widely different localities and found that environment influenced nicotinic acid content. Gustafson[52] found more nicotinic acid in tomatoes, beans, and soybeans grown at 28 to 30° than at 10 to 15°; the reverse was true with broccoli, cabbage, spinach, clover, peas, and wheat.

However, the magnitude of the effects produced by soil and environment seems to be much less than the influence of heredity, within the limits of reasonable production yields. McElroy and Simonson[53] found no correlation between soil type and nicotinic acid content for oats, wheat, and barley grown in three different parts of Alberta. Richey and Dawson[54] found that extreme differences in production practices, i e., fertilizers, green manures, etc., had no significant influence on the nicotinic acid content of corn, although different inbred strains of corn varied from 13.9 to 53.3 γ per gram of nicotinic acid. Hunt et al.[55] examined samples of nine corn hybrids grown at five different locations for 2 years. There were differences in nicotinic acid content for both years and at all locations. However, the variations were small compared to the variations in nicotinic acid content characteris-

[44] R. M. Griswold, L. M. Jans, and E. G. Halliday, *J. Am. Dietet. Assoc.* **25**, 866 (1949).

[45] E. Hartzler, W. Ross, and E. L. Willett, *Food Research* **14**, 15 (1949).

[46] A. Lopez-Matas and C. R. Fellers, *Food Research* **13**, 387 (1948).

[47] B. S. Schweigert, J. M. McIntyre, and C. A. Elvehjem, *J. Nutrition* **27**, 419 (1944).

[48] K. Causey, E. G. Andreassen, M. E. Hausrath, C. Along, P. E. Ramstad, and F. Fenton, *Food Research* **15**, 237, 249, 256 (1950).

[49] T. A. McCoy, S. M. Free, R. G. Langston, and J. Q. Snyder, *Soil Sci.* **68**, 375 (1949).

[50] C. H. Hunt, L. D. Rodriquez, and R. M. Bethke, *Cereal Chem.* **27**, 79 (1950).

[51] H. W. Gough and E. M. Lantz, *Food Research* **15**, 308 (1950).

[52] F. G. Gustafson, *Plant Physiol.* **25**, 150 (1950).

[53] L. W. McElroy and H. Simonson, *Can. J.Research* **26F**, 201 (1948).

[54] F. D. Richey and R. F. Dawson, *Plant Physiol.* **23**, 238 (1948).

[55] C. H. Hunt, L. Ditzler, and R. M. Bethke, *Cereal Chem.* **24**, 355 (1947).

tic for each hybrid. Carroll and Lee Peng[56] analyzed two varieties of corn, four of wheat, two of oats, and two of soybeans all grown under the same environmental conditions and found the nicotinic acid content to be more characteristic of the species than the soil. Futhermore, Leng et al.[57] grew corn which was a cross between a high nicotinic acid sugar line (48.3 γ per gram) and a low nicotinic acid waxy line (18.0 γ per gram). From each ear of the resultant corn they could pick kernels which were sugary in type (33.8 γ of nicotinic acid per gram), waxy (26.0 γ per gram), and dent (21.4 γ per gram). This certainly demonstrates the predominance of heredity over environment in this regard.

Different strains of corn are known to vary greatly in their nicotinic acid content (Table XV). Sugary corns are generally higher than starchy strains.

TABLE XV

Nicotinic Acid in Various Strains of Corn (from Burkholder et al. [31])

(γ/g. air-dried mature grain)

Type of corn	Number of strains	Average nicotinic acid	Range
Yellow field	94	21.4	11.3–36.3
White field	86	20.1	12.7–29.3
Sweet	46	34.6	18.2–62.1
Popcorn	7	17.4	7.9–21.6

F. NICOTINIC ACID IN U. S. DIETS

Studies made by the U. S. Department of Agriculture indicate that our food in 1951 supplied 24% more nicotinic acid than in the 1935–1939 period.[58] Much of this increase can be accounted for by the widespread enrichment of white flour, the Federal Standard for which provides a minimum of 10 mg. and a maximum of 15.0 mg. of nicotinic acid per pound.[59] Booher and Behan[60] have analyzed composite food samples representative of the national dietary for nicotinic acid, as well as other nutrients. According to their results a 3050-calorie diet provides 20.2 mg. of nicotinic acid, considerably in excess of the recommended allowances of the National Research Council (15 mg.).[61] Earlier studies making direct analyses on foods representative of the national dietary in 1940 and 1941 indicated that the

[56] J. C. Carroll and C. A. Lee Peng, Science 113, 211 (1951).

[57] E. R. Leng, J. J. Curtis, and M. C. Shekleton, Science 111, 665 (1950).

[58] C. M. Coons, Chicago Med. Soc. Bull. 53, 1015 (1951).

[59] Federal Register, Aug. 3, 1943.

[60] L. E. Booher and I. T. Behan, J. Nutrition 39, 495 (1949).

[61] Recommended Dietary Allowances, Bull. Natl. Research Council, Reprint and Circ. Ser. 129, (1948).

average American diet provided about 11 mg. of nicotinic acid daily (no allowance included for enriched bread).[62, 63] These data are in contrast to the 4.25 to 10.49 mg. of nicotinic acid per day which Frazier and Friedemann,[64] using Goldberger's diet records, have calculated were consumed by families in which pellagra was prevalent. These facts, plus the virtual disappearance of pellagra, indicate that the average American diet is adequate in pellagra-preventive factors.

G. ANTIVITAMINS IN FOOD

The existence of substances in food which have antinicotinic acid properties has not been proved. There are innumerable reports in the older literature suggesting or citing evidence for the presence of pellagragenic factors in corn, particularly spoiled corn. More recently, Woolley[65] extracted a substance from corn which caused a pellagra-like syndrome in mice which could be prevented by nicotinamide. Borrow and associates[66] attempted to repeat Woolley's work but were in doubt as to whether the toxicity they obtained was due to residual chloroform in the extract. The latter group did, however, find evidence of a pellagragenic factor for mice in corn bran. No further reports on this finding have appeared thus far. Raska[67] reported producing "pellagra" in dogs by feeding large amounts of adenine and phosphate. Apparently no attempt was made to prevent or treat this condition with nicotinic acid. Hence, there is no assurance that the condition was actually a nicotinic acid deficiency. Kodicek et al.[68] reported that indole-3-acetic acid, which does occur in corn, was pellagragenic in rats. However, this claim has been denied[69-71] and was later retracted.[72]

Woolley et al.[73] found that 3-acetylpyridine was toxic in nicotinic acid-deficient dogs but, in the same dosage, harmless to normal dogs. Woolley later reported[74, 75] that 3-acetylpyridine caused a "pellagra-like" condition

[62] R. L. Lane, E. Johnson, and R. R. Williams, J. Nutrition 23, 613 (1942).

[63] V. H. Cheldelin and R. R. Williams, J. Nutrition 26, 417 (1943).

[64] E. I. Frazier and T. E. Friedemann, Quart. Bull. Northwestern Univ. Med. School 20, 24 (1946).

[65] D. W. Woolley, J. Biol. Chem. 163, 773 (1946).

[66] A. Borrow, L. Fowden, M. M. Stedman, J. C. Waterlow, and R. A. Webb, Lancet 254, 752 (1948).

[67] S. B. Raska, J. Biol. Chem. 165, 743 (1946); Science 105, 126 (1947).

[68] E. Kodicek, K. J. Carpenter, and L. J. Harris, Lancet 251, 491 (1946).

[69] L. M. Henderson, T. Deodhar, W. A. Krehl, and C. A. Elvehjem, J. Biol. Chem. 170, 261 (1947).

[70] F. Rosen and W. A. Perlzweig, Arch. Biochem. 15, 111 (1947).

[71] Y. Raoul and C. Marnay, Compt. rend. 226, 1043 (1948).

[72] E. Kodicek, K. J. Carpenter, and L. J. Harris, Lancet 253, 616 (1947).

[73] D. W. Woolley, F. M. Strong, R. J. Madden, and C. A. Elvehjem, J. Biol. Chem. 124, 715 (1938).

[74] D. W. Woolley, J. Biol. Chem. 157, 455 (1945).

in mice which could be counteracted by nicotinic acid or tryptophan. These findings have not been confirmed. Indeed, Gaebler and Beher[76] found that 3-acetylpyridine caused large increases in urinary N^1-methylnicotinamide excretion in dogs and rats, indicating that this compound could serve as a precursor of nicotinic acid. Beher et al.[77] later used an isotope tracer technique to prove the conversion of 3-acetylpyridine to nicotinic acid. However, Ackermann and Taylor[77a] found that 3-acetylpyridine induced rapid

TABLE XVI

NICOTINIC ACID CONTENT OF VARIOUS ORGANS AND TISSUES

(γ/g. of wet tissue)

	Man[79]	Human fetus[80]	Rat[81]	Rat[82]	Pig[83]	Ox[83]
Heart	34	50	125	114	53	59
Liver	60	49	180	157	118	122
Brain	19.5	23	64	47	—	—
Lung	20	—	51	48	—	—
Kidney	40	38	115	87	68	58
Spleen	26	—	69	58	40	44
Thyroid	—	25	—	—	16	30
Muscle, smooth	31	—	—	—	—	—
Muscle, skeletal	42	26	80	78	47	49
Adrenal	25	—	—	—	—	57
Stomach	22	33	—	—	—	—
Ileum	21	31	—	—	—	—
Colon, mucosa	16	—	—	—	—	—
Ovary	18	—	—	—	38	—
Testes seminiferous tubules	16	—	—	—	47	—
Seminal ducts	8.2	—	—	—	—	—
Skin	8.6	20	—	—	—	—
Cartilage	—	9.7	—	—	—	—
Bone	—	13.0	—	—	—	—

death in embryonating eggs, an effect competitively reversed by nicotinamide but much less successfully reversed with nicotinic acid or tryptophan. Hull et al.[78] reported that 3-acetylpyridine and pyridine-3-sulfonic

[75] D. W. Woolley, J. Biol. Chem. **162**, 179 (1946).

[76] O. H. Gaebler and W. T. Beher, J. Biol. Chem. **188**, 343 (1951).

[77] W. T. Beher, W. M. Holliday, and O. H. Gaebler, Abstr. 12th Intern. Congr. Pure and Appl. Chem., New York, p. 84 (1951).

[77a] W. W. Ackermann and A. Taylor, Proc. Soc. Exptl. Biol. Med. **67**, 449 (1948).

[78] W. Hull, J. C. Perrone, and P. L. Kirk, J. Gen. Physiol. **34**, 75 (1950).

[79] Averaged from the data of A. Taylor, M. A. Pollack, and R. J. Williams, Univ. Texas Publ. **4237**, 41–55 (1942).

[80] A. Lwoff and L. Digonnet, Compt. rend. **213**, 1030 (1941).

[81] H. K. Mitchell and E. R. Isbell, Univ. Texas Publ. **4237**, 37–40 (1942).

acid produced deleterious effects in embryonic chick heart cultures, but nicotinic acid would not reverse this effect. Available evidence seems to support the view that 3-acetylpyridine is a nicotinic acid antagonist under certain conditions. However, animals (rat and dog at least) possess the ability to convert this compound to nicotinic acid. If the antagonist is administered in doses large enough to exceed the animal's capacity to convert it to nicotinic acid, then it acts as an antagonist. If given in lower doses it does not act as an antagonist but will actually substitute for nicotinic acid. There is no evidence that either 3-acetylpyridine or pyridine-3-sulfonic acid occurs in food.

H. OCCURRENCE IN VARIOUS TISSUES

The data in Table XVI are presented to give a picture of the relative distribution of nicotinic acid in various mammalian tissues and organs. The data are not necessarily exactly comparable from one species to another, because different analytical methods were used. Gounelle and associates[84] found considerably higher values for normal human liver (150 γ per gram) than that reported by Taylor et al.[79] (Table XVI).

X. Effects of Deficiency

A. IN MICROORGANISMS

E. E. SNELL

Subsequent to the discovery of diphospho- and triphosphopyridine nucleotides and the demonstration that these nicotinamide-containing coenzymes were identical with the long-known factor V required for growth of *Hemophilus influenza*, nicotinic acid itself was shown to be an essential growth factor for *Staphylococcus aureus*[1] and for *Corynebacterium diphtheriae*.[2] Since then, it has been shown to be essential for a great variety of other bacteria (e.g., *Proteus vulgaris*, *Acetobacter*, all lactobacilli so far examined, *Clostridium tetani*, and others[3, 4]), and for some yeasts.[5, 6] Natu-

---

[82] S. A. Singal, V. P. Sydenstricker, and J. M. Littlejohn, *J. Biol. Chem.* **176**, 1069 (1948).

[83] E. Bandier, *Biochem. J.* **33**, 1130 (1939).

[84] H. Gounelle, Y. Raoul, and J. Marche, *Compt. rend.* **139**, 30 (1945).

[1] B. C. J. G. Knight, *Biochem. J.* **31**, 731, 966 (1937).

[2] J. H. Mueller, *J. Biol. Chem.* **120**, 219 (1937).

[3] B. C. J. G. Knight, *Vitamins and Hormones* **3**, 105 (1945).

[4] W. H. Peterson and M. S. Peterson, *Bacteriol. Revs.* **9**, 49 (1945).

[5] A. S. Schultz, L. Atkin, and C. N. Frey, *J. Am. Chem. Soc.* **60**, 1514 (1938).

[6] P. R. Burkholder, I. McVeigh, and D. Moyer, *J. Bacteriol.* **48**, 385 (1944).

ral populations of fungi other than yeast that require nicotinic acid have not been observed; however, mutant cultures of *Neurospora crassa* that require it are readily obtained.[7] All organisms that do not require it preformed in the medium appear to synthesize it; many intermediates in the route of this synthesis, which proceeds from tryptophan to niacin through a series of intermediates, were first indicated by use of mutant cultures of *N. crassa.*[7]

In all cultures that require a source of nicotinic acid (or its amide) in the medium, a deficiency in supply is reflected in decreased growth of the culture. Concomitant with such decreased growth there is, of course, a decreased production of the metabolic end products of the particular culture (e.g., lactic acid production by lactic acid bacteria). Microbiological assays for the vitamin depend upon these effects.[8] Aside from these over-all effects upon growth, no effects of nicotinic acid deficiency upon specific phases of metabolism of microorganisms have been reported. Because of the role of the nicotinamide-coenzymes in metabolism, one might expect the ability of resting cells to carry out certain dehydrogenation reactions to be impaired by deficiency of nicotinic acid. Few studies of a sufficiently quantitative character to detect such alterations have been made. Hughes, however, reported that in a nicotinic acid-low medium, *L. arabinosus* synthesized DPN at a considerably higher rate (24 mμ moles per milligram of cells per hour) than was true in the presence of an excess of nicotinic acid (3 mμ moles per milligram per hour).[9]

B. IN MAN AND ANIMALS

J. M. HUNDLEY

1. RELATION OF BIOCHEMICAL FUNCTIONS OF NICOTINIC ACID TO DEFICIENCY STATES

A dietary deficiency of nicotinic acid produces deficiency states by virtue of the fact that nicotinamide is an essential component of coenzymes I and II. These coenzymes are required for normal metabolism, indeed, for life itself. If the dietary supply of nicotinic acid is insufficient and the organism is unable to synthesize sufficient amounts of the vitamin (see Section VI), normal metabolism becomes impossible, a deficiency state develops, and the organism eventually dies, if the deficiency is sufficiently severe.

A great mass of precise information is available on the many biochemical

---

[7] G. W. Beadle, H. K. Mitchell, and J. F. Nyc, *Proc. Natl. Acad. Sci. U. S.* **33**, 155 (1947).

[8] E. E. Snell *in* Vitamin Methods, Vol. 1, p. 327. Academic Press, New York, 1951.

[9] D. E. Hughes, *Biochem. J.* **45**, xxxvi (1949).

reactions which are catalyzed by these coenzymes. The chemistry of the reactions and the manner in which the coenzymes function are known. Yet with all this precise information, it is still impossible to offer any comprehensive explanation for the origin of many of the characteristic pathological manifestations of human nicotinic acid deficiency such as dermatitis, skin sensitivity to solar radiation, glossitis, atrophy of tongue papillae, and mental abnormalities. An extensive field, still largely unexplored, exists in which the biochemical reactions catalyzed by these coenzymes must be integrated into the normal physiology and biochemistry of the intact animal. This will be necessary before any real picture of the specific effects of malfunction of the enzyme systems can be drawn. Such will be a difficult task, but until it is done our explanations for the manifestations of nicotinic acid deficiency will be mostly educated guesswork based on reasoning rather than demonstrated facts.

2. The Deficiency State

Only two mammalian species, man and dog, develop nicotinic acid deficiency states which are characteristic and which can be readily differentiated by their external manifestations from other vitamin deficiencies and other diseases. The four D's of pellagra in man, dermatitis, diarrhea, delirium, and death, form a characteristic picture which is readily diagnosed by an experienced clinician. Milder and atypical syndromes are frequently observed. Many excellent clinical descriptions of pellagra have been published and need not be repeated here.[10] Pellagra has been produced experimentally in man on two occasions. The original demonstration of the nutritional etiology of pellagra by Goldberger and associates in 1915[11-17] is a classic and well-known story in nutrition. Their work represented the first experimental production of pellagra in man and clearly demonstrated the role of diet in the origin and prevention of the disease. It is of more than passing interest, in view of the recently demonstrated tryptophan-nicotinic acid relationship, that Goldberger suspected that an amino acid

---

[10] T. D. Spies *in* Clinical Nutrition, p. 531. Paul B. Hoeber, New York, 1950.

[11] J. Goldberger and G. A. Wheeler, *Public Health Repts.* (*U. S.*) **30**, 3336 (1915).

[12] J. Goldberger, *Public Health Repts.* (*U. S.*) **31**, 3159 (1916).

[13] J. Goldberger, C. H. Waring, and D. G. Willets, *Public Health Repts.* (*U. S.*) **30**, 3117 (1915).

[14] J. Goldberger and G. A. Wheeler, *U. S. Public Health Service Hyg. Lab. Bull.* **120** (1920).

[15] M. X. Sullivan and K. K. Jones, *U. S. Public Health Service Hyg. Lab. Bull.* **120**, 117–126 (1920).

[16] J. Goldberger and W. F. Tanner, *Public Health Repts.* (*U. S.*) **39**, 87 (1924).

[17] J. Goldberger, G. A. Wheeler, E. Sydenstricker, W. I. King, W. S. Bean, R. E. Dyer, J. D. Reichard, P. M. Stewart, M. C. Edmonds, R. E. Tarbett, D. Wiehl, and J. C. Goddard, *U. S. Public Health Service Hyg. Lab. Bull.* **153**, (1929).

deficiency, as well as a vitamin deficiency, was involved in the etiology of pellagra. He singled out cystine and tryptophan as the probable culprits and with W. F. Tanner conducted therapeutic trials in three patients.[18] The results were cautiously evaluated as a marked improvement in the dermal lesions of two patients given cystine and a steady gain in weight with some improvement in diarrhea when both cystine and tryptophan were administered to the third patient. Apparently, tests with tryptophan alone were conducted but they were never reported. The author of this review is in possession of a copy of a progress report to Goldberger from Tanner, dated August 5, 1921, which has never been publicly reported. In it, Tanner relates the course of one pellagrous patient who was given "one-half dram" of tryptophan before each meal. There was no improvement in the diarrhea at the time of the report, but prompt and marked improvement in the patient's extensive dermatitis was noted. After describing the progress of the skin lesions, Tanner stated: "I might add that the improvement in this patient's skin condition has surpassed anything I have ever seen in a case of pellagra in an equal period of time." There is no record of the final result.

The second instance of the production of pellagra in man by dietary means was recently described by Goldsmith et al.[19] These experiments are of special interest, since the importance of tryptophan was realized and both the tryptophan and nicotinic acid intakes were controlled. These workers also provided supplementary vitamins such as riboflavin and folic acid. It has long been a debatable issue as to the extent to which the pellagra syndrome, as commonly seen clinically, may be modified by concomitant deficiencies of other vitamins. It is, therefore, of interest that essentially typical pellagrous lesions appeared in spite of added vitamins (not including nicotinic acid). These workers were also able to cure pellagra with tryptophan, a clear demonstration of the ability of this amino acid to cure pellagra in man.[19a] Other interesting aspects of these investigations are discussed in later sections.

Dogs also develop a very characteristic reaction to nicotinic acid deficiency, the so-called blacktongue. The severe oral lesions, drooling of saliva, the very foul and characteristic oral odor, diarrhea, often bloody, the emaciated appearance, and the complete lack of appetite for food and water form a typical picture. This syndrome is described in detail in Section XI.

[18] J. Goldberger and W. F. Tanner, *Public Health Repts.* (*U. S.*) **37,** 462 (1922).

[19] G. A. Goldsmith, H. P. Sarett, U. D. Register, and J. Gibbens, *J. Clin. Invest.* **31,** 533 (1952).

[19a] W. B. Bean, M. Franklin, and K. Daum, *J. Lab. Clin. Med.* **38,** 167 (1951), also reported that tryptophan produced rapid improvement in the tongue of two patients with pellagrous glossitis.

In all other species, except possibly the cat (p. 570), a deficiency of nicotinic acid is manifested by the same signs and symptoms as can be produced by many other deficiencies. Actually, there are only six deficiency phenomena which can be found in all species susceptible to the deficiency. These are: (1) reduced growth in young animals, (2) weight loss in either young or adult animals if the deficiency is severe, (3) loss of appetite, (4) reduced concentration of nicotinic acid and coenzymes I and II in some but not all tissues, (5) reduced excretion of nicotinic acid and its derivatives in the urine, and (6) death, if the deficiency is severe or long continued. Difficulties in reproduction and lactation could probably be added to this list, but these subjects have received little attention. All these phenomena, except possibly the reduced tissue and urine levels, can be produced by other deficiencies.

The general signs and symptoms and the pathology observed in various species is described in Section XI. The discussion in this section will deal with some of the physiological and biochemical defects which have been reported in various species as well as some of the interesting and fairly characteristic defects which are seen in human pellagra.

3. NICOTINIC ACID AND COENZYME TISSUE LEVELS

Nicotinic acid-deficient chicks,[20, 21] dogs,[22-24] pigs,[23, 24] rats,[25-29] rabbits,[30] and men[31] exhibit a lowered concentration of nicotinic acid (and nicotinic acid-containing coenzymes) in tissues such as liver, muscle, and, in some species, brain. Other tissues such as red blood cells, heart, lung, spleen, and kidney may maintain normal concentrations.[22-25, 31-34] The level of nicotinic

[20] E. G. Anderson, L. J. Teply, and C. A. Elvehjem, *Arch. Biochem.* **3**, 357 (1944).

[21] G. M. Briggs, Jr., T. D. Luckey, L. J. Teply, C. A. Elvehjem, and E. B. Hart, *J. Biol. Chem.* **148**, 517 (1943).

[22] H. I. Kohn, J. R. Klein, and W. J. Dann, *Biochem. J.* **33**, 1432 (1939).

[23] A. E. Axelrod, R. J. Madden, and C. A. Elvehjem, *J. Biol. Chem.* **131**, 85 (1939).

[24] A. E. Axelrod and C. A. Elvehjem, *Nature* **143**, 282 (1939).

[25] S. A. Singal, V. P. Sydenstricker, and J. M. Littlejohn, *J. Biol. Chem.* **176**, 1069 (1948).

[26] J. M. Hundley, *J. Nutrition* **34**, 253 (1947).

[27] J. N. Williams, Jr., P. Feigelson, and C. A. Elvehjem, *J. Biol. Chem.* **187**, 597 (1950).

[28] J. M. Hundley, *J. Biol. Chem.* **181**, 1 (1949).

[29] S. A. Singal, V. P. Sydenstricker, and J. M. Littlejohn, *J. Biol. Chem.* **171**, 203 (1947); **176**, 1063 (1948).

[30] J. G. Wooley, *Proc. Soc. Exptl. Biol. Med.* **65**, 315 (1947).

[31] H. Gounelle, Y. Raoul, A. Vallette, and J. Marche, *Bull. mém. soc. méd. hôp. Paris* **21**, 1225 (1945).

[32] A. E. Axelrod, T. D. Spies, and C. A. Elvehjem, *J. Biol. Chem.* **138**, 667 (1941).

[33] A. E. Axelrod, E. S. Gordon, and C. A. Elvehjem, *Am. J. Med. Sci.* **199**, 697 (1940).

[34] H. I. Chu, P. T. Kuo, and K. P. Chang, *Chinese Med. J.* **61**, 181 (1942).

acid (or coenzymes) in liver and muscle shows a much better correlation with the degree of nicotinic acid deficiency than most other tissues. There seems to be little or no correlation between nicotinic acid levels in blood and the deficiency. Furthermore, blood nicotinic acid may be depressed in several pathological states other than nicotinic acid deficiency.[31, 35-37] The degree of depression in coenzyme levels in tissues such as liver and muscle from deficient animals has varied greatly in different studies. In dogs with acute blacktongue Kohn et al.[22] found coenzyme levels 70 % below normal in liver and 35 % below normal in striated muscle. Paradoxically, the liver, which showed a decreased coenzyme level, exhibited an increase of 35 % in O_2 consumption, whereas kidney which showed no lowering of coenzymes showed a 50 % decrease in lactate oxidation. More recent studies by Williams and Elvehjem[38] with rat liver homogenates from deficient animals have shown a low endogenous respiratory rate which could be restored to normal by the addition of coenzyme I *in vitro*. Other studies[28] in rats have shown that survival and some growth is possible in animals having a concentration of nicotinic acid 70 % of normal in liver and 50 % of normal in muscle. The type of carbohydrate in the diet appeared to influence growth and survival in animals having these lowered nicotinic acid tissue levels. Glucose and carbohydrates containing glucose exerted a favorable effect, but fructose and sucrose had the opposite effect.[28]

Factors other than nicotinic acid deficiency have been reported to lower nicotinic acid tissue levels. Although simple starvation does not have this effect,[39] a protein-free diet,[40, 41] a low protein diet,[42] and a vitamin B-free ration[43] do have this effect in rats. Deficiencies of thiamine and riboflavin also have been reported to lower liver nicotinic acid.[44, 45] Cobalt deficiency has been reported to lower blood nicotinic acid in sheep.[46]

Administration of nicotinic acid or tryptophan to deficient or normal subjects results in a rise in blood and tissue nicotinic acid sometimes, especially

[35] H. I. Kohn, F. Bernheim, and A. V. Felsovanyi, *J. Clin. Invest.* **18,** 585 (1939).
[36] S. P. Vilter, M. B. Koch, and T. D. Spies, *J. Lab. Clin. Med.* **26,** 31 (1940).
[37] C. W. Carter and J. R. P. O'Brien, *Quart. J. Med.* [N. S.] **14,** 197 (1945).
[38] J. N. Williams, Jr., and C. A. Elvehjem, *J. Biol. Chem.* **183,** 539 (1950).
[39] B. C. Flinn, F. J. Pilgrim, H. S. Gregg, and A. E. Axelrod, *Proc. Soc. Exptl. Biol. Med.* **63,** 523 (1946).
[40] J. N. Williams, Jr., P. Feigelson, C. A. Elvehjem, and S. S. Shahinian, *J. Biol. Chem.* **189,** 659 (1951).
[41] S. Seifter, D. M. Harkness, L. Rubin, and E. Muntwyler, *J. Biol. Chem.* **176,** 1371 (1948).
[42] L. D. Wright and H. R. Skeggs, *Proc. Soc. Exptl. Biol. Med.* **63,** 327 (1946).
[43] H. von Euler, F. Schlenk, L. Melzer, and B. Högberg, *Hoppe-Seyler's Z. physiol. Chem.* **258,** 219 (1939).
[44] K. Bhagvat and P. Devi, *Biochem. J.* **45,** 32 (1949).
[45] Y. Raoul, *Bull. soc. chim. biol.* **27,** 371 (1945).
[46] S. N. Ray, W. C. Weir, A. L. Pope, and P. H. Phillips, *J. Nutrition* **34,** 595 (1947).

in non-deficient subjects, to levels temporarily above normal.[20, 30, 33, 47-5] Wooley[30] found that tryptophan was less effective than nicotinic acid in increasing the nicotinic acid level in skeletal muscle of deficient rabbits, although both substances were equally effective in increasing the liver nicotinic acid level and in alleviating deficiency symptoms. On the other hand Williams et al.[27] found that nicotinic acid was less effective than tryptophan in maintaining levels of coenzyme I and II in the liver of rats. This seemed to be particularly true when protein-free rations were fed.[40] However, in later studies Feigelson et al.[57a] found that nicotinic acid and tryptophan were equally effective, on an equimolecular basis, as precursors for liver pyridine nucleotides, except that administration of tryptophan at levels considerably in excess of requirements seemed to increase liver pyridine nucleotides above "normal." This effect was not observed with nicotinic acid.

4. URINARY EXCRETION OF NICOTINIC ACID AND OTHER SUBSTANCES

a. Urinary Pigments

For the first two or three years following the discovery of nicotinic acid as the pellagra-preventive vitamin, interest in using urine for diagnostic purposes centered about the excretion of porphyrin and other pigments. Beckh, Ellinger, and Spies[58] devised a test (the B.E.S. test) which they believed to measure urinary porphyrin and which seemed to have a diagnostic relationship to pellagra. However, further investigations by Watson and associates[59-62] showed that the B.E.S. test measured urorosein, which

[47] I. G. Leder and P. Handler, *J. Biol. Chem.* **189,** 889 (1951).

[48] C. L. Hoagland, S. M. Ward, and R. E. Shank, *J. Biol. Chem.* **151,** 369 (1943).

[49] E. Leifer, J. R. Hogness, L. J. Roth, and W. Langham, *J. Am. Chem. Soc.* **70,** 2908 (1948).

[50] L. J. Roth, E. Leifer, J. R. Hogness, and W. H. Langham, *J. Biol. Chem.* **176,** 249 (1948).

[51] A. Bonsignore and L. Bevilacqua, *Bull. soc. ital. biol. sper.* **23,** 1219 (1947).

[52] W. J. Dann and H. I. Kohn, *J. Biol. Chem.* **136,** 435 (1940).

[53] C. Ling, D. M. Hegsted, and F. J. Stare, *J. Biol. Chem.* **174,** 803 (1948).

[54] H. I. Kohn, *Biochem. J.* **32,** 2075 (1938).

[55] H. I. Kohn and J. R. Klein, *J. Biol. Chem.* **130,** 1 (1939).

[56] A. Bonsignore and C. Ricci, *Boll. soc. ital. biol. sper.* **24,** 171 (1948).

[57] M. Duncan and H. P. Sarett, *J. Biol. Chem.* **193,** 317 (1951).

[57a] P. Feigelson, J. N. Williams, Jr., and C. A. Elvehjem, *J. Biol. Chem.* **193,** 737 (1951).

[58] W. Beckh, P. Ellinger, and T. D. Spies, *Quart. J. Med.* [N. S.] **6,** 305 (1937).

[59] C. J. Watson, *Proc. Soc. Exptl. Biol. Med.* **39,** 514 (1938); **41,** 591 (1939).

[60] C. J. Watson and J. A. Layne, *Ann. Internal Med.* **19,** 183 (1943).

[61] J. A. Layne and C. J. Watson, *Ann. Internal Med.* **19,** 200 (1943).

[62] S. Schwartz, J. F. Marvin, J. A. Layne, and C. J. Watson, *Ann. Internal Med.* **19,** 206 (1943).

is a normal constituent of many urines. No relation between urorosein excretion and nicotinic acid malnutrition could be observed. Furthermore, results of the B.E.S. test could not be correlated with the amount of urinary porphyrin, and the excretion of porphyrin had no constant relation to nicotinic acid deficiency. A red pigment which was observed in urine from patients with pellagra and from dogs with blacktongue was identified as a mixture of several related pigments similar to but not identical with synthetic indirubin. These pigments were found in normal animals as well as in those with nicotinic acid deficiency. Thus, it seems clear that these urinary pigments have no special relationship to nicotinic acid deficiency.

b. Urinary Fluorescent Substances

In 1940 Najjar and Wood[63] noted a substance in urine which gave a bluish fluorescence with ultraviolet light, the concentration of which seemed to be increased when nicotinic acid was administered. Shortly thereafter Najjar et al.[64, 65] noted that this substance (F_2) seemed to be absent in the urine of patients with pellagra and of dogs with blacktongue. They also noted another fluorescent substance (F_1) in the urine of patients with pellagra and of dogs with blacktongue which they did not find in normal urine. These investigators suggested that measurement of F_1 and F_2 in urine would be a useful diagnostic tool in pellagra. Later, Field and associates,[66] Perlzweig et al.[67] Raoul,[68] and Ellinger and Coulson[69] noted similar fluorescent substances in urine. The latter workers found that N^1-methyl-nicotinamide (nicotinamide methochloride) gave a reaction similar to F_2 in urine. In 1943 Huff and Perlzweig[70] isolated F_2 from urine and identified it as N^1-methylnicotinamide. Considerable controversy developed as to whether the substance they isolated was identical with F_2.[71-74] In any event, it is now well established that N^1-methylnicotinamide is one of the principal

[63] V. A. Najjar and R. W. Wood, *Proc. Soc. Exptl. Biol. Med.* **44,** 386 (1940).

[64] V. A. Najjar and L. E. Holt, Jr., *Science* **93,** 20 (1941).

[65] V. A. Najjar, H. J. Stein, L. E. Holt, Jr., and C. A. Kabler, *J. Clin. Invest.* **21,** 263 (1942).

[66] H. Field, Jr., D. Melnick, W. D. Robinson, and C. F. Wilkinson, Jr., *J. Clin. Invest.* **20,** 379 (1941).

[67] W. A. Perlzweig, H. P. Sarett, and L. H. Margolis, *J. Am. Med. Assoc.* **118,** 28 (1942).

[68] Y. Raoul, *Bull. soc. chim. biol.* **25,** 266, 271, 279 (1943).

[69] P. Ellinger and R. A. Coulson, *Nature* **152,** 383 (1943).

[70] J. W. Huff and W. A. Perlzweig, *J. Biol. Chem.* **150,** 395 (1943).

[71] J. W. Huff and W. A. Perlzweig, *Science* **97,** 538 (1943); **100,** 28 (1944).

[72] J. W. Huff, *J. Biol. Chem.* **167,** 151 (1947).

[73] V. A. Najjar and V. White, *Science* **99,** 284 (1944); **100,** 247 (1944).

[74] V. A. Najjar, V. White, and D. B. M. Scott, *Bull. Johns Hopkins Hosp.* **74,** 378 (1944).

urinary nicotinic acid excretion products and that it reflects the state o:
nicotinic acid nourishment to some extent. F_1 has never been identifiec
nor has it been studied in recent years.

c. Nicotinic Acid and Its Derivatives in Urine

It is now known that there are a number of forms in which nicotinic
acid is excreted (Fig. 11) and that different species vary markedly as tc
which derivatives predominate in their urine (Tables IX and X). In man
the principal derivatives are N^1-methylnicotinamide and the 6-pyridone
of N^1-methylnicotinamide. The dog, however, excretes none of the latter

Niacin → Niacinamide → N^1-Methyl-
nicotinamide → 6-Pyridone of N^1-Methyl-nicotinamide

CH₂—CH₂—CH₂—CH—COOH

2,5-Dinicotinylornithine
(birds only)

Nicotinuric acid

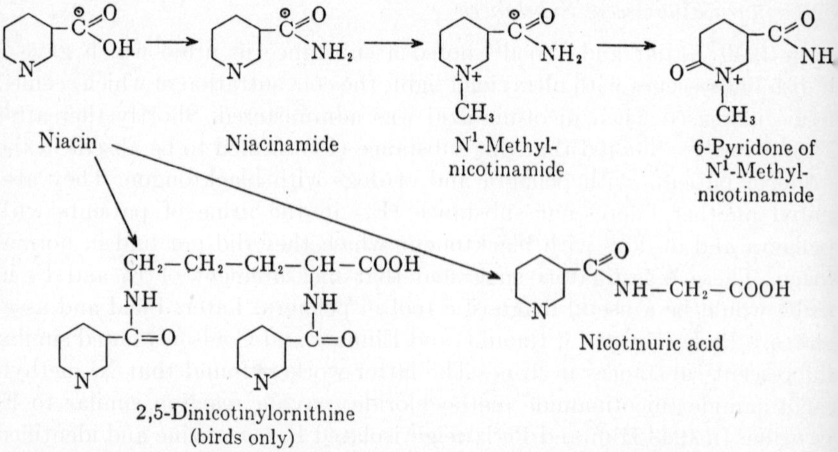

Fig. 11. Derivatives of nicotinic acid found in urine. The symbol (⊙) refers tc
steps which have been proved by means of isotope tracer techniques.

compound. There have been innumerable studies of the urinary excretion
of one or more of these nicotinic acid derivatives in relation to nicotinic
acid deficiency or nicotinic acid intake. Some of the early studies were
complicated, intentionally or unintentionally, by the fact that the assay
methods measured trigonelline as well as nicotinic acid derivatives. It is
now known that trigonelline is not a product of nicotinic acid metabolism
in mammals.

In man, dog, and rat, the most studied species, it seems clear that urinary
N^1-methylnicotinamide and the 6-pyridone of this compound (in man) reflect the amount of nicotinic acid available to the host. It also seems clear
especially from the recent carefully controlled studies of Goldsmith and
her associates,[19] that the finding of low or even zero amounts of these
nicotinic acid metabolites in urine does not necessarily mean that the
patient is actually suffering from pellagra. This is true, since the excretion
of these substances drops rapidly to a low and constant level soon afte

nicotinic acid restriction is instituted and considerably before any symptoms of the deficiency become evident. This finding might be anticipated from animal studies and in view of the fact that the tissues would undoubtedly attempt to conserve all available nicotinic acid if the supply were limited, hence leaving little available for excretion.

It should be mentioned that there are several published reports which have failed to find any significant correlation between nicotinic acid intake and excretion of nicotinic acid metabolites and hence are in seeming contradiction to the conclusions stated above.[75-78] It is obvious, however, that if the dietary circumstances are such that appreciable and undeterminable amounts of nicotinic acid are synthesized from tryptophan, or possibly by intestinal microorganisms or from any other source, then it would be almost impossible to establish any correlation of intake to excretion or to the state of nicotinic acid nourishment of the tissues. As pointed out by Ellinger and Coulson[75] the urinary excretion of nicotinic acid derivatives is influenced by the intake, the need in the body, the amount of methyl donors, the efficiency of the methylating mechanisms, the amount of biosynthesis, and other factors.

Consequently, it is not surprising that most studies in which an attempt has been made to determine nutritional status with respect to nicotinic acid by determining the amount of urinary nicotinic acid derivatives have encountered much variability and overlapping of results between normal and presumably deficient groups.[79-84b] Studies in animals, where the dietary and environmental circumstances can be controlled, have given much more consistent results.[26, 28, 85]

4. Load Tests

Attempts have been made to increase the sensitivity and diagnostic usefulness of urinary excretion by employing the "load" principle. The theory

[75] P. Ellinger and R. A. Coulson, *Biochem. J.* **38**, 265 (1944).

[76] V. A. Najjar, L. E. Holt, Jr., G. A. Johns, G. C. Mediary, and G. Fleischmann, *Proc. Soc. Exptl. Biol. Med.* **61**, 371 (1946).

[77] A. P. Briggs, S. A. Singal, and V. P. Sydenstricker, *J. Nutrition* **29**, 331 (1945).

[78] O. Mickelsen and L. L. Erickson, *Proc. Soc. Exptl. Biol. Med.* **58**, 33 (1945).

[79] G. A. Goldsmith, *Arch. Internal Med.* **73**, 410 (1944).

[80] G. A. Goldsmith, *Proc. Soc. Exptl. Biol. Med.* **51**, 42 (1942).

[81] H. C. Hou and M. Y. Dju, *Chinese Med. J.* **61**, 192 (1942).

[82] W. A. Perlzweig, J. M. Ruffin, and D. Cayer, *Federation Proc.* **4**, No. 1 (1945).

[83] J. J. Angulo, *Rev. med. trop. parasitol. bacteriol. (Habana)* **11**, 79 (1945).

[84] F. Sargent, P. Robinson, R. E. Johnson, and M. Castiglione, *J. Clin. Invest.* **23**, 714 (1944).

[84a] H. Field, Jr., P. P. Foa, and N. L. Foa, *Arch. Biochem.* **9**, 45 (1946).

[84b] C. W. Denko, W. E. Grundy, J. W. Potter, and G. H. Berryman, *Arch. Biochem.* **10**, 33 (1946).

[85] P. Ellinger and M. M. Abdel Kader, *Biochem. J.* **44**, 77, 627 (1949).

of this test is simple. If an organism is suffering from nicotinic acid deficiency, its tissues are depleted of the vitamin and urinary excretion should be low. A standard dose of nicotinic acid (usually as the amide) should then go principally to replete the tissue stores; less should be excreted in the urine than when the same amount is given to individuals whose tissues are already normally saturated with the vitamin. This test undoubtedly has some usefulness, but interpretation of individual tests is often difficult. It has been useful as a research tool.[19, 75, 77, 79, 80, 82, 86-87b] Doses of 50 to 500 mg. of nicotinamide and urine collection periods of 2 to 24 hours have been recommended. There seems to be no agreement on any "standard" technique for doing the test.

5. STOMACH

About 60% of pellagrins have histamine-resistant achlorhydria.[10, 88] A return of normal gastric secretion frequently follows therapy with nicotinamide. It is of interest that one of the human subjects in whom Goldsmith and associates[19] induced pellagra developed a histamine-resistant achlorhydria with return of acid secretion following therapy. Another patient developed a slight reduction in gastric acidity. It has also been reported that swine on a Goldberger type of blacktongue-producing diet develop achlorhydria, although nicotinic acid-deficient dogs[89] and rats[90] show essentially normal gastric secretion. It is also well known that nicotinic acid and the amide are capable of stimulating gastric secretion in normal individuals as well as in patients with pellagra (p. 575). The acid-secreting (oxyntic) cells of the stomach are known to have a very high concentration of coenzyme I (DPN) (see Table VII).

These facts have led to considerable speculation that DPN and TPN may play a vital role in the mechanism by which gastric hydrochloric acid is secreted. Patterson and Stetten[91] have evolved a theory, and supported it with some experimental evidence, that DPN is an essential component of a stratified sequence of enzyme systems which transport the hydrogen necessary for gastric hydrochloric acid production. Hawk and Hundley[9] were unable to obtain supporting evidence in nicotinic acid-deficient rats but these experiments certainly do not rule out the possibility of such a mechanism.

[86] H. P. Sarett and G. A. Goldsmith, *J. Biol. Chem.* **167**, 293 (1947); **177**, 461 (1949) **182**, 679 (1950).

[87] W. A. Perlzweig, E. D. Levy, and H. P. Sarett, *J. Biol. Chem.* **136**, 729 (1940).

[87a] D. Melnick, W. D. Robinson, and H. Field, Jr., *J. Biol. Chem.* **136**, 145 (1940).

[87b] P. Ellinger and R. Benesch, *Lancet* **II**, 197 (1945).

[88] V. P. Sydenstricker and E. S. Armstrong, *Arch. Internal Med.* **59**, 883 (1937).

[89] J. A. Layne and J. B. Carey, *Gastroenterology* **2**, 133 (1944).

[90] E. A. Hawk and J. M. Hundley, *Proc. Soc. Exptl. Biol. Med.* **78**, 318 (1951).

[91] W. B. Patterson and D. Stetten, Jr., *Science* **109**, 256 (1949).

These and other facts have led some observers to speculate that the stomach may have a special relationship to the etiology of pellagra.[92] Sydenstricker and associates[93] treated six cases of pellagra with gastric juice from normal individuals and obtained very favorable results. These investigators proposed that there was an "intrinsic factor" produced in the stomach of normal individuals but absent in pellagrins which was essential in curing pellagra, as well as an "extrinsic factor" present in food which was also required. Díaz-Rubio and Lorente[94] treated thirty-six cases of pellagra with gastric juice from normal individuals and failed to obtain very dramatic results (nine of the thirty-six died). They did note an improvement in diarrhea in a few patients and a striking improvement in the neurological symptoms of many patients. The medical literature has been singularly free of any reference to an "intrinsic factor" in pellagra since the discovery that nicotinic acid was the pellagra-preventive vitamin.

6. HEART

Nicotinic acid deficiency is not known to selectively damage the heart, such as occurs frequently in beriberi. Pathological studies have shown no gross and only minor microscopic lesions. There is no reason to believe that the biochemical defects present in this deficiency affect the heart any more or less than any other organ. Yet, several independent studies of human pellagra have shown a very high incidence of abnormal electrocardiograms. These defects were mainly of the myocardial type rather than conduction defects. Inverted T_I and/or T_{II}, Pardee-type S-T intervals, notched or low-voltage ventricular complexes, and other defects were noted. Most of these abnormalities disappeared promptly following therapy with nicotinic acid.[95-97]

7. BRAIN

Man is apparently unique among mammals in that no other species develops such a striking and profound mental disturbance in nicotinic acid deficiency as occurs frequently in man. Deficient animals customarily develop apathy and other mild disturbances which might be referable to the central nervous system. Pathological lesions have been observed in the spinal cord of nicotinic acid-deficient dogs (p. 566). The hind limb paralysis and acute collapse syndrome sometimes seen in dogs on Goldberger-type

[92] V. P. Sydenstricker and J. W. Thomas, *Southern Med. J.* **30**, 14 (1937).

[93] V. P. Sydenstricker, E. S. Armstrong, C. J. Derrick, and P. S. Kemp, *Am. J. Med. Sci.* **192**, 1 (1936).

[94] M. Díaz-Rubio and L. Lorente, *Rev. clin. españ.* **16**, 72 (1944); Author's summary in *Rev. asoc. méd. argentina* **59**, 1178 (1945).

[95] H. Feil, *Am. Heart J.* **11**, 173 (1936).

[96] F. Mainzer and M. Krause, *Brit. Heart J.* **2**, 85 (1940).

[97] M. Rachmilewitz and K. Braun, *Am. Heart J.* **27**, 203 (1944).

blacktongue-producing rations is due to riboflavin deficiency rather than nicotinic acid. Man, however, frequently develops a marked "encephalopathy"[98] with irritability, insomnia, headaches, dizziness, tremor, jerky movements, and rigidity of the body. Altered tendon reflexes, numbness, and later paralysis of the extremities may develop. Insanity may occur if the patients are not treated.[10] Alcoholism, with its mental disturbances, and concomitant thiamine deficiency, with its effect on the nervous system, frequently complicates the picture.

DPN and TPN are known to be required for the biochemical reactions by which the brain obtains energy from fuels such as fructose. It is easy to imagine that a deficiency of these vital coenzymes could impede essential biochemical reactions and permit the accumulation of metabolites such as lactic acid which could cause some of these mental symptoms. However, this is speculation and not experimental fact. Actually, no adequate biochemical explanation can be offered for the occurrence of these striking mental abnormalities.

8. SKIN

One of the most puzzling lesions in human pellagra is the rather typical dermatitis and the pigmentation which usually accompanies it. Man, again, is unique, since these lesions are not seen in deficient animals. It has long been known that the dermatitis occurs principally on those parts of the body normally exposed to the sun and that sunlight frequently precipitates the lesions. The suggestion has been made repeatedly that the photosensitive skin of pellagrins may be due to a disturbance in porphyrin metabolism.[58, 99-102] This has never been proved (p. 556). Alcoholic pellagrins do appear to show an increased amount of coproporphyrin III in their urine and stools, but this does not seem to be specifically related to nicotinic acid.[59, 103-105]

Again, no adequate biochemical explanation can be offered for these interesting phenomena.

[98] N. Jolliffe, K. M. Bowman, L. A. Rosenblum, and H. D. Fein, J. Am. Med. Assoc. 114, 307 (1940).
[99] U. Bassi, Clin. med. ital. 65, 241 (1934).
[100] P. Ellinger and F. Dojmi, Chemistry & Industry 54, 507 (1935).
[101] M. Massa, Riforma med. 48, 1669 (1932).
[102] T. D. Spies, Y. Sasaki, and E. S. Gross, Southern Med. J. 31, 483 (1938).
[103] K. Dobriner, W. H. Strain, and S. A. Localio, Proc. Soc. Exptl. Biol. Med. 38, 748 (1938).
[104] R. Kark and A. P. Meikeljohn, Am. J. Med. Sci. 201, 380 (1941).
[105] L. A. Rosenblum and N. Jolliffe, Am. J. Med. Sci. 199, 853 (1940).

9. EYES

Hubbard and Wald[106] have shown that DPN is necessary for the conversion of vitamin A_1 to rhodopsin, a process essential to vision. In this instance, a ready-made biochemical explanation is available for a defect which has not been noted in either human or animal nicotinic acid deficiency.

Simonelli[107] found that cataractous lens (produced by massage) in rabbits have a nicotinic acid concentration one-fifth to one-half of normal. The same was true for cataracts induced by naphthalene. The concentration of nicotinic acid in the crystalline lens from two humans with cataract seemed to be slightly reduced. Pike[108] found that nicotinic acid had an effect in preventing congenital cataract in rats. The effect seemed to be due to the "sparing" effect of nicotinic acid on tryptophan. Large amounts of nicotinic acid were ineffective if dietary tryptophan was too low. Cataract from tryptophan deficiency is well known.

10. BLOOD

Anemia is an almost constant finding in human pellagra. It is generally mild and may be macrocytic or normocytic hypochromic in type. The white cell count is generally normal.[88] There is no certainty that this anemia is due specifically to nicotinic acid deficiency. It does generally improve following nicotinic acid therapy, but most often other B vitamins, yeast, or wheat germ as well as a generous diet are used in therapy. This could provide adequate amounts of other vitamins, such as folic acid, which may be more directly concerned in the anemia. Complicating deficiencies of vitamins other than nicotinic acid almost certainly were present in some of the early experiments showing that dogs and swine on Goldberger diets developed anemia as well as leucopenia and granulocytopenia.[109-112] However, later studies in swine, where complicating deficiencies were minimized, revealed a normocytic anemia.[113] Wooley[30] found a mild anemia, leucopenia, and granulocytopenia in nicotinic acid-deficient rabbits which responded to therapy with either nicotinic acid or tryptophan. Rats and dogs do not usually develop anemia in nicotinic acid deficiency on diets otherwise com-

[106] R. Hubbard and G. Wald, *Science* **115**, 60 (1952).
[107] M. Simonelli, *Boll. soc. ital. biol. sper.* **20**, 692 (1945).
[108] R. L. Pike, *J. Nutrition* **44**, 191 (1951).
[109] D. K. Miller and C. P. Rhoads, *J. Clin. Invest.* **14**, 153 (1935).
[110] C. P. Rhoads and D. K. Miller, *J. Exptl. Med.* **58**, 585 (1933).
[111] D. K. Miller and C. P. Rhoads, *J. Exptl. Med.* **61**, 173 (1935).
[112] T. Spies and A. Dowling, *Am. J. Physiol.* **114**, 25 (1935).
[113] G. E. Cartwright, B. Tatting, and M. M. Wintrobe, *Arch. Biochem.* **19**, 109 (1948).

plete in known growth factors.[114, 115] However, Handler and associates have shown that, if the life of their dogs was prolonged beyond the stage of blacktongue by parenteral saline therapy, then a macrocytic or normocytic anemia and leucopenia developed.[116-118] These abnormalities would respond to nicotinic acid even though the food intake was restricted during therapy. This subject has been very carefully reviewed by Handler.[119] It should also be noted that nicotinic acid-deficient dogs are much more susceptible to the hemolytic effect of indole than are normal dogs.[120, 121] These results seem to indicate that nicotinic acid is necessary for the formation of red and white blood cells but that this can be demonstrated only if proper conditions are found. It should be noted that none of Goldsmith's experimental pellagra patients developed an anemia which could be attributed to nicotinic acid deficiency.[19]

There seems to be nothing characteristic about other constituents of blood such as sugar, non-protein nitrogen, and lactate-pyruvate ratios in human pellagra.[19, 88, 122, 123]

11. MISCELLANEOUS

a. Nitrogen Balance

Very few data are available on the subject. The patients of Goldsmith et al.[19] maintained positive nitrogen balance. Mancini and Fabriani[124] studied three cases of pellagra and noted a positive balance in each. One patient treated with nicotinic acid showed an improved nitrogen retention after therapy. Sure and associates[125] used a paired-feeding technique to show that nicotinic acid had a "specific" effect in improving food utilization.

b. Pregnancy and Lactation

Lojkin et al.[126] found that pregnant women, as well as pregnant rats, showed a progressive tendency to excrete more urinary nicotinic acid de-

[114] W. A. Krehl, P. S. Sarma, L. J. Teply, and C. A. Elvehjem, J. Nutrition 31, 85 (1946).
[115] W. A. Krehl and C. A. Elvehjem, J. Biol. Chem. 158, 173 (1945).
[116] P. Handler and W. J. Dann, J. Biol. Chem. 145, 145 (1942).
[117] P. Handler, Proc. Soc. Exptl. Biol. Med. 52, 263 (1943).
[118] P. Handler and W. P. Featherston, J. Biol. Chem. 151, 395 (1943).
[119] P. Handler, Z. Vitaminforsch. 19, 393 (1948).
[120] C. P. Rhoads, W. H. Barker, and D. K. Miller, J. Exptl. Med. 67, 299 (1938).
[121] W. H. Sebrell and J. M. Hundley, Trans. Assoc. Am. Physicians 61, 288 (1948).
[122] G. A. Goldsmith, Federation Proc. 6, 408 (1947).
[123] M. Díaz-Rubio, E. Monsalvez, and J. M. Masaguer, Rev. clin. españ. 21, 299 (1946).
[124] F. Mancini and G. Fabriani, Boll. soc. ital. biol. sper. 20, 342 (1945).
[125] B. Sure, L. Easterling, and S. Jeu, J. Nutrition 46, 55 (1952).
[126] M. E. Lojkin, A. W. Wertz, and C. G. Dietz, J. Nutrition 46, 335 (1952).

rivatives as pregnancy progressed. During the last month of pregnancy women excreted considerably more of these derivatives in the urine than they ingested. Coryell and associates[127] studied nicotinic acid intake in relation to the nicotinic acid content of human milk at various intervals postpartum. Nicotinic acid in the milk increased from the first to the tenth day postpartum. During mature milk production, about 7 % of daily nicotinic acid intake appeared in the milk and 3 % in the urine.

c. Corn and Alcohol in the Etiology of Pellagra

The consumption of maize and the excessive consumption of alcohol are the two outstanding factors known to show a positive correlation with the incidence of pellagra. The role of maize in pellagra has been covered very competently in two recent reviews, one by Handler[119] and one by Chick.[128] This subject has also been considered in other sections of this chapter (p. 548).

Pellagra is known to be frequent in alcoholics. The effect of alcohol seems to be only that it inhibits consumption of a normal diet and therefore leads to a deficient intake of nicotinic acid. There is no evidence that alcohol increases the requirement for nicotinic acid. The few metabolic studies which have been done indicate that ingestion of alcohol increases the urinary output of N^1-methylnicotinamide, possibly due to a "sparing" action of alcohol on the nicotinic acid requirement.[75, 129]

XI. Pathology

J. M. HUNDLEY

A. IN ANIMALS

1. Dogs

Chittenden and Underhill[1] were the first to produce experimentally the dietary deficiency in dogs which later became established as the canine equivalent of pellagra. Wheeler et al.[2] called attention to the similarity of this syndrome to what was known to American veterinarians as black-

[127] M. N. Coryell, C. E. Roderuck, M. E. Harris, S. Miller, M. M. Rutledge, H. H. Williams, and I. G. Macy, J. Nutrition 34, 219 (1947).

[128] H. Chick, Nutrition Abstr. and Revs. 20, 523 (1951).

[129] R. E. Butler and H. P. Sarett, J. Nutrition 35, 539 (1948).

[1] R. H. Chittenden and F. P. Underhill, Am. J. Physiol 44, 13 (1917).

[2] G. A. Wheeler, J. Goldberger, and V. Blackstock, Public Health Repts. (U.S.) 37, 1063 (1922).

tongue. Goldberger *et al.*[3] studied a case of naturally occurring blacktongue and later described a similar disease in dogs which was produced experimentally.[4] Dogs suffering from this deficiency show very characteristic findings. The first abnormality is, usually, refusal to eat. The animals are quiet and apathetic. After a day or two the inner surfaces of the lips, cheeks, and gums become diffusely inflamed and develop superficial yellowish necrotic patches. There is an intensely foul odor. Excessive drooling of thick ropy saliva is characteristic. The tip and margins of the tongue become red and later develop dark bluish patches. Ulceration frequently appears on or under the tongue. A diarrhea, generally bloody, is present. Scrotal dermatitis may be found. Vomiting usually develops. Body temperature may reach 40 or 41°. At autopsy, the tongue is found generally to have assumed a deep bluish-black color. The inflammatory changes in the mouth may extend to affect the epiglottis, the soft palate, and even into the esophagus. The stomach may show small areas of congestion, although during life it is apparently normal to endoscopic examination.[5] Small and large intestine, and particularly the rectum usually show patches of intense congestion, less commonly small hemorrhages. Duodenal or colonic ulcers may be found.

Denton[6] studied the pathological changes in Goldberger's dogs. He found degenerative lesions in the mucous membranes of the mouth, pharynx, esophagus, intestines, and epithelium of the scrotum. The lesions seemed to originate in the supporting tissues of the membranes and terminated in extensive necrotic and diphtheritic inflammation. Lillie[7] made a detailed histologic study of the tissues of blacktongue dogs. In addition to previously described findings, he noted degenerative changes in the nerves regional to the oral lesions, granular degeneration of heart muscle fibers, moderate passive congestion, and relatively little fatty infiltration of the liver. The spleen was fibrotic and contained atrophic follicles. Albuminous degeneration of the epithelium of the convoluted tubules of the kidney, injection of the meninges, tigrolysis of the brain stem ganglia, nerve cell atrophy, and pericellular vacuolation in the cortex and basal ganglia were found. Jensenius and Norgaard[8] also found extensive histological changes in the central nervous system, particularly the spinal cord.

The fatty livers (yellow liver) sometimes seen in dogs on blacktongue-

[3] J. Goldberger, W. F. Tanner, and E. B. Saye, *Public Health Repts.* (*U. S.*) **38**, 2711 (1923).

[4] J. Goldberger and G. A. Wheeler, *Public Health Repts.* (*U.S.*) **43**, 172 (1928).

[5] J. A. Layne and J. B. Carey, *Gastroenterology* **2**, 133 (1944).

[6] J. Denton, *Am. J. Pathol.* **4**, 341 (1928).

[7] R. D. Lillie, *Natl. Insts. Health Bull.* **162**, 13 (1933).

[8] H. Jensenius and F. Norgaard, *Acta Pathol. Microbiol. Scand.* **19**, 433 (1942).

producing diets[9, 10] were undoubtedly due to concomitant riboflavin deficiency as shown by Sebrell and associates.[11] Smith *et al.*[12] were apparently the first to note the large number of fuso-spirochetal organisms in the mouths of blacktongue dogs. The almost universal occurrence of this Vincent's-type infection is one of the most puzzling features of canine blacktongue.

Nicotinic acid deficiency may occur in dogs without blacktongue, especially in puppies and when purified diets are used.[13] Handler and Dann[14] found that dogs could be cured of blacktongue by treatment with intravenous saline only to continue to lose weight and develop a severe anemia and leucopenia (p. 564). The bone marrow of such dogs has not, apparently, been studied.

2. HOGS

Miller and Rhoads[15] fed swine a modified Goldberger diet and observed a syndrome similar but not identical to blacktongue in dogs, i.e., stomatitis, achlorhydria, anemia, diarrhea, loss of appetite, and weakness. Both macrocytic and microcytic anemias were observed. These deficiency symptoms could be relieved with oral or parenteral liver extract. Several other investigators gave similar diets and observed the beneficial effect of nicotinic acid on the deficiency state.[16-20] Braude *et al.*[21] used Chick's diet[16] and made a study of the gross pathology of pig pellagra. In their experiments, the pigs had a rough, "staring" coat but showed no actual dermatitis. Several pigs had small ulcerations of the buccal mucosa and most had a severe enteritis with necrotic ulceration of the cecum and large bowel. Fibrinous pleurisy, mild anemia, and, frequently, pneumonia were found in animals which died of the deficiency.

Unfortunately, most of the experiments referred to above were undoubtedly complicated by deficiencies of nutrients other than nicotinic acid.

[9] W. H. Sebrell, *Natl. Insts. Health Bull.* **162**, 23 (1933).
[10] W. H. Sebrell and R. D. Lillie, *Natl. Insts. Health Bull.* **162**, 37 (1933).
[11] W. H. Sebrell, R. H. Onstott, and D. J. Hunt, *Public Health Repts.* (*U.S.*) **52**, 427 (1937).
[12] D. T. Smith, E. L. Persons, and H. I. Harvey, *J. Nutrition* **14**, 373 (1937).
[13] P. Handler, *Z. Vitaminforsch*, **19**, 393 (1948).
[14] P. Handler and W. J. Dann, *J. Biol. Chem.* **145**, 145 (1942).
[15] D. K. Miller and C. P. Rhoads, *J. Clin. Invest.* **14**, 153 (1935).
[16] H. Chick, T. F. Macrae, A. J. P. Martin, and C. J. Martin, *Biochem. J.* **32**, 10, 844 (1938).
[17] E. H. Hughes, *Hilgardia* **11**, 595 (1938).
[18] L. C. Madison, R. C. Miller, and T. B. Keith, *Science* **89**, 490 (1939).
[19] M. M. Wintrobe, *Am. J. Physiol.* **126**, 375 (1939).
[20] A. N. Worden and G. Slavin, *J. Comp. Pathol. Therap.* **54**, 77 (1944).
[21] R. Braude, S. K. Kon, and E. G. White, *Biochem. J.* **40**, 843 (1947).

However, more recent studies using purified diets more adequately supplied with vitamins have shown findings generally similar to the observations already reported.[22-25]

3. RATS

Most investigators have observed little pathology in nicotinic acid-deficient rats except retarded growth and non-specific deficiency signs such as rough hair coat, porphyrin-caked whiskers and, occasionally, alopecia.[26, 27] Animals allowed to eat a nicotinic acid-deficient ration *ad lib* voluntarily restrict their food intake and may thereby protect themselves to some extent. Spector and associates[28, 29] force-fed a diet severely deficient in both nicotinic acid and tryptophan to rats and observed striking pathology. Alopecia, bloating, diarrhea, hunchback, jumping, screeching, convulsions, mild anemia, kidney enlargement, degeneration of the testes, fatty infiltration of the liver, atrophy and degeneration of visceral and cardiac muscle, and keratinization of the cornea were observed. Most of these abnormalities were undoubtedly due primarily to tryptophan deficiency rather than nicotinic acid. The addition of nicotinic acid in the absence of added tryptophan was without any substantial effect on the deficiency syndrome. Nicotinic acid can protect to some extent against congenital cataract in rats when the diet contains marginal amounts of tryptophan as shown by Pike.[30] The stomach of deficient rats is normal to gross inspection, and acid-pepsin secretion is normal.[31] However, Bourne[32] found that the gastric mucosa was reduced in thickness, mainly at the expense of the oxyntic cells. Only slight degenerative changes were noted in the rest of the gastrointestinal tract. Johnston and Weitz,[33] on the other hand, found marked degenerative changes in the Golgi apparatus in the columnar absorbing cells of the duodenum in nicotinic acid-deficient rats. Bourne[32] also noted loss of staining ability and decrease in number of acidophile cells

[22] G. E. Cartwright, B. Tatting, and M. M. Wintrobe, *Arch. Biochem.* **19**, 109 (1948).
[23] M. M. Wintrobe, H. J. Stein, R. H. Follis, Jr., and S. Humphreys, *J. Nutrition* **30**, 395 (1945).
[24] W. C. Powick, N. R. Ellis, L. L. Madsen, and C. N. Dale, *J. Animal Sci.* **6**, 310 (1947).
[25] W. Burroughs, B. H. Edgington, W. L. Robinson, and R. M. Bethke, *J. Nutrition* **41**, 51 (1950).
[26] W. A. Krehl, P. S. Sarma, L. J. Teply, and C. A. Elvehjem, *J. Nutrition* **31**, 85 (1946).
[27] W. A. Krehl, L. J. Teply, and C. A. Elvehjem, *Science* **101**, 283 (1945).
[28] H. Spector, *J. Biol. Chem.* **173**, 659 (1948).
[29] H. Spector and F. B. Adamstone, *J. Nutrition* **40**, 213 (1950).
[30] R. L. Pike, *J. Nutrition* **44**, 191 (1951).
[31] E. A. Hawk and J. M. Hundley, *Proc. Soc. Exptl. Biol. Med.* **78**, 318 (1951).
[32] G. H. Bourne, *Brit. J. Nutrition* **4**, xvi (1950).
[33] P. M. Johnston and E. M. Weitz, *J. Morphol.* **91**, 79 (1952).

in the anterior pituitary, cessation of bone formation at the costochondral junctions, cessation of spermatogenesis, and a reduction in size of the adrenal cortex. The spleen was reduced in size and showed fibrosis and reduction of the red pulp. The epithelium of the trachea showed degeneration. The tubular epithelium of the kidneys was severely degenerated. Bourne did not report the use of pair fed controls to rule out the nonspecific effects of simple inanition in the etiology of these lesions.

4. Cotton Rats and Mice

Only poor growth has been reported as a symptom of nicotinic acid deficiency in the cotton rat.[34, 35] As reported by Woolley,[36] mice given 3-acetylpyridine, a "nicotinic acid antagonist" (p. 548), developed difficulty in controlling their hind legs and finally became almost completely paralyzed. The hair coat became wet and unkempt. Weight loss and emaciation developed. The skin of the chest wall, the sides of the abdomen, and the legs became very red and inflamed. Fiery red tongues developed late in about half of the animals.

5. Rabbits

Subnormal weight gain, anemia, leucopenia, and a terminal diarrhea, sometimes bloody, were observed in nicotinic acid-deficient rabbits by Wooley and Sebrell.[37, 38] No oral lesions were found. Histological examination showed nothing that could be attributed to nicotinic acid deficiency aside from a few animals showing superficial ulcerations in the colon. Olcese et al.[39] observed only subnormal weight gain in their nicotinic acid-deficient rabbits.

6. Chicks, Turkeys, and Ducks

Growing chicks on nicotinic acid-deficient rations showed diminished growth, increased mortality, and inflammation of the entire mouth cavity as well as the esophagus and the crop (blacktongue) except for the tip of the tongue, which remained white. Excessive mucus may be found in the mouth. Diarrhea, perosis, and poor feathering have been described.[40-43] The

[34] J. M. McIntire, B. S. Schweigert, and C. A. Elvehjem, *J. Nutrition* **27**, 1 (1944).

[35] B. S. Schweigert and P. B. Pearson, *J. Biol. Chem.* **172**, 485 (1948).

[36] D. W. Woolley, *J. Biol. Chem.* **157**, 455 (1945).

[37] J. G. Wooley, *Proc. Soc. Exptl. Biol. Med.* **65**, 315 (1947).

[38] J. G. Wooley and W. H. Sebrell, *J. Nutrition* **19**, 191 (1945).

[39] O. Olcese, P. B. Pearson, and P. Sparks, *J. Nutrition* **39**, 93 (1949).

[40] G. M. Briggs, Jr., R. C. Mills, C. A. Elvehjem, and E. B. Hart, *Proc. Soc. Exptl. Biol. Med.* **51**, 59 (1942).

[41] G. M. Briggs, A. C. Groschke, and R. J. Lillie, *J. Nutrition* **32**, 659 (1946).

[42] L. R. Richardson, A. G. Hogan, and H. L. Kempster, *Missouri Agr. Expt. Sta. Research Bull.* **390**, (1945).

[43] H. M. Scott, E. P. Singsen, and L. D. Matterson, *Poultry Sci.* (Research Notes) **25**, 303 (1946).

rather marked dermatitis noted in some of the early work of Briggs and associates[44] has not been found in more recent studies where the diets were more adequately supplemented with vitamins other than nicotinic acid. Nicotinic acid-deficient turkey poults exhibited similar findings.[45-47]

Nicotinic acid-deficient ducks show diminished weight gain, weakness, and diarrhea. In some of the birds there was an accumulation of food under the tongue and necrotic tissue beneath this.[48]

7. OTHER SPECIES

Cats have been reported to develop a disease in nature which resembles canine blacktongue and which responds to nicotinic acid.[49] Nicotinic acid-deficient foxes showed cessation of weight gain and anorexia, and, if the deficiency was severe, they developed symptoms similar to blacktongue.[50] Rainbow trout developed swollen gills when deprived of nicotinic acid.[51]

B. IN MAN

Sundwall[52] and Harris[53] have reviewed the European and early American literature up to about 1915. These authors and, more recently, Denton,[54] Moore et al.,[55] and Follis[56] have published their observations of the pathology of pellagra in the United States.

The usual pathological features of pellagra in this country include changes in the skin, oral cavity, esophagus, colon, nervous system, and blood. Skin from clinically involved areas shows dilatation of blood vessels, some rarefaction of tissue, hyperkeratosis, parakeratosis, acanthosis, and, in severe cases, bullae. The sebaceous glands may be atrophic, although the sweat glands appear normal. Abnormalities of keratinization may be found in clinically normal skin. The mucous membrane of the mouth, tongue, esophagus, vagina, and colon show somewhat similar changes with

[44] G. M. Briggs, Jr., T. D. Luckey, L. J. Teply, C. A. Elvehjem, and E. B. Hart, J. Biol. Chem. 148, 517 (1943).
[45] G. M. Briggs, J. Nutrition 31, 79 (1946).
[46] T. H. Jukes, E. L. R. Stokstad, and M. Belt, J. Nutrition 33, 1 (1947).
[47] B. G. Lance and A. G. Hogan, J. Nutrition 36, 369 (1948).
[48] D. M. Hegsted, J. Nutrition 32, 467 (1946).
[49] M. K. Heath, J. W. MacQueen, and T. D. Spies, Science 92, 514 (1940).
[50] A. E. Schaefer, C. K. Whitehair, and C. A. Elvehjem, J. Nutrition 34, 131 (1947).
[51] B. A. McLaren, E. B. Keller, D. J. O'Donnell, and C. A. Elvehjem, Arch. Biochem. 15, 169 (1947).
[52] J. Sundwall, U. S. Public Health Service Hyg. Lab. Bull. 106, 5–74 (1917).
[53] H. F. Harris, Pellagra, pp. 138–180. The Macmillan Co., New York, 1919.
[54] J. Denton, Am. J. Trop. Med. 5, 173 (1925).
[55] R. A. Moore, T. D. Spies, and Z. K. Cooper, Arch. Dermatol and Syphilol. 46, 100 (1942).
[56] R. H. Follis, Jr., The Pathology of Nutritional Disease, p. 169. Charles C Thomas, Springfield, Ill., 1948.

considerable atrophy of the epithelium. The buccal mucous membrane may disappear entirely in some areas with grayish ulcerations which are loaded with microorganisms. Cysts filled with mucus and inflammatory material and, in advanced cases, ulcers are found in the colon. Chromatolysis of ganglion cells in the brain and, in some cases, myelin degeneration of peripheral nerves can be observed. Peripheral blood may show either microcytic or macrocytic anemia. Bone marrow appears to have been studied but little.

The specificity of these pathological changes in relation to possible concomitant deficiencies of other essential nutrients has been discussed elsewhere (p. 553). The "pellagra" of Africans, as characterized by the Gillmans,[57] almost certainly is complicated by other deficiencies, since it does not respond to nicotinic acid but does respond to certain materials which contain high-quality protein. The extensive pathology of this severe nutritional disease has been described thoroughly by the Gillmans.[57]

XII. Pharmacology

J. M. HUNDLEY

A. TOXICITY

Both nicotinamide and nicotinic acid are quite non-toxic, there being a ratio of at least 1:1000 between the effective therapeutic dose and the toxic dose.

1. RATS AND MICE

The LD_{50}'s of nicotinic acid (sodium salt when given parenterally) and nicotinamide range from 3.5 to 5 g. per kilogram subcutaneously and 5 to 7 g. orally. Nicotinamide is almost twice as toxic as nicotinic acid.[1-3] The methyl ester of nicotinic acid injected into mice was tolerated at a level of 1.0 g. per kilogram, whereas the methoiodide of this compound was fatal at 0.6 g. per kilogram. The methyl ester of N^1-methyltetrahydronicotinic acid (arecoline) was fatal at a dosage of 0.065 g. per kilogram.[4] N^1-Methylation of nicotinic acid and related compounds does not result in a consistent

[57] J. Gillman and T. Gillman, Perspectives in Human Malnutrition. Grune & Stratton, New York, 1951.
[1] K. K. Chen, C. L. Rose, and E. B. Robbins, Proc. Soc. Exptl. Biol. Med. 38, 241 (1938).
[2] K. Unna, J. Pharmacol. Exptl. Therap. 65, 95 (1939).
[3] F. G. Brazda and R. A. Coulson, Proc. Soc. Exptl. Biol. Med. 62, 19 (1946).
[4] R. Hunt and R. R. Renshaw, J. Pharmacol. Exptl. Therap. 35, 75 (1929).

effect on toxicity. Brazda and Coulson[3] found the following LD_{50}'s in rats given the following compounds subcutaneously (grams per kilogram): nicotinic acid 5.0, trigonelline 5.0, nicotinamide 1.68, N^1-methylnicotinamide 2.4, N,N-diethylnicotinamide (coramine) 0.24, coramine methochloride 1.90, pyridine 1.00, and pyridine methochloride 0.28. Nicotinamide, coramine, and their N^1-methyl derivatives caused paralysis of the respiratory centers. Pyridine and its methyl derivative caused deep anesthesia. Karasek and coworkers[5] reported considerably lower LD_{50}'s for nicotinic acid in mice (1.8 g. per kilogram) than those recorded above. They also found that as little as 0.4 g. per kilogram caused preglomerular, corticomedullary, and interstitial hemorrhages in rats. Unna,[2] on the other hand, fed 1.0 g. per kilogram of sodium nicotinate daily for 40 days to rats and observed no effect on growth or on tissue histology. Chen and associates[1] found no abnormalities in mice injected with 0.5 g. per kilogram daily for four weeks. McCrea[6] gave 0.05 to 0.2 g. of nicotinic acid to rats intraperitoneally for 24 days with no ill effects. Unna[2] suggested that the toxic effect of nicotinic acid and its amide may be due, at least in part, to simple osmotic effects, since the same volumes of a solution of sodium chloride equimolecular to the sodium nicotinate solutions caused some deaths in their animals.

2. Dogs

Dogs tolerated up to 2 g. of sodium nicotinate per kilogram of body weight orally for 35 to 63 days without toxicity.[2] Chen and associates[1] gave dogs 1 g. of nicotinic acid per day orally for eight weeks with no toxic symptoms, although 2 g. per dog per day produced marked toxic symptoms in 11 to 20 days.

3. Other Species

Chickens tolerated sodium nicotinate up to 2 g. per kilogram of body weight orally each day for periods as long as two months.[2] The minimum lethal dose of sodium nicotinate by injection into guinea pigs was 3.5 g. per kilogram. Rabbits tolerated 0.02 to 0.06 g. per kilogram per day for ten days.[6] As much as 5.4 g. of nicotinic acid per day has been given orally to man with no harmful effects.[7] Hawker[8] reported a 20% increase in ovary weight and a decrease in pituitary gland weight of virgin guinea pigs receiving nicotinic acid in amounts up to 150 mg. daily. This report must be accepted with reservations because of the very small number of animals used.

[5] F. Karasek, O. Poupa, and V. Jelinek, *Minerva med.* **39**, 28 (1948) [*C. A.* **43**, 6291 (1949)].

[6] F. D. McCrea, *J. Pharmacol. Exptl. Therap.* **63**, 25 (1938).

[7] C. M. Kurtz, O. S. Orth, and G. Sepulveda, *Wisconsin Med. J.* **44**, 761 (1945).

[8] R. W. Hawker, *Med. J. Australia* **I**, 872 (1946).

B. TOXICITY IN DIETS

Handler and Dann[9] found that inclusion of 1 % nicotinamide in a low protein diet almost completely inhibited growth in rats. This growth inhibition could be prevented by methionine or by choline plus homocystine but not by choline, betaine, homocystine, or cystine alone. One per cent nicotinic acid in the same diet did not inhibit growth but did induce fatty liver, an effect preventable by methionine, choline, and betaine but aggravated by cystine or homocystine.[9, 10] Randoin and Causeret[11] confirmed the dietary toxicity of 0.5 to 2.0 % nicotinamide but failed to obtain reversal with methionine.[12] They did obtain reversal of toxicity with liver powder or folic acid plus calcium pantothenate.[13] One or two per cent nicotinamide in the diet of rabbits and guinea pigs did not depress growth and did not cause fatty liver.[14] It is of interest that the latter two species do not methylate nicotinamide to any extent, whereas the rat does. Two per cent nicotinamide reduced the growth of chicks but did not produce fatty liver; neither glycine nor choline restored growth. Two per cent nicotinic acid in this diet had no effect on chick growth.[14]

Coulson and Brazda[15] fed rats a series of pyridine derivatives, including the N^1-methyl derivatives of each, at a level of 1 % in a high protein diet. None of the N^1-methyl derivatives affected liver fat. N^1-Methylation had no consistent effect when the growth depression obtained with methylated compounds was compared with that obtained with non-methylated compounds. γ-Picoline, nicotinic acid, and nicotinamide increased liver fat. β-Picoline and coramine produced larger increases in liver fat, but this could be prevented by methionine or choline. Coramine produced a large increase in fat-free liver weight which could not be prevented by choline or methionine. These results suggest that the toxicity of pyridine derivatives may be only partially explained by the fact that the tissues are robbed of the methyl groups necessary for their methylation and excretion.

C. CIRCULATION

Nicotinic acid, 20 to 30 mg. given intravenously or 100 to 500 mg. orally, produces a transient vasodilatation of the cutaneous vessels, particularly of the ears, face, neck, upper extremities, and trunk in most human subjects. The reaction is accompanied by itching, burning, and tingling of the

[9] P. Handler and W. J. Dann, *J. Biol. Chem.* **146**, 357 (1942).

[10] A. Aschkenasy and J. Mignot, *Compt. rend. soc. biol.* **140**, 261 (1946).

[11] L. Randoin and J. Causeret, *Compt. rend.* **227**, 367 (1948).

[12] L. Randoin and J. Causeret, *Compt. rend.* **228**, 504 (1949) [*C. A.* **43**, 6296 (1949)].

[13] L. Randoin and J. Causeret, *Compt. rend.* **227**, 399 (1948).

[14] P. Handler, *J. Biol. Chem.* **154**, 203 (1944).

[15] R. A. Coulson and F. G. Brazda, *Proc. Soc. Exptl. Biol. Med.* **65**, 1 (1947).

affected areas.[16] The skin temperature may[16] or may not[17] be elevated. In spite of this reaction, blood pressure, pulse, and body temperature are little affected. There is an increased blood flow in the hand and the forearm but little in the leg.[17] The increase in blood flow is largely in the skin and subcutaneous tissue, there, apparently, being a compensatory decrease in the muscles[18] and the viscera[19, 20] so that there is little change in blood pressure and perhaps only a slight increase in circulating blood volume.[21] Some dilatation of the arteries of the retina may occur,[19] but there is no increase in cerebral blood flow, according to Scheinberg.[22] The latter is somewhat surprising, since flushing doses of nicotinic acid are reported to have a beneficial effect in certain types of headaches.[23, 24] Nicotinamide and many other related compounds do not cause this flushing reaction,[25] although a few derivatives such as methyl nicotinate, other alkyl nicotinates, and the alcohol of nicotinamide (Roniacol) do.[26, 27] Prior dosage with 30 to 60 g. of glycine is said to prevent or retard the flushing action of nicotinic acid in man.[16, 25] Coramine (N,N-diethylnicotinamide) has a marked stimulant action on the central nervous system. Other nicotinic acid derivatives such as tetrahydrofurfuryl nicotinate[28] have a direct hyperemic action on the skin. The reported ability of nicotinic acid or nicotinamide to increase the resistance of rats to anoxia may be related to some of these circulatory effects.[29]

Although nicotinic acid itself is quite inactive in lowering blood pressure, its methyl ester, the methyl ester of N^1-methylnicotinamide, and the methyl ester of N^1-methyltetrahydronicotinic acid (arecoline) are, in the order given, quite active in that respect.[4]

D. BLOOD SUGAR

The extensive and contradictory literature on this subject has been reviewed by Díaz-Rubio and associates.[30] Various investigators seem about

[16] T. D. Spies, W. B. Bean, and R. E. Stone, J. Am. Med. Assoc. 111, 584 (1938).
[17] D. I. Abramson, H. H. Katzenstein, and F. A. Senior, Am. J. Med. Sci. 200, 96 (1940).
[18] R. A. Murphy, Jr., J. N. McClure, Jr., F. W. Cooper, Jr., and L. D. Crowley, Surgery 27, 655 (1950).
[19] S. Artunkal, Bull. fac. méd. Instanbul I, 4024 (1944).
[20] M. Salvini, Boll. soc. ital. biol. sper. 23, 907 (1947).
[21] M. Salvini and C. Dal Palu, Boll. soc. ital. biol. sper. 24, 986 (1948).
[22] P. Scheinberg, Circulation 1, 1148 (1950).
[23] M. Atkinson, Ann. Internal Med. 21, 990 (1944).
[24] J. W. Goldzieher and G. L. Popkin, J. Am. Med. Assoc. 131, 103 (1946).
[25] W. B. Bean and T. D. Spies, J. Am. Med. Assoc. 114, 439 (1940).
[26] L. Chevillard, R. Charonnat, and H. Giono, Compt. rend. soc. biol. 144, 194 (1950).
[27] W. Huber, U. S. Pat. 2,431,558 (November 25, 1947).
[28] CIBA Ltd. Swiss Pat. 258,714 (June 1, 1949).
[29] R. M. Calder, Proc. Soc. Exptl. Biol. Med. 68, 642 (1948).
[30] M. Díaz-Rubio, E. Monsalvez, and J. M. Masaguer, Rev. clin. españ. 21, 299 (1946).

equally divided among those who find a hyperglycemia, those who find no effect, and those who find a hypoglycemia after intravenous nicotinic acid. More recent reports concerning both animals and man have not clarified this subject, although most reports indicate either no effect or a slight hypoglycemic action.[31-37] Poppalardo[38] found a marked hypoglycemic action when nicotinic acid or nicotinamide was given by subarachnoid injection in man. Insulin injected into the developing egg embryo induced developmental defects. Nicotinamide prevented this effect, although α-ketoglutaric acid also had a similar action.[39]

E. KETOSIS

Janes and Meyers[40] discovered that rather large amounts of nicotinic acid would induce ketosis in alloxan diabetic rats. The alcohol of nicotinic acid (Roniacol) was more active, and nicotinamide less active, than nicotinic acid in this action.[41] Banerjee[42] found that nicotinic acid, and several other compounds having a pyridine nucleus and a carboxyl group, would inhibit the diabetogenic action of alloxan in rabbits. However, there is nothing specific about the action of nicotinic acid in either the induction or the progress of alloxan diabetes. Janes and Brady[43] found that excessive doses of nicotinic acid induced ketosis even in normal rats. Banerjee and Ghosh[37] could detect no effect of large doses of nicotinamide on blood acetone bodies in either normal or diabetic subjects.

F. GASTRIC SECRETION

Both nicotinic acid and nicotinamide have the ability to increase gastric secretion, including free and total acid, in normal individuals[44-46] and in

31 F. K. Permyakov, *Klin. Med.* (*U.S.S.R.*) **24**, 65 (1946).
32 C. Pelosio, *Fisiol. e med.* (*Rome*) **15**, 481 (1947).
33 S. Eser, *Bull. fac. méd. Instanbul* **11**, 82 (1948).
34 S. Banerjee, N. C. Ghosh, and G. Bhattacharya, *Indian J. Med. Research* **36**, 341 (1948).
35 G. Benedetti, B. Tortori-Donati, and F. Ferri, *Rass. fisiopatol. clin. e terap.* (*Pisa*) **20**, 233 (1948).
36 E. M. Alesker, *Klin. Med.* (*U.S.S.R.*) **27**, 70 (1949).
37 S. Banerjee and N. C. Ghosh, *J. Biol. Chem.* **177**, 789 (1949).
38 P. Poppalardo, *Acta. Neurol.* (*Naples*) **1**, 102 (1946).
39 W. Landauer, *J. Exptl. Zool.* **109**, 283 (1948).
40 R. G. Janes and L. Meyers, *Proc. Soc. Exptl. Biol. Med.* **63**, 410 (1946).
41 R. G. Janes, *Proc. Soc. Exptl. Biol. Med.* **75**, 246 (1950).
42 S. Banerjee, *Science* **106**, 128 (1947).
43 R. G. Janes and J. Brady, *Am. J. Physiol.* **159**, 547 (1949).
44 C. Malaguzzi-Valeri and P. Paterno, *Boll. soc. ital. biol. sper.* **14**, 377 (1939); *Gazz. ospedali e clin.* **60**, 925 (1939).
45 G. Gabor, *Orvosi Hetilap* **85**, 629 (1941).
46 I. S. Snitzer, *Klin. Med.* (*U.S.S.R.*) **27**, 77 (1949).

pellagrins,[16, 47-50] but usually not in achylic individuals.[44] Other investigators[51] confirmed this action of nicotinic acid and nicotinamide in normal individuals but could find little or no increase in patients with pellagra.

G. SERUM BILIRUBIN

Intravenous sodium nicotinate (30 to 300 mg.) induces a rather striking rise in indirect reading serum bilirubin in both normals and those with hepatic disease.[52-55] The increase is generally higher and more prolonged in patients with hepatic diseases than in normal subjects. A copious excretion of bile and increased urinary urobilin were also noted.[54, 56] Nicotinamide given intravenously did not elevate serum bilirubin but did increase bile flow to some extent.[56]

H. ANTIALLERGIC EFFECTS

There are quite a number of reports in recent European medical literature attributing antihistaminic and smooth muscle pharmacological effects to nicotinic acid and nicotinamide. These reports constitute an interesting facet of the pharmacology of nicotinic acid which has been largely overlooked in the American literature except for the flushing (smooth muscle?) action of nicotinic acid.

In 1941 Scaffidi and Molino[57] noted that intravenous sodium nicotinate caused a transient increase in tone and amplitude of the rhythmic contractions of rabbit uteri. In 1944 Halpern and Dainow[58] discovered that nicotinamide would protect against anaphylactic shock and histamine aerosol asthma but not against bronchospasm induced by acetylcholine in guinea pigs. These investigators also noted an antagonism between nicotinamide and histamine on the isolated intestine and uteri of guinea pigs. Nicotinamide diminished the stimulant action of acetylcholine and barium chloride

[47] G. A. Goldsmith, H. P. Sarett, U. D. Register, and J. Gibbens, *J. Clin. Invest.* **31**, 533 (1952).

[48] V. Rao, *Riv. patol. sper.* **26**, 49 (1941).

[49] G. Gotgiu and L. Romano, *Otti. soc. med. chir. Padova* **7**, 3 (1939), quoted in ref. 44.

[50] G. A. Goldsmith, H. P. Sarett, U. D. Register, and J. Gibbens, *Federation Proc.* **10**, 383 (1951).

[51] D. Zamfir, C. C. Dimitriu, P. Ionescu-Stoian, and N. Neculescu, *Rev. stürnt. med.* **31**, 420 (1942), abstract in *Ber. ges. Physiol.* **131**, 585 (1943).

[52] C. Mattei, *Minerva med.* **37**, 308 (1946).

[53] L. Marfori, M. Stefanini, and P. Bramante, *Il Policlinico (Rome) Sez. med.* **53**, 243 (1946); *Am. J. Med. Sci.* **213**, 150 (1947).

[54] M. Stefanini, *J. Lab. Clin. Med.* **34**, 1039 (1949).

[55] M. Salvini and F. S. Feruglio, *Boll. soc. ital. biol. sper.* **24**, 979 (1948).

[56] M. Stefanini, *Am. J. Digestive Diseases* **17**, 337 (1950).

[57] V. Scaffidi and N. Molino, *Boll. soc. ital. biol. sper.* **16**, 284 (1941).

[58] B. N. Halpern and I. Daïnow, *Z. Vitaminforsch.* **15**, 217, 250, 260 (1944).

on the isolated intestine but seemed without effect on uterine contractions induced by posterior pituitary extracts. Alechinsky[59] found that 100 mg. of nicotinamide would protect guinea pigs against one MLD of histamine. Frommel and associates[60] tested a number of nicotinamide derivatives against histamine aerosol in guinea pigs. None of the compounds had greater efficacy than nicotinamide itself, although others have found it less effective than sodium nicotinate.[61] Nicotinamide has also been reported to modify the systemic effects of histamine and to decrease the local effect of histamine on skin.[62]

Nicotinic acid and nicotinamide increased the force of contraction of the isolated intestine of rabbits.[63] A number of esters of nicotinic acid have been studied for their spasmolytic potency on smooth, cardiac and striped muscle.[64] Both nicotinic acid and nicotinamide have been found to antagonize curare and to reinforce the action of acetylcholine on the gastrocnemius and soleus muscles of anesthetized cats. Nicotinic acid antagonized whereas nicotinamide reinforced the action of prostigmine in this type of preparation.[65] Nicotinic acid has been reported to shorten the period of spasms in mice given strychnine and to give some protection against metrazole shock in rats, rabbits, and guinea pigs[66] and in dogs.[67]

I. OTHER EFFECTS

There are a number of reports dealing with unexpected effects of nicotinic acid administration in man and animals which have not been studied extensively enough for their significance to be determined. These are reduction in electrical excitability of the cerebral cortex in dogs[68]; increased absorption and increased blood levels of iron[69, 70]; prevention and treatment of bromidism in man and dogs;[71] changes in blood electrolytes;[72, 73] counter-

[59] A. Alechinsky, *Compt. rend. soc. biol.* **141**, 524 (1947).

[60] E. Frommel, A. Bischler, I. T. Beck, F. Vallette, and M. Favre, *Intern. Z. Vitaminforsch.* **19**, 193 (1947).

[31] E. Ginoulhiac and F. Semenza, *Acta Vitaminol.* **3**, 20 (1949).

[32] U. Butturini, *Giorn. clin. med. (Parma)* **27**, 681 (1946).

[3] R. Savini, *Boll. soc. ital. biol. sper.* **24**, 819 (1948).

[64] R. Charonnat, L. Chevillard, H. Giono, M. Harispe, and J. V. Harispe, *Ann. pharm. franç.* **6**, 489, 490 (1948).

[65] F. Valenzuela and F. Huidobro, *J. Pharmacol. Exptl. Therap.* **92**, 1 (1948).

[66] N. V. Sapezhinskaya, *Farmakol. i Toksikol.* **10**, 11 (1947) [*C. A.* **42**, 3081 (1948)].

[67] Q. Calabro and R. Savini, *Boll. soc. ital. biol. sper.* **24**, 823 (1948).

[68] R. Savini, *Boll. soc. ital. biol. sper.* **24**, 822 (1948).

[69] A. Lattanzi, *Boll. soc. ital. biol. sper.* **24**, 561 (1948); *Intern. Z. Vitaminforsch.* **21**, 307 (1949).

[70] L. Marinelli and C. Tramontana, *Giorn. clin. med. (Parma)* **31**, 152 (1950).

[71] R. S. Harris and P. S. Derian, *Southern Med. J.* **42**, 973 (1949).

[72] L. Biana, *Boll. soc. ital. biol. sper.* **15**, 1051, 1054 (1940).
M. Sacca, *Boll. soc. ital. biol. sper.* **22**, 477 (1946).

action of the toxicity of crystalline borrilidin in rats;[74] decreased serum cholinesterase;[75] and an increase (with thiamine) of basal metabolic rate.[76]

XIII. Requirements and Factors Influencing Them

J. M. HUNDLEY

A. ANIMALS

Table XVII presents a summary of published information on the nicotinic acid requirement of various species. The figures for tryptophan listed in

TABLE XVII

NICOTINIC ACID REQUIREMENT AND AMOUNT OF TRYPTOPHAN REQUIRED TO REPLACE NICOTINIC ACID

Species	Nicotinic acid, mg./100 g. of diet	Tryptophan, mg./100 g. of diet	Remarks
Rat	1.5 (1, 2)[a]	L or DL, 50 (1, 2)	Corn diets
	0.5–1.5 (3)		Diets with various carbohydrates
Mouse	1.0 (4)	[b]	—
Cotton rat	<2.5 (5, 6)	[b]	—
Dog	5.0 (7)	—	Corn diets
	0.130–0.225/kg. body wt./day (8–10)	—	Adult dogs
	0.250–0.360 kg. body wt./day (9)	DL, 100 or L, 50 (11)	Puppies
Swine	6.5–17.0/day/animal (12–14)	DL, 250 (15, 16)	Young pigs
	0.6–1.0/kg. body wt./day (15, 16)	DL, 200/day (12, 14)	Young pigs
Rabbit	60 (17)	DL, 220 (17)	Glucose diet
	10/kg. body wt./day (18)	DL, 400/kg. body wt./day (19)	Sucrose diet
Monkey	10–35 wk. (20)	DL, 1000–4000/wk. (20)	—
Chicken	1.8–2.0 (21–23)	—	Young chicks
	3.0 (24, 25)	L or DL, 200 (24)	Young chicks
	4.0–5.0 (26–28)	L, 100 or DL, 200 (27–29)	Young chicks
Turkey	3.0–10.0 (30–32)	[c]	Poults
Duck	2.5 (33)	DL, 400 (34)	Ducklings
Cat	1.7/day (35)	[d]	—

a Figures in parentheses are references.
b Tryptophan can replace nicotinic acid in the mouse and cotton rat, but this has not been determined quantitatively.
c The ability of tryptophan to replace nicotinic acid in the turkey has not been determined.
d Trypotophan does not appear to replace nicotinic acid in cats.

[74] J. M. Cooperman, S. H. Rubin, and B. Tabenkin, Proc. Soc. Exptl. Biol. Med. **76**, 18 (1951).

Table XVII represent the approximate amount required to substitute for the nicotinic acid requirement. These figures do not include tryptophan

[75] P. Salvi and A. Morelli, *Acta neurol. (Naples)* **2**, 986 (1947).

[76] C. Malaguzzi-Valeri, G. Conese, and D. Angarano, *Intern. Z. Vitaminforsch.* **22**, 174 (1950).

[1] W. A. Krehl, P. S. Sarma, L. J. Teply, and C. A. Elvehjem, *J. Nutrition* **31**, 85 (1946).

[2] L. V. Hankes, L. M. Henderson, W. L. Brickson, and C. A. Elvehjem, *J. Biol. Chem.* **174**, 873 (1948).

[3] J. M. Hundley, *J. Biol. Chem.* **181**, 1 (1949).

[4] B. S. Schweigert and P. B. Pearson, *J. Biol. Chem.* **172**, 485 (1948).

[5] J. M. McIntire, B. S. Schweigert, and C. A. Elvehjem, *J. Nutrition* **27**, 1 (1944).

[6] B. S. Schweigert, *Proc. Soc. Exptl. Biol. Med.* **68**, 522 (1948).

[7] W. A. Krehl, L. J. Teply, and C. A. Elvehjem, *Proc. Soc. Exptl. Biol. Med.* **58**, 334 (1945).

[8] T. W. Birch, *J. Nutrition* **17**, 281 (1939).

[9] A. E. Schaefer, J. M. McKibbin, and C. A. Elvehjem, *J. Biol. Chem.* **144**, 679 (1942).

[10] W. H. Sebrell, R. H. Onstott, H. F. Fraser, and F. S. Daft, *J. Nutrition* **16**, 355 (1938).

[11] S. A. Singal, V. P. Sydenstricker, and J. M. Littlejohn, *J. Biol. Chem.* **176**, 1051 (1948).

[12] R. W. Luecke, W. N. McMillen, F. Thorp, Jr., and C. Tull, *J. Nutrition* **36**, 417 (1948).

[13] R. E. Butler and H. P. Sarett, *J. Nutrition* **35**, 539 (1948).

[14] R. W. Luecke, W. N. McMillen, F. Thorp, Jr., and C. Tull, *J. Nutrition* **33**, 251 (1947).

[15] W. C. Powick, N. R. Ellis, L. L. Madsen, and C. N. Dale, *J. Animal Sci.* **6**, 310 (1947).

[16] W. C. Powick, N. R. Ellis, and C. N. Dale, *J. Animal Sci.* **7**, 228 (1948).

[17] O. Olcese, P. B. Pearson, and P. Sparks, *J. Nutrition* **39**, 93 (1949).

[18] J. G. Wooley and W. H. Sebrell, *J. Nutrition* **19**, 191 (1945).

[19] J. G. Wooley, *Proc. Soc. Exptl. Biol. Med.* **65**, 315 (1947).

[20] D. V. Tappan, U. J. Lewis, U. D. Register, and C. A. Elvehjem, *J. Nutrition* **46**, 75 (1952).

[21] G. M. Briggs, R. C. Mills, C. A. Elvehjem, and E. B. Hart, *Proc. Soc. Exptl. Biol. Med.* **51**, 59 (1942).

[22] H. M. Scott, E. P. Singsen, and L. D. Matterson, *Poultry Sci. (Research Notes)* **25**, 303 (1946).

[23] P. S. Sarma and C. A. Elvehjem, *Poultry Sci.* **25**, 39 (1946).

[24] J. W. West, C. W. Carrick, S. M. Hauge, and E. T. Mertz, *Poultry Sci.* **31**, 479 (1952).

[25] G. R. Childs, C. W. Carrick, and S. M. Hauge, *Poultry Sci.* **31**, 551 (1952).

[26] M. E. Coates, S. K. Kon, and E. E. Shepheard, *Brit. J. Nutrition* **4**, 203 (1950).

[27] G. M. Briggs, A. C. Groschke, and R. J. Lillie, *J. Nutrition* **32**, 659 (1946).

[28] G. M. Briggs, *J. Biol. Chem.* **161**, 749 (1945).

[29] J. O. Anderson, G. F. Combs, and G. M. Briggs, *J. Nutrition* **42**, 463 (1950).

[30] G. M. Briggs, *J. Nutrition* **31**, 79 (1946).

[31] T. H. Jukes, E. L. R. Stokstad, and M. Belt, *J. Nutrition* **33**, 1 (1947).

[32] B. G. Lance and A. G. Hogan, *J. Nutrition* **36**, 369 (1948).

[33] D. M. Hegsted, *J. Nutrition* **32**, 467 (1946).

in the basal diet and hence do not represent the absolute tryptophan requirement. The figures listed, both for nicotinic acid and tryptophan, can be regarded as valid only under the particular conditions of the experiments cited, in view of the well-known conversion of tryptophan to nicotinic acid and the many other factors which influence requirements.

As indicated in Table XVII, rats, mice, cotton rats, dogs, swine, rabbits, monkeys, chickens, turkeys, ducks, and cats require a dietary source of nicotinic acid except, in some species, when sufficient tryptophan is supplied. Fox puppies require nicotinic acid (0.39 to 2.0 mg. per kilogram of body weight per day).[36] The activity of tryptophan has not been reported in this species. Guinea pigs require nicotinic acid.[37, 38] Banerjee *et al.*[38] could demonstrate no activity with tryptophan, although Cannon and associates[37] obtained some evidence that tryptophan could substitute for nicotinic acid and Henderson *et al.*[39] found that tryptophan increased the urinary excretion of nicotinic acid and related compounds in guinea pigs.

Calves,[39-42] horses,[43, 44] and sheep[39, 45, 46] do not require a dietary source of nicotinic acid, although they can convert tryptophan to nicotinic acid.

a. Tryptophan

The conversion of tryptophan to nicotinic acid is described in detail in Section VI. Tryptophan may be added to the diet either as the pure amino acid or as protein. Thus, dogs will develop blacktongue on a 20 % casein ration but will not if the casein is increased to 42 %.[11] Rats develop nicotinic acid deficiency on 9 % casein, cystine-supplemented rations but do not if the casein level is increased to 15 to 25 %.[4, 47-51] Swine develop nicotinic

---

[34] R. Bernard and J. M. Demers, *Rev. can. biol.* **8**, 504 (1949).

[35] A. C. da Silva, *Acta Physiol. Latinoamer.* **1**, 20 (1950); A. C. da Silva, R. Fried, and R. C. de Angelis, *J. Nutrition* **46**, 399 (1952).

[36] A. E. Schaefer, C. K. Whitehair, and C. A. Elvehjem, *J. Nutrition* **34**, 131 (1947).

[37] M. D. Cannon, G. J. Mannering, C. A. Elvehjem, and E. B. Hart, *Proc. Soc. Exptl. Biol. Med.* **63**, 414 (1946).

[38] S. Banerjee, R. Banerjee, and C. C. Deb, *Indian J. Med. Research* **38**, 161 (1950).

[39] L. M. Henderson, G. B. Ramasarma, and B. C. Johnson, *J. Biol. Chem.* **181**, 731 (1949).

[40] B. C. Johnson, A. C. Wiese, H. H. Mitchell, and W. B. Nevens, *J. Biol. Chem.* **167**, 729 (1947).

[41] B. C. Johnson, *Euclides (Madrid)* **8**, 161 (1948).

[42] G. C. Esh and T. S. Sutton, *J. Dairy Sci.* **31**, 909 (1948).

[43] J. W. Huff, P. B. Pearson, and W. A. Perlzweig, *Arch. Biochem.* **9**, 99 (1946).

[44] B. S. Schweigert, P. B. Pearson, and M. C. Wilkening, *Arch. Biochem.* **12**, 139 (1947).

[45] A. H. Winegar, P. B. Pearson, and H. Schmidt, *Science* **91**, 508 (1940).

[46] P. B. Pearson, A. H. Winegar, and H. Schmidt, *J. Nutrition* **20**, 551 (1940).

[47] J. M. Hundley, *J. Nutrition* **34**, 253 (1947).

[48] W. A. Krehl, L. J. Teply, and C. A. Elvehjem, *Science* **101**, 283 (1945).

acid deficiency on low casein diets but not if the casein level is increased
to 25 or 26 %.[12, 51]

There is considerable evidence that tryptophan added to the diet as the
free amino acid results in considerably greater synthesis of nicotinic acid
than when an equivalent amount of tryptophan is added as protein.[52, 53]
This interesting phenomenon might be explained by assuming that tryptophan presented to the tissues along with a well-balanced mixture of other
amino acids is used primarily in association with other amino acids in
processes involved in protein synthesis and replacement. However, when
tryptophan is presented to the tissues so that it is in excess of the available
amount of other amino acids, the excess tryptophan is diverted into the
channels which lead to nicotinic acid synthesis.

b. Other Amino Acids

Several groups of investigators have shown that proteins lacking or low
in tryptophan, amino acid mixtures simulating these proteins, and certain
amino acids, singly or in combinations, have a marked ability to increase
nicotinic acid requirements when added to deficient rations in rats[2, 47, 54-57]
and in chicks.[27, 58-60] Anderson *et al.*,[61] using chicks on a nicotinic acid
deficient diet, have recently shown that amino acids may be divided into
two groups, those which cause a growth depression correctable by nicotinic
acid and those which cause a growth depression not influenced by the
vitamin.

In each of the experiments cited above, the basal ration to which the
various protein and amino acid supplements were added contained a limited
amount of tryptophan as well as being deficient in nicotinic acid. In general,

[49] W. D. Salmon, *J. Nutrition* **33**, 169 (1947).
[50] W. D. Salmon, *J. Nutrition* **33**, 155 (1947).
[51] M. M. Wintrobe, H. J. Stein, R. H. Follis, Jr., and S. Humphreys, *J. Nutrition* **30**, 395 (1945).
[52] S. A. Singal, A. P. Briggs, V. P. Sydenstricker, and J. M. Littlejohn, *J. Biol. Chem.* **166**, 573 (1946).
[53] G. H. Bell, B. T. Scheer, and H. J. Deuel, Jr., *J. Nutrition* **35**, 239 (1948).
[54] W. A. Krehl, L. M. Henderson, J. de la Huerga, and C. A. Elvehjem, *J. Biol. Chem.* **166**, 531 (1946).
[55] F. Rosen, J. W. Huff, and W. A. Perlzweig, *J. Biol. Chem.* **163**, 343 (1946).
[56] S. A. Singal, V. P. Sydenstricker, and J. M. Littlejohn, *J. Biol. Chem.* **171**, 203 (1947); **176**, 1063 (1948).
[57] F. Rosen and W. A. Perlzweig, *J. Biol. Chem.* **177**, 163 (1949).
[58] A. C. Groschke, J. O. Anderson, and G. M. Briggs, *Proc. Soc. Exptl. Biol. Med.* **68**, 564 (1948).
[59] G. M. Briggs, *J. Biol. Chem.* **161**, 749 (1945).
[60] A. C. Groschke and G. M. Briggs, *J. Biol. Chem.* **165**, 739 (1946).
[61] J. O. Anderson, G. F. Combs, A. C. Groschke, and G. M. Briggs, *J. Nutrition* **45**, 345 (1951).

the more of the supplements which were added, the more severe the apparent nicotinic acid deficiency became. In most instances nicotinic acid and tryptophan were equally effective in overcoming the growth depression (within certain limits).

Most, if not all, of these observations can be explained according to the concept of amino acid balance. When the diet contains more tryptophan, in proportion to available amounts of other amino acids, than is required for protein synthesis and other anabolic demands, then a portion of the tryptophan is converted into nicotinic acid in an efficient fashion. When, however, the supply of tryptophan is restricted so that it is the most limiting amino acid, then the tissues seem to metabolize it in a different fashion. Its utilization becomes quite inefficient and very little nicotinic acid is formed, as shown by Krehl and associates.[62] The greater the deficit of tryptophan in proportion to the other amino acids, the more severe the nicotinic acid deficiency seems to be. If nicotinic acid is supplied in these low-tryptophan rations, the tissues seem to be relieved of the necessity for converting tryptophan to nicotinic acid and the metabolism of tryptophan becomes efficient once again; i.e., the added nicotinic acid seems to "spare" tryptophan.

This concept, if valid, implies that the metabolic channels into which an amino acid can be directed may vary according to the needs of the tissues for essential substances. It also implies that the metabolic utilization of an amino acid may become quite inefficient when it is the most limiting amino acid. Further, it is evident that the absolute requirement of an organism for an amino acid varies not only with the relative supply of other amino acids but with the dietary supply of essential substances which can, in case of need, be made from the amino acid.

The role of amino acid balance in nutrition has been reviewed by Elvehjem and Krehl[63] and by Krehl.[64]

c. Influence of Carbohydrates

Krehl and associates[1] were the first to note that dextrin, starch, glucose, and lactose had a nicotinic acid sparing action when compared to diets containing sucrose in the rat. These findings have been confirmed and extended.[4, 54, 65] A similar phenomenon may exist in the rabbit,[17, 18] although the reverse apparently obtains in chicks; i.e., starch increases nicotinic acid requirements.[29] The explanation usually given these phenomena is that different carbohydrates alter the intestinal flora and thereby

[62] W. A. Krehl, J. de la Huerga and C. A. Elvehjem, *J. Nutrition* **164**, 551 (1946).

[63] C. A. Elvehjem and W. A. Krehl, *J. Am. Med. Assoc.* **135**, 279 (1947).

[64] W. A. Krehl, *Vitamins and Hormones* **7**, 111 (1949).

[65] L. M. Henderson, T. Deodhar, W. A. Krehl, and C. A. Elvehjem, *J. Biol. Chem.* **170**, 261 (1947).

change the amount of nicotinic acid consumed or produced by the micro-organisms, which in turn influences the amount of nicotinic acid available to the host. This may be the true explanation, although Hundley[3] has advanced the idea, with some supporting data, that fructose and sugars containing fructose require more nicotinic acid in their metabolism than do glucose and sugars containing glucose. According to this theory, fructose, or a portion of it, may be metabolized in a different manner from glucose, a metabolic pathway which necessitates a greater utilization of nicotinic acid-containing coenzymes, and may thereby increase the dietary nicotinic acid requirement.

d. Intestinal Synthesis of Nicotinic Acid

The exact explanation for the effect of various carbohydrates on nicotinic acid requirement is still in doubt. Indeed, much has been written about the role of intestinal microorganisms in supplying the host with essential nutrients. Ellinger[66] has reviewed the extensive and excellent work he and his associates have done, as well as that of other workers, which supports the position that intestinal microbes play an important role in providing nicotinic acid for the host. There is no doubt whatsoever that bacteria, such as are found in the intestine, can and do synthesize nicotinic acid, but on the other hand they may also consume and destroy it.[67, 68] There is also no doubt that dietary variations such as changing the type of carbohydrate will alter the microbial population of the intestine and will change the amount of free nicotinic acid found in the intestine, as shown by the numerous studies on carbohydrates cited previously.

The essential question is whether any of these changes result in any substantial difference in the nicotinic acid economy of the host. The evidence is conflicting. Ellinger and associates have found that some sulfa drugs, but not others, taken orally result in a substantial decrease in urinary N^1-methylnicotinamide excretion.[69, 70] There are clinical reports of nicotinic acid deficiency being induced by oral "sulfa" drugs or antibiotics.[71, 72] On the other hand, numerous attempts to produce nicotinic acid deficiency in animals by means of sulfa drugs have been unsuccessful. Several investigators have found no decrease in the urinary excretion of N^1-methylnicotinamide or other nicotinic acid metabolites after sulfa drugs

[66] P. Ellinger, *Experentia* **6**, 144 (1950).
[67] S. A. Koser and G. R. Baird, *J. Infectious Diseases* **75**, 250 (1944).
[68] R. Benesch, *Lancet* **I**, 718 (1945); *Prensa med. (Argentina)* **33**, 1335 (1946).
[69] P. Ellinger, R. A. Coulson, and R. Benesch, *Nature* **154**, 270 (1944).
[70] P. Ellinger, R. Benesch, and W. W. Kay, *Lancet* **I**, 432 (1945).
[71] S. W. Hardwick, *Lancet* **250**, 267 (1946).
[72] P. Ellinger and F. M. Shattock, *Brit. Med. J.* **II**, 611 (1946).

were given orally in man and animals,[73-75] although some drugs seem to produce an increased excretion of nicotinic acid metabolites.[76-78] The final solution to this knotty question will have to await the availability of tools which will permit a more direct approach to the problem.

e. Influence of Fat

Salmon[79] has shown that diets high in fat result in a lowered dietary requirement for nicotinic acid, in a fashion similar to the well-known thiamine-sparing action of fat. This has been interpreted as providing additional evidence for the role of nicotinic acid in carbohydrate metabolism, although the correctness of this interpretation has been questioned.[64]

f. Other Influences

(1) *Corn.* The fact that the occurrence of human pellagra is so often associated with the consumption of diets high in corn, and the fact that pellagra will develop when corn diets are fed whereas other diets with less nicotinic acid do not cause pellagra,[80, 81] have led to innumerable attempts to find some substance in corn which increases nicotinic acid requirements (pp. 548 and 565). Although it has been shown that corn, under certain circumstances, will increase nicotinic acid requirements in several species of animals,[7, 48, 82] there is no conclusive evidence that this effect of corn is due to anything more than the effect of its low tryptophan protein.[49, 58, 83] The weight of evidence seems to favor the view that these effects of corn can be adequately explained on this basis plus perhaps a relatively low digestibility and a low availability of the nicotinic acid in corn.[84, 85]

(2) *Vitamin B₆.* A deficiency of pyridoxine in the rat, if sufficiently severe, reduces the excretion of urinary nicotinic acid derivatives after

[73] V. A. Najjar, L. E. Holt, Jr., G. A. Johns, G. C. Mediary, and G. Fleischmann, *Proc. Soc. Exptl. Biol. Med.* **61**, 371 (1946).

[74] H. N. De, M. C. Malaker, and A. K. Paul, *Indian Med. Gaz.* **84**, 542 (1949).

[75] A. E. Teeri, M. Leavitt, D. Josselyn, N. F. Caloves, and H. A. Keener, *J. Biol. Chem.* **182**, 509 (1950).

[76] H. Spector, *J. Biol. Chem.* **173**, 659 (1948).

[77] P. Ellinger and A. Emmanuelowa, *Lancet* **251**, 716 (1946).

[78] P. Ellinger, M. M. Abdel Kader, and A. Emmanuelowa, *Brit. J. Exptl. Pathol.* **28**, 261 (1947).

[79] W. D. Salmon, *J. Nutrition* **33**, 155 (1947).

[80] E. I. Frazier and T. E. Friedemann, *Quart. Bull. Northwestern Univ. Med. School* **20**, 24 (1946).

[81] W. R. Aykroyd and M. Swaminathan, *Indian J. Med. Research* **27**, 667 (1940).

[82] P. Handler, *Proc. Soc. Exptl. Biol. Med.* **52**, 263 (1943).

[83] W. A. Krehl, P. S. Sarma, and C. A. Elvehjem, *J. Biol. Chem.* **162**, 403 (1946).

[84] E. Kodicek, *Biochem. J.* **48**, viii (1951).

[85] R. G. Chitre and D. B. Desai, *Ind. J. Med. Research* **3**, 471, 479 (1949).

tryptophan administration[53, 86-88] and prevents the normal increase of pyridine nucleotides in red blood cells following tryptophan.[89] In most instances these defects were overcome promptly after pyridoxine therapy. Since pyridoxine deficiency is known to result in abnormal tryptophan metabolism [90-93] it was logical to believe that pyridoxine deficiency might also interfere with the synthesis of nicotinic acid from tryptophan.

However, several reports[94-96] appeared indicating that the liver of pyridoxine-deficient rats could still transform tryptophan to nicotinic acid derivatives. Furthermore, deficiencies of thiamine or riboflavin or simple reduction in caloric intake also appeared to result in a reduced excretion of urinary nicotinic acid derivatives after tryptophan.[88] Spector[76] found no interference with the tryptophan to nicotinic acid conversion in force-fed pyridoxine-deficient rats. Heimberg *et al.*[97] obtained evidence that the involvement of pyridoxine in nicotinic acid synthesis was not a direct metabolic effect. These seemingly contradictory reports may be explained by a recent investigation by Kring and associates,[98] who also found that pyridoxine deficiency did not inhibit the formation of liver pyridine nucleotides from tryptophan. However, if they intensified the deficiency state by using the antagonist desoxypyridoxine, they could demonstrate such an interference. However, even this severe deficiency did not interfere with the formation of liver pyridine nucleotides from nicotinic acid.

So far as is known, this interesting interrelationship between pyridoxine and tryptophan has no practical significance in altering the nicotinic acid requirements of either animals or man.

(3) *Folic Acid.* Krehl and associates[99, 100] found that folic acid improved

[86] F. Rosen, J. W. Huff, and W. A. Perlzweig, *J. Nutrition* **33**, 561 (1947).

[87] B. S. Schweigert and P. B. Pearson, *J. Biol. Chem.* **168**, 555 (1947).

[88] P. B. Junqueira and B. S. Schweigert, *J. Biol. Chem.* **174**, 605 (1948).

[89] C. Ling, D. M. Hegsted, and F. J. Stare, *J. Biol. Chem.* **174**, 803 (1948).

[90] P. J. Fouts and S. Lepkovsky, *Proc. Soc. Exptl. Biol. Med.* **50**, 221 (1942).

[91] S. Lepkovsky and E. Nielsen, *J. Biol. Chem.* **144**, 135 (1942).

[92] S. Lepkovsky, E. Roboz, and A. J. Haagen-Smit, *J. Biol. Chem.* **149**, 195 (1943).

[93] C. C. Porter, I. Clark, and R. H. Silber, *J. Biol. Chem.* **167**, 573 (1947).

[94] J. N. Williams, Jr., P. Feigelson, C. A. Elvehjem, and S. S. Shahinian, *J. Biol. Chem.* **189**, 659 (1951).

[95] W. W. Hurt, B. T. Scheer, and H. J. Deuel, Jr., *Arch. Biochem.* **21**, 87 (1949).

[96] J. N. Williams, Jr., P. Feigelson, S. S. Shahinian, and C. A. Elvehjem, *Proc. Soc. Exptl. Biol. Med.* **76**, 441 (1951).

[97] M. Heimberg, F. Rosen, I. G. Leder, and W. A. Perlzweig, *Arch. Biochem.* **28**, 225 (1950).

[98] J. P. Kring, K. Ebisuzaki, J. N. Williams, Jr., and C. A. Elvehjem, *J. Biol. Chem.* **195**, 591 (1952).

[99] W. A. Krehl and C. A. Elvehjem, *J. Biol. Chem.* **158**, 173 (1945).

[100] W. A. Krehl, N. Torbet, J. de la Huerga, and C. A. Elvehjem, *Arch. Biochem.* **11**, 363 (1946).

the response of nicotinic acid-deficient dogs to nicotinic acid and helped to maintain a more normal blood picture. Ruegamer *et al.*[101] reported that both folic acid and nicotinic acid were required to obtain a response with liver extract in an anemia which developed in dogs on rations which were probably deficient in all three factors. Teply *et al.*[102] found an interrelation between folic acid and nicotinic acid in the ceca of rats under various dietary circumstances. Junqueira and Schweigert[103] found that sulfasuxidine interfered with the conversion of tryptophan to nicotinic acid if folic acid was not in the diet, but had no effect if the diet was supplemented with folic acid. The significance, if any, of these reports in relation to the nicotinic acid requirement of animals is not clear.

(4) *Age.* Adult animals require less nicotinic acid than growing animals, as might be expected.[1, 12, 104]

(5) *Climate.* Mills and associates[105] found no difference in nicotinic acid requirement between chicks kept at temperate coolness and at tropical heat.

(6) *Alcohol.* Available evidence (p. 565) suggests that alcohol "spares" nicotinic acid in man. However, in view of the high incidence of pellagra in alcoholics, one might doubt the practical importance of this effect.

B. MAN

The recommended daily dietary allowance of nicotinic acid which is generally applied in the United States is that of the Food and Nutrition Board of the National Research Council.[106] According to this standard, the daily diet of man should provide 12 to 18 mg. of nicotinic acid, depending on activity, that for women 10 to 15 mg., depending on activity and whether they are pregnant or lactating. Infants and children should receive from 4 to 17 mg. daily, depending on age up to 13 years, and on age and sex from 13 to 20 years of age.

These allowances were based primarily on animal experiments and on analyses of diets which were known to be pellagra preventive.[106] They contain a deliberate margin of safety to provide for those who may have requirements above average or who by reason of illness or injury might have a temporarily increased need for the vitamin. It should be emphasized that the figures cited above are recommended allowances, not minimum physiological requirements.

[101] W. R. Ruegamer, W. L. Brickson, N. J. Torbet, and C. A. Elvehjem, *J. Nutrition* **36**, 425 (1948).
[102] L. J. Teply, W. A. Krehl, and C. A. Elvehjem, *Am. J. Physiol.* **148**, 91 (1947).
[103] P. B. Junqueira and B. S. Schweigert, *J. Biol. Chem.* **175**, 535 (1948).
[104] R. Braude, S. K. Kon, and E. G. White, *Biochem. J.* **40**, 843 (1947).
[105] C. A. Mills, E. Cottingham, and E. Taylor, *Am. J. Physiol.* **149**, 376 (1947).
[106] Recommended Dietary Allowances, *Bull. Natl. Research Council (U. S.) Reprint and Circ. Ser.* **129**, (1948).

However, the validity of these recommended allowances has recently received important confirmation from two sources. Frazier and Friedemann[80] recalculated the nicotinic acid and other nutrients in diets known to be pellagra producing or pellagra preventive, using dietary records gathered by Goldberger and others. They concluded that the minimum daily intake of nicotinic acid in a marginal diet containing corn products is about 7.5 mg. per day. More recently, Goldsmith and associates[107] produced pellagra experimentally in women with corn-containing diets which provided 4.7 mg. of nicotinic acid and 190 mg. of tryptophan daily. Other subjects who received the same diet supplemented with 2 mg. of nicotinic acid, or "wheat" diets providing 5.7 mg. of nicotinic acid and 230 mg. of tryptophan, failed to develop pellagra.

Much less precise information is available on factors which influence requirements in man than in animals. Tryptophan can substitute, at least in part, for nicotinic acid in human diets. The possible influence of corn products (p. 548) and alcohol (p. 565) has been mentioned elsewhere. Several factors are known which, clinically, seem to precipitate or predispose man to attacks of pellagra. These are sunlight, heavy work, disturbed gastrointestinal function, intestinal parasitism, and surgery. Whether these increase requirements or act in an indirect manner is not established. Likewise, it is uncertain whether the peak incidence of pellagra in the early spring months is due to the effect of sunlight, to increased exercise, or simply to the development of a deficit of nicotinic acid during the winter months.

[107] G. A. Goldsmith, H. P. Sarett, U. D. Register, and J. Gibbens, *J. Clin. Invest.* **31**, 533 (1952).

I. Nomenclature

ROBERT S. HARRIS

Accepted name: Pantothenic acid[1]
Obsolete names: Liver factor 2[2]
             Antidermatitis factor[3]
             Chick antidermatitis factor[4]
             Liver filtrate factor[5]
             Yeast filtrate factor[6]
             Chick antipellagra (A.P.) factor[7]
Empirical formula: $C_9H_{17}O_5N$
Chemical name: α,γ-Dihydroxy-β,β-dimethylbutyryl-β'-alanine
Structural formula:

$$\underset{\underset{CH_3}{|}}{\overset{\overset{CH_3}{|}}{HOCH_2-C-CHOH-CO-NH-CH_2-CH_2-COOH}}$$

II. Chemistry

SAMUEL LEPKOVSKY

A. ISOLATION

The isolation of pantothenic acid was accomplished during a period in the history of nutrition that was characterized by confusion and misunderstanding. This was caused by the mistaken notion that vitamin G or B_2 was a single factor instead of a multiplicity of factors which had similar chemical properties and were associated together in such foodstuffs as yeast, liver, and wheat germ. Goldberger and Lillie[1] predicted this in what became a masterpiece of understatement. "The possibility, remote though it seems, is not excluded that there may be in yeast more

[1] R. J. Williams, C. M. Lyman, G. H. Goodyear, T. H. Truesdail, and D. Holaday, J. Am. Chem. Soc. 55, 2012 (1932).

[2] S. Lepkovsky, T. H. Jukes, and M. E. Krause, J. Biol. Chem. 115, 557 (1936).

[3] J. C. Bauernfeind, A. E. Schumacher, A. Z. Hodson, L. C. Norris, and G. F. Heuser, Proc. Soc. Exptl. Biol. Med. 39, 108 (1938).

[4] O. Mickelsen, H. A. Waisman, and C. A. Elvehjem, J. Biol. Chem. 124, 313 (1938).

[5] T. H. Jukes and S. Lepkovsky, J. Biol. Chem. 111, 119 (1935).

[6] C. E. Edgar and T. F. Macrae, Biochem. J. 31, 886, 893 (1937).

[7] C. J. Koehn, Jr., and C. A. Elvehjem, J. Biol. Chem. 118, 693 (1937).

[1] J. Goldberger and R. D. Lillie, Public Health Repts. (U. S.) 41, 297 (1926).

than one such thermostable factor which further study may succeed in differentiating. Moreover, it is not clear that all essential factors, or necessary relations among such factors, for the nutrition of the albino rat, have as yet been determined." The confusion was largely attributable to three causes:

1. Different species of animals such as the chicken, the turkey, the rat, and the human being showed superficially similar symptoms, such as dermatitis, which were very frequently and uncritically referred to as "pellagra." This resulted in the mistaken implication that one vitamin only was involved when in fact each so-called "pellagrous" condition was due to the deficiency of a different vitamin.

2. Not all species reacted similarly to all vitamin deficiencies. Man, dog, and pig were sensitive to the deficiency of nicotinic acid, but the rat and the chick were not.[2] It took some time for investigators to realize that a pig developed pellagra on a diet whereas a rat on the same diet did not.

3. Adsorbing agents such as fuller's earth and charcoal which were used in the fractionation of different vitamins were not so specific as the investigators using them believed, leading to considerable misunderstanding.

Slowly and laboriously the weight of accumulating evidence brought to light the chemical nature of pantothenic acid. Two completely independent lines of investigations, proceeding simultaneously, one with microorganisms and the other with chicks, finally merged, and together they were largely responsible for the isolation of pantothenic acid and its recognition as a vitamin.

The pioneering investigations of Williams, an organic chemist using microorganisms and microbiological methods, were in large part responsible for the isolation and characterization of pantothenic acid. The term was coined by Williams and his coworkers and it comes from the Greek meaning "from everywhere"[3, 3a] because it was found in all of a considerable number of plant and animal tissues from widely divergent sources, and they correctly felt that it must play a fundamentally important biological role. The retention of the name pantothenic acid and the failure to use any letter-number designation for it marks the early departure from the traditional alphabetical-number vitamin nomenclature. Williams et al.[4, 4a] used the following techniques in the isolation of pantothenic acid from liver.

[2] S. Lepkovsky, Nutrition Abstr. & Revs. 11, 363 (1942). This article carries an extensive bibliography on the subject.

[3] R. J. Williams, C. M. Lyman, G. H. Goodyear, J. H. Truesdail, and D. Holaday, J. Am. Chem. Soc. 55, 2912 (1933).

[3a] R. J. Williams, Advances in Enzymol. 3, 253 (1943). This article carries an extensive bibliography on the subject.

[4] R. J. Williams, J. H. Truesdail, H. H. Weinstock, Jr., E. Rohrmann, C. M. Lyman, and C. H. McBurney, J. Am. Chem. Soc. 60, 2719 (1938).

[4a] F. A. Robinson, The Vitamin B Complex. John Wiley and Sons, New York, 1951.

1. Autolysis to obtain a clear filtrate.

2. Adsorption on fuller's earth to remove bases.

3. Adsorption of the vitamin on charcoal and its subsequent elution.

4. Preparation of brucine derivatives by evaporation to dryness on kieselguhr in the presence of brucine and brucine oxalate.

5. Extraction of brucine pantothenate with chloroform.

6. Fractional distribution of the brucine salts between chloroform and water.

7. Conversion of the pantothenic acid to its calcium salt.

8. Fractionation of the calcium salts with various solvents and solvent mixtures.

The success of this procedure depended upon a rapid and accurate quantitative assay method which was made possible by the use of yeast as test organisms.[3, 5] Without such a rapid test, this procedure would have been hopeless. This work foreshadowed the wide use of microorganisms for the assay of vitamins and amino acids.

Pure pantothenic acid has never been isolated by this or any other procedure. Only a small quantity of pantothenic acid of 90% purity has been prepared. It was a colorless "varnish," which, when ground, yielded a white amorphous hygroscopic powder which was about 11,000 times as potent as their "standard" rice bran preparation.[3a, 4]

Long before pantothenic acid was isolated, Williams and his coworkers obtained extensive preliminary information about it, made possible in large part by the extensive use of a relatively new tool, i.e., fractional electrical transport.[3a, 6, 7]

1. The compound was an acid with a molecular weight[3] of about 150 and with an ionization constant[8] of about 3.9×10^{-5}.

2. It was unstable in hot acids and alkalies.

3. It had a nitrogen atom with barely detectable basic properties.[9]

4. It had in its structure no olefin double bond, aldehyde, ketone, sulfhydryl, basic nitrogen, aromatic, or sugar group.

5. It possessed several hydroxyl groups.[3]

Snell et al.[10] were independently studying an essential nutrient for lactic acid bacteria. They concluded that it was an acid, was adsorbed on charcoal, lacked basic properties, and was unstable in hot acid or alkaline solution.

[5] R. J. Williams, E. D. McAlister, and R. R. Roehm, J. Biol. Chem. 83, 315 (1929).

[6] R. J. Williams and J. H. Truesdail, J. Am. Chem. Soc. 53, 4171 (1931).

[7] R. J. Williams, J. Biol. Chem. 110, 589 (1935).

[8] R. J. Williams and R. J. Moser, J. Am. Chem. Soc. 56, 169 (1934).

[9] R. J. Williams, H. H. Weinstock, Jr., E. Rohrmann, J. H. Truesdail, H. K. Mitchell, and C. E. Meyer, J. Am. Chem. Soc. 61, 454 (1939).

[10] E. E. Snell, F. M. Strong, and W. H. Peterson, Biochem. J. 31, 1789 (1937).

They recognized a rough similarity between their factor and pantothenic acid but concluded that the available evidence was too limited to warrant discussion of the relationship of the two factors.

A clue to the nature of pantothenic acid was found with the discovery that β-alanine was a yeast growth stimulant.[11] This discovery led Williams and his coworkers to suspect that there was a structural relationship between β-alanine and pantothenic acid. This suspicion was soon confirmed with the discovery that β-alanine was in fact a cleavage product of pantothenic acid,[12] and they succeeded in isolating it in the form of β-naphthalene-sulfo-β-alanine.[3a] They also found that their yeasts (G.M.) were capable of synthesizing physiologically active pantothenic acid when β-alanine was supplied in the medium.[12]

Attention was now concentrated upon the other cleavage product. The evidence indicated that it was an α-hydroxy-γ-lactone.[13] Elementary analysis of the most potent pantothenic acid concentrates yielded the misleading information that this lactone possessed five carbon atoms[14] instead of the six actually present. A partial synthesis of physiologically active pantothenic was effected by condensing β-alanine ester with impure lactone obtained from a pantothenic acid concentrate.[15] This amazing information, obtained about a compound before it had been obtained in pure form, proved to be decisive in the ultimate isolation and synthesis of pantothenic acid.

In the meantime, Snell et al.[16] continued their investigations of the acidic compound required by lactic acid bacteria. In general their information paralleled that obtained by Williams and his coworkers. They[17] also succeeded in accomplishing a partial synthesis of physiologically active pantothenic acid and concluded that their factor was indeed identical with the pantothenic acid of Williams and his coworkers.[3a, 16, 17]

Norris and Ringrose[18] described in chicks a "pellagrous" dermatitis which was destined to play a key role in the isolation and characterization of pantothenic acid. The cure of the "pellagrous" condition was attributed

11 R. J. Williams and E. J. Rohrman, J. Am. Chem. Soc. 58, 695 (1936).
12 H. H. Weinstock, Jr., H. K. Mitchell, E. F. Pratt, and R. J. Williams, J. Am. Chem. Soc. 61, 1421 (1939).
13 H. K. Mitchell, H. H. Weinstock, Jr., E. E. Snell, S. R. Stanberry, and R. J. Williams, J. Am. Chem. Soc. 62, 1776 (1940).
14 R. J. Williams, H. H. Weinstock, Jr., E. Rohrmann, J. H. Truesdail, H. K. Mitchell, and C. E. Meyer, J. Am. Chem. Soc. 61, 454 (1939).
15 R. J. Williams, H. K. Mitchell, H. H. Weinstock, Jr., and E. E. Snell, J. Am. Chem. Soc. 62, 1784 (1940).
16 E. E. Snell, F. M. Strong, and W. H. Peterson, J. Am. Chem. Soc. 60, 2825 (1938).
17 E. E. Snell, F. M. Strong, and W. H. Peterson, J. Bacteriol. 38, 293 (1939).
18 L. C. Norris and R. C. Ringrose, Science 71, 643 (1930).

by these workers to vitamin B_2 or G. By the use of a heat-treated ration composed largely of yellow corn, middlings, and casein, Kline et al.[19] developed a basal ration which regularly produced dermatitis in chicks and was very useful in studies of a factor referred to as the chick antidermatitis vitamin. Using this technique for the quantitative determination of this vitamin, Woolley et al.[20] obtained evidence that it was a hydroxy acid. Further study indicated a close similarity between the properties of the chick antidermatitis vitamin and those of pantothenic acid. Like pantothenic acid, the chick antidermatitis vitamin contained β-alanine in its molecule. Moreover, these workers succeeded in producing a partial synthesis of physiologically active chick antidermatitis vitamin by coupling β-alanine with the acidic part of alkali-inactivated concentrates of the chick antidermatitis vitamin.[21, 22]

As a result of their investigations, Woolley et al.[21, 22] suggested that the chick antidermatitis vitamin was identical with pantothenic acid for the following reasons.

1. Both are acids composed of β-alanine with an hydroxy acid in amide linkage.

2. Both are labile to hot acid and alkali.

3. Both form heat-stable acetyl derivatives which distill at approximately the same temperature and pressure.

4. The solubilities in various solvents of the free acids and salts of both these vitamins are similar.

Jukes[23] fed a crude preparation of pantothenic acid, which he obtained from Williams, to chicks with dermatitis and cured them. Although his results are of limited significance because of impurity of the preparation, they did serve to strengthen the evidence of Woolley and his coworkers. In a later communication with a highly potent concentrate of pantothenic acid, also obtained from Williams, Jukes[24] was able to strengthen the evidence still further for the identity of pantothenic acid and the chick antidermatitis vitamin by the similarity in their dissociation constants and by the constancy in the ration of chick activity to yeast growth activity of the pantothenic acid preparations that he fed. Final proof of the identity of

[19] O. L. Kline, J. A. Keenan, C. A. Elvehjem, and E. B. Hart, J. Biol. Chem. 99, 295 (1932).

[20] D. W. Woolley, H. A. Waisman, O. Mickelsen, and C. A. Elvehjem, J. Biol. Chem. 125, 715 (1938).

[21] D. W. Wooley, H. A. Waisman, and C. A. Elvehjem, J. Am. Chem. Soc. 61, 977 (1939).

[22] D. W. Wooley, H. A. Waisman, and C. A. Elvehjem, J. Biol. Chem. 129, 673 (1939).

[23] T. H. Jukes, J. Am. Chem. Soc. 61, 975 (1939).

[24] T. H. Jukes, J. Biol. Chem. 129, 225 (1939).

the chick antidermatitis vitamin with pantothenic acid came with the synthesis of pantothenic acid.[3a, 4a, 25, 26]

Williams and Major[27] announced the synthesis of pantothenic acid which was made possible by the isolation from pantothenic acid concentrates of the lactone moiety in pure form. They named this compound pantoic lactone. The lactone and β-alanine were coupled to form pure pantothenic acid. Pure pantothenic acid thus was first prepared as a synthetic compound. Its preparation clarified its relation to the "filtrate factor" of the English workers[28, 29] who were also well along toward its isolation. They suggested that their factor and pantothenic acid were identical.[2] Pantothenic acid also seemed to be identical with factor 2 of Lepkovsky et al.[30]

B. CHEMICAL AND PHYSICAL PROPERTIES

Pantothenic acid is a pale-yellow viscous oil with a molecular weight of 219. It has weak basic properties. It has never been prepared in crystalline form, but its sodium, potassium, and calcium salts crystallize readily. It is generally distributed commercially as its calcium salt. It is readily soluble in water, ethyl alcohol, dioxane, and glacial acetic acid.[31] It is somewhat soluble in ether acetone and amyl alcohol and practically insoluble in benzene, chloroform, and the hydrocarbon solvents. It is hydrophilic and is adsorbed on charcoal but not on fuller's earth.[31] It is readily esterified Its methyl or ethyl esters are active for animals but have little activity for microorganisms. The vitamin activity of pantothenic acid is lost when the OH groups in the pantoic acid part of the molecule are esterified. The activity is regenerated by careful saponification.[31] Its acetyl derivative can be distilled at approximately 10^{-5} mm. Hg.[20]

Panthothenic acid is quite stable in neutral solution, but its activity is destroyed by hot acid or alkaline solutions. Under these conditions, it decomposes largely into pantoic acid or its lactone and β-alanine.

The vitamin is optically active, owing to an asymmetric carbon atom in pantoic lactone. Free pantothenic acid has a rotatory power $[\alpha]_D^{26} + 37.5$

[25] E. T. Stiller, J. C. Keresztesy, and J. Finkelstein, *J. Am. Chem. Soc.* **62,** 1779 (1940).

[26] E. T. Stiller, S. A. Harris, J. Finkelstein, J. C. Keresztesy, and K. Folkers, *J. Am. Chem. Soc.* **62,** 1785 (1940).

[27] R. J. Williams and R. T. Major, *Science* **91,** 246 (1940).

[28] T. F. Macrae, A. R. Todd, B. Lythgoe, C. E. Work, H. G. Hind, and M. M. E. Sadr, *Biochem. J.* **33,** 1681 (1939).

[29] B. Lythgoe, T. F. Macrae, R. H. Stanley, A. R. Todd, and C. E. Work, *Biochem. J.* **34,** 1335 (1940).

[30] S. Lepkovsky, T. H. Jukes, and M. E. Krause, *J. Biol. Chem.* **115,** 557 (1936).

[31] H. R. Rosenberg, Chemistry and Physiology of the Vitamins. Interscience Publishers, New York, 1945.

Its calcium salt is also dextrorotatory $[\alpha]_D^{26}$ + 24.3. It has an ionization constant of about 3.9×10^{-5}.[3a, 31]

C. CONSTITUTION

Pantothenic acid has the empirical formula $C_9H_{17}O_5N$. It consists essentially of two compounds, pantoic acid and β-alanine, combined in acid-amide linkage by the coupling of the carboxyl group of pantoic acid with the amino group of β-alanine. It has been assigned the following structure.

$$\underset{\overset{\displaystyle |}{CH_3}}{\overset{\overset{\displaystyle CH_3}{\displaystyle |}}{HOCH_2-C-CHOH-CO-NH-CH_2-CH_2-COOH}}$$

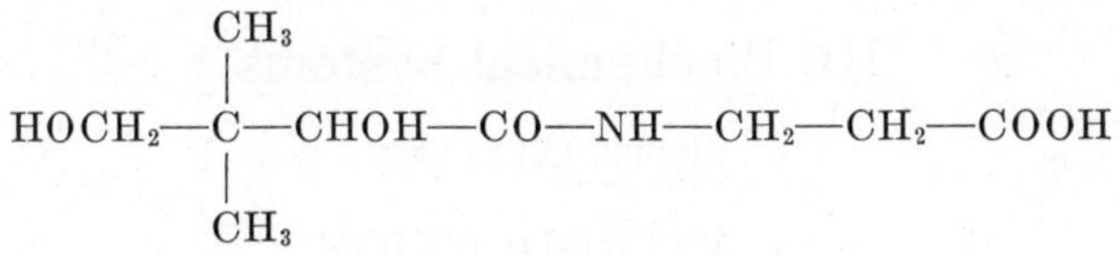

α-γ-Dihydroxy-β,β-dimethyl butyryl-β-alanine

Pantoic acid has two hydroxy groups, one of them in the α- and the other in the γ position. In acid solution, especially upon heating, it forms a lactone which is represented by the following structure.[3a, 4a, 31]

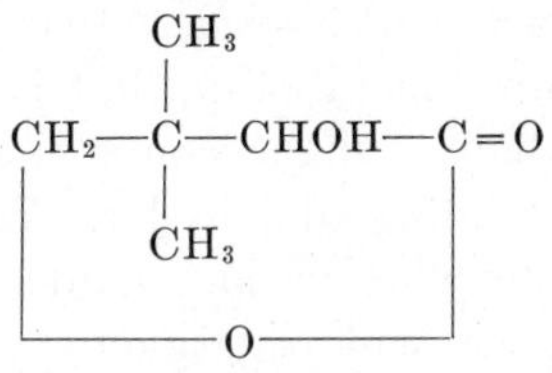

$$CH_2-\underset{\overset{\displaystyle |}{CH_3}}{\overset{\overset{\displaystyle CH_3}{\displaystyle |}}{C}}-CHOH-C=O$$

α-Hydroxy-β,β-dimethyl-γ-butyrolactone[31]

D. SYNTHESIS

A partial synthesis of pantothenic acid was effected before its structure was known. The total synthesis of pantothenic acid involves essentially the synthesis of pantoic acid or its lactone followed by its condensation with β-alanine. The synthesis of pantoic acid is carried out as follows.[31] Isobutyraldehyde is condensed with formaldehyde to give α,α-dimethyl-β-hydroxy-propionaldehyde. This compound is condensed with hydrocyanic acid or potassium cyanide in the presence of calcium chloride to form racemic α-hydroxy-β,β-dimethyl-γ-butyrolactone. This lactone may then be condensed with β-alanine to form racemic pantothenic acid. Both the racemic pantothenic acid and the pantoic lactone can be resolved by the fractional crystallization of their quinine salts.[31] The salts of quinine methohydroxide, quinidine methohydroxide, and cinchonine methohydroxide have also been used to resolve racemic mixtures of these compounds.[3a, 31]

Many methods are available for the condensation of pantoic lactone with β-alanine. A simple and effective method is the direct condensation of

β-alanine with the lactone. An approximately theoretical yield may thu
be obtained. This type of condensation has also been carried out with th•
dry sodium salt of β-alanine and yields directly the sodium salt of panto
thenic acid. Pantothenic acid has also been obtained by the condensatio𝗋
of the lactone with β-alanine benzyl ester followed by the catalytic hydro
genation of the pantothenic benzyl ester to free pantothenic acid.[3a, 4a, 31]

III. Biochemical Systems

FRITZ LIPMANN

A. INTRODUCTION

In 1943 Roger Williams wrote in *Advances in Enzymology*:[1] "The pre𝖾
sumption, in view of the known function of other vitamins, is that panto•
thenic acid fits into some enzyme system or systems which is essential t•
metabolism. What this enzyme system is or what these systems are is no•
known. There are some facts which suggest that pantothenic acid may b•
concerned with carbohydrate metabolism, but it is not certain."

At that time, other than a slight connection between carbohydrat•
storage and pantothenic acid,[2] found in Dr. Williams' laboratory, ther•
existed only one promising observation, namely, a demonstration of 𝖺
specific stimulation of pyruvic acid oxidation by pantothenic acid in *Proteu*
morgani by Dorfman *et al.*[3] in this country, and independently by Hills
in England. However, this observation remained an isolated fact for severa
years.

In 1946, during the study of the acetylation of sulfonamide in cell-fre
systems of pigeon liver, Lipmann[5, 6] observed that a coenzyme was in
volved in this reaction, which could not be replaced by any of the ther
known coenzymes. Independently, in the study of acetylcholine synthesi
in brain extracts, Feldberg and Mann[7] and Nachmansohn and Behrma𝗇
found that for acetylation of choline a stable cofactor seemed necessary
In view of the indication that a novel factor may be involved in acetylatio𝗇
reactions, an isolation of the coenzyme was started and after preliminar𝗒
purification it was shown, as illustrated by Fig. 1, that the cofactors fo•

[1] R. J. Williams, *Advances in Enzymol.* **3**, 253 (1943).
[2] R. J. Williams, W. A. Mosher, and E. Rohrmann, *Biochem. J.* **30**, 2036 (1936).
[3] A. Dorfman, S. Berlman, and S. A. Koser, *J. Biol. Chem.* **144**, 393 (1942).
[4] G. M. Hills, *Biochem. J.* **37**, 418 (1943).
[5] F. Lipmann, *J. Biol. Chem.* **160**, 173 (1945).
[6] F. Lipmann and N. O. Kaplan, *Federation Proc.* **5**, 145 (1946).
[7] W. Feldberg and T. Mann, *J. Physiol.* **104**, 411 (1946).
[8] D. Nachmansohn and M. Behrman, *J. Biol. Chem.* **165**, 551 (1946).

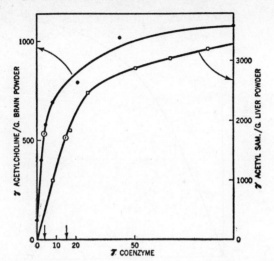

FIG. 1. Coenzyme A, the common activator of sulfanilamide acetylation in liver xtract and choline acetylation in brain extract.[9a] A highly purified preparation of ʃoA was used.

he acetylation of sulfonamide in liver and for the acetylation of choline in ▸rain were identical.[9] An effort was then made to purify the coenzyme more igorously, and preparations were obtained which appeared to be far nough advanced in purity to justify a chemical study of the product.

B. IDENTIFICATION OF PANTOTHENIC ACID AS PART OF COENZYME A

1. CoA[9b] ASSAY

As a convenient assay system for the coenzyme, the sulfanilamide ace-ylation system in liver was used.[10] In this enzyme system, sulfanilamide is cetylated in the presence of ATP and acetate. After autolysis of the ace-one-pigeon liver extract for 3 hours at room temperature, the originally resent CoA is completely decomposed. The autolyzed extract serves as poenzyme for measuring CoA. As a unit of CoA, such an amount was efined as giving a half reactivation of the apoenzyme system under spec-ied conditions. A standard curve obtained with this system is shown in ʹig. 2. It may be seen that between 0.5 and 1.5 units the curve is nearly a

[9] F. Lipmann and N. O. Kaplan, *J. Biol. Chem.* **162**, 743 (1946).

[9a] F. Lipmann, *Advances in Enzymol.* **6**, 231 (1946).

[9b] The following abbreviations are used: AMP = adenosine monophosphate; ADP = adenosine diphosphate; ATP = adenosine triphosphate; CoA = coenzyme A; P = phosphate; PP = pyrophosphate; and Ac = acetate, acetyl.

[10] N. O. Kaplan and F. Lipmann, *J. Biol. Chem.* **174**, 37 (1948).

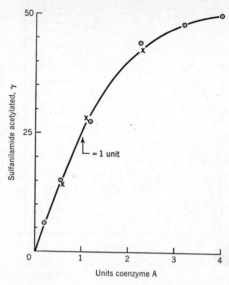

FIG. 2. Coenzyme A assay. Concentration-activity curves for coenzyme A prepa rations of different purity. The arrow indicates the half-reactivation point whic represents our unit. ○ = crude coenzyme, 0.25 unit per milligram; X = purifie coenzyme, 130 units per milligram.

straight line. A modified assay procedure with the same enzyme solutio using the color change caused by acetylation of 4-aminoazobenzene wa recently described by Handschumacher *et al.*[11] This color change may b measured directly. On the same principle, Bessman[11a] in our laboratory re cently worked out a more convenient procedure using the much more solu ble 4-aminoazobenzene sulfonate.

In view of the likelihood that a new coenzyme may contain one of th vitamins not covered then by coenzyme activity, the preparation wa analyzed for its vitamin content. Fortunately, in this task we were helpe by the experience of Dr. Roger Williams' laboratory with vitamin assa in general, and in particular with pantothenic acid assay. Dr. Beverl Guirard, who carried out the analysis of our coenzyme preparations, foun little or no activity with *Lactobacillus arabinosus.* However, after incubatio for a prolonged period with clarase and papain—at that time considere enzymes which liberated the "protein-bound" pantothenic acid of natura sources—a small amount started to appear, still only of the order of

[11] R. E. Handschumacher, G. C. Mueller, and F. M. Strong, *J. Biol. Chem.* **189,** 3: (1951).

[11a] S. P. Bessman and F. Lipmann, *Arch. Biochem. and Biophys.* **46,** 252 (1953 cf. also M. E. Jones, S. Black, R. M. Flynn, and F. Lipmann, *Biochim. et Biophy Acta* **12,** 143 (1953).

fraction of a per cent. This was, however, enough to make Dr. Guirard suspect that pantothenic acid might be present but might not be liberated effectively by the procedure used. She therefore tested for the presence of β-alanine in the acid hydrolyzate of the coenzyme preparations; indeed, the yeast assay showed β-alanine to be present in amounts corresponding to a pantothenic acid content of 11 %.[12, 13] In view of the rare occurrence of β-alanine, it was then considered almost certain that pantothenic acid was part of CoA.

Because of the instability of pantothenic acid to alkali or acid, chemical hydrolysis of CoA could not be applied for its liberation. Eventually the unhinging of pantothenic acid from its links in CoA was accomplished by enzymatic hydrolysis with intestinal phosphatase in conjunction with a particular peptidase present in bird liver,[14] in pig kidney,[15] and, to a lesser extent, in other organs.

2. RELATION OF THE ENZYMATICALLY DETERMINED CoA UNIT TO ITS PANTOTHENIC ACID CONTENT

A unit of CoA corresponds to 0.7 γ of pantothenic acid per milligram.[12, 13] This ratio has been of great value for assessment of purity; 1 μM. of CoA containing 1 μM. of pantothenic acid corresponds to 310 units of CoA. The molecular weight of the coenzyme was earlier determined by the Northrup diffusion method[16] to be around 800. Therefore, pure CoA was expected to contain approximately 400 units per milligram. Analytical data obtained with our purest preparations,[17] which will be discussed below in detail, indicate a molecular weight of 767 and a content of 410 units per milligram of pure CoA, in excellent agreement with earlier predictions.

3. ARSENOLYSIS ASSAY

During the work on isolation, we became aware that the assay system with crude pigeon liver extract is not specific for intact CoA, but responds to certain fragments.[18] This is due to enzymatic resynthesis of CoA from partially dephosphorylated coenzyme in the presence of ATP. Products which may be resynthesized to CoA have been obtained by controlled

[12] F. Lipmann, N. O. Kaplan, G. D. Novelli, L. C. Tuttle, and B. M. Guirard, *J. Biol. Chem.* **167**, 869 (1947).

[13] F. Lipmann, N. O. Kaplan, G. D. Novelli, L. C. Tuttle, and B. M. Guirard, *J. Biol. Chem.* **186**, 235 (1950).

[14] G. D. Novelli, N. O. Kaplan, and F. Lipmann, *J. Biol. Chem.* **177**, 97 (1949).

[15] L. Levintow and G. D. Novelli, *Abstr. Papers, Meeting Am. Chem. Soc. Atlantic City*, p. 33C (Sept. 14–19, 1952).

[16] G. D. Novelli, R. M. Flynn, and F. Lipmann, *J. Biol. Chem.* **177**, 493 (1949).

[17] J. D. Gregory, G. D. Novelli, and F. Lipmann, *J. Am. Chem. Soc.* **74**, 854 (1952).

[18] G. D. Novelli, N. O. Kaplan, and F. Lipmann, *Federation Proc.* **9**, 209 (1950).

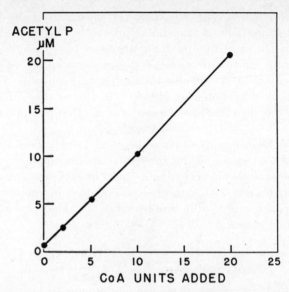

Fig. 3. Proportionality of arsenolysis with coenzyme A concentration. The acetyl phosphate values represent micromoles of acetyl phosphate decomposed in 15 minutes. Coenzyme A values are recorded in units per milliliter. Conditions: 0.05 M potassium arsenate; 0.1 tris(hydroxymethyl)aminomethane (pH 8.0); 22 μM. acetyl phosphate; 0.01 M cysteine; 0.002 M $MgCl_2$; 0.5 mg. of enzyme (from Lot L); ammonium sulfate fraction, between 70 and 90% saturation. Final volume 1 ml. (Drawn from Table IV in Stadtman et al.[21a])

degradation. This procedure has been useful in the study of the structure, in particular, in conjunction with assay procedures more specific for intact CoA. As such, the arsenolysis assay[19] has been very important.

In many microorganisms, in particular, in Clostridium kluyveri, an enzyme, transacetylase,[19, 20] is present which equilibrates acetyl phosphate and CoA to acetyl-CoA and phosphate. If arsenate is added to this system it equilibrates with arsenate, yielding acetyl arsenate, which decomposes immediately.[20] The arsenolysis of acetyl phosphate is CoA-dependent and may be measured easily by following acetyl phosphate decomposition with the hydroxamic acid reaction.[19] CoA can be removed from microbial extracts by shaking with Dowex-1 chloride.[19, 21] The Dowex-treated apoenzyme may be used for CoA assay. Over a wide range, the rate of acetyl phosphate disappearance is proportional with CoA concentration, as shown

[19] E. R. Stadtman, G. D. Novelli, and F. Lipmann, J. Biol. Chem. **191,** 365 (1951).
[20] E. R. Stadtman and H. A. Barker, J. Biol. Chem. **184,** 769 (1950).
[21] H. Chantrenne and F. Lipmann, J. Biol. Chem. **187,** 757 (1950).
[21a] E. R. Stadtman, M. Doudoroff, and F. Lipmann, J. Biol. Chem. **191,** 377 (1951).

in Fig. 3. In contrast to the pigeon liver assay, the arsenolysis assay is sharply specific for intact CoA.

4. Other CoA Assay Systems

Assay systems have recently been devised where CoA concentration may be measured spectrophotometrically in CoA-dependent DPN-reducing systems. Sanadi and Littlefield in Green's laboratory[22, 23] found that DPN reduction by ketoglutarate in a muscle extract is CoA-dependent, and this system may be used for assay. Stadtman[24] found that the acetaldehyde-DPN reaction in extracts of *Clostridium kluyveri* is CoA-dependent, and this system likewise represents a promising assay system.

C. THE CHEMISTRY OF COENZYME A

1. Phosphate and Adenylic Acid Content

Nearly pure preparations of CoA contain 1 mole of adenosine and 3 moles of phosphate per mole of pantothenic acid.[25] Only 1 of the 3 moles of phosphate is split off by phosphomonoesterases (prostate phosphatase).[17] The partially dephosphorylated product is easily rephosphorylated by ATP through a kinase present in pigeon liver extract (Novelli[26]). This fragment, therefore, assays in pigeon liver acetylation assay as CoA but is inactive in the arsenolysis assay. It may be reactivated for arsenolysis by incubation with ATP in pigeon liver extract. The monoester-linked phosphate is located at the ribose of adenosine (Baddiley[27]).

Kaplan discovered an enzyme which specifically attacks *a* nucleotides (-phospho-2-), but not the *b* form (-phospho-3-).[28] With this enzyme he studied the position of the monoester-linked phosphate in CoA and found that it corresponded to the *b* nucleotide series. Interestingly enough, the monoester phosphate in TPN corresponds to the *a* series, according to his analysis.

If CoA is treated with an enzyme preparation from potato similar to the nucleotide pyrophosphatase of Kornberg,[29] it is inactivated for arsenolysis, but not for crude pigeon liver assay.[26] The pH optimum for the

[22] H. Beinert, R. W. Van Korff, D. E. Green, D. A. Buyske, R. E. Handschumacher, H. Higgins, and F. M. Strong, *J. Am. Chem. Soc.* **74**, 854 (1952).
[23] D. R. Sanadi and J. W. Littlefield, *J. Biol. Chem.* **193**, 683 (1951).
[24] R. M. Burton and E. R. Stadtman, *J. Biol. Chem.* **202**, 873 (1953).
[25] W. H. DeVries, W. M. Govier, J. S. Evans, J. D. Gregory, G. D. Novelli, M. Soodak, and F. Lipmann, *J. Am. Chem. Soc.* **72**, 4838 (1950).
[26] G. D. Novelli, *in* Phosphorus Metabolism, Vol. I, p. 414. Johns Hopkins Press, Baltimore, 1951.
[27] J. Baddiley and E. M. Thain, *J. Chem. Soc.* **1951**, 3421.
[28] L. Shuster and N. O. Kaplan, *Federation Proc.* **11**, 286 (1952).
[29] A. Kornberg and W. E. Pricer, Jr., *J. Biol. Chem.* **182**, 763 (1950).

splitting of the pyrophosphate bridge in CoA, however, was found to be different from that of the pyridine nucleotides, being 4.5 rather than 7.[26] No phosphate, however, may be liberated with this enzyme. If the nucleotidase-treated preparation is exposed, subsequently, to phosphomonoesterase, then all three phosphates are split off and almost complete inactivation for all assay systems results. In analogy to the results of Kornberg on DPN and, in particular, on TPN with a similar enzyme,[29] it is concluded that the nucleotidase splits a pyrophosphate bridge between a phosphopantothenate derivative and diphosphoadenosine. The phosphopantothenate derivative, now identified as phosphopantothenylthioethanolamine,[30] was found to be resynthesized to CoA with ATP and pigeon liver enzyme.[31]

Evidence for the pyrophosphate bridge is further offered by the complete inactivation with intestinal phosphatase, which, by virtue of its phosphodiesterase activity, opens the bridge and dephosphorylates completely. The same effect obtains as mentioned, by a combination of dinucleotidase treatment and partial dephosphorylation.[27, 32]

The nature of the phosphate attachment to pantothenic acid has recently been settled definitely after pantothenate-2'-phosphate, pantothenate-4'-phosphate, the diphosphate, and the cyclic phosphate had been synthesized and made available for comparison.[26, 33] Baddiley chromatographically identified a fragment of CoA obtained by cautious alkaline hydrolysis with pantothenate-4'-phosphate. This observation had already made it most likely that the pyrophosphate bridge links between the 5' position on ribose and the 4' position on pantothenic acid.[27, 34, 35] Recently, Baddiley and Thain[36] have synthesized pantethine-4'-phosphate. This was established as a fragment of CoA by enzymatic synthesis to CoA in a pigeon liver fraction isolated by Levintow and Novelli[15] which acts specifically on phosphorylated pantethine.[36]

Final proof for the structure outlined was obtained recently by Hoagland and Novelli,[36a] who synthesized dephospho-CoA from ATP and synthetic pantetheine-4'-phosphate and showed equivalent liberation of pyrophosphate according to the following equation:

[30] E. E. Snell, G. M. Brown, V. J. Peters, J. A. Craig, E. L. Wittle, J. A. Moore, V. M. McGlohon, and O. D. Bird, *J. Am. Chem. Soc.* **72**, 5349 (1950).
[31] W. M. Govier and A. J. Gibbons, *Arch. Biochem. and Biophys.* **32**, 347 (1951).
[32] G. D. Novelli, J. D. Gregory, R. M. Flynn, and F. J. Schmetz, Jr., *Federation Proc.* **10**, 229 (1951).
[33] T. E. King and F. M. Strong, *J. Biol. Chem.* **189**, 315 (1951); **191**, 515 (1951).
[34] J. Baddiley and E. M. Thain, *J. Chem. Soc.* **1951**, 246.
[35] J. Baddiley and E. M. Thain, *J. Chem. Soc.* **1951**, 2253.
[36] J. Baddiley, E. M. Thain, G. D. Novelli, and F. Lipmann, *Nature* **171**, 76 (1953).
[36a] M. B. Hoagland and G. D. Novelli, *J. Biol. Chem.* **207**, 767 (1954).

$$\text{Pantetheine-4'-P} + \text{adenosine-P-P-P} \rightleftharpoons \text{Pantetheine-}$$
$$\text{4'-P-P-5-adenosine} \; (= \text{dephospho-CoA}) + \text{PP} \tag{1}$$

Dephospho-CoA was then converted to CoA with ATP.

$$\text{Pantetheine-4'-P-P-adenosine} + \text{ATP pantetheine-4'-}$$
$$\text{P-P-5-adenosine-3-P} \; (= \text{CoA}) \tag{2}$$

The enzymatic synthetis has been reviewed expertly by Novelli in the CoA Symposium at the Federation Meeting of 1953.[36b]

2. THE SULFUR-CONTAINING MOIETY

It was early observed that CoA preparations contained sulfur in disulfide linkage.[13, 37] The preparations gave a typical purple nitroprusside reaction for SH-compounds, but only after reduction, for example, by treatment with cyanide. The preparation in which the presence of pantothenic acid was discovered[12, 13] contained 1.97 % sulfur and 11 % pantothenic acid, corresponding to 1.2 moles of sulfur per mole of pantothenic acid.

Initially, however, so much attention was centered on the evaluation of the presence of pantothenic acid in this coenzyme that little attention was paid to the sulfur-containing part. Eventually, through a number of circumstances, information was gained on the nature of the compound as well as on its linkage to pantothenic acid. Very stimulatory in this respect was the discovery by Williams et al.[38] of a new growth factor for *Lactobacillus bulgaricus* (LBF). This factor was identified as a pantothenic acid derivative and a fragment of CoA.[39, 40] Brown et al. showed that intact CoA was inactive as their factor.[39] However, CoA could be activated by dephosphorylation with intestinal phosphatase. Very significant was the further observation by Snell's group that the bird liver enzyme, which we had found to be necessary for complete liberation of pantothenic acid from CoA, destroyed LBF activity. By following the lead of these observations on Snell's new factor, we obtained by degradation of CoA with intestinal phosphatase and subsequent chromatography[25] a product containing the pantothenic acid linked to a ninhydrin-reactive sulfur compound which, however, was not cystine, as had previously been tentatively assumed. Chromatographically, this degradation product behaved like LBF. A chromatogram of intestinal phosphatase-treated CoA is shown in Fig. 4.

[36b] G. D. Novelli, *Federation Proc.* **12**, 675 (1953).
[37] F. Lipmann, N. O. Kaplan, and G. D. Novelli, *Federation Proc.* **6**, 272 (1947).
[38] W. L. Williams, E. Hoff-Jørgensen, and E. E. Snell, *J. Biol. Chem.* **177**, 933 (1949).
[39] G. M. Brown, J. A. Craig, and E. E. Snell, *Arch. Biochem.* **27**, 473 (1950).
[40] R. A. McRorie, P. M. Masley, and W. L. Williams, *Arch. Biochem.* **27**, 471 (1950).

Independently, in a brilliant piece of work, Snell and his associates arrived,[30] by isolation and synthesis, at a final identification of the LBF fragment of CoA. They found it to be N-pantothenylthioethanolamine; this compound was named "pantetheine" for the sulfhydryl form and "pantethine" for the disulfide form. A new and relatively simple method of synthesis for pantethine was recently described by Baddiley.[41, 42]

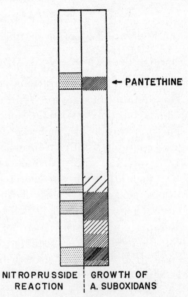

NITROPRUSSIDE   GROWTH OF
REACTION   A. SUBOXIDANS

FIG. 4. Paper chromatogram of phosphatase-treated coenzyme A (cf. ref. 18)· The right-hand side represents the assay for pantothenic acid in all bound forms, using *Acetobacter suboxydans*.
The left-hand side represents the disulfide test by cyanide-nitroprusside spray.

By this identification at the same time, the sulfur compound in CoA was identified as the decarboxylation product of cysteine, also known under the name of "cysteamine", a short and handy name. The synthesis of pantetheine has been studied by various workers and appears to involve a condensation of pantothenic acid with cysteine. This is followed by decarboxylation of the pantothenyl-cysteine to yield pantethine eventually.

Some differences between the synthetic compounds and substances isolated from natural materials have been explained through a cross-linking of various SH- compounds to reduced pantethine by simultaneous oxidation

[41] J. Baddiley and E. M. Thain, *J. Chem. Soc.* **1951**, 3425.
[42] J. Baddiley and E. M. Thain, *J. Chem. Soc.* **1952**, 800.
[43] G. Medes and N. Floyd, *Biochem. J.* **36**, 2591 (1942).

in the process of isolation.[44] Such S-S- cross-links also contaminate all cruder CoA preparations.[17, 45]

Govier and Gibbons[31] obtained an independent support for the presence of pantethine in CoA. They found that aged pigeon liver extract could synthesize small but appreciable amounts of CoA from synthetic pantethine + ATP. Levintow and Novelli[15] in this laboratory recently found that such a synthesis occurs much more readily in very fresh liver extracts.

3. ACETYL-CoA

The analysis of various acetylation systems involving CoA had led to the recognition of its acetyl carrier function, a shuttling back and forth between acetyl donor and acceptor systems.[19, 46, 47] Recently, Lynen and Reichert[48, 49] succeeded in isolating acetyl-CoA in substance from yeast. They furthermore became aware of the possibility that the SH-group in CoA[13, 25] may be the point of attachment of the acetyl group. In confirmation, they could show in a brilliant piece of work that acetyl-CoA, which is nitroprusside negative, becomes SH-positive by such alkali treatment as is known to split the mercaptoesters. The nature of the acetyl-S-CoA link was further verified by the lability of the acetyl group in CoA to mercuric salt, a rather specific property of mercaptoesters.[50] It reminds one interestingly enough of the similar behavior of enol phosphate, which likewise is easily split catalytically by mercuric salts.

Lynen and Reichert also showed that, with the acceptor enzyme of liver extract, acetyl-CoA donates acetyl to sulfanilamide, and that SH- is liberated by this enzymatic acetyl transfer. Acetyl-CoA was furthermore identified as acetyl donor in citric acid synthesis.[51]

More recently, Stadtman,[24] in continuation of earlier experiments on transacetylase, worked out a rather efficient enzymatic method for the preparations of acetyl-CoA. He used acetyl phosphate with the transacetylase, for example, of *Clostridium kluyveri*, as the acetyl donor system, with which CoA can be preparatively acetylated. Acetyl phosphate is destroyed by heating at a pH of 4.5, whereas acetyl-CoA is stable. M. E. Jones, in our laboratory, found that the product of enzymatic acetylation,

[44] G. M. Brown and E. E. Snell, *Proc. Soc. Exptl. Biol. Med.* **77**, 138 (1951).
[45] J. D. Gregory and F. Lipmann, *Abstr. Papers 12th Intern. Congr. Pure and Appl. Chem. New York*, p. 74 (1951).
[46] T. C. Chou, G. D. Novelli, E. R. Stadtman, and F. Lipmann, *Federation Proc.* **9**, 160 (1950).
[47] E. R. Stadtman, *Federation Proc.* **9**, 233 (1950).
[48] F. Lynen and E. Reichert, *Angew. Chem.* **63**, 47 (1951).
[49] F. Lynen, E. Reichert, and L. Rueff, *Ann.* **574**, 1 (1951).
[50] G. Sachs, *Ber.* **54**, 1849 (1921).
[51] S. Ochoa, J. R. Stern, and M. C. Schneider, *J. Biol. Chem.* **193**, 691 (1951).

TABLE I[17]

	Calcd., %[a]	Found, %	Ratio
Pantothenic acid	28.6	26.8 (enzymatic assay)	1
		25.6 (microbiological)	
Adenine	17.6	17.0 (spectrophotometric)	1.05
Phosphorus (total)	12.12	10.6	2.83
Monoester phosphorus[b]	—	3.6	0.96
Sulfur	4.18	4.13	1.07

[a] Pantothenic acid, 2-mercaptoethylamine, 3-phosphoric acid, adenosine, −5H₂O; molecular weight 767.
[b] Liberated by prostate phosphomonoesterase.

acetyl-CoA, may be purified easily by resin chromatography. She obtained in this manner practically pure acetyl-CoA.

A very convenient method for a preparation of various CoA derivatives was recently described by Simon and Shemin,[51a] using the great affinity of SH-compound for acid anhydrides. For example, they synthesized, in aqueous solution, succinyl-SCoA from CoA-SH and succinic anhydride in excellent yield, using only a slight excess of anhydride. This reaction is very generally applicable.

4. THE STRUCTURE OF CoA

Analytical data on a nearly pure CoA preparation[17] are represented in Table I. The data agree with the composition of pantothenic acid, thio-ethanolamine, adenosine, and three phosphates, minus 5H₂O. In conjunction with this analytical data, the results of structural analysis presented in the previous paragraphs lead to the formulation shown in Fig. 5. (This structure is now definitely established by analysis as well as by enzymatic synthesis.)

To summarize, the biosynthesis of CoA from pantothenic acid involves the following steps:

1. Pantetheine, by condensation of pantothenic acid and cysteine, with subsequent decarboxylation.

2. Phosphorylation of pantetheine in the 4′-position by ATP. This reaction is catalyzed by Kinase I, which was partially purified from pigeon liver extract.

3. Condensation of pantetheine-4′-phosphate and ATP, with elimination of inorganic pyrophosphate, by a condensing enzyme in pigeon liver extract. The resulting product is "dephospho-CoA" also obtained from CoA by dephosphorylation with prostate phosphomonoesterase.

4. The final step is catalyzed by Kinase II, which phosphorylates dephospho-CoA in the 3-position on the ribose part of adenylic acid.

[51a] E. J. Simon and D. Shemin, J. Am. Chem. Soc., **75**, 2590 (1953).

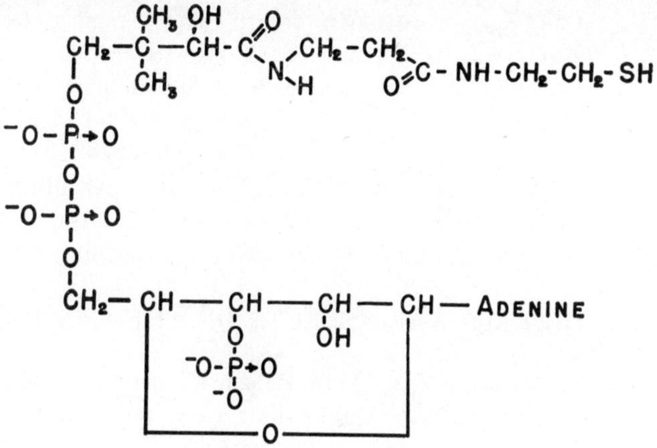

FIG. 5. The structure of coenzyme A.

For further details, the reader is referred to Novelli's review in the CoA Symposium of the Federation Meeting, 1953.[51b]

5. PREPARATION OF CoA

The early preparations of CoA were obtained from pig liver.[12, 13, 37] In view of the easy destruction of CoA by autolysis, only very fresh pig liver can be used for the isolation. A rather complicated procedure was originally used, involving metal precipitation and acetone fractionation.[13] More recently, in collaboration with Dr. Evans, Dr. Govier, and Mr. DeVries of the Upjohn Research Laboratory, a simpler procedure was elaborated for isolation of CoA from cultures of *Streptomyces fradiae*.[25] The coenzyme was repeatedly adsorbed from acid solution on charcoal and eluted with acetone-ammonia.

Final purification was worked out by Gregory after it had been observed that a reduction step had to be included in the purification procedure to remove cross-linking from sulfur compounds.[45] The best preparation described in the previous paragraph was obtained by following up the adsorption procedure with reduction with zinc and hydrochloric acid and mercury precipitation.[17] After removal of mercury by hydrogen sulfide, the solution was chromatographed over Duolite-CS 100. Most of the impurities were removed by washing with hydrochloric acid, and the coenzyme was eventually eluted with water and freeze-dried.

More recently, Green, Strong,[22] and their group at the University of Wisconsin described a relatively simple, promising isolation procedure. Yeast was used as the starting material, and preliminary purification was

[51b] G. D. Novelli, *Federation Proc.* **12**, 675 (1953).

carried out by charcoal adsorption as described by Gregory *et al.*[17, 25] The prepurified material was then coprecipitated with reduced glutathione by the Hopkins reagent, cuprous oxide. The glutathione was removed by resin chromatography. In this manner, in a rather good yield, 75 % pure CoA was obtained.

A very good preparation of CoA, averaging 360 units per milligram (about 75 to 80 % pure) is now commercially available from the Pabst Laboratories, 1037 McKinley Avenue, Milwaukee 3, Wisconsin.

D. SOME NUTRITIONAL ASPECTS OF THE CoA PROBLEM

1. ASSAY OF PANTOTHENIC ACID BASED ON THE METHODOLOGY OF PANTOTHENIC ACID LIBERATION FROM CoA

The difficulties encountered with the liberation of pantothenic acid from its coenzyme, which have been described above, eventually resulted in the elaboration of the dual enzyme treatment.[14] Since, as shown in Table II, fresh tissues contain almost solely CoA and very little free pantothenic acid, it is obvious that the methodology for liberation of pantothenic acid from the coenzyme should be generally applicable for microbiological determination of pantothenic acid in natural sources, including foodstuffs. With the treatment by intestinal phosphatase and liver enzyme, the first fully satisfactory method for a complete liberation of pantothenic acid from natural sources was developed as an accidental result of our studies on CoA. The data in Table III may serve as an example of the effectiveness of the method for reaching all bound pantothenic acid.

The importance of this method for the evaluation of true pantothenic acid content in food is amplified by the work of Neilands and Strong,[52] who compared the old clarase-papain procedure with the phosphatase-liver enzyme method (cf. Table III). They found that the new method yielded in some cases up to four times as much pantothenic acid as the old one. A somewhat troublesome high blank in the liver enzyme has recently been eliminated by Novelli and Schmetz[53] through Dowex treatment of the liver enzyme solution. Recent work in our laboratory by Levintow indicates that pig kidney may even be a better and more convenient source of the second enzyme than bird liver.

Earlier discrepancies of pantothenic acid values obtained with the chick and microbiological assays[54] have now found their explanation in the difference in availability of CoA-bound pantothenic acid. Hegsted and Lip-

[52] J. B. Neilands and F. M. Strong, *Arch. Biochem.* **19**, 287 (1948).
[53] G. D. Novelli and F. J. Schmetz, Jr., *J. Biol. Chem.* **192**, 181 (1951).
[54] T. H. Jukes, *Biol. Symposia* **12**, 253 (1947).

TABLE II[14]

RELATION OF COENZYME A ACTIVITY AND PANTOTHENIC ACID CONTENT IN ORGANS
OF RABBIT

(All values are given per gram of wet weight of tissue)

		Pantothenic acid, γ			
	Coenzyme A, units			Bound	
		Free	Total	Found	Calculated[a]
Liver	112	1.2	75	74	73
Heart	26.4	3.3	20.7	17	17
Kidney	49.5	2.7	45	42	32
Brain (cortex)	40.5	3.0	18	15	26
Testes	25.6	6.0	20.4	14	17
Muscle (skeletal)	6	5.1	9.9	5	4

[a] Calculated by multiplication of the unit value by 0.65, the average pantothenic acid content in micrograms of a unit of coenzyme A.

mann[55] could show that the chick almost completely utilized CoA-bound pantothenic acid. Therefore, in contrast to most microorganisms, the animal body is able to utilize the vitamin fully when bound in the coenzyme.

2. THE ALKALI STABILITY OF "NATURAL PANTOTHENIC ACID"

It has been observed by various workers that natural pantothenic acid in tissues and other fresh material resists alkali treatment much better than free pantothenic acid, where the peptide bond between the β-alanine and pantoic acid is very labile to alkali (Jukes[54]). Strong and King,[33] and, independently, Baddiley,[35] have now explained this discrepancy. They show that phosphorylation of pantothenic acid confers to it resistance to alkali. Since pantothenic acid in CoA is phosphorylated, the alkali resistance now is explained through the presence of the phosphorylated pantothenic acid derivative coenzyme A.

E. SPLIT PRODUCTS OF CoA AS MICROBIAL GROWTH FACTORS

In two instances a growth factor has been identified as a fragment of CoA. These are the *Acetobacter suboxydans* factor (PAC) of Cheldelin[16, 56] and the *Lactobacillus bulgaricus* factor (LBF, pantethine), of Snell and Williams.[30, 39, 40] In a stricter sense, both factors are rather to be termed growth stimulants. *Acetobacter* will grow relatively easily with pantothenic acid, although with a pronounced lag period. The *Lactobacillus bulgaricus* family responds poorly or not at all to small amounts of pantothenic acid but will grow if rather large quantities are supplied. Since both organisms

[55] D. M. Hegsted and F. Lipmann, *J. Biol. Chem.* **174**, 89 (1948).
[56] T. E. King, I. G. Fels, and V. H. Cheldelin, *J. Am. Chem. Soc.* **71**, 131 (1949).

TABLE III

PANTOTHENIC ACID RELEASED FROM BIOLOGICAL MATERIALS BY VARIOUS TREATMENTS[52]

Enzyme treatment	Liver enzyme plus phosphatase[a]		Mylase P	None
	Pantothenic acids, γ/g.			
	A	B		
Spinach	27.5	30.0	11.5	7.2
	21.8	23.6	11.4	7.8
Alfalfa	41.0	65.0	43.8	29.8
	46.8	58.7	37.9	26.0
Wheat germ meal	30.0	30.0	15.2	14.6
	29.3	28.6	17.2	17.3
Beef, dried	33.3	46.6	16.7	6.9
	45.6	64.6	17.3	8.9
Whole liver powder	365	400	70.0	50.4
	343	386	67.5	53.7
Yeast, dried	400	400	106	57.0
	443	486	100	58.8
Vitab	385	400	132	121
	418	436	138	130
Egg, fresh	50.7	53.3	13.0	9.9
	49.0	57.4	12.6	10.4
Sardines, Pacific[b]	15.0	12.5	6.0	5.0
	18.4	19.3	6.0	3.9
Tuna	—	—	4.2	1.1
	8.4	14.3	4.2	1.1
Sardines, Atlantic	12.0	11.5	4.7	4.1
	17.1	19.0	4.7	4.0
Mackerel, Pacific	11.3	11.0	4.7	2.7
	15.9	16.8	4.7	2.5
Salmon	15.7	—	5.8	4.8
	20.9	26.4	5.8	4.8
Mackerel, Atlantic	11.3	—	3.1	2.7
	12.0	19.3	3.1	2.4

[a] In column B the substrate concentration was half that in column A. Enzyme concentrations were identical.

[b] All the fish samples assayed were canned products.

convert pantothenic acid into its functional form, namely, CoA, the growth effect of the CoA fragment indicates the lack of one of the enzymatic reactions needed for the synthesis of CoA from free pantothenic acid. The sluggish response of both *Acetobacter suboxydans* an *Lactobacillus bulgaricus* to pantothenic acid indicates a certain capacity for adaptive formation of the lacking enzymatic step.

1. PANTOTHENIC ACID CONJUGATE OF CHELDELIN

In the case of the *Acetobacter suboxydans* factor, Cheldelin showed that it is destroyed by intestinal phosphatase.[56] It was found, subsequently, that intact CoA as well as some of its fragments are active, and it was confirmed that intestinal phosphate destroys activity or reduces it to a low level. During studies on the constitution of CoA, as already mentioned, Novelli studied the *Acetobacter* factor in detail.[26] He found that, if the organism had been grown on CoA, it would respond best to intact CoA. But if it had been grown on partially decomposed CoA, it would respond most actively to a phosphorylated fragment obtained by treatment with potato dinucleotidase, by mild acid hydrolysis, or with an enzyme obtained from snake venom. This *Acetobacter* factor has now been identified as phospho-4-pantethine which was recently synthesized by Baddiley and Thain and biologically tested in this laboratory.[36]

Acetobacter is the only organism known so far which responds reasonably well to all bound forms of pantothenic acid. This organism has frequently been used in this laboratory for a qualitative detection of pantothenic acid in all bound forms, e.g., in chromatograms of CoA fragments.[25]

2. PANTETHINE (*Lactobacillus bulgaricus* FACTOR)

In 1947, Williams *et al.*[38] discovered a new growth factor for *Lactobacillus bulgaricus*. Snell *et al.*[39] and Williams *et al.*[40] independently observed that large amounts of pantothenic acid would replace the factor. In their concentrates, pantothenic acid was found to be present in a bound form. As mentioned already, Snell and his group compared this factor with CoA.[39] They found that the intact coenzyme was inactive. But dephosphorylation with intestinal phosphatase liberated a very active compound comparable to their factor. On the other hand, treatment with liver enzyme completely destroyed the activity of the LBF. This group of organisms, therefore, seemed to be lacking in the enzyme which synthesizes the link to pantothenic acid, specifically hydrolyzed by the liver enzyme. This is now known to be a peptidic link between pantothenic acid carboxyl and the amino group of cysteamine. In summary, the anomaly in *Lactobacillus bulgaricus* appears to be the lack of or slow adaptation to the enzymatic synthesis of the link between thioethanolamine (or rather cysteine; cf. above) and the carboxyl group of pantothenic acid.

In conclusion, it seems worth mentioning that the two fragments of CoA, which are active as growth factors, mirror, in the direction of synthesis, the two degrading steps essential for the liberation of pantothenic acid from CoA. The *Acetobacter* factor is destroyed by intestinal phosphatase and the *Lactobacillus bulgaricus* factor by bird liver "peptidase," the combination of which is necessary to liberate pantothenic acid fully for the assay with *Lactobacillus arabinosus* or *Proteus morgani*.[14]

F. THE METABOLIC FUNCTION OF CoA

1. Distribution of CoA

All living material so far tested for CoA was found to contain this coenzyme in variable amounts.[10, 14] The highest content in animal tissues is found in the liver. Rat liver assays from 100 to 250 units per gram wet weight. In Table II, which appears on p. 611, the enzymatically assayed CoA content of various animal tissues is compared with the total amount of pantothenic acid obtained by *Lactobacillus arabinosus* assay after double enzyme treatment. There is very little free pantothenic acid present in fresh tissues.[14] Practically all pantothenic acid was found to be bound as CoA. This may be seen from the close correspondence of the amounts of pantothenic acid determined directly by microbial assay and calculated from CoA assay by multiplying with the pantothenic acid factor of 0.7 γ per unit of CoA. It appears, therefore, unlikely that there is another pantothenic acid-containing coenzyme in animal tissue.

It is noteworthy that the adrenal gland is next highest to liver in CoA content. The well-known relationship between pantothenic acid and adrenal cortex[57, 58] is further emphasized by the decline of CoA in adrenal gland in pantothenic acid deficiency,[59] as shown in Fig. 6. A similar depletion of CoA in pantothenic acid deficiency in other organs is shown in the same figure for liver, heart, and kidney. With *Lactobacillus arabinosus*, the depletion of CoA in a pantothenic acid-deficient organism is shown in Table IV.[60] It is compared with an increase in coenzyme of the same organism after incubation with pantothenic acid. Very large amounts of CoA are present in microorganisms carrying out 4-carbon fermentations. *Clostridium butylicum* contains 1000 units per gram dry weight. *Clostridium kluyveri* contains 500 units per gram. Some examples of the CoA content in plants are shown in Table V.

It was to a large extent the early recognized presence of CoA in all living matter which made us expect that this coenzyme had to fulfill important functions in intermediary metabolism.

[57] A. F. Morgan, *Vitamins and Hormones*. **9**, 162 (1951).
[58] E. P. Ralli, *Trans. 1st Conf. on Adrenal Cortex, New York*, p. 159 (1949).
[59] R. E. Olson and N. O. Kaplan, *J. Biol. Chem.* **175**, 515 (1948).
[60] G. D. Novelli and F. Lipmann, *Arch. Biochem.* **14**, 23 (1947).

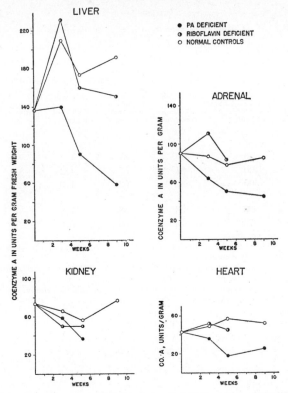

Fig. 6. Changes in the coenzyme A content of liver, adrenal, heart, and kidney in rats on normal, riboflavin-deficient, and pantothenic acid-deficient diets. Coenzyme A content in units per gram of fresh weight of tissue plotted against the time on the diet in weeks. Each point represents the mean value for pooled tissues from two rats.

2. ACETYL AND ACYL TRANSFER

CoA was discovered during a study which was essentially undertaken to elucidate the nature of the active acetate.[5] Isotope work had indicated a great variety of synthetic reactions with the mysteriously reactive acetyl as starting material.[61] This is illustrated by Fig. 7.[62]

Then a connection of CoA with a great variety of primary processes involved in acetyl transfer soon indicated that the coenzyme may act as an acetyl carrier.[63-66] This view was substantiated through a separation of

[61] K. Bloch, *Physiol. Revs.* **27**, 574 (1947).

[62] F. Lipmann, *Harvey Lectures, Ser.* **XLIV**, 99 (1948–1949).

[63] N. O. Kaplan and F. Lipmann, *Federation Proc.* **7**, 163 (1948).

[64] R. C. Millican, S. M. Rosenthal, and H. Tabor, *J. Pharmacol. Exptl. Therap.* **97**, 4 (1949).

[65] G. D. Novelli and F. Lipmann, *J. Biol. Chem.* **182**, 213 (1950).

TABLE IV[60]
COENZYME SYNTHESIS IN *L. arabinosus*
(Pantothenic acid was determined microbiologically. Coenzyme was determined enzymatically.)

No.	Pantothenic acid added to growth medium, γ/100 ml.	Units coenzyme	Per gram dry weight of harvested cells			
			Pantothenic acid bound in coenzyme, calculated[a]	Yield of coenzyme, %	Free pantothenic acid	Bound pantothenic acid[b]
1	1	0[c]	—	—		
	50	44	31	4.8		
	100	81	57	4.2		
	500	89	62	1.0		
2	30	54	38	7.8	7	33
	75	94	66	5.8	7	51

[a] This value is calculated by multiplying the number of coenzyme units with the constant factor of 0.7 γ of pantothenic acid per unit of coenzyme.

[b] Bound pantothenic acid is determined after liberation through incubation with a mixture of acetone pigeon liver extract and intestinal phosphatase. This enzyme mixture was shown to liberate pantothenic acid from coenzyme A. Intact coenzyme does not test as pantothenic acid microbiologically.

[c] Too little to be determined accurately.

TABLE V[10]
COENZYME A IN PLANT MATERIAL

	Units per gram fresh weight
Spinach	0.74
Tomato	1.3
Frozen peas	4.5
Wheat germ (commercial sample)	30
Royal jelly (bee)	0

CoA-requiring reactions into two distinct classes, namely, acetyl donor and acetyl acceptor enzyme systems.[67] Particularly useful for the identification of partial reactions in acetyl transfer was the separation of the various donor and acceptor enzymes present in pigeon liver extract by Chou in our laboratory. Very important, furthermore, was the recognition of an activating system in bacterial extract for acetyl phosphate to act as an acetyl donor.[19, 65] This enzymatic process of activation was identified with the transacetylase reaction of Stadtman and Barker.[19, 20] This reaction has been described in a previous paragraph as an assay system for intact CoA. The CoA dependence of the phosphate exchange of acetyl-bound and inorganic phosphate, as well as of the arsenolysis of acetyl

[66] M. Soodak and F. Lipmann, *J. Biol. Chem.* **175**, 999 (1948).

[67] T. C. Chou and F. Lipmann, *J. Biol. Chem.* **196**, 89 (1952).

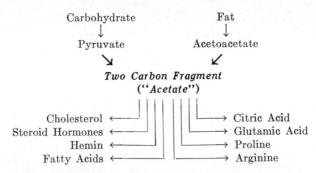

FIG. 7. Synthetic products derived from the 2-carbon fragment.

phosphate, led to the formulation of the enzyme-catalyzed process as essentially the conversion of acetyl phosphate to acetyl-CoA by an equilibration reaction; this observation furnished definite evidence for the existence of acetyl-CoA and its identity with "active" acetate.[62] This was further substantiated by the interchangeability of a great variety of donor systems to donate acetyl by way of CoA to the sulfanilamide acetyl-acceptor enzyme.[19, 21, 67, 68] It was shown that acetyl phosphate, through phosphotransacetylase,[19] pyruvate,[21, 69] and, furthermore, the ATP-CoA-acetate reaction of animal tissues and of yeast could furnish a common acetyl donor, acetyl-CoA, for the same acceptor system.[19, 21, 67]

The just-mentioned ATP-CoA-acetate reaction represents one of the most important acetyl donor reactions in animal tissues. Its mechanism remained for a long time obscure. It recently was clarified through the work of Lipmann et al.[70] The reaction was found unexpectedly to yield inorganic pyrophosphate according to an over-all reaction:

$$CoA + acetate + ATP \rightleftharpoons Acetyl\ CoA + AMP + pyrophosphate$$

The reaction is freely reversible.[70a] The finer mechanism of the reaction was recently further clarified through use of isotope exchange reactions by Jones et al.[70b]

Integrating the reactions just discussed, we are led to the construction of what may be called a general acetyl transfer field, separated into donor

[68] J. R. Stern, B. Shapiro, E. R. Stadtman, and S. Ochoa, J. Biol. Chem. **193**, 703 (1951).

[69] S. Korkes, A. Del Campillo, I. C. Gunsalus, and S. Ochoa, J. Biol. Chem. **193**, 721 (1951).

[70] F. Lipmann, M. E. Jones, S. Black, and R. M. Flynn, J. Am. Chem. Soc. **74**, 2384 (1952).

[70a] M. E. Jones, S. Black, R. M. Flynn, and F. Lipmann, Biochim. et Biophys. Acta **12**, 141 (1953); M. E. Jones, Federation Proc. **12**, 708 (1953).

[70b] M. E. Jones, F. Lipmann, H. Hilz, and F. Lynen, J. Am. Chem. Soc. **75**, 3285 (1953).

DONOR SYSTEMS
TRANSACETYLASES:

ACCEPTOR SYSTEMS
ACETOKINASES:

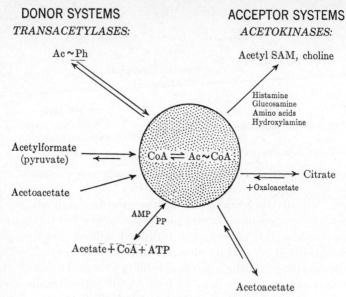

FIG. 8. The acetyl transfer system.

and acceptor territories, which are bridged by the acetyl-CoA carrier system. This is illustrated by Fig. 8.[67]

As mentioned, a final confirmation and amplification was obtained by Lynen and Reichert[48, 49] when they isolated acetyl-CoA from yeast. Of great importance is their finding that the SH- group of CoA is the functional group, that is to say, when functioning, CoA shuttles back and forth between sulfhydryl- and thioacetyl-CoA. This explains the long-known need of large amounts of SH-compounds like cysteine or glutathione to activate all acetylation systems.[10, 71] This activation occurs by conversion of inactive CoA disulfide into the active sulfhydryl-CoA.

It is quite remarkable that in CoA-linked acetyl the methyl end—we call this in our laboratory the "tail" end—as well as the carboxyl end or "head" is activated. Accordingly, we speak of "tail" or "head" condensations.[72] Thus citric acid synthesis is a tail condensation. Straightforward acetylation reactions are, of course, head condensations. One of the most interesting reactions in this respect is acetoacetate synthesis. Stadtman *et al.* showed that acetoacetate is synthesized by interaction of two active acetyls, i.e., two acetyl-CoA's, the head of one reacting with the tail of another.[73]

[71] D. Nachmansohn and A. L. Machado, *Neurophysiol.* **6,** 397 (1943).

[72] F. Lipmann, *Cold Spring Harbor Symposia Quant. Biol.* **13,** 127 (1948).

[73] E. R. Stadtman, M. Doudoroff, and F. Lipmann, *J. Biol. Chem.* **191,** 377 (1951).

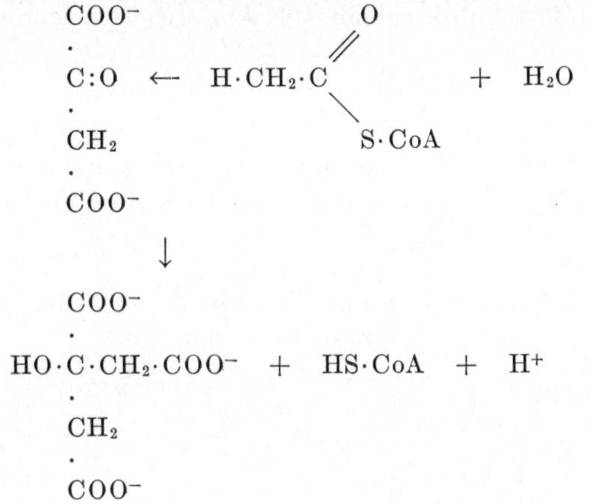

$$
\begin{array}{l}
\text{COO}^- \qquad\qquad \text{O} \\
\,\cdot \qquad\qquad\qquad \nearrow\!\!/ \\
\text{C:O} \quad \leftarrow \quad \text{H}\cdot\text{CH}_2\cdot\text{C} \qquad\qquad + \quad \text{H}_2\text{O} \\
\,\cdot \qquad\qquad\qquad\quad \searrow \\
\text{CH}_2 \qquad\qquad\qquad \text{S}\cdot\text{CoA} \\
\,\cdot \\
\text{COO}^-
\end{array}
$$

$$\downarrow$$

$$
\begin{array}{l}
\text{COO}^- \\
\,\cdot \\
\text{HO}\cdot\text{C}\cdot\text{CH}_2\cdot\text{COO}^- \;+\; \text{HS}\cdot\text{CoA} \;+\; \text{H}^+ \\
\,\cdot \\
\text{CH}_2 \\
\,\cdot \\
\text{COO}^-
\end{array}
$$

Fig. 9. Citric acid synthesis from acetyl-CoA and oxalacetate.

This reaction has now been fully clarified by the work of Lynen and his group[73a], by parallel work in Green's laboratory[73b] and by Stern and del Campillo in Ochoa's laboratory.[73c] The reaction is formulated as follows:

$$\text{CH}_3\cdot\text{CO}\cdot\text{S}\cdot\text{CoA} \;+\; \text{CH}_3\cdot\text{CO}\cdot\text{S}\cdot\text{CoA}$$

$$\rightleftharpoons \text{CH}_3\cdot\text{CO}\cdot\text{CH}_2\cdot\text{CO}\cdot\text{S}\cdot\text{CoA} \;+\; \text{HS}\cdot\text{CoA}$$

The equilibrium favors greatly the split of acetoacetyl-S-CoA + CoA-SH to two moles of acetyl-S-CoA, the "thioclastic split" of Lynen.[73d] In the process of fatty acid synthesis the condensation is followed by DPN-linked hydrogenation of acetoacetyl-CoA to β-hydroxybutyryl-CoA. The β-hydroxybutyryl-CoA, unlike the free l-compound, belongs to the d-series.[73e] It now is dehydrated to crotonyl-CoA, which then is hydrogenated by a flavin enzyme to butyryl-CoA. The butyryl-CoA condenses further with a new molecule of acetyl-CoA to the 6-carbon-β-keto acyl-CoA and DPN-linked hydration reduction; flavin-linked reduction and condensation continues until the 16- or 18-carbon chain is completed. Then stearyl or palmityl-CoA condenses with glycerophosphate to form the phospholipids[73f] and presumably with glycerol to yield neutral fat.

[73a] F. Lynen, *Harvey Lectures*, Ser. **XLVIII,** 210 (1954); F. Lynen, *Federation Proc.* **12,** 683 (1953).
[73b] H. Beinert, R. M. Bock, D. S. Goldman, D. E. Green, H. R. Mahler, S. Mii, P. G. Stansly, and S. J. Wakil, *J. Am. Chem. Soc.* **75,** 4111 (1953).
[73c] J. R. Stern and A. del Campillo, *J. Am. Chem. Soc.* **75,** 2277 (1953).
[73d] F. Lynen, *Federation Proc.* **12,** 683 (1953).
[73e] A. L. Lehninger and G. D. Greville, *J. Am. Chem. Soc.* **75,** 1515 (1953).
[73f] A. Kornberg and W. E. Pricer, Jr., *J. Am. Chem. Soc.* **74,** 1617 (1952).

Fatty acid oxidation proceeds by the same reaction chain in an opposite direction. For further reference the reader is referred to Lynen's *Harvey Lecture*[73g] and to papers by Lynen,[73h] and by Mahler[73i] in the Symposium on CoA. A list of CoA-linked reactions known at the present time is given in Tables VI and VII. It is quite notable that CoA is by no means exclusively

TABLE VI

COENZYME A-CATALYZED ENZYMATIC REACTIONS I

ACETYL TRANSFER

Type of reaction	Enzyme systems, extracts	References
Donor Systems		
ATP-CoA-acetate:		
ATP + CoA + Ac $\rightleftharpoons$ Ac-CoA +		5, 67, 70, 74
AMP + PP	Pigeon liver, yeast	75
Phosphotransacetylation:		
Ac-P + CoA $\rightleftharpoons$ Ac-CoA + P	*Cl. kluyveri, E. coli*	19, 20, 24
Formotransacetylation:		
Pyruvate + CoA $\rightleftharpoons$ Ac-CoA +	*E. coli*	21, 69
formate		
Transacetylase:		
Ac-CoA + butyrate $\rightleftharpoons$ Butyryl-	*Cl. kluyveri*	76
CoA + acetate		
Acetoacetate	Pigeon liver	77
Citrate in reverse	Pigeon liver	68
Acetaldehyde + CoA + DPN →	Glyceraldehyde dehydro-	78, 79, 80
Ac-CoA	genase, *E. coli, Cl. kluyveri*	
Pyruvate + CoA + DPN → Ac-	*E. coli, Strep. faecales*, heart	81, 82
CoA + DPNH$_2$ + CO$_2$	and muscle	
Acceptor Systems		
Acetokinases		
Aromatic amines	Pigeon liver	5
Choline	Rat brain	71
Histamine	Pigeon liver	64
Amino acids	*Cl. kluyveri*	20
Glucosamine	Pigeon liver	83
Condensation		
Acetoacetate	Pigeon liver	66, 73
Citric acid	Pigeon liver, yeast	68, 68
Pyruvate	*E. coli*	21, 84–86

[73g] F. Lynen, *Harvey Lectures*, Ser. **XLVIII**, 210 (1954).
[73h] F. Lynen, *Federation Proc.* **12**, 683 (1953).
[73i] H. R. Mahler, *Federation Proc.* **12**, 694 (1953).
[74] F. Lipmann and L. C. Tuttle, *J. Biol. Chem.* **159**, 21 (1945).
[75] F. Lipmann and L. C. Tuttle, *J. Biol. Chem.* **161**, 415 (1945).
[76] E. R. Stadtman, *J. Cellular Comp. Physiol.* **41**, *Suppl.* **1**, 89 (1953).

TABLE VII
COENZYME-CATALYZED REACTIONS II

Type of reaction	Acyl Transfer Enzyme systems, extracts	References
Succinyl Transfer		
Donor system		
Ketoglutarate + DPN + CoA →Succinate-CoA + DPNH₂ + CoA	Heart muscle	23, 87, 88
ATP-succinate	*E. coli*	89
Acceptor system		
Heme synthesis	Red cells hemolyzate	90
Benzoyl Transfer		
Hippuric synthesis	Rat liver	91, 92
Stearyl Transfer		
Phospholipid synthesis	Rat liver	93

Type of reaction	Complex Reaction Systems Enzyme systems	References
Fatty acid synthesis	*Cl. kluyveri* extracts	20, 94
Butyrate oxidation	*Cl. kluyveri* extracts	95
Fatty acid oxidation	Liver homogenate	96
Steroid and fat synthesis	Resting yeast cells	97
	Liver slices	98

[77] M. Soodak *in* Phosphorus Metabolism, Vol. I, p. 291. Johns Hopkins Press, Baltimore, 1951.

[78] J. Harting, *Federation Proc.* **10**, 195 (1951).

[79] G. B. Pinchot and E. Racker, *Federation Proc.* **10**, 233 (1951).

[80] R. M. Burton and E. R. Stadtman, cf. *in* Phosphorus Metabolism, Vol. I, p. 229. Johns Hopkins Press, Baltimore, 1951.

[81] S. Korkes *in* Phosphorus Metabolism, Vol. I, p. 259. Johns Hopkins Press, Baltimore, 1951.

[82] R. S. Schweet, M. Fuld, K. Cheslock, and M. H. Paul *in* Phosphorus Metabolism, Vol. I, p. 246. Johns Hopkins Press, Baltimore, 1951.

[83] T. C. Chou and M. Soodak, *J. Biol. Chem.* **196**, 105 (1952).

[84] F. Lipmann and L. C. Tuttle, *J. Biol. Chem.* **154**, 725 (1944).

[85] H. J. Strecker, H. G. Wood, and L. O. Krampitz, *J. Biol. Chem.* **182**, 525 (1950).

[86] M. F. Utter, C. H. Werkman, and F. Lipmann, *J. Biol. Chem.* **154**, 723 (1944).

[87] D. E. Green and H. Beinert, *in* Phosphorus Metabolism, Vol. I, p. 330. Johns Hopkins Press, Baltimore, 1951.

[88] S. Kaufman *in* Phosphorus Metabolism. Vol. I, p. 370. Johns Hopkins Press. Baltimore, 1951.

[89] G. D. Novelli, unpublished results.

[90] D. Shemin and R. Rittenberg, *J. Biol. Chem.* **192**, 315 (1951).

[91] H. Chantrenne, *J. Biol. Chem.* **189**, 227 (1951).

[92] R. W. McGilvery and P. P. Cohen, *J. Biol. Chem.* **183**, 179 (1950).

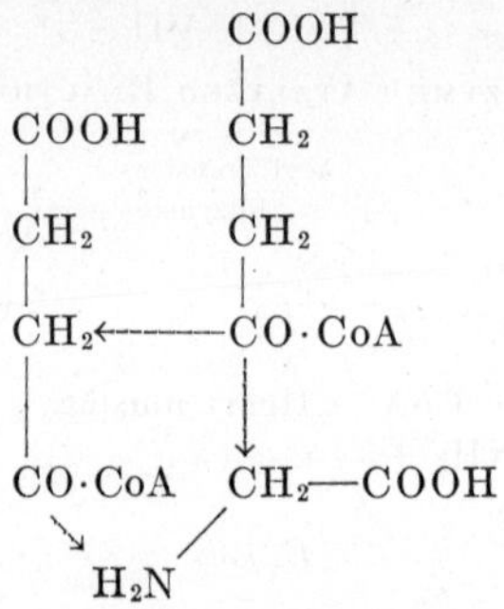

$$
\begin{array}{cc}
 & \mathrm{COOH} \\
 & | \\
\mathrm{COOH} & \mathrm{CH_2} \\
| & | \\
\mathrm{CH_2} & \mathrm{CH_2} \\
| & | \\
\mathrm{CH_2}\!\leftarrow\!\!-\!\!-\!\!-\!\mathrm{CO\cdot CoA} \\
| & \downarrow \\
\mathrm{CO\cdot CoA} & \mathrm{CH_2}\!-\!\mathrm{COOH} \\
\searrow & \diagup \\
 & \mathrm{H_2N}
\end{array}
$$

FIG. 10. The mechanism of pyrrole synthesis from succinyl-CoA and glycine. (From Shemin et al.[90])

an *acetyl* carrier but is more broadly used by the cell as an *acyl* transfer system.

Of major importance is the succinyl transfer function of CoA now studied by Green's group[87] and in Ochoa's laboratory.[88] The principal background of this reaction is the observation that ketoglutarate oxidation, e.g., in heart muscle extracts, is CoA-dependent.[23] An ATP-succinate reaction was shown by Kaufman[88] and has recently been also found by Novelli[89] to occur in *Escherichia coli*. Of particular interest appear the indications obtained by Shemin[90] that succinyl-CoA is likely to be a building stone of the pyrrole ring in the heme molecule. The tentative scheme of condensation of two succinyl-CoA's with glycine is reproduced here from Shemin's paper as an illustration. This scheme, if further substantiated, would confirm on the enzymatic level a previously suspected relationship of pantothenic acid to erythrocyte metabolism.[99]

3. FAT AND STEROID SYNTHESIS

The identification of acetate by isotope analysis as a precursor of fatty acid, cholesterol, and steroid hormones[61] indicated that the initial condensation reactions leading to these syntheses should belong to the acetyl

[93] A. Kornberg and W. E. Pricer, Jr., *Federation Proc.* **11**, 242 (1952).

[94] H. A. Barker *in* Phosphorus Metabolism, Vol. I, p. 204. Johns Hopkins Press, Baltimore, 1951.

[95] E. P. Kennedy, cf. *in* Phosphorus Metabolism, Vol. I, p. 240. Johns Hopkins Press, Baltimore, 1951.

[96] V. H. Cheldelin, A. P. Nygaard, O. M. Hale, and T. E. King, *J. Am. Chem. Soc.* **73**, 5004 (1951).

[97] H. P. Klein, *Federation Proc.* **10**, 209 (1951).

[98] H. P. Klein and F. Lipmann, *J. Biol. Chem.* **203**, 95 (1953); H. P. Klein and F. Lipmann, *J. Biol. Chem.* **203**, 101 (1953).

[99] R. J. Williams, R. E. Eakin, E. Beerstecher, Jr., and W. Shieve, The Biochemistry of the B Vitamins, p. 423. Reinhold Publishing Corp., New York, 1950.

TABLE VIII[98]
LIPID SYNTHESIS WITH CoA-POOR AND CoA-RICH RESTING CELLS
OF *Saccharomyces cerevisiae*[a]

Experiment	Pantothenic acid added, γ/ml.	CoA, units/g. cells	Net synthesis, steroid	Total lipid, mg./g. cells
1	0	37	−0.2	
	0.02	67	1.2	
2	0	47	0.2	2.4
	10	280	2.5	12.7
3	0	60	0.4	1.0
	10	310	1.8	8.6
4	0	57	0.2	1.2
	10	300	1.7	9.6
5	0	60	1.8	
	10	165	6.2	

[a] Identical pantothenic acid-deficient yeast samples were incubated with and without pantothenic acid for 2 to 3 hours, washed, and assayed for CoA. Subsequently, the yeast samples were incubated for 16 hours in an acetate-phosphate medium and analyzed for total lipid and steroid.

acceptor territory and derive acetyl from acetyl-CoA. In confirmation a still rather general connection between CoA and fat and steroid synthesis has evolved from studies in this laboratory with Klein.[97] By a comparison of CoA-poor and CoA-rich yeast samples (Table VIII), he showed that that fat and ergosterol synthesis runs parallel with CoA concentrations.

A similar parallel between fat and cholesterol synthesis and CoA levels was obtained in experiments with pantothenic acid-deficient rats.[98] The incorporation of isotopic acetate into fat and cholesterol in liver slices from normal and pantothenic acid-deficient animals is shown in Table IX.

TABLE IX[98]
$CH_3C^{14}OOH$ INCORPORATION INTO PANTOTHENIC ACID-DEFICIENT RAT LIVER SLICES

Group	Age, weeks	Pantothenic acid	CoA in liver, units/g.	Incorporation per gram of fatty acids, %	Liver cholesterol, %
1	6	+	98	14.9	7.1
		−	55	6.6	2.0
2	10	+	85	2.7	1.4
		−	62	0.4	0.4
3	11	+	85	7.4	0.9
		−	65	0.3	0.8

TABLE X[98]

INHIBITION OF LIPID SYNTHESIS BY PANTOYL-TAURYL-ANISIDIDE (PTA); PARTIAL RELEASE BY LBF

No.	PTA	LBF, mg./7.5 ml.	C.p.m./g. tissue Fatty acids	Cholesterol
1	—	—	2450	315
	—	0.5	2300	305
	$3.7 \times 10^{-3} M$	—	550	1000
	$3.7 \times 10^{-3} M$	0.5	825	245
2	—	—	1650	725
	—	1.0	2000	680
	$1.5 \times 10^{-3} M$	—	365	210
	$1.5 \times 10^{-3} M$	1.0	800	525

In view of the sensitivity of fat and steroid synthesis to various nutritional effects,[99a] results obtained by the use of a pantothenic acid antimetabolite are of significance. Klein found (cf. Table X) that pantoyl-tauryl-anisidide suppresses fat and steroid synthesis without appreciably influencing respiration. Under certain conditions he also could demonstrate an antagonism between pantethine[30] and pantoyl-tauryl-anisidide,[98] while free pantothenic acid appeared inactive.

In view of the much-discussed, rather specific relationship of pantothenic acid to the adrenal cortex, recently reviewed by A. F. Morgan[57] (cf. also ref. 58), a participation of CoA in the synthesis of steroids assumes special importance. As mentioned before, CoA is very abundant in the adrenal gland,[59] and it declines in pantothenic acid deficiency obviously in parallel with a depletion of steroids. A confirmation of this view seems to derive from the recent work of Cowgill and his associates,[100] who report that adrenal degeneration in pantothenic acid-deficient rats may be prevented by corticosterol.

G. CONCLUSION

Since the discovery of CoA, the function of pantothenic acid has been relegated to the metabolic territory of acetyl transfer in particular, and to that of acyl transfer in a more general sense. The relative abundance of pantothenic acid as CoA in living cells, e.g., up to 400 mg. of CoA per kilogram of liver is explained by the variety of the metabolic reactions mediated by this coenzyme. It appears that CoA is involved in the primary

[99a] S. Gurin, private communication.
[100] G. R. Cowgill, R. W. Winters, R. B. Schultz, and W. A. Krehl, International Congress on Vitamins (Havana, Cuba), report in The New York Times, January 26, 1952.

pathway of carbohydrate oxidation through citric acid synthesis and through its function in ketoglutarate and pyruvate oxidation. Through its function in citrate and ketoglutarate metabolism, furthermore, it is involved in the synthesis of various amino acids, like glutamic acid,[101] proline, and others from carbohydrate sources. Through succinyl transfer, it seems to enter into synthesis of the pyrrole ring in the heme molecule. Its role in acetoacetate synthesis and its well established role in fatty acid and cholesterol synthesis illustrate the instrumental part of the coenzyme in fat and steroid synthesis.

The unequivocal identification of acetyl-CoA with "active acetate" makes it appear legitimate to presume that any incorporation of isotopically marked acetate indicates the intermediacy of acetyl-CoA at some stage of the process. In this manner, by aiming at a closer recognition of the role of acetyl-CoA, an opening is found for an enzymatic understanding of such complex reactions as steroid, rubber, carotenoid, and terpene biosynthesis where acetate incorporation has been shown to occur. It is presumed that such structures are built up from 2-carbon residues exclusively, as was shown to be the case for cholesterol by Bloch's investigations.[102] James Bonner's work on the synthesis of latex in certain plants[103] indicates that the isoprene unit may be derived from 2-carbon residues.

It is, however, obvious that an incorporation of acetate into a biological structure has to be viewed judiciously because, for example, by milling through the citric acid cycle, acetate incorporates into a large number of molecular species, as amino acid, carbohydrates, and others. These, in their turn, represent building stones and will spread acetate secondarily into many compounds. Although initially acetyl-CoA participates in a derivation of such building stones, eventual synthetic mechanisms may easily not involve this coenzyme.

A few concluding remarks on the role of pantothenic acid in CoA appear in order. Comparing CoA structurally to the pyridine and flavin adenine dinucleotide, one finds that pantothenic acid, through its terminal hydroxyl on the one side and the carboxyl on the other, links the reactive base cysteamine through the pyrophosphate bridge to the adenyl moiety, the latter a common feature in many coenzymes. The question as to why in the case of CoA this "tie" molecule has to have such an unusual structure remains open, and the essentiality of the "precious" vitamin in this coenzyme still presents a challenge to our biochemical imagination.

[101] S. Shive, W. W. Ackermann, and J. E. Sutherland, *J. Am. Chem. Soc.* **69,** 2567 (1947).
[102] K. Bloch, *Recent Progr. Hormone Research* **6,** 111 (1951).
[103] J. Bonner and B. Arreguin, *Arch. Biochem.* **21,** 109 (1949).

IV. Specificity of Action

SAMUEL LEPKOVSKY

The activity of pantothenic acid resides only in its dextrorotatory form which has been indicated to be the D configuration by application of Hudson's amide rule.[1-3] L(−)-Pantothenic acid appears to be inactive for organisms requiring the intact vitamin. Pantothenic acid appears to be highly specific and is incapable of modification without loss of activity unless the organisms metabolizing it are capable of regenerating it *in vivo*.[3] The following are examples which illustrate this.

1. The methyl and ethyl esters of pantothenic acid are comparable in activity to the vitamin in promoting growth of rats,[3, 4] but ethyl pantothenate is only about 6.8 % as effective as pantothenic acid for *Lactobacillus casei*.[3-5] The rats apparently can hydrolyze the esters *in vivo*, but the bacteria cannot.

2. The alcohol corresponding to pantothenic acid (pantothenyl alcohol) has been found to be effective in animals,[3, 6] but it cannot replace pantothenic acid in the nutrition of lactic acid bacteria and it even inhibits its utilization in these organisms.[7] The utilization of pantothenyl alcohol by animals depends upon its *in vivo* conversion to pantothenic acid. Lactic acid bacteria apparently cannot make this conversion.

3. Acetylation of pantothenic acid concentrates from natural sources destroys its activity for chicks[8] and for bacteria.[9] However, synthetic ethyl monoacetyl D-pantothenate is as active as pantothenic acid for rats and chicks but is only 0.7 % as effective as the vitamin for *Lactobacillus casei*.[3-5] These are impressive examples of the relationship between the potency of a vitamin and the presence of enzyme systems in the organism capable of modifying the vitamin so that it can be metabolized.

Many analogs of pantothenic acid have been prepared. The β-alanine has been replaced with other amino acids such as α-alanine, β-aminobutyric acid, aspartic acid, lysine, and leucine. All such preparations were devoid of

[1] H. C. Park and E. J. Lawson, *J. Am. Chem. Soc.* **63**, 2869 (1941)

[2] C. S. Hudson, *J. Am. Chem. Soc.* **39**, 462 (1917).

[3] R. J. Williams, R. E. Eakin, E. Beerstecher, Jr., and W. Shive, The Biochemistry of the B Vitamins. Reinhold Publishing Corp., New York, 1950. The chapter on pantothenic acid carries an extensive bibliography.

[4] K. Unna and C. W. Muschett, *Am. J. Physiol.* **135**, 267 (1942).

[5] S. A. Harris, G. A. Boyack, and K. Folkers, *J. Am. Chem. Soc.* **63**, 2662 (1941).

[6] S. H. Rubin, J. M. Cooperman, M. E. Moore, and J. Scheiner, *J. Nutrition* **35**, 499 (1948).

[7] E. E. Snell and W. Shive, *J. Biol. Chem.* **158**, 551 (1945).

[8] D. W. Woolley, H. A. Waisman, O. Mickelsen, and C. A. Elvehjem, *J. Biol. Chem.* **125**, 715 (1938).

[9] E. E. Snell, F. M. Strong, and W. H. Peterson, *Biochem. J.* **31**, 1789 (1937).

activity.[10] The pantoic lactone portion of the pantothenic acid molecule has also been modified in many ways, all of them resulting in great loss of activity.[3] The only modifications of pantothenic acid which retain appreciable, but by no means full, activity are hydroxypantothenic acid[10] and methylpantothenic acid.[3, 10] It is not known whether modifications *in vivo* account for all or part of the activity of these analogs.

V. Biogenesis

SAMUEL LEPKOVSKY

Microorganisms differ in their ability to synthesize pantothenic acid. Some are capable of its total synthesis. This has been demonstrated by the rumen microorganisms in cattle and sheep.[1] Its synthesis also takes place in the intestinal tract of rats, apparently by the bacteria in the cecum. Some organisms can produce only the pantoic lactone fragment but not β-alanine,[2,] whereas others can synthesize β-alanine but not pantoic lactone.[2,]

β-Alanine is apparently formed by the decarboxylation of aspartic acid.[3]

$$
\begin{array}{c}
\text{COOH} \\
| \\
\text{CH}_2 \\
| \\
\text{CH}\!-\!\text{NH}_2 \\
| \\
\text{COOH}
\end{array}
\quad \xrightarrow{\;-CO_2\;} \quad \text{NH}_2\text{CH}_2\text{CH}_2\text{COOH}
$$

Aspartic acid β-Alanine

β-Alanine is then coupled with pantoic acid to form pantothenic acid. The steps in the biosynthesis of pantoic acid remains to be worked out.

[10] R. J. Williams, *Advances in Enzymol.* **3,** 253 (1943).
[1] L. W. McElroy and H. Goss, *J. Nutrition* **21,** 405 (1941).
[2] R. J. Williams, R. E. Eakin, E. Beerstecher, Jr., and W. Shive, The Biochemistry of the B Vitamins. Reinhold Publishing Corp., New York, 1950.
[3] H. R. Rosenberg, Chemistry and Physiology of the Vitamins. Interscience Publishers New York, 1945.

VI. Estimation

A. CHEMICAL AND PHYSICAL METHODS

GEORGE M. BRIGGS and FLOYD S. DAFT

Several chemical methods for estimation of pantothenic acid are available, although they seem especially suited only for relatively pure mixtures. Two proposed methods are based on the liberation of β-alanine by chemical means and its subsequent determination by colorimetric tests.[1, 1a] Recently this has been extended to the determination of pantothenic acid in crude materials (urine and wheat), and the values agree well with the results obtained by biological assay.[1b, 1c] Further studies are necessary, however, before chemical methods can be routinely used for biological materials.

The estimation of pantothenic acid in pure vitamin mixtures is possible by the chemical release and determination of pantoyl lactone or of pantoic acid.[1d, 1e] This method does not differentiate pantothenic acid from its inactive lactone moiety, however.

Also, it is known that pantothenic acid is reduced at the dropping mercury electrode[2] and may be measured by polarimetric analysis.[3] These methods are not specific enough, however, to be used to assay pantothenic acid in natural materials.

B. BIOLOGICAL METHODS

GEORGE M. BRIGGS and FLOYD S. DAFT

Biological methods of assay are the only satisfactory methods thus far suggested. Microbiological assays (discussed elsewhere) and animal assays are both used with success. Microbiological methods are more rapid and are the method of choice for routine purposes, whereas animal assays are helpful chiefly for checking the accuracy of microbiological methods in the determination of total pantothenic acid activity.

In general, an animal assay of crude material measures not only pantothenic acid but also any "sparing" factor which might be present.[4] This gives a greater significance to animal assays than to microbiological assays as far as animal "pantothenic acid activity" of a material is concerned.

[1] R. Crokaert, *Bull. soc. chim. biol.* **31**, 903 (1949).

[1a] C. R. Szalkowski, W. J. Mader, and H. A. Frediani, *Cereal Chem.* **28**, 218 (1951).

[1b] R. Crokaert, S. Moore, and E. J. Bigwood, *Bull. soc. chim. biol.* **33**, 1209 (1951).

[1c] F. Y. Refai and B. S. Miller, *Cereal Chem.* **29**, 469 (1952).

[1d] E. G. Wollish and M. Schmall, *Anal. Chem.* **22**, 1033 (1950).

[1e] C. R. Szalkowski and J. H. Davidson, *Anal. Chem.* **25**, 1192 (1953).

[2] J. J. Lingane and O. L. Davis, *J. Biol. Chem.* **137**, 567 (1941).

[3] D. V. Frost, *Ind. Eng. Chem. Anal. Ed.* **15**, 306 (1943).

[4] F. S. Daft and K. Schwarz, *Federation Proc.* **11**, 201 (1952).

However, such assays have less significance in terms of the content of pantothenic acid itself.

1. Rat Growth Assays

Satisfactory assays for pantothenic acid activity may be made by removing pantothenic acid from any of the good, highly purified diets for rats in use today. The pantothenic acid activity of crude materials may then be calculated by comparing the growth obtained with such materials with standard growth curves obtained by feeding graded levels of crystalline calcium pantothenate.

As an example of the use of this principle, a successful rat growth assay was used by Wisconsin workers[5] in 1951 to determine the activity of bound forms of pantothenic acid. Total pantothenic acid activity of certain samples of liver, yeast, wheat bran, and rice bran was greater than indicated by microbiological assay. A few other laboratories have also used rat assays,[6, 7] but older rat assays now need modification because of newer vitamins which have since been discovered.

2. Chick Growth Assays

Assays for pantothenic acid activity may be made with chicks by the same general method as that used with rats. Chick assays have the advantage over rat assays of being somewhat less expensive and of shorter duration. For instance, Hegsted and Lipmann,[8] in 1948, measured the pantothenic acid content of coenzyme A by using a purified-type diet low in pantothenic acid. Day-old chicks were fed a commercial chick mash for 4 days and then placed on the pantothenic acid-low diet. After a short depletion period the chicks were divided into uniform groups for assay purposes. The length of the actual assay period was only 8 to 10 days.

Animal assays, especially chick assays, have been very useful as a standard in the development of improved microbiological methods for pantothenic acid. This is true because the animal can utilize bound forms of pantothenic acid which usually are not available to bacteria unless released by special techniques.[8-15]

[5] H. Lih, T. E. King, H. Higgins, C. A. Baumann, and F. M. Strong, *J. Nutrition* **44**, 361 (1951).

[6] J. S. D. Bacon, G. N. Jenkins, and J. O. Irwin, *Biochem. J.* **37**, 492 (1943).

[7] N. B. Guerrant, M. G. Vavich, and O. B. Fardig, *Ind. Eng. Chem. Anal. Ed.* **17**, 710 (1945).

[8] D. M. Hegsted and F. Lipmann, *J. Biol. Chem.* **174**, 89 (1948).

[9] D. Pennington, E. E. Snell, H. K. Mitchell, J. R. McMahan, and R. J. Williams, *Univ. Texas Publ.* **4137**, 14 (1941).

[10] A. L. Neal and F. M. Strong, *J. Am. Chem. Soc.* **65**, 1659 (1943).

[11] A. L. Neal and F. M. Strong, *Ind. Eng. Chem. Anal. Ed.* **15**, 654 (1943).

Several laboratories have used the chick assay to study the distribution of pantothenic acid in a wide variety of foods, animal tissues, and feedstuffs.[8, 16-19] (See the review on this subject by Jukes.[14]) However, some of this work was done before the importance of the more recently discovered vitamins was known, so that many of the values may be somewhat high. Also, much of the older work was done with natural-type diets heated in the dry state to destroy the pantothenic acid content. This heating process undoubtedly affected other nutrients as well, some of which could not be added back satisfactorily.

3. ASSAYS FOR COENZYME A

It is now possible to measure coenzyme A by *in vitro* methods from which pantothenic acid values may be computed. Kaplan and Lipmann proposed a method depending upon the reactivation by coenzyme A of an acetylating system derived from pigeon liver extract.[20] Assay values could be obtained in a few hours. Various modifications of this method have since been suggested.

C. MICROBIOLOGICAL METHODS

E. E. SNELL

Pantothenic acid was discovered independently as a growth factor for yeast[21, 22] and for lactic acid bacteria[23] before its role in animal nutrition was recognized. Following demonstration of its importance for animal life, representatives of these two groups of organisms were used widely for its determination.

The assay of this vitamin is complicated by its occurrence in bound forms,

---

[12] E. H. Hoag, H. P. Sarett, and V. H. Cheldelin, *Ind. Eng. Chem. Anal. Ed.* **17**, 60 (1945).

[13] E. Willerton and H. W. Cromwell, *Ind. Eng. Chem. Anal. Ed.* **14**, 603 (1942).

[14] T. H. Jukes, *Biol. Symposia* **12**, 253 (1947).

[15] M. E. Coates, J. E. Ford, G. F. Harrison, S. K. Kon, E. E. Shepheard, and F. W. Wilby, *Brit. J. Nutrition* **6**, 75 (1952).

[16] H. A. Waisman, O. Mickelsen, and C. A. Elvehjem, *J. Nutrition* **18**, 247 (1939).

[17] T. H. Jukes, *J. Nutrition* **21**, 193 (1941).

[18] T. H. Jukes and S. Lepkovsky, *J. Biol. Chem.* **114**, 117 (1936).

[19] H. A. Waisman and C. A. Elvehjem, Vitamin Content of Meat. Burgess, Minneapolis, 1941.

[20] N. O. Kaplan and F. Lipmann, *J. Biol. Chem.* **174**, 37 (1948).

[21] R. J. Williams, C. M. Lyman, G. H. Goodyear, and J. H. Truesdail, *J. Am. Chem. Soc.* **54**, 3462 (1932).

[22] R. J. Williams, *Advances in Enzymol.* **3**, 257 (1943).

[23] E. E. Snell, F. M. Strong, and W. H. Peterson, *Biochem. J.* **31**, 1789 (1937); *J. Am. Chem. Soc.* **60**, 2825 (1938).

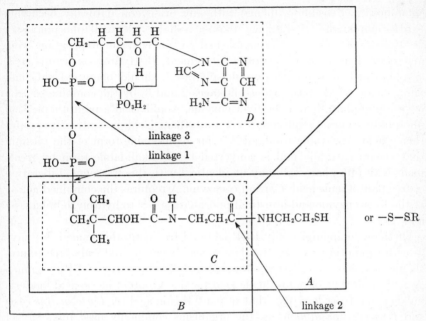

Diagram giving suggested formula for coenzyme A.

of which coenzyme A and its various degradation products are quantitatively the most important.[24] Our present knowledge of the relationships of these products is summarized in the diagram, which gives a suggested formula for coenzyme A.[25, 26] This formula will serve to illustrate the types of linkages that must be broken to liberate pantothenic acid.

A variety of different products containing pantothenic acid are possible, depending upon whether one hydrolyzes linkages 1, 2, or 3, or various combinations of these. Hydrolysis of linkage 1 yields one or more forms of the growth factor, LBF, closely related to or identical with synthetic pantetheine, A.[27-29a] This growth factor, and coenzyme A itself, exist in a variety of forms, depending upon whether their —SH group is free or

[24] N. O. Kaplan and F. Lipmann, *J. Biol. Chem.* **174**, 37 (1948).

[25] J. Baddiley and E. M. Thain, *J. Chem. Soc.* **1951**, 2253.

[26] T. P. Wang, L. Shuster, and N. O. Kaplan, *J. Am. Chem. Soc.* **74**, 3204 (1952).

[27] G. M. Brown, J. A. Craig, and E. E. Snell, *Arch. Biochem.* **27**, 473 (1950).

[28] E. E. Snell, G. M. Brown, V. J. Peters, J. A. Craig, E. I. Wittle, J. A. Moore, V. M. McGlohon, and O. D. Bird, *J. Am. Chem. Soc.* **72**, 5349 (1950).

[29] J. A. Craig and E. E. Snell, *J. Bacteriol.* **61**, 283 (1951).

[29a] E. E. Snell and G. M. Brown, *Advances in Enzymol.* **14**, 49 (1953).

combined in a disulfide linkage with any of several naturally occurring —SH compounds.[30, 31] Linkage 1 is cleaved by intestinal phosphatase.[32] Hydrolysis of linkage 2, accomplished by an enzyme preparation from pigeon or chicken liver,[32] liberates a fragment, *B*. Hydrolysis of linkage 3, accomplished by a potato pyrophosphatase,[33] should liberate 4-phospho-pantetheine. Hydrolysis of both linkages 2 and 3, by the combined action of pyrophosphatase and the liver enzyme, would yield a pantothenic acid phosphate. Synthetic phosphates of pantothenic acid, in contrast to pantothenic acid, are stable to alkali;[25, 34] an alkali-stable form of the vitamin that occurs naturally and is converted to an alkali-labile form by treatment with phosphatases[35] may be identical with this fragment. Liberation of free pantothenic acid, *C*, from coenzyme A requires the combined action of the liver enzyme and intestinal phosphatase[32, 36] to hydrolyze linkages 1 and 2.

Of these compounds, only LBF (*A*) and free pantothenic acid (*C*) have growth-promoting activity for lactic acid bacteria, and only free pantothenic acid has such activity for yeasts.[29] The activity of LBF is much greater than that of pantothenic acid for one group of lactic acid bacteria but is equal to or less than that of pantothenic acid for *Lactobacillus casei* and *Lactobacillus arabinosus*, the organisms commonly used for assay of pantothenic acid. Whichever of the methods of assay is used, it is therefore necessary to liberate pantothenic acid by the combined action of liver enzyme and intestinal phosphatase to obtain true values. Procedures for this purpose have been summarized elsewhere.[32, 36-38] Since such procedures were unknown until recently, many of the early figures for the pantothenic acid content of natural materials obtained by microbiological procedures are low, a fact that was indicated quite early by their failure to agree with chick assay procedures.[39]

The most widely used microbiological procedure for pantothenic acid employs *Lactobacillus arabinosus* as the test organism.[37] The procedure and medium are very similar to those used for determination of biotin and nicotinic acid; they have been described in detail several times.[37-39] Growth in the pantothenic acid-free medium increases with the pantothenic acid

[30] G. M. Brown and E. E. Snell, *Proc. Soc. Exptl. Biol. Med.* **77**, 138 (1951).
[31] G. M. Brown and E. E. Snell, *J. Biol. Chem.* **198**, 375 (1952).
[32] G. D. Novelli, N. O. Kaplan, and F. Lipmann, *J. Biol. Chem.* **177**, 97 (1949).
[33] G. D. Novelli, N. O. Kaplan, and F. Lipmann, *Federation Proc.* **9**, 209 (1950).
[34] T. E. King and F. M. Strong, *Science* **112**, 562 (1950).
[35] A. L. Neal and F. M. Strong, *J. Am. Chem. Soc.* **65**, 1659 (1943).
[36] J. B. Neilands and F. M. Strong, *Arch. Biochem.* **19**, 287 (1948).
[37] E. E. Snell, *in* Vitamin Methods, Vol. I, p. 327. Academic Press, 1950.
[38] Association of Vitamin Chemists, Methods of Vitamin Assay, 2nd ed., p. 290. Interscience Publishers, New York, 1951.
[39] T. H. Jukes, *Biol. Symposia* **12**, 253 (1947).

concentration in the range from 0 to about 0.2 γ of calcium pantothenate per 10 ml. The pure vitamin and samples which supply it at several levels within this range are added to individual tubes containing 5 ml. of the double-strength medium. Each tube is then diluted to 10 ml., capped, autoclaved, cooled, and inoculated. Response of the test organism is customarily determined by acid titration after 72 hours of incubation at 30 to 37°, or turbidimetric estimations of growth can be made as early as 24 hours. β-Alanine does not replace pantothenic acid; fatty acids may interfere slightly, and should be removed by filtration of the samples at pH 4.5 before assay.

Lactobacillus casei was used in many of the earlier procedures,[37] but it was more troublesome than *L. arabinosus* because of its more complex nutrition and because fatty acids interfered much more markedly with its response to pantothenic acid. With present knowledge, both disadvantages could be overcome, and further work might lead to a simpler assay procedure with this test organism, inasmuch as it is one of the few investigated for which pantethine (LBF) and pantothenic acid have equimolar activity.[29]

Early yeast assay methods for pantothenic acid were relatively nonspecific when applied to natural materials because of the presence of toxic materials, because β-alanine could be used in place of pantothenic acid, and because other components of the sample stimulated growth in the simple media originally used.[37] None of these objections apply to a more recently developed procedure utilizing *Saccharomyces carlsbergensis*.[37, 40] For suitably equipped laboratories, this method should be found equally as suitable as that utilizing *L. arabinosus*.

VII. Standardization of Activity

GEORGE M. BRIGGS and FLOYD S. DAFT

Now that the crystalline calcium salt of pantothenic acid is readily available, the older "units" are obsolete. Since the calcium salt is usually used in biological studies, it is sometimes convenient to know that 1.087 g. of calcium pantothenate equals 1.0 g. of pantothenic acid. Pure pantothenic acid is not used as a standard, since it is an unstable viscous oil and extremely hygroscopic. The sodium salt is also hygroscopic, whereas calcium pantothenate in the dry form is reasonably stable to air and light.

A unit of coenzyme A has been defined as the amount which will activate the *in vitro* system of Kaplan and Lipmann to half the maximum activity.[1] It contains approximately 0.7 γ of bound pantothenic acid.

[40] L. Atkin, W. L. Williams, A. S. Schultz, and C. N. Frey, *Ind. Eng. Chem. Anal. Ed.* **16,** 67 (1944).

[1] N. O. Kaplan and F. Lipmann, *J. Biol. Chem.* **174,** 37 (1948).

VIII. Occurrence

GEORGE M. BRIGGS and FLOYD S. DAFT

There is somewhat of a scarcity of reliable figures in the literature on the pantothenic acid content of natural materials. This is because only in very recent years have methods become available by which the various bound forms of pantothenic acid are released to make them available for the growth of microorganisms. Older values obtained by microbiological assay tend to be somewhat low, especially for materials rich in bound forms.

Pantothenic acid is universally distributed in all living cells and tissues. In general, liver, kidney, yeast, egg yolk, royal jelly, and fresh vegetables are the best sources of pantothenic acid, and milk, meat, grains, fruits, and nuts are considered fair to good sources. Certain canned products, as well as egg white, beets, corn, and rice, may be considered relatively poor sources.

A. ASSAY VALUES IN FOODS, FEEDS, TISSUES, AND MISCELLANEOUS MATERIALS

The tables, which appear at the end of this section give the approximate pantothenic acid content of various classes of materials of natural origin. The values given were selected as much as possible from the most recent and reliable values found in the literature. Not all values, however, have been determined by the use of modern methods of enzymatic release of pantothenic acid, and, hence, they tend to be low. In a few instances, values obtained by several methods are given for the sake of comparison.

The tables are separated according to the following classification:

Table XI (p. 638): Foodstuffs.
Table XII (p. 642): Feedstuffs (grains, animal by-products, etc.).
Table XIII (p. 644): Various varieties of oats, wheat, and soybeans.
Table XIV (p. 645): Diet ingredients, enzymes, and miscellaneous.
Table XV (p. 646): Organisms of different biological phyla.
Table XVI (p. 647): Normal tissues of rat, mouse, beef, hog, chick, and human being.
Table XVII (p. 648): Milk of various species.
Table XVIII (p. 648): Blood of various species.
Table XIX (p. 649): Coenzyme A distribution.

B. EFFECT OF VARIOUS FACTORS ON PANTOTHENIC ACID DISTRIBUTION

Various factors are known to affect the pantothenic acid content of natural materials as discussed below.

1. Effect of Variety, Species, and Breed

Table XIII gives the pantothenic acid content of various varieties of grains.[1-3] It is obvious that considerable variation exists which might be expected from genetic, environmental, and other considerations. This variation convincingly demonstrates the importance of directly assaying any diet or food if a true pantothenic acid value is wanted rather than relying too heavily on published "average" values.

Myint et al.[4] have reported that highly significant differences were observed in the pantothenic acid content of different breeds of chickens fed similar diets (containing 10 % alfalfa) as follows:

Breed	Pantothenic acid content of leg tissue, γ/g.
White Jersey Giant	11.6
New Hampshire	14.7
White Plymouth Rock	10.7
White Leghorn	11.0

No significant differences could be found in the pantothenic acid content of milk of various breeds of cattle.[4a] Individual variation was greater than differences in breed in the few samples studied.

2. Effect of Environment during Period of Growth

The pantothenic acid content of fresh plants, such as alfalfa and clover, is surprisingly not influenced by the stage of growth according to Bondi et al.[5] These authors reported, however, that there were various seasonal effects on pantothenic acid content of plants; e.g., plants grown in a dry season had more pantothenic acid than plants grown during a rainy season.

In this same connection, Tepley et al.[2] have shown that the pantothenic acid content of wheat samples of the same variety differed with the locality in which they were grown. For instance, wheat samples from Ohio were lower in pantothenic acid than the same variety from other areas. These differences are probably explained by soil and seasonal effects. Also, it is known that rain may cause a leaching effect on pantothenic acid during the period of field curing[6] which may then also be a factor in the final pantothenic acid content of hays or grains. The pantothenic acid content of

[1] K. J. Frey and G. I. Watson, *Agron. J.* **42**, 434 (1950).
[2] L. J. Teply, F. M. Strong, and C. A. Elvehjem, *J. Nutrition* **24**, 167 (1942).
[2a] F. Y. Refai and B. S. Miller, *Cereal Chem.* **29**, 469 (1952).
[3] P. R. Burkholder and I. McVeigh, *Plant Physiol.* **20**, 301 (1945).
[4] T. Myint, C. I. Draper, and D. A. Glenwood, *Abstr. Meeting, Am. Chem. Soc.* p. 3A (Sept. 3-8, 1950).
[4a] J. M. Lawrence, B. L. Herrington, and L. A. Maynard, *J. Nutrition* **32**, 73 (1946).
[5] A. Bondi, R. Etinger, and H. Meyer, *J. Agr. Sci.* **39**, 104 (1949).
[6] L. G. Blaylock, L. R. Richardson, and P. B. Pearson, *Poultry Sci.* **29**, 692 (1950).

corn is known to be affected by environmental factors[6a, 6b] and is markedly affected by stage of maturity (the pantothenic acid level becomes less as the stage of maturity increases).[6b]

It is known that the composition of the soil may affect the vitamin content of a plant. For instance, the pantothenic acid content of oat plants has been reported to be lowered by soils low in phosphorus[6c] or in calcium.[6d] Also, a soil high in phosphorus[6c] or high in nitrate[6e] produces oat plants with higher than normal amounts of pantothenic acid.

3. Effect of Germination and Embryonic Development

Burkholder[7] has reported that the pantothenic acid content of germinated oats, wheat, barley, and corn seeds is approximately double the content of ungerminated seeds. Similar increases due to germination have also been seen in the pea, the soybean, and the mung bean.[3] This increase in the synthesis of pantothenic acid during germination is no doubt a reflection of the increased rate of metabolism, and hence of the requirement for coenzyme A, in the germinating seed.

No change occurs in the pantothenic acid content of incubating hen eggs over the course of the entire period of incubation according to Snell and Quarles.[8]

4. Effect of Diet on Tissue Composition

The pantothenic acid content of tissues may be influenced by the dietary level of pantothenic acid, as well as other substances, although more information on this subject is needed. In studies with chicks it has been shown that there is a direct correlation between the pantothenic acid content of the diet and the pantothenic acid content of various tissues.[9] Deficient chicks had from only 10 to 40% as much pantothenic acid as normal chicks. Likewise, in studies with hens, it has been determined that the pantothenic acid content of blood,[10, 11] eggs,[11-13] and other tissues[10] is directly related to that of the diet. A similar relationship between dietary

[6a] L. Ditzler, C. H. Hunt, and R. M. Bethke, *Cereal Chem.* **25**, 273 (1948).

[6b] C. H. Hunt, L. D. Rodriguez, S. Taylor, and R. M. Bethke, *Cereal Chem.* **29**, 142 (1952).

[6c] T. A. McCoy, D. G. Bostwick, and A. C. Devich, *Plant Physiol.* **26**, 784 (1951).

[6d] D. S. Bostwick and T. A. McCoy, *Proc. Oklahoma Acad. Sci.* **31**, 112 (1950).

[6e] R. Langston, *Plant Physiol.* **26**, 115 (1951).

[7] P. R. Burkholder, *Science* **97**, 562 (1943).

[8] E. E. Snell and E. Quarles, *J. Nutrition* **22**, 483 (1941).

[9] E. E. Snell, D. Pennington, and R. J. Williams, *J. Biol. Chem.* **133**, 559 (1940).

[10] P. B. Pearson and V. H. Melass, *Federation Proc.* **5**, 237 (1946).

[11] M. B. Gillis, G. F. Heuser, and L. C. Norris, *J. Nutrition* **35**, 351 (1948).

[12] E. E. Snell, E. Aline, J. R. Couch, and P. B. Pearson, *J. Nutrition* **21**, 201 (1941).

[13] P. B. Pearson, V. H. Melass, and R. M. Sherwood, *Arch. Biochem.* **7**, 353 (1945).

and tissue pantothenic acid content has been seen in swine[14] and in other animals[14a] (see also section on deficiency symptoms).

It is also interesting that the pantothenic acid, or coenzyme A, content of certain animal tissues is changed as a result of deficiencies of other vitamins, as shown in studies with chicks,[15, 15a] rats,[15b] and humans[16] (with beriberi, pellagra, or riboflavin deficiency).

5. EFFECT OF STORAGE

Pantothenic acid is reasonably stable in foods and feedstuffs during long periods of storage, provided that oxidation and high temperatures are avoided. For instance, it has been shown that grains may be stored for periods up to a year in the intact or ground state without appreciable loss of pantothenic acid.[17] Also, it is known that the pantothenic acid content of pork[17a] and of eggs[18] is reduced very little after 12 months' cold storage, or longer.

6. EFFECT OF HEAT AND COOKING

It is well known that heating or cooking of feeds or foods may cause some destruction of pantothenic acid. In usual cooking or baking procedures only relatively small amounts of pantothenic acid are lost.[4a, 17a, 19] Normal dehydration temperatures over very short periods do not cause any loss of pantothenic acid, as shown with studies on dehydrated alfalfa meal.[6] High temperatures (100° to 150°) over long periods of time (2 to 6 days), however, do cause considerable loss of pantothenic acid. In fact, this is the method by which pantothenic acid-low diets were obtained in the early studies with this vitamin in chick nutrition.[20, 21]

[14] B. D. Owen and J. P. Bowland, *J. Nutrition* **48**, 317 (1952).

[14a] R. M. Melampy and L. C. Northrop, *Arch. Biochem.* **30**, 180 (1951).

[15] E. M. Popp and J. R. Totter, *J. Biol. Chem.* **199**, 547 (1952).

[15a] R. J. Evans, A. C. Groschke, and H. A. Butts, *Arch. Biochem. and Biophys.* **31**, 454 (1951).

[15b] T. Terroine and J. Adrian, *Arch. sci. physiol.* **4**, 435 (1950).

[16] S. R. Stanberry, E. E. Snell, and T. D. Spies, *J. Biol. Chem.* **135**, 353 (1940).

[17] C. C. Lardinois, C. A. Elvehjem, and E. B. Hart, *J. Dairy Sci.* **27**, 875 (1944).

[17a] B. D. Westerman, G. E. Vail, J. Kalen, M. Stone, and D. L. Mackintosh, *J. Am. Dietet. Assoc.* **28**, 49 and 331 (1952).

[18] R. J. Evans, J. A. Davidson, and H. A. Butts, *Poultry Sci.* **31**, 777 (1952).

[19] F. M. Strong, A. Earle, and B. Zeman, *J. Biol. Chem.* **140**, cxxviii (1941); V. H. Cheldelin, A. M. Woods, and R. J. Williams, *J. Nutrition* **26**, 477 (1943); B. S. Schweigert, and B. T. Guthneck, *J. Nutrition* **51**, 283 (1953); S. Cover and W. H. Smith, Jr., *Food Research* **17**, 148 (1952).

[20] O. L. Kline, J. A. Keenan, C. A. Elvehjem, and E. B. Hart, *J. Biol. Chem.* **99**, 295 (1932); T. H. Jukes, *J. Biol. Chem.* **117**, 11 (1937).

[21] A. M. Pearson, J. E. Burnside, H. M. Edwards, R. S. Glasscock. T. J. Cunha, and A. F. Novak, *Food Research* **16**, 85 (1951).

A factor affecting the pantothenic acid content of meat, which may become more important in the future, is the loss found in the drip from defrosting frozen meat. Pearson *et al.* report a 33 % loss of pantothenic acid in this manner.[21]

7. Effect of Stage of Lactation

The pantothenic acid content of colostrum milk is significantly lower than in milk obtained at a later stage of lactation, as determined in studies with milk of the cow,[4a, 21a] human,[21b] ewe,[21a] and sow.[21c] This is rather a surprising fact, since colostrum milk is known to be richer than normal milk in most nutrients.

C. DISTRIBUTION OF COENZYME A

Only a few values for the distribution of coenzyme A in natural materials are available at this time and are given in Table XIX. Coenzyme A is present in large amounts in certain dried microorganisms and is in relatively high amounts in animal tissues.

TABLE XI

PANTOTHENIC ACID CONTENT OF FOODSTUFFS[22-30a]

(Fresh basis unless otherwise noted)

Food	Pantothenic acid, γ/g.	Method of assay, if given	Reference and year
Almonds	4.0	—	30, 1943
Apples	0.6	Microb.	28, 1942
Apricots, canned	0.9	Microb.	29, 1945
Artichoke	4.0	Chick	24, 1941
Asparagus, green, canned	2.0	Microb.	29, 1945

[21a] P. B. Pearson and A. L. Darnell, *J. Nutrition* **31**, 51 (1946).

[21b] M. N. Coryell, M. E. Harris, S. Miller, H. H. Williams, and I. G. Macy, *Am. J. Diseases Children* **70**, 150 (1945).

[21c] V. E. Davis, A. A. Heidebrecht, R. W. MacVicar, O. B. Ross, and C. K. Whitehair, *J. Nutrition* **44**, 17 (1951).

[22] N. G. Guerrant, M. G. Vavich, and O. B. Fardig, *Ind. Eng. Chem. Anal. Ed.* **17** 710 (1945).

[23] A. L. Neal and F. M. Strong, *Ind. Eng. Chem. Anal. Ed.* **15**, 654 (1943).

[24] T. H. Jukes, *J. Nutrition* **21**, 193 (1941).

[25] H. A. Waisman and C. A. Elvehjem, Vitamin Content of Meat. Burgess, Minneapolis, 1941.

[26] J. B. Neilands and F. M. Strong, *Arch. Biochem.* **19**, 287 (1948).

[27] M. Ives and F. M. Strong, *Arch. Biochem.* **9**, 251 (1946).

[28] V. H. Cheldelin and R. J. Williams, *Univ. Texas Publ.* **4237**, 105 (1942).

[29] M. Ives, M. Zepplin, S. R. Ames, F. M. Strong, and C. A. Elvehjem, *J. Am. Diet. Assoc.* **21**, 357 (1945).

[30] W. H. Peterson, J. T. Skinner, and F. M. Strong, Elements of Food Biochemistry, p. 272. Prentice-Hall, New York, 1943.

[30a] A. J. Ihde, and H. A. Schuette, *J. Nutrition* **22**, 527 (1941).

TABLE XI—*Continued*

Food	Pantothenic acid, γ/g.	Method of assay, if given	Reference and year
Bacon, sample 1	⎰2.8	Microb.	28, 1942
Bacon, sample 2	⎱9.8	Microb.	28, 1942
Beans, green string, canned	0.7	Microb.	29, 1945
Beans, green string, fresh	1.5	—	30, 1943
Beans, kidney, dried	5.5	—	30, 1943
Beans, lima, canned	1.1	Microb.	29, 1945
Beans, lima, dried	8.3	Microb.	28, 1942
Beans, navy, dried	6.0	—	30, 1943
Beans, yellow wax	0.6	—	30, 1943
Beef, brain	18.0	Microb.	28, 1942
Beef, dried	55.6	Microb.	26, 1948
Beef, heart	20.0	Microb.	28, 1942
Beef, kidney	35.0	—	30, 1943
Beef, liver	76.0	Microb.	28, 1942
Beef, round	4.9	Microb.	28, 1942
Beef, steak	6.5	—	30, 1943
Beef, tongue	11.0	Microb.	25, 1941
Beets	2.0	—	30, 1943
Beet greens	5.0	—	30, 1943
Blackberries, canned	0.8	Microb.	29, 1945
Blueberries, canned	0.7	Microb.	29, 1945
Brazil nuts	2.5	—	30, 1943
Bread, rye (40%)	5.0	—	30, 1943
Bread, white	4.0	—	30, 1943
Bread, white enriched	4.6	Microb.	28, 1942
Bread, whole wheat	8.0	—	30, 1943
Broccoli	14.0	Chick	24, 1941
Brussels sprouts	6.0	—	30, 1943
Buckwheat	26.0	—	30, 1943
Cabbage	1.8	Microb.	28, 1942
Cantaloupe	2.3	Microb.	28, 1942
Carrots, canned	1.1	Microb.	29, 1945
Carrot, fresh	2.5	Microb.	28, 1942
Cauliflower	9.2	Microb.	28, 1942
Celery, bleached	3.0	—	30, 1943
Cheese, American	2.8	—	30, 1943
Cheese, cottage	2.5	—	30, 1943
Cheese, Swiss	3.5	—	30, 1943
Cherries, red sour, canned	1.2	Microb.	29, 1945
Chicken, dark	13.0	Microb.	25, 1941
Chicken, light	8.0	Microb.	25, 1941
Chocolate	1.9	Microb.	28, 1942
Codfish	5.0	—	30, 1943
Corn, white, meal	3.1	Microb.	28, 1942
Corn, yellow, sweet, dried	8.0	—	30, 1943
Corn, cream style, canned	2.2	Microb.	29, 1945

TABLE XI—*Continued*

Food	Pantothenic acid, γ/g.	Method of assay, if given	Reference and year
Corn, sweet, canned	2.9	Rat	22, 1945
Cowpeas, dried	18.0	—	30, 1943
Cucumbers	3.9	—	30, 1943
Egg, hen's, whole	55.4	Microb.	26, 1948
Egg, hen's, white	1.3	—	30, 1943
Egg, hen's, yolk	63.0	Chick	24, 1941
Endive	2.3	—	30, 1943
Flour, rye (dark)	14.1	Microb.	30a, 1941
Flour, rye (white)	7.2	Microb.	30a, 1941
Flour, white, patent	3.5	Microb.	28, 1942
Flour, whole wheat	10.0	—	30, 1943
Grapefruit	2.9	Microb.	28, 1942
Grapefruit juice, canned	1.7	Microb.	29, 1945
Halibut	1.5	Microb.	28, 1942
Hominy grits	1.0	Microb.	28, 1942
Kale	3.0	Chick	24, 1941
Kohlrabi	1.6	—	30, 1943
Lamb, leg of	6.0	Microb.	28, 1942
Lamb, liver	53.0	Microb.	25, 1941
Lettuce, head	1.3	—	30, 1943
Lettuce, leaf	1.1	Microb.	28, 1942
Lima beans	1.7	Microb.	27, 1946
Mackerel	13.9	Microb.	26, 1948
Milk, pasteurized	3.0	—	30, 1943
Milk, powder, skim	36.0	Chick	24, 1941
Milk, powder, whole	24.0	Microb.	28, 1942
Milk, skim, fresh	3.6	Chick	24, 1941
Milk, whole, raw	2.9	Microb.	28, 1942
Molasses	25.0	—	30, 1943
Mushrooms, canned	9.4	Microb.	29, 1945
Mushrooms, fresh	17.0	Microb.	28, 1942
Mutton, shoulder	4.3	Microb.	28, 1942
Oats, rolled	11.0	Chick	24, 1941
Onions, dry	1.3	Microb.	28, 1942
Oranges	3.4	Microb.	28, 1942
Orange juice, canned	1.3	Microb.	29, 1945
Oysters	4.9	Microb.	28, 1942
Parsley	6.0	—	30, 1943
Peaches, canned	0.6	Microb.	29, 1945
Peaches, fresh	1.7	Microb.	28, 1942
Pears, halves, canned	2.5	Microb.	29, 1945
Peanuts, roasted	25.0	Microb.	28, 1942
Peas, blackeyed	10.4	Microb.	28, 1942
Peas, dried	18.0	—	30, 1943
Peas, fresh green	1.8	Microb.	23, 1943
	5.8	—	30, 1943
Peas, green, canned	1.3	Microb.	29, 1945
	2.0	Rat	22, 1945

TABLE XI—*Concluded*

Food	Pantothenic acid, γ/g.	Method of assay, if given	Reference and year
Pecans	14.0	—	30, 1943
Peppers, green	1.2	—	30, 1943
Peppers, red, canned	1.0	Microb.	29, 1945
Pineapple, canned	0.8	Microb.	23, 1943
Pork, ham, fresh	{ 3.4	Microb.	28, 1942
	{ 13.0	—	30, 1943
Pork, ham, smoked	9.0	Microb.	25, 1941
Pork, heart	21.0	Microb.	25, 1941
Pork, kidney	30.0	—	30, 1943
Pork, liver	{ 16.0	Microb.	23, 1943
	{ 49.0	Microb.	25, 1941
Pork, loin	11.0	Microb.	28, 1942
Potatoes, sweet, canned	4.3	Microb.	29, 1945
Potatoes, sweet	9.4	Microb.	28, 1942
Potatoes, white	6.5	Chick	24, 1941
Prunes, Italian, canned	1.0	Microb.	29, 1945
Pumpkin, canned	4.0	Chick	24, 1941
Raisins	0.9	Microb.	28, 1942
Rice Krispies	3.4	Microb.	28, 1942
Rice, bran	22.0	Chick	24, 1941
Rice, white	8.0	—	30, 1943
Salmon, canned	{ 26.4	Microb.	26, 1948
	{ 5.1	Rat	22, 1945
Sardines	15.9	Microb.	26, 1948
Sauerkraut, canned	0.9	Microb.	29, 1945
Spinach, canned	0.6	Microb.	29, 1945
Spinach, fresh	{ 26.8	Microb.	26, 1948
	{ 1.8	Microb.	28, 1942
Squash, Zucchini	3.0	Chick	24, 1941
Strawberries	2.6	Microb.	28, 1942
Tomatoes, canned	{ 2.3	Microb.	28, 1942
	{ 3.8	Rat	22, 1945
Tomatoes, ripe	3.7	Rat	28, 1942
Tomato juice, canned	3.0	Rat	29, 1945
Tunafish	14.3	Microb.	26, 1948
Turnips	0.37	Microb.	28, 1942
Turnip greens, canned	0.7	Microb.	29, 1945
Veal, chop	1.1	Microb.	28, 1942
Veal, heart	31.0	Microb.	25, 1941
Veal, liver	52.0	Microb.	25, 1941
Veal, round	16.9	Microb.	27, 1946
Walnuts, English	8.0	Chick	24, 1941
Watercress	1.5	—	30, 1943
Watermelon	3.1	Microb.	28, 1942
Wheat, bran	30.0	—	30, 1943
Wheat, germ meal	29.3	Microb.	26, 1948
Wheat, whole	12.0	Microb.	28, 1942
Yeast, brewer's, dry	200.0	Chick	24, 1941

TABLE XII

PANTOTHENIC ACID CONTENT OF FEEDSTUFFS[5, 24, 31-34]

(Air-dry basis unless otherwise noted)

Feedstuff	Pantothenic acid, γ/g.	Method of assay, if given	Reference and year
Alfalfa meal, dehydrated			
17% protein	38.4	Microb.	32, 1942
20% protein	41.0	—	33, 1947
Barley	10.0	Chick	24, 1941
	4.1	Microb.	5, 1949
Barley malt	8.6	—	33, 1947
Beet pulp, dried	1.8	—	33, 1947
Blood flour	5.5	—	33, 1947
Blood meal	1.1	—	33, 1947
Bone meal, raw	2.2	—	33, 1947
Bone meal, steamed	1.8	—	33, 1947
Brewer's dried grains	14.6	—	33, 1947
Buckwheat	12.3	—	33, 1947
Buttermilk, dried	34.2	Microb.	32, 1942
Buttermilk, fresh	4.6	Chick	24, 1941
Citrus pulp, dried	13.2	—	33, 1947
Coconut meal	7.3	Microb.	5, 1949
Corn, dent, white	3.5	—	33, 1947
Corn, dent, yellow	4.6	Microb.	5, 1949
Corn gluten feed	17.2	—	33, 1947
	2.1	Microb.	5, 1949
Corn gluten meal (41% protein)	13.8	Microb.	32, 1942
Corn oil meal	4.0	—	33, 1947
Cottonseed meal (41% protein)	14.0	Chick	24, 1941
Cowpeas	17.6	—	33, 1947
Distiller's dried corn grains	11.7	—	33, 1947
Distiller's dried grains, wheat with solubles	13.2	—	33, 1947
Distiller's solubles	25.0	—	34, 1951
Fish meal, herring	8.2	Microb.	5, 1949
	8.8	—	33, 1947
Fish meal, salmon	7.1	—	33, 1947
Fish meal, sardine	15.8	Microb.	5, 1949
Fish solubles, condensed	40.1	—	33, 1947
Hominy feed	7.4	—	33, 1947
Kafir	12.6	—	33, 1947

[31] H. Lih, T. E. King, H. Higgens, C. A. Baumann, and F. M. Strong, *J. Nutrition* **44**, 361 (1951).

[32] J. C. Bauernfeind, L. C. Norris, and G. F. Heuser, *Poultry Sci.* **21**, 136 (1942).

[33] R. V. Boucher and Committee on Feed Composition, *Rept. Natl. Research Council* (*U. S.*) **1**, *Suppl.* (1947).

[34] K. L. Smiley, M. Sobolov, F. L. Austin, R. A. Rasmussen, M. B. Smith, J. M. Van Lanen, L. Stone, and C. S. Boruff, *Ind. Eng. Chem.* **43**, 1380 (1951).

TABLE XII—*Concluded*

Feedstuff	Pantothenic acid, γ/g.	Method of assay, if given	Reference and year
Linseed oil meal	16.5	—	33, 1947
	7.1	Microb.	5, 1949
Liver meal	105.0	Chick	24, 1941
Meat scraps, 52% protein	4.6	—	33, 1947
Meat scraps, 60% protein	5.1	—	33, 1947
Meat and bone scrap, 50% protein	3.3	—	33, 1947
Millet	7.9	Microb.	5, 1949
Milo	13.2	—	33, 1947
Molasses, cane, Cuban	39.5	—	33, 1947
Molasses, cane, Hawaiian	57.5	Microb.	32, 1942
Oats	15.0	—	33, 1947
Oat middlings	22.9	—	33, 1947
Oats, rolled	11.0	—	33, 1947
Peanut kernels	35.1	—	33, 1947
Peanut oil meal, 43% protein	53.0	—	33, 1947
Peanut oil meal, 51% protein	34.8	Microb.	5, 1949
Rice bran	22.7	—	33, 1947
Rice polishings	12.1	—	33, 1947
Rye	9.3	—	33, 1947
Rye germ	13.9	Microb.	30a, 1941
Rye middlings	23.1	Microb.	30a, 1941
Sesame oil cake	5.6	Microb.	5, 1949
Skim milk, dried	29.9	Microb.	5, 1949
	35.0	—	33, 1947
Soybeans, yellow varieties, whole	15.7	—	33, 1947
Soybean oil meal, 43% protein	11.0	Microb.	5, 1949
Soybean oil meal, 44% protein	13.9	—	33, 1947
Soybean oil meal, solvent extracted	16.1	—	33, 1947
Sunflower seed oil meal	11.0	Microb.	5, 1949
Tankage, digester, 60% protein	2.4	—	33, 1947
Wheat, hard red, winter	10.6	—	33, 1947
Wheat, northern, spring	14.1	—	33, 1947
Wheat, soft, white	11.5	—	33, 1947
Wheat bran	48.0	Rat	31, 1951
	23.4	Microb.	5, 1949
Wheat germ	11.5	—	33, 1947
Wheat standard middlings	20.0	—	33, 1947
Whey, dried	60.0	Chick	24, 1941
	42.4	Microb.	5, 1949
Whey, fresh	4.0	Chick	24, 1941
Yeast, brewer's, dried	62.8	Microb.	32, 1942
	200.0	Chick	24, 1941

TABLE XIII
Pantothenic Acid Content of Varieties of Grain
(Air-dry basis)

Oats[1]	Pantothenic acid, γ/g.	Wheat[2]	Pantothenic acid, γ/g.[a]	Soybeans[3]	Pantothenic acid, γ/g.
Andrew	6.3	Turkey	13.2	Peking	36.3
Beaver	8.6	Tenmarq	12.4	Manchu	19.3
Bonda	7.2	Chiefkan	11.8	Mukden	20.0
Clinton	8.5	Blackhull	12.9	Lincoln	22.0
Eaton	8.7	Kawvale	15.1	Dunfield	15.9
Forvic	10.6	Fulcaster	10.4	Illini	19.6
Huron	9.4	Wabash	9.3	Anwei	17.6
Mohawk	7.2	Purdue	9.4		—
Overland	8.9	American Banner	11.4	Average	21.5
Vicland	10.7	Hymar	11.4		
Wolverine	12.7	Ceres	15.0		
Worthy	9.0	Marquis	15.3		
Colo	8.3	Thatcher	14.8		
Michigan 44720	9.2	Garnet	10.4		
	—	Blue Stem	15.2		
Average	9.0	Burbank	15.0		
		Dicklow	11.9		
			—		
		Average	12.6		

[a] Expressed as calcium pantothenate. Other values for wheat also given in refs. 2 and 2a.

TABLE XIV

PANTOTHENIC ACID CONTENT OF EXPERIMENTAL DIET INGREDIENTS, AND
MISCELLANEOUS MATERIALS[a]
(Air-dry basis unless otherwise noted)

Sample	Pantothenic acid, γ/g.	Method of assay	Reference and year
Beef heart infusion	70.0	Microb.	35, 1944
Casein, commercial	5.3	Microb.	32, 1942
Casein, alcohol-extracted	0.8	Microb.	36, 1945
Casein, acid-washed	0.57	Microb.	36, 1945
Fermented solubles of *A. gossypi*	210.0	—	34, 1951
Gelatin	0.8	Microb.	35, 1944
Lactoglobulin, crystalline	2.1	Microb.	37, 1944
Liebig meat extract	15.5	Microb.	35, 1944
Liver powder 1:20 (Wilson)	612.0	Rat	31, 1951
Liver powder, whole (Wilson)	393.0	Microb.	26, 1948
Malt extract	7.2	Microb.	35, 1944
Peptone	5.0	Microb.	35, 1944
Phosphorylase, muscle (crystalline)	2.1	Microb.	37, 1944
Rice brain extract	210.0	Rat	31, 1951
Royal jelly (honey bee)	89.0	Microb.	28, 1942
Trypsin, crystalline	1.2	Microb.	37, 1944
Tryptone	5.3	Microb.	35, 1944
Vitab	418.0	Microb.	26, 1948
Yeast, dried brewer's, strain G	130.0	Microb.	32, 1942
Yeast, dried	$\begin{cases} 252.0 \\ 443.0 \end{cases}$	Rat / Microb.	31, 1951 / 26, 1948
Yeast extract, Group A	197.0	Microb.	35, 1944
Yeast extract, Group B	138.0	Microb.	35, 1944

[a] See ref. 37 for assay values in other purified proteins and enzymes.

[35] J. L. Stokes, M. Gunness, and J. W. Foster, *J. Bacteriol.* **47**, 293 (1944).
[36] M. D. Cannon, R. K. Boutwell, and C. A. Elvehjem, *Science* **102**, 529 (1945).
[37] R. J. Williams, F. Schlenk, and M. A. Eppright, *J. Am. Chem. Soc.* **66**, 896 (1944).

TABLE XV

PANTOTHENIC ACID IN ORGANISMS OF DIFFERENT BIOLOGICAL PHYLA[a]

(γ/g. of moist tissue)

	Pantothenic acid, γ/g.
Fish (*Cryprinidae*)	7.5
Frog (*Rana*)	3.7
Snake (*Thamnophis*)	5.1
Chick embryo	26.0
Red ant (*Dolichederus*)	12.5
Cockroach	17.5
Termites	16.0
Dros. virilis larvae, N. Y.	20.0
Oyster (*Mytilus*)	4.9
Earthworm	3.2
Protozoa (*Tetrahymena geleii*)	13.8
A. aerogenes	30.0
C. butylicum	26.9
Mushrooms	17.0
Yeast, brewer's	42.5
Mold	3.0
Rat (whole)	13.0

[a] Data from the University of Texas.[38] Values determined by microbiological assay.

[38] A. M. Woods, J. Taylor, M. J. Hofer, G. A. Johnson, R. L. Lane, and J. R. McMahan, *Univ. Texas Publ.* **4237,** 84 (1942).

TABLE XVI
PANTOTHENIC ACID CONTENT OF NORMAL TISSUES[a]

(Dry basis)

Tissue	Mature rat, γ/g.	Mouse, γ/g.	Beef, γ/g.	Hog, γ/g.	Embryo rat (12-day), γ/g.	Embryo chick (12 day), γ/g.	Chicken, γ/g.	Mature human, γ/g.
Entire carcass	37	—	—	—	—	—	—	—
Liver	370	120	150	160	140	300	190	136
Spleen	59	7.6	31	37	—	—	—	25
Heart	200	150	63	83	140	400	180	78
Kidney	190	150	73	150	—	—	—	99
Muscle	32	25	28	28	—	—	—	53
Lung	58	26	36	44	—	—	—	26
Brain	71	82	66	55	240	380	310	68
Ovary	40	—	78	—	—	—	—	18
Pancreas	52	—	44	—	—	—	—	—
Thymus	150	—	25	—	—	—	—	—
Thyroid	80	—	7	—	—	—	—	—
Testes	150	—	70	—	—	—	—	32
Skin (with hair)	5.2	—	—	—	—	—	—	7.5
Intestinal tract	63	—	—	—	—	—	—	24
Adrenal cortex	—	—	64	—	—	—	—	—
Anterior pituitary	—	—	31	—	—	—	—	—
Posterior pituitary	—	—	31	—	—	—	—	—
Adrenal gland (whole)	—	—	—	—	—	—	—	20

[a] Data from the University of Texas.[39-41] Values determined by microbiological assay. Other values for various tissues[25] and for 13 different chicken muscles[42] are available.

[39] L. D. Wright, J. R. McMahan, V. H. Cheldelin, A. Taylor, E. E. Snell, and R. J. Williams, *Univ. Texas Publ.* **4137,** 38 (1941).

[40] R. J. Williams, A. Taylor, and V. H. Cheldelin, *Univ. Texas Publ.* **4137,** 61 (1941).

[41] A. Taylor, M. A. Pollack, and R. J. Williams, *Univ. Texas Publ.* **4237,** 41 (1942).

[42] E. E. Rice, E. J. Strandine, E. M. Squires, and B. Lyddon, *Arch. Biochem.* **10,** 251 (1946).

TABLE XVII
Pantothenic Acid Content of Milk of Various Species[a]

Source of milk	γ/ml.
Human being, white	1.6
Mare, thoroughbred	2.9
Cow	2.9
Goat	2.4
Dog, English bull	4.9
Mouse, albino	23.0

[a] Data from the University of Texas.[43] Values given in terms of γ/ml. fresh milk determined by microbiological assay. Additional values for the pantothenic acid content of milk of the guinea pig,[43a] ewe,[21a] sow,[21c] mare,[43b] human,[21b] and cow,[4a, 21a, 43c] are available.

TABLE XVIII
Pantothenic Acid Content of the Blood of Various Species[44, 45]
(Microbiological assay, 1941 and 1946)[a]

Species	Cells, %	Pantothenic acid, γ/100 ml.		
		Blood	Plasma	Cells
Dog	46.7	26.3	31.8	22.4
Horse	32.9	44.8	37.4	51.9
Human being	47.8	19.4	17.0	23.6
Pig	42.8	33.5	34.7	29.6
Rabbit	32.3	71.7	57.8	84.6
Sheep	33.2	26.6	24.1	29.0
Chick[45]	27.3	43.6	51.6	21.9

[a] Also see section on effect of diet on tissue composition for additional references.

[43] R. J. Williams, V. H. Cheldelin, and H. K. Mitchell, *Univ. Texas Publ.* **4237,** 97 (1942).

[43a] W. L. Nelson, A. Kaye, M. Moore, H. H. Williams, and B. L. Herrington, *J. Nutrition* **44,** 585 (1951).

[43b] A. D. Holmes, B. V. McKey, A. W. Wertz, H. G. Lindquist, and L. R. Parkinson, *J. Dairy Sci.* **29,** 163 (1946).

[43c] A. Z. Hodson, *J. Nutrition* **29,** 137 (1945).

[44] P. B. Pearson, *J. Biol. Chem.* **140,** 423 (1941).

[45] P. B. Pearson, V. H. Melass, and R. M. Sherwood, *J. Nutrition* **32,** 187 (1946).

TABLE XIX

CoenZYME A DistributioN[a]

(Fresh basis unless otherwise noted)

	Coenzyme A, units/g.[a]
Plant materials	
Peas, frozen	4.5
Royal jelly (bee)	0
Spinach	0.74
Tomato	1.3
Wheat germ	30.0
Clostridium butylicium, dried extract	2000.0
Escherichia coli, dried	320.0
Tissues, rat	
Liver	132
Adrenal	91
Kidney	74
Brain	28
Heart	42
Intestine	26
Thymus	20
Human red blood cells	3–4
Human plasma	0

[a] A coenzyme A unit contains 0.7 γ of bound pantothenic acid. Data from Kaplan and Lipmann.[46]

IX. Effects of Deficiency

A. IN ANIMALS

GEORGE M. BRIGGS and FLOYD S. DAFT

The effects of pantothenic acid deficiency vary greatly from species to species. In one species, the rat, some of the deficiency signs have been obtained in rather low incidence or even only sporadically. In addition, in some laboratories, certain of the generally recognized deficiency signs have either not been observed at all or their relationship to a lack of pantothenic acid has appeared questionable. Despite these unexplained discrepancies, many interesting lesions may be ascribed with confidence to a low level of this vitamin in the diet. Among the earliest deficiency signs correctly ascribed to pantothenic acid deficiency were growth failure in the chick and rat, dermatitis in the chick, achromotrichia (graying of the hair) in rats and other animals, and adrenal necrosis and hemorrhage in the rat. These and other pathological changes will be discussed in the following sections.

[46] N. O. Kaplan and F. Lipmann, *J. Biol. Chem.* **174,** 37 (1948).

1. Rats

The signs of pantothenic acid deficiency observed in the rat are failure of growth, achromotrichia (in black, hooded, or brown animals), dermatitis, porphyrin staining of the fur and whiskers, "spectacled" eyes (circumocular loss of hair), a characteristic spastic gait, closure of the eyes by a sticky exudate, and, in some animals, an obvious anemia. At autopsy, the adrenals may be enlarged, very dark red in color, and apparently engorged with blood. This advanced stage of adrenal damage has not been observed in all laboratories but when present, it presents a striking picture that cannot be overlooked. There is a marked reduction of body fat. Histological examination has revealed lesions in skin, adrenal, thymus, bone marrow, testis, intestine, bone, and kidney. In mature pantothenic acid-deficient rats, reproduction is impaired.

a. Adrenal Necrosis and Hemorrhage

One of the most interesting and significant of these changes is a fatal cortical necrosis and hemorrhage of the adrenal gland.[1, 2] Hyperemia and hemorrhage in the adrenal cortex and medulla had been described earlier as part of a panmyelophthisis syndrome due to an unknown deficiency,[3] and atrophy of the adrenal without mention of necrosis or hemorrhage had also been described and attributed to filtrate factor deficiency.[4] Daft et al.[2] demonstrated the effectiveness of pantothenic acid in the prevention or correction of the adrenal necrosis, hemorrhage, and other changes which they had observed, and these results have been repeatedly confirmed.[5-7] Gross and histological examinations of the adrenals have been made in several laboratories.[8-10] Grossly, the adrenals are swollen and dark. Ashburn[9] described the microscopic findings as congestion, hemorrhage, atrophy, necrosis, scarring, fibrosis, hemosiderin deposition, and cortical fat depletion. Deane and McKibbin[10] studied the sequence of events in the development of the adrenal lesions. The first changes noted were a disappearance of

[1] F. S. Daft and W. H. Sebrell, Public Health Repts. (U.S.) 54, 2247 (1939).

[2] F. S. Daft, W. H. Sebrell, S. H. Babcock, Jr., and T. H. Jukes, Public Health Repts. (U.S.) 55, 1333 (1940).

[3] P. György, H. Goldblatt, F. R. Miller, and R. P. Fulton, J. Exptl. Med. 66, 579 (1937).

[4] A. F. Morgan and H. D. Simms, Science 89, 565 (1939).

[5] R. C. Mills, J. H. Shaw, C. A. Elvehjem, and P. H. Phillips, Proc. Soc. Exptl. Biol. Med. 45, 482 (1940).

[6] W. D. Salmon and R. W. Engel, Proc. Soc. Exptl. Biol. Med. 45, 621 (1940).

[7] K. Unna, J. Nutrition 20, 565 (1940).

[8] A. A. Nelson, Public Health Repts. (U.S.) 54, 2250 (1939).

[9] L. L. Ashburn, Public Health Repts. (U.S.) 55, 1337 (1940).

[10] H. W. Deane and J. M. McKibbin, Endocrinology 38, 385 (1946).

ketosteroid from the inner cortical zones (reticularis and fasciculata), accompanied and followed by progressive depletion of sudanophilic droplets from the same area. Shortly thereafter, foci of necrosis and hemorrhage appeared in these zones. This progressed in severe cases to almost total destruction of the cortex, only a thin layer of intact cells remaining in the zona glomerulosa.

A number of laboratories have reported failure to observe the more advanced stages of adrenal damage, and some investigators have found no pathological changes observable in gross or by microscopic examination. Cowgill and coworkers[11] have obtained consistent, rapid, and marked changes by using weanling rats from mothers placed on the deficient diet immediately after birth of the offspring.

Because of the fact that depletion of the lipoids of the adrenal cortex preceded cortical necrosis and hemorrhage, it was proposed by Ashburn[9] that the adrenals of pantothenic acid-deficient rats might be functionally insufficient. It had earlier been suggested by Morgan and Simms[4] that the graying and other physical changes of senescence, which they reported as being associated with a deficiency of filtrate factor, might be mediated through the adrenal. These investigators reported further that graying in rats could be cured by relatively large doses of adrenal cortical extract[4] or by thyroid extract.[12] These results have not been confirmed.[13, 14] In further support of the concept of adrenal insufficiency in pantothenic acid deficiency in rats are the results of Gaunt and coworkers,[15] who demonstrated a greater sensitivity of their animals to water intoxication.

In opposition to the suggestions that the adrenal of the pantothenic acid-deficient rat might be functionally insufficient, Deane and McKibbin[10] proposed that there might be overstimulation of the gland due to a stress reaction. They presented cytological and physiological data in support of this point of view. McQueeney et al.[16] showed also that deficient animals on drastically restricted sodium intake showed no defect in sodium conservation. Perry and coworkers[17] reported that pantothenic acid-deficient rats showed no loss in ability to react to stress as judged by discharge of ascorbic acid from the adrenal. Ershoff et al.[18] presented evidence that there was no

[11] G. R. Cowgill, R. W. Winters, R. B. Schultz, and W. A. Krehl, *Intern. Rev. Vitamin Research* 23, 275 (1952).
[12] A. F. Morgan and H. D. Simms, *J. Nutrition* 19, 233 (1940).
[13] C. W. Mushett and K. Unna, *J. Nutrition* 22, 565 (1941).
[14] R. B. Schultz, Thesis, Yale University School of Medicine, 1952, quoted by Cowgill *et al.* in ref. 11.
[15] R. Gaunt, M. Liling, and C. W. Mushett, *Endocrinology* 38, 127 (1946).
[16] A. J. McQueeney, L. L. Ashburn, F. S. Daft, and R. R. Faulkner, *Endocrinology* 41, 441 (1947).
[17] W. F. Perry, W. W. Hawkins, and G. R. Cumming, *Am. J. Physiol.* 172, 259 (1953).
[18] B. H. Ershoff, R. B. Alfin Slater, and J. G. Gaines, *J. Nutrition* 50, 299 (1953).

impairment of pituitary-adrenal function in deficient animals as judged by resistance to egg white intoxication or as judged by the extent of adrenal ascorbic acid depletion and peripheral lymphocyte response following epinephrine or ACTH administration.

Morgan and associates[19] have also investigated adrenal function in their animals and have concluded that pantothenic acid deficiency imposes a stress on the adrenal cortex, resulting in exhaustion of the gland and adrenal hypofunction. Dumm et al.[20] have presented evidence that the deficient rat's ability to resynthesize adrenal cholesterol, after stress, is decreased.

Cowgill and associates[11] and Winters et al.[21] have made a further study of the physiological events leading to and accompanying adrenal damage. Using weanling rats which had suckled mothers receiving a pantothenic acid-deficient diet, they were able to secure striking alterations of the adrenals. Large doses of ACTH (4 mg. per rat per day) produced a marked intensification of the adrenal lesion, while cortisone at a level of 2 mg. per rat per day protected the rats completely from cortical necrosis and hemorrhage. The adrenals in the latter animals (cortisone-treated and pantothenic acid-deficient) were indistinguishable from control animals given cortisone. These investigators concluded that a depletion of coenzyme A in the adrenal cortex leads to increased secretion of ACTH and consequent adrenal hypertrophy; that the adrenal becomes increasingly unable to produce and secrete steroid hormone; and that the sustained high level of circulating ACTH acting upon the enfeebled gland leads, directly or indirectly, to "hemorrhagic necrosis" of the adrenal cortex.

It is interesting that, although all observers are agreed that in pantothenic acid deficiency there is a depletion of adrenal cholesterol and other steroids, it has been reported by Guggenheim and Olson[21a] that lipogenesis per se does not appear to be altered. In their experiments cholesterol concentrations of the liver, heart and blood serum in deficient animals were normal and C^{14} incorporation into cholesterol was not significantly reduced.

[19] L. S. Hurley and A. F. Morgan, J. Biol. Chem. **195,** 583 (1952); R. R. Guehring, L. S. Hurley, and A. F. Morgan, ibid. **197,** 485 (1952); A. F. Morgan and E. M. Lewis, J. Biol. Chem. **200,** 839 (1953).

[20] M. E. Dumm, H. Gershberg, E. M. Beck, and E. P. Ralli, Proc. Soc. Exptl. Biol. Med. **82,** 659 (1953).

[21] R. W. Winters, R. B. Schultz, and W. A. Krehl, Proc. Soc. Exptl. Biol. Med. **79,** 695 (1952); R. W. Winters, R. B. Schultz, and W. A. Krehl, Endocrinology **50,** 377 (1952); R. W. Winters, R. B. Schultz, and W. A. Krehl, ibid. **50,** 388 (1952); R. B. Schultz, R. W. Winters, and W. A. Krehl, ibid. **51,** 336 (1952).

[21a] K. Guggenheim and R. E. Olson, J. Nutrition **48,** 345 (1952).

b. Blood Dyscrasias

A second lesion, which has been observed in a few laboratories in pantothenic acid-deficient rats, is a fatal aplasia of the bone marrow with anemia, leucopenia, and granulocytopenia.[3, 22-24] In 1937, before the isolation of pantothenic acid, György and coworkers[3] observed panmyelophthisis in 72 of 319 rats on various deficient diets. Twenty-four of the 72 animals had hyperemic and hemorrhagic adrenals. The authors stated that the panmyelophthisis was not cured or prevented by the known B vitamins available (thiamine, riboflavin, and pyridoxine) or by a supposedly active filtrate factor preparation. In view of subsequent investigations it appears very probable that pantothenic acid in sufficient amount would have prevented the appearance of the described syndrome even though it may not be a sign of an uncomplicated pantothenic acid deficiency. Attempts to duplicate the hematopoietic findings in other laboratories were unsuccessful until 1945 at which time Daft et al.[22] and Carter and coworkers[24] described very similar blood changes in rats receiving purified diets deficient in pantothenic acid. Daft and coworkers reported that therapy with pantothenic acid was usually unsuccessful unless folic acid also was administered. Adequate amounts of pantothenic acid, but not of folic acid, prevented the development of the blood dyscrasias. Carter et al. did not test folic acid but reported that therapy with pantothenic acid was successful in only 25 % of their animals.

A surprising aspect of the situation is that this striking deficiency syndrome has been observed in so few of the laboratories which have studied pantothenic acid deficiency in rats and that even in those few laboratories its appearance apparently has been sporadic. It appears probable that special conditions must be necessary, possibly the simultaneous deficiency of other food essentials.

c. Achromotrichia

A third aspect of pantothenic acid deficiency in black, hooded, or brown rats is achromotrichia or graying of the hair. Morgan and coworkers[25] and Lunde and Kringstad[26] showed that this condition could be prevented or corrected by the inclusion of filtrate factor concentrates in the diet. This

[22] F. S. Daft, A. Kornberg, L. L. Ashburn, and W. H. Sebrell, *Public Health Repts.* (*U.S.*) **60**, 1201 (1945).

[23] L. L. Ashburn, F. S. Daft, and R. R. Faulkner, *Blood* **2**, 451 (1947).

[24] C. W. Carter, R. G. Macfarlane, J. R. P. O'Brien, and A. H. T. Robb-Smith, *Biochem. J.* **39**, 339 (1945).

[25] A. F. Morgan, B. B. Cook, and H. G. Davison, *J. Nutrition* **15**, 27 (1938).

[26] G. Lunde and H. Kringstad, *Avhandl. Norske Videnskaps—Akad. Oslo.* I *Mat. Naturv. Kl.*, No. 1 (1938).

finding was confirmed by others using concentrates,[27-29] impure pantothenic acid,[30] and finally the pure compound.[31-37] Considerable controversy developed, however, as to how completely the achromotrichia of filtrate factor deficiency (i.e., factors not adsorbed on fuller's earth and known to be different from thiamine, riboflavin, and pyridoxine) could be prevented or cured by pantothenic acid. Williams[38] reported completely negative results, and Frost et al.[39] found only a slight effect of the pure vitamin in preventing graying in their animals. Dimick and Lepp[40] reported that some measure of graying persisted in rats given 50 γ of synthetic pantothenic acid daily, and György and Poling[32] indicated that depigmentation of a less striking nature reappeared in their animals which had been cured of graying even though pantothenic acid supplementation was continued. Emerson and Evans[41] and Pavcek and Baum[42] stated that pantothenic acid, although quite effective, did not restore the hair of rats to its original color but resulted in stippling. Despite the occasional negative findings and the incomplete repigmentation frequently observed, it is generally conceded that pantothenic acid is an important factor in the prevention or treatment of dietary achromotrichia. It is also recognized that under appropriate experimental conditions other dietary deficiencies may be involved. The effect of a copper deficiency on graying of the hair in rats is well established.[43-46]

[27] J. J. Oleson, C. A. Elvehjem, and E. B. Hart, Proc. Soc. Exptl. Biol. Med. 42, 283 (1939).

[28] A. Mohammad, O. H. Emerson, G. A. Emerson, and H. M. Evans, J. Biol. Chem. 133, 17 (1940).

[29] H. Chick, T. F. Macrae, and A. N. Worden, Biochem. J. 34, 580 (1940).

[30] P. György, C. E. Poling, and Y. SubbaRow, J. Biol. Chem. 132, 789 (1940).

[31] P. György and C. E. Poling, Science 92, 202 (1940).

[32] P. György and C. E. Poling, Proc. Soc. Exptl. Biol. Med. 45, 773 (1940).

[33] K. Unna and W. L. Sampson, Proc. Soc. Exptl. Biol. Med. 45, 309 (1940).

[34] K. Unna, Am. J. Physiol. 133, 473 (1941).

[35] C. A. Elvehjem, L. M. Henderson, S. Black, and E. Nielsen, J. Biol. Chem. 140 xxxvi (1941).

[36] K. Unna, G. V. Richards, and W. L. Sampson, J. Nutrition 22, 553 (1941).

[37] L. M. Henderson, J. M. McIntire, H. A. Waisman, and C. A. Elvehjem, J. Nutrition 23, 47 (1942).

[38] R. R. Williams, Science 92, 561 (1940).

[39] D. V. Frost, R. C. Moore, and F. P. Dann, Proc. Soc. Exptl. Biol. Med. 46, 507 (1941).

[40] M. K. Dimick and A. Lepp, J. Nutrition 20, 413 (1940).

[41] G. A. Emerson and H. M. Evans, Proc. Soc. Exptl. Biol. Med. 46, 655 (1941).

[42] P. L. Pavcek and H. M. Baum, Proc. Soc. Exptl. Biol. Med. 47, 271 (1941).

[43] H. L. Keil and V. E. Nelson, J. Biol. Chem. 93, 49 (1931).

[44] A. H. Free, Proc. Soc. Exptl. Biol. Med. 44, 371 (1940).

[45] J. M. Hundley, Proc. Soc. Exptl. Biol. Med. 74, 531 (1950).

[46] J. M. Hundley and R. B. Ing, Endocrinology 48, 482 (1951); J. M. Hundley and R. B. Ing, Federation Proc. 10, 385 (1951)

A deficiency of zinc[47] appears to produce a similar effect on the color of the hair. Folic acid deficiency induced by sulfonamides has been shown to produce achromotrichia in rats[48, 49] as well as in other species, and reports have appeared on chromotrichial effects from cystine,[42] choline,[50] biotin,[32] and sodium chloride.[51] p-Aminobenzoic acid, also, was reported from one laboratory to be a chromotrichial agent,[52, 53] but this finding was not confirmed by other investigators.[36, 37, 54, 55]

An extremely interesting finding in regard to the graying in pantothenic acid deficiency is that of Ralli and Graef[56] that rapid and diffuse, though somewhat transitory, repigmentation, observable first in the skin and then in the hair, occurs following adrenalectomy. The pigmentation of the skin was even more pronounced in adrenalectomized control animals receiving adequate amounts of pantothenic acid. Injections of desoxycortisone inhibited the adrenalectomy-induced melanin deposition.[57, 58] Hypophysectomy caused an effect similar to removal of the adrenal but less striking.[59] The significance of these results is not entirely clear. They appear to demonstrate quite convincingly that the adrenal is in some way concerned with melanin production or deposition. It is tempting to conclude further that the achromotrichia of pantothenic acid deficiency is mediated through the adrenal. However, since the initial pigment deposition is greater than normal, since it occurs in supplemented control rats as well as deficient animals, and since the effect is transitory, such a conclusion does not, at this time, appear to be justified.

d. Nasal Discharge of Porphyrin

Most of the earlier reports on pantothenic acid deficiency in rats, including those on studies carried out on "filtrate factor deficiency" before the actual isolation and identification of the vitamin, referred to the accumulation of red material around the nose, staining the whiskers and fur, as "nosebleed" or "blood-caked" whiskers. Chick et al.[29] and McElroy and

[47] F. E. Stirn, C. A. Elvehjem, and E. B. Hart, J. Biol. Chem. **109**, 347 (1935).
[48] G. J. Martin, Proc. Soc. Exptl. Biol. Med. **51**, 353 (1942).
[49] L. D. Wright and A. D. Welch, J. Nutrition **27**, 55 (1944).
[50] H. S. Owens, M. Trautman, and E. Woods, Science **93**, 502 (1941).
[51] E. P. Ralli, D. H. Clarke, and E. Kennedy, J. Biol. Chem. **141**, 105 (1941).
[52] S. Ansbacher, Science **93**, 164 (1941).
[53] G. J. Martin and S. Ansbacher, J. Biol. Chem. **138**, 441 (1941).
[54] G. A. Emerson, Proc. Soc. Exptl. Biol. Med. **47**, 448 (1941).
[55] F. P. Dann, R. C. Moore, and D. V. Frost, Federation Proc. **1**, 107 (1942).
[56] E. P. Ralli and I. Graef, Endocrinology **32**, 1 (1943).
[57] H. J. Spoon and E. P. Ralli, Endocrinology **35**, 325 (1944).
[58] E. P. Ralli and I. Graef, Endocrinology **37**, 252 (1945).
[59] E. P. Ralli, Trans. 1st Conf. on Adrenal Cortex, New York, p. 159 (1950).

associates,[60] however, showed that the material was porphyrin in nature. Chick and coworkers[29] tentatively identified it as protoporphyrin, but McElroy *et al.*[60] presented evidence for its identity with synthetic coproporphyrin I. The latter workers showed, also, by ablation experiments that the source of the porphyrin was the Harderian glands. Figge and Atkinson[61] reported that limitation of the drinking water of pantothenic acid-supplemented rats led to a similar porphyrin deposition and concluded that pantothenic acid may be involved in the regulation of water metabolism. It has been pointed out by Smith[62] that similar deposits had been observed earlier in riboflavin deficiency and that they, also, had been attributed to dehydration.[63]

e. Growth Failure

The effect of pantothenic acid concentrates (factor 2 concentrates) on rat growth was clearly shown by Lepkovsky and coworkers[64] in 1936. Their sharp separation of factor 1 (pyridoxine) from factor 2 (pantothenic acid) by adsorption of factor 1 on fuller's earth contributed greatly to progress in the field of the B vitamins. Their conclusion that both factors were needed for growth of rats was repeatedly confirmed in the following years with concentrates of pantothenic acid[65-70] and with the pure compound.[2-5, 7, 31-42, 71-73] In large measure the curtailment of growth in pantothenic acid deficiency is due to inanition, but it has been shown by paired feeding experiments that the administration of this vitamin results in a specific growth-promoting effect not related to appetite.[74]

f. Dermatitis

The first clear differentiation of the dermatitis of pantothenic acid deficiency in the rat from that of other B-vitamin deficiencies appears to have

[60] L. W. McElroy, K. Salomon, F. H. J. Figge, and G. R. Cowgill, *Science* **94**, 467 (1941).

[61] F. H. J. Figge and W. B. Atkinson, *Proc. Soc. Exptl. Biol. Med.* **48**, 112 (1941).

[62] S. G. Smith, *Proc. Soc. Exptl. Biol. Med.* **49**, 691 (1942).

[63] S. G. Smith and D. H. Sprunt, *J. Nutrition* **10**, 481 (1935).

[64] S. Lepkovsky, T. H. Jukes, and M. E. Krause, *J. Biol. Chem.* **115**, 557 (1936).

[65] C. E. Edgar and T. F. Macrae, *Biochem. J.* **31**, 893 (1937).

[66] Y. SubbaRow and G. H. Hitchings, *J. Am. Chem. Soc.* **61**, 1615 (1939).

[67] M. M. El-Sadr, H. G. Hind, T. F. Macrae, C. E. Work, B. Lythgoe, and A. R. Todd, *Nature* **144**, 73 (1939).

[68] G. H. Hitchings and Y. SubbaRow, *J. Nutrition* **18**, 265 (1939).

[69] J. J. Oleson, D. W. Woolley, and C. A. Elvehjem, *Proc. Soc. Exptl. Biol. Med.* **42**, 151 (1939).

[70] D. W. Woolley, *Science* **91**, 245 (1940).

[71] K. Unna, *Am. J. Med. Sci.* **200**, 848 (1940).

[72] K. Schwarz, *Z. physiol. Chem.* **275**, 245 (1942).

[73] K. Unna and G. V. Richards, *J. Nutrition* **23**, 545 (1942).

[74] L. Voris, A. Black, R. W. Swift, and C. E. French, *J. Nutrition* **23**, 555 (1942).

been made by György and associates[75-77] soon after pyridoxine first became available. These investigators described the lesion as an exfoliative dermatitis. Scaliness was observed most frequently in the region of the abdomen, head, groin, and acillae. In the following years, most other investigators in the field observed some degree of dermatitis in animals receiving thiamine, riboflavin, and pyridoxine but deficient in pantothenic acid. After pure pantothenate became available, it was widely noted that these lesions responded to its administration.[2-5, 31-42, 71-73] Sullivan and Nicholls, in their series of studies on nutritional dermatoses in the rat, investigated the effect of this deficiency.[78] They described the lesions of pantothenic acid deficiency as generalized scaling, small eczematous crusted plaques, diffuse alopecia of the venter and the preauricular regions, and alopecia with or without inflammation in the circumocular regions. They reported that the histological lesions consisted of milk hyperkeratosis, acanthosis, occasionally parakeratosis, a small amount of edema and vesiculation, dilatation of the hair follicles, and, in the late stages, disintegration of the sebaceous glands in the areas of alopecia. To most observers, the dermatitis has not been a striking feature of pantothenic acid deficiency in the rat.

Collins et al.[78a] have reported that rats kept under conditions of low relative humidity developed dermatitis, whereas those kept at 50% relative humidity or above did not.

g. Other Pathological Changes

Other pathological changes reported as occurring in pantothenic acid-deficient rats are hemorrhages into the gastrointestinal tract with abscesses and macrophage accumulation in the submucosa;[8, 78b] reduction of spermatogenesis and other signs of damage to the testes;[8, 9] lesions of the kidney,[8, 10, 79] liver,[8, 10] and heart;[8, 79] hemosiderin deposition in the spleen;[8, 9] inhibition of skeletal growth (cartilage hypoplasia);[9, 16, 80] atrophy of the thymus;[10, 16, 23] and changes in the bone marrow, ranging from impairment of hematopoiesis[80] to the almost complete aplasia which has been discussed in an earlier paragraph.[3, 22-24] Although some degree of some of the above changes can be brought about by inanition alone (e.g., reduc-

[75] P. György, *J. Am. Chem. Soc.* **60**, 983 (1938).

[76] P. György and R. E. Eckardt, *Nature* **144**, 512 (1939).

[77] P. György, C. E. Poling, and Y. SubbaRow, *Proc. Soc. Exptl. Biol. Med.* **42**, 738 (1939).

[78] M. Sullivan and J. Nicholls, *Arch. Dermatol. and Syphilol.* **45**, 917 (1942).

[78a] R. A. Collins, M. Schreiber, and C. A. Elvehjem, *J. Nutrition* **49**, 589 (1953).

[78b] J. J. Vitale, D. M. Hegsted, J. Di Giorgio, and N. Zamcheck, *Metabolism* **2**, 367 (1953).

[79] G. C. Supplee, R. C. Bender, and O. J. Kahlenberg, *Endocrinology* **30**, 355 (1942).

[80] M. M. Nelson, E. Sulon, H. Becks, W. W. Wainwright, and H. M. Evans, *Proc. Soc. Exptl. Biol. Med.* **73**, 31 (1950).

tion of spermatogenesis and inhibition of skeletal growth), it does not appear that any of the changes reported can be accounted for entirely in this way.

2. CHICKS

Deficiency signs, now known to be due chiefly to a lack of pantothenic acid, were described in chicks fed heated diets by Kline et al.[81] in 1932. Even before this time, studies with chickens had indicated that there were unidentified factors of the B complex yet to be discovered (for example, vitamin B_3 of Eddy et al.[82] and the unidentified factor of Norris and co-workers[83, 84]). It is now evident that perhaps a part, but not all, of these early deficiencies can be accounted for by a lack of pantothenic acid. (See the review by Williams.[85]) Since 1932, basal diets have been improved for the study of this vitamin and deficiency signs have been more adequately described by a number of workers.[86-101] That the use of purified or synthetic pantothenic acid in the diet would prevent the occurrence of certain deficiency signs was first shown in 1939–1940 by Woolley et al.,[102, 103] Jukes,[104, 105] Babcock and Jukes,[106] and Stiller et al.[107]

[81] O. L. Kline, J. A. Keenan, C. A. Elvehjem, and E. B. Hart, J. Biol. Chem. 99, 295 (1932).

[82] W. H. Eddy, S. Gurin, and J. C. Keresztesy, J. Biol. Chem. 87, 729 (1930).

[83] L. C. Norris and A. T. Ringrose, Science 71, 643 (1930).

[84] A. T. Ringrose, L. C. Norris, and G. F. Heuser, Poultry Sci. 10, 166 (1931).

[85] R. J. Williams, Advances in Enzymol. 3, 253 (1943).

[86] D. M. Hegsted and F. Lipmann, J. Biol. Chem. 174, 89 (1948).

[87] M. E. Coates, J. E. Ford, G. F. Harrison, S. K. Kon, E. E. Shepheard, and F. W. Wilby, Brit. J. Nutrition 6, 75 (1952).

[88] H. A. Waisman, O. Mickelsen, and C. A. Elvehjem, J. Nutrition 18, 247 (1939).

[89] T. H. Jukes, J. Nutrition 21, 193 (1941).

[90] T. H. Jukes and S. Lepkovsky, J. Biol. Chem. 114, 117 (1936).

[91] J. G. Lease and H. T. Parsons, Biochem. J. 28, 2109 (1934).

[92] C. A. Elvehjem and C. J. Koehn, Jr., J. Biol. Chem. 108, 709 (1935).

[93] S. Lepkovsky and T. H. Jukes, J. Biol. Chem. 114, 109 (1936).

[94] A. T. Ringrose and L. C. Norris, J. Nutrition 12, 553 (1936).

[95] O. Mickelsen, H. A. Waisman, and C. A. Elvehjem, J. Biol. Chem. 124, 313 (1938).

[96] M. K. Dimick and A. Lepp, J. Nutrition 20, 413 (1940).

[97] H. A. Waisman, R. C. Mills, and C. A. Elvehjem, J. Nutrition 24, 187 (1942).

[98] T. H. Jukes and L. W. McElroy, Poultry Sci. 22, 438 (1943).

[99] T. Ram, Poultry Sci. 28, 425 (1949).

[100] J. L. Milligan and G. M. Briggs, Poultry Sci. 28, 202 (1949).

[101] M. E. Coates, S. K. Kon, and E. E. Shepheard, Brit. J. Nutrition 4, 203 (1950).

[102] D. W. Woolley, H. A. Waisman, and C. A. Elvehjem, J. Am. Chem. Soc. 61, 977 (1939).

[103] D. W. Woolley, H. A. Waisman, and C. A. Elvehjem, J. Biol. Chem. 129, 673 (1939).

[104] T. H. Jukes, J. Am. Chem. Soc. 61, 975 (1939).

[105] T. H. Jukes, J. Biol. Chem. 129, 225 (1939).

[106] S. H. Babcock, Jr., and T. H. Jukes, J. Am. Chem. Soc. 62, 1628 (1940).

A unique feature of acute pantothenic acid deficiency in the young chick
is the occurrence of a severe dermatitis in the corners of the mouth, often
extending under the lower mandible and to the nostrils. The dermatitis is
the first specific symptom seen, usually when the chicks are 14 to 21 days
old. The eyelids become granular and eventually stick together in severely
affected birds unless they are manually separated. Mild dermatitis between
the toes and on the upper surface of the foot may also occur, but, if so,
this is not generally seen until several days after appearance of the mouth
and eye symptoms. The foot symptoms may never appear in borderline
deficiencies.

The dermatitis symptoms closely resemble those of a biotin deficiency in
the chick. Early reports of Norris and coworkers[83, 84] in 1930 and 1931 described symptoms chiefly of a biotin dermatitis in chicks, sometimes mis-
takenly attributed in the literature since then to be due mainly to a pantothenic acid deficiency. The deficiency described by these investigators was
produced, in part, by diets containing unheated egg white, which is now
known to cause a biotin deficiency. Distinction between the dermatitis of
pantothenic acid and of biotin deficiencies has been since described by Lease
and Parsons,[91] Ringrose and Norris,[94, 108] Lepkovsky and Jukes,[109] Hegsted
et al.,[110] and others.[111] In true pantothenic acid deficiency the mouth and
eyelids are chiefly affected and the feet are involved to a minor extent,
whereas in a biotin deficiency the feet are severely affected before the oral
symptoms appear.

Other signs of pantothenic acid deficiency in the chick include poor feathers (which may become brittle and drop off),[100] lowered efficiency of feed
utilization,[100] lowered pantothenic acid content (and no doubt coenzyme A)
of blood and tissues,[112] slow growth rate or weight loss, and, in severe cases,
incoordination, paralysis, and death at as early as 3 to 4 weeks of age.[91-101]
Although graying of hair has been associated with pantothenic acid deficiency in certain other animals, no loss of feather pigment has been noted
in colored breeds of chicks. The feather depigmentation reported by Groody
and Groody in 1942[113] attributed to a pantothenic acid deficiency, is un-
confirmed and was more likely due to inanition which itself may cause depigmentation.[114] The positive control birds fed pantothenic acid in the

[07] E. T. Stiller, S. A. Harris, J. Finkelstein, J. C. Keresztesy, and K. Folkers, J.
Am. Chem. Soc. 62, 1785 (1940).
[08] A. T. Ringrose and L. C. Norris, J. Nutrition 12, 535 (1936).
[09] S. Lepkovsky and T. H. Jukes, J. Biol. Chem. 111, 119 (1935).
[10] D. M. Hegsted, J. J. Oleson, R. C. Mills, C. A. Elvehjem, and E. B. Hart, J.
Nutrition 20, 599 (1940).
[11] T. H. Jukes, Biol. Symposia 12, 253 (1947).
[12] E. E. Snell, D. Pennington, and R. J. Williams, J. Biol. Chem. 133, 559 (1940).
[13] T. C. Groody and M. E. Groody, Science 95, 655 (1942).
[14] G. M. Briggs, Poultry Sci. 15, 41 (1946).

studies of Groody and Groody gained only 151 g. in 66 days, showing that other growth factors were lacking also.

Histological study of the tissue of pantothenic acid-deficient chicks, as reported by Phillips and Engel[115] and Shaw and Phillips,[116] showed lesions in the spinal cord characterized by myelin degeneration of myelinated fibers distributed widely throughout the white matter but chiefly in the lateral and anterior columns and extending to all segments of the cord. Axon degeneration also occurred to some extent. The spinal cord alone and not the peripheral nerves seemed to be involved.[116] Thymus involution and, occasionally, liver damage were also seen. Coates et al.[101] have also reported liver damage ("dark and patchy livers") in pantothenic acid-deficient chicks.

Ram[99] found myelin degeneration in the motor apparatus of the brain in addition to the spinal cord. Ram also found eroded gizzard lining, slightly thickened proventriculus, and distended gall bladder. It is questionable whether or not these symptoms are specific, since the diet of Ram contained only 10 γ each of added biotin and folic acid per 100 g. of diet, and no weight values of the positive control birds were given for proper evaluation of the results.

That hens also require pantothenic acid was suggested by Bauernfeind and Norris in 1939[117, 118] and later confirmed by Gillis et al. (1942),[119] who first used crystalline pantothenic acid. Deficient hens, as demonstrated by more recent work, may not have the typical dermatitis symptoms seen in the chick, but in severe cases they show loss of weight, possible drop in egg production, poor hatchability of eggs (due to death of the 18 to 21-day-old embryo), poor qualtity of down on the embryo, and loss of viability and growth of progeny, as indicated chiefly by the work of Gillis et al.[119-121]

A deficiency in the hen also results in a lowering of the pantothenic acid content of the egg,[120, 122, 123] the blood, and the tissues.[120, 124, 125] Low pantothenic acid content of eggs is associated with lowered amounts in hatched chicks.[123] Higher than normal pantothenic acid content of eggs may give

[115] P. H. Phillips and R. W. Engel, J. Nutrition 18, 227 (1939).
[116] J. H. Shaw and P. H. Phillips, J. Nutrition 29, 107 (1945).
[117] J. C. Bauernfeind and L. C. Norris, Science 89, 416 (1939).
[118] J. C. Bauernfeind and L. C. Norris, J. Nutrition 18, 579 (1939).
[119] M. B. Gillis, G. F. Heuser and L. C. Norris, J. Nutrition 23, 153 (1942).
[120] M. B. Gillis, G. F. Heuser, and L. C. Norris, J. Nutrition 35, 351 (1948).
[121] M. B. Gillis, G. F. Heuser, and L. C. Norris, J. Nutrition 26, 285 (1943).
[122] E. E. Snell, E. Aline, J. R. Couch, and P. B. Pearson, J. Nutrition 21, 201 (1941).
[123] P. B. Pearson, V. H. Melass, and R. M. Sherwood, Arch. Biochem. 7, 353 (1945).
[124] P. B. Pearson, V. H. Melass, and R. M. Sherwood, J. Nutrition 32, 187 (1946).
[125] P. B. Pearson and V. H. Melass, Federation Proc. 5, 237 (1946).

rise to depressed size of embryonic heart and brain and higher concentration of hemoglobin as compared with the normal.[126]

It is interesting that there have recently been occasional reports showing that pantothenic acid resulted in small (and often insignificant) growth responses when added to practical poultry rations, chiefly of the corn-soybean oil meal type.[127-129] As a result of these reports many feed manufacturers are today adding supplementary synthetic calcium pantothenate to certain poultry rations, especially turkey starters. In spite of this, at present there is no clear-cut evidence that supplements of this vitamin need to be added routinely to any commercial poultry feed. For every report showing a possible positive effect from pantothenic acid addition there have been many more showing negative results. Obviously, future studies on this aspect are needed.

3. TURKEYS

Symptoms of pantothenic acid deficiency in the turkey poult are similar to those in chickens and include dermatitis of the mouth, adhesions of the eyelids, weakness, lowered growth rate, and, in severe cases, death.[130] The deficiency was first studied by Jukes[131] in 1938, before the availability of pure pantothenic acid. More recent studies, with pure pantothenic acid, have been made by Lepkovsky et al. (1945),[132] who showed that the requirement was higher than that of chickens, and by Kratzer and Williams (1948)[130] who used an improved basal diet. No information is available on pantothenic acid deficiency in the mature turkey, although it could be assumed that it is necessary.

4. DUCKS, PIGEONS, AND OTHER FOWL

Probably the first report of a pantothenic acid deficiency in the duck was made by Trager[133] in 1943, who used a heated grain-casein diet. Deficient

26 A. Taylor, J. Thacker, and D. Pennington, Science 94, 542 (1941).

27 J. A. Marvel, C. W. Carrick, R. E. Roberts, and S. M. Hauge, Poultry Sci. 24, 253 (1945); H. R. Bird and M. Rubin, ibid. 25, 87 (1946); D. H. Mishler, C. W. Carrick, R. E. Roberts, and S. M. Hauge, ibid. 25, 479 (1946).

28 A. R. Robblee and D. R. Clandinin, Poultry Sci. 28, 781 (1949); 29, 777 (1950); 32, 579 (1953).

29 S. J. Slinger, W. F. Pepper, D. C. Hill, and E. S. Snyder, Poultry Sci. 31, 193 (1952); M. L. Sunde, J. R. Vedvik, H. W. Bruins, and W. W. Cravens, ibid. 31, 571 (1952).

30 F. H. Kratzer and D. Williams, Poultry Sci. 27, 518 (1948).

31 T. H. Jukes, Poultry Sci. 17, 227 (1938).

32 S. Lepkovsky, F. H. Bird, F. H. Kratzer, and V. S. Asmundson, Poultry Sci. 24, 335 (1945).

33 W. Trager, J. Exptl. Med. 77, 557 (1943).

ducks became weak, grew poorly, had lowered pantothenic acid content of the blood, and had sticky eyelids, while the control ducks fed pantothenic acid appeared "entirely normal." More extensive studies have been made by Hegsted and Perry,[134] who found that 3- to 4-day-old ducks very rapidly develop acute pantothenic acid deficiency when placed on a synthetic diet low in pantothenic acid. In these studies ducks failed to grow after only 2 or 3 days on the diet and usually died within 4 to 7 days, whereas positive control ducks with pantothenic acid gained as much as an average of 35 g. per day for 10 days. It may be pointed out that no other animal has been reported to show such marked effects in such a short period when fed pantothenic acid-low diets.

Because of the obvious importance of pantothenic acid for the duck, this species has been useful in studying the effect of a deficiency of this vitamin on the metabolism of tissues. Olson and Kaplan,[135] in 1948, and Olson and Stare,[136] in 1951, reported that coenzyme A values of liver and heart tissues of pantothenic acid-deficient ducks fell 50 to 70 % in only 5 days and that there was a decreased ability of the tissues to metabolize pyruvic acid. In these two studies, ducks 7 days old were used in order to obtain better survival. The authors reported the occurrence of anorexia, conjunctivitis, and decreased feed efficiency in the deficient ducks. Dermatitis was noted in these studies,[135] although Hegsted and Perry[134] did not observe dermatitis in their ducks.

Some of the earliest studies on what is now known as pantothenic acid were made with the pigeon, although the diets were complicated with other deficiencies.[82, 85, 137-140] At least part of the activity of vitamin B_3,[82] first discovered in 1928, may probably be explained by pantothenic acid. Lee and Hogan first used pure pantothenic acid in the pigeon and reported, in 1942, that this vitamin was needed for growth and for prevention of anemia.[141] Additional studies with the pigeon, with the use of nutritionally complete diets, are needed.

No reports have appeared on pantothenic acid deficiency in pheasants, quail, geese, guinea, and other fowl, although presumably these animals also require pantothenic acid.

[134] D. M. Hegsted and R. L. Perry, *J. Nutrition* **35,** 411 (1948).
[135] R. E. Olson and N. O. Kaplan, *J. Biol. Chem.* **175,** 515 (1948).
[136] R. E. Olson and F. J. Stare, *J. Biol. Chem.* **190,** 149 (1951).
[137] R. R. Williams and R. E. Waterman, *J. Biol. Chem.* **78,** 311 (1928).
[138] C. W. Carter and J. R. O'Brien, *Biochem. J.* **30,** 43 (1936).
[139] C. W. Carter and J. R. O'Brien, *Biochem. J.* **33,** 1810 (1939).
[140] C. W. Carter, H. W. Kinnersley, and R. A. Peters, *Biochem. J.* **24,** 1832 (1930).
[141] J. G. Lee and A. G. Hogan, *Missouri Agr. Expt. Sta. Research Bull.* **342** (1942).

5. Dogs

Before the availability of pure pantothenic acid, several reports in 1939 indicated that this vitamin may be important in dog nutrition.[12, 142-144] These studies were obviously complicated with other deficiencies, and it wasn't until Morgan (1941),[145] Schaefer *et al.* (1942),[146] Scudi and Hamlin (1942),[147] and Silber (1944)[148] used pure pantothenic acid that convincing evidence was obtained for its need. Even these diets were inadequate by today's standards, however.

Pantothenic acid-deficient dogs usually show the following symptoms:[146, 148] lowered growth rate, decreased appetite, irritability and sudden prostration or coma, rapid respiratory and heart rate, convulsions, gastrointestinal symptoms, and, eventually, death. Spasticity may occur in the hind quarters during the last week. The hair of deficient dogs may appear coarser, but there has been no evidence of alopecia, graying, or other skin or hair disorder. The corneal reflex is sluggish at the time of collapse, and there may be excessive salivation.

Gross examination of tissues of pantothenic acid-deficient dogs revealed fatty livers (as high as 55 % fat), evidence of hemorrhagic kidney degeneration in the cortex and medulla, frequently gastritis or enteritis and intussusception, and possibly mottled thymuses, The occurrence of mottled thymuses and hemorrhagic kidneys has been questioned.[148] No histological studies have been presented except preliminary liver pathology.[147]

In addition to these signs, deficient dogs show lowered pantothenic acid content of liver, muscle, brain, and blood,[148] lowered blood sugar,[146] a lowering of cholesterol, cholesterol esters, lipoid phosphorus, and total lipoids in the blood (correlated with occurrence of liver damage),[147] and possible decreased gastrointestinal motility and poor digestion and absorption of carbohydrate and protein.[149] Although hemorrhagic adrenals were not seen in earlier studies,[146, 148] Morgan and Guehring[150] stated that they obtained hemorrhagic adrenals in their pantothenic acid-deficient dogs unless 1 % of cholesterol was added to the diet. Fatty livers occurred whether or not cholesterol was fed.[150]

[142] P. J. Fouts, O. M. Helmer, and S. Lepkovsky, *J. Nutrition* **19**, 393 (1940).
[143] J. M. McKibbin, R. J. Madden, S. Black, and C. A. Elvehjem, *Am. J. Physiol.* **128**, 102 (1939).
[144] J. M. McKibbin, S. Black, and C. A. Elvehjem, *Am. J. Physiol.* **130**, 365 (1940).
[145] A. F. Morgan, *Science* **93**, 261 (1941).
[146] A. E. Schaefer, J. M. McKibbin, and C. A. Elvehjem, *J. Biol. Chem.* **143**, 321 (1942).
[147] J. V. Scudi and M. Hamlin, *J. Nutrition* **24**, 273 (1942).
[148] R. H. Silber, *J. Nutrition* **27**, 425 (1944).
[149] C. G. Bly, F. W. Heggeness, and E. S. Nasset, *J. Nutrition* **26**, 161 (1943).
[150] A. F. Morgan and R. R. Guehring, *Federation Proc.* **10**, 226 (1951).

The amount of pantothenic acid excreted in the urine is in proportion to the amount in the diet (Silber and Unna[151] and Silber[148]). Only a small fraction of ingested pantothenic acid may appear in the urine, whereas fecal excretion is rather constant (Silber[152]).

Adult dogs are more resistant to a deficiency than are puppies, apparently requiring less dietary pantothenic acid.[146-148, 153] Little is known about pantothenic acid requirements for reproduction of the dog.

6. GUINEA PIGS

Reid in 1952[154] demonstrated that young guinea pigs require a dietary source of pantothenic acid when fed a synthetic-type diet. Symptoms of deficiency include decrease in growth rate and loss of weight, anorexia accompanied by inactivity and weakness, rough hair coat, cyanosis at the margin of the ears, and diarrhea. The report of Reid is the first study of a clear-cut pantothenic acid deficiency in the guinea pig. A previous study by Morgan and Simms[12] showing gray hair in guinea pigs was inadequate to prove that pantothenic acid was the limiting factor.

7. SWINE

It would be difficult to determine who first described signs of pantothenic acid deficiency in swine, because abnormal gait, now known to be associated with pantothenic acid deficiency, had been seen in pigs many years before the discovery of pantothenic acid (see the review by Wintrobe, et al.[155]). Between 1938 and 1941 deficiency symptoms were obtained in pigs by a number of workers, but it is clear now that the diets used were deficient in other factors as well as in pantothenic acid.[155-159]

The first studies in which responses were obtained with pure pantothenic acid were made independently in 1942 by Hughes[160] and Wintrobe et al.[161] with the use of diets very similar to those used previously. Since 1942, a number of workers have made careful studies of pantothenic acid-deficiency

[151] R. H. Silber and K. Unna, *J. Biol. Chem.* **142**, 623 (1942).

[152] R. H. Silber, *Arch. Biochem.* **7**, 329 (1945).

[153] A. O. Seeler and R. H. Silber, *J. Nutrition* **30**, 111 (1945).

[154] M. E. Reid, *Federation Proc.* **11**, 453 (1952).

[155] M. M. Wintrobe, J. L. Miller, Jr., and H. Lisco, *Bull. Johns Hopkins Hosp.* **67** 377 (1940).

[156] H. Chick, T. F. Macrae, A. J. P. Martin, and C. J. Martin, *Biochem. J.* **32**, 220 (1938).

[157] E. H. Hughes, *J. Nutrition* **17**, 527 (1939).

[158] M. M. Wintrobe, *Am. J. Physiol.* **126**, 375 (1939).

[159] N. R. Ellis and L. L. Madsen, *J. Agr. Research* **62**, 303 (1941).

[160] E. H. Hughes, *J. Agr. Research* **64**, 185 (1942).

[161] M. M. Wintrobe, M. H. Miller, R. H. Follis, Jr., H. J. Stein, C. Mushatt, and S Humphreys, *J. Nutrition* **24**, 345 (1942).

symptoms in swine, although again much of this work was complicated by other vitamin deficiencies.[162-165]

As a result of the above-mentioned studies, further clarified by studies made since 1947 with more complete diets,[166-171] it may be concluded that the following symptoms of pantothenic acid deficiency may be seen in young swine (given approximately in the order of appearance): excessive lachrymation, coughing, decrease in appetite, dermatitis, incoordinated movements of the hind legs and a spastic gait ("goose-stepping"—one of the most characteristic symptoms), dull and roughened hair coat and skin and eventually some alopecia, brown exudate around the eyes, diarrhea, poor weight gains, loss of sucking reflexes and control of tongue, rectal hemorrhages, and low urinary excretion of pantothenic acid. Postmortem gross examination reveals loss of subcutaneous and internal fat, soft ribs and long bones, and light bone marrow.[169] Gastritis[160] and diffuse hyperemia, formation of small ulcers, and inflammatory changes of the bowel[163] may also be seen.

Changes in the tissues may include development of a moderate normocytic anemia, a fall in serum chlorides, increase in the carbon dioxide combining power of the blood, a terminal rise in non-protein nitrogen, and sometimes hypoglycemia.[163] A lowering of the pantothenic acid content of blood has also been observed in deficient animals[167] as well as a lowering of creatinine, total lipids, total cholesterol, cholesterol esters, and free cholesterol.[172]

Histological examination[163] may show atrophy of the cells lining the glands of the mucosa, abscess formation, and ulceration of the large intestine. Sensory nerve degeneration is also seen.[165] The dorsal root ganglion cells exhibit chromatolysis. The Nissl bodies become finer and finally dissolve, leaving a homogeneous ground substance. Loss of myelin of the peripheral nerves and axis cylinder degeneration is also found, as well as cer-

[162] E. H. Hughes and N. R. Ittner, J. Animal Sci. 1, 116 (1942).

[163] M. M. Wintrobe, R. H. Follis, Jr., R. Alcayaga, M. Paulson, and S. Humphreys, Bull. Johns Hopkins Hosp. 73, 313 (1943).

[164] N. R. Ellis, L. L. Madsen, and C. O. Miller, J. Animal Sci. 2, 365 (1943).

[165] R. H. Follis and M. M. Wintrobe, J. Exptl. Med. 81, 539 (1945).

[166] R. W. Colby, T. J. Cunha, C. E. Lindley, D. R. Cordy, and M. E. Ensminger, J. Am. Vet. Med. Assoc. 113, 589 (1948).

[167] R. W. Luecke, F. Thorp, Jr., W. N. McMillen, and H. W. Dunne, J. Animal Sci. 8, 464 (1949).

[168] R. W. Luecke, W. N. McMillen, and F. Thorp, Jr., J. Animal Sci. 9, 78 (1950).

[168a] G. L. Sharma, R. L. Johnston, R. W. Luecke, J. A. Hoefer, M. L. Gray, and F. Thorp, Jr., Am. J. Vet. Research 13, 298 (1952).

[169] A. C. Wiese, W. P. Lehrer, P. R. Moore, O. F. Pahnish, and W. V. Hartwell, J. Animal Sci. 10, 80 (1951).

[170] R. W. Luecke, J. A. Hoefer, and F. Thorp, Jr., J. Animal Sci. 11, 238 (1952).

[171] Committee on Animal Nutrition, Recommended Nutrient Allowances for Swine. National Research Council, Washington, D. C., 1950.

[172] W. C. Russell and A. E. Teeri, Federation Proc. 7, 297 (1948).

tain other changes.[165] No changes in the adrenal gland have been noted in swine.[163]

The heated diet, used to a great extent in pantothenic acid studies with poultry, has not been used to any great extent with swine. However, Ellis and Madsen[159] in 1941, showed that incoordination and myelin degeneration developed in animals fed a heated diet.

In experiments with sows, Hodgskiss *et al.* in 1950[173] demonstrated for the first time that pantothenic acid-deficiency signs may develop in the adult animal. Deficient sows showed loss of appetite, reduced water intake, "goose-stepping" with hind legs, diarrhea, and rectal hemorrhages. Reproduction was abnormal because of death of the fetus. Autopsy of pregnant sows showed macerating fetuses in the uterine horns as well as "hemorrhagiconecrotic cecocolitis," gastroenteritis, and catarrh of the stomach and small intestine.

It is of interest that in practical swine feeding there is some evidence that the usual amount of pantothenic acid in corn-soybean oil meal type rations is often not enough to provide for optimal growth.[167, 168, 174] This is especially true if the diet is low in protein (less than 15 %) since higher levels of soybean oil meal may protect pigs from a deficiency of pantothenic acid[17] owing either to increased levels of protein or to some other sparing factor. Several reports to the contrary, showing no effect of pantothenic acid in practical rations, have appeared.[174a] Whether this vitamin should be added to all commercial swine rations of a corn-soybean meal nature can only be answered by further research.

8. Cattle and Sheep

Although it is well known that all the B vitamins, including pantothenic acid, are synthesized by the microflora in the rumen of cattle and sheep, it is becoming increasingly evident that dietary sources of the B vitamins are needed in the very young animal before the rumen starts to function. For instance, the newborn calf requires a dietary source of pantothenic acid when fed "synthetic-type" diets, according to Johnson *et al.* in 1947.[17] Signs of pantothenic acid deficiency included diarrhea, cessation of growth, weakness of the legs with inability to stand, and decreased urinary level

[173] H. W. Hodgskiss, M. E. Ensminger, R. W. Colby, and T. J. Cunha, *J. Animal Sci.* **9**, 619 (1950); M. E. Ensminger, R. W. Colby, and T. C. Cunha, *Washington Agr. Expt. Sta. Circ.* **134**, 1951.

[174] J. E. Briggs and W. M. Beeson, *J. Animal Sci.* **10**, 813 (1951); R. W. Luecke, J. A. Hoefer, and F. Thorp, Jr., *J. Animal Sci.* **12**, 605 (1953).

[174a] D. V. Catron, R. W. Bennison, H. M. Maddock, G. C. Ashton, and P. G. Homeyer, *J. Animal Sci.* **12**, 51 (1953).

[175] B. C. Johnson, H. H. Mitchell, T. S. Hamilton, and W. B. Nevens, *Federation Proc.* **6**, 410 (1947).

of pantothenic acid. These results are only preliminary, and more work is necessary with this vitamin in cattle. Pantothenic acid deficiency has not been studied in the young lamb as yet, but it would be expected they would need this vitamin.

9. MONKEYS

Very little information is available concerning pantothenic acid in monkey nutrition. McCall et al.[176] in 1946 reported that pantothenic acid deficiency in rhesus monkeys was characterized by lack of growth, ataxia, graying and thinning of the fur, anemia, diarrhea, and cachexia. Dermatitis was noted in one animal. These studies were complicated by a concurrent deficiency of a factor present in liver, and complete recovery was not obtained with the administration of pantothenic acid. Additional studies in monkeys are needed, especially because of the close relationship between this animal and the human being.

The daily intake of 3 mg. of pantothenic acid appears to be fully adequate to prevent the occurrence of deficiency symptoms.

10. MICE

In most, but not all, respects, pantothenic acid deficiency in the mouse resembles its counterpart in the rat. The most striking differences are the absence of necrotic and hemorrhagic adrenals in the mouse and the development of paralysis of the hind legs with nerve tissue degeneration in this species.

Achromotrichia and growth failure of C57 black mice and repigmentation and growth resumption following pantothenic acid therapy were described by György and Poling.[32] Martin[177] reported that graying in Rockland strain black mice was partially, but not completely, reversed by similar therapy. Norris and Hauschildt[178] observed the development of dermatitis in mice receiving thiamine, riboflavin, niacin, pyridoxine, and "filtrate factor." There is considerable question, however, as to whether their animals were receiving adequate amounts of filtrate factor, i.e., pantothenic acid. Cerecedo and coworkers[179, 180] and Martin[177] noted a very similar dermatitis, together with alopecia and growth failure, in mice which were deficient in this vitamin. All these changes were prevented or reversed by pantothenic acid administration.

[176] K. B. McCall, H. A. Waisman, C. A. Elvehjem, and E. S. Jones, J. Nutrition 31, 685 (1946).
[177] G. J. Martin, Science 93, 422 (1941).
[178] E. R. Norris and J. Hauschildt, Science 92, 316 (1940).
[179] J. G. Sandza and L. R. Cerecedo, J. Nutrition 21, 609 (1941).
[180] J. R. Foy and L. R. Cerecedo, J. Nutrition 22, 439 (1941).

Morris and Lippincott[181-183] made histopathological as well as other studies of pantothenic acid deficiency in C3H mice. They reported growth failure, followed by depilation and a dermatosis which presented a scaly "chalklike" appearance. An additional deficiency sign was a partial paralysis of the hind legs. Histologically, the dermatosis was described as hyperkeratotic and desquamative; myelin degeneration of the spinal cord, posterior roots, and sciatic nerves was noted. The adrenal cortex was found to be normal. These observations were, in general, confirmed by Woolley,[184] who observed hyperirritability, lack of muscular control followed by paralysis, and closure of the eyes by a sticky exudate. Jones et al.[185] found no signs of paralysis in their deficient albino mice but noted spasticity of the extremities, arching of the spine, and an awkward gait as well as a striking alopecia, scaly desquamation of the skin, and hyperemia and edema of the eyelids. Melampy and coworkers[185a] noted lipid depletion of the adrenal in adult mice of CF No. 1 strain kept on a pantothenic acid-deficient diet but reported an even more rapid depletion in starvation. A strain variation in susceptibility to pantothenic acid deficiency has been reported.[185b, 185c]

11. Other Species of Animals

Pantothenic acid has been studied in several other animal species, and it has been shown to be required for fish (McLaren et al.[186]), the fox (Lunde and Kringstad[187] and Morgan and Simms[188]), the hamster (Routh and Houchin[189]), various insects (see reviews on this subject[190, 191]), and the toad (tadpole stage, Catolla-Cavalcanti[192]). In this connection, Shock and Sebrell[193] found that the work output of frog muscles was improved by the addition of calcium pantothenate to the perfusion fluid.

[181] H. P. Morris and S. W. Lippincott, J. Natl. Cancer Inst. 2, 29 (1941).

[182] S. W. Lippincott and H. P. Morris, J. Natl. Cancer Inst. 2, 39 (1941).

[183] S. W. Lippincott and H. P. Morris, Am. J. Pathol. 17, 588 (1941).

[184] D. W. Woolley, Proc. Soc. Exptl. Biol. Med. 46, 565 (1941).

[185] J. H. Jones, C. Foster, F. Dorfman, and G. L. Hunter, J. Nutrition 29, 127 (1945).

[185a] R. M. Melampy, D. W. Cheng, and L. C. Northrop, Proc. Soc. Exptl. Biol. Med. 76, 24 (1951).

[185b] P. F. Fenton, G. R. Cowgill, M. A. Stone, and D. H. Justice, J. Nutrition 42, 257 (1950).

[185c] D. R. Weir, J. Nutrition 49, 425 (1953).

[186] B. A. McLaren, B. E. Keller, D. J. O'Donnell, and C. A. Elvehjem, Arch. Biochem, 15, 169 (1947); L. E. Wolf, Progressive Fish Culturist, 13, No. 1, 17 (1951).

[187] G. Lunde and H. Kringstad, Naturwissenschaften 27, 755 (1939).

[188] A. F. Morgan and H. D. Simms, J. Nutrition 20, 627 (1940).

[189] J. I. Routh and O. B. Houchin, Federation Proc. 1, 191 (1942).

[190] F. A. Robinson, The Vitamin B Complex. John Wiley and Sons, New York, 1951.

[191] R. J. Williams, R. E. Eakin, E. Beerstecher, Jr., and W. Shive, The Biochemistry of B Vitamins. Reinhold Publishing Corp., New York, 1950.

[192] A. Catolla-Cavalcanti, Acta Vitaminol. 5, 162 (1951).

[193] N. W. Shock and W. H. Sebrell, Am. J. Physiol. 142, 274 (1944).

The pantothenic acid content of the urine of the horse is influenced by the amount of pantothenic acid in the diet, although this vitamin does not appear to be low in natural-type diets for this species.[194, 195] As yet, there is no proof that this vitamin is needed in the diet of the horse at any stage of growth.

Studies with the growing rabbit show that dietary pantothenic acid may not be needed (Olcese et al.[196]). The rabbit is known to consume a considerable amount of soft, or night, feces which contain a large amount of pantothenic acid (50 γ/g.) produced by synthesis within the gastrointestinal tract.[197] The pantothenic acid content of the soft feces is approximately six times as great as the content of hard feces.[197] These facts probably account for the apparent non-essentiality of dietary pantothenic acid for the rabbit.

B. IN MAN

ELAINE P. RALLI

1. Introduction

Up to the present, no definite pathological lesions due to a deficiency of pantothenic acid have been described in the human being. This is in contrast to the detailed description of the pathological effects of a deficiency of this vitamin in experimental animals.[198-202] In view of the paucity of pathological data in man, the only approaches open to a reviewer are, first, to examine those conditions in which pantothenic acid has been used therapeutically and, second, to examine the pathological findings reported in situations of gross deficiency in human subjects and see wherein these might compare with the pathological lesions described in experimental animals on pantothenate-deficient diets. For this reason the pathological findings in pantothenic acid-deficient animals are listed briefly.

2. Summary of the Pathological Findings in Animals Fed Diets Deficient in Pantothenic Acid

a. Atrophy of the hair follicles and bulbs and loss of melanin with resulting graying of the fur.[199, 203] Rusting of the fur and porphyrin-caked

194 P. B. Pearson and H. Schmidt, Federation Proc. 1, 191 (1945).
195 P. B. Pearson and H. Schmidt, J. Animal Sci. 7, 78 (1948).
196 O. Olcese, P. B. Pearson, and B. S. Schweigert, J. Nutrition 35, 577 (1940).
197 R. Kulwich, L. Struglia, and P. B. Pearson, J. Nutrition 49, 639 (1953).
198 L. L. Ashburn, Public Health Repts. (U.S.) 55, 1337 (1940).
199 A. F. Morgan and H. D. Simms, Science 89, 565 (1939).
200 W. D. Salmon and R. W. Engel, Proc. Soc. Exptl. Biol. Med. 45, 621 (1940).
201 F. S. Daft and W. H. Sebrell, Public Health Repts. (U. S.) 54, 2247 (1939).
202 H. W. Deane and J. M. McKibbin, Endocrinology 38, 385 (1946).
203 E. P. Ralli and I. Graef, Endocrinology 32, 1 (1943).

whiskers have also been observed in white rats. These findings have been observed in mice,[204] rats,[205] foxes,[206] dogs,[207] and monkeys.[208]

b. Corneal changes, consisting of vascularization, thickening, and opacity of the cornea.[209]

c. A tendency for fatty infiltration of the liver.[207]

d. Atrophy of the adrenal cortex with necrosis and hemorrhage in about 50% of the animals.[198-202] The hemorrhagic lesion is probably present in animals on the deficient diet who are stressed.

e. Failure of spermatogenesis due to necrosis of the tubular cells of the testes.[205]

f. Delay or absence of the estrus cycle.[210]

g. Neurological lesions. Deficiency of pantothenic acid in the chick causes widespread myelin degeneration of the spinal cord[211, 212] and in swine[213-215] ataxia with sensory neuron damage.

h. Reproduction. Hatchability of eggs is decreased in hens on a deficient diet and can be markedly increased when pantothenic acid is added to the diet.[216] In rats, fetal abnormalities[217] have been observed as a result of pantothenic acid deficiency, and interestingly enough the lesions involved principally the nervous system. Absence of the eyes occurred and the ocular globe and optic nerve could not be found. Massive diencephalus and alteration in the morphology of the brain were also observed.

3. Pathological Lesions in Human Beings Suggestive of a Deficiency of Pantothenic Acid

a. Effect of Administration of Large Doses of Pantothenic Acid in Certain Clinical Conditions

(1) Graying of the Hair. Human subjects with gray hair have been given large amounts of calcium pantothenate orally, and its effect on the color of

[204] J. H. Jones, C. Foster, F. Dorfman, and G. L. Hunter, J. Nutrition 29, 127 (1945).

[205] A. F. Morgan and H. D. Simms, J. Nutrition 19, 233 (1940).

[206] A. E. Schaefer, C. K. Whitehair, and C. A. Elvehjem, J. Nutrition 34, 131 (1947).

[207] R. H. Silber, J. Nutrition 27, 425 (1944).

[208] K. B. McCall, H. A. Waisman, C. A. Elvehjem, and E. S. Jones, J. Nutrition 31, 685 (1946).

[209] L. L. Bowles, W. K. Hall, V. P. Sydenstricker, and C. W. Hock, J. Nutrition 37, 9 (1949).

[210] F. H. J. Figge and E. Allen, Endocrinology 30, S1028 (1942).

[211] J. H. Shaw and P. H. Phillips, J. Nutrition 29, 107 (1945).

[212] P. H. Phillips and R. W. Engel, J. Nutrition 18, 227 (1939).

[213] M. M. Wintrobe, M. H. Miller, R. H. Follis, Jr., H. J. Stein, C. Mushatt, and S. Humphreys, J. Nutrition 24, 345 (1942).

[214] R. H. Follis, Jr., and M. M. Wintrobe, J. Exptl. Med. 81, 539 (1945).

[215] R. L. Swank and R. D. Adams, J. Neuropathol. Exptl. Neurol. 7, 274 (1948).

[216] M. B. Gillis, G. F. Heuser, and L. C. Norris, J. Nutrition 35, 351 (1948).

[217] J. Boisselot, Arch. franç. pédiat. 6, 225 (1949).

the hair has been observed. The majority of subjects have been people in whom premature graying of the hair had occurred, but the vitamin was also given to elderly individuals with gray hair. The dosage used was more than adequate (from 20 to 100 mg. of calcium pantothenate daily), so that had the condition been due to deficiency of pantothenic acid it should have responded. Except in an occasional subject, investigators[218, 219] did not find that the administration of calcium pantothenate had any consistent effect in overcoming graying of the hair. Frankly, there seems little reason to infer that, because the fur of animals grayed as a result of pantothenate deficiency, pantothenic acid would cure gray hair in man. In the animal, the "skin" is composed of the hair follicles and bulbs with a thin overlying layer of cutis. The various hair follicles and bulbs go through phases of atrophy and regeneration, and the melanin content, which is responsible for the pigmentation, varies according to the state of the hair follicles and bulbs. In the animal, pantothenic acid is clearly responsible for maintaining the integrity of the hair apparatus and in its absence atrophy of the hair follicles and bulbs and loss of melanin occur. In man, obviously, the question of graying of the hair depends on many factors.

(2) *Therapeutic Effects of Calcium Pantothenate or Pantothenyl Alcohol on Various Skin Lesions.* Therapeutic use of pantothenic acid has been reported in a variety of skin lesions. The vitamin has been given orally or applied topically as an ointment.[220, 221] Goldman[220] treated patients with discoid erythematosus of the scalp, giving 400 mg. per day, and noted improvement in the subacute type. Combes and Zuckerman[221] applied the vitamin as an ointment to patients with ulcerations of the skin due to a variety of causes, including ulcers due to radium therapy, traumatic ulcers, arteriosclerotic ulcers, and ulcerations in patients with sickle cell anemia. Pantothenic acid ointment has also been used locally in the treatment of burns and infected wounds,[222] apparently with beneficial results.

These findings suggest that pantothenic acid may be important to the nutrition of the skin, and this may offer a parallel to the skin lesions, such as scaliness and crusting, seen in animals on a pantothenic acid-deficient diet.

(3) *Effect of Pantothenic Acid on the Hematopoietic System.* Crisalli[223] reported that pantothenic acid has a stimulating action on the hematopoietic system in infants. However, in this respect it should be borne in mind that

[218] H. Brandaleone, E. Main, and J. M. Steele, *Proc. Soc. Exptl. Biol. Med.* **53,** 47 (1943).

[219] I. Kerlan and R. P. Herwick, *J. Am. Med. Assoc.* **123,** 391 (1943).

[220] L. Goldman, *J. Invest. Dermatol.* **11,** 95 (1948).

[221] F. C. Combes and R. Zuckerman, *J. Invest. Dermatol.* **16,** 379 (1951).

[222] F. Sciclounoff and E. Naz, *Schweiz. med. Wochschr.* **75,** 767 (1945).

[223] M. Crisalli, *Boll. soc. ital. biol. sper.* **23,** 1047 (1947).

the intestinal synthesis of folic acid and biotin is affected in pantothenic acid deficiency,[224] and it may be that any effects on the hematopoietic system are the result of an associated deficiency of folic acid.

(4) *Pantothenic Acid Therapy in Metabolic Disease.* In view of the fact that an absence of pantothenic acid in animals was associated with atrophy and, in many instances, necrosis and hemorrhage of the adrenal cortex, the use of this vitamin in the treatment of patients with Addison's disease naturally has suggested itself. The author has personally given three patients with Addison's disease massive doses of calcium pantothenate (10 to 20 g. daily). There was no evidence of any effect on the course of the disease or on the hormone requirement of these patients. In two of them the etiological cause of the Addison's disease was presumably tuberculosis, as other evidences of tuberculosis were present in the patients. It may be that the different etiological factors involved, i.e., pantothenic acid deficiency in the rat and a chronic infection in the human being, explain the fact that no clinical effect was observed.

Disturbances of carbohydrate metabolism have been reported as associated with pantothenic acid deficiency in many species.[225-229] Gershberg *et al.*[230] studied the ability of patients to acetylate PABA and sulfadiazine after having been administered large amounts of this vitamin (from 10 to 20 g.). No depression of acetylation was observed in patients with liver disease or in patients with rheumatoid arthritis, diabetes mellitus, hypothyroidism, sprue, or leukemia. In patients with hyperthyroidism, a diminished capacity to acetylate was observed, which was improved by the administration of sodium acetate, suggesting that in hyperthyroidism there is a decrease in available acetate due to its rapid utilization. One might infer that patients with hyperthyroidism would be more susceptible to pantothenic acid deficiency than normal subjects. In this respect it is interesting that Drill and Overman[231] found that the requirement for pantothenic acid increased in experimental hyperthyroidism in rats.

(5) *Pantothenic Acid in Other Clinical Situations.* Jacques[232] reported the use of pantothenic acid in the treatment of surgical patients with severe

[224] B. N. Berg, T. F. Zucker, and L. M. Zucker, *Proc. Soc. Exptl. Biol. Med.* **71**, 374 (1949).

[225] L. D. Wright, *J. Biol. Chem.* **142**, 445 (1942).

[226] A. E. Schaefer, J. M. McKibbin, and C. A. Elvehjem, *J. Biol. Chem.* **143**, 321 (1942).

[227] A. Dorfman, S. Berkman, and S. A. Koser, *J. Biol. Chem.* **144**, 393 (1942).

[228] H. McIlwain and D. E. Hughes, *Biochem. J.* **38**, 187 (1944).

[229] R. E. Olson and N. O. Kaplan, *J. Biol. Chem.* **175**, 515 (1948).

[230] H. Gershberg, S. H. Rubin, and E. P. Ralli, *J. Nutrition* **39**, 107 (1949).

[231] V. A. Drill and R. Overman, *Am. J. Physiol.* **135**, 474 (1942).

[232] J. E. Jacques, *Lancet* **II**, 861 (1951).

postoperative ileus. He was stimulated to try pantothenic acid in this situation as a result of the observations of Jurgens and Pfaltz[233] that rats kept on a diet deficient in pantothenic acid showed atony and distension of the gastrointestinal tract. Sixteen cases were studied. Pantothenic acid was given intramuscularly in doses of 50 mg., and most of the patients received two or three injections. Jacques reported a very encouraging response to the use of pantothenic acid in that a return of bowel motility took place as evidenced by the passage of flatus. Many of the patients did not receive pantothenic acid until they had been under treatment with either pituitary extract, neostigmine, or other drugs. The clinical observations should be confirmed, but they are suggestive of a possible therapeutic role of pantothenic acid.

Ralli et al.[234] have reported the effects of large amounts of calcium pantothenate by mouth in normal male adults stressed by immersing them in water of 9° for 8 minutes. When this stress was repeated after 6 weeks of pantothenine therapy, it was observed that the initial eosinophile count was higher and that there was less of an eosinopenia. The whole blood ascorbic acid was significantly elevated, and there was no decrease in the blood ascorbic acid following the stress. In the urine the uric acid/creatinine ratio was decreased after therapy. The oral administration of vitamin B_{12} was not associated with any changes of this type. The authors suggest that pantothenic acid may possibly increase the capacity of the tissues to withstand stress, and this might result from the fact that pantothenic acid constitutes part of coenzyme A. This coenzyme[235] functions catalytically in the condensation of pyruvate with oxalacetate to form citrate. An intermediary in this reaction is acetyl-CoA, which is believed to represent an essential step in the oxidative metabolism of carbohydrate. Therefore pantothenate is an essential part of one of the key reactions for the oxidative metabolism of cells, and when excessive amounts of pantothenate are provided to the tissues the production of coenzyme A might be facilitated and so influence the response to stress.

b. Pathological Lesions among Prisoners of War in the Far East, Suggestive of a Deficiency of Pantothenic Acid

It is obvious that more than one nutritional factor was involved in the cases of gross malnutrition that occurred among the prisoners of war in the Japanese prison camps. The diets were deficient in all fractions of the vitamin B complex, in protein, and in fat. It is interesting that scurvy was

[233] R. Jurgens and H. Pfaltz, *Z. Vitaminforsch.* **14**, 243 (1944).

[234] E. P. Ralli, *Nutrition Symposium Natl. Vitamin Found. Ser.* **5**, 78 (1952).

[235] S. Korkes, A. Del Campillo, I. C. Gunsalus, and S. Ochoa, *J. Biol. Chem.* **193**, 721 (1951).

rarely encountered among the prisoners. Among prisoners of war it was noted by physicians, who themselves were in prison camps and were able to make observations at first hand, and among investigators, who had an opportunity of studying the prisoners when they were released from the camps, that many of the pathological lesions present did not respond to specific fractions of the B complex, such as thiamine, riboflavin, or nicotinic acid, but did respond to dried brewers' yeast or to liver extract. The lesions that did not respond to specific fractions of the B complex were in some instances suggestive of pantothenic acid deficiency in experimental animals, and it is these findings that will be discussed.

(1) *Ocular Changes.* Among prisoners of war visual disturbances ranging from complete blindness to just blurring of vision were reported by many investigators. Pallor of the optic discs and central scotoma were also observed.[236] Improvement did not occur on high vitamin diets. The fact that there was no improvement with therapy may well have been due to the fact that the visual symptoms had developed two to three years prior to any therapy. Scott[237] reported that in some of the British West Indies islands the eye changes were associated with itching and burning of the eyes and inflammatory lesions in the mouth and fissures. Pallor of the optic disc was noted in children in Kingston, and treatment with brewers' yeast and cod liver oil improved the visual disturbances, but not if the disease had existed for some time.[238, 239] Bell and O'Neill[240] observed 95 cases of partial optic atrophy from malnutrition occurring in liberated prisoners of war from Hong Kong, which was an incidence of 20 %. The main findings were scotomata and contraction of the peripheral visual fields. In discussing the ophthalmology, they felt that the lack of vitamin B and the hypoproteinemia were factors and that, in addition, there was possibly a toxic factor. Invasion of the cornea was also noted by Kark.[241] Some observers felt that this was due to riboflavin deficiency.

The fact that many of the prisoners of war had had symptoms of beriberi and pellagra, the fact that the response to these fractions of the B complex were not uniformly satisfactory, and the fairly high incidence of eye lesions obviously suggest that other factors were involved in the production of these lesions. In view of the corneal vascularization that occurs in pantothenic acid deficiency in animals, and in view of the other eye lesions occurring in animals, it seems reasonable to suggest that pantothenic acid may

[236] W. L. Roberts and T. H. Willcockson, *Am. J. Ophthalmol.* **30,** 165 (1947).
[237] H. H. Scott, *Ann. Trop. Med. Parasitol.* **12,** 109 (1918).
[238] D. Whitebourne, *Am. J. Ophthalmol.* **30,** 169 (1947).
[239] F. D. Carroll, *Am. J. Ophthalmol.* **30,** 172 (1947).
[240] P. G. Bell and J. C. O'Neill, *Can. Med. Assoc. J.* **56,** 475 (1947).
[241] R. Kark, H. F. Aiton, and E. D. Pease, *Ann. Internal Med.* **25,** 266 (1946).

have been one of the factors responsible for some of the eye lesions, possibly those involving the cornea.

(2) *Burning Feet Syndrome.* Probably the findings in humans most suggestive of pantothenic acid deficiency are those related to the syndrome known as "burning feet."[242, 243] This has no exact counterpart in the experimental animal, and there is no justification for concluding that it is due soley to a deficiency of pantothenic acid. This condition, seen in so many of the men who were in prisoner-of-war camps in Japan and Burma, had a characteristic syndrome, was associated with neurological and mental disturbances, did not respond satisfactorily to therapy with thiamine chloride, riboflavin, or nicotinic acid, and was reported by Gopalan[244] as responding to calcium pantothenate. The other fractions of the vitamin B complex improved the nutritional state of the individual although they were not successful in completely correcting the feet symptoms or the mental disturbance. Dried brewers' yeast was apparently the most successful therapy, and this, of course, contains all fractions of the B complex.

Glusman,[245] who himself was a prisoner of the Japanese from the time of the fall of Corregidor until the war was over, had an opportunity of observing prisoners of war in the Philippines and in Japan. He reports that evidence of weight loss and malnutrition became apparent soon after the American troops were taken prisoner in the Philippines, but that three or four months elapsed before the first patients with burning feet began to appear. The incidence then increased rapidly so that approximately 300 of some 800 patients were complaining of this symptom. In other camps, such as Cabanatuan, some 2000 more cases were observed. In these patients evidences of pellagra were common, as well as corneal ulcerations, constriction of the visual fields, central scotomata, scrotal dermatitis, glossitis, and cheilosis. Diarrhea was almost universal. The burning feet syndrome occurred in conjunction with evidences of these other deficiencies, but Glusman reports that "it could occur as a distinct symptom complex by itself." As described by all authors, the onset was gradual, with numbness and tingling in the toes, usually bilateral. The paresthesias then gave way to burning pains in the toes and soles of the feet, and then the shooting pains began. These radiated from the dorsa of the feet up the legs. There seemed to be a relationship in these pains to the time of day, and they were much more severe at night. In the most advanced cases, pains in the palms of the hands also occurred. Relief occurred to a certain extent when the feet were immersed in cold water. Preservation of the reflexes was the rule, and motor

242 G. F. Harrison, *Lancet* I, 961 (1946).

243 E. K. Cruickshank, *Lancet* II, 369 (1946).

244 C. Gopalan, *Indian Med. Gaz.* **81**, 22 (1946).

245 M. Glusman, *Am. J. Med.* **3**, 211 (1947).

power was preserved. No paralysis of the extremities occurred; there was no evidence of foot drop. The gait is best described by quoting from Glusman's report: "The gait was peculiar but this appeared to be due to pain and hypersensitivity of the soles of the feet rather than to disturbance of motor power or equilibrium. The patient walked as if the ground beneath the soles of his feet were hot. He walked cautiously, gingerly, and on a somewhat widened base. Because of his reluctance to use his oversensitive toes to grip the ground, the gait had a characteristic flat-footed quality. In standing, patients frequently shifted their weight from one foot to the other in a restless and repetitious fashion. It seemed as if they could not endure the discomfort of resting their weight on one foot for more than a few moments at a time. The same restlessness was frequently noted while the patient was in bed. Often when the pain was severe patients would sit cross legged in bed, holding the distal portions of their feet in their hands and rock rhythmically backward and forward with the pain. This last attitude was not only pitiful but it was so pathognomonic that any observer walking into a ward could pick out those with burning feet at a glance."

Attempts at therapy were, according to Glusman, disappointing. Nicotinic acid, as reported by other observers also, relieved the associated signs of pellagra "but was without effect on the symptoms of burning feet." The same was true of thiamine chloride.

Glusman also mentions discussing the matter with Professor Kinosita, and the report was the same as published in Page's article.[246] Kinosita claimed that the Japanese had been unfamiliar with the syndrome of burning feet before the war. However, they began to see patients with this condition among the Japanese military personnel who had been cut off by allied operations in the southern battle areas for variable periods of time before rescue. Professor Kinosita autopsied a small number of these Japanese soldiers. He observed that the spinal cords and peripheral nerves in these patients were normal. He found changes in the small arteries "whose walls were diffusely thickened, and he commented on the absence of new vessels."

A clue to the etiology of the syndrome is provided by Gopalan's report,[244] which was done in the Nutrition Research Laboratories in South India. This author very kindly provided me with a microfilm copy of his report. He points out that the "differences between 'burning feet' and the peripheral neuritis associated with thiamine deficiency are so fundamental that it is surprising that the two conditions have been confused." He found that the incidence was greatest among the poorer classes and that the diet consumed was mostly rice gruel and cheap vegetables, the rice being of the parboiled type which contains enough thiamine to prevent beriberi. Again, the signs

[246] J. A. Page, *Brit. Med. J.* **II**, 260 (1946).

of riboflavin deficiency and other deficiencies were present in many of the subjects. The description of the symptoms was much the same as Glusman's, but probably the most significant finding was the result of treatment. Gopalan found that 50 mg. of thiamine chloride daily, 300 mg. of nicotinic acid, and 10 mg. of riboflavin resulted in the disappearance of the deficiencies such as glossitis, stomatitis, and some of the ocular symptoms but had no effect on the burning feet. A striking improvement occurred following the administration intramuscularly of 20 to 40 mg. of calcium pantothenate daily. The burning and hyperhidrosis disappeared first, and the pins-and-needles sensation later. Up to 80 mg. of calcium pantothenate was given in some cases and in fact was necessary in the more severe cases. No untoward reactions occurred. Gopalan points out the resemblance to the neurological lesions occurring in pantothenate-deficient swine. Spies has reported that riboflavin or biotin injections increased the blood level of pantothenic acid.[247] This may account for the moderate improvement reported by some other authors after treatment with the other fractions of the B complex. The probability is that the other fractions of the B vitamin complex also are involved to a certain extent in the syndrome. However, it would seem that the burning feet syndrome was associated with a deficiency of pantothenic acid and suggests that in humans a deficiency of this vitamin will affect the small arteries and may involve the central nervous system as it does in the experimental animal.[213-215] Major Bruce Hunt, of the Australian Army Medical Corps,[248] who was taken prisoner by the Japanese at Singapore, told me that personality changes and mental disturbances were also present in many of the men suffering from the burning feet syndrome.

(3) There were no reports on pathological examination of fatty infiltration of the liver or atrophy of the adrenals in men dying as a result of starvation in the prison camps, but apparently complete pathological examinations were not feasible.

(4) Apparently some decrease in the secretion of the male sex hormone occurred, as a common observation among the prisoners was the fact that they had to shave much less frequently than normally, and loss of libido was frequently reported. Whether or not this was due to atrophy or changes in the tubular cells of the testes is not known, but undoubtedly it was the result of malnutrition.

c. Summary

Obviously, at the present time one can only surmise, on the basis of animal experimentation, what the possible pathological changes in humans

[247] T. D. Spies, S. R. Stanbery, R. J. Williams, T. H. Jukes, and S. H. Babcock, *J. Am. Med. Assoc.* **115**, 523 (1940).
[248] B. Hunt, personal communication, Perth, Australia.

would be as a result of a deficiency of pantothenic acid. The pathological effects of a deficiency of this vitamin have not been clearly defined in humans. In view of the ubiquitous occurrence of the vitamin in nature, it is probable that pantothenic acid deficiency is a rare occurrence in humans, except possibly for the burning feet syndrome seen in the prisoners of war and among some malnourished peoples in the Far East. Apparently, the most propitious place to pursue the study of the deficiency would be in that part of the world where this syndrome is most often encountered. Glusman feels that the syndrome is due to a nutritional deficiency and suggests calling it "nutritional melalgia" (nutritional limb pain); he apparently considers pantothenic acid one of the major nutritional factors involved.

C. IN MICROORGANISMS

E. E. SNELL

Pantothenic acid was discovered independently as a growth factor for yeast[249, 250] and for lactic acid bacteria;[251] it was only after extensive work on its properties, distribution, and purification had been carried out with these microorganisms that the active compound present in the concentrates was shown to be identical with a relatively uncharacterized substance required for growth of animals.[250, 252, 253] The vitamin is required for growth by a large variety of microorganisms;[250, 254, 255] those that do not require it preformed synthesize it. In the absence of the vitamin, organisms that do not synthesize it fail to grow, and in the presence of suboptimal amounts of it, growth increases with the vitamin concentration. Microbiological assays for the vitamin are based upon this fact.[256]

In addition to its effects on growth, several rather specific relationships of pantothenic acid to the metabolism of microorganisms have been noted. Glycogen storage by yeast is reported to increase definitely when pantothenic acid is supplied to the growing cultures.[257] The requirement of many lactic acid bacteria for pantothenic acid is considerably decreased by the

[249] R. J. Williams, C. M. Lyman, G. H. Goodyear, J. H. Truesdail, and D. Holaday, J. Am. Chem. Soc. **55**, 2912 (1933).

[250] R. J. Williams, Advances in Enzymol. **3**, 253 (1943).

[251] E. E. Snell, F. M. Strong, and W. H. Peterson, Biochem. J. **31**, 1789 (1937); J. Am. Chem. Soc. **60**, 2825 (1938).

[252] D. W. Woolley, H. A. Waisman, and C. A. Elvehjem, J. Am. Chem. Soc. **61**, 977 (1939).

[253] T. H. Jukes, J. Am. Chem. Soc. **61**, 975 (1939).

[254] B. C. J. G. Knight, Vitamins and Hormones **3**, 105 (1945).

[255] W. H. Peterson and M. S. Peterson, Bacteriol. Revs. **9**, 49 (1945).

[256] E. E. Snell in Vitamin Methods, Vol. I, p. 327. Academic Press, New York, 1950.

[257] R. J. Williams, W. A. Mosher, and E. Rohrmann, Biochem. J. **30**, 2036 (1936).

presence of fatty acids in the medium;[256, 258] similarly, the inhibitory effect on these organisms of antivitamins related to pantothenic acid in structure is greatly decreased by addition of free or combined fatty acids to the medium.[259] Pantothenic acid greatly increases the synthesis of acetylcholine by *Lactobacillus plantarum*.[260]

Dorfman and coworkers[261] found that the rate of pyruvate oxidation by cells of *Proteus morganii* was depressed when the cells were grown with suboptimal amounts of pantothenic acid; the rate of oxidation was increased by addition of pantothenic acid to the resting cell suspension. Similar observations were made by Hills.[262] Both authors considered that the vitamin takes part in the oxidation of pyruvic acid to acetic acid. Novelli and Lipmann[263] showed that this increased oxidation was mediated by coenzyme A, which is formed almost quantitatively by such organisms from the pantothenic acid which they take up. This coenzyme is concerned in the initial reactions (condensation of acetate with oxalacetate) leading to the oxidation of acetate.[264, 265] This was shown in striking fashion by the demonstration that acetate accumulated from ethanol in the presence of a pantothenic acid-deficient yeast suspension, but not in the presence of a similar suspension rich in pantothenic acid. The latter preparation of cells also removed acetate from solution (by oxidation) much more rapidly than the former deficient cells.[264]

As a result principally of the work of Lipmann and his group, pantothenic acid is now known to be essential for a whole series of reactions (and possibly all reactions) involving the acetyl group. As a preliminary to participation in such reactions, it must be built into its coenzyme form, coenzyme A.[263, 266] The latter coenzyme, together with various degradation products of it, accounts for essentially all the "bound" pantothenic acid present in tissues. Knowledge of these facts permits a ready explanation of most of the metabolic effects described above. Thus, coenzyme A is required for formation of fatty acids from acetate, and hence the addition of preformed fatty acids in a form directly utilizable for cell synthesis might be expected to decrease the pantothenic acid requirement of organisms such as *L*.

[258] H. P. Broquist, Ph.D. Thesis, University of Wisconsin, 1950.
[259] W. Shive, W. W. Ackermann, J. M. Ravel, and J. E. Sutherland, *J. Am. Chem. Soc.* **69**, 2567 (1947).
[260] E. Rowett, *J. Gen. Microbiol.* **2**, 25 (1948).
[261] A. Dorfman, S. Berkman, and S. A. Koser, *J. Biol. Chem.* **144**, 393 (1942).
[262] G. M. Hills, *Biochem. J.* **37**, 418 (1943).
[263] G. D. Novelli and F. Lipmann, *J. Bacteriol.* **54**, 19 (1947); *Arch. Biochem.* **14**, 23 (1947).
[264] G. D. Novelli and F. Lipmann, *J. Biol. Chem.* **171**, 833 (1947).
[265] J. R. Stern, B. Shapiro, and S. Ochoa, *Nature* **166**, 403 (1950).
[266] G. D. Novelli, N. O. Kaplan, and F. Lipmann, *J. Biol. Chem.* **177**, 97 (1949).

arabinosus. Since coenzyme A is essential for acetylcholine formation, it is readily seen why pantothenic acid-deficient cells of *L. plantarum* form decreased amounts of this ester. Since oxidation of acetate (and hence of pyruvate) in many organisms proceeds through the Krebs cycle, and since coenzyme A is necessary for the initial formation of citric acid in this cycle, the reason for the stimulation of oxidation of pyruvate by pantothenate in deficient cells of *Proteus* becomes apparent. By way of contrast, the anaerobic fermentation of glucose by yeast juice was not decreased in pantothenic acid deficiency.[267]

The extensive studies of McIlwain on the mechanism of the inhibitory action of pantoyltaurine for pantothenic acid-requiring bacteria may also be explained on this basis. McIlwain showed that addition of pantoyltaurine increased the lag phase and decreased the rate of growth during the first half of the logarithmic phase of *Streptococcus hemolyticus*, observations consistent with the assumption that pantoyltaurine slowed incorporation of the vitamin into a substance necessary for normal growth.[268] Pantothenic acid disappeared from cultures of this organism; this disappearance was dependent upon the simultaneous occurrence of glycolysis, but was prevented by pantoyltaurine even though glycolysis was not. It may now be assumed that the pantothenic acid was being converted to coenzyme A, an endergonic process that was dependent upon glycolysis,[269] and that this conversion was the process inhibited by pantoyltaurine. Related antimetabolites of pantothenic acid probably inhibit growth by a similar mechanism.[270]

The observation that *either* pantothenic acid *or* tryptophan suffices to permit growth of a strain of *Staphylococcus aureus* under specified conditions[271] indicates a relationship of the vitamin to metabolism of this amino acid. The nature of this relationship has not been clarified.

X. Pharmacology

SAMUEL LEPKOVSKY

Little is known concerning the pharmacology of pantothenic acid. Its toxicity is very low and varies with different animals.[1-4] Acute toxicity was

---

[267] P. C. Teague and R. J. Williams, *J. Gen. Physiol.* **25,** 777 (1942).
[268] H. McIlwain, *Biochem. J.* **36,** 364 (1942).
[269] H. McIlwain and D. E. Hughes, *Biochem. J.* **38,** 184 (1944).
[270] H. McIlwain and D. E. Hughes, *Biochem. J.* **39,** 133 (1945).
[271] M. G. Sevag and M. N. Green, *J. Biol. Chem.* **154,** 719 (1944); *J. Bacteriol.* **48,** 631 (1944).
[1] K. Unna and J. G. Greslin, *J. Pharmacol. Exptl. Therap.* **73,** 85 (1941).

studied in mice, rats, dogs, and monkeys. The LD_{50} after subcutaneous injection is 2.7 g. per kilogram in mice and 3.4 g. per kilogram in rats. The LD_{50} after oral administration in mice is 10 g. per kilogram of body weight, but rats fed the same amount of pantothenic acid survived without showing toxic symptoms. After intraperitoneal and intravenous injections the LD_{50} for mice is 0.92 and 0.91 g. per kilogram, respectively, and for rats it is 0.82 and 0.83.[1] Lethal doses produced prostration and respiratory failure in rats and mice. No toxic symptoms were observed in five dogs and one monkey fed 1 g. of calcium pantothenate per kilogram of body weight.[1] Pantothenic acid is essentially non-toxic to human beings. At least 100 mg. may be injected intravenously in man without producing any toxic reactions.[2]

Chronic toxicity was studied in rats, dogs, and monkeys. Daily doses of 50 and 200 mg., respectively, of calcium pantothenate were fed to young male and female rats over a period of 190 days. Growth was normal, and autopsies at the end of the feeding period did not reveal any gross or microscopic changes in the organs. Offsprings of the group of rats receiving 50 mg. of calcium pantothenate daily were given this dose of pantothenic acid from the day that they were weaned. These second-generation animals also developed normally.[1]

Adult dogs were fed daily 50 mg. of calcium pantothenate per kilogram, and monkeys 1.0 g. per kilogram over a period of 6 months. Neither the dogs nor the monkeys showed any toxic symptoms or loss of weight. Histopathological examination of these animals failed to reveal any changes.[1]

Local effects of calcium pantothenate were studied on rabbits by subcutaneous injections and instillation into the conjunctival sac. No irritation, inflammation, or abscess formation was observed following the subcutaneous injection of 1.0 ml. of 1, 2, 5, and 10 % solutions of the vitamin. The infiltration of the subcutaneous tissue subsided about as rapidly as that following an injection of 1.0 ml. of saline solution. Instillation of 0.5 ml. of a 10 % solution into the conjunctival sac did not produce any irritation.[1]

Calcium pantothenate did not influence the metabolism, circulatory and respiratory systems, or the smooth muscle organs of normal animals.[1]

[2] T. D. Spies, D. P. Hightower, and L. H. Hubbard, *J. Am. Med. Assoc.* **115**, 292 (1940).

[3] F. A. Robinson, The Vitamin B Complex. John Wiley and Sons, New York, 1951.

[4] H. Molitor and G. A. Emerson, *Vitamins and Hormones* **6**, 69 (1948).

XI. Requirements and Factors Influencing Them

A. OF ANIMALS

GEORGE M. BRIGGS and FLOYD S. DAFT

The pantothenic acid requirement of animals varies with species, age, type of diet, period of depletion, various stresses, and other factors to be considered. Many careful attempts have been made to determine the minimal level required for optimum growth for many animals but considerably more work is needed. Accepted values of today may need to be changed as new nutritional developments unfold.

1. MINIMAL LEVELS

The requirements for pantothenic acid which are available are given in Table XX with key references. The values given are minimal levels, with

TABLE XX

MINIMAL CALCIUM PANTOTHENATE REQUIREMENTS FOR OPTIMUM GROWTH, PERFORMANCE, OR PRODUCTION

Animal	Mg./100 g. of diet	Mg./kg. body weight per day	Mg./day	Other key references to studies on requirement
Rat				
Weanling			0.08[1, 2]	
			0.04–0.10[a, 3]	
			0.10[4]	
			0.08–0.10[5, 6, 8]	
			0.05–0.10[7]	
	0.6[9]			
Young adult (10 wk. old)			0.025[6]	
Breeding	2.0[5]			
Chicken				
Chick	0.9[10]			11–17
Laying hen	0.15[18]			19
Breeding hen	1.0[18]			19
Turkey	1.25[17]			20, 21
Duck	1.18[22]			
Swine	1.0–2.0[23]	0.17–0.26[24]	10–20[25]	
Dog		0.1[26]		
Mouse			0.03[27]	
		1.0[28]	0.023–0.029[28]	

[a] 40 γ daily for maximum growth; 100 γ daily for prevention of graying.

[1] K. Unna, *J. Nutrition* **20**, 565 (1940).
[2] K. Unna and W. L. Sampson, *Proc. Soc. Exptl. Biol. Med.* **45**, 309 (1940).
[3] G. A. Emerson and H. M. Evans, *Proc. Soc. Exptl. Biol. Med.* **46**, 655 (1941).

no added "allowance," and are based on the latest figures available. Many of the older values were obtained with diets considered incomplete by today's standards or with depleted animals. Values for many animals have not been determined as yet.

2. Factors Influencing Requirements

Many factors are known to influence the pantothenic acid requirement of any one species, so actually it is difficult to give one figure as the "requirement." A discussion of some of these factors follows:

a. State of Maturity of the Animal

As has been seen in the former section, adult animals, in general, require less dietary pantothenic acid than growing animals. Deficiency symptoms are most readily obtained in the very young animal (see section on pathology and deficiency symptoms).

[4] C. A. Elvehjem, L. M. Henderson, S. Black, and E. Nielsen, *J. Biol. Chem.* **140,** xxxvi (1941).

[5] L. M. Henderson, J. M. McIntire, H. A. Waisman, and C. A. Elvehjem, *J. Nutrition* **23,** 47 (1942).

[6] K. Unna and G. V. Richards, *J. Nutrition* **23,** 545 (1942).

[7] J. S. D. Bacon and G. N. Jenkins, *Biochem. J.* **37,** 492 (1943).

[8] C. A. Slanetz, *Am. J. Vet. Research* **4,** 182 (1943).

[9] C. A. Mills, *Arch. Biochem.* **1,** 73 (1942).

[10] D. M. Hegsted and T. R. Riggs, *J. Nutrition* **37,** 361 (1949).

[11] H. A. Waisman, R. C. Mills, and C. A. Elvehjem, *J. Nutrition* **24,** 187 (1942).

[12] T. H. Jukes and L. W. McElroy, *Poultry Sci.* **22,** 438 (1943).

[13] J. L. Milligan and G. M. Briggs, *Poultry Sci.* **28,** 202 (1949).

[14] S. Lepkovsky, F. H. Bird, F. H. Kratzer, and V. S. Asmundson, *Poultry Sci.* **24,** 335 (1945).

[15] G. F. Heuser, M. B. Gillis, and L. C. Norris, *Rept. 8th World's Poultry Congr.* p. 114 (1948).

[16] J. C. Bauernfeind, L. C. Norris, and G. F. Heuser, *Poultry Sci.* **21,** 142 (1942).

[17] A. G. Hogan, *Nutrition Abstr. & Revs.* **19,** 751 (1949–1950).

[18] M. B. Gillis, G. F. Heuser, and L. C. Norris, *J. Nutrition* **35,** 351 (1948).

[19] M. B. Gillis, G. F. Heuser, and L. C. Norris, *J. Nutrition* **26,** 285 (1943).

[20] F. H. Kratzer and D. Williams, *Poultry Sci.* **27,** 518 (1948).

[21] T. H. Jukes, *Poultry Sci.* **17,** 227 (1938).

[22] W. Trager, *J. Exptl. Med.* **77,** 557 (1943).

[23] S. C. Stothers, R. R. Johnston, J. A. Hoefer, and R. W. Luecke, *J. Animal Sci.* **11,** 777 (1952).

[24] E. H. Hughes and N. R. Ittner, *J. Animal Sci.* **1,** 116 (1942).

[25] A. C. Wiese, W. P. Lehrer, P. R. Moore, O. F. Pahnish, and W. V. Hartwell, *J. Animal Sci.* **10,** 80 (1951).

[26] A. E. Schaefer, J. M. McKibbin, and C. A. Elvehjem, *J. Biol. Chem.* **143,** 321 (1942).

[27] J. G. Sandza and L. R. Cerecedo, *J. Nutrition* **21,** 609 (1941).

[28] H. P. Morris and S. W. Lippincott, *J. Natl. Cancer Inst.* **2,** 29 (1941).

b. Environmental Effects

Spector et al.[29] reported that the urinary and dermal excretion of pantothenic acid was greater in human subjects under hot moist conditions than under comfortable conditions. Mills,[9] however, found no difference in the dietary concentration of this vitamin required for maximum growth of the rat at 68° F. and at 91° F.

c. Effect of Other Nutrients

It has long been known that the type of carbohydrate in the diet may affect profoundly the requirements of rats and other animals for the B vitamins. It was reported in 1926 by Fridericia[30] that some rats receiving uncooked rice-starch as the source of carbohydrate developed a condition designated as "refection" and required no "B vitamin" in their food. Animals on the rice-starch diet which did not become refected spontaneously developed the condition after ingestion of feces from refected animals (Fridericia and coworkers[31]). It was also shown by Roscoe[32] that in order to continue in a refected state an animal must continue to ingest his own or similar feces. Morgan and coworkers[33] showed that rats receiving starch as the source of carbohydrate grew well without filtrate factor and that supplementation of the diet of these animals with filtrate factor concentrates improved the growth rate only slightly.

The level of protein, also, has been shown by Nelson and coworkers to affect the dietary requirement of the rat for pantothenic acid.[34-36] Animals deficient in this vitamin receiving casein at a level of 64 % grew better and survived longer than littermates maintained on a 24 % casein diet.[34] When intermediate levels of casein were used, the sparing effect was proportional to the protein level.[35] When washed beef blood fibrin, which was even lower in its pantothenic acid content than the casein, was used as the protein component of the diet, even more pronounced differences between 64 % and 24 % levels of protein were seen.[36] The pantothenic acid requirement of the pig has also been shown to be similarly dependent on the level of protein in the diet.[37]

Yacowitz et al.[38] reported that the presence or absence of vitamin B_{12} in

[29] H. Spector, T. S. Hamilton, and H. H. Mitchell, J. Biol. Chem. **161**, 145 (1945).

[30] L. S. Fridericia, Skand. Arch. Physiol. **2**, 55 (1926).

[31] L. S. Fridericia, P. Freudenthal, S. Gudjonnsson, G. Johansen, and N. Schoubye, J. Hyg. **27**, 70 (1927).

[32] M. H. Roscoe, J. Hyg. **27**, 103 (1927).

[33] A. F. Morgan, B. B. Cook, and H. G. Davidson, J. Nutrition **15**, 27 (1938).

[34] M. M. Nelson and H. M. Evans, Proc. Soc. Exptl. Biol. Med. **60**, 319 (1945).

[35] M. M. Nelson, F. van Nouhuys, and H. M. Evans, J. Nutrition **34**, 189 (1947).

[36] M. M. Nelson and H. M. Evans, Proc. Soc. Exptl. Biol. Med. **66**, 299 (1947).

[37] R. W. Luecke, J. A. Hoefer, and F. Thorp, Jr., J. Animal Sci. **11**, 238 (1952).

[38] H. Yacowitz, L. C. Norris, and G. F. Heuser, J. Biol. Chem. **192**, 141 (1951).

the diet of chicks influences the requirement of pantothenic acid; without B_{12} it was reported as 2 mg. per 100 g. of diet, whereas with adequate B_{12} it was only 1 mg. per 100 g. of diet. Jukes, however, concluded from his experiments[39] that the requirement of chicks for pantothenic acid is not significantly affected by the lack of B_{12} if the diet is adequate in methionine and choline. In young pigs fed practical rations with only 14% protein, Catron et al.,[39a] in 1953, also found a sparing action of vitamin B_{12} on the pantothenic acid requirement.

Wright and Welch[40] reported that a relationship exists between deficiencies of folic acid and biotin and the development of signs of pantothenic acid deficiency. Following the administration of succinylsulfathiazole to rats, changes appeared which were very similar to those seen in pantothenic acid deficiency, and a low level of this vitamin in the liver was demonstrated. Administration of additional pantothenic acid did not correct these conditions in any way, but administration of folic acid and biotin corrected them completely. These investigators interpreted their results as indicating that deficiencies of folic acid and biotin prevent the proper utilization of pantothenic acid.

Daft[41] showed that the inclusion of ascorbic acid at a level of 2% in diets deficient in pantothenic acid prevented the development of the usual pantothenic acid deficiency syndrome in weanling rats. Daft and Schwarz[42] reported on these and similar experiments after the animals had remained on the deficient diet for one year. Some rats grew to a weight of over 500 g. during this period, having received from weaning a highly purified diet with no supplementary pantothenic acid. Hundley and Ing[42a] showed that glucuronolactone and other related compounds could successfully replace ascorbic acid in similar experiments. Everson et al.[42b] reported that the inclusion of 2% of ascorbic acid in a pantothenic acid-deficient diet had a beneficial effect on reproduction.

d. Effect of Antibiotics

In 1951, Swick et al.[43] and Lih and Baumann[44] reported that penicillin, aureomycin, and streptomycin stimulated the growth of rats receiving

[39] T. H. Jukes, Federation Proc. 11, 447 (1952).

[39a] D. V. Catron, R. W. Bennison, H. M. Maddock, G. C. Ashton, and P. G. Homeyer, J. Animal Sci. 12, 51 (1953).

[40] L. D. Wright and A. D. Welch, Science 97, 426 (1943).

[41] F. S. Daft, Federation Proc. 10, 380 (1951).

[42] F. S. Daft and K. Schwarz, Federation Proc. 11, 201 (1952).

[42a] J. M. Hundley and R. B. Ing, Federation Proc. 12, 417 (1953).

[42b] G. Everson, L. Northrop, N. Y. Chung, and R. Getty, Federation Proc. 12, 413 (1953).

[43] R. W. Swick, H. Lih, and C. A. Baumann, Federation Proc. 10, 395 (1951).

[44] H. Lih and C. A. Baumann, J. Nutrition 45, 143 (1951).

limited amounts of pantothenic acid. The increase was that to be expected from doubling or tripling the pantothenic acid content of the diet. Aureomycin and streptomycin were reported as superior to penicillin in these experiments. A few months later Sauberlich[45] showed that aureomycin or penicillin increased the growth of pantothenic acid-deficient rats during a four-week period and concluded that these antibiotics have a marked influence upon the pantothenic acid requirement of the weanling rat. In 1952 Daft and Schwarz reported on experiments which had lasted for a year[42] and showed that weanling rats grew at an almost normal rate during this period on highly purified diets unsupplemented with pantothenic acid but containing small amounts of aureomycin. Somewhat similar results with a variety of antibiotics have been reported by other investigators.[45a-d] Luecke et al.[46] reported that in his experiments aureomycin did not spare the pantothenic acid requirement of pigs, although Catron et al.[39a] did find a sparing effect in pigs when the protein level was low (14 %).

e. Effects of Hormones

Drill and Overman[47] have shown that the pantothenic acid requirement of rats is increased during experimental hyperthyroidism. Haque et al.,[48] on the other hand, observed a partial counteraction of pantothenic acid deficiency signs in chicks by thyroxine injections.

The effects of adrenal and pituitary hormones on the development of the pantothenic acid deficiency syndrome in rats have been discussed in a previous section.

f. Effects of Stress and Miscellaneous Factors

Dumm et al.[49] have reported that rats deficient in pantothenic acid, which were subjected to the stress of swimming or given injections of ACTH, failed to show the expected lymphopenia. Following therapy with

[45] H. E. Sauberlich, *J. Nutrition* **46**, 99 (1952).

[45a] A. Fidanza, G. Giunchi, M. L. Rutigliano, L. A. Scuro, and F. Sorice, *Boll. soc. ital. biol. sper.* **28**, 1393 (1952).

[45b] G. Giunchi, A. Fidanza, L. A. Scuro, and F. Sorice, *Acta Vitaminol.* **7**, 75 (1953).

[45c] G. Giunchi, A. Fidanza, L. A. Scuro, and F. Sorice, *Boll. ist. sieroterap. milan.* **32**, 159 (1953).

[45d] K. Guggenheim, S. Halevy, I. Hartmann, and R. Zamir, *J. Nutrition* **50**, 245 (1953).

[46] R. W. Luecke, J. A. Hoefer, and F. Thorp, Jr., *J. Animal Sci.* **11**, 769 (1952); **12**, 605 (1953).

[47] V. A. Drill and R. Overman, *Am. J. Physiol.* **135**, 474 (1942).

[48] M. E. Haque, R. J. Lillie, C. S. Shaffner, and G. M. Briggs, *Endocrinology* **42**, 273 (1948).

[49] M. E. Dumm, P. Ovando, P. Roth, and E. P. Ralli, *Proc. Soc. Exptl. Biol. Med.* **71**, 368 (1949).

pantothenic acid, the animals showed the usual lymphopenia after swimming or ACTH administration. Dumm and Ralli[50] also stated that a daily intake of at least 4 mg. of calcium pantothenate is necessary to obtain prolonged survival in adrenalectomized rats. Ralli and coworkers[51, 52] have also observed a decreased excretion of ascorbic acid during pantothenic acid deficiency or following adrenalectomy or hypophysectomy.

Rats depleted in pantothenic acid are less able to withstand exposure to cold than their pair-fed or normal controls, according to Ershoff.[52a]

B. OF MAN

ELAINE P. RALLI

The widespread occurrence of pantothenic acid in foods precludes the possibility that a deficiency state due to the absence of this vitamin would be readily produced. There have been no experiments on human subjects maintained for long periods on diets deficient in pantothenic acid. Therefore, the question of the nutritional requirement of human beings for pantothenic acid will be approached on the basis of the approximate daily intake of this vitamin provided in an average diet in this country, on the studies of the excretion of pantothenic acid in human subjects, and, finally, by estimating the human requirement on the basis of the known requirement of animals of different species.

1. PANTOTHENIC ACID CONTENT OF FOODS

Numerous analyses have been made of the pantothenic acid content of uncooked foods.[53-58] From the data in Table XI (see p. 638) the average American diet, which would include two glasses of milk, two helpings of fruit, two helpings of vegetables, a generous helping of potatoes, 5 oz. of meat, 4 oz. of beans, two eggs, and several slices of bread, would contain about 9 mg. of pantothenic acid. Even if the diet consisted mainly of vegetables and two glasses of milk daily, the pantothenic acid intake would

[50] M. E. Dumm and E. P. Ralli, *Endocrinology* **43**, 283 (1948); M. E. Dumm and E. P. Ralli, *Metabolism* **2**, 153 (1953).

[51] M. E. Dumm and E. P. Ralli, *Endocrinology* **45**, 188 (1949).

[52] M. E. Dumm, E. P. Ralli, and I. Graef, quoted by E. P. Ralli and M. E. Dumm, *Endocrinology* **51**, 135 (1952).

[52a] B. H. Ershoff, *J. Nutrition* **49**, 373 (1953).

[53] M. L. Thompson, E. Cunningham, and E. E. Snell, *J. Nutrition* **28**, 123 (1944).

[54] A. J. Ihde and H. A. Schuette, *J. Nutrition* **22**, 527 (1941).

[55] L. J. Teply, F. M. Strong, and C. A. Elvehjem, *J. Nutrition* **24**, 167 (1942).

[56] J. M. Lawrence, B. L. Herrington, and L. A. Maynard, *J. Nutrition* **32**, 73 (1946).

[57] V. H. Cheldelin and R. R. Williams, *J. Nutrition* **26**, 417 (1943).

[58] T. H. Jukes, *J. Nutrition* **21**, 193 (1941).

still be approximately 6 to 7 mg. The widespread distribution of pantothenic acid in foods undoubtedly guards against a deficiency of this vitamin. The absorption of the vitamin is apparently fairly complete and is not impaired even in such a disease as pernicious anemia.[59]

On the basis of the dietary intake of pantothenic acid, the requirement would seem to be about 7 mg. daily. This is lower than the 10 to 12 mg. suggested by Williams.[60]

2. URINARY EXCRETION AND BLOOD LEVELS OF PANTOTHENIC ACID IN HUMAN BEINGS

The urinary excretion of pantothenic acid has been measured in man by many investigators,[61-66] and Oldham et al.[62] have determined the fecal excretion. The data from the various reports on urinary excretion are in good agreement and show that on normal diets the excretion ranges from 1.3 to 5.3 mg. per 24 hours. The excretion of pantothenic acid is influenced by the intake. The excretion is not altered in elderly people.[67] Oldham et al. have done a very complete study on the excretion of pantothenic acid in urine and feces at different levels of intake, and the data in Table XXI are taken from their report. Approximately 54 to 84 % of the excreted vitamin was found in the urine, and 25 to 38 % in the feces.

Rubin and his associates[68] found that when pantothenic acid was given in the form of pantothenyl alcohol a greater portion of the pantothenic acid was excreted than when administered in the form of calcium pantothenate. They gave doses of 100 mg. of calcium pantothenate or an equivalent dose of pantothenyl alcohol. Their interpretation was that the pantothenyl alcohol was physiologically more available than calcium pantothenate. However, I would question this interpretation and would suggest rather that the blood levels may have risen more rapidly following the administration of the pantothenyl alcohol, and that this was associated with an increased rate of excretion. In renal clearance studies, Wright et al.[69] have studied the relation of the excretion of pantothenic acid to the blood

[59] C. E. Meyer, I. F. Burton, and C. C. Sturgis, Proc. Soc. Exptl. Biol. Med. 49, 363 (1942).

[60] R. J. Williams, J. Am. Med. Assoc. 119, 1 (1942).

[61] H. P. Sarett, J. Biol. Chem. 159, 321 (1945).

[62] H. G. Oldham, M. V. Davis, and L. J. Roberts, J. Nutrition 32, 163 (1946).

[63] L. D. Wright and E. Q. Wright, Proc. Soc. Exptl. Biol. Med. 49, 80 (1942).

[64] M. J. Pelczar, Jr., and J. R. Porter, Proc. Soc. Exptl. Biol. Med. 47, 3 (1941).

[65] P. B. Pearson, Am. J. Physiol. 135, 59 (1941).

[66] H. Krahnke and E. S. Gordon, J. Am. Med. Assoc. 116, 2431 (1941).

[67] V. Schmidt, J. Gerontol. 6, 132 (1951).

[68] S. H. Rubin, J. M. Cooperman, M. E. Moore, and J. Scheiner, J. Nutrition 35, 499 (1948).

[69] L. D. Wright, K. H. Beyer, H. R. Skeggs, H. F. Russo, and E. A. Patch, Am. J. Physiol. 145, 633 (1946).

TABLE XXI

Average Daily Pantothenic Acid Excretions on Different Intakes[a]

(Excretion in mg.)

Subject	Period Ia				Period Ib				Period II				Period III				Period IV				Period V			
																	Week 1		Week 2					
	Intake	Urine	Feces	Total	Intake	Urine	Feces	Total	Intake	Urine	Feces	Total	Intake	Urine	Feces	Total	Intake	Urine	Intake	Urine	Intake	Urine	Feces	Total
1	2.1	1.7	—	—	2.3	1.5	0.7	2.2	3.9	1.7	0.5	2.2	4.9	1.7	1.0	2.7	5.0	4.4	5.0	4.2	4.8	3.6	0.5	4.1
2	—	—	—	—	1.7	1.1	0.5	1.6	3.1	1.3	1.9	3.2	3.3	1.6	1.0	2.6	4.1	3.8	3.9	2.4	3.7	3.3	1.0	4.3
3	2.1	1.8	0.7	2.5	2.7	1.7	0.9	2.6	3.4	2.0	1.3	3.3	4.2	2.6	1.6	4.2	4.8	3.8	5.0	5.0	4.6	4.1	1.6	5.7
4	1.7	1.6	0.6	2.2	2.1	1.7	0.7	2.4	3.7	2.5	1.5	4.0	—	—	—	—	—	—	—	—	—	—	—	—
5	2.0	1.7	1.1	2.8	1.9	1.8	1.4	3.2	3.2	2.2	—	—	—	—	—	—	—	—	—	—	—	—	—	—
6	—	—	—	—	—	—	—	—	—	—	—	—	4.7	4.6	2.1	6.7	4.8	4.5	5.2	5.4	4.8	4.0	1.3	5.3
7	2.6	1.7	0.8	2.5	3.0	1.7	—	—	—	—	—	—	—	—	—	—	—	—	—	—	—	—	—	—
8	3.3	1.6	—	—	2.4	1.5	—	—	—	—	—	—	—	—	—	—	—	—	—	—	—	—	—	—
9	2.3	1.8	—	—	—	—	—	—	—	—	—	—	—	2.3	—	—	—	—	—	—	4.7	2.8	—	—
10	—	—	—	—	2.5	1.6	—	—	—	—	—	—	4.7	2.3	—	—	4.5	3.9	4.8	3.3	—	—	—	—
11	2.2	1.4	—	—	—	—	—	—	—	—	—	—	4.3	2.2	2.1	4.3	4.5	3.2	4.6	3.9	4.0	2.9	1.1	4.0
12	—	—	—	—	—	—	—	—	—	—	—	—	—	—	—	—	—	—	—	—	—	—	—	—
Av.	2.1	1.7	0.8	2.5	2.1	1.6	0.8	2.4	3.5	1.9	1.3	3.2	4.3	2.5	1.6	4.1	4.6	3.9	4.8	4.0	4.4	3.6	1.1	4.7

[a] All figures in this table are based on collections made for 3 days during the last week of each period. The data are from the report of Oldham et al.[62]

levels. They found that at ordinary normal plasma concentrations (0.10 to 0.32 γ per milliliter) only a trace of pantothenic acid was excreted in the urine and that the renal clearance was of the order of 0.2 to 0.5 milliliter per minute. On increasing the plasma concentration by oral or intravenous administration to about 0.5 γ per milliliter, there was an abrupt rise in the calculated clearance. When the plasma concentration was increased to 1.2 γ per milliliter, the renal clearance approximated the glomerular filtration rate and the further increase of the plasma concentration to or above 100 γ per milliliter did not alter materially the clearance ratio. These experiments were done with dogs.

Pelczar and Porter[64] determined the plasma concentration of pantothenic acid in seventeen normal subjects and found that it ranged from 0.030 to 0.099 γ per milliliter of blood and averaged 0.059 γ per milliliter. These levels are lower than those observed in 1946 by Wright et al. at the time they did renal clearances.[69] Pearson[65] reported the blood levels as varying from 0.020 to 0.28 γ per milliliter. The discrepancy is probably due to the organism that was used in the microbiological assays. Wright et al. used Lactobacillus arabinosus. Pearson used Lactobacillus casei ϵ, and Pelczar and Porter used Proteus morganii.

Spies et al.[70] made the interesting observation that the pantothenic acid content of the blood was decreased in patients with pellagra, beriberi, and riboflavin deficiency. They found that the administration of 20 mg. of pantothenate daily increased the blood pantothenic acid and riboflavin levels. Siegel et al.[71] studied blood pantothenic acid in patients with multiple sclerosis and did not observe any significant differences from the blood levels in normal subjects.

Another group of workers studied the pantothenic acid content of cancerous tissue and analyzed malignancies of liver, myocardium, brain, lung, spleen, kidney, and muscle.[72] The pantothenic acid content in micrograms per gram of fresh tissue was highest in carcinoma of the liver and lowest in carcinoma of the lung and spleen. The pantothenic acid content of liver was 31 γ per gram, of kidney 16 γ per gram, and of lung and spleen 5 γ per gram. The figures were lower than determined in rat liver carcinoma.

In Oldham's study, the dietary intake of pantothenic acid was lower (2 to 5 mg.) than what would normally be consumed in an ordinary diet (7 mg.). It seems obvious that the subjects in this study had adequate supplies of pantothenic acid in their tissues because the excretion paralleled

[70] T. D. Spies, S. R. Stanbery, R. J. Williams, T. H. Jukes, and S. H. Babcock, J. Am. Med. Assoc. 115, 523 (1940).

[71] L. Siegel, T. J. Putnam, and J. G. Lynn, Proc. Soc. Exptl. Biol. Med. 47, 362 (1941).

[72] A. Taylor, M. A. Pollack, M. J. Hofer, and R. J. Williams, Cancer Research 2, 752 (1942).

the intake, and as the intake was increased the total excretion increased. The effect of test doses of various magnitudes confirms this observation, and as was shown by Rubin et al.[68] the dose response relationship is quite constant—the greater the test dose, the greater the excretion.

The question arises as to what use one can make of the data on the excretion of pantothenic acid in estimating the daily requirement. The fecal excretion remains fairly constant on different intakes, and it is the urinary excretion which reflects the daily intake. If one assumes that the amount of the vitamin excreted in the urine represents an excess of the bodily need, then subtraction of the amount excreted daily from the amount ingested might be considered as the amount required daily in a normal, well-nourished subject. The average daily excretion (3.7 mg. in the urine and 1.0 mg. in the feces) subtracted from an approximate average intake of 10.4 mg., would leave approximately 6.4 mg. as the daily requirement.

3. Approximate Pantothenic Acid Requirement of Man as Based on the Known Requirement of the Experimental Animal

In all experimental studies in animals, the physiological state of the animal influences its requirement for pantothenic acid. The requirement of the growing animal is much greater than that of the adult. Similarly, stress increases the animal's requirement for pantothenate. As an example of this, it was reported by Lotspeich[73] that symptoms of pantothenic acid deficiency, which are very slow to appear in the adult rat on a deficient diet, can be induced fairly rapidly if the animal is given injections of an anterior pituitary hormone. Other forms of stress, such as pregnancy and hyperthyroidism, will also increase the requirement for this vitamin.[74, 75]

The pantothenic acid requirement for the rat decreases from about 2.5 mg. per kilogram of body weight daily at weaning to approach 0.1 mg. per kilogram for the adult rat.[76] More than 3 mg. is required daily by the weanling mouse,[77] whereas the young dog requires only 0.1 mg.[78] Since adult dogs survive much longer on diets deficient in pantothenic acid than do pups, the adult requirement is thought to be less than 0.1 mg. per kilogram. I am indebted to Dr. Mary E. Dumm for the graphic summary of these data, shown in Fig. 11, in which the requirement of pantothenic acid

[73] W. D. Lotspeich, Proc. Soc. Exptl. Biol. Med. **73,** 85 (1950).

[74] J. Boisselot, Arch. franç. pédiat. **6,** 225 (1949).

[75] V. A. Drill and R. Overman, Am. J. Physiol. **135,** 474 (1942).

[76] K. Unna and G. V. Richards, J. Nutrition **23,** 545 (1942).

[77] J. G. Sandza and L. R. Cerecedo, J. Nutrition **21,** 609 (1941).

[78] A. E. Schaefer, J. M. McKibbin, and C. A. Elvehjem, J. Biol. Chem. **143,** 321 (1942).

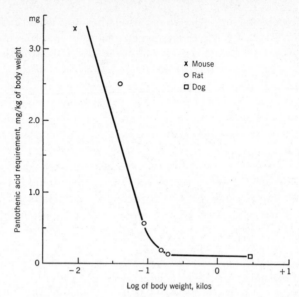

FIG. 11. Pantothenic acid requirement of the mouse, the rat, and the dog, in milligrams per kilogram of body weight. (Prepared by M. E. Dumm.)

per kilogram of body weight (at the beginning of the experiment) is shown with reference to the log of the body weight in kilograms for the three species on which quantitative data are available. In general, the data suggest that the requirement for pantothenic acid, expressed per kilogram of body weight, is greater for small mammals than for large ones, and that within a given species the requirement may be considerably greater for the young animal than for the adult.

Although the estimation of the human requirement on the basis of information obtained from other species is notably uncertain, the data in Fig. 11 might be interpreted as suggesting that the human requirement is probably less than 0.1 mg. per kilogram, or no more than 6 to 8 mg. daily for adults.

4. Toxicity of Pantothenic Acid

In discussing pantothenic acid intake and requirement, it seems reasonable to mention briefly what is known of the toxicity of this vitamin.

The toxicity of pantothenic acid was studied by Unna and Greslin[79] in mice, rats, dogs, and monkeys. Very large doses, up to 1 g. per kilogram in monkeys and 50 mg. per kilogram in dogs, seemed to have no toxic effect. The author and associates[80, 81] have administered from 10 to 20 g.

[79] K. Unna and J. Greslin, *Proc. Soc. Exptl. Biol. Med.* **45,** 311 (1940).
[80] H. Gershberg, S. H. Rubin, and E. P. Ralli, *J. Nutrition* **39,** 107 (1949).
[81] H. Gershberg and W. J. Kuhl, Jr., *J. Clin. Invest.* **29,** 1625 (1950).

of calcium pantothenate daily to human subjects—these are, of course, excessively large doses. The evidences of toxicity were an occasional diarrhea and, in three subjects with rheumatoid arthritis, retention of water with edema of the face, the feet, and the lower parts of the leg occurred, but it disappeared when calcium pantothenate was discontinued. This latter observation is interesting because of the report by Gaunt *et al.*[82] concerning the disturbance in water tolerance tests in rats on diets deficient in pantothenic acid, and also because of the effects of large doses of calcium pantothenate on the survival of the completely adrenalectomized rat.[83, 84] In our own experiments on intact rats on high pantothenate intakes[85] we observed a decrease in the water tolerance test. One would judge that calcium pantothenate under certain circumstances was associated with the retention of water.

5. SUMMARY

On the basis of the data reported, it would appear that the approximate daily intake of pantothenic acid in human subjects on a diet in the United States varies from 3 to 12 mg. Judging from this and from the amounts excreted daily, the amount of pantothenic acid in the diet is more than adequate and protects against a deficiency of this vitamin. Combined with the data in Fig. 11, it would appear that the daily requirement of pantothenic acid for adults is approximately 3 to 5 mg. The intake of pantothenic acid is reflected in the urinary excretion, and when the diet is excessively high the excretion will increase. The highest excretion reported on normal diets was 5.3 mg. per 24 hours. The constancy of the fecal excretion indicates good absorption of the vitamin. Probably the infant and growing child would need relatively more pantothenic acid than the adult, approximately 5 mg. daily. On the basis of data previously mentioned on the effects of the administration of very large doses of pantothenic acid to individuals with a variety of metabolic disturbances, there seems to be no indication that the requirement is significantly altered in these diseases. The proof that the average human, at least in this country, has an adequate supply of pantothenic acid is provided by the acetylation studies done in patients with such severe diseases as cirrhosis of the liver, Addison's disease, and diabetes mellitus. It is significant in this respect that patients with hyperthyroidism[81] did not acetylate PABA as well as did normal subjects, and probably in conditions of stress in humans and in situations where the metabolic rate is significantly increased the pantothenic acid requirement would be increased.

[82] R. Gaunt, M. Liling, and C. W. Mushett, *Endocrinology* **38,** 127 (1946).
[83] E. P. Ralli, *Endocrinology* **39,** 225 (1946).
[84] M. E. Dumm and E. P. Ralli, *Endocrinology* **43,** 283 (1948).
[85] M. E. Dumm and E. P. Ralli, unpublished data.

The nutritional requirement of pantothenic acid is, in all probability, influenced by the intake of some of the other fractions of the vitamin B complex. There are experimental data to show an interrelation between vitamin B_{12} and pantothenic acid in chicks.[86] Apparently B_{12} will spare the pantothenic requirement for growth and survival and will prevent the dermatosis. Pantothenic acid similarly showed a sparing effect on the vitamin B_{12} requirement for the growth of normal chicks. Other data indicate an interrelationship between biotin and pantothenic acid[87] and also between ascorbic acid and pantothenic acid.[88] As mentioned in the previous section, the development of the burning feet syndrome in the prisoners of war as a rule was preceded by the development of symptoms of thiamine, riboflavin, and nicotinic acid deficiency. Similarly, the administration of these fractions in some instances decreased the severity of the burning feet syndrome although it definitely was not successful in clearing up this syndrome. Obviously, our knowledge of the requirement of pantothenic acid will depend on further data concerning the interrelation of other vitamins and pantothenic acid.

The data for the human requirement are inferential, and the daily requirement arrived at by these means should under no circumstances be taken as the final word on the subject.

[86] H. Yacowitz, L. C. Norris, and G. F. Heuser, *J. Biol. Chem.* **192**, 141 (1951).
[87] G. A. Emerson and E. Wurtz, *Proc. Soc. Exptl. Biol. Med.* **57**, 47 (1944).
[88] M. E. Dumm and E. P. Ralli, *Endocrinology* **45**, 188 (1949).

Author Index

Numbers in parentheses are footnote numbers. They are inserted to indicate the reference when an author's name is cited but his name does not appear on the page.

A

Aaes-Jorgensen, E., 286
Abbott, L. D., Jr., 41
Abbott, O. D., 96
Abdel Kader, M. M., 515, 518 (2, 32), 523
524 (26), 530, 533, 536, 537 (26), 559,
584
Abdon, N. O., 57, 90, 91
Abelin, I., 380
Abels, J. C., 347, 371
Abraham, E. P., 525, 526 (55, 56)
Abrahamson, E. M., 229
Abramson, D. I., 574
Abramson, H., 247, 248
Ackermann, D., 7, 8, 52, 92, 335, 457, 459
(43)
Ackermann, W. W., 532, 549, 625, 679
Adams, R. D., 670, 677 (215)
Adamstone, F. B., 568
Adler, B., 422, 448
Adler, E., 488, 493 (42), 503 (76), 507 (44),
508, 511 (80)
Adler, R., 495
Adrian, J., 637
Aggeler, P. M., 436
Agnew, M. C., 248
Agnew, R. C., 248
Ahlström, L., 312
Ahrens, E. H., 373
Ahrens, F. B., 475
Aiton, H. F., 674
Åkeson, Å., 458
Albanese, A. A., 532
Albers, H., 453, 458 (8), 480, 481 (3), 482
(3), 485 (3), 488 (3)
Albert, P. W., 519 (53), 527
Alberti, C. G., 142
Albright, F., 249, 250, 265
Alcayaga, R., 665, 666 (163)
Aldridge, W. N., 17
Alechinsky, A., 577

Alesker, E. M., 575
Alexander, H. D., 87
Alfin Slater, R. B., 651
Aline, E., 636, 660
Allan, F. N., 19, 100
Allen, E., 670
Allen, E. V., 427, 428
Allen, J. G., 100
Alles, G. A., 124
Allison, J. B., 92, 126
Almquist, H. J., 28, 46, 94, 95, 389 (15),
390 (14), 391 (15), 393 (16), 394, 395,
396 (29, 34), 397 (35, 45), 398, 399, 400,
401, 402, 403, 404, 405, 406 (14), 407,
408 (9), 409, 410 (31), 411, 412, 413,
414, 415, 416, 417(1), 422, 423, 425,
426 (26), 429, 435, 439, 441, 444, 445
(1), 446, 447, 531
Aloisi, M., 8, 12, 19, 89
Along, C., 546
Alscher, R. P., 418, 426
Altman, K. I., 506
Ambo, H., 54
Ambrose, B. A., 461, 462 (64), 463 (64),
464 (64)
Ames, S. R., 638, 639 (29), 640 (29), 641
(29)
Amiard, G., 177, 194, 202, 204 (316)
Amos, E. S., 84
Anderlik, B., 365
Anderson, A. B., 336
Anderson, B. A., 247
Anderson, E. G., 508, 554, 556 (20)
Anderson, F. W., 197, 204 (297a)
Anderson, G. W., 442
Anderson, J. O., 522, 531, 578 (29), 581,
582 (29), 584 (58)
Anderson, L., 323, 324 (2), 327, 328, 329
(21), 330, 331 (5), 333 (5), 336 (5)
Anderson, R. C., 338

726 AUTHOR INDEX

Pfiffner, J. J., 44
Phelps, E. T., 436, 437, 442
Philippot, E., 345
Philips, A., 472
Phillips, P. H., 39, 81, 342, 343 (9), 344
  (19), 368, 369, 555, 650, 656 (5), 657
  (5), 660, 670
Phillips, R. V., 438
Philpot, J. St. L., 181, 182 (241), 189, 192
  (263), 195 (241, 263), 196 (263), 198
  (263), 204 (263), 216
Piacentini, C., 441
Pichat, P., 442
Pigman, W. W., 323, 363
Pike, E. F., 476
Pike, R. L., 563, 568
Pilgrim, F. J., 508, 555
Pinchot, G. B., 620 (79)
Pinkos, J. A., 102
Pinner, A., 479
Pirk, L. A., 426
Pirlot, G., 215, 217
Pisciotta, A. V., 428
Pittman, M., 518 (33)
Pitzer, K. S., 331, 332 (20)
Plass, M., 493, 511 (80)
Platt, A. P., 40, 46, 48 (20), 69, 72, 76 (52),
  77
Platt, B. S., 359, 360
Platt, J. R., 275
Platz, B. R., 283, 315
Plaut, G. W. E., 84, 85
Plum, C. M., 427
Plum, P., 433
Pohl, R., 138, 139, 175, 178 (28, 30), 199
Pohle, F. J., 427
Poirot, G., 337
Polgár, P., 442
Polglase, W. J., 328, 365
Poling, C. E., 654, 655 (32), 656 (31, 32),
  654 (31, 32), 657, 667
Pollack, M. A., 377, 549, 550 (79), 647, 690
Pollak, F., 476
Pollak, O, J., 373
Pollard, A., 153
Polskin, L. J., 296
Pons, W. A., Jr, 339
Poole, A. G., 359
Poole, H. H., 171
Pope, A. L., 555
Pope, H., 354

Popkin, G. L., 574
Popp, E. M., 637
Poppalardo, P., 575
Popper, H., 90, 108, 113 (428), 127, 128,
  130
Porter, C. C., 585
Porter, F., 475
Porter, J. R., 688, 690
Porter, R. R., 72
Porterfield, V. T., 74
Portman, O. W., 44, 45
Portmann, A., 377
Post, A. L., 81
Post, J., 372
Posternak, T., 323, 326, 327, 329 (19), 330,
  331, 335, 337 (7, 8), 338 (59), 344, 346,
  347, 351, 352, 357, 365
Potter, E. L., 422
Potter, J. W., 559
Potter, V. R., 15, 509
Poulsson, E., 222
Poulsson, E. A., 399
Pounden, W. D., 223
Poupa, O., 572
Powell, D., 533
Powell, M. J., 216
Power, M. H., 448
Powick, W. C., 568, 578 (15, 16)
Pramanik, B. N., 366
Pratt, E. F., 594
Preisler, P. W., 358
Prelog, V., 159
Present, C. H., 100
Preston, F. W., 429, 431 (90)
Prestrud, M. C., 426
Pricer, W. E., Jr., 458, 489, 494 (55), 498,
  506 (55, 115), 507 (55), 603, 604 (29),
  619, 621 (93)
Prickett, P. S., 153, 157, 160
Provost, R. C., Jr., 466, 467 (68)
Pruess, L. M., 156
Pugsley, L. I., 167
Puig Muset, P., 384
Pullman, M. E., 494
Pulver, R., 427
Putnam, T. J., 690

Q

Quackenbush, F. W., 283, 315, 316
Quadbeck, G., 338
Quarles, E., 357, 636

Subject Index

A

Acetaldehyde,
  formation from pyruvate, 499
  in coenzyme A assay, 603
Acetic acid, 91
  as inositol precursor, 355
  formation from pyruvic acid, 499
  in coenzyme A assay, 599
  in lipid synthesis, 622–624
  pantothenic acid and, 679
Acetoacetic acid, 502, 625
  synthesis of, 618–619
Acetobacter suboxydans, inositol oxidation by, 326, 331, 333, 337, 347–348, 353–354
Acetone, in methyl group synthesis, 27
Acetylase, 16
Acetylation, in disease, 672
Acetylcholine, 2, 49, 123, 380, 381
  adenosine triphosphatase and, 15
  comparative activity of, 124
  fatty acids and, 317
  inactivation of, 17
  in choline estimation, 57
  in growth of microorganisms, 50, 55
  isolation of, 7–8
  niacin and, 576–577
  oxidation of, 33
  pantothenic acid and, 679, 680
  synthesis of, 598–599
  vitamin K and, 440
Acetylcholinesterase, 17
Acetyl-coenzyme A, 16, 602
  isolation of, 607, 618
Acetyl compounds, oxidation of, 502
Acetylkinase, 16–17
Acetyl-β-methylcholine, resemblance to acetylcholine, 124
Acetyl phosphate, 607
  arsenolysis of, 602
  as acetyl donor, 616, 617
3-Acetylpyridine,
  antiniacin effect of, 548–550, 569
  niacin and, 517

synthesis of, 477
  toxicity of, 532
Acetyl transfer, coenzyme A and, 615–621
Acetyl tryptophan, 531
Achlorhydria, in pellagra, 560
Achromotrichia, in pantothenic acid deficiency, 653–655, 667
Acidosis, effect on rickets, 260
"Active acetate," 615, 617, 625, see also
  Acetyl coenzyme A
Actomyosin, 15
Acyl transfer, coenzyme A and, 620–622
Addison's disease, pantothenic acid, and, 672
Adenine, 455, 481, 482
  antiniacin effect of, 548
  as inhibitor, 508
  in pyridine nucleotides, 485, 489
Adenine dinucleotide, as inhibitor, 508
Adenosine, as inhibitor, 508
Adenosine phosphate, 15
Adenosine triphosphatase, 15
Adenosine triphosphte, 16, 17, 33
  as inhibitor, 508
  estimation of, 511
  in acetyl transfer, 617
  in active methionine formation, 33
  in choline phosphorylation, 19
  in coenzyme A assay, 599
  in coenzyme A synthesis, 603
  in creatine formation, 30–31
  in methylation of niacinamide, 32, 516
  pyridine nucleotides and, 496–498, 506
S-Adenosylmethionine, 29
  in transmethylation, 25, 33
Adenylic acid, 507
  in coenzyme A, 603
Adrenal cortical hormones, coenzyme A and, 624
Adrenal gland,
  achromotrichia and, 655
  coenzyme A in, 614
  fatty liver and, 72–73
  in choline deficiency, 66

in methyl group synthesis, 23, 84–85
in pantothenic acid deficiency, 653, 671–672, 685
in pellagra, 553, 563
leucocytes and, 90–91
niacin toxicity and, 573
relation to choline, 49, 83–84, 129
Folinic acid, *see* Citrovorum factor
Formaldehyde,
formation from glycine, 41, 42
in methyl group synthesis, 27, 33
formation from sarcosine, 41
Formic acid, 83
formation of, 41, 127
in creatine formation, 31
in histidine synthesis, 28
methyl groups and, 22–23, 27, 33, 43–44
in serine synthesis, 27, 41–42
in transmethylation, 29
metabolism of, 83–84, 86
10-Formylfolic acid, in creatine formation, 31
N-Formylkynurenine, in niacin synthesis, 527
Fructose-1,6-diphosphate, 498, 501, 510–511
Fucosterol, 135, 136
Fumaric acid, 509
in creatin formation, 31

G

Galactose,
reaction with sphingosine, 58–61
Gammexane, 336, *see also* Hexachlorocyclohexane
Gastric ulcers,
choline and, 90, 98
pyridoxine and, 90
Gastrointestinal tract,
inositol and, 379–380
pantothenic acid and, 672–673
Gelatin,
effect in choline deficiency, 76, 78
effect on perosis, 93–94, 97
Gliadin, effect in choline deficiency, 77
Glucose, inositol and, 354, 355–356, 377–378
Glucose dehydrogenase,

coenzyme of, 493
inhibition of, 508
in triphosphopyridine nucleotide estimation, 511
Glucose-1-phosphate, pyridine nucleotides and, 497–498
Glucose-6-phosphate, 511
oxidation of, 482
Glucosides, cardiac, 134
Glucuronolactone, pantothenic acid and 685
Glutamic acid, 625
niacin synthesis and, 522–523
pyridine nucleotides and, 502
Glutamic dehydrogenase, coenzyme of, 493
Glutamine, 32
in niacinamide synthesis, 505
niacin synthesis and, 523
Glutathione, 51
in acetylation systems, 618
vitamin K and, 440
L-Glyceraldehyde, 325
Glyceraldehyde-3-phosphate, in diphosphopyridine nucleotide estimation, 510
Glycerol, 501, 619
in inositol estimation, 360
Glycerophosphate, 8, 510
hydrolysis of, 19
in lecithin synthesis, 99
phospholipid synthesis and, 70
pyridine nucleotides and, 501
Glycerylphosphorylcholine, 2, 8–9, 12, 62
in lecithin synthesis, 52
in tissues, 18–19
Glycine, 574
conversion to glyoxylate, 42
effect on perosis, 93–94, 97
formate formation from 41
formation from sarcosine, 41
in aminoethanol formation, 83–84
in heme synthesis, 622
in serine synthesis, 27, 41, 42, 85
leucocytosis and, 91
methyl derivatives of, 40
niacin toxicity and, 573
relation to betaine, 40
relation to choline, 2, 40, 71, 79

Lecithinase, 52
  effect on adenosine triphosphatase, 15
  in bone-forming cells, 237
Lentine, *see* Carbaminoylcholine
Leuconostoc mesenteroides, in differential
  niacin assay, 540
Leucopenia, choline and, 90–91
Line test, in vitamin D estimation, 220
Linoleic acid, 268, 274, 280, 281
  conjugated, 283
  conversion to arachidonate, 281
  effect in deficiency, 278–280
  effect in double deficiency, 284–285
  isolation of, 270–272
  synthesis of, 272
Linolelaidic acid, 283
Linolenic acid, 268, 274
  effect in deficiency, 280
  effect in double deficiency, 284–285
  effect on enzymes, 278
  isolation of, 271–272
trans-Linolenic acid, 282
Lipase, in fat deficient diet, 277
Lipids,
  in bone-forming cells, 237
  in choline deficiency, 68–76, 98
  inositol in, 334, 366–367
  tissue, in fatty acid deficiency, 307,
    308–309, 310–311
Lipocaic, 371
  choline and, 100–101
  composition of, 86
Lipogenesis,
  in choline deficiency, 91
  in pantothenic acid deficiency, 652
Lipoprotein, 15
Lipositol, 334–335
  composition of, 346
Lipoxidase, 280
  in estimation of fatty acids, 289
  specificity of, 312
  substrates of, 278
Liver,
  coenzyme A in, 614
  dicoumarol and, 428–429
  in choline deficiency, 63, 67
  in fatty acid deficiency, 299–300
  in prothrombin production, 426–427
  vitamin K and, 401, 437
Liver factor 2, *see* Pantothenic acid
Liver filtrate factor, *see* Pantothenic acid

Lomiatol, vitamin K and, 397
Long bones, deformation in rickets, 240
Lumisterol, 181, 196, 205
  as provitamin D, 144
  formation of, 142, 178
  properties of, 191–192, 202
Lymph, in vitamin K absorption, 426
Lysine, fatty liver and, 87

M

Malic acid, formation of, 499, 500
Malic dehydrogenase, 499
  coenzyme of, 493
  inhibition of, 508
"Malic" enzyme, 499
  in carbon dioxide fixation, 504
Malonic acid,
  choline oxidase and, 36
  reversal of inhibition by, 366
Manganese, 93
Meat sugar, *see* Inositol
Mecholyl, *see* Acetyl-β-methylcholine
Melanin, formation of, 655
Menadione, *see* *also* Vitamin K, 2-
  Methyl-1,4-naphthoquinone
  inhibitory effects of, 439–440
Mercaptoesters, behavior of, 607
β-Mercaptoethylamine, 16
Metals, effect on choline oxidase, 36
Mercury salts, in choline isolation, 7
Metaphysis, in rickets, 245
Methanol, in methyl group synthesis, 27,
  84
Methionine, 23, 26, 90, 101
  active, 25, 29, 31
  as source of cysteine, 29
  choline oxidase and, 38
  creatine and, 21–22, 30–31
  effect on fatty liver, 20, 76, 78
  effect on perosis, 94, 97
  ethionine and, 80
  formation, 29, 40, 41
  in epinephrine formation, 32
  in growth of microorganisms, 49, 50, 55
  in inositol deficiency, 368
  in methylation of nicotinamide, 32,
    516, 517
  in niacin toxicity, 573
  in thiomethyladenosine formation, 51
  in transmethylation, 21–23
  oxidation of, 43

Monoethylcholine, 45
Monoiodocalciferol, vitamin D activity
 of, 208
Monomethylamine, formation of, 92
p-Monomethylaminoazobenzene, 89
Monomethylaminoethanol, 17
 as methyl donor, 28
 effect in choline deficiency, 68, 70, 128
 formation by chick, 40
 in growth of microorganisms, 50-51, 55
 in perosis, 94
 phosphorylation of, 19
Monomethylglycine, see also Sarcosine,
 degradation of, 41
Monomethyltryptophan, 531
Mouse,
 choline deficiency in, 103
 fatty acid deficiency in, 297, 315
 niacin deficiency in, 569
 pantothenic acid deficiency in, 667-668
Mucopolysaccharides, in calcification,
 236
Muscarine, resemblance to choline, 123
Myosin, 15
Mytilitol, 335, 363
 vitamin activity of, 351, 352-353

N

β-Naphthylamine, methylation of, 44
Nerves, in pantothenic acid deficiency,
 665-666, 667-668
Neurine, 3
 formation of, 11
 in growth of microorganisms, 50, 55
Neuromuscular system, inositol and, 380
Neurospora,
 in choline estimation, 55-57
 in inositol assay, 362
 niacin synthesis and, 525-526
Niacin, see also Nicotinic acid
 absorption spectrum, 461-462
 acidic character of, 465-466
 antihistaminic effect of, 576-577
 antivitamins in food, 548-550
 as inhibitor, 508
 basic character of, 464-465
 biochemical systems, 480-517
 biosynthesis of, 505, 521-533
 chemistry, 452-478
 constitution of, 473
 crystal structure, 461

decarboxylation of, 513
differential assay of, 535-536
dissociation constants, 462
effects of deficiency,
 in man and animals, 551-565
 in microorganisms, 550-551
effect on bilirubin, 576
effect on blood sugar, 574-575
effect on circulation, 573-574
effect on gastric secretion, 575-576
estimation,
 biological, 534
 chemical, 534-538
 microbiological, 538-540
excretion of, 513, 522, 556-560
industrial preparation, 478-479
in U. S. diets, 547-548
isolation, 452-454
isotopic, 476
ketosis and, 575
load tests of deficiency, 559-560
niacinamide synthesis from, 476, 505
nomenclature and formulas, 452
occurrence of, 541-550
pathology,
 in animals, 565-570
 in humans, 570-571
pharmacology, 571-578
requirements,
 in animals, 578-586
 in human, 586-587
separation from niacinamide, 456
solubility, 460
specificity of action, 517-521
stability, 460, 545-546
standardization of activity, 540
synthesis of, 474-478
tissue, 514, 554-556
toxicity,
 in dogs, 572
 in other species, 572
 in rodents, 571-572
urinary metabolites of, 514-516
Niacinamide, see also Nicotinamide
 absorption spectrum, 470-472
 chemical properties, 472-473
 crystal structure, 467-470
 differential assay of, 540
 dissociation constants, 472
 in destruction of pyridine nucleotides,
 507, 508

effect in inositol deficiency, 343, 357, 367, 384, 385
effect of storage on, 637
effects of deficiency,
    in animals, 649–669
    in humans, 669–678
    in microorganisms, 678–680
esters of, 626
estimation of,
    biological methods, 628–630
    chemical and physical methods, 628
    microbiological methods, 630–633
excretion of, 688–691
factors affecting distribution, 634–638
fatty liver and, 80, 88
hair-color and, 670–671
human intake of, 687–688
in coenzyme A, 599–601
in red cell metabolism, 622
isolation, 591–596
levels in blood, 690
losses in cooking, 637–638
niacin toxicity and, 573
nomenclature, 591
occurrence, 634–649
pharmacology of, 680–681
release from coenzyme A, 610–611
requirements,
    of animals, 682–687
    of humans, 687–694
specificity of action, 626–627
standardization of activity, 633
synthesis of, 597–598
toxicity of, 692–693
Pantothenic acid conjugate, as growth factor, 613
Pantothenic acid phosphate, coenzyme A and, 604, 632
Pantothenyl alcohol, biological activity of, 626
N-Pantothenylthioethanolamine, 606
Pantoyl-tauryl-anisidide, as antimetabolite, 624
Pantoyltaurine, effect on growth, 680
Parathormone, in bone resorption, 237
Parathyroid gland, effect on calcium levels, 250–252, 260
Pellagra, 453, 480, 674, 675, see also Niacin, deficiency
in vitamin deficiency, 592

pantothenic acid and, 637, 690
symptoms of, 552–553
Pellagramine, see Niacin
Pellagra preventive factor, see Niacin
Pelvis, deformation in rickets, 239–240
Penicillin, pantothenic acid requirement and, 685–686
Pentaenoic acid, 273, 283
formation from linoleate, 281
Pentose phosphate, 512
Peptidase, coenzyme A and, 601
Perchloric acid, in vitamin D estimation, 217
Perhydro-1,2-cyclopentenophenanthrene, 134
Periodic acid, in inositol estimation, 359–360
Periodide,
    in choline estimation, 52–53
    in choline isolation, 7
Peristalsis, effect of choline on, 123
Perosis, in choline deficiency, 93, 97
Phaseomannite, see Inositol
Phenanthraquinone, vitamin K and, 398
Phenylhydrazine, effect on choline oxidase, 36
Phenylindanedione, 427–428
Phlorizin, 19
Phloroglucinol, inositol and, 356
Phosphatase, 16
    choline and, 15, 67, 98
    coenzyme A and, 601, 632
    in bone formation, 235–236, 237
    in phosphorylcholine synthesis, 8
    in rickets, 226–227, 253
    effect on choline oxidase, 34
    in coenzyme A, 603
Phosphatides, 19
Phosphocholine, in lecithin synthesis, 49
6-Phosphogluconic acid,
    in pentose synthesis, 500
    in photosynthesis, 503–504
    in triphosphopyridine nucleotide estimation, 512
3-Phosphoglyceraldehyde, 498
Phosphoglyceraldehyde dehydrogenase, 492
3-Phosphoglyceric acid, 498–499
Phospholipids, 2, 15, 40, 90, 94, 347, 619
    aminoethanol in, 30
    distribution of, 52

absorption of, 400
biochemical systems, 400–402
chemical and physical properties, 390–393
chemistry, 389–399
comparative potencies of, 410–413, 424, 446, 447
consitution, 393–395
dosages, 435–436
effect of deficiency,
  in animals, 419
  in humans, 419–435
effect of route of administration, 405–406
effect on bacteria, 417
estimation of,
  biological, 402–413
  chemical and physical, 413–414
  sources of error, 403
estrogens and, 440
forms used therapeutically, 435
industrial preparation of, 399–400
isolation of, 389–390
miscellaneous effects, 440–441
mode of action, 437–442
mode of administration, 436–437
natural antagonists of, 418
nomenclature and formulas, 388
occurrence of, 415–418
pharmacology of, 435–444
requirements,
  chick, 444–446
  dog, 447
  human, 447–448
  rat, 446–447

specificity of, 396–399
standards of potency, 409–410
synthesis of, 395
toxicity of, 442–444
water soluble forms of, 400
Vitamin P,
  antivitamins K and, 432
  dicoumarol and, 439
Vitamin PP, *see* Niacin

W

Warburg's coferment, *see* Triphospho-pyridine nucleotide
Water metabolism, pantothenic acid and, 693

X

Xanthine oxidase, vitamin B_{12} and, 85
Xanthophyll, vitamin K and, 415
X-rays,
  choline oxidase and, 39
  in vitamin D estimation, 220

Y

Yeast, in inositol assay, 362
Yeast filtrate factor, *see* Pantothenic acid
Yellow fever,
  choline and, 103

Z

Zinc, deficiency, 655
Zwischenferment, coenzyme of, 482